CONCORDIA UNIVERSITY
W9-CXT-519

ANNUAL REVIEW OF PHYSIOLOGY

ANNUAL REVIEW OF PHYSIOLOGY

I. S. EDELMAN, *Editor*
Columbia University College of Physicians and Surgeons

STANLEY G. SCHULTZ, *Associate Editor*
University of Texas Medical School

VOLUME 42

1980

ANNUAL REVIEWS INC. 4139 EL CAMINO WAY PALO ALTO, CALIFORNIA 94306

ANNUAL REVIEWS INC.
Palo Alto, California, USA

REPRINTS The conspicuous number aligned in the margin with the title of each article in this volume is a key for use in ordering reprints. Available reprints are priced at the uniform rate of $1.00 each postpaid. The minimum acceptable reprint order is 5 reprints and/or $5.00 prepaid. A quantity discount is available.

International Standard Serial Number: 0066-4278
International Standard Book Number: 0-8243-0342-3
Library of Congress Catalog Card Number: 39-15404

PRINTED AND BOUND IN THE UNITED STATES OF AMERICA

PREFACE

Volume 41 (1979) of the *Annual Review of Physiology* introduced a new format consisting of seven sections, each under the editorship of an established specialist, representing major fields in physiology. The present volume (Volume 42) continues this format but is organized into eight sections: Renal & Electrolyte Physiology (T. E. Andreoli, Section Editor); Cardiovascular Physiology (R. M. Berne, Section Editor); Comparative and Integrative Physiology (W. R. Dawson, Section Editor); Respiratory Physiology (A. P. Fishman, Section Editor); Cell and Membrane Physiology (J. Gergely, Section Editor); Special Topic: Receptors in Excitable Cells (A. Karlin, Section Editor); Endocrinology and Metabolism (S. M. McCann, Section Editor); Gastrointestinal and Nutritional Physiology (S. G. Schultz, Section Editor).

The section format was dictated by the rapid and massive accumulation of information in physiology, where various domains and even sub-domains now require periodic coherent synthesis and reassessment. Therefore, in each Section each year a strategically circumscribed theme will be covered by a group of complementary reviews. By means of systematic coverage, year-by-year, of various component themes, we hope to provide a comprehensive progress report of the realm of physiology. (The field of neurophysiology, covered comprehensively by the *Annual Review of Neuroscience,* will be represented in the *Annual Review of Physiology* Special Topics Section.)

The new format should serve the need of the specialist to maintain an up-to-date store of information and should also encourage a global view of physiology. Moreover, thematic analysis, which is not confined to cataloging masses of observations, provides authors with the opportunity for creative advancement of knowledge. Because the ultimate judgment of the success of the sectional format must come from our readership, we welcome and await with uncommon interest the expression, both direct and indirect, of your views.

The substance and value of the reviews, no matter what the format, are determined by the insights and scholarship of the authors. Their efforts are acknowledged with gratitude and admiration. Equally deserving of accolades are the Section Editors, whose orchestrations determine the quality of the whole. A special commendation has been earned by Dr. W. R. Dawson, whose six years of service on the Editorial Committee have been marked by exceptional skill and devotion. It is appropriate to close the Preface with acknowledgment of the indispensable and expert efforts of the Production Editor, R. L. Burke, and his associates.

I. S. EDELMAN, EDITOR

SOME RELATED ARTICLES IN OTHER *ANNUAL REVIEWS*

From the *Annual Review of Biochemistry,* Volume 48, 1979

The Assembly of Proteins into Biological Membranes: The Membrane Trigger Hypothesis, William Wickner

Epidermal Growth Factor, Graham Carpenter and Stanley Cohen

Photoaffinity Labeling of Biological Systems, Vinay Chowdhry and F. H. Westheimer

Regulation of Protein Synthesis in Eukaryotes, Severo Ochoa and Cesar de Haro

From the *Annual Review of Microbiology,* Volume 33, 1979

Dynamics of the Macrophage Plasma Membrane, Steven H Zuckerman and Steven D. Douglas

Perspectives on the In Vivo Location of Cellular Interactions in the Humoral Immune Response, Judith Rae Lumb

The Biology of Gastrointestinal Bacteroides, Joan M. Macy and Irmelin Probst

From the *Annual Review of Neuroscience,* Volume 2, 1979

Visual Transduction in Vertebrate Photoreceptors, Wayne L. Hubbell and M. Deric Bownds

Biochemistry of Neurotransmitter Release, Regis B. Kelly, James W. Deutsch, Steven S. Carlson, and John A. Wagner

Axonal Transport: Components, Mechanisms, and Specificity, James H. Schwartz

The Development of Behavior in Human Infants, Premature and Newborn, Peter H. Wolff and Richard Ferber

From the *Annual Review of Pharmacology and Toxicology,* Volume 19, 1979

Salt in Hypertension and the Effects of Diuretics, Edward D. Freis

H-2 Histamine Receptors, Basil I. Hirschowitz

β-Adrenoceptor Blocking Drugs in Hypertension, Alexander Scriabine

Perinatal Renal Pharmacology, Jerry B. Hook and Michael D. Bailie

Annual Review of Physiology
Volume 42, 1980

CONTENTS

ANNUAL REVIEWS INC. is a nonprofit corporation established to promote the advancement of the sciences. Beginning in 1932 with the *Annual Review of Biochemistry,* the Company has pursued as its principal function the publication of high quality, reasonably priced Annual Review volumes. The volumes are organized by Editors and Editorial Committees who invite qualified authors to contribute critical articles reviewing significant developments within each major discipline.

Annual Reviews are published in the following sciences: Anthropology, Astronomy and Astrophysics, Biochemistry, Biophysics and Bioengineering, Earth and Planetary Sciences, Ecology and Systematics, Energy, Entomology, Fluid Mechanics, Genetics, Materials Science, Medicine, Microbiology, Neuroscience, Nuclear and Particle Science, Pharmacology and Toxicology, Physical Chemistry, Physiology, Phytopathology, Plant Physiology, Psychology, Public Health, and Sociology. In addition, five special volumes have been published by Annual Reviews Inc.: *History of Entomology* (1973), *The Excitement and Fascination of Science* (1965), *The Excitement and Fascination of Science, Volume Two* (1978), *Annual Reviews Reprints: Cell Membranes, 1975–1977* (published 1978), and *Annual Reviews Reprints: Immunology, 1977–1979* (published 1980). For the convenience of readers, a detachable order form/envelope is bound into the back of this volume.

Hans H. Ussing

Ann. Rev. Physiol. 1980. 42:1–16

LIFE WITH TRACERS ❖1250

Hans H. Ussing

Institute of Biological Chemistry A, University of Copenhagen, Copenhagen, Denmark

OPENING

In New York in 1952 I participated in a symposium on kidney physiology sponsored by the Macy Foundation. As a part of the program we were interviewed about what had motivated us to become physiologists. The organizer of the meeting asked his first victim: "Why did you become a physiologist?" The answer came without hesitation: "I was without a job and Homer Smith offered me one." The organizer put the same question to the next participant. Answer: "I was without a job and Homer Smith offered me one." When it was my turn I answered: "I was without a job and August Krogh offered me one." I mention this incident not only to illustrate the element of sheer luck that determines one's destiny, but also to emphasize the role played by influential scientific personalities in directing the interest of young people toward particular fields. Becoming a physiologist, however, requires both motive and opportunity. I graduated from the University of Copenhagen in 1934 during the Great Depression, and opportunities for a University career were few, even when one was motivated. And motivated I was. As far back as I can remember, I had no doubt that I wanted to become a scientist. During high school my main interest oscillated between biology and chemistry. Finally biology got the upper hand.

MARINE BIOLOGIST

In 1933 I was offered the chance of participating as marine biologist and hydrographer in *The Lauge Koch's* 3 year expedition to East Greenland.

My own collections from that year plus all samples of plankton collected by other zoologists of the expedition during a three year period were placed

0066-4278/80/0315-0001$01.00

at my disposal and served as the basis for my dissertation on the biology of some important planktons in the fiords of East Greenland. My scientific future seemed to have been settled: I was to become a marine biologist.

But I was detoured. During my work with planktons I had been hindered by the fact that the larval stages of various species of copepods (a group of small crustaceans that, due to their number, play an enormous role in the biology of the sea) seemed virtually indistinguishable. I then got the idea that it might be possible to prepare antibodies against the various larvae and precipitate one species at a time.

ENCOUNTER WITH D_2O

Before starting on such an enterprise I discussed the idea with my professor of physiology, August Krogh. He found it attractive but advised me to contact the Serum Institute concerning the procedure. Then he switched to another subject, showing me a small glass vial that contained 1 ml of a clear fluid and asking me what I thought it was. I looked at it and shook it, judging its surface tension and viscosity. "It looks like water," I said. "It is water," he answered, "but not ordinary water. It is heavy water." Krogh anticipated that heavy water and heavy hydrogen compounds might become enormously important in the study of permeability problems, and H. C. Urey, the discoverer of deuterium, had given him this little sample. Krogh told me at some length about his plans for using heavy water in his research. Two days later he telephoned to tell me that I could start in his laboratory the following Monday to help him discover the uses of heavy water in biology. It never occurred to either of us that my answer could be anything but yes. For me, then, marine biology and the precipitation of plankton larvae were things of the past. Isotopes had entered my life to stay.

The use of isotopes in biology was not entirely new. G. Hevesy, who invented the use of isotopic tracers, had been living in Copenhagen for some time as a permanent guest in Niels Bohr's Institute for Theoretical Physics. Hevesy, a close friend of Krogh and a frequent guest at our afternoon coffee break, tried to stimulate the interest of biologists in the use of tracers. But before deuterium was discovered all available tracers had been nonbiological elements such as uranium, lead, bismuth, etc. A tracer for hydrogen was of infinitely greater biological importance.

LIFE IN THE ZOOPHYSIOLOGICAL LABORATORY

At the time I started my career as a physiologist, August Krogh's zoophysiological laboratory exhibited a whole spectrum of activities. Over the years Krogh had worked successfully on many aspects of physiology, each time attracting new students and collaborators. A sizable group worked on respiratory metabolism both in man and in marine animals. Capillary physiology was also represented. Landis had just left, but among our guests were Knisely and Beecher.

Krogh's new interest, osmotic regulation, was represented by A. Keys from the United States, R. Dean (who first proposed the term "sodium pump"), H. Koch from Louvain, and Wigglesworth from England, to mention just a few of the visitors. Among the Danish staff members I must mention Marie Krogh, August Krogh's wife; his first assistant and later successor, P. Brandt Rehberg (the inventor of the creatinine-clearance method); and the heavy labor physiologist, Hohwü Christensen.

It was a fascinating experience for me to land in that international milieu. The afternoon coffee break at 3 P.M. was a permanent institution. Invariably the gathering resulted in a lively scientific discussion in which everybody took part, though most of the time Krogh and Rehberg were the main actors. Problems of physiological interest were defined, and the possible lines of attack were mustered. In these discussions Krogh was usually the *advocatus celesti* and Rehberg the *advocatus diaboli.* Rehberg, with his enormous learnedness and keen critical intelligence, would prove that a certain experiment could not be done, Krogh would then counter by proposing an elegant approach that might make the experiment feasible after all. This benevolent intellectual fencing was an invaluable drill for us young scientists, more valuable than formal teaching. For good or bad, the atmosphere in the laboratory led us to believe that no problem was too difficult if approached with clear analysis and common sense.

The reader may wonder how the activities in the lab were financed at a time of world depression. Grants from the Carlsberg Foundation, the Rockefeller Foundation, and other granting agencies played a role, but an equally important part was played by the production and sale of equipment for use in hospitals and research institutions. Instruments like respirometers, bicycle ergometers, etc, were developed on the basis of Krogh's inventions, and the profits helped to finance the lab. This also meant that we had a first-class mechanical shop, invaluable for our research. Furthermore, inventing and producing equipment for our own research became second nature for all of us. Krogh was an expert glassblower and taught me the art.

My first task was to develop a method for estimating the toxicity of heavy water. In the meantime Hevesy, Hofer & Krogh (3) studied the permeability of frog skin to water, comparing osmotic permeability to diffusion permeability, as measured with heavy water. The data did not agree; osmotic permeability was several times larger than diffusion permeability when expressed in the same units (e.g. $cm^2 \ sec^{-1}$).

We shall return to this discrepancy later. At the time Krogh concluded that until the reason for the discrepancy was found it would not be safe to use heavy water for determining water permeabilities.

USE OF DEUTERIUM LABELLING FOR ESTIMATING PROTEIN SYNTHESIS

My interests temporarily shifted to something entirely different: In connection with our early permeability studies on living animals we found that some deuterium disappeared from the water and had entered organic substances (mostly proteins) in the tissues. This problem fascinated me and I wanted to find out how deuterium could enter stable positions in the proteins.

Krogh felt that this study required more chemical experience than our laboratory could muster and arranged for me to do the protein work, including separation of the amino acids, at the Carlsberg Laboratory. That was a piece of good luck for me. The head of the Carlsberg Lab was S. P. L. Sørensen, a prominent protein chemist and the inventor of the term pH. He was friendly and benevolent towards me, but the problem of hydrogen-deuterium exchange did not interest him very much. However, his first assistant (and later his successor) K. Linderström-Lang immediately realized the importance of using deuterium in protein chemistry and helped me in every respect to aquire the necessary knowledge of protein chemistry and other aspects of biochemistry. More than that, he became a friend to whom I could always turn when I wanted to discuss difficult physico-chemical problems.

The use of deuterium in the study of protein metabolism opened new horizons for me. In all directions lay unbroken soil. Independently of the Schoenheimer-Rittenberg group at Columbia University (and slightly earlier), I demonstrated (21) that deuterium-labelled amino acids were introduced into certain body proteins at a surprising speed so that, in mice and rats, the renewal time was only a few days. I worked out a method for quantitative determination of the renewal rate for proteins by maintaining a constant level of D_2O in the body water of the animals and following the kinetics of build-up of stably bound deuterium in various protein fractions (22). I saw clearly my future as a protein biochemist.

Then came the war, and Denmark was occupied. This hampered our research. When the Norwegian heavy water plant at Riukan was blown up by the Norwegian resistance movement our deuterium work was brought to a complete stop.

Three lucky things happened to me during the otherwise miserable years of occupation. In 1940 I married Annemarie Fuchs, in 1942 our daughter

Kirsten was born, and the same year I became lecturer in biochemistry for the science students while keeping my research position at the Zoophysiological Laboratory. The teaching job induced me to study not only biochemistry but also physical chemistry and organic chemistry. In particular, the contact with the brilliant but rather awe inspiring professor of physical chemistry, Brønsted, was valuable for my later work.

The years of occupation became increasingly grim. I lectured to my students in our home for fear that they should be rounded up by the Gestapo (some of my students were very active in the resistance movement). Krogh sought refuge in Sweden because he was known to be on the list of potential hostages. Rehberg was finally arrested by the Gestapo (and later had a very narrow escape from the burning Gestapo headquarters). Thus the laboratory limped along with a skeleton staff and no supplies.

TRACER STUDIES OF ACTIVE AND PASSIVE TRANSPORT

The war ended. Our son Niels was born the day Allied forces entered Copenhagen. I expected to continue isotope work with proteins and amino acid metabolism, but things turned out differently.

In 1945 Krogh retired as head of the Zoophysiological Laboratory and was succeeded by Poul Brandt Rehberg. Krogh moved his research to a private laboratory (in the basement of his house) where he wanted to devote his time to his new interest, the flight of insects. Before retirement he had planned to initiate and supervise a program at the Lab to study active and passive exchanges of inorganic ions through the surface of living cells, using radioactive isotopes. He developed the rationale behind the project in an important review, his Croonian Lecture of 1946 (11), and had already done an experimental paper on the giant cells of the brackish water characean, *Nitella* (5). The idea was that the constant exchange of inorganic ions between cells and their surroundings must mean an active transport of certain (or maybe all?) species in one direction and leakage in the opposite direction. If a certain ion species exhibits a sufficiently large concentration drop across the cell membrane, one must assume that the flow of ions is almost exclusively active in one direction and passive in the other. In such cases the ion exchange as measured with an isotope under steady-state conditions should simultaneously yield the rate of active transport and the leak permeability.

As we shall see in a moment this argument does not always hold, but conceptually it was a very important step forward. The work of Hevesy and other pioneers in the use of isotopes had revealed that many ionic species, thought to be nonpenetrating, exhibited a more or less lively "exchange" across cell membranes, but the mechanisms underlying the exchanges had not been rigorously analyzed. Such mechanisms were hardly discussed in the papers describing the exchanges. Now Krogh postulated that the process could be resolved into two well-defined processes: an active transport that consumed metabolic energy, and a passive leak that was a simple physical process.

Originally he planned to locate the project in the Zoophysiological Laboratory and to staff it with a few young physiologists working under his guidance. Because the start of the project was delayed until after his retirement, Krogh asked me to supervise it until it was well on its way. I had two good reasons for joining the new project. In the first place it was essential that so important a project not go astray in its initial phase. Second, as Krogh pointed out, the fact that our University had a cyclotron at the Bohr Institute and that Niels Bohr actively supported biological applications of isotopes gave us a unique chance to do pioneer work with respect to transport of inorganic ions. Carbon 14 had just become available for biochemical applications and everybody in the isotope field would soon rush to apply carbon-labelled substances in metabolic studies. In the meantime, we might have the inorganic ions for ourselves for a while. I therefore accepted the task and decided to join the project for a year or two before returning to my beloved amino acids and proteins; but I never returned. The supposedly temporary task has lasted until this day.

The team that started on the project consisted of Hilde Levi (one of Hevesy's former associates), C. Barker Jørgensen, a young physiologist who had done his thesis work at our lab, and myself. We decided to try the isotope experiments in two very different systems: live axolotls submerged in water, and isolated frog sartorius muscle.

ANTIDIURETIC HORMONE STIMULATES ACTIVE SODIUM TRANSPORT

Ten years earlier Krogh and his associates had demonstrated that frogs and many other freshwater animals take up sodium chloride from the surrounding water. This capacity is very well developed in axolotls. Krogh had assumed that the active salt uptake was regulated by a sort of mass action effect, so that low salt levels in the blood would induce an increased uptake. For the sake of argument I then proposed that the uptake might be regulated hormonally. In our storeroom I could find only one candidate (aldosterone had not yet been isolated): antidiuretic hormone. I had happily forgotten that, according to the kidney physiologists, ADH had no effect whatsoever on salt resorption. We injected ADH into the axolotls and, lo and behold, both sodium and chloride uptake were dramatically increased. This could be seen both from chemical analysis and from changes in the rate of uptake of ^{38}Cl and ^{24}Na (6). Later, as is well known, it turned out that ADH and related hormones stimulate sodium transport in many epithelia.

SODIUM EXCHANGE IN SARTORIUS MUSCLE

One thing worried me, though. Clearly sodium chloride was taken up, but the uptake was often different for the two ions. Thus they behaved like independent species. Was the uptake active for both species, or was only one transported actively, creating an electric potential difference that in turn brought about the uptake of the other? We turned to our second experimental object, muscle, where the sign and magnitude of the electric potential drop were known so that one could say with certainty which of the ions had to move against an electrochemical potential gradient.

It was well-established that muscle fibers were negative inside, that their cellular concentration of sodium was low, and that their potassium concentration was high. Now, we could easily show that ^{24}Na in the medium exchanged with all of the sodium in the muscle. By following the washout of radio-sodium from the muscle we resolved the process into two first-order processes: the wash-out of interspace sodium, and the exchange of sodium across the fiber membrane. Since sodium moved out across the fiber membrane against an electric potential gradient as well as against a concentration gradient, the process clearly involved active transport.

EXCHANGE DIFFUSION

I did a quick calculation to find out what fraction of the energy output of the muscle would be necessary to drive the "sodium pump." I found to my horror that the energy requirement surpassed the total available energy output as estimated from the oxygen consumption. This led me to ask whether any of our original assumptions could be false.

Finally it dawned on me that an exchange of an ion species across a membrane can proceed without consumption of free energy even if the ion is present at different electrochemical potentials in the two bathing solutions, but it is only possible under very particular conditions: The passage of an ion in one direction must be strictly coupled to the passage of a similar ion in the opposite direction, so that the free energy gained by the downhill transport is used for the uphill transport. On the molecular level this could be achieved if, for instance, there existed in the membrane phase a carrier molecule that could only pass from one boundary to the other in association with the ion species in question. This would inevitably lead to a one-to-one exchange of the ion, irrespective of the potential difference or concentration difference between the bathing solutions. Instead of by a diffusing carrier, the exchange might be brought about by a specific ion-binding molecule or site that could flip-flop between two positions, alternately exposing the binding site to the two bathing solutions (15, 23). Clearly, the phenomenon that I named "exchange diffusion" will also occur even for carriers that can pass the membrane in the free state if the ion in question is present in so high a concentration on both sides of the membrane that all carrier molecules are saturated at both boundaries (cf 26).

The phenomenon of exchange diffusion later turned out to be quite widespread in nature. As is well known, it is of great functional importance in physiology and biochemistry in cases where two or more molecular or ionic species share the same carrier system (counter-transport of Cl and bicarbonate in erythrocytes, antiport systems in mitochondria, etc). At the time, however, it meant that an abyss opened under the original plan of our experiments. Without additional information one obviously could not use steady-state fluxes of isotopes for measuring either active transport or leak permeability because part of the flux might be exchange diffusion. In our experiments with axolotls, active transport certainly occurred, because salt moved from a lower to a higher concentration; but unless one knew the direction and magnitude of the electric potential difference between blood and bath it was impossible to tell whether sodium, chloride, or possibly both, were actively transported. Thus we had to look for a system where all necessary parameters could be measured simultaneously.

THE FROG SKIN AS TEST OBJECT

I decided to begin with the isolated frog skin, mostly because I found it easier to skin a frog than an axolotl but also because Krogh had demonstrated that frogs can take up both sodium and chloride from very dilute solutions.

When mounted as a diaphragm separating suitable solutions (e.g. Ringer's), the isolated frog skin maintains high and rather stable potential differences, the inside bath being positive relative to that on the outside. One can then add radioisotopes of Na and Cl to the bathing solutions and measure the rates of appearance of tracers on each side. This approach soon gave a qualitatively clear answer: Sodium moved faster in the inward than in the outward direction, even when the movement took place against a concentration or a potential gradient. Hence, at least part of the sodium transport must be an active process. At least part of the chloride transfer might take place due to the electric field, but it was not possible at that time to tell which part of the chloride transport could be accounted for by "simple" electrodiffusion, i.e. the combined effect of concentration gradient and electric field.

THE FLUX RATIO EQUATION

Could an equation describing electrodiffusion of isotopic tracers through a biological structure be worked out? Having discussed this problem with Linderstrøm-Lang one Saturday afternoon, I worked hard on the problem and Monday morning called him with a solution. He, too, had worked out a solution, which was not identical to mine. In order to solve the appropriate differential equation he had used the constant concentration gradient assumption, whereas I had used the constant field assumption.

The worrisome thing was that although I now had two solutions to my problem I could trust neither. In a frog skin, or any epithelium for that matter, there must be several diffusion barriers in series: cell membranes, basement membrane, connective tissue, etc. To assume a constant field or a constant concentration gradient in such a system would be rash. However, while I was playing around with the two equations I made an odd observation: If I divided the expression for the forward flux by that for the backward flux both solutions then yielded the same equation. I suspected that the flux ratio for an ion that moves without interacting with other moving particles was a sort of state function, being independent of the properties of the barriers along its path (25).

By the time I worked out the proof for the flux ratio equation I had a temporary appointment as Rockefeller Fellow at the Donner Laboratory, University of California. It was customary for staff members at the Zoophysiological Laboratory in Copenhagen to spend one year abroad as Rockefeller Fellows after they had obtained tenure, and in 1948 it was my turn. Annemarie and I and our children Kirsten (5 year) and Niels (3 years) were installed in a one-room apartment in Oakland (later two rooms in Berkeley), and I started working in the Radiation Laboratory. Unfortunately, I had not forseen the need for a supply grant. In Copenhagen I obtained isotopes free from the Bohr Institute, but in Berkeley one had to pay. I found, however, that the clinicians at the Donner Lab used large amounts of isotopes, notably ^{24}Na and ^{131}I, for treating patients; by rinsing their empty bottles I recovered plenty of tracer material for my own work. Thus I was able to illustrate the usefulness of the flux ratio equation by showing that iodide behaved as a passive ion when passing the frog skin whereas sodium moved almost exclusively by active transport (16).

Although most of the staff at the Donner Lab used radioisotopes for one purpose or another, nobody worked on problems even remotely related to mine. Yet I was far from feeling lost. Among the senior staff Drs. Hardin Jones and Nello Pace were particularly helpful and I developed a lasting friendship with the scientists with whom I shared laboratory space. Furthermore, Berkeley was (I guess it still is?) a fascinating place. I remember that I was particularly impressed by the work of Calvin and Benzon on photosynthesis, which had just gotten underway.

THE SHORT-CIRCUITED FROG SKIN

During my stay in Berkeley I gave a seminar on sodium transport across the frog skin and one student expressed doubt that active sodium transport is the main source of the frog skin potential. He pointed out that his former teacher, Professor E. J. Lund, had shown the frog skin potential to be a redox potential. I found that assumption extremely unlikely since redox potentials cannot be picked up via a KCl bridge. Nevertheless I accepted the student's offer to lend me Lund's book, *Bioelectric Fields and Growth* (19). The book did not change my view, but I noticed something of great importance for my future work: Lund & Stapp (19) had attempted to draw electric current from frog skins via reversible lead-lead chloride electrodes. When I recalculated the currents drawn from frog skins in terms of sodium fluxes they turned out to be roughly the same order of magnitude as the isotope fluxes I had measured. Of course this similarity might have been fortuitous. Nevertheless, a plan took shape: If one could "short-circuit" the skin via suitable electrodes so that the potential drop across was reduced to zero and if the bathing solutions were identical then only actively transported ions could contribute to the current passing the skin; the flux ratio for passive ions would become one. By then, however, my stay at Berkeley was over and I had to return to Copenhagen. The idea of short-circuiting frog skins was put aside for a while.

After my return to Denmark we succeeded in showing that the fluxes of chloride through frog skin obeyed the flux ratio equation, indicating that virtually all of the chloride passed the skin passively, even when there was a net inward transport against a concentration gradient (9).

In the meantime the 18th International Physiology Congress to be held in Copenhagen in 1950 had been organized with August Krogh as President. (Krogh died before the congress began and Einar Lundsgaard had to take over the presidency; Poul Brandt Rehberg served as General Secretary.) Among the introductory talks, three were to be devoted to membrane transport problems. The speakers were to be Conway, Hodgkin, and myself. Of course I was pleased but also a bit worried. I planned to talk about the use of the flux ratio equation for distinguishing between active and passive transport, but did this justify that I, a relative newcomer in the ion transport field, was to give a main talk in front of oldtimers? I felt that I needed some striking finding that would justify my place in the program. I looked at my list of future projects and settled on the short-circuiting experiments. But time was running out. It was essential for me to find an efficient co-worker then and there. Dr. K. Zerahn, one of professor Hevesy's former associates, was working on phosphate metabolism of yeast; but when I told him about my plan and its significance, in less than an hour, he decided to join the frog skin team. He never returned to yeast.

Zerahn wired up the circuit; I did the glass blowing and, helped by our mechanic, designed the chamber. Within a week we had the first results: During short-circuiting, the entire current drawn from the skin is accounted for by the net sodium flux (influx minus outflux). We had shown that the active sodium transport alone is responsible for the electric asymmetry of the frog skin. Within two weeks we had enough data to confirm the first findings and to warrant publication of the result (31).

SOLVENT DRAG

We now had the tools for analyzing transport processes in epithelia: The flux ratio equation and the short-circuiting technique were both theoretically satisfactory as long as there was no osmotic flow through the system. I felt that as long as solutes and solvent follow separate pathways through the system the interaction could be neglected. But if there is bulk flow through narrow channels, ions and other solutes diffusing through the system will be speeded up in the direction of flow and slowed down in the opposite direction. Consequently the flux ratio, even for a passive species, would deviate from the predictions of the ideal flux ratio equation. Since such a "solvent drag" would also act on water it might explain the strange observation made by Hevesy, Hofer & Krogh (3) that the osmotic permeability of frog skin seemed larger than the diffusion permeability as measured with heavy water (see above).

A theory for the dependency of the flux ratio on solvent drag in composite systems was developed (7, 26). Predictions were verified in experiments on toad skin and frog skin: During osmotic flow, solvent drag effects do exist. These effects, however, were small compared to those bringing about active transport of sodium. Our equations for solvent drag are in complete agreement with those derived later from irreversible thermodynamics.

EXPLORING THE ROLE OF ACTIVE SODIUM TRANSPORT

In the fertile and stimulating years following the Copenhagen Physiological Congress a steady stream of visitors came to work with us. Most of the time the foreign and Danish visiting scientists outnumbered the permanent staff.

I must postpone telling the story of this period, except to mention a few developments that added to the store of concepts and tools having some general scientific applicability.

With the love for sweeping generalizations that is characteristic of mankind in general and of general physiologists in particular, I thought for a while that active sodium transport might be the charging device for all bioelectric potentials, at least in the animal kingdom. As early as 1951 we learned otherwise. Adrian Hogben (4), working in our lab, found that the potential developed across isolated toad gastric mucosa stems from active transport of chloride. In the following year we found that when stimulated by adrenaline (10) the skin glands of frog skin transported chloride in the outward direction. On the other hand we showed that active sodium transport was solely responsible for the electric asymmetry of isolated mucosa from toad large intestine and Guinea pig cecum. Of greater potential value was the isolated toad urinary bladder preparation developed by Alex Leaf (14) during his stay with us in 1954. This preparation later became the preferred test object in innumerable transport studies from many laboratories. Important developments were also triggered by Csaky & Thale's finding (1) that sodium is absolutely essential for the uptake of 3-methyl glucose through isolated toad small intestine. As is well known, the correct interpretation of this finding was later given by Crane in the form of the cotransport theory. One of my former associates, the late Peter Curran (visitor in our lab from 1959 to 1961) was to contribute greatly to our understanding of the role of cotransport for intestinal uptake of amino acids and other nutrients.

THE TWO-MEMBRANE THEORY FOR THE FROG SKIN POTENTIAL

For several years our main object was to sort out the transport processes due to active transport from those that were secondary consequences of active transport. For the exploratory stage of the studies the black-box treatment of the epithelium as a transporting entity was acceptable. After a while it became imperative to localize the mechanisms within the system. From the very beginning of my work with epithelia I had held the (rather obvious) opinion that the net transport of ions must depend on the inward and outward facing cell membranes' having different transport properties. The finding that in frog skin sodium transport was active while chloride transport was passive made it almost imperative that the sodium pump was located at the inward-facing boundary of the transporting cells (cf 24). Otherwise the cell interior would be overloaded with sodium. Another implication is that the outward-facing cell membrane must be tight to potassium. Otherwise the uptake of sodium in the cells would lead to an enormous loss of potassium.

Testing this hypothesis required a study of the ion selectivities of the outward- and inward-facing cell membranes of the epithelium. Our experimental approach was based upon the following consideration: If the skin potential results from the activity of the sodium pump, shunted by a chloride leak, it is clear that the potential measured must approach the electromotive force of the pump when the shunt conductance is reduced to zero. This situation can be approached, for instance, using the poorly permeating sulfate ion instead of chloride. Under these conditions when the compositions of the bathing solutions were varied the outward-facing side of the epithelium behaved like an almost ideal sodium electrode and the inward-facing membrane behaved like a potassium electrode.

The minimum requirements for a system that could take care of net salt transport and regulate the cell electrolyte composition at the same time would then be the following: The inward-facing membrane would have the same properties as any body cell. It would be permeable to potassium and chloride, be nearly tight to passively diffusing sodium ions, and would possess a sodium pump. We imagined that the sodium transport was performed by a sodium-potassium exchange pump (but any type of sodium pump would do). The outward-facing membrane (permeable to chloride and tight to potassium) was considered to be without active transport systems but to have a strictly selective sodium channel allowing passive sodium entry (8, 27).

This theory has had a peculiar destiny. At first it was generally accepted as a model for many epithelia. Then gradually each of its assumptions was contested. In recent years the pendulum has been swinging back: All of the original assumptions were essentially correct (28, 32). Larsen & Kristensen (12, 13) have worked out a computer program based on the assumptions of the two-membrane theory. This program predicts the steady-state electric properties of the frog skin quite satisfactorily under various conditions. Lew et al (17) have recently developed a similar program that predicts correctly even the potential and resistance transients when the system is suddenly modified. Very recently my associate Robert Nielsen has produced strong evidence (in preparation) that the ion pump is really a sodium-potassium exchange pump, with a coupling ratio of 3 Na for 2 K.

SHUNT PATHS

In our original version of the theory, based mainly on early microelectrode studies, we assumed the transporting cell layer to be the stratum germinativum in frog skin. Experiments with an improved technique (29, 30) have shown that the sodium-selective membrane must be the outward-facing surface of the outermost living cell layer, just underneath the cornified layer (which is mostly only one cell layer thick). We have modified the original model in two other respects: (*a*) Besides the transcellular chloride pathway we now assume a variable intercellular shunt pathway (via the "tight" seals) open to small ions, including sodium; (*b*) the different layers of epithelial cells are electrically coupled via a resistive cell-to-cell permeability to ions. Independently Farquhar & Palade (2) reached a similar conclusion, which also agreed with the concept of cell coupling advanced by Loewenstein (18). The idea of intercellular shunts was developed further by Windhager, Boulpaep & Giebisch (34) to describe the conductance of proximal kidney tubule. Later it was generally accepted as a property of "leaky epithelia."

COUPLING BETWEEN CELL LAYERS

The concept of coupling between different layers of epithelial cells has given rise to problems and apparent contradictions. Some studies have given clear evidence for the coupling in frog skins (20) while others have indicated very limited coupling (33). Current work by our group (R. Nielsen and H. H. Ussing, in preparation) indicates that both views may be correct, depending on the experimental circumstances. The coupling seems to vary with the degree of contact between the cells, which in turn depends on the intraepithelial pressure.

CODA

My academic position has undergone a few changes over the years. In 1951 I obtained a research professorship in zoophysiology but continued to teach biochemistry to science students. In 1960 I was asked to take over the chairmanship of the Institute of Biological Chemistry. With some reluctance I accepted the offer, because I assumed that biological transport phenomena were then ripe for study on the molecular level. As it turned out, epithelial transport studies took more time to pass from biophysics to biochemistry than anticipated. With retirement looming less than three years ahead I can no longer hope to take an active part in this development; but as long as I live I shall be an interested onlooker. In the meantime there are still plenty of tempting problems of a more biophysical nature to which I can devote my time.

Literature Cited

1. Csàky, T. Z., Thale, M. 1960. Effect of ionic environment on intestinal sugar transport. *J. Physiol. London* 151:59–65
2. Farquhar, M. G., Palade, G. E. 1964. Functional organization of amphibian skin. *Proc. Natl. Acad. Sci. USA* 51:569–77
3. Hevesy, G., Hofer, E., Krogh, A. 1935. The permeability of the skin of frogs to water as determined by D_2O and H_2O. *Skand. Arch. Physiol.* 72:199–214
4. Hogben, C. A. M. 1955. Active transport of chloride by isolated frog gastric epithelium. *Am. J. Physiol.* 180:641–49
5. Holm-Jensen, I., Krogh, A., Wartiovaara, V. 1944. Some experiments on the exchange of potassium and sodium between single cells of Characeae and the bathing fluid. *Acta Bot. Fenn.* 36:1–22
6. Jörgensen, C. B., Levi, H., Ussing, H. H. 1946. On the influence of the neurohypophyseal principles on the sodium metabolism in the axolotl (*Ambystoma mexicanum*). *Acta Physiol. Scand.* 12:350–71
7. Koefoed-Johnsen, V., Ussing, H. H. 1953. The contributions of diffusion and flow to the passage of D_2O through living membranes. *Acta Physiol. Scand.* 28:60–76
8. Koefoed-Johnsen, V., Ussing, H. H. 1958. The nature of the frog skin potential. *Acta Physiol. Scand.* 42:298–308
9. Koefoed-Johnsen, V., Levi, H., Ussing, H. H. 1952. The mode of passage of chloride ions through the isolated frog skin. *Acta Physiol. Scand.* 25:150–63
10. Koefoed-Johnsen, V., Ussing, H. H. Zerahn, K. 1952. The origin of the short-circuit current in the adrenaline stimulated frog skin. *Acta Physiol. Scand.* 27:38–48
11. Krogh, A. 1946. Croonian Lecture: The active and passive exchanges of inorganic ions through the surface of living cells and through living membranes generally. *Proc. R. Soc. Ser. B* 133:140–200
12. Larsen, E. H., Kristensen, P. 1978. Properties of a conductive cellular chloride pathway in the skin of the toad (*Bufo bufo*). *Acta Physiol. Scand.* 102:1–21
13. Larsen, E. H. 1978. Computed steady-state ion concentrations and volume of epithelial cells. Dependence on transcellular Na^+ transport. *Alfred Benzon Symp. XI, Munksgaard,* pp. 438–56
14. Leaf, A. 1955. Ion transport by the isolated bladder of the toad. *Res. Comm. 3^e Congr. Int. Biochim., Brussels,* p. 107.
15. Levi, H., Ussing, H. H. 1948. The exchange of sodium and chloride across the fibre membrane of the isolated frog sartorius. *Acta Physiol. Scand.* 16:232–49
16. Levi, H., Ussing, H. H. 1949. Resting potential and ion movements in the frog skin. *Nature* 164:928–30
17. Lew, V. L., Ferreira, H. G., Moura, T. 1979. The behaviour of transporting epithelial cells. I. Computer analysis of a basic model. *Proc. R. Soc. Ser. B.* In press
18. Loewenstein, W. R., Kanno, Y. 1964. Studies on an epithelial (gland) cell junction. I. Modifications of surface membrane permeability. *J. Cell Biol.* 22:565
19. Lund, E. J., Stapp, P. 1947. Biocoulometry 1. Use of iodine coulometer in the measurement of bioelectrical energy and the efficiency of the bioelectrical process. In *Bioelectric Fields and Growth,* pp. 235–80. Austin: Univ. Texas Press
20. Rick, R., Dörge, A., von Arnum, E., Thurau, K. 1978. Electron microprobe analysis of frog skin epithelium: Evidence for a syncytial sodium transport compartment. *J. Membr. Biol.* 39:313–31
21. Ussing, H. H. 1938. Use of amino acids containing deuterium to follow protein production in the organism. *Nature* 142:399
22. Ussing, H. H. 1941. The rate of protein renewal in mice and rats studied by means of heavy hydrogen. *Acta Physiol. Scand.* 2:209–21
23. Ussing, H. H. 1947. Interpretation of the exchange of radio-sodium in the isolated muscle. *Nature* 160:262
24. Ussing, H. H. 1948. The use of tracers in the study of active ion transport across animal membranes. *Cold Springs Harbor Symp. Quant. Biol.* 13:193–200
25. Ussing, H. H. 1949. The distinction by means of tracers between active transport and diffusion. *Acta Physiol. Scand.* 19:43–56
26. Ussing, H. H. 1952. Some aspects of the application of tracers in permeability studies. *Adv. Enzymol.* 13:21–65
27. Ussing, H. H., Koefoed-Johnsen, V. 1956. Nature of the frog skin potential. *Abstr. Commun. 20th Int. Physiol. Congr., Brussels.* 568 pp.
28. Ussing, H. H., Leaf, A. 1978. Transport across multimembrane systems. In

Membrane Transport in Biology, ed. G. Giebisch, D. C. Tosteson, H. H. Ussing, 3:1–26. Berlin/Heidelberg/New York: Springer. 459 pp.

29. Ussing, H. H., Windhager, E. E. 1964. Nature of shunt path and active sodium transport path through frog skin epithelium. *Acta Physiol. Scand.* 61:484–504
30. Ussing, H. H., Windhager, E. E. 1964. Active sodium transport at the cellular level. In *Water and Electrolyte Metabolism,* ed. J. de Graeff, B. Leijnse, 2:3–19. Amsterdam: Elsevier
31. Ussing, H. H., Zerahn, K. 1951. Active transport of sodium as the source of electric current in the short-circuited isolated frog skin. *Acta Physiol. Scand.* 23:110–27
32. Ussing, H. H., Erlij, D., Lassen, U. 1974. Transport pathways in biological membranes. *Ann. Rev. Physiol.* 36: 17–49
33. Voûte, C. L., Ussing, H. H. 1968. Some morphological aspects of active sodium transport. The epithelium of the frog skin. *J. Cell Biol.* 36:625–38
34. Windhager, E. E., Boulpaep, E. L., Giebisch, G. 1967. Electrophysiological studies on single nephrons. *Proc. 3rd Int. Congr. Nephrol. Washington DC, 1966,* 1:35–47. Basel/New York: Karger

ENDOCRINOLOGY AND METABOLISM

Ann. Rev. Physiol. 1980. 42:17–35

DYNAMICS OF STEROID HORMONE RECEPTOR ACTION

❖1251

Benita S. Katzenellenbogen

Department of Physiology and Biophysics, University of Illinois, and School of Basic Medical Sciences, University of Illinois College of Medicine, Urbana, Illinois 61801

INTRODUCTION

The steroid hormones—estrogens, progestins, androgens, glucocorticoids, and mineralocorticoids—are chemically quite simple molecules, yet their biological activities are exquisitely specific. Their diverse effects include metabolic, morphological, and behavioral changes. At least part of their hormonal specificity resides in the fact that different tissues contain proteins that selectively bind only certain classes of active steroids; hence, the tissue "selects" the hormone with which it will interact by possessing high affinity binding proteins, or "receptors," for a particular class of steroid hormones.

Here I review recent information on (*a*) the multihormonal regulation of steroid hormone receptors and steroid hormone action in selected tissues and (*b*) the temporal and quantitative relationships between hormone receptor binding and the stimulation of biological responses in target tissues. I discuss only briefly some recent advances in the biochemistry of steroid hormone receptors since several excellent reviews have covered the state of knowledge through 1976 (15, 41, 55, 114). In view of my own interests and because this review serves as a prelude to reports on the reproductive system, I emphasize receptors for the sex steroid hormones, in particular the estrogen receptor.

THE CONCEPT OF "RECEPTORS" AND "TARGET TISSUES"

The accumulation of studies on steroid hormone–target tissue interactions has led to an increasing refinement of the concepts of target tissue and receptor. Prolonged hormone retention was the initial hallmark of a target

0066-4278/80/0315-0017$01.00

tissue (39, 51) and still remains a most important characteristic of target tissues. Increasingly sensitive hormone binding assays have revealed, however, that some tissues previously considered to be nontarget tissues do contain low but significant levels of receptor, and that such tissues do respond to hormone under certain circumstances. Hence, there appears to be a spectrum in terms of receptor content and the responsiveness of different tissues to a given class of steroid hormones.

For example, estrogen receptor levels are highest in tissues of the reproductive system including the uterus, vagina, and mammary glands (where estrogen exerts a major growth promoting influence) and in the pituitary and certain regions of the hypothalamus (which serve as feedback sites regulating pituitary hormone output and influencing sexual behavior in some species). However, high affinity estrogen binding proteins are also found, in lower concentrations, in liver (4), kidney (65), adrenal (23, 78), and ovary (91). Most of these tissues do show characteristic changes in response to estrogenic hormones. In the mammalian liver, the administration of estrogens (including the use of oral contraceptives) increases the production of plasma renin substrate, some blood clotting factors, and other serum proteins that normally increase during pregnancy. In avian and amphibian species, estrogen plays an essential role in the induction of the egg yolk protein, vitellogenin. In the ovary, estrogen modulation of the binding of follicle stimulating hormone and of follicular development may be mediated via ovarian estrogen receptors.

Recent studies reemphasize the differential effects of hormones on different cell populations within a tissue or organ. Autoradiographic studies of estrogen receptor localization in uterus and pituitary (107, 108) and studies utilizing fluorescent estrogens as tags for the estrogen receptor in mammary tumors and normal rat uterus (25, 89) indicate the nonhomogeneous distribution of receptors throughout target tissues. These considerations are fundamental to understanding the highly specific actions of hormones and also the effects of both physiological and pharmacological doses of steroid hormones on the biology of normal tissues and on the growth and regression of tumors.

HORMONE RECEPTOR DYNAMICS AND THE INDUCTION OF BIOLOGICAL RESPONSES

The general model of initial steroid hormone interaction with a cytoplasmic receptor, followed by activation of the hormone receptor complex and its translocation to the nucleus where its interaction alters the pattern of gene expression (41, 114), still appears to provide a suitable outline for receptor interactions at the target cell level. The receptors for steroid hormones are found in the cytoplasm of most, but not all (see below), target cells in the absence of hormone; a cytoplasmic exclusion hypothesis (34) and the presence of specific nuclear components that "accept" or bind the hormone-receptor complex ["acceptor" sites, reviewed in (41) and (109)] have been proposed to account for these changes in distribution of receptor in the absence and presence of hormone.

Advances that promise further elucidation of receptor dynamics include the isolation of highly purified receptors and the preparation of antibodies to receptors, the development of affinity labeling receptor reagents (57), kinetic studies on nuclear and cytoplasmic receptor forms (83), and the synthetic development of ligands with a high affinity for tissue receptors but a greatly reduced interaction with serum binding proteins (84). Purification of the progesterone receptor from the chick oviduct has clearly progressed the furthest (102), and the availability of defined fragments of hormone inducible chick genes cloned in bacterial plasmids has enabled a detailed analysis of the genomic interaction of receptor (101). The estrogen receptor from calf endometrium has been purified greatly by conventional protein purification methods, and the generation of antibodies to this receptor has revealed immunological crossreactivity between nuclear and cytoplasmic estrogen receptors and between estrogen receptors of different mammalian species and target tissues (43).

Receptor Activation

The process of receptor activation, whereby the initial steroid cytoplasmic receptor complex is converted into a form with high affinity for the nucleus and capacity for the induction of biological responses, continues to be investigated vigorously. Elegant kinetic and molecular analyses (83) support a model for estrogen receptor activation involving estrogen-induced receptor dimerization or association with a dissimilar protein, with the resultant conversion of the 4S cytoplasmic estradiol binding protein ($\sim$75,000 mol wt) to the 5S estradiol binding protein ($\sim$140,000 mol wt). This receptor transformation is both hormone- and temperature-dependent, and only the activated 5S receptor form shows a high affinity for uterine nuclei and is reported capable of increasing RNA polymerase activity (76). Other studies (113) have also concluded that the 5S estrogen binding protein consists of the 4S estrogen receptor plus an additional protein. This additional protein was found (113) in nontarget, as well as target, tissues. Analyses (83) also suggest that in the absence of hormone the 4S binding protein is associated with an inhibitory macromolecule from which it must dissociate before it can form the 5S estrogen binding protein.

Evidence has been presented for a dialyzable (and hence presumably low molecular weight) inhibitory molecule(s) in cytosol of mouse Leydig cell tumors (98) and rat uterus (99) that inhibits estrogen receptor activation. A similar low molecular weight inhibitor of glucocorticoid receptor activation has also been reported (5, 40). In the glucocorticoid receptor system, activation is associated with a change in isoelectric point of the receptor but does not involve any significant change in sedimentation behavior, as is seen for the estrogen receptor (53, 86). The observation, in the case of the estrogen receptor, that activation of cytosol by dialysis does not require the presence of hormone, makes it of special interest (99).

The progesterone receptor of chick oviduct can also be transformed by warming, as well as by high salt treatment, to acquire the capacity to bind to nuclei or to certain resins, such as ATP-Sepharose, DNA-cellulose, or phosphocellulose (75). Recent studies have shown that sodium molybdate, a potent phosphatase inhibitor that has been shown to stabilize glucocorticoid receptors (81) and androgen and progesterone receptors (82), appears to interfere with the transformation of the progesterone receptor (82). Since molybdate is a phosphatase inhibitor, one interpretation of the data is that receptor transformation may involve a dephosphorylation process.

Still unresolved is whether receptor transformation normally occurs in vivo in the cell cytoplasm or nucleus. While temperature-activated receptor transformation can occur in the cytoplasm in vitro, Yamamoto (113) has reported that the 4S to 5S conversion occurs much more rapidly in the presence of DNA. In addition, Siiteri et al (105) report finding 4S receptor in nuclei; their pulse-chase experiments reveal that the nuclear 4S form decreases as the 5S form increases, which suggests that the 4S estrogen binding protein is transformed within the nuclear compartment. This 4S to 5S conversion within the nucleus was reported for several target tissues—hypothalamus, pituitary, and uterus—though rates of receptor activation differed considerably among the three tissues (67).

The steroid binding portion of the receptor is distinguishable from the portion of receptor that is required for nuclear binding. Mild proteolysis of cytoplasmic receptors for a variety of steroid classes generates a small ($\sim$2–4 $\times$ 10^4 daltons) fragment of the receptor, called the mero-receptor, that retains the steroid binding domain intact but lacks the capacity to bind to nuclei (104).

Further information on the relatedness of nuclear and cytoplasmic forms of the estrogen receptor comes from recent immunological studies. Jensen and co-workers (43) have generated antibodies to highly purified nuclear estradiol-receptor complexes from calf uterus, an approach taken with only limited success earlier. These antibodies crossreact with both the nuclear and cytoplasmic estrogen receptors from a variety of mammalian species (calf, rat, mouse, guinea pig, and human) and target tissues (uterus and breast). They do not crossreact with androgen or progesterone receptor complexes, which indicates immunochemical differences among receptor proteins for different classes of steroid hormones (43). Monoclonal antibody preparations to the nuclear estradiol receptor have been generated (44), and these should provide novel reagents for detailed studies of receptor structure and function.

Heterogeneity of Hormone Binding Sites

Recently a second class of nuclear and cytoplasmic estrogen binding sites (called type II sites) have been reported that are of lower affinity and differ from the classical nuclear and cytoplasmic estrogen receptor sites (called type I sites) described above. The cytoplasmic type II sites (19) have an affinity for estradiol about forty times lower than that of the type I sites ($K_d \sim 30$ nM vs 0.8 nM). Hence, these sites are not detected by direct labeling with low concentrations of [^{3}H]estradiol and do not retain radiolabeled ligand upon gradient centrifugation; however, these sites can be detected by postlabeling of gradient fractions with [^{3}H]estradiol, and they are found in the 4S region. They are present in higher concentrations in target tissue cytosols (uterus and vagina) but are found at low levels in other tissue cytosols (kidney and spleen). As opposed to the classical cytoplasmic receptor (type I) sites, which are translocated to the nucleus by hormone, these type II sites always remain in the cytoplasm. Their function is unknown at present. It has been suggested that they may serve as a mechanism for concentrating estrogen in target cells.

Type II nuclear estrogen binding sites do not originate from either type I or II cytoplasmic sites. These sites are revealed in the nucleus after exposure of uteri or mammary tumor tissue to estrogen in vivo, and they have been detected by nuclear exchange assay using high concentrations of [^{3}H]estradiol (27). These sites have a lower affinity for estradiol than do the nuclear receptor (type I) sites (half saturated at ~20 nM estradiol, type II nuclear sites vs $K_d = 0.6$ nM for type I nuclear sites), but they are present in higher concentration than type I sites. It is not clear whether these sites are ever occupied by physiological concentrations of estrogen ($\sim 10^{-11}$–10^{-9} M) unless the local concentration of hormone in the target tissue or nucleus is greatly enhanced over that in the blood. However, these sites may come into play when pharmacological concentrations of hormones are utilized, as in hormonal therapy for breast cancer.

Of interest also is the finding (28) of two types of nuclear binding sites for aldosterone (type I, $K_d = 3 \times 10^{-9}$ M; type II, $K_d = 5 \times 10^{-7}$ M). Occupancy of type I sites correlates with aldosterone-induced increases in transepithelial sodium transport. Occupancy of type II sites occurs at higher hormone concentrations, but no further increase in sodium transport is evoked.

Additional reports have described the presence of specific binding sites for estrogen on the cell membrane of isolated target cells (90) and associated with the lysosomal (108a) and microsomal fractions of target cells (111). The role of these sites in recognition of hormone and/or hormone action remains to be elucidated.

Nuclear Receptor Binding and the Induction of Responses

Many investigators have sought to elucidate the relationships between the binding of the steroid receptor complexes in the nucleus and the magnitude of hormone induced responses. In many cases, the binding and responses are linearly related. Studies with estrogens of different biological potencies and with different concentrations of estradiol in vitro and in vivo indicate a linear relationship between the induction of a specific early estrogen-induced protein (abbreviated IP) and the relative saturation of receptors (54). The relationship between tyrosine aminotransferase induction and the relative saturation of glucocorticoid receptors in hepatoma cells is also a linear one (7), as is the relationship between receptor occupation and induction of mouse mammary tumor virus RNA production by glucocorticoids, which occurs within minutes in mammary tumor cells (115). Time-course and hormone-dosage experiments also indicate that the degree of saturation of the glucocorticoid receptor by steroid in vivo coincides with its inducing effects upon hepatic tryptophan oxygenase and tyrosine aminotransferase (29).

However, the simple linear relationship between hormone binding and response does not appear to hold in all cases. Evidence has accumulated recently for differential induction of specific cellular responses depending on the doses of hormone administered. For example, although the increase in uterine wet weight and induction of induced protein synthesis are at half-maximum when nuclear receptors are 50% saturated, stimulation of glucose oxidation by estrogen is maximal at very low levels of nuclear receptor occupancy (18). In urinary bladder, there is a curvilinear relationship between aldosterone-induced increases in transepithelial Na^+ transport and nuclear receptor occupancy (28). In chick oviduct, the concentration of nuclear receptors is related to the rate of accumulation of ovalbumin and conalbumin mRNA; however, the relationship between receptor and response is a linear one in the case of conalbumin mRNA production, while half-maximal induction of ovalbumin mRNA requires higher (80%) saturation of nuclear receptors (79). These differential responses may be related either to different numbers of binding sites regulating the production of these two mRNAs or to different affinities of regulatory sites for estrogen receptors (79).

Questions have frequently been raised concerning the large numbers of steroid hormone receptors (~15,000–20,000 per cell) and whether all of these are needed for hormonal response (41). Although some of the studies described above indicate a linear relationship between receptor binding and the magnitude of induction of early biological responses, it does not appear that occupancy of all of these is required to elicit more long-term responses to the hormone. Low doses of estradiol, which result in both the nuclear localization of ~20% of the maximal level of estrogen receptor and the maintenance of these receptor levels for certain critical periods of time (see the section below on Temporal Relationships), are capable of eliciting full uterine growth even though early responses are not maximally stimulated (21). Furthermore, regardless of the initial number of estrogen receptor complexes moved to the nucleus by different doses of estradiol, only 2000–3000 remain in the nucleus for longer than 6 hr.

In studies of the relationships between hormone receptor binding and the induction of hormonal responses, attempts have been made to determine whether different populations of receptors are involved in differential hormone responses (cf preceding section). Differential extractability of nuclear receptor complexes by salt or by DNase treatment has been examined in several systems. Since Clark & Peck (21) have found the number of salt-resistant nuclear estrogen binding sites to be similar to the number of sites required for maximal uterine growth, they have suggested that the low level of salt-inextractable sites may be of importance in long-term estrogen-mediated events. Other findings (77, 110) have raised questions, however, about the existence of salt-inextractable receptor sites in uterine nuclei. It seems that the method of salt extraction of nuclei (77, 94, 110) and whether exposure to radiolabeled estradiol is by direct binding in vivo or in vitro or by exchange assay in vitro (6) can influence markedly the quantity of receptor sites determined to be salt-inextractable. These methodologic differences have made comparisons between studies difficult. It seems likely, however, that the relative sensitivity of different receptor populations to liberation by salt from chromatin or the nuclear matrix may vary (6, 21, 95) and may serve, as does sensitivity to liberation by DNase (7, 29), as a means of probing for different receptor binding sites in the nucleus.

The Fate of Nuclear Receptor

Still unclear is the fate of receptor after its interaction in the nucleus. Studies (52, 72, 97) with inhibitors of RNA and protein synthesis (actinomycin D and cycloheximide) suggest that approximately 40% of the estrogen receptors that reappear in the uterine cytoplasm after their initial depletion by an estrogen injection do not depend on de novo RNA or protein synthesis and most likely arise from recycling of estrogen receptor from the nucleus. The remaining 60% fail to appear in the cytoplasm when protein or RNA synthesis is inhibited; hence, they are presumed to be newly synthesized. A similar protein-synthesis-dependent regulation of cytoplasmic receptor populations occurs in other estrogen target tissues, including the anterior pituitary and hypothalamus (16).

In hepatoma cells, removal of hormone from the medium results in a rapid dissociation of hormone from the receptor and a return of receptor to the cytoplasm. In this system, maximal return of receptor to the cytoplasm occurs when protein and RNA syntheses are inhibited (7), which indicates that only the preexisting receptors, and not newly synthesized ones, are responsible for replenishment of receptors in the cytoplasm. In thymus cells, a similar protein-synthesis-independent mechanism exists; it has been proposed that ATP (energy) is required for the reappearance of these cytoplasmic glucocorticoid receptors (80).

Although receptors for steroid hormones are found almost always in the extranuclear regions of target cells in the absence of hormone and become associated with nuclear components following association with hormone, fascinating studies with human breast cancer cells in culture (68, 117) indicate that these cells contain approximately 75% of their total estrogen receptors in the nucleus in the apparent absence of hormone. Many human breast tumor biopsies also contain substantial levels of "free" nuclear receptor [unoccupied by hormone (38, 85)], which indicates that this unusual distribution is not an artifact of in vitro culture conditions. In an interesting series of studies (48, 49), association with estrogen has been found to result in the release or processing of these nuclear receptors and the induction of progesterone receptor synthesis.

Interestingly, nuclear receptor complexes with antiestrogens are either only partially processed (as in the case of tamoxifen) or are not processed at all (nafoxidine-bound nuclear receptors); in nafoxidine-treated cells, there is also no alteration of progesterone receptor content (49). Hence, this receptor "processing" has been considered an important aspect of hormone action in human breast cancer (MCF-7) cells since the decline in estrogen receptor content correlates with the appearance of an estrogenic response, the induction of the progesterone receptor.

In dispersed rat uterine cells in which estrogen receptors are localized in the cytoplasm in the absence of hormone, exposure to estradiol results in a movement of receptors to the nucleus followed by a period during which ~50% of estrogen receptors progressively disappear from the nucleus (88). In both cell systems, when estrogen receptor is processed it can no longer be detected as a hormone binding protein in either the nuclear or cytoplasmic compartment. Actinomycin D (1–2 μM) and chromomycin A3, which intercalate at G-C base pairs on DNA, rather selectively and completely prevent nuclear estrogen receptor processing (48), even though estrogen binding, translocation of receptor complexes, and the accumulation of filled nuclear receptors are unaffected. The mechanistic basis for this effect is not presently understood.

Hence, the requirements for receptor cycling and replenishment appear to differ in different cells. How these apparent differences might relate to the physiology of these target cells is not known. In several of these systems, however, the absence of unfilled receptor sites renders the tissue insensitive to hormone, and the return or regeneration of receptors parallels the return of sensitivity to hormone (2, 32).

Temporal Relationships in Hormone Receptor Action

It is clear that many of the responses to steroid hormones appear to be dependent upon the binding of the hormone to its receptor protein. Both the binding and the response, however, are complex processes that have distinct temporal elements. In the immature rat uterus, the biochemical and physiological events that follow the cytoplasmic binding and nuclear localization of estrogen unfold in a rigidly programmed sequence that culminates in tissue growth (55). The relationship between the presence of the hormone receptor complex in the nucleus (in particular, the duration of its presence) and the "turning on" of temporally early (0–6 hr) and late events and stimulation of tissue growth remains a subject of considerable interest and active research.

It has long been recognized that the biological potency of compounds depends on both their receptor affinity and their persistence in the target tissue. However, only recently have these relationships been elucidated at the molecular level. The studies of Anderson, Clark & Peck (18) on the relationships between the magnitude of nuclear receptor estrogen binding and early and late uterotrophic responses, which have been confirmed and extended by others (42, 56, 61), suggest that stimulations of various early responses are not sufficient in themselves to cause the later responses. In brief, the estrogens, estriol and estradiol, are found to be almost equally effective in stimulating early estrogen responses, such as the induction of IP synthesis (55), and in promoting increases in uterine fluid imbibition, glucose oxidation (18), 2-deoxyglucose metabolism (42, 61), RNA polymerase II activity (45), and RNA and protein synthesis during the first few ($\sim$6) hours after injection. However, estriol has little or no effect on late responses, which are stimulated by estradiol: 2-deoxyglucose metabolism at 18–24 hr (42), elevations in the activities of RNA polymerase I and II at 9–24 hr (45), uterine weight at 24–72 hr, and DNA synthesis at 18–24 hr (61); this appears to be due to the fact that estriol is lost from the tissue at a faster rate (42, 61).

However, estriol can be made as effective as estradiol in stimulating later uterine responses if its circulating levels are maintained, either by multiple injection, administration via paraffin implants (3, 20, 74), or chemical modification to a long-acting (prohormonal) form (61); and in these cases, sufficient nuclear levels of receptor are maintained for the periods required to elicit the late responses. Within a series of short- and long-acting derivatives of estriol there is an excellent correlation between the ability of the compound to stimulate uterine growth and to maintain elevated levels of nuclear receptor (61). Likewise, dimethylstilbestrol acts as a more potent estrogen if it occupies receptor sites for a sufficient length of time; this can be achieved by administering it as the dimethyl ether derivative (56). These observations imply that the presence of estrogen in the nucleus must be sustained in order to elicit growth responses. Recent studies contrasting the actions of estradiol and estriol (B. Markaverich, J. H. Clark, in preparation) suggest that estrogen stimulation of uterine growth may require, or is at least accompanied by, both long-term (6–24 hr) retention of nuclear type I sites and sustained elevations of type II sites.

Similar temporal patterns of estrogen receptor translocation and nuclear retention are seen in hypothalamus and pituitary (1, 71). The rather long-term nuclear receptor interaction in these tissues may also be involved in mediating estrogenic regulation of the synthesis and secretion of various pituitary hormones, estrogen facilitation of the luteinizing hormone surge and of lordosis behavior, and changes in pituitary enzyme activities (70).

However, studies have shown that estrogen is probably not required continuously in order to obtain maximal DNA synthesis and uterine growth. In studies using the short-acting estrogen, estriol, exciting data have been obtained, suggesting that the requirement for estrogen in the stimulation of DNA synthesis in the uterus is discontinuous (46). If estriol is present during certain critical phases (0–2 hr and 9–15 hr after the initial injection), it is rendered equipotent to estradiol in eliciting the full uterotrophic response.

Other studies suggest that pituitary factors or additional hormonal factors may be required directly or indirectly for the uterus or oviduct to respond completely to estrogen under certain circumstances (62). In immature rats, hypophysectomy or hypothyroidism does not alter the magnitude of temporally early responses to estradiol, but either diminishes long-term uterine responses occurring $\geqslant$24 hr after a single estradiol treatment. These effects of hypophysectomy or hypothyroidism do not appear to be due to changes in estrogen receptor populations or hormone retention times in the uteri of these young animals (37, 58).

HORMONAL MODULATION OF STEROID RECEPTOR LEVELS

The sequential presentation of different hormones at the target tissue is often accompanied by changes in receptor populations and in sensitivity of the responding tissue to hormones. There is now abundant evidence that some hormones modulate the levels of their own receptors or of receptors for other hormones and thereby influence tissue sensitivity to multiple hormones. For example, the biological effects of progestational compounds are often dependent on prior exposure to estrogen. This estrogen priming has been shown to increase the concentration of progesterone receptor in the uterus, oviduct, vagina, anterior pituitary, and hypothalamus of a variety of species; this increase in receptor may be part of the molecular mechanism by which estrogens potentiate the biological effects of progesterone (63). It is of interest that progesterone administration to a previously estrogen-primed animal results in a rapid fall in the levels of uterine progesterone receptor (73). These effects of estrogen to increase and of progesterone to decrease progesterone receptor content in the uterus appear compatible with the cyclic changes observed physiologically in intact animals (10) and women (8).

In addition to regulating the levels of its own receptor as described above, progesterone modulates the level of the estrogen receptor. This has been well documented in the rat uterus (50, 87) and in the reproductive tract of other animals (11, 59). Estrogen receptor concentrations are higher in proliferative than in secretory endometrium in the human (8) and are highest in the oviduct and endometrium of monkeys during the follicular phase (112). In monkeys, the high follicular phase levels of estrogen receptor decline soon after ovulation as progesterone levels increase, and receptor levels rise again when serum progesterone levels fall below 1 ng ml^{-1} following luteolysis. These data provide strong evidence that progesterone can suppress estrogen receptor levels in the reproductive tract in the presence of continuously elevated serum estradiol (112).

Simultaneous administration of progesterone and estrogen results in a diminished uterine growth compared with that elicited by estradiol alone, probably because progesterone interferes with the replenishment of the cytoplasmic estrogen receptor and thereby reduces the number of receptor estrogen complexes that are translocated and retained by uterine nuclei (9, 50, 87). Studies with RNA and protein synthesis inhibitors suggest that progesterone antagonism of receptor replenishment occurs by actual interference with de novo synthesis of receptors or required protein factors (9). These mechanisms may explain numerous observations indicating that progesterone is an antagonist of estrogen action; however, they may not account for them all (60).

Of great interest in this regard are the observations that the morphological response to progesterone differs in different tissues of the reproductive tract even though progesterone results in equally diminished levels of cytoplasmic and nuclear estrogen receptor in these tissues (11). In cats and monkeys, the endometrium hypertrophies and undergoes marked secretory development while the oviduct atrophies, loses its ciliation, and dedifferentiates.

Despite the generality for progesterone suppression of the estrogen receptor system in several diverse animal species, it appears that progesterone is not an equally effective antiuterotrophic agent in all species (106), and it may exert differential effects on estrogen receptor levels in the endometrium and myometrium in some species (69). In addition, the estrogen : progesterone ratio is very important in determining the synergistic and/or antagonistic effects of these hormones on different tissues of the reproductive tract (10). Further, progesterone modulation of lordosis behavior and of the estrogen-induced luteinizing hormone surge does not appear to be accompanied by changes in estrogen receptor content or patterns of depletion-replenishment of the estrogen receptor in the hypothalamus or pituitary (4a, 26), as is seen in uterus.

Several other hormones also influence estrogen receptor levels in specific target tissues. Prolactin has been shown to increase estrogen receptor levels in the rat mammary gland under in vitro (64) and in vivo (66) conditions and to increase estrogen receptor levels in human (103) and rat (47) mammary tumors. Prolactin also increases estrogen receptor levels in the liver (14), but prolactin has no effect on estrogen receptor levels in the uterus (66). Thyroid hormones also influence the levels of cytoplasmic estrogen receptor in the uterus and pituitary without any effect on hypothalamic estrogen receptor content. The effects of thyroid hormone depend as well on the endocrine status of the animal (whether the female rat is castrate or intact) and the relationships appear to be complex (17).

These studies point out that the regulation of receptor levels is frequently under multihormonal control and that the regulation of a particular receptor may involve different hormones in different tissues. However, it must be stressed that in some cases where hormones appear to modulate sensitivity to a particular hormone [(26) and see the section above on Temporal Relationships] the modulation has not been shown to be associated with changes in hormone receptor levels but may instead reflect alterations at some later stage in the hormone response pathway, including the possible involvement of permissive factors.

PHARMACOLOGICAL VS PHYSIOLOGICAL ACTIONS OF HORMONES

When steroid hormones are present at physiological levels their interaction is generally restricted to the specific receptor protein for that class of hormone. However, when hormones are given in higher pharmacological doses there is sometimes a "spillover" of specificity. This results in "illicit" occupancy of receptors, with interesting and sometimes unexpected biological results.

Several laboratories have documented the initial observations (93) that although low doses of androgens interact solely with the androgen receptor system in the uterus, pharmacological doses are capable of interacting with the estrogen receptor system to elicit responses typically evoked by estrogens, such as nuclear translocation of estrogen receptor, synthesis of the induced protein, and stimulation of uterine growth and progesterone receptor synthesis (35, 96, 99a, 100). In human breast cancer (MCF-7) cells in culture, 10^{-8} M androgen depletes only cytoplasmic androgen receptor while other hormone receptors are unaltered, and no growth stimulation occurs. Pharmacological (10^{-6} M) androgen depletes both the androgen and estrogen receptor, increases MCF cell growth, and stimulates synthesis of progesterone receptor, a specific product of estrogen action (118). High doses of androgens also interact with estrogen receptors and increase protein synthesis in dimethylbenz(a)anthracene-induced rat mammary tumors, but it is not clear whether the regression of rat (36, 116) and human breast cancers by androgen treatment can be explained by androgen interaction with the tumor estrogen receptor system.

Excellent examples of spillovers of specificity have been documented in the occupancy of glucocorticoid receptors by mineralocorticoids and mineralocorticoid occupancy of the glucocorticoid receptor sites. Thus, at physiological concentrations aldosterone is bound principally to mineralocorticoid receptors (31, 33), while at higher concentrations it occupies both glucocorticoid and mineralocorticoid receptors and demonstrates increased glucocorticoid properties while retaining its mineralocorticoid actions. Additionally, the glucocorticoids, which are devoid of intrinsic mineralocorticoid activity at physiological levels, have considerable mineralocorticoid activity and occupy mineralocorticoid receptors when administered at higher concentrations (13).

The androgenic properties of progestins are well known, and their use can result in fetal virilization or masculinization in humans and other animals. Studies have demonstrated that progestins can either mimic androgen effects, potentiate androgen effects (be synandrogenic), or inhibit androgen effects (be antiandrogenic) depending on the steroid structure, dose, and tissue. These actions of progestins are mediated via interaction with androgen receptors, and a steric-allosteric model has been applied to analyze this interesting situation (12).

Unexpected receptor interactions may also arise when certain steroid drugs are used pharmacologically for therapy. Spironolactone, an antimineralocorticoid that interacts primarily with mineralocorticoid receptors, also interacts with the androgen receptor, and this later interaction is believed responsible for its antiandrogenic effects (22); other derivatives have now been synthesized that possess greatly reduced affinity for the androgen receptor (24). The binding of a large series of synthetic steroids to four different hormone receptors (androgen, estrogen, progestin, and glucocorticoid) has been examined systematically (84). These compounds span a spectrum from those very specific for a single receptor system to others having affinities for all four. Such structure–function analyses should aid in elucidating the functional substituents important in distinguishing among receptor binding sites.

Nonsteroidal drugs can also interact with steroid receptors. Digitalis is found to interact with the estrogen receptor in both the rat and human (92), a possible mechanism by which the drug may produce its estrogen-like side effects. Several anti-inflammatory drugs (phenylbutazone, aspirin, and indomethacin) have intrinsic mineralocorticoid properties that appear to be mediated through the receptor pathway, and their mineralocorticoid actions would likely be manifest within the therapeutic range for these agents (30).

SUMMARY AND CONCLUSION

The relationships between hormone receptor binding and receptor initiation of responses are proving to be complex and multifaceted, with distinct temporal components. The interaction of steroid hormones with their receptors is generally specific at physiological levels of the natural hormones, but the specificity may be compromised when pharmacological doses or hormone analogs with altered structures are used. The process by which the hormone receptor complex becomes "activated" appears to differ for different hormone classes and may involve dissociation of inhibitory factors and changes in conformation or macromolecular associations. The levels of steroid hormone receptors and consequent tissue responsiveness are often regulated by multiple hormones; individual receptors are controlled by different hormones in different tissues.

Several models appear necessary to explain the relationships between the nuclear binding of the hormone receptor complex and the induction of various responses; these may involve different classes of nuclear binding or regulatory sites, with responses requiring differing degrees and durations of nuclear receptor occupancy. These dynamic features of hormone receptor interaction provide numerous points at which hormone action may be regulated to provide the fine physiological control seen in diverse target tissues.

Acknowledgments

Work from my laboratory discussed in this review was supported in part by research grants NIH HD 06726 and CA 18119 from the United States Public Health Service and Ford Foundation Grant 700-0333. I thank the Physiology Department secretaries and the School of Basic Medical Sciences Word Processing Center for excellent secretarial assistance.

Literature Cited

1. Anderson, J. N., Peck, E. J. Jr., Clark, J. H. 1973. Nuclear receptor estrogen complex: accumulation, retention, and localization in the hypothalamus and pituitary. *Endocrinology* 93:711–17
2. Anderson, J. N., Peck, E. J. Jr., Clark, J. H. 1974. Nuclear receptor estradiol complex: a requirement for uterotrophic responses. *Endocrinology* 95:174–78
3. Anderson, J. N., Peck, E. J. Jr., Clark, J. H. 1975. Estrogen-induced uterine responses and growth: relationship to receptor estrogen binding by uterine nuclei. *Endocrinology* 96:160–67
4. Aten, R. F., Weinberger, M. J., Eisenfeld, A. J. 1978. Estrogen receptor in rat liver: translocation to the nucleus in vivo. *Endocrinology* 102:433–42

4a. Attardi, B. 1979. Effects of progesterone on cytoplasmic estrogen receptors in the hypothalamus-preoptic area and pituitary in relation to the LH surge in the rat. *Proc. Ann. Endocrine Soc. Meet., 61st, Anaheim,* p. 307 (Abstr. 939)

5. Bailly, A., Sallas, N., Milgrom, E. 1977. A low molecular weight inhibitor of steroid receptor activation. *J. Biol. Chem.* 252:858–63
6. Barrack, E. R., Hawkins, E. F., Allen, S. L., Hicks, L. L., Coffey, D. S. 1977. Concepts related to salt resistant estradiol receptors in rat uterine nuclei: nuclear matrix. *Biochem. Biophys. Res. Commun.* 79:829–36
7. Baxter, J. D., Ivarie, R. D. 1978. Regulation of gene expression by glucocorticoid hormones: studies of receptors and responses in cultured cells. In *Receptors and Hormone Action,* ed. B. W. O'Malley, L. Birnbaumer, 2:252–96. NY: Academic. 602 pp.
8. Bayard, F., Damilano, S., Robel, P., Baulieu, E.-E. 1978. Cytoplasmic and nuclear estradiol and progesterone receptors in human endometrium. *J. Clin. Endocrinol. Metab.* 46:635–48
9. Bhakoo, H. S., Katzenellenbogen, B. S. 1977. Progesterone modulation of estrogen-stimulated uterine biosynthetic events and estrogen receptor levels. *Mol. Cell. Endocrinol.* 8:121–34
10. Brenner, R. M., West, N. B. 1975. Hormonal regulation of the reproductive tract in female mammals. *Ann. Rev. Physiol.* 37:273–302
11. Brenner, R. M., West, N. B., Norman, R. L., Sandow, B. A., Verhage, H. G. 1979. Progesterone suppression of the estradiol receptor in the reproductive tract of macaques, cats, and hamsters. *Adv. Exp. Med. Biol.* 117:173–96
12. Bullock, L. P., Bardin, C. W., Sherman, M. R. 1978. Androgenic, antiandrogenic, and synandrogenic actions of progestins: role of steric and allosteric interactions with androgen receptors. *Endocrinology* 103:1768–82
13. Cake, M. H., Litwack, G. 1975. The glucocorticoid receptor. In *Biochemical Actions of Hormones,* ed. G. Litwack, 3:317–90. NY: Academic. 415 pp.
14. Chamness, G. C., Costlow, M. E., McGuire, W. L. 1975. Estrogen receptor in rat liver and its dependence on prolactin. *Steroids* 26:363–71
15. Chan, L., O'Malley, B. W. 1976. Mechanisms of action of the sex steroid hormones. *N. Engl. J. Med.* 294:1322–28, 1372–81, 1430–37
16. Cidlowski, J. A., Muldoon, T. G. 1974. Estrogenic regulation of cytoplasmic receptor populations in estrogen-responsive tissues of the rat. *Endocrinology* 95:1621–29
17. Cidlowski, J. A., Muldoon, T. G. 1975. Modulation by thyroid hormones of cytoplasmic estrogen receptor concentrations in reproductive tissues of the rat. *Endocrinology* 97:59–67
18. Clark, J. H., Anderson, J. N., Peck, E. J. Jr. 1973. Nuclear receptor estrogen complexes of rat uteri: concentration-time-response parameters. *Adv. Exp. Med. Biol.* 36:15–59
19. Clark, J. H., Hardin, J. W., Upchurch, S., Eriksson, H. 1978. Heterogeneity of estrogen binding sites in the cytosol of the rat uterus. *J. Biol. Chem.* 253: 7630–34
20. Clark, J. H., Paszko, Z., Peck, E. J. Jr. 1977. Nuclear binding and retention of the receptor estrogen complex: relation to the agonistic and antagonistic properties of estriol. *Endocrinology* 100: 91–96
21. Clark, J. H., Peck, E. J. Jr. 1976. Nuclear retention of receptor-oestrogen complex and nuclear acceptor sites. *Nature* 260:635–37
22. Corvol, P., Michaud, A., Menard, J., Freifeld, M., Mahoudeau, J. 1975. Antiandrogenic effect of spirolactones: mechanism of action. *Endocrinology* 97:52–58
23. Cutler, G. B. Jr., Barnes, K. M., Sauer, M. A., Loriaux, D. L. 1978. Estrogen receptor in rat adrenal gland. *Endocrinology* 102:252–57
24. Cutler, G. B. Jr., Pita, J. C. Jr., Rifka, S. M., Menard, R. H., Sauer, M. A.,

Loriaux, D. L. 1978. SC 25152: a potent mineralocorticoid antagonist with reduced affinity for the 5α-dihydrotestosterone receptor of human and rat prostate. *J. Clin. Endocrinol. Metab.* 47: 171–75

25. Dandliker, W. B., Brawn, R. J., Hsu, M. L., Brawn, P. N., Levin, J., Meyers, C. Y., Kolb, V. M. 1978. Investigation of hormone-receptor interactions by means of fluorescence labeling. *Cancer Res.* 38:4212–24
26. DeBold, J. F., Martin, J. V., Whalen, R. E. 1976. The excitation and inhibition of sexual receptivity in female hamsters by progesterone: time and dose relationships, neural localization and mechanisms of action. *Endocrinology* 99:1519–27
27. Eriksson, H., Upchurch, S., Hardin, J. W., Peck, E. J. Jr., Clark, J. H. 1978. Heterogeneity of estrogen receptors in the cytosol and nuclear fractions of the rat uterus. *Biochem. Biophys. Res. Commun.* 81:1–7
28. Farman, N., Kusch, M., Edelman, I. S. 1978. Aldosterone receptor occupancy and sodium transport in the urinary bladder of *Bufo marinus. Am. J. Physiol.* 235:C90-C96
29. Feigelson, P., Ramanarayanan-Murthy, L., Colman, P. D. 1978. Studies on the cytoplasmic glucocorticoid receptor and its nuclear interaction in mediating induction of tryptophan oxygenase messenger RNA in liver and hepatoma. See Ref. 7, pp. 226–49
30. Feldman, D., Couropmitree, C. 1976. Intrinsic mineralocorticoid agonist activity of some nonsteroidal anti-inflammatory drugs. *J. Clin. Invest.* 57:1–7
31. Feldman, D., Funder, J. W., Edelman, I. S. 1973. Evidence for a new class of corticosterone receptors in the rat kidney. *Endocrinology* 92:1429–41
32. Ferguson, E. R., Katzenellenbogen, B. S. 1977. A comparative study of antiestrogen action: temporal patterns of antagonism of estrogen stimulated uterine growth and effects on estrogen receptor levels. *Endocrinology* 100:1242–51
33. Funder, J. W., Feldman, D., Edelman, I. S. 1973. The role of plasma binding and receptor specificity in the mineralocorticoid action of aldosterone. *Endocrinology* 92:994–1004
34. Gannon, F., Katzenellenbogen, B. S., Stancel, G., Gorski, J. 1976. Estrogen-receptor movement to the nucleus: discussion of a cytoplasmic-exclusion hypothesis. In *The Molecular Biology of Hormone Action,* ed. J. Papaconstantinou, pp. 137–149. NY: Academic. 197 pp.
35. Garcia, M., Rochefort, H. 1977. Androgens on the estrogen receptor, II. Correlation between nuclear translocation and protein synthesis. *Steroids* 29: 111–26
36. Garcia, M., Rochefort, H. 1978. Androgen effects mediated by estrogen receptor in 7,12-dimethylbenz(a)anthracene-induced rat mammary tumors. *Cancer Res.* 38:3922–29
37. Gardner, R. M., Kirkland, J. L., Ireland, J. S., Stancel, G. M. 1978. Regulation of the uterine response to estrogen by thyroid hormone. *Endocrinology* 103:1164–72
38. Garola, R. E., McGuire, W. L. 1977. An improved assay for nuclear estrogen receptor in experimental and human breast cancer. *Cancer Res.* 37:3333–37
39. Glascock, R. F., Hoekstra, W. G. 1959. Selective accumulation of tritium-labelled hexoestrol by the reproductive organs of immature female goats and sheep. *Biochem. J.* 72:673–82
40. Goidl, J. A., Cake, M. H., Dolan, K. P., Parchman, L. G., Litwack, G. 1977. Activation of the rat liver glucocorticoid-receptor complexes. *Biochemistry* 16:2125–30
41. Gorski, J., Gannon, F. 1976. Current models of steroid hormone action: a critique. *Ann. Rev. Physiol.* 38:425–50
42. Gorski, J., Raker, B. 1974. Estrogen action in the uterus: the requisite for sustained estrogen binding in the nucleus. *Gynecol. Oncol.* 2:249–58
43. Greene, G. L., Closs, L. E., Fleming, H., DeSombre, E. R., Jensen, E. V. 1977. Antibodies to estrogen receptor: immunochemical similarity of estrophilin from various mammalian species. *Proc. Natl. Acad. Sci. USA* 74:3681–85
44. Greene, G. L., Jensen, E. V., Fitch, F. W. 1979. Monoclonal antibodies to estrophilin: new probes for the study of estrogen receptors. *Proc. Ann. Endocrine Soc. Meet., 61st, Anaheim,* p. 74 (Abstr. 8)
45. Hardin, J. W., Clark, J. H., Glasser, S. R., Peck, E. J. Jr. 1976. RNA polymerase activity and uterine growth: differential stimulation by estradiol, estriol, and nafoxidine. *Biochemistry* 15: 1370–74
46. Harris, J., Gorski, J. 1978. Evidence for a discontinuous requirement for estrogen in stimulation of deoxyribonucleic acid synthesis in the immature rat uterus. *Endocrinology* 103:240–45

47. Hawkins, R. A., Hill, A., Freedman, B., Killen, E., Buchan, P., Miller, W. R., Forrest, A. P. M. 1977. Oestrogen receptor activity and endocrine status in DMBA-induced rat mammary tumors. *Eur. J. Cancer* 13:223–28
48. Horwitz, K. B., McGuire, W. L. 1978. Actinomycin D prevents nuclear processing of estrogen receptor. *J. Biol. Chem.* 253:6319–22
49. Horwitz, K. B., McGuire, W. L. 1978. Nuclear mechanisms of estrogen action: effects of estradiol and antiestrogens on estrogen receptors and nuclear receptor processing. *J. Biol. Chem.* 253:8185–91
50. Hseuh, A. J. W., Peck, E. J. Jr., Clark, J. H. 1976. Control of uterine estrogen receptor levels by progesterone. *Endocrinology* 98:438–44
51. Jensen, E. V., Jacobson, H. I. 1962. Basic guides to the mechanism of estrogen action. *Rec. Prog. Horm. Res.* 18:387–414
52. Jensen, E. V., Suzuki, T., Numata, M., Smith, S., DeSombre, E. R. 1969. Estrogen-binding of target tissues. *Steroids* 13:417–27
53. Kalimi, M., Colman, P. D., Feigelson, P. 1975. The "activated" hepatic glucocorticoid-receptor complex. *J. Biol. Chem.* 250:1080–86
54. Katzenellenbogen, B. S., Bhakoo, H. S., Ferguson, E. R., Lan, N. C., Tatee, T., Tsai, T. L., Katzenellenbogen, J. A. 1979. Estrogen and antiestrogen action in reproductive tissues and tumors. *Rec. Prog. Horm. Res.* 35:259–300
55. Katzenellenbogen, B. S., Gorski, J. 1975. Estrogen actions on syntheses of macromolecules in target cells. See Ref. 13, pp. 187–243
56. Katzenellenbogen, B. S., Iwamoto, H. S., Heiman, D. F., Lan, N. C., Katzenellenbogen, J. A. 1978. Stilbestrols and stilbestrol derivatives: estrogenic potency and temporal relationships between estrogen receptor binding and uterine growth. *Mol. Cell. Endocrinol.* 10:103–13
57. Katzenellenbogen, J. A. 1978. Photoaffinity labeling of estrogen receptors. *Fed. Proc.* 73:174–78
58. Kirkland, J. L., Gardner, R. M., Ireland, J. S., Stancel, G. M. 1977. The effect of hypophysectomy on the uterine response to estradiol. *Endocrinology* 101:403–10
59. Koligian, K. B., Stormshak, F. 1977. Progesterone inhibition of estrogen receptor replenishment in ovine endometrium. *Biol. Reprod.* 17:412–16
60. Koseki, Y., Zava, D. T., Chamness, G. C., McGuire, W. L. 1977. Progesterone interaction with estrogen and antiestrogen in the rat uterus: receptor effects. *Steroids* 30:169–77
61. Lan, N. C., Katzenellenbogen, B. S. 1976. Temporal relationships between hormone receptor binding and biological responses in the uterus: studies with short- and long-acting derivatives of estriol. *Endocrinology* 98:220–27
62. Laugier, C., Sandoz, D., Brard, E., Sonnenschein, C. 1978. The effect of hypophysectomy on the quail's oviduct response to low and high doses of estradiol benzoate. *Endocrinology* 103:1425–33
63. Leavitt, W. W., Chen, T. J., Do, Y. S., Carlton, B. D., Allen, T. C. 1978. Biology of progesterone receptors. See Ref. 7, pp. 157–88
64. Leung, B. S., Sasaki, G. H. 1973. Prolactin and progesterone effect on specific estradiol binding in uterine and mammary tissues in vitro. *Biochem. Biophys. Res. Commun.* 55:1180–84
65. Li, J. J., Talley, D. J., Li, S. A., Villee, C. A. 1974. An estrogen binding protein in the renal cytosol of the intact, castrated, and estrogenized golden hamster. *Endocrinology* 95:1134–41
66. Lignon, F., Rochefort, H. 1976. Regulation of estrogen receptors in ovarian-dependent rat mammary tumors, I. Effect of castration and prolactin. *Endocrinology* 98:722–29
67. Linkie, D. M. 1977. Estrogen receptors in different target tissues: similarities of form-dissimilarities of transformation. *Endocrinology* 101:1862–70
68. Lippman, M. E., Osborne, C. K., Knazek, R., Young, N., Frei, E. 1977. In vitro model systems for the study of hormone-dependent human breast cancer. *N. Engl. J. Med.* 296:154–59
69. Martel, D., Psychoyos, A. 1978. Progesterone-induced oestrogen receptors in the rat uterus. *J. Endocrinol.* 76:145–54
70. McEwen, B. S. 1978. Gonadal steroid receptors in neuroendocrine tissues. See Ref. 7, pp. 354–400
71. McEwen, B. S., Pfaff, D. W., Chaptal, C., Luine, V. N. 1975. Brain cell nuclear retention of [^{3}H]estradiol doses able to promote lordosis: temporal and regional aspects. *Brain Res.* 86:155–61
72. Mester, J., Baulieu, E. E. 1975. Dynamics of oestrogen-receptor distribution between the cytosol and nuclear fractions of immature rat uterus after oestradiol administration. *Biochem. J.* 146:617–23

73. Milgrom, E., Thi, L., Atger, M., Baulieu, E.-E. 1973. Mechanisms regulating the concentration and conformation of progesterone receptor(s) in the uterus. *J. Biol. Chem.* 248:6366–74
74. Miller, B. G. 1969. The relative potencies of oestriol, oestradiol and oestrone on the uterus and vagina of the mouse. *J. Endocrinol.* 43:563–70
75. Miller, J. B., Toft, D. O. 1978. Requirement for activation in the binding of progesterone receptor to ATP-sepharose. *Biochemistry* 17:173–77
76. Mohla, S., DeSombre, E. R., Jensen, E. V. 1972. Tissue-specific stimulation of RNA synthesis by transformed estradiol-receptor complex. *Biochem. Biophys. Res. Commun.* 46:661–67
77. Muller, R. E., Traish, A. M., Wotiz, H. H. 1977. Interaction of receptor-estrogen complex (R-E) with uterine nuclei. *J. Biol. Chem.* 252:8206–11
78. Muller, R. E., Wotiz, H. H. 1978. Estrogen-binding protein in mouse and rat adrenal glands. *J. Biol. Chem.* 253: 740–45
79. Mulvihill, E. R., Palmiter, R. D. 1977. Relationship of nuclear estrogen receptor levels to induction of ovalbumin and conalbumin mRNA in chick oviduct. *J. Biol. Chem.* 252:2060–68
80. Munck, A., Wira, C., Young, D. A., Mosher, K. M., Hallahan, C., Bell, P. A. 1972. Glucocorticoid-receptor complexes and the earliest steps in the action of glucocorticoids on thymus cells. *J. Steroid Biochem.* 3:567–78
81. Nielsen, C. J., Sando, J. J., Pratt, W. B. 1977. Evidence that dephosphorylation inactivates glucocorticoid receptors. *Proc. Natl. Acad. Sci. USA* 74:1398–1402
82. Nishigori, H., Toft, D. 1979. Studies on the transformation of avian progesterone receptor. *Proc. Ann. Endocrine Soc. Meet. 61st, Anaheim,* p. 270 (Abstr. 791).
83. Notides, A. C. 1978. Conformational forms of the estrogen receptor. See Ref. 7, pp. 33–61
84. Ojasoo, T., Raynaud, J. P. 1978. Unique steroid congeners for receptor studies. *Cancer Res.* 38:4186–98
85. Panko, W. B., MacLeod, R. M. 1978. Uncharged nuclear receptors for estrogen in breast cancers. *Cancer Res.* 38:1948–51
86. Parchman, L. G., Litwack, G. 1977. Resolution of activated and unactivated forms of the glucocorticoid receptor from rat liver. *Arch. Biochem. Biophys.* 183:374–82
87. Pavlik, E. J., Coulson, P. B. 1976. Modulation of estrogen receptors in four different target tissues: differential effects of estrogen and progesterone. *J. Steroid Biochem.* 7:369–76
88. Pavlik, E. J., Rutledge, S., Eckert, R. L., Katzenellenbogen, B. S.1979. Localization of estrogen receptors in uterine cells: an appraisal of translocation. *Exper. Cell Res.* In press
89. Pertschuk, L. P., Tobin, E. H., Brigati, D. J., Kim, D. S., Bloom, N. D., Gaetjens, E., Berman, P. J., Carter, A. C., Degenshein, G. A. 1978. Immunofluorescent detection of estrogen receptors in breast cancer. *Cancer* 41:907–11
90. Pietras, R. J., Szego, C. M. 1977. Specific binding sites for oestrogen at the outer surfaces of isolated endometrial cells. *Nature* 265:69–72
91. Richards, J. S., Ireland, J. J., Rao, M. C., Bernath, G. A., Midgley, A. R. Jr., Reichert, L. E. Jr. 1976. Ovarian follicular development in the rat: hormone receptor regulation by estradiol, follicle stimulating hormone and luteinizing hormone. *Endocrinology* 99:1562–70
92. Rifka, S. M., Pita, J. C., Vigersky, R. A., Wilson, Y. A., Loriaux, D. L. 1978. Interaction of digitalis and spironolactone with human sex steroid receptors. *J. Clin. Endocrinol. Metab.* 46:338–44
93. Rochefort, H., Vignon, F., Capony, F. 1972. Formation of estrogen nuclear receptor in uterus: effect of androgens, estrone and nafoxidine. *Biochem. Biophys. Res. Commun.* 47:662–70
94. Roy, E. J., McEwen, B. S. 1977. An exchange assay for estrogen receptors in cell nuclei of the adult rat brain. *Steroids* 30:657–69
95. Ruh, T. S., Baudendistel, L. J. 1977. Different nuclear binding sites for antiestrogen and estrogen receptor complexes. *Endocrinology* 100:420–26
96. Ruh, T. S., Ruh, M. F. 1975. Androgen induction of a specific uterine protein. *Endocrinology* 97:1144–50
97. Sarff, M., Gorski, J. 1971. Control of estrogen binding protein concentration under basal conditions and after estrogen administration. *Biochemistry* 10: 2557–63
98. Sato, B., Huseby, A., Samuels, L. T. 1978. Evidence of a small molecule in mouse Leydig cell tumors which inhibits the conversion of estrogen receptor from 4S to 5S. *Endocrinology* 102: 545–55
99. Sato, B., Nishizawa, Y., Noma, K., Matsumoto, K., Yamamura, Y. 1979. Estrogen-independent nuclear binding

of receptor protein of rat uterine cytosol by removal of low molecular weight inhibitor. *Endocrinology* 104:1474–79

99a. Schmidt, W. N., Katzenellenbogen, B. S. 1979. Androgen-uterine interactions: An assessment of androgen interaction with the testosterone and estrogen receptor systems and stimulation of uterine growth and progesterone receptor synthesis. *Mol. Cell. Endocrinol.* In press

100. Schmidt, W. N., Sadler, M. A., Katzenellenbogen, B. S. 1976. Androgen-uterine interaction: nuclear translocation of the estrogen receptor and induction of the synthesis of the uterine-induced protein (IP) by high concentrations of androgens in vitro but not in vivo. *Endocrinology* 98:702–16

101. Schrader, W. T., Hughes, M. R., O'Malley, B. W. 1979. Progesterone receptor subunits of chick oviduct: analysis of the DNA binding site. *Proc. Ann. Endocrine Soc. Meet., 61st Anaheim,* p. 76 (Abstr. 14)

102. Schrader, W. T., O'Malley, B. W. 1978. Structure of chick oviduct progesterone receptors. *Cancer Res.* 38:4100–3

103. Shafie, S., Brooks, S. C. 1977. Effect of prolactin on growth and the estrogen receptor level of human breast cancer cells (MCF-7). *Cancer Res.* 37:792–99

104. Sherman, M. R., Pickering, L. A., Rollwagen, F. M., Miller, L. K. 1978. Meroreceptors: proteolytic fragments of receptors containing the steroid-binding site. *Fed. Proc.* 37:167–73

105. Siiteri, P. K., Schwarz, B. E., Moriyama, I., Ashby, R., Linkie, D., MacDonald, P. C. 1973. Estrogen binding in the rat and human. *Adv. Exp. Med. Biol.* 36:97–112

106. Stone, G. M., Murphy, L., Miller, B. G. 1978. Hormone receptor levels and metabolic activity in the uterus of the ewe: regulation by estradiol and progesterone. *Aust. J. Biol. Sci.* 31:395–403

107. Stumpf, W. E. 1968. Estradiol-concentrating neurons: topography in the hypothalamus by dry mount autoradiography. *Science* 162:1001–3

108. Stumpf, W. E. 1968. Subcellular distribution of ^{3}H-estradiol in rat uterus by quantitative autoradiography—a comparision between ^{3}H-estradiol and ^{3}H-norethynodrel. *Endocrinology* 83: 777–82

108a. Szego, C. M. 1974. The lysosome as a mediator of hormone action. *Rec. Prog. Horm. Res.* 30:171–233

109. Thrall, C. L., Webster, R. A., Spelsberg, T. C. 1978. Steroid receptor interaction with chromatin. In *The Cell Nucleus,* ed. H. Busch, 6:461–529. NY: Academic. 600 pp.

110. Traish, A. M., Muller, R. E., Wotiz, H. H. 1977. Binding of estrogen receptor to uterine nuclei: salt-extractable versus salt-resistant receptor estrogen complexes. *J. Biol. Chem.* 252:6823–30

111. Watson, G. H., Muldoon, T. G. 1977. Microsomal estrogen receptors in rat uterus and anterior pituitary. *Fed. Proc.* 36:912

112. West, N. B., Hess, D. L., Sandow, B. A., Brenner, R. M. 1979. Nuclear and cytoplasmic estrogen receptor levels in the oviducts and endometria of cynomolgus monkeys during the menstrual cycle. *Proc. Ann. Endocrine Soc. Meet., 61st, Anaheim,* p. 157 (Abstr. 338)

113. Yamamoto, K. R. 1974. Characterization of the 4S to 5S forms of the estradiol receptor protein and their interaction with deoxyribonucleic acid. *J. Biol. Chem.* 249:7068–75

114. Yamamoto, K. R., Alberts, B. M. 1976. Steroid receptors: elements for modulation of eukaryotic transcription. *Ann. Rev. Biochem.* 45:721–46

115. Yamamoto, K. R., Ringold, G. M. 1978. Glucocorticoid regulation of mammary tumor virus gene expression. See Ref. 7, pp. 298–322

116. Zava, D. T., McGuire, W. L. 1977. Estrogen receptors in androgen-induced breast tumor regression. *Cancer Res.* 37:1608–10

117. Zava, D. T., McGuire, W. L. 1977. Estrogen receptor: unoccupied sites in nuclei of a breast tumor cell line. *J. Biol. Chem.* 252:3703–8

118. Zava, D. T., McGuire, W. L. 1978. Androgen action through estrogen receptor in a human breast cancer cell line. *Endocrinology* 103:624–31

Ann. Rev. Physiol. 1980. 42:37–57

THE ROLE OF CYCLIC NUCLEOTIDES IN REPRODUCTIVE PROCESSES

❖1252

Barbara M. Sanborn

Department of Reproductive Medicine and Biology, University of Texas Medical School, Houston, Texas 77030

Jerrold J. Heindel

Department of Reproductive Medicine and Biology and Department of Pharmacology, University of Texas Medical School, Houston, Texas 77030

G. Alan Robison

Department of Pharmacology, University of Texas Medical School, Houston, Texas 77030

INTRODUCTION[1]

Cyclic nucleotides are involved in almost every aspect of the reproductive process. This article summarizes current knowledge (as of September, 1978) about the role of cyclic nucleotides in several areas of reproductive physiology: the synthesis and release of gonadotropins, the regulation of gonadal function, the function of spermatozoa, the regulation of smooth muscle function, and the maintenance of reproductive tract function.

[1]Abbreviations: cAMP: 3',5'-cyclic AMP; cGMP: 3',5'-cyclic GMP; dbcAMP: N^6, $O^{2'}$-dibutyryl cyclic AMP; FSH: follicle stimulating hormone; GnRH: gonadotropin releasing hormone; LH: luteinizing hormone; MIX: 1-methyl-3-isobutylxanthine.

0066-4278/80/0315-0037$01.00

REGULATION OF GONADOTROPIN RELEASE AND SYNTHESIS

Several lines of evidence support the hypothesis that cAMP is involved in regulating the release of LH and FSH from the anterior pituitary (reviewed in 83, 84). However, a number of investigators have been unable to demonstrate an effect of dbcAMP or 8-Br-cAMP on LH release during a 3–4 hr incubation of male rat pituitaries in vitro (83, 111, 157). Since dbcAMP has been shown to stimulate only the acute phase of LH release in a perfusion system (76), an effect might not be measurable after prolonged incubation.

A number of workers have also failed to observe GnRH stimulation of cAMP accumulation accompanying LH release in rat pituitaries in vitro (110, 112). It is perhaps surprising that such an elevation should ever be observed, since gonadotrophs comprise only about 5% of pituitary cells. Furthermore, phosphodiesterase inhibitors were not present in most of these studies. Nonetheless it is noteworthy that those studies in which GnRH stimulation of cAMP accumulation was reported used male rat pituitaries (84, 111, 112), while those in which no such correlation was found used tissues or cells from female rats (110, 112). However, such an effect was noted using immature female pituitaries in the presence of theophylline (106).

Sex-related differences in GnRH binding as well as differences in GnRH-stimulated LH release exist and probably derive from differences in the influence of sex hormones on the gland (157, 180). The sensitivity of pituitary cells to GnRH was increased by estrogens and decreased by testosterone (77, 84). Thus under estrogenic influence the pituitary may be capable of responding to small changes in cAMP, which are not detectable by current methods. Estrogens also augmented the stimulation of LH release by 8-Br-cAMP (37), suggesting that the site of steroid hormone action was distal to cAMP formation.

The mechanism by which cAMP influences gonadotropin release has not been clarified. Cyclic AMP-dependent phosphorylation of proteins from pituitary ribosomes, secretory granules, plasma membranes, and nuclei has been described, but the functions of these proteins and the effect of phosphorylation upon that function have not been defined (84).

Cyclic GMP has recently been implicated in GnRH-stimulated gonadotropin release from hemipituitaries and dispersed cells from female rats (110, 130). However, the tenuous nature of this association is indicated by the finding that LH was released by GnRH in the presence or absence of phosphodiesterase inhibitors but that cGMP rose in the former instance and fell in the latter.

The role of GnRH in the synthesis of the gonadotropins is unclear at present. GnRH has been reported to stimulate pituitary protein synthesis, glycoprotein synthesis, LH synthesis, and glucosamine incorporation into LH (90, 106, 169), but interpretation of these data is complicated by the existence of several pools of pituitary LH that may be affected differently by GnRH (77). Moreover, to date there has been no direct demonstration of the ability of dbcAMP or phosphodiesterase inhibitors to stimulate incorporation of amino acids or sugar moieties into immunoprecipitable LH or FSH.

REGULATION OF OVARIAN FUNCTION

Molecular Aspects of Steroidogenesis

Evidence for the involvement of cAMP in hormone-mediated increases in steroid production has been obtained in whole ovaries, Graafian follicles, and corpora lutea (70, 96, 98, 107, 176). Recent studies have focused on the molecular mechanisms involved. Ovarian adenylate cyclase has been solubilized and putative follicular inhibitors of LH-stimulated cAMP elevation have been described (1, 22, 38, 136). The multiple forms of cAMP-dependent protein kinases found in the ovary have been reported to change cellular distribution depending on reproductive stage and hormonal stimulation and to exhibit apparent compartmentalization with respect to responsiveness to cAMP (5, 70, 75, 166). However, aside from the fact that purified cAMP-dependent protein kinase has been shown to activate a reconstituted luteal cell cholesterol side-chain cleavage system (19, 96, 176), little is known about the specific mechanisms by which elevations in cAMP increase ovarian steroidogenesis. The evidence currently available does not support earlier suggestions that prostaglandins are obligatory intermediates in LH-induced steroidogenesis (11, 96, 97, 181).

Two other aspects of ovarian steroidogenic capability are currently receiving considerable attention. Desensitization or tachyphylaxis of the ovarian LH-adenylate cyclase system has been noted following in vivo LH injection, subsequent to the endogenous LH surge, and to varying degrees in the corpora lutea of pregnancy [(58, 70); Midgley, this volume]. Such changes almost certainly play a role in regulating tissue responsiveness to LH. The apparent ability of the cells of the ovarian follicle to act synergistically to produce several steroids is discussed extensively by Armstrong elsewhere in this volume.

Follicular Maturation, Ovulation, and Corpus Luteum Function

Follicular maturation appears to involve exposure of the follicular cells to a variety of locally synthesized steroid hormones, prostaglandins, and other substances in a precise sequence [(89, 127–129); Armstrong, this volume], but the roles played by cyclic nucleotides in these events have not been defined. Cyclic AMP has been implicated in the protein synthetic actions of the gonadotropins (6, 96) and has been linked with the ability of FSH to increase ovarian LH receptor levels in vivo (128) but not in vitro (115). Estrogen has been reported to enhance the ability of FSH to increase cAMP in granulosa cells by increasing cAMP binding capacity (127).

Gonadotropins have also been implicated in the resumption of meiosis by oocytes [(8); Armstrong, this volume]. Dibutyryl cAMP was reported by one group (163) to trigger the resumption of meiosis after intrafollicular injection and to mimic the effect of gonadotropins on the cumulus oophorus but was found by others (24, 29, 93) to prevent oocyte maturation if present in the medium. Recently the interesting suggestion has been advanced (29) that the termination of the cumulus-oocyte communication network near the time of ovulation may result in a fall in cAMP in the oocyte and subsequent resumption of meiosis.

The ovulatory process involves complex changes in follicular steroid, cyclic nucleotide, prostaglandin, and protein concentrations as well as changes in sensitivity of the cAMP-responsive systems (70, 107). Prostaglandins and plasminogen activator produced in response to cAMP or LH have been implicated in the physical aspects of follicle wall rupture (154), but biochemical mechanisms beyond these steps are unknown.

In this volume, Midgley discusses in some detail the hormonal requirements for the maintenance of the corpus luteum. With regard to the degeneration of the corpus luteum, prostaglandin $F_{2\alpha}$, the suggested luteolysin in several species, has been shown to rapidly inhibit LH-stimulated adenylate cyclase and progesterone production by luteal cells and the corpora lutea of pregnancy and to cause subsequently a gradual decline in the number of LH receptors (11, 85, 160).

MOLECULAR ASPECTS OF TESTICULAR FUNCTION

The Regulation of Steroidogenesis in Leydig Cells

LH (or hCG) initiates its actions in the testis by binding to specific membrane receptors on Leydig cells. The protein comprising the gonadotropin acceptor site of the receptor has recently been extensively characterized (4, 38, 92, 96). It has been proposed that the LH receptor is coupled to adenylate cyclase and that stimulation of androgen production depends on the production of cAMP (39, 96, 105, 132, 175). However, quantitative discrepancies were noted such that the stimulation of testosterone production by LH could be demonstrated with concentrations of the hormone that did not alter basal cAMP levels (104). Nonetheless, it has recently been demonstrated that LH stimulation of testosterone is indeed accompanied by a rapid simultaneous increase in endogenous cAMP bound to the intracellular receptor protein and in cAMP-independent protein kinase activity in purified Leydig cell preparations (25, 41, 121). LH stimulated testosterone production 100-fold more efficiently than cholera toxin under conditions where cAMP levels were elevated to the same degree by both agents (39). Consequently, it has been suggested that the cAMP produced by LH stimulation is more closely associated with the cellular machinery responsible for eliciting the steroidogenic response than is that produced by cholera toxin.

Two cAMP-dependent protein kinase isozymes, a typical type I and an atypical type II, have been characterized in interstitial cells (25, 122). LH increased ^{32}P incorporation into several protein species, the specific location and function of which are not known (26). The major acute effect of LH or cAMP on the steroidogenic pathway is thought to be to increase the conversion of cholesterol to pregnenolone by the mitochondrial cholesterol side-chain cleavage enzyme complex (96). However, LH or cAMP had no direct effect on pregnenolone production by isolated mitochondrial preparations (168). It would therefore be of considerable interest to determine whether side-chain cleavage could be stimulated in vitro by the addition of cAMP and protein kinase as has been done using ovarian components (19).

Protein and RNA synthesis were found to be required for the stimulation of steroidogenesis by LH (71, 96, 103). Addition of LH, dbcAMP, MIX, or cholera toxin to Leydig cell suspensions from adult rats stimulated the synthesis of a specific protein with a half-life longer than 30 minutes (72). However, Leydig tumor cells and cells from immature rats each responded to LH with the synthesis of individually distinct protein patterns (73). The role of the specific proteins stimulated by LH and/or cAMP in the regulation of testosterone production is not yet clear.

Modification of LH receptors and the LH-adenylate cyclase systems of Leydig cells has been reported. Administration of LH or hCG in vivo or in vitro resulted in an initial rise in total receptor content followed by a progressive loss of receptors (40, 120, 123, 135, 144, 164). In general, the cAMP response to hCG in vitro was reduced in proportion to receptor loss (164). However, recovery of the cAMP response lagged behind the return of LH receptors (68, 164). It is interesting to note that exogenous cAMP failed to evoke a maximal testosterone response despite apparently normal protein kinase activation in Leydig cells desensitized to LH (164). A loss of steroidogenic enzyme activity (in particular the C-17,20 lyase) was noted (164), thus underscoring the fact that the cholesterol side-chain cleavage enzyme system is not the only enzyme affected by chronic stimulation with LH.

The Regulation of Sertoli Cell Function

The evidence implicating the Sertoli cell as the primary target cell for FSH in the testes has been extensively reviewed (44, 101, 102, 151) and is considered in detail by Means in this volume. See also (10, 36, 59, 149, 150).

Cyclic Nucleotides in Developing Germ Cells

Rat testis has been found to contain both particulate and soluble adenylate cyclase, the latter appearing coincident with the formation of the first wave of late spermatocytes and early spermatids (17, 18). The soluble enzyme, presumably associated with advanced germ cells, was fluoride- and gonadotropin-insensitive, was active only in the presence of Mn^{2+}, and was classified as a "Class III" cyclase (17, 18, 113). The study of the acquisition of this enzyme by mature germ cells and of the changes in cyclase activity that occur when the mature spermatozoa traverse the epididymis is of potential interest.

Testicular guanylate cyclase was found to exist in particulate and soluble forms, the latter being ascribed to either Sertoli cells or spermatogonia (118, 148). The association of cGMP with the premeiotic chromosomes of rat pachytene spermatocytes (148) and with the genetically active regions of the polytene chromosomes of *Drosophila melanogaster* (147) has led to the suggestion that this nucleotide may be involved in regulating gene expression.

ACQUISITION OF FUNCTIONAL CAPACITY BY SPERM

Components of Cyclic Nucleotide Systems in Spermatozoa

Adenylate cyclase has been described in several mammalian species of sperm as Mn^{2+}-dependent and fluoride-insensitive (18, 53, 65, 66, 161). Recent data suggest that while the total concentration of adenylate cyclase decreases during the transit of the sperm through the epididymis, the proportion of particulate enzyme increases (21). Guanylate cyclase has been demonstrated in invertebrate sperm membranes but has not been found in mammalian sperm (53, 138).

Mammalian sperm adenylate cyclase was not stimulated by polypeptide hormones or catecholamines but was activated by high concentrations of triiodothyronine, Mn^{2+}, and Ca^{2+} (16, 18, 53, 65, 66), by Gpp(NH)p (21), and by spermine and spermidine at concentrations comparable to those found in seminal plasma (21, 143). More recently, factors released from sea urchin eggs were found to elevate specifically adenylate cyclase and cAMP levels in sea urchin sperm by a process that required Ca^{2+} (49, 50, 165, 171). These substances may represent physiological stimulatory factors.

Multiple soluble and particulate forms of cAMP-dependent phosphodiesterase in sperm have been characterized (152, 159). The proportion of particulate enzyme activity increased as bovine sperm traversed the epididymis, but the total amount of particulate enzyme decreased during transit (152). Cyclic GMP phosphodiesterase levels in vertebrate sperm were low compared to sea urchin sperm, where the enzyme was mostly particulate; cAMP phosphodiesterase in this species was predominantly soluble (53, 138, 174).

Data on sperm protein kinases, which occur in multiple forms and in large amounts relative to total protein, have been extensively reviewed (65, 66). It has also been reported that cAMP can bind to the membrane of human spermatozoa in an apparently saturable manner (134). In contrast to the enzyme in vertebrate sperm, sea urchin protein kinase was activated equally by cAMP and cGMP (86).

The definition of specific substrates of the cAMP-dependent protein kinases has proved difficult. Initial attempts to detect significant phosphorylation of the particulate fraction from bovine spermatozoa were unsuccessful, though some cAMP-dependent phosphorylation of cytosol proteins was noted (65, 66). More recently, stimulation by cAMP of ^{33}P-inorganic phosphate incorporation into three protein bands in whole sperm and membrane fractions has been reported (69). Phosphorylation of only the 50,000 dalton species exhibited an absolute requirement for cAMP. The roles of these proteins and the effect of phosphorylation on their function are presently unknown. Finally, phosphoprotein phosphatase has been localized to the cytosol and tail fragments of bovine epididymal spermatozoa (158).

Cyclic Nucleotides and Sperm Metabolism

The accumulated evidence linking cyclic nucleotides with the control of metabolism in sperm includes the ability of phosphodiesterase inhibitors and both dbcAMP and cGMP to increase respiratory rate and carbohydrate metabolism, the absolute increase being dependent upon the metabolic state of the cells (65, 66, 108). The effect of cyclic nucleotides on respiration was considered to be secondary to the effect on motility and the subsequent decrease in energy charge (65, 66). Caffeine and theophylline could do more than inhibit phosphodiesterases (131). However, in the absence of phosphodiesterase inhibitors, dilution of two species of sea urchin in sea water led to a statistically significant correlation between the increase in cAMP levels and respiratory rates that ensued (79).

Cyclic Nucleotides and Sperm Motility

Dibutyryl cAMP and several phosphodiesterase inhibitors have been shown to maintain sperm motility in the presence of substrate in a number of species (31, 65, 66). Conflicting results have been obtained using demembranated (modeled) sperm. Ejaculated bull sperm treated with Triton X-100 responded to cAMP and cGMP but not to theophylline with increased motility even in the presence of metabolic inhibitors, suggesting that cyclic nucleotides directly affect the contractile apparatus (88). In contrast, bovine epididymal sperm treated with dithiothreitol and polyoxyethylene alcohol (Brij-35) responded with increased motility to caffeine but not to cAMP (156). Perhaps definition of the biochemical state of each model will give insight into the source of the apparent difference in responsiveness.

Recently attention has been focused on the relationship between cAMP and the progressive acquisition of motility potential that occurs as sperm pass through the epididymis. It had previously been observed that the cAMP content of sperm increased during transit through the epididymis (65, 66). Although testicular, caput, caudal, and ejaculated sperm all possessed adenylate cyclase, protein kinase, and phosphodiesterase, treatment of testicular sperm with caffeine raised cAMP and glucose utilization without affecting motility or O_2 consumption (20). In contrast, dilution of freshly isolated caudal sperm in such diverse mixtures as caput epididymal fluid, sex accessory gland fluid, or synthetic buffer resulted in an increase in cAMP, a drop in ATP, and an increase in motility (65, 66). Furthermore, exposure of caput sperm to phosphodiesterase inhibitors resulted, after a lag phase, in an increase in cAMP and the initiation of a twitching motion but not forward motility (67). Seminal plasma had no effect on either motility or cAMP levels but, in the presence of theophylline, promoted forward motility. A glycoprotein forward motility factor that is postulated to bind to sperm during transit through the epididymis has since been isolated (64). In addition, the existence in hamster caudal fluid of a small-molecular-weight substance that enhances sperm motility has been reported (9). Presumably the combination of the binding of one or more of these factors and the progressive elevation of cAMP levels is responsible for the acquisition of the capacity for forward motility demonstrated by caudal sperm upon dilution.

Sperm Capacitation and the Fertilization Process

Sperm capacitation, i.e. induction of the capacity to fertilize an ovum, results from a complex series of events. Although increased respiration, glycolysis, motility, and loss of tetracycline binding capacity are temporally correlated with capacitation, these phenomena may be the results rather than the causes of the process; hence an ability of cAMP to trigger these events cannot at present be linked with causality (65, 66). Nonetheless, during in vitro capacitation both follicular fluid and cAMP derivatives increased oxygen uptake and fertilizing ability, released bound tetracycline, and destabilized the sperm plasma membrane (30, 61, 126, 133, 162). In contrast, other investigators noted that dbcAMP and phosphodiesterase inhibitors actually reduced the percentage of sperm undergoing the acrosome reaction and, when present in the fertilization medium, decreased fertilizing ability while imidazole potentiated it (51). In this regard, a high level of calmodulin, the Ca^{2+}-dependent modulator protein that activates at least one form of phosphodiesterase as well as myosin light chain kinase, has recently been found in the head and presumably the acrosomal region of mammalian, avian, and sea urchin sperm and may play a role in acrosomal activation (74). High levels of calmodulin have also been found in sea urchin eggs and may play a role in fertilization (74). Finally, factors from sea urchin eggs have been shown to elevate sperm cAMP levels in a Ca^{2+}-dependent process and to increase sperm fertilizing ability (49, 50, 165). It seems quite likely that secretions from both male and female reproductive tracts and perhaps secretions from the egg itself influence the processes of sperm capacitation and fertilization by way of cAMP.

REGULATION OF SMOOTH MUSCLE IN THE REPRODUCTIVE TRACT

Contractions of the Female Reproductive Tract

The relationship of cyclic nucleotides to the regulation of uterine contractility has been extensively reviewed recently (3, 33, 34, 55, 80, 81, 140). Considerable evidence has accumulated favoring a role for cAMP in the relaxation that occurs as a result of β-adrenergic stimulation and includes correlations between these two parameters with respect to time, dose, and relative activity of analogs. There is some disagreement, however, about whether all phases of the relaxation caused by β-adrenergic agents involve changes in cAMP (114, 119).

As is true for almost all cases where cAMP has been implicated as an effector, considerable evidence also indicates that not all mechanisms for uterine relaxation involve this cyclic nucleotide (3, 33, 34, 55). Chemicals such as D600 have been shown to relax the uterus without elevating tissue cAMP. In addition, a number of investigators failed to find a correlation between cAMP levels and spontaneous activity or a fall in cAMP concomitant with contractions. Furthermore, while a number of agents that contracted the uterus antagonized the effect of β-adrenergic agonists on uterine cAMP, substances such as PGE_2 elevated cAMP while stimulating contractions. However, multiple cell types or mechanisms may be involved, since PGE_2 antagonized the ability of isoproterenol to elevate cAMP at lower doses than required for PGE_2-stimulated elevation (12). Also, prostaglandin inhibitors blocked the contractile responses but not the ability of PGE_2 to elevate cAMP (55). The argument for compartmentalization of cAMP effects apparently does not account for the difference in action of the contractant PGE_1 and the relaxant epinephrine. When present at the appropriate concentrations, both of these agents elevated total uterine cAMP, decreased uterine cytoplasmic cAMP binding capacity, and increased cAMP-independent protein kinase activity and translocation to the particulate fraction to the same degree (55).

The postulated obligatory role for cGMP in promoting uterine contractions has not been strongly substantiated. Elevation of uterine cGMP by contractile agents was reported by some investigators but not others, while cGMP elevations were found to accompany drug-induced relaxation in some cases (34, 55).

Components of both cAMP- and cGMP-sensitive systems have been demonstrated in the uterus (146). Isoproterenol activated cytoplasmic cAMP-dependent protein kinase activity and promoted the apparent translocation of the catalytic subunit to the particulate fraction (55, 82). Endogenous protein kinase activity was also measurable in the particulate fraction in the presence of detergent (82). Pretreatment of myometrial tissue with isoproterenol or treatment of the nonmitochondrial membrane preparations with cAMP enhanced ^{32}P incorporation into at least three protein species, which suggested that one or more of these might be involved in the sequestration of Ca^{2+} in analogy with proteins of cardiac sarcoplasmic reticulum (80, 82, 117). While cGMP stimulated phosphorylation of two of these proteins, phosphorylation of the third (mol wt 48,000) was strictly dependent on cAMP (116). A stimulation by cAMP and isoproterenol of Ca^{2+} uptake by myometrial membranes has been observed by some but not all investigators (80, 82, 117, 124, 179). Very recently, cAMP and its derivatives have been reported to enhance the phosphorylation of the 48,000 dalton membrane protein by endogenous protein kinase and the binding of Ca^{2+} in a parallel fashion (116). It will be important to attempt to correlate these events with physical relaxation.

Since the uterus is a multicellular organ whose contractile responsiveness is regulated by the interrelated effects of steroids, biogenic amines, polypeptide hormones, and prostaglandins (80, 81, 99), investigators in this field must attempt dose-related correlations between contractility and biochemical parameters in strictly defined hormonal models.

Information about the effect of cyclic nucleotides on the motility of the remainder of the female reproductive tract is sparse. Ovarian contractions were stimulated by α-adrenergic agents and prostaglandins but inhibited by β-adrenergic agonists or dbcAMP (27, 99). The relationship of these contractions to ovulation has been questioned (43).

The musculature of the fallopian tube was reported to be responsive to catecholamines and to relax when β-adrenergic sensitivity predominated (52, 99), but the role of these contractions in ovum transport is disputed (54). Dibutyryl cAMP, theophylline, and aminophylline have been shown to affect both electrical and physical contractile parameters (94). Regional differences in the ability of hCG to elevate rabbit oviductal cAMP and cGMP were noted, but these did not correlate with patterns of electrical activity (167).

A potentially important probe for further exploring the role of cAMP in reproductive tract smooth muscle relaxation is relaxin, a polypeptide produced by the corpus luteum of pregnancy (2), which has been shown to cause relaxation of the pubic symphysis ligament, the uterus, and the cervix (100). Purified relaxin has recently been shown to increase cAMP levels and ornithine decarboxylase activity in the pubic symphysis ligament (14, 15) and to elevate uterine and cervical cAMP levels (23, 137). Neither the effect of relaxin on uterine cAMP elevation in the presence of phosphodiesterase inhibitors nor its effect on relaxation in their absence was blocked by the β-adrenergic antagonist propranolol (137). This suggests that the relaxin effect was not mediated via release of catecholamines as had been previously proposed. Further work is required to establish whether relaxin has a direct effect on adenylate cyclase and whether its effects on spontaneous uterine activity and cAMP are in any way related.

Contractions of the Male Reproductive Tract

Contractions of the testicular capsule and seminiferous tubules have been implicated in sperm transport from the testis to the epididymis (56). In general, contractions of testicular capsules have been reported to be stimulated by prostaglandins and inhibited by β-adrenergic agonists, adenosine, caffeine, cAMP, and dbcAMP (42, 57, 142). While the spontaneous contractile activity of the epididymis and the effect of adrenergic agents and other drugs have been recorded (28, 60), correlations with cyclic nucleotide levels have not been made.

In the vas deferens, stimulation of contraction has been found to be accompanied by elevations in cGMP in some but not all instances (35, 139). With regard to relaxation, MIX relaxed the vas deferens but elevated both cAMP and cGMP (139). Numerous other relaxants did not change cAMP levels, and some, such as sodium nitroprusside, even increased cGMP levels (7, 13, 35, 141). In addition to these direct effects, the release of norepinephrine in the vas deferens by dbcAMP has been observed by one group (177) but not by another (153).

The actin binding protein, filamin, has recently been reported to be phosphorylated by a cAMP-stimulated mechanism in intact vas deferens and by cAMP-dependent protein kinase in an in vitro system (170). Since this protein apparently interferes with the interaction between actin and myosin and could therefore be involved in relaxation events, its phosphorylation is of potential interest although not as yet linked to a change in function.

MAINTENANCE OF REPRODUCTIVE TRACT FUNCTION

Relationship to the Action of Steroid Hormones

The differentiation, growth, and maintenance of reproductive tract function are dependent upon sex hormones in both the male and female. The evidence for a role for cyclic nucleotides in the mediation of these aspects of steroid hormone action in the uterus and prostate has been extensively reviewed (145, 146, 155). These data include the ability of steroid hormones to increase adenylate cyclase and cAMP and/or cGMP levels, the potentiation of steroid hormone-stimulated activation of certain enzymes in carbohydrate metabolism by theophylline, and the in vivo effects of cAMP on protein and RNA synthesis in estrogen- and androgen-dependent tissues.

Conversely, other data indicate that cyclic nucleotides cannot be obligatory second messengers mediating all actions of steroid hormones. These data include the failure of a number of investigators to demonstrate acute elevation of cyclic nucleotides in response to steroid hormones, the dichotomy in the ability of steroid antagonists to block sex hormone–stimulated and cyclic nucleotide–stimulated events, and the lack of correlation between cyclic nucleotide elevation and long-term effects such as cell division (47, 95, 145). The elevation of cyclic nucleotides and their subsequent action may be part of a generalized tissue response to sex steroid hormones, and hence they may be mediators in that sense; but unfortunately little new information has been forthcoming to elucidate this point.

Steroid hormones can influence the cyclic nucleotide responsive systems in reproductive tissues in a way other than by direct interaction. For example, androgens have been reported to restore prostatic adenylate cyclase (91) and protein kinase I (48) in castrates or animals treated with antiandrogens. It remains to be established, however, whether these responses are specific consequences of androgen action or simply part of a generalized growth response.

The interrelationship between steroid hormones and cyclic nucleotides with respect to the secretory function of reproductive tissues is also not well understood. In this regard, both testosterone and dbcAMP have been reported to stimulate the incorporation of ^{32}P into secreted protein and to increase the discharge of specific proteins from rat seminal vesicle (78).

Implantation and Blastocyst Development

Cyclic AMP has been reported to stimulate RNA and protein synthesis in both the uterus and the blastocyst (109). Since estrogen was known to stimulate implantation in the rodent and cAMP had been implicated in estrogen action, a number of workers sought to replace estradiol with cAMP or dbcAMP in ovariectomized, pregnant rodent models but met with little success (87, 172, 178). Others found that cAMP was capable of producing implantation and mimicking early estrogenic effects on the morphology of the blastocyst surface but was incapable of maintaining the tissues and promoting live births (62, 63). The specificity of the requirement for cAMP in the implantation reaction has recently been questioned (45).

Dibutyryl cAMP increased stromal and epithelial mitoses in uteri of ovariectomized, progesterone-treated mice; it sensitized these uteri to undergo the decidual reaction in the absence of an embryo (173). The response was quantitatively inferior to that produced by estrogens. Elevation of cAMP levels in the traumatized uterus and specifically in the uterine horn undergoing the decidual reaction in response to trauma or oil injection has been observed (87, 125). However, saline injection increased cAMP but did not cause a decidual reaction, while oil injection elevated cGMP in both horns (125).

Data on the level of cAMP and cGMP in the developing blastocyst are few. Decreases in cAMP from two-cell embryos to Day 4 blastocysts (46), and increases in both cAMP and cGMP and an increase in the cAMP/cGMP ratio in the Day 5–6 transition have been reported (32).

The data cited are difficult to interpret but do suggest that while cAMP may affect either the uterine epithelium, the blastocyst, or both, it is not solely responsible for the implantation process. In addition, it seems clear that the action of estrogen in this process is not solely mediated by cAMP.

CONCLUSION

Understanding of the roles of cyclic nucleotides in at least some reproductive processes is at a level comparable with elucidation of their roles in other tissues. However, it is also apparent from this review that the roles of cyclic nucleotides in several areas of reproductive function have not been extensively explored. Finally, as in other systems where multiple regulators impinge on the same process, the physiological roles of cyclic nucleotides in the regulation of reproductive processes in vivo remain to be firmly established.

Acknowledgments

The authors wish to thank the many investigators who provided articles and manuscripts in press during the writing of this review. They are grateful to Ms. Arlene Lee for editorial assistance and to Ms. Pat Dirba for secretarial assistance. BMS is the recipient of NIH Research Career Development Award 5-K04-HD00126.

Literature Cited

1. Amsterdam, A., Shemesh, M., Salomon, Y. 1979. Inhibition by follicular fluid of luteinizing hormone–sensitive adenylate cyclase in ovarian plasma membranes. In *Ovarian Follicular and Corpus Luteum Function,* ed. C. P. Channing, J. M. Marsh, W. A. Sadler, pp. 401–6. NY: Plenum Press
2. Anderson, M. L., Long, J. A. 1978. Localization of relaxin in the pregnant rat: Bioassay of tissue extracts and cell fractionation studies. *Biol. Reprod.* 18: 110–17
3. Andersson, R. G. G., Nilsson, K. B. 1977. Role of cyclic nucleotides: Metabolism and mechanical activity in smooth muscle. In *The Biochemistry of Smooth Muscle,* ed. N. L. Stephans, pp. 263–91. Baltimore: University Park Press
4. Ascoli, M., Puett, D. 1978. Gonadotropin binding and stimulation of steroidogenesis in Leydig tumor cells. *Proc. Natl. Acad. Sci. USA* 75:99–102
5. Azhar, S., Clark, M. R., Menon, K. M. J. 1976. Regulation of cyclic adenosine 3',5'-monophosphate dependent protein kinase of rat ovarian cells by luteinizing hormone and human chorionic gonadotropin. *Endocrinol. Res. Commun.* 3:93–104
6. Azhar, S., Menon, K. M. J. 1978. Stimulation of ribonucleic acid synthesis in luteinized rat ovary by cyclic 3',5'-adenosine monophosphate. *Biol. Reprod.* 19:346–57
7. Baer, H. P., Paton, D. M. 1978. Adenosine receptors in smooth muscle and other tissues. *Adv. Cyclic Nucleotide Res.* 9:315–26
8. Baker, T. G. 1979. The control of oogenesis in mammals. In *Ovarian Follicular Development and Function,* ed. A. R. Midgley, W. A. Sadler, pp. 353–64. NY: Raven Press
9. Bavister, B. D., Rogers, B. J., Yanagimachi, R. 1978. The effects of caudal epididymal plasma on the motility and acrosome reaction of hamster and guinea pig spermatozoa *in vitro. Biol. Reprod.* 19:358–63
10. Beale, E. G., Dedman, J. R., Means, A. R. 1977. Isolation and regulation of the protein kinase inhibitor and the calcium-dependent cyclic nucleotide phosphodiesterase regulator in the Sertoli cell enriched testes. *Endocrinology* 101:1621–34
11. Behrman, H. R., Caldwell, B. V. 1974. Role of prostaglandins in reproduction. In *Reproductive Physiology* (*MTP Int. Rev. Sci. Ser. 1, Vol. 8*), ed. R. O. Greep, pp. 63–94. Baltimore: University Park Press
12. Bhalla, R. C., Sanborn, B. M., Korenman, S. G. 1972. Hormonal interactions in the uterus: Inhibition by oxytocin and prostaglandins of isoproterenol-induced accumulation of cyclic AMP. *Proc. Natl. Acad. Sci. USA* 69:3761–64
13. Böhme, E., Graf, H., Schultz, G. 1978. Effects of sodium nitroprusside and other smooth muscle relaxants in cyclic GMP formation in smooth muscle and platelets. See Ref. 7, pp. 131–44
14. Braddon, S. A. 1978. Stimulation of ornithine decarboxylase by relaxin. *Biochem. Biophys. Res. Commun.* 80: 75–80
15. Braddon, S. A. 1978. Relaxin-dependent adenosine 3',5'-monophosphate concentration changes in the mouse pubic symphysis. *Endocrinology* 102: 1292–99
16. Braun, T. 1975. The effect of divalent cations on bovine spermatozoal adenylate cyclase activity. *J. Cyclic Nucleotide Res.* 1:271–81
17. Braun, T., Dods, R. F. 1975. Development of a Mn^{2+}-sensitive, "soluble" adenylate cyclase in rat testis. *Proc. Natl. Acad. Sci. USA* 72:1097–1101
18. Braun, T., Frank, H., Dods, R., Sepsenwol, S. 1977. Mn^{2+}-sensitive, soluble adenylate cyclase in rat testis. Differentiation from other testicular nucleotide cyclases. *Biochim. Biophys. Acta* 481: 227–35
19. Caron, M. G., Goldstein, S., Savard, K., Marsh, J. M. 1975. Protein kinase stimulation of a reconstituted cholesterol side chain cleavage enzyme system in the bovine corpus luteum. *J. Biol. Chem.* 250:5137–43
20. Cascieri, M., Amann, R. P., Hammerstedt, R. H. 1976. Adenine nucleotide changes at initiation of bull sperm motility. *J. Biol. Chem.* 251:787–93
21. Casillas, E. R., Elder, C. M., Hoskins, D. D. 1978. Adenylate cyclase activity in maturing bovine spermatozoa: Activation by GTP and polyamines. *Fed. Proc.* 37(6):2307 (Abstr.)
22. Channing, C. P. 1979. Intraovarian inhibitors of follicular function. See Ref. 8, pp. 59–64
23. Cheah, S. H., Sherwood, O. D. 1979. Target tissues for relaxin in the rat: Tissue distribution of injected ^{125}I-labeled relaxin and tissue changes in cyclic AMP levels after *in vitro* relaxin incu-

bation. *Progr. 61st Meet. Endocrine Soc., Anaheim, Calif.,* Abstr. 579

24. Cho, W. K., Stern, S., Biggers, J. D. 1974. Inhibitory effect of dibutyryl cAMP on mouse oocyte maturation *in vitro. J. Exp. Zool.* 187:383–86
25. Cooke, B. A., Lindh, M. L., Janszen, F. H. A. 1976. Correlation of protein kinase activation and testosterone production after stimulation of Leydig cells with luteinizing hormone. *Biochem. J.* 160:439–46
26. Cooke, B. A., Lindh, M. L., Janszen, F. H. A. 1977. Effect of lutropin on phosphorylation of endogenous proteins in testes Leydig cells. *Biochem. J.* 168:43–48
27. Coutinho, E. M., Maia, H., Maia, H. Jr. 1974. Ovarian contractility. In *Physiology and Genetics of Reproduction,* ed. E. M. Coutinho, F. Fuchs, Part B, pp. 127–37. NY: Plenum Press
28. Da Silva e Souza, M. C., Gimeno, A. L., Gimeno, M. F. 1975. Pharmacological influences upon the contractile activity of isolated guinea pig epididymis. *Acta Physiol. Latinoamericana* 25:225–26
29. Dekel, N., Beers, W. H. 1978. Rat oocyte maturation *in vitro:* Relief of cyclic AMP inhibition by gonadotropins. *Proc. Natl. Acad. Sci. USA* 75:4369–73
30. Delgado, N. M., Huacuja, L., Pancardo, R. M., Merchant, H., Rosado, A. 1976. Changes in the protein conformation of human spermatozoal membranes after treatment with cyclic adenosine 3',5'-monophosphate and human follicular fluid. *Fert. Steril.* 27:413–20
31. de Turner, E. A., Aparicio, N. J., Turner, D., Schwarzstein, L. 1978. Effect of two phosphodiesterase inhibitors, cyclic adenosine 3',5'-monophosphate, and a β-blocking agent on human sperm motility. *Fert. Steril.* 29: 328–31
32. Dey, S. K., Kimura, F., Mukherjee, A., Dickmann, Z. 1978. Cyclic AMP and cyclic GMP in rabbit blastocysts. *J. Reprod. Fert.* 52:235–37
33. Diamond, J. 1977. Evidence for dissociation between cyclic nucleotide levels and tension in smooth muscle. See Ref. 3, pp. 343–60
34. Diamond, J. 1978. Role of cyclic nucleotides in control of smooth muscle contraction. See Ref. 7, pp. 327–40
35. Diamond, J., Janis, R. A. 1978. Increases in cyclic GMP levels may not mediate relaxant effects of sodium nitroprusside, verapamil, and hydralazine in rat vas deferens. *Nature* 271:472–73
36. Dorrington, J. H., Fritz, I. B. 1974. Effects of gonadotropins on cyclic AMP production by isolated seminiferous tubules and interstitial cell preparations. *Endocrinology* 94:395–403
37. Drouin, J., Lavoie, M., Labrie, F. 1978. Effect of gonadal steroids on the luteinizing hormone and follicle stimulating hormone response to 8 Bromo-adenosine 3',5'-monophosphate in anterior pituitary cells in culture. *Endocrinology* 102:358–61
38. Dufau, M. L., Baukal, A. J., Ryan, D., Catt, K. J. 1977. Properties of detergent-solubilized adenylate cyclase and gonadotropin receptors of testis and ovary. *Molec. Cell. Endocrinol.* 6:253–69
39. Dufau, M. L., Horner, K. A., Hayashi, K., Tsuruhara, T., Conn, P. M., Catt, K. J. 1978. Actions of choleragen and gonadotropin in isolated Leydig cells. Functional compartmentalization of the hormone-activated cyclic AMP response. *J. Biol. Chem.* 253:3721–29
40. Dufau, M. L., Hsueh, A. J., Cigorraga, S., Baukal, A. J., Catt, K. J. 1978. Inhibition of Leydig cell function through hormonal regulatory mechanisms. *Int. J. Androl.* 1978: Suppl. 2, pp. 193–239
41. Dufau, M. L., Tsuruhara, T., Horner, K. A., Podesta, E., Catt, K. J. 1977. Intermediate role of adenosine 3',5'-cyclic monophosphate and protein kinase during gonadotropin-induced steroidogenesis in testicular interstitial cells. *Proc. Natl. Acad. Sci. USA* 74:3419–23
42. Ellis, L. C., Buhrley, L. E. Jr. 1978. Inhibitory effects of melatonin, prostaglandin E_1, cyclic AMP, dibutyrylcyclic AMP and theophylline on rat seminiferous tubular contractility *in vitro. Biol. Reprod.* 19:217–22
43. Espey, L. L. 1978. Ovarian contractility and its relationship to ovulation: A review. *Biol. Reprod.* 19:540–51
44. Fakunding, J. L., Tindall, D. J., Dedman, J. R., Mena, C. R., Means, A. R. 1976. Biochemical actions of follicle-stimulating hormone in the Sertoli cell of the rat testes. *Endocrinology* 98:392–402
45. Fernandez-Noval, A., Leroy, F. 1978. Induction of implantation in the mouse by intrauterine injection of adenosine monophosphate. *J. Reprod. Fert.* 53: 7–8
46. Fisher, D. L., Gunaga, K. P. 1975. Theophylline induced variations in cyclic AMP content of the superovulated

preimplantation mouse embryo. *Biol. Reprod.* 12:471–76

47. Flandroy, F., Galand, P. 1978. Changes in cGMP and cAMP content in the estrogen-stimulated rat uterus: Temporal relationship with other parameters of hormonal stimulation. *J. Cyclic Nucleotide Res.* 4:145–58
48. Fuller, D. J. M., Byus, C. V., Russell, D. H. 1978. Specific regulation by steroid hormones of the amount of type I cyclic AMP-dependent protein kinase holoenzyme. *Proc. Natl. Acad. Sci. USA* 75:223–27
49. Garbers, D. L., Kopf, G. S. 1978. Effect of factors released from eggs and other agents on cyclic nucleotide concentrations of sea urchin spermatozoa. *J. Reprod. Fert* 52:135–40
50. Garbers, D. L., Watkins, H. D., Tubb, D. J., Kopf, G. S. 1978. Regulation of spermatozoan cyclic nucleotide metabolism by egg factors. See Ref. 7, pp. 583–95
51. Garcia, L., Rogers, B. J. 1978. Effect of cyclic AMP on capacitation and fertilization. *Progr. 11th Ann. Meet. Soc. Stud. Reprod.*, #176 (Abstr.)
52. Gimeno, M. F., Rettori, V., Gimeno, A. L. 1974. Motility of the isolated oviduct of rats and guinea pigs. See Ref. 27, pp. 147–58
53. Gray, J. P., Drummond, G. I., Luk, D. W. T., Hardman, J. G., Sutherland, E. W. 1976. Enzymes of cyclic nucleotide metabolism in invertebrate and vertebrate sperm. *Arch. Biochem. Biophys.* 172:20–30
54. Halbert, S. A., Tam, P. Y., Blandau, R. J. 1976. Egg transport in the rabbit oviduct: The role of cilia and muscle. *Science* 191:1052–53
55. Harbon, S., Vesin, M. F., Khac, L. D., Leiber, D. 1978. Cyclic nucleotides in the regulation of rat uterus contractility. In *Molecular Biology and Pharmacology of Cyclic Nucleotides,* ed. G. Eolco, R. Paoletti, pp. 279–96. Amsterdam: Elsevier/North-Holland Biomedical Press
56. Hargrove, J. L., MacIndoe, J. H., Ellis, L. C. 1977. Testicular contractile cells and sperm transport. *Fert. Steril.* 28:1146–57
57. Hargrove, J. L., Seeley, R. R., Ellis, L. C. 1973. Contractions of rabbit testes *in vitro:* Permissive role of prostaglandins for the actions of Ca and some smooth-muscle stimulating agents. *Prostaglandins* 3:469–80
58. Harwood, J. P., Conti, M., Conn, P. M., Dufau, M. L., Catt, K. J. 1978. Receptor regulation and target cell responses: Studies in the ovarian luteal cell. *Molec. Cell. Endocrinol.* 11:121–35
59. Heindel, J. J., Hintz, M. I., Steinberger, E., Strada, S. J. 1977. Effects of FSH on cyclic nucleotide accumulation in testes of rats of various ages. *Endocrinol. Res. Commun.* 4:311–28
60. Hib, J., Caldeyro-Barcia, R. 1974. Neurohormonal control of epididymal contractions. See Ref. 27, pp. 111–26
61. Hicks, J. J., Martinez-Manautou, J., Pedron, N., Rosado, A. 1972. Metabolic changes in human spermatozoa related to capacitation. *Fert. Steril.* 23: 172–79
62. Holmes, P. V., Bergstrom, S. 1975. Induction of blastocyst implantation in mice by cyclic AMP. *J. Reprod. Fert.* 43:329–32
63. Holmes, P. V., Bergstrom, S. 1976. Cyclic adenosine monophosphate–induced changes in the surface morphology of diapausing blastocysts and the effects on implantation. *Am. J. Obstet. Gynecol.* 124:301–6
64. Hoskins, D. D., Brandt, H., Acott, T. S. 1978. Initiation of sperm motility in the mammalian epididymis. *Fed. Proc.* 37:2534–42
65. Hoskins, D. D., Casillas, E. R. 1975. Function of cyclic nucleotides in mammalian spermatozoa. In *Handbook of Physiology,* ed. R. O. Greep, E. B. Astwood, 5:453–60. Washington DC: Am. Physiol. Soc.
66. Hoskins, D. D., Casillas, E. R. 1975. Hormones, second messengers, and the mammalian spermatozoan. In *Molecular Mechanisms of Gonadal Hormone Action* (*Adv. Sex Horm. Res. Vol 1*), ed. J. A. Thomas, R. L. Singhal, pp. 283–324. Baltimore: University Park Press
67. Hoskins, D. D., Hall, M. L., Munsterman, D. 1975. Induction of motility in immature bovine spermatozoa by cyclic AMP phosphodiesterase inhibitors and seminal plasma. *Biol. Reprod.* 13: 168–76
68. Hsueh, A. J. W., Dufau, M. L., Catt, K. J. 1977. Gonadotropin-induced regulation of luteinizing hormone receptors and desensitization of testicular 3',5'-cyclic AMP and testosterone responses. *Proc. Natl. Acad. Sci. USA* 74:592–95
69. Huacuja, L., Delgado, N. M., Merchant, H., Pancardo, R. M., Rosado, A. 1977. Cyclic AMP induced incorporation of ^{33}P into human spermatozoa membrane components. *Biol. Reprod.* 17:89–96
70. Hunzicker-Dunn, M., Jungmann, R. A., Birnbaumer, L. 1979. Hormone ac-

tion in ovarian follicles: Adenylyl cyclase and protein kinase enzyme systems. See Ref. 8, pp. 267–304

71. Janszen, F. H. A., Cooke, B. A., van der Molen, H. J. 1977. Specific protein synthesis in isolated rat testes Leydig cells. Influence of luteinizing hormone and cycloheximide. *Biochem. J.* 162: 341–46
72. Janszen, F. H. A., Cooke, B. A., van Driel, M. J. A., van der Molen, H. J. 1978. Regulation of the synthesis of lutropin-induced protein in rat testes Leydig cells. *Biochem. J.* 170:9–15
73. Janszen, F. H. A., Cooke, B. A., van Driel, M. J. A., van der Molen, H. J. 1978. The effect of lutropin on specific protein synthesis in tumor Leydig cells and in Leydig cells from immature rats. *Biochem. J.* 172:147–53
74. Jones, H. P., Bradford, M. M., McRorie, R. A., Cormier, M. J. 1978. High levels of a calcium-dependent modulator protein in spermatozoa and its similarity to brain modulator protein. *Biochem. Biophys. Res. Commun.* 82: 1264–72
75. Jungmann, R. A., Hiestand, P. C., Schweppe, J. S. 1974. Mechanism of action of gonadotropin. IV. Cyclic adenosine monophosphate–dependent translocation of ovarian cytoplasmic cyclic adenosine monophosphate–binding protein and protein kinase to nuclear acceptor sites. *Endocrinology* 94: 168–83
76. Kercret, H., Benoist, L., Duval, J. 1977. Acute release of gonadotropins mediated by dibutyryl cyclic AMP *in vitro*. *FEBS Lett.* 83:222–24
77. Kercret, H., Duval, J. 1978. Gonadoliberin-promoted release of gonadotropins and increased sensitivity of the pituitary by oestradiol-17β. *J. Steroid Biochem.* 9:761–66
78. Koenig, H., Lu, C. Y., Bakay, R. 1976. Testosterone and 6-N, 2'-0-dibutyryladenosine 3',5'-cyclic monophosphate stimulate protein and lysosomal enzyme secretion in rat seminal vesicle. *Biochem. J.* 158:543–47
79. Kopf, G. S., Garbers, D. L. 1978. Correlation between sea urchin sperm respiratory rates and cyclic AMP concentrations as a function of cell dilution. *Biol. Reprod.* 18:229–33
80. Korenman, S. G., Krall, J. F. 1977. The role of cyclic AMP in the regulation of smooth muscle cell contraction in the uterus. *Biol. Reprod.* 16:1–17
81. Krall, J. F., Korenman, S. G. 1977. Mechanisms in the control of uterine contractility. In *Regulatory Mechanisms Affecting Gonadal Hormone Action* (*Adv. Sex Horm. Res., Vol 3*), ed. J. A. Thomas, R. L. Singhal, pp. 75–101. Baltimore: University Park Press
82. Krall, J. F., Schindler, A. M., Korenman, S. G. 1978. Myometrial protein kinase: Hormone stimulated translocation and membrane binding of the soluble enzyme. *Arch. Biochem. Biophys.* 187:1–11
83. Labrie, F., DeLean, A., Lagace, L., Drouin, J., Ferland, L., Beaulieu, M., Morin, O. 1978. Interactions of TRH, LH-RH and somatostatin in the anterior pituitary gland. In *Receptors and Hormone Action,* ed. L. Birnbaumer, B. W. O'Malley, III:493–511. NY: Academic
84. Labrie, F., Drouin, J., Ferland, L., Lagace, L., Beaulieu, M., DeLean, A., Kelly, P. A., Caron, M. G., Raymond, V. 1978. Mechanism of action of hypothalamic hormones in the anterior pituitary gland and specific modulation of their activity by sex steroids and thyroid hormones. *Recent Prog. Horm. Res.* 35:25–93
85. Lahav, M., Freud, A., Lindner, H. R. 1976. Abrogation by prostaglandin $F_{2\alpha}$ of LH-stimulated cyclic AMP accumulation in isolated rat corpora lutea of pregnancy. *Biochem. Biophys. Res. Commun.* 68:1294–1300
86. Lee, M. Y. W., Iverson, R. M. 1976. An adenosine 3',5'-monophosphate dependent protein kinase from sea urchin spermatozoa. *Biochim. Biophys. Acta* 429:123–36
87. Leroy, F., Vansande, J., Shetgen, G., Brasseur, D. 1974. Cyclic AMP and the triggering of the decidual reaction. *J. Reprod. Fert.* 39:207–11
88. Lindemann, C. B. 1978. A cAMP-induced increase in the motility of demembranated bull sperm models. *Cell* 13:9–18
89. Lindner, H. R., Amsterdam, A., Salomon, Y., Tsafriri, A., Nimrod, A., Lamprecht, S. A., Zor, U., Koch, Y. 1977. Intraovarian factors in ovulation: Determinants of follicular response to gonadotrophins. *J. Reprod. Fert.* 51: 215–35
90. Liu, T. C., Jackson, G. L. 1978. Modification of luteinizing hormone biosynthesis and release by gonadotropin-releasing hormone, cycloheximide and actinomycin D. *Endocrinology* 103: 1253–63
91. Lubek, B. M., Tsang, B. K., Singhal, R. L. 1977. Responsiveness of the prostatic adenylate cyclase–cyclic AMP system

to cyproterone acetate treatment in male rats. *J. Med.* 8:349–65
92. Maghuin-Rogister, G., Closset, J., Combarnous, Y., Hennen, G., Dechenne, C., Ketelslegers, J. M. 1978. Study of follitropin receptors in testes using a homologous system. *Eur. J. Biochem.* 86:121–31
93. Magnusson, C., Hillensjö, T. 1977. Inhibition of maturation and metabolism in rat oocytes by cyclic AMP. *J. Exp. Zool.* 201:139–47
94. Maia, H. Jr., Coutinho, E. M. 1974. Cyclic AMP and oviduct contractility. See Ref. 27, pp. 167–76
95. Mainwaring, W. I. P. 1977. *The Mechanism of Action of Androgens.* NY: Springer. 178 pp.
96. Marsh, J. M. 1975. The role of cyclic AMP in gonadal function. *Adv. Cyclic Nucleotide Res.* 6:137–99
97. Marsh, J. M., LeMaire, W. J. 1974. The role of cyclic AMP and prostaglandins in the actions of LH. In *Gonadotropins and Gonadal Function,* ed. N. R. Moudgal, pp. 376–90. NY: Academic
98. Marsh, J. M., LeMaire, W. J. 1976. The interrelationship of follicular cyclic AMP, steroids and prostaglandins during the ovulatory process. In *The Endocrine Function of the Human Ovary,* ed. V. H. T. James, M. Serio, G. Giusti, pp. 25–35. NY: Academic
99. Marshall, J. M. 1973. Effects of catecholamines on the smooth muscle of the female reproductive tract. *Ann. Rev. Pharmacol.* 13:19–32
100. Martin, G. J., Schoenbach, U. 1958. Historical aspects of relaxin. *Ann. NY Acad. Sci.* 75:923–30
101. Means, A. R., Dedman, J. R., Fakunding, J. L., Tindall, D. J. 1978. Mechanism of action of FSH in the male rat. In *Receptors and Hormone Action,* ed. L. Birnbaumer, B. W. O'Malley, III:363–92. NY: Academic
102. Means, A. R., Dedman, J. R., Tindall, D. J., Welsh, M. J. 1978. Hormonal regulation of Sertoli cells. *Int. J. Androl.* 2: Suppl. 403–23
103. Mendelson, C., Dufau, M., Catt, K. 1975. Dependence of gonadotropin-induced steroidogenesis upon RNA and protein synthesis in the interstitial cells of the rat testes. *Biochem. Biophys. Acta* 411:222–30
104. Mendelson, C., Dufau, M., Catt, K. 1975. Gonadotropin binding and stimulation of cyclic adenosine 3',5'-monophosphate and testosterone production in isolated Leydig cells. *J. Biol. Chem.* 250:8818–23
105. Menon, K. M. J., Gunaga, K. P. 1974. Role of cyclic AMP in reproductive processes. *Fert. Steril.* 25:732–50
106. Menon, K. M. J., Gunaga, K. P., Azhar, S. 1977. GnRH action in rat anterior pituitary gland: Regulation of protein, glycoprotein and LH syntheses. *Acta Endocrinol.* 86:473–88
107. Midgley, A. R., Sadler, W. A., eds. 1979. *Ovarian Follicular Development and Function.* NY: Raven Press. 414 pp.
108. Milkowski, A. L., Babcock, D. F., Lardy, H. A. 1976. Activation of bovine epididymal sperm respiration by caffeine. *Arch. Biochem. Biophys.* 176: 250–56
109. Mohla, S., Prasad, M. R. N. 1970. Stimulation of RNA synthesis in the blastocyst and uterus of rat by adenosine 3',5'-monophosphate (cyclic AMP). *J. Reprod. Fert.* 23:327–29
110. Nakano, H., Fawcett, C. P., Kimura, F., McCann, S. M. 1978. Evidence for the involvement of guanosine 3',5'-cyclic monophosphate in the regulation of gonadotropin release. *Endocrinology* 103:1527–33
111. Naor, Z., Koch, Y., Chobsieng, P., Zor, U. 1975. Pituitary cyclic AMP production and mechanism of luteinizing hormone release. *FEBS Lett.* 58:318–21
112. Naor, Z., Zor, U., Meidan, R., Koch, Y. 1978. Sex differences in pituitary cyclic AMP response to gonadotropin-releasing hormone. *Am. J. Physiol.* 235: E37–41
113. Neer, E. J. 1978. Multiple forms of adenylate cyclase. See Ref. 7, pp. 69–84
114. Nesheim, B. I. 1975. Action of β-adrenoceptor antagonists on the response to isoprenaline in the oestrogen dominated rabbit uterus. *Br. J. Pharmacol.* 53:393–401
115. Nimrod, A., Tsafriri, A., Lindner, H. R. 1977. *In vitro* induction of binding sites for hCG in rat granulosa cells by FSH. *Nature* 267:632–33
116. Nishikori, K., Maeno, H. 1979. Close relationship between adenosine 3',5'-monophosphate-dependent endogenous phosphorylation of a specific protein and stimulation of calcium uptake in rat uterine microsomes. *J. Biol. Chem.* 254:6099–106
117. Nishikori, K., Takenaka, T., Maeno, H. 1977. Stimulation of microsomal calcium uptake and protein phosphorylation by adenosine cyclic 3',5'-monophosphate in rat uterus. *Mol. Pharmacol.* 13:671–78

118. Ong, S. H., Whitley, T. H., Stowe, N. W., Steiner, A. L. 1975. Immunolocalization of 3',5'-cyclic AMP and 3',5'-cyclic GMP in rat liver, intestine and testis. *Proc. Natl. Acad. Sci. USA* 72:2022–26
119. Overweg, N. I. A., Schiff, J. D. 1978. Two mechanisms of isoproterenol inhibition of smooth muscle. *Eur. J. Pharmacol.* 47:231–33
120. Payne, A. H., Zipf, W. B. 1973. Regulation of Leydig cell function by prolactin, growth hormone and luteinizing hormone. *Int. J. Androl.* Supp 2:329–44
121. Podesta, E. J., Dufau, M. L., Catt, K. J. 1976. Adenosine 3',5'-monophosphate-dependent protein kinase of Leydig cells: *In vitro* activation and relationship to gonadotropin action upon cyclic AMP and steroidogenesis. *FEBS Lett.* 70:212–16
122. Podesta, E. J., Dufau, M. L., Catt, K. J. 1978. Cyclic adenosine 3',5'-monophosphate dependent protein kinases of rat Leydig cells: Physical characteristics of two holoenzymes and their subunits. *Biochemistry* 17:1566–73
123. Purvis, K., Torjesen, P. A., Haug, E., Hansson, V. 1977. HCG suppression of LH receptors and responsiveness of testicular tissue to hCG. *Mol. Cell Endocrinol.* 8:73–80
124. Rangachari, P. K., Pernollet, M. G., Worcel, M. 1976. Calcium uptake by myometrial membranes: Effect of A23187, a calcium ionophore. *Eur. J. Pharmacol.* 40:291–94
125. Rankin, J. C., Ledford, B. E., Baggett, B. 1977. Early involvement of cyclic nucleotides in the artificially stimulated decidual cell reaction in the mouse uterus. *Biol. Reprod.* 17:549–54
126. Reyes, A., Goicoechea, B., Rosado, A. 1978. Calcium ion requirement for rabbit spermatozoal capacitation and enhancement of fertilizing ability by ionophore A23187 and cyclic adenosine 3',5'-monophosphate. *Fert. Steril.* 29:451–55
127. Richards, J. S. 1979. Hormonal control of ovarian follicular development: A 1978 perspective. *Recent Prog. Horm. Res.* 36: In press
128. Richards, J. S., Midgley, A. R. Jr. 1976. Protein hormone action: A key to understanding ovarian follicular and luteal cell development. *Biol. Reprod.* 14:82–94
129. Richards, J. S., Rao, M. C., Ireland, J. J. 1978. Actions of pituitary gonadotrophins on the ovary. In *The Control of Ovulation,* ed. D. B. Crighton, pp. 197–216. London: Butterworth
130. Rigler, G. L., Peake, G. T., Ratner, A. 1978. Effect of luteinizing hormone releasing hormone on accumulation of pituitary cyclic AMP and GMP *in vitro. J. Endocrinol.* 76:367–68
131. Robison, G. A. 1976. Cyclic nucleotides as mediators of drug action. In *Receptors and Cellular Pharmacology,* ed. J. Tuomisto, M. K. Paasonen, pp. 185–91. Oxford: Pergamon Press
132. Rommerts, F. F. G., Cooke, B. A., van der Molen, H. J. 1974. The role of cyclic AMP in the regulation of steroid biosynthesis in the testes tissue. *J. Steroid Biochem.* 5:279–85
133. Rosado, A., Hicks, J. J., Reyes, A., Blanco, I. 1974. Capacitation *in vitro* of rabbit spermatozoa with cyclic adenosine monophosphate and human follicular fluid. *Fert. Steril.* 25:821–24
134. Rosado, A., Huacuja, L., Delgado, N. M., Hicks, J. J., Pancardo, R. M. 1975. Cyclic-AMP receptors in the human spermatozoa membrane. *Life Sci.* 17:1707–14
135. Saez, J. M., Haour, F., Cathiard, A. M. 1978. Early hCG-induced desensitization in Leydig cells. *Biochem. Biophys. Res. Commun.* 81:552–58
136. Salomon, Y., Amsterdam, A. 1977. Heparin: A potent inhibitor of ovarian luteinizing hormone–sensitive adenylate cyclase. *FEBS Lett.* 83:263–66
137. Sanborn, B. M., Kuo, H. S., Weisbrodt, N. W., Sherwood, O. D. 1979. Effect of relaxin on uterine cAMP levels and contractile activity. See Ref. 23, Abstr. 848
138. Sano, M. 1976. Subcellular localizations of guanylate cyclase and 3',5'-cyclic nucleotide phosphodiesterase in sea urchin sperm. *Biochim. Biophys. Acta* 428:525–31
139. Schultz, G., Hardman, J. G. 1975. Regulation of cyclic GMP levels in the ductus deferens of the rat. *Adv. Cyclic Nucleotide Res.* 5:339–51
140. Schultz, G., Hardman, J. G. 1976. Possible roles of cyclic nucleotides in the regulation of smooth muscle tonus. In *Eukaryotic Cell Function and Growth,* ed. J. E. Dumont, B. L. Brown, N. J. Marshall, pp. 667–83. NY: Plenum
141. Schultz, K. D., Schultz, K., Schultz, G. 1977. Sodium nitroprusside and other smooth muscle–relaxants increase cyclic GMP levels in rat ductus deferens. *Nature* 265:750–51
142. Seeley, R. R., Hargrove, J. L., Sanders, R. T., Ellis, L. C. 1973. Response of

rabbit testicular capsular contractions to testosterone, prostaglandin E_1, and isoproterenol *in vitro* and *in vivo*. *Proc. Soc. Exp. Biol. Med.* 144:329–32

143. Shah, G. V., Sheth, A. R., Mugatwala, P. P., Roa, S. S. 1975. Effect of spermine on adenyl cyclase activity of spermatozoa. *Experientia* 31:631–32
144. Sharpe, R. M. 1977. Gonadotropin-induced reduction in the steroidogenic responsiveness of the immature rat testes. *Biochem. Biophys. Res. Commun.* 76:957–62
145. Singhal, R. L., Sutherland, D. J. B. 1975. Cyclic 3',5'-adenosine monophosphate and accessory sex organ responses. In *Molecular Mechanisms of Gonadal Hormone Action,* ed. J. A. Thomas, R. L. Singhal, 1:225–82. Baltimore: University Park Press
146. Singhal, R. L., Tsang, B. K., Sutherland, D. J. B. 1976. Regulation of cyclic nucleotide and prostaglandin metabolism in sex steroid-dependent cells. In *Cellular Mechanisms Modulating Gonadal Hormone Action,* ed. R. L. Singhal, J. A. Thomas, 2:325–424. Baltimore: University Park Press
147. Spruill, W. A., Hurwitz, D. R., Lucchesi, J. C., Steiner, A. L. 1978. Association of cyclic GMP with gene expression of polytene chromosomes of *Drosophila Melanogaster. Proc. Natl. Acad. Sci. USA* 75:1480–84
148. Spruill, A., Steiner, A. 1976. Immunohistochemical localization of cyclic nucleotides during testicular development. *J. Cyclic Nucl. Res.* 2:225–39
149. Steinberger, A., Hintz, M., Heindel, J. J. 1978. Changes in cyclic AMP responses to FSH in isolated rat Sertoli cells during sexual maturation. *Biol. Reprod.* 19:566–71
150. Steinberger, A., Walther, J., Heindel, J. J., Sanborn, B. M., Tsai, Y. H., Steinberger, E. 1979. Hormone interactions in the Sertoli cell. *In Vitro* 15:23–31
151. Steinberger, E., Steinberger, A., Sanborn, B. M. 1978. Molecular mechanisms concerned with hormonal control of the seminiferous epithelium. *Rec. Prog. Androl.* 14:143–78
152. Stephens, D. T., Wang, J. L., Hoskins, D. D. 1979. The cyclic AMP phosphodiesterase of bovine spermatozoa: Multiple forms, kinetic properties and changes during development. *Biol. Reprod.* 20:483–91
153. Stjarne, L. 1976. Relative importance of calcium and cyclic AMP for noradrenaline secretion from sympathetic nerves of guinea pig vas deferens and for prostaglandin induced depression of noradrenaline secretion. *Neuroscience* 1:19–22
154. Strickland, S., Beers, W. H. 1979. Studies of the enzymatic basis and hormonal control of ovulation. See Ref. 8, pp. 143–53
155. Szego, C. M. 1978. Parallels in the modes of action of peptide and steroid hormones: Membrane effects and cellular entry. In *The Structure and Function of Gonadotropins,* ed. K. W. McKerns, pp. 431–72. NY: Plenum
156. Tamblyn, T. M., First, N. L. 1977. Caffeine-stimulated ATP-reactivated motility in a detergent-treated bovine sperm model. *Arch. Biochem. Biophys.* 181:208–215
157. Tang, L. K. L. 1978. Sex difference in LH response to LHRH and dbcAMP and effect of testosterone. *Am. J. Physiol.* 235:291–94
158. Tang, F. Y., Hoskins, D. D. 1975. Phosphoprotein phosphatase of bovine epididymal spermatozoa. *Biochem. BioPhys. Res. Commun.* 62:328–35
159. Tash, J. S. 1976. Investigations on adenosine 3',5'-monophosphate phosphodiesterase in ram semen and initial characterization of a sperm-specific isozyme. *J. Reprod. Fert.* 47:63–72
160. Thomas, J. P., Dorflinger, L. J., Behrman, H. R. 1978. Mechanism of the rapid antigonadotropic action of prostaglandins in cultured luteal cells. *Proc. Natl. Acad. Sci. USA* 75:1344–48
161. Towns, K. M., Like, R. K. J. 1976. Measurement of adenylate cyclase activity in ram spermatozoa. *J. Reprod. Fert.* 47:355–57
162. Toyoda, Y., Chang, M. C. 1974. Capacitation of epididymal spermatozoa in a medium with high K/Na ratio and cylic AMP for the fertilization of rat eggs *in vitro. J. Reprod. Fert.* 36:125–34
163. Tsafriri, A., Lindner, H. R., Zor, U., Lamprecht, S. A. 1972. *In vitro* induction of meiotic division in follicle-enclosed rat oocytes by LH, cyclic AMP, and prostaglandin E_2. *J. Reprod. Fert.* 31:39–50
164. Tsuruhara, T., Dufau, M., Cigorraga, S., Catt, K. 1977. Hormonal regulation of testicular luteinizing hormone receptors. *J. Biol. Chem.* 252:9002–9
165. Tubb, D. J., Kopf, G. S., Garbers, D. L. 1978. The elevation of sperm adenosine 3',5'-monophosphate concentrations by factors released from eggs requires calcium. *Biol. Reprod.* 18:181–85

166. Vaitukaitis, J. L., Albertson, B. D. 1979. Mechanisms modulating gonadotropin action. See Ref. 8, pp. 247–53
167. Valenzuela, G., Antonini, R., Hodgson, B. J., Jones, D. J., Harper, M. J. K. 1977. Cyclic nucleotides and prostaglandins produced by the rabbit oviduct: Effects of estrogen treatment. *Res. Commun. Chem. Pathol. Pharmacol.* 17:361–64
168. van der Vusse, G. J., Kalkman, M. L., van Wensen, M. P. I., van der Molen, H. J. 1975. Short term effect of luteinizing hormone and cycloheximide *in vivo* and Ca^{2+} *in vitro* on steroid production in cell-free systems. *Biochem. Biophys. Acta* 398:28–38
169. Vilchez-Martinez, J. A., Arimura, A., Schally, A. V. 1976. On the effect of actinomycin D on the pituitary response to LHRH. *Acta Endocrinol.* 81:73–81
170. Wallach, D., Davies, P. J. A., Pastan, I. 1978. Cyclic AMP-dependent phosphorylation of filamin in mammalian smooth muscle. *J. Biol. Chem.* 253: 4739–45
171. Watkins, H. D., Kopf, G. S., Garbers, D. L. 1978. Activation of sperm adenylate cyclase by factors associated with eggs. *Biol. Reprod.* 19:890–94
172. Webb, F. T. G. 1975. The inability of dibutyryl adenosine 3',5'-monophosphate to induce the decidual reaction in intact pseudo-pregnant mice. *J. Reprod. Fert.* 42:187–88
173. Webb, F. T. G. 1977. Cyclic AMP and the preparation of the mouse uterus for implantation. *J. Reprod. Fert.* 50:83–89
174. Wells, J. N., Garbers, D. L. 1976. Nucleoside 3',5'-monophosphate phosphodiesterases in sea urchin sperm. *Biol. Reprod.* 15:46–53
175. Williams, C. D., Horner, A. K., Catt, K. J. 1976. The effect of methylxanthines on gonadotropin-induced steroidogenesis and protein synthesis in isolated testes interstitial cells. *Endocrinol. Res. Commun.* 3:343–58
176. Williams, M. T., Clark, M. R., Ling, W. Y., LeMaire, W. J., Caron, M. G., Marsh, J. M. 1978. Role of cyclic AMP in the actions of luteinizing hormone on steroidogenesis in the corpus luteum. See Ref. 7, pp. 573–82
177. Wooten, G. F., Thoa, N. B., Kopin, I. J., Axelrod, J. 1973. Enhanced release of dopamine β-hydroxylase and NE from sympathetic nerves by dibutyryl cAMP and theophylline. *Mol. Pharmacol.* 9:178–83
178. Wu, J. T., Chang, M. C. 1977. Failure of dibutyryl cyclic AMP to induce implantation in rats and mice. *Biol. Reprod.* 17:355–60
179. Zelck, U., Karnstedt, U. 1977. ATP-dependent Ca^{2+} binding by mitochondrial and microsomal fractions isolated from different smooth muscles: Influence of cyclic nucleotides. In *Excitation-Contraction Coupling in Smooth Muscle,* ed. R. Casteels, T. Godfraind, J. C. Ruegg, pp. 171–80. Amsterdam: Elsevier/North Holland
180. Zolman, J. C., Valenta, L. J. 1978. Sex dependent differences in LH secretion and GnRH binding in bovine anterior pituitary. *Progr. 60th Meet. Endocrine Soc., Miami, Fla.,* #755 (Abstr.)
181. Zor, U., Lamprecht, S. A. 1977. Mechanism of prostaglandin action in endocrine glands. In *Biochemical Actions of Hormones,* ed. G. Litwack, IV:85–133. NY: Academic

Ann. Rev. Physiol. 1980. 42:59–70

REGULATION OF THE TESTIS SERTOLI CELL BY FOLLICLE STIMULATING HORMONE ❖1253

A. R. Means, J. R. Dedman, J. S. Tash, D. J. Tindall, M. van Sickle and M. J. Welsh

Department of Cell Biology, Baylor College of Medicine, Houston, Texas 77030

INTRODUCTION

The Sertoli cell is the only somatic cell within the confines of the seminiferous epthelium of the testis. This cell to a large degree dictates the development and maintenance of spermatogenesis in all mammals. Spermatogenesis is a hormonally regulated process, but controversy exists concerning which steps in the complex series of events are regulated by hormones. The Sertoli cell is regulated by both a steroid hormone, testosterone, and a peptide hormone, follicle stimulating hormone (FSH). All hormonal regulation of spermatogenesis is probably mediated by the Sertoli cell. Several recent reviews concern the hormonal regulation of spermatogenesis and the mechanism of action of FSH (14, 25, 26). Here we review the effects of FSH on Sertoli cells in tissue culture and discuss three major areas: (*a*) the temporal sequence of events following the addition of FSH to Sertoli cells in culture; (*b*) why the Sertoli cell becomes refractory to FSH as the animal ages; and (*c*) the mechanisms by which FSH controls secretion of proteins from the Sertoli cell.

Peptide hormones regulate many cellular processes in a variety of target cells, including ion flux, enzyme activity, RNA and protein synthesis, steroid synthesis and secretion, protein secretion, cell division, cell motility, and cell-to-cell communication. The Sertoli cell is unique in that it participates in each of these diverse processes, all of which are regulated by FSH at some time during the development and differentiation of the Sertoli cell. Table 1 lists these events and the specific process in the Sertoli cell regulated by FSH. Thus the study of FSH regulation of the Sertoli cell offers insight

0066-4278/80/0315-0059$01.00

Table 1 Cellular processes regulated by peptide hormones

Process	FSH and Sertoli cells	References
Ion flux	Ca^{2+} redistribution	26
Enzyme activity	Adenylyl cyclase	4, 26, 40
	Phosphodiesterase	13, 26
	Protein kinase	12, 13, 25, 40
	Ornithine decarboxylase	27
Protein synthesis	General cell proteins	13
	Protein kinase inhibitor	36, 37
Protein secretion	Androgen binding protein	13, 14, 15, 23, 26, 30, 40
	Plasminogen activator	22
	Inhibin	35
Steroid synthesis	Estrogen	11
Cell division	DNA synthesis & mitosis	18
Cell motility	Microtubule polymerization	24
	Microfilament organization	9, 10, 25, 26, 40
	Cell shape	25, 26, 32, 39, 40
Cell-cell communication	Junctional complexes	7, 17, 28

not only into regulation of spermatogenesis but also into mechanisms involved in the modulation of a variety of intracellular events important in cell biology.

FSH BINDING AND CYCLIC NUCLEOTIDE METABOLISM

Sertoli cells can be isolated from both normal and Sertoli cell–enriched testis (13, 25, 26) in high yields using very simple procedures. To a large extent the cultures are primary—i.e. even though some cell division has been reported, the mitotic index is very low. In addition, this low rate of mitotic activity is restricted to cells derived from animals less than 20 days of age. FSH binds to specific receptors on the membranes of Sertoli cells (1, 5, 13). This interaction is both tissue- and cell-specific, is dependent on both temperature and time, is of high affinity ($K_d \sim 10^{-10}$ M), and is of limited capacity (10^4 sites per cell). Binding of ^{125}I- or ^{3}H-FSH can be detected within 1 min, and saturation is achieved by 20 min. FSH-membrane interaction coincides with stimulation of adenylyl cyclase (4, 26, 40). Cyclase stimulation can be observed either in homogenates prepared from Sertoli cells, intact Sertoli cells incubated with ATP^{32}, or in membranes isolated from the cultured Sertoli cells (40). In the latter case, a significant stimulation is noted within 2 min, and a linear increase in activity continues for at least 20 min. Thus the temporal kinetics of the interaction of FSH with plasma membrane receptors and the activation of membrane bound adenylyl cyclase are similar.

Adenylyl cylase is the only enzyme known to synthesize cylic AMP (cAMP) in cells. Likewise, cyclic nucleotide–dependent phosphodiesterase is the only enzyme to degrade cAMP. It has been established kinetically that a change in the V_{max} of adenylyl cyclase is equal to an equivalent change in the K_m of phosphodiesterase, which is inversely related to the V_{max} of phosphodiesterase (26). Therefore, in considering the steady-state concentration of cAMP, activities of phosphodiesterase must be taken into account. Indeed, FSH results in a decrease in the activity of cAMP phosphodiesterase in isolated Sertoli cells that can be measured within 5 min; inhibition is maximal at 20 min (13, 25, 26). Again, the temporal effects of FSH on phosphodiesterase are similar to FSH binding and stimulation of adenylyl cyclase. Subsequent studies have shown that the phosphodiesterase isoform affected by FSH is a high affinity cAMP enzyme that requires calcium (10^{-6} M) for activity (26). The stimulation of adenylyl cyclase and inhibition of phosphodiesterase result in an elevation of intracellular levels of cAMP (34). Statistically significant effects can be seen at 10^{-11} M hormone and maximal effects occur at 10^{-9} M (13). Thus over a two log dose range of FSH, a linear increase in Sertoli cell cAMP is observed.

The rapid increase in the intracellular concentration of cAMP results in the activation of cAMP-dependent protein kinase (12, 13, 25, 26, 40). Again, this activation can be seen within 2 min, is maximal within 30 min, and even in the continued presence of hormone declines to basal levels by 4 hr. The activated catalytic subunit of cAMP-dependent protein kinase phosphorylates proteins in virtually every subcellular compartment. To date no specific protein substrate has been shown to be phosphorylated in response to FSH. Clearly, the specific substrate must be elucidated before phosphorylation can be shown to underwrite the subsequent effects of FSH. In fact, this step represents the major missing link between hormone binding, altered cyclic nucleotide metabolism, and the subsequent intracellular events to be discussed.

PROTEIN SYNTHESIS AND SECRETION

Within 30 min after addition of FSH to tissue culture cells, an increase in the incorporation of tritiated uridine into RNA is observed and protein synthesis measured by incorporation of amino acids into proteins is stimulated (13, 40). It has been known for some time that FSH results in an overall stimulation of protein synthesis (25). Recently it has been possible to demonstrate the specific synthesis of an intracellular protein in response to this hormone. The protein is a low-molecular-weight, heat-stable molecule reported to inhibit the catalytic subunit of cAMP-dependent protein kinase and the calcium-dependent form of cAMP phosphodiesterase (3). This protein has been called the protein kinase inhibitor (PKI). Stimulation of PKI by FSH can be seen within 4 hr after addition of the gonodatropin to tissue culture cells (37). Stimulation continues to increase for at least 24 hr, at which time PKI levels are four times that observed in control cells. The response of PKI to FSH is dose-dependent, can be mimicked by cAMP or by substances that increase Sertoli cell cAMP, and can be inhibited by actinomycin D and cycloheximide. Androgen binding protein (ABP) levels are also stimulated in the Sertoli cell, but the precise mechanism of regulation of the synthesis of ABP is unclear (13–15, 23, 25, 26, 30, 40). The data indicate that both testosterone and FSH may control this process (23). On the other hand, ABP secretion seems to be an FSH-specific event (25, 26). Secretion can be detected within 3 hr; it peaks at 12–24 hr and tends to plateau at that point (40). Thus FSH controls both the synthesis and secretion of specific Sertoli cell proteins.

SERTOLI CELL SENSITIVITY TO FSH

FSH has been reported to increase the incorporation of thymidine into DNA and to increase the mitotic activity of isolated Sertoli cells (14, 32). These data suggest that the proliferation of Sertoli cells during the early development of the testis may be dependent upon this gonadotropin. However, stimulation of DNA synthesis and mitotic activity by FSH is dependent upon the age of the animals from which Sertoli cells are isolated. Maximum sensitivity to this gonadotropin occurs between 12 and 15 days of age, and by 20 days of age little effect can be seen (14). This age dependency is true for all intracellular events stimulated by FSH in isolated Sertoli cells (14, 25, 26). Thus increased cAMP, inhibition of phosphodiesterase, activation of protein kinase, RNA and protein synthesis, and mitotic activity all peak at about 20 days of age, the time at which the tight junctions between Sertoli cells first appear in vivo (17, 25). This age is also the time at which meiotic activity is first seen among the germ cells and marks the onset of complete spermatogenesis in the rat.

The lack of responsiveness of the Sertoli cell to FSH is not due to the absence or diminution of FSH receptors. The number of FSH receptors per cell continues to increase for the first 60–80 days of Sertoli cell development

(13, 21, 38). This persistence of receptors occurs in normal testis and Sertoli cell–enriched testis in vivo as well as in isolated Sertoli cells in vitro. At first glance, stimulation of Sertoli cell adenylyl cyclase seems to be age-dependent (26, 34). This observation is true if cyclase is measured in homogenates of isolated Sertoli cells. However, the stimulation by FSH can be recovered by the addition of the guanyl nucleotide, GMP-P(NH)P (40). In addition, stimulation is observed by centrifuging the homogenate at 1000 *g* and measuring activity in the supernatant fraction, or by diluting the homogenate considerably. When plasma membranes are isolated from mature Sertoli cells, the basal activity is no different from that observed in membranes from immature animals (40). The response to FSH is identical. These observations suggest that the functional FSH-receptor–adenylyl-cyclase coupling mechanism is viable in isolated Sertoli cell membranes regardless of age. The defect seems to lie in the accumulation of some component that can be diluted out or removed by differential centrifugation. This putative compound remains unidentified.

The effect of FSH on inhibition of phosphodiesterase is also age-dependent (13, 25, 26). The inhibition seems to be due to a calcium-dependent form of the enzyme in isolated Sertoli cells. Fractionation studies have demonstrated that the immature cell contains two isoforms of the enzyme separable by ion exchange chromatography. The first form to elute is calcium-sensitive whereas the second does not require calcium for activity. The mature Sertoli cell, on the other hand, seems to have lost the calcium-sensitive form, but the amount of the calcium insensitive form has increased so that total levels of cAMP phosphodiesterase are the same in mature and immature cells. These data suggest that the lack of inhibition of phosphodiesterase might result in a more rapid hydrolysis of cAMP so that intracellular concentrations of this nucleotide could not reach the same levels as in the immature cells. Indeed, inhibition of phosphodiesterase by the addition of 1-methyl-3-isobutylxanthine results in the restoration of the ability of FSH to elevate cAMP, to activate protein kinase, and to stimulate protein synthesis (13, 25, 26). Thus one of the changes that occurs during age-dependent development of the Sertoli cell may be a change in the isoforms of cAMP phosphodiesterase.

The increased synthesis of PKI is also age-dependent (36, 37). FSH causes the stimulation at both 12 and 19 days of age, but by 40 days of age no stimulation can be seen. In the immature Sertoli cell, increased PKI is first demonstrable at the time when protein kinase activity ratios are returning to normal. In FSH-responsive cells PKI may thus help to terminate the response to the gonodatropin. It is also interesting that in cells isolated from 10-day-old animals enough PKI is present to inhibit completely 41% of the total catalytic subunit. Between 19 and 43 days of age, the amount of catalytic subunit increases 10-fold, but the specific activity of the PKI does not increase. Thus even in the absence of hormone the mature Sertoli cell has more free catalytic subunit available than does the immature Sertoli cell when maximally stimulated by FSH. Thus the diminished sensitivity of the cells to FSH may be due in part to the fact that phosphorylation events normally regulated by FSH in immature cells proceed constitutively in the older cells.

Beta-adrenergic agonists stimulate adenylyl cyclase in isolated Sertoli cells (26, 40). These compounds, typified by isoproterenol, stimulate cyclase and increase intracellular concentrations of cAMP. This increased cAMP accumulation is not age-dependent. Indeed, isoproterenol results in the stimulation of protein kinase activity and stimulation of PKI synthesis in animals of all ages. Thus the defect in response to FSH seems to be hormone-specific and not directly related to cyclic nucleotide metabolism within the Sertoli cell.

REGULATION OF THE CYTOSKELETON

The Sertoli cell clearly continues to function in the adult animal. At least three roles seem obvious. First, it continues to secrete ABP throughout the adult life of the animal. The second involves cell-cell communication: These junctional complexes that form between the Sertoli cells may be involved in information transfer during various stages of the cycle of the seminiferous epithelium. The third deals with the release of sperm into the lumen of the seminiferous tubule. In all three of these events, the microtubules and microfilaments that comprise the cell cytoskeleton are involved. Changes in the distribution or organization of the cytoskeleton can frequently be visualized by changes in the shape of the cell. Indeed, Tung et al (39) have reported that treatment of Sertoli cells with FSH results within 24 hr in morphological changes. Our own laboratory has investigated whether alteration in the shape of the cell might occur more rapidly and thus be involved in the control of the secretory process in the Sertoli cell in culture (26, 40). Soon after plating, Sertoli cells form a flattened confluent monolayer in tissue culture. Within 1 hr, addition of FSH or dibutyryl cAMP caused the cells to round but did not promote detachment from the anchorage sites. Similar changes in cell shape occurred when intracellular cAMP was elevated by isoproterenol. In addition, propranolol prevented the shape change induced by this beta-adrenergic agonist.

Calcium has been implicated both in the control of cell shape and in the regulation of protein secretion (9). In an attempt to determine whether calcium was involved in the regulation of Sertoli cell shape, the effect of depleting calcium from the media surrounding cultured Sertoli cells was examined. This depletion was accomplished by the addition of EGTA, which chelates free calcium. EGTA caused the rapid rounding of Sertoli cells, which could be reversed by the addition of excess calcium. This effect was specific for Sertoli cells since testis fibroblasts cultured with the Sertoli cells did not round when EGTA was added.

The next question was whether cytoskeletal elements were involved in the regulation of the shape changes in response to elevated cAMP or depletion of extra-cellular calcium (26, 40). In these experiments we used indirect immunofluorescence microscopy as described by Fuller et al (16). Cells were plated onto glass coverslips and were fixed with 3% formalin. After washing, the cells were treated with cold acetone to increase the permeability of the cell membrane. An antibody to tubulin (the major component of the microtubule network) was added and cells were incubated. The excess antibody was washed off the coverslip, and a second antibody conjugated to fluorescein was added. Following incubation and removal of excess antibody, the cells were visualized using immunofluorescence microscopy. Sertoli cells were shown to possess numerous microtubules. When cells were treated for one hour with dibutyryl cAMP or EGTA, microtubules remained evident, though their shape was altered, which suggested redistribution of the cytoplasmic microtubule network. When the microtubules were disrupted by the addition of the drug colcemid, no shape change was noted. These data suggested that hormones affect the distribution of the microtubules but that this component of the cytoskeleton is not involved in the regulation of cell shape.

The second major component of the cytoskeleton is the microfilament network. These structures are composed primarily of actin and myosin. When antibodies to actin were used in the immunofluorescence procedure, untreated Sertoli cells were shown to possess an abundant array of parallel bundles of microfilaments (26, 40). Treatment of these cells by agents that increased cAMP within the cells or decreased extracellular calcium resulted in a marked reduction of cell microfilaments visualized with anti-actin antibody, and a concomitant change in cell shape. Cytochalasin B is known to destroy microfilament structure. When this drug was added to Sertoli cells, again the number of microfilaments was markedly reduced, and the shape was again altered. These data suggest that the hormonal control of cell shape is regulated via the microfilaments and not the microtubules.

CALCIUM, CALMODULIN, AND CYCLIC AMP

Both microfilaments and protein secretion are controlled by calcium (9). In an attempt to determine whether FSH induced a change in the flux or distribution of calcium within the Sertoli cell (26, 40), Sertoli cells were incubated in the presence of $^{45}Ca^{2+}$ until equilibrium was achieved. FSH was then added to half the cells, and both control and hormone-treated cells were examined for calcium flux with respect to time. No marked change in calcium flux occurred, though there did appear to be an increase in the nonexchangeable calcium pool in response to the treatment. The interpretation of these data is preliminary and must be viewed with caution since measurements of calcium redistribution and flux are subject to technical difficulties. However, it seems clear that FSH, via an increase in cAMP, affects either the level or distribution of calcium within the Sertoli cells.

The next task was to determine how to relate changes in calcium distribution to an alteration in microfilament organization and protein secretion. Calmodulin is a multifunctional calcium binding protein that exists in all eukaryotic cells (9). Immunofluorescence microscopy has been used to show that in interphase cells this protein is localized on the microfilaments (9, 10). Calmodulin has also been shown to regulate microfilaments biochemically (8). Calcium regulates the contraction-relaxation cycle of microfilaments in nonmuscle cells. This regulation is accomplished by the calmodulin-calcium activation of a cyclic-nucleotide-independent protein kinase (myosin light chain kinase) that specifically phosphorylates the 20,000 Mr light chain of myosin (8). This phosphorylation promotes the association of actin with the myosin heavy chain, thus stimulating ATPase and allowing tension development (31). Calmodulin exists in cells in two forms—bound to plasma membranes and free in the cytoplasm (or associated with cytoplasmic organelles, such as microfilaments and microtubules) (9). Hormonal treatment of cells tends to cause a decrease in membrane-bound and an increase in free calmodulin. This apparent redistribution could explain the changes in calcium distribution and offer a testable hypothesis for how FSH and calcium control the microfilaments of the Sertoli cell and protein secretion. Indeed, treatment of cells with EGTA causes rapid release of ABP, and cytochalasin B abolishes this EGTA effect. These results offer further support for the hypothesis that cyclic nucleotides and calcium are involved in microfilament regulation and the process of protein secretion.

FSH AND EXOCYTOSIS: A MODEL

From our results and the information reported by others concerning regulation of actomyosin in different nonmuscle cell types, we can outline the cascade of activities in the Sertoli cell in response to FSH that may result in the eventual secretion of specific proteins (Figure 1). FSH binds to receptors on the cell surface and concomitantly activates membrane-bound adenylyl cyclase. In addition, calcium-dependent cAMP phosphodiesterase is inhibited. Regulation of these two enzyme activities results in the intracellular accumulation of cAMP, which promotes dissociation of inactive cAMP-dependent protein kinase and release of the free catalytic subunit of this enzyme. The active catalytic subunit of cyclic nucleotide–dependent

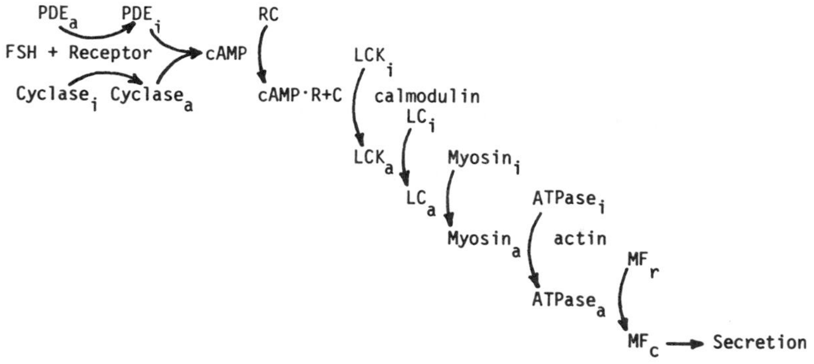

$$
\begin{array}{l}
PDE_a \rightarrow PDE_i \\
FSH + Receptor \rightarrow cAMP \\
Cyclase_i \rightarrow Cyclase_a \\
RC + cAMP \rightarrow cAMP \cdot R + C \\
C + LCK_i \rightarrow LCK_a \\
LCK_a + calmodulin;\ LC_i \rightarrow LC_a \\
LC_a;\ Myosin_i \rightarrow Myosin_a \\
Myosin_a + actin;\ ATPase_i \rightarrow ATPase_a \\
ATPase_a;\ MF_r \rightarrow MF_c \rightarrow Secretion
\end{array}
$$

Figure 1 Proposed temporal sequence of events by which FSH regulates protein exocytosis from Sertoli cells. PDE_a=active, and PDE_i=inactive phosphodiesterase.

protein kinase phosphorylates a multitude of proteins in virtually every subcellular compartment. No specific protein substrate has been identified that undergoes an activity change when phosphorylated in the Sertoli cell. However, when considering the regulation of cell shape and protein secretion, only a limited number of enzymatic events need occur. One substrate shown to be phosphorylated by cyclic nucleotide–dependent protein kinase is the myosin light chain kinase (2). The Sertoli cell contains large amounts of this protein kinase. Upon activation the myosin light chain kinase associates with calmodulin and promotes the phosphorylation of the 20,000 Mr light chain of myosin (8). Only in the phosphorylated state can myosin undergo the conformational change that results in the association of actin with myosin (31). This protein-protein interaction stimulates myosin ATPase activity. Hydrolysis of ATP produces energy required for the restructuring of the microfilaments and tension development. To date we can only theorize that this generation of motile force is involved in the regulation of secretion. However, the few steps required to support this hypothesis can easily be tested experimentally.

CONCLUSIONS

FSH seems to be one of the primary regulators of exocytosis in the Sertoli cell. Indeed, many peptide hormones regulate this process in other cells. Exocytosis is a multiphased process involving intracellular synthesis of the exportable substances, packaging and intracellular transport of the protein to the cell periphery, and finally membrane fusion and extracellular discharge. Regulation of secretion may occur at any one of these steps. Data from many laboratories show conclusively that microfilaments and microtubules are involved in the normal functioning of the secretory process.

The precise role played by each of these cytoskeletal components remains to be determined. Microtubules could provide a structural lattice to define and orient the flow of secretory granules, and the microfilaments could provide the motile force for granule movement. This model would be compatible with the requirement for both cAMP and calcium. Both of these second messengers are involved in the regulation of microtubules and microfilaments, and both act through an intracellular receptor. The receptor for cAMP is the regulatory subunit for protein kinase, and it is interesting to note that no role for cAMP has been demonstrated that does not require the association of cAMP with this protein. The intracellular receptor for calcium is calmodulin. This protein is highly constitutive, and intracellular levels are not affected by most peptide hormones. Calcium flux and redistribution, however, are highly regulated events (9). Most of the known roles for calcium have been demonstrated to require calmodulin. These roles include the already discussed regulation of myosin ATPase activity (2, 8, 31), but also include the polymerization-depolymerization of microtubules (24), the transport of calcium between and within cells (19, 20), and the regulation of glycogenolysis (6, 29, 33).

Investigation of the interrelationships among cyclic nucleotides, calcium, and the cytoskeletal components will help to elucidate the mechanism of action of FSH in the Sertoli cell. Every cellular process described above that is regulated by FSH (Table 1) involves at least one cytoskeletal component and either calcium or cAMP. During the development and differentiation of the Sertoli cell, the response to FSH is dramatically reduced at the time when tight junctions are formed between the Sertoli cells. One of the first microscopic clues that tight junctions will be formed is the appearance of numerous microfilament bundles juxtaposed with the cell membrane at the locale of eventual fusion (7, 17). Once fusion occurs these microfilament bundles seem to span the junctional complex. In addition, smooth endoplasmic reticulum is found associated with the junctional complexes. Even when these complexes are disrupted in order to allow movement of the proliferated germ cell population from basal to adlumenal compartments, the half junctional complexes characterized by a thickening of the membrane, microfilament bundles, and smooth endoplasmic reticulum remain. As new membrane is synthesized (or recycled) and the cytoplasmic processes of the Sertoli cells enlarge, these half junctional complexes can be found associated with the head of developing spermatids during spermatogenesis (28). It is possible that the smooth endoplasmic reticulum acts as a calcium-sequestering site and that cAMP regulates the movement of calcium from sequestered to free. This calcium could become associated with calmodulin and promote generation of motile force of the microfilaments. This force would allow the expulsion of the developed spermatids via a microfilament contraction-relaxation cycle.

Intracellular processes involving cyclic nucleotides, calcium, microtubules, and microfilaments do not require effects of peptide hormones such as FSH at the level of the cell nucleus. Instead, these are mechanisms involving translational or post-translational control, which can be modulated via a few discrete enzymatic steps within the cell. Thus the most direct way to define a specific action of FSH in chemically precise terms would be to determine the processes involved in junctional complex formation, generation of motile force that results in contraction of the Sertoli cell cytoplasm, or exocytosis of specific proteins. These new avenues of approach and the availability of isolated Sertoli cells in tissue culture should allow the eventual definitive description of the mechanisms by which FSH controls Sertoli cell function.

Literature Cited

1. Abou-Issa, H., Reichert, L. E. Jr. 1977. Solubilization and some characteristics of the follitropin receptor from calf testis. *J. Biol. Chem.* 252:4166–74
2. Adelstein, R. S., Conti, M. A., Hathaway, D. R., Klee, C. 1978. Phosphorylation of smooth muscle myosin light chain kinase by the catalytic subunit of adenosine 3':5'-monophosphate-dependent protein kinase. *J. Biol. Chem.* 253:8347–50
3. Beale, E. G., Dedman, J. R., Means, A. R. 1977. Isolation and characterization of a protein from rat testis which inhibits cyclic AMP–dependent protein kinase and phosphodiesterase. *J. Biol. Chem.* 252:6322–27
4. Braun, T., Sepsenwol, S. 1976. LH- and FSH-stimulation of adenylate cyclase in seminiferous tubules from young rats: functional FSH and LH receptors unmasked by homogenization. *Mol. Cell Endocrinol.* 4:183–94
5. Cheng, K.-W. 1975. Properties of FSH receptor in cell membrane of bovine testis. *Biochem. J.* 149:123–32
6. Cohen, P., Burchell, A., Foulkes, J. G., Cohen, P. T., Vanaman, T. C., Nairn, A. 1978. Identification of the calcium dependent modulator protein as the 4th subunit of rabbit skeletal muscle phosphorylase kinase. *FEBS Lett.* 92:287–91
7. Connell, C. J. 1978. A freeze-fracture and lanthanum tracer study of the complex junction between Sertoli cells of the canine testis. *J. Cell Biol.* 76:57–75
8. Dabrowska, R., Sherry, J. M. F., Aromatorio, D. K., Hartshorne, D. J. 1978. Modulator protein as a component of the myosin light chain kinase in chicken gizzard. *Biochemistry* 17: 253–58
9. Dedman, J. R., Brinkley, B. R., Means, A. R. 1979. Regulation of microfilaments and microtubules by calcium and cyclic AMP. *Adv. Cyclic Nucleotide Res.* 11:131–74
10. Dedman, J. R., Welsh, M. J., Means, A. R. 1978. Ca^{2+}-dependent regulator: production and characterization of a monospecific antibody. *J. Biol. Chem.* 253:7515–21
11. Dorrington, J. H., Fritz, I. B., Armstrong, D. T. 1978. Control of testicular estrogen synthesis. *Biol. Reprod.* 18: 55–64
12. Fakunding, J. L., Means, A. R. 1977. Characterization and follicle stimulating hormone activation of Sertoli cell cyclic AMP-dependent protein kinase. *Endocrinology* 101:1358–68
13. Fakunding, J. L., Tindall, D. J., Dedman, J. R., Mena, C. R., Means, A. R. 1976. Biochemical actions of follicle-stimulating hormone in the Sertoli cell of the rat testis. *Endocrinology* 98:392–402
14. Fritz, I. B. 1979. In *Biochemical Actions of Hormones*, ed. E. Litwack, 5:249–81. NY: Academic
15. Fritz, I. B., Rommerts, F. G., Louis, B. G., Dorrington, J. H. 1976. Regulation by FSH and dibutyryl cyclic AMP of the formation of androgen-binding protein in Sertoli cell-enriched cultures. *J. Reprod. Fert.* 46:17–24
16. Fuller, G. M., Brinkley, B. R. 1976. Structure and control of assembly of cytoplasmic microtubules in normal and transformed cells. *J. Supramol. Struct.* 5:497–514

17. Gilula, N. B., Fawcett, D. W., Aoki, A. 1976. The Sertoli cell occluding junctions and gap junctions in mature and developing mammalian testis. *Dev. Biol.* 50:142–68
18. Griswold, M. D., Solari, A., Tung, P. S., Fritz, I. B. 1977. Stimulation by follicle-stimulating hormone of DNA synthesis and of mitosis in cultured Sertoli cells prepared from testes of immature rats. *Mol. Cell. Endocrinol.* 7:151–65
19. Hinds, T. R., Larsen, F. L., Vincenzi, F. F. 1978. Plasma membrane Ca^{2+} transport: stimulation by soluble proteins. *Biochem. Biophys. Res. Commun.* 81:455–61
20. Katz, S., Remtulla, M. A. 1978. Phosphodiesterase protein activator stimulates calcium transport in cardiac microsomal preparations enriched in sarcoplasmic reticulum. *Biochem. Biophys. Res. Commun.* 83:1373–79
21. Kettleslegers, J. M., Hetzel, W. D., Sherins, R. J., Catt, K. J. 1978. Developmental changes in testicular gonadotropin receptors, plasma gonadotropins and plasma testosterone in the rat. *Endocrinology* 103:212–22
22. Lacroix, M., Smith, F. E., Fritz, I. B. 1977. Secretion of plasminogen activator by Sertoli cell-enriched cultures. *Mol. Cell. Endocrinol.* 9:227–36
23. Louis, B. G., Fritz, I. B. 1979. Follicle-stimulating hormone and testosterone independently increase the production of androgen-binding protein by Sertoli cells in culture. *Endocrinology* 104:454–61
24. Marcum, J. M., Dedman, J. R., Brinkley, B. R., Means, A. R. 1978. Control of microtubule assembly-disassembly by Ca^{2+}-dependent regulator protein. *Proc. Natl. Acad. Sci. USA* 75:3771–75
25. Means, A. R., Dedman, J. R., Fakunding, J. L., Tindall, D. J. 1978. In *Receptors and Hormone Action,* ed. L. Birnbaumer, B. W. O'Malley, 3:363–93. NY: Academic
26. Means, A. R., Dedman, J. R., Welsh, M. J., Marcum, M., Brinkley, B. R. 1979. In *Ontogeny of Receptors and Reproductive Hormone Action,* ed. T. Hamilton, J. Clark, W. Sadler, pp. 207–24. NY: Raven
27. Reddy, P. R. K., Villee, C. A. 1975. Stimulation of ornithine decarboxylase activity by gonadotropic hormones and cyclic AMP in the testis of immature rats. *Biochem. Biophys. Res. Commun.* 65:1350–54
28. Russell, L. 1977. Observations on rat Sertoli ectoplasmic ('junctional') specializations and their association with germ cells of the rat testis. *Tissue & Cell* 9:475–98
29. Rylatt, D. B., Embi, N., Cohen, P. 1979. Glycogen synthase kinase-2 from rabbit skeletal muscle is activated by the calcium-dependent regular protein. *FEBS Lett.* 98:76–80
30. Sanborn, B. M., Elkington, J. S. H., Steinberger, A., Steinberger, E., Meistrich, M. L. 1975. In *Hormonal Regulation of Spermatogenesis,* ed. F. French, V. Hansson, E. Ritzen, S. Nayfeh, pp. 293–310. NY: Plenum
31. Scordilis, S. P., Adelstein, R. S. 1977. Myoblast myosin phosphorylation is a prerequisite for actin-activation. *Nature* 268:558–60
32. Solari, A. J., Fritz, I. B. 1978. The ultrastructure of immature Sertoli cells. Maturation-like changes during culture and the maintenance of mitotic potentiality. *Biol. Reprod.* 18:329–45
33. Srivastava, A. K., Waisman, D. M., Brostrom, C. O., Soderling, T. R. 1979. Stimulation of glycogen synthase phosphorylation by calcium-dependent regulator protein. *J. Biol. Chem.* 254:583–86
34. Steinberger, A., Hintz, M., Heindel, J. J. 1978. Changes in cyclic AMP responses to FSH in isolated rat Sertoli cells during sexual maturation. *Biol. Reprod.* 19:566–72
35. Steinberger, A., Steinberger, E. 1976. Secretion of an FSH-inhibiting factor by cultured Sertoli cells. *Endocrinology* 99:918–21
36. Tash, J. S., Dedman, J. R., Means, A. R. 1979. Protein kinase inhibitor in Sertoli cell-enriched rat testis. Specific regulation by follicle-stimulating hormone. *J. Biol. Chem.* 254:1241–47
37. Tash, J. S., Welsh, M. J., Means, A. R. 1979. In *Testicular Development, Structure and Function,* ed. E. Steinberger, A. Steinberger, pp. 159–67. NY: Raven
38. Thanki, K. H., Steinberger, A. 1977. Effect of age and hypophysectomy on FSH binding by rat testis. *Andrologia* 9:307–12
39. Tung, P. S., Dorrington, J. H., Fritz, I. B. 1975. Responsiveness of cultured Sertoli cells to FSH. *Proc. Natl. Acad. Sci. USA* 72:1838–42
40. Welsh, M. J., van Sickle, M., Means, A. R. 1979. See Ref. 37, pp. 89–98

Ann. Rev. Physiol. 1980. 42:71–82

INTERACTIONS OF STEROIDS AND GONADOTROPINS IN THE CONTROL OF STEROIDOGENESIS IN THE OVARIAN FOLLICLE ❖1254

Peter C. K. Leung and David T. Armstrong[1]

Departments of Physiology and of Obstetrics & Gynaecology, University Hospital, University of Western Ontario, London, Ontario, Canada N6A 5A5

INTRODUCTION

The primary role of the pituitary gonadotropic hormones, follicle-stimulating hormone (FSH) and luteinizing hormone (LH), in the physiological regulation of ovarian functions is well established. The interactions of these protein hormones with the ovarian cell types within the ovary and the mechanisms of their action have been the subjects of numerous recent reviews. Steroid hormones secreted in response to gonadotropic stimulation are important components of feedback mechanisms that regulate gonadotropin secretion via actions upon the hypothalamic-pituitary system. Evidence has accumulated recently that ovarian steroids may also modulate the responses of the ovary to gonadotropins through direct actions upon the ovarian cells involved. The sites and mechanisms of these local intraovarian actions of steroids, and the manner in which they interact with the pituitary gonadotropins in regulation of ovarian steroid biosynthesis, are the subjects of this review.

[1]Associate of the Medical Research Council (Canada). Research of the authors reviewed here was supported by the M.R.C. of Canada and the World Health Organization.

0066-4278/80/0315-0071$01.00

CONTROL OF STEROID BIOSYNTHESIS IN THE OVARY

Regulation of Estrogen Biosynthesis

ROLE OF ANDROGEN AS SUBSTRATE IN GONADOTROPIN-INDUCED ESTROGEN BIOSYNTHESIS The histories both of our understanding of the roles gonadotropic hormones play in the control of estrogen biosynthesis and of the ovarian cell types involved in this process have been reviewed recently (3, 12). Androgens, i.e. androstenedione and/or testosterone, are essential intermediates in estrogen biosynthesis. In vivo studies with hypophysectomized rats (5) have shown LH to increase androgen production markedly. The increased ovarian androgen levels observed in hypophysectomized rats following LH treatment were accompanied by increased ovarian levels of estradiol-17β (estradiol) and by increased uterine weights only when FSH was administered concomitantly. Substitution of an aromatizable androgen (testosterone or androstenedione, but not 5α-dihydrotestosterone) for LH led to similarly increased estrogen production in FSH-treated hypophysectomized rats (5). These observations were interpreted to mean that the well-known ability of LH to stimulate estrogen production could be explained by its ability to stimulate production of aromatizable substrates, and that FSH was important for induction of the aromatase enzyme system necessary for converting these androgens to estrogens.

Numerous studies of isolated ovarian cell types from several species have attempted to elucidate the relative contributions of the various cells and gonadotropins in the overall process of estrogen biosynthesis. From investigations of hamster (33), rat (16), sheep (36), and human (47) follicles, the theca cell has emerged as the follicular cell responsible for androgen biosynthesis in mammals; LH is the pituitary gonadotropin primarily responsible for its control. That the theca cell can also produce estrogen is less certain. In vitro culture studies using isolated thecal tissues from several species—e.g. rat (17) and human (35)—have either failed to detect or have detected small amounts of estrogen production. The possibility cannot be excluded that appropriate conditions of culture have not yet been found for thecal tissues.

The steroid biosynthetic capability of granulosa cells differs from that of theca cells in two significant ways. First, in contrast to theca cells, granulosa cells lack the 17α-hydroxylase and $C_{17,20}$-lyase enzymes necessary to produce androgens from C_{21} precursors (e.g. 16). Second, granulosa cells from all mammalian species so far examined have abundant aromatase activity. They can therefore readily convert androgens to estrogens, provided they have been obtained from sufficiently developed follicles—e.g. hamster (33), rabbit (15), ewe (36), and human (35). Furthermore, FSH induces aromatase activity, both in vivo (14) and in vitro (13), in rat granulosa cells at less mature stages of development.

Studies of the type reviewed above suggest that the theca and granulosa cells cooperate in the production of estrogens, with the theca cells, under the influence of LH, providing the C_{19} substrate that is then converted to estrogen by the granulosa cells under the influence of FSH (3).

In the sheep, injection of an antiserum to testosterone during the follicular phase of the cycle markedly depressed the secretion of estradiol into the ovarian vein (7). On the assumption that the antibodies were unable to enter cells, this was interpreted as evidence that the androgen precursors must leave the ovarian cells (presumably theca) before aromatization can occur. The relative contributions of the granulosa versus theca cells to the secretion of estrogen into the ovarian vein have been investigated recently in the sheep (6). Granulosa cells were surgically removed from the major follicle(s) on one ovary of ewes during the preovulatory period. Mean estradiol secretion rates declined during the first 30 min after "granulosectomy" to 30% of the preoperative level, and further to 21% during the next 30 min. Mean estradiol secretion rates following sham treatment of the contralateral control ovaries during the same periods were 86% and 75%, respectively, of the pretreatment levels (6). Results from this in vivo experiment support those obtained from in vitro cell culture experiments (e.g 36) in demonstrating a probable role for the granulosa cells in estrogen secretion by the preovulatory sheep follicle. They do not exclude the possibility of a contribution by the theca cells.

The above in vivo studies with sheep contrast with results obtained using a similar in vivo approach in the rhesus monkey (9), which suggest that the theca rather than the granulosa cells may be the major source of follicular estrogen secretion during the immediate preovulatory period in this species. Studies with cultured granulosa cells from rhesus monkeys, on the other hand, are in general agreement with those from other species: Unless an aromatizable substrate is provided, granulosa cells cannot produce significant amounts of estrogen (10). When cocultured with theca cells, especially in medium containing exogenous testosterone, granulosa cells from preovulatory monkey follicles produced amounts of estrogen far in excess of the amounts produced by isolated thecal tissue from the same follicles. Since in vivo granulosa cells of preovulatory follicles exist in an environment (the follicular fluid) containing high concentrations of aromatizable androgens, they are probably active in converting these androgens to estrogens.

Evidence with human ovarian follicles also suggests an important role for granulosa cells in estrogen production. A close correlation has been found between the number of granulosa cells and the levels of FSH and estradiol in the follicular fluid, irrespective of the stage of the cycle; in human ovaries up to 90% of the estradiol in follicular fluid may originate from the granulosa cells (34). When cultured in the presence of aromatizable substrates, large amounts of estradiol are produced by granulosa cells isolated from human Graafian follicles (8, 18). The addition of FSH, but not of human chorionic gonadotropin (hCG), stimulated aromatization of testosterone in cultured human granulosa cells isolated from medium-sized follicles at varying stages of the menstrual cycle (35). Thecal preparations from the same follicles produced negligible amounts of estradiol when cultured in the absence or presence of gonadotropins but responded to hCG with increased production of cyclic adenosine monophosphate (cAMP) and androgens (35). Thecal preparations from somewhat larger human follicles produced significant amounts of estradiol when cultured alone (8). However, the combined cultures of theca and granulosa cells from the same follicles produced substantially more estradiol than was produced by the theca and granulosa cells separately, which confirmed for the human the importance of interactions between the two follicular cell types in the biosynthesis of estradiol.

STIMULATORY ACTION OF ANDROGEN AND FSH ON OVARIAN AROMATASE ACTIVITY Purified FSH preparations (13) stimulate estrogen biosynthesis by granulosa cells (from immature follicles) cultured in medium containing aromatizable androgens. This stimulation may be the result of an increased aromatizing activity caused entirely by FSH, the androgen acting solely as a substrate. Alternatively, the increase in aromatizing activity may depend upon the cooperative actions of FSH and androgens. A specific role for FSH in the stimulation of aromatase enzyme activity in granulosa cells is substantiated by both in vivo and in vitro findings in immature, hypophysectomized, estrogen-primed rats (14). After a lag period of 24 hr, twice-daily injection of FSH increased the ability of isolated granulosa cells to aromatize androstenedione in vitro. The FSH effect appeared to be time-dependent; after 48 hr the aromatizing ability of the cells reached a level comparable to that in preovulatory follicles. When isolated granulosa cells were cultured in the presence of androstenedione for one or two days, purified FSH but not purified LH stimulated estradiol production, an effect which was dose-dependent. Two-day culture of granulosa cells with FSH in vitro enhanced the subsequent ability of these cells to convert androstenedione to estradiol in a short-term incubation, thereby indicating a direct action of FSH in the induction of the aromatase enzyme system (14).

Although the above studies clearly show that FSH by itself is capable of inducing aromatase activity in granulosa cells, they do not exclude a role of androgens in the enzyme-inducing process. Recent in vitro evidence supports such a role for androgens. In experiments involving sequential cultures of rat granulosa cells with FSH and various androgens, either alone or in combination, followed by culture with testosterone alone to determine aromatizing activity, evidence was obtained that androgens enhance the ability of FSH to induce aromatase activity (11). Although somewhat less effective than testosterone in this regard, the nonaromatizable androgens, 5α-dihydrotestosterone and androsterone, also significantly enhanced the FSH effect. In vivo evidence also suggests a role of androgens in maintenance of aromatase activity. Administration of LH to rats treated with pregnant mare's serum gonadotropin (PMSG) causes a marked fall in ovarian androgen levels after an initial short-lived stimulation; this fall is followed shortly by a marked decrease in ovarian aromatase activity (25). If the fall in ovarian androgen levels is prevented by administration of high levels of exogenous testosterone, then the subsequent drop in aromatase activity is smaller. This suggests that testosterone, in addition to serving as substrate for estrogen biosynthesis, may also have a role in the maintenance of aromatase enzyme activity (26).

ROLE OF ANDROGEN IN THE INHIBITORY ACTION OF LH ON ESTROGEN BIOSYNTHESIS An inhibitory action of LH on estrogen secretion is suggested by the close temporal association between the elevation of endogenous LH concentration and the fall in serum estrogen levels during the preovulatory period in many species, and decreases in serum, ovarian, and/or follicular levels of estradiol have been reported following exogenous LH stimulation in vivo or in vitro (see 3). The mechanism of this LH-induced decrease in estrogen levels is not known, though evidence is accumulating to suggest that inhibition of androgen synthesis is the primary cause. The decline in ovarian androgen levels following LH treatment in vivo coincides closely with a decline in ovarian levels of estradiol, which suggests a cause-effect relationship (4, 25). As discussed above, when the decline in ovarian androgen levels was prevented by administration of exogenous testosterone, the fall in ovarian estradiol levels was much smaller, which indicates that lack of androgen substrate was probably primarily responsible for the fall (26).

Similar conclusions have been reached on the basis of in vitro studies with cultured preovulatory follicles. Follicles explanted on the morning of proestrus from PMSG-primed immature rats produced predominantly androstenedione and estradiol with little progesterone, whereas the reverse was true in those explanted after the endogenous gonadotropin surge (22). Blockade of the gonadotropin surge with Nembutal prevented this reversal. Addition of testosterone or androstenedione (but not dihydrotestosterone or 17α-hydroxyprogesterone) to the incubation medium of follicles isolated after the endogenous gonadotropin surge restored estradiol biosynthesis to levels observed before the gonadotropin surge; addition of exogenous LH, FSH, or dibutyryl cyclic AMP (dbcAMP) was without effect in this regard (23).

This LH-induced alteration in the pattern of steroidogenesis in whole follicles has been extended to isolated cells of preovulatory follicles. While theca cells isolated from rats killed before the gonadotropin surge secreted predominantly androstenedione and were able to convert 17α-hydroxyprogesterone to androstenedione in vitro, those isolated after the gonadotropin surge produced mainly progesterone and appeared to lack $C_{17,20}$-lyase activity (20). In parallel experiments with isolated granulosa cells, addition of exogenous testosterone in vitro enhanced the production of estradiol, irrespective of whether the cells were isolated before or after the gonadotropin surge (20).

Although results from the above in vivo and in vitro studies can be interpreted to agree that androgen availability may have played a major role in the inhibitory action of LH on estradiol biosynthesis, LH in vivo appears to exert an additional inhibitory effect at the level of the aromatase enzyme (25). However, this decreased aromatase activity may be secondary to decreased androgen levels within the ovary if, as suggested above, androgens are involved in induction or at least in maintenance of activity of the aromatase system.

Regulation of Progesterone Biosynthesis

STIMULATORY ACTION OF ANDROGEN ON GONADOTROPIN-INDUCED PROGESTERONE BIOSYNTHESIS Evidence from in vitro studies implicates androgens in the regulation of progesterone biosynthesis in the ovary. Addition of androgens to the culture medium stimulated progestin (progesterone and/or 20α-hydroxyprogesterone) accumulation in granulosa cells isolated from porcine ovarian follicles (21, 41). Androgens also stimulated progesterone production by cultured granulosa cells from preantral follicles of immature hypophysectomized estrogen-treated rats (32, 39) and from preovulatory follicles of mature rats (39). In the latter studies either testosterone, androstenedione, or dihydrotestosterone, but not estradiol, was effective; thus this stimulation appears to be a true androgen effect, rather than one dependent on aromatization of androgens to estrogens by granulosa cells. Indeed, androgenic stimulation of progesterone production by granulosa cells is a specific receptor-mediated event, its occurrence being suppressed by a 100-fold molar excess of either steroidal or nonsteroidal anti-androgens (24). A stimulatory action of androgens has also been observed in cultures of bovine ovarian follicles: Intrafollicular injection of androstenedione but not estradiol enhanced progesterone accumulation by both small and large follicles (44).

Granulosa cells isolated from immature hypophysectomized, estrogen-treated rats are capable of secreting progesterone in response to FSH (but not LH) in vitro, and androgens, in addition to causing a stimulatory effect on their own, have been shown to synergize markedly with FSH in enhancing progesterone secretion by these cells (2, 39). While the exact mechanism of this interaction between FSH and androgens has yet to be elucidated, several important aspects have been delineated. Addition of androgens to rat granulosa cells cultured with FSH increases their subsequent ability to produce cAMP in response to a further acute stimulation with either FSH or LH (19), which suggests an interaction at the gonadotropin receptor–adenylate cyclase level. However, this is probably not the explanation for the synergism, since exogenous cyclic AMP alone (dbcAMP) was as effective as the combined treatment with FSH and androgen in stimulating progesterone secretion (38). Furthermore, addition of androstenedione was able to enhance still further the stimulatory action of dbcAMP. Thus, the synergistic action of androgens and FSH on progesterone secretion by rat granulosa cells is likely exerted at a step distal to cAMP production.

What are the sites of action of androgens on specific enzymes involved in progesterone biosynthesis or metabolism? On the metabolic side, the possibility that androgens act by inhibiting progesterone catabolism by 5α-reductase appears to have been ruled out by the observation that conversion of labelled progesterone to 5α-reduced metabolites by rat granulosa cells in vitro was not altered by the presence of androstenedione in the culture medium (37). On the biosynthetic side, FSH has been observed to stimulate markedly the activity of 3β-hydroxysteroid dehydrogenase in cultured rat granulosa cells, but this stimulation was not enhanced by concomitant treatment with androgens (12). It seems likely, therefore, that the stimulatory action of androgens in enhancing progesterone biosynthesis is exerted at a level different from that of FSH—possibly at the level of the cholesterol side-chain cleavage enzymes.

Administration of anti-androgens (flutamide or its active metabolite) by means of local implants in the ovary in vivo has been shown to reduce the subsequent secretion of progestins by porcine granulosa cells in vitro (42). In the immature rat, testosterone administered systemically, or dihydrotestosterone administered locally, enhanced the subsequent responsiveness of the ovary to stimulation by both FSH and LH in vivo, as well as of isolated granulosa cells to both FSH and LH in vitro (29). Thus direct in vivo evidence supports a role for androgens in the regulation of ovarian progesterone biosynthesis. Since these alterations could be demonstrated in intact but not in hypophysectomized rats (29), it appears that some pituitary factor (presumably FSH) is required to enable androgens to enhance progesterone production in vivo. This conclusion is supported by the in vitro demonstration that androgens on their own have little or no effect in increasing subsequent responsiveness of rat granulosa cells in the secretion of progestin, whereas combined treatment with androgen plus FSH results in marked stimulation of progesterone synthesis (19, 38).

INTERACTION OF ESTROGEN AND GONADOTROPINS ON PROGESTERONE BIOSYNTHESIS The first conclusive evidence of a direct intraovarian action of one steroid on the biosynthesis of another in vivo was the demonstration of the stimulatory action of estrogen on progesterone secretion in the hypophysectomized rabbit, which led to the concept that estrogen is the luteotropic hormone in this species (40). More recently, both in vivo and in vitro evidence from other species indicates a direct inhibitory action of estrogen on progesterone biosynthesis by ovarian cells. In cultures of porcine granulosa cells isolated from small (1–2 mm) follicles, addition of estradiol decreased progesterone secretion in both the absence and presence of FSH (45). Both dihydrotestosterone and testosterone stimulate progestin secretion by porcine granulosa cells isolated from medium-sized (3–5 mm) follicles (41) or from large (8–10 mm) follicles (21), but estradiol markedly depressed progestin synthesis in these cultures.

Antagonistic actions of estrogens and androgens on progesterone biosynthesis have also been observed in cultures of preantral granulosa cells from immature hypophysectomized estrogen-primed rats. In this in vitro system, an intriguing pattern of interaction between estrogen and androgens has been revealed that depends on their relative concentrations. High estrogen concentrations (diethylstilbestrol, 10^{-5} M) suppressed, whereas low concentrations (10^{-9} M) enhanced, the stimulatory effect of low concentrations of testosterone (10^{-9} M) on progesterone production. The response to high concentrations of testosterone (10^{-7} M) was not affected by either high or low concentrations of the estrogen (24). Since the androgen receptors in rat granulosa cells also are capable of binding estrogens (43), the ability of estrogens to alter androgen responsiveness may be an indication of interaction between the two classes of steroids at the androgen receptor level.

In vivo evidence has also been obtained for an inhibitory action of estrogen on progesterone biosynthesis. Treatment of immature hypophysectomized rats with estradiol resulted in impaired ovarian response to LH in the production of progesterone in vivo (30). This inhibitory action of estrogen was not observed in intact rats and was antagonized by the administration of purified FSH in hypophysectomized rats in vivo (31). Thus it appears that in addition to its ability to interact with androgens estrogen may also interact with gonadotropic hormones in the regulation of progesterone biosynthesis in the ovary.

Regulation of Androgen Biosynthesis

INHIBITORY ACTION OF ESTROGEN ON GONADOTROPIN-INDUCED ANDROGEN BIOSYNTHESIS Estrogen may act within the ovary of the immature rat to inhibit androgen production (30). Administration of estradiol to intact immature rats significantly decreases ovarian testosterone levels and inhibits ovarian responsiveness to LH in the production of testosterone. That the action is exerted directly upon the ovary is suggested strongly from the unilateral nature of this inhibition in experiments in which Silastic capsules containing various dosages of estradiol were implanted unilaterally beneath the ovarian bursae. A similar inhibition by estradiol of the ovarian testosterone response to LH also was demonstrated in hypophysectomized rats (30), which, by indicating that the inhibition is not mediated via the pituitary, provides additional evidence for a direct ovarian site of action.

What is the biochemical site of the inhibition by estrogen? The ability of LH to increase cAMP production by ovaries from intact rats (P. C. K. Leung, D. T. Armstrong, unpublished observations) and by thecal tissues from pig follicles (46) was not decreased by estrogen under conditions in which the androgen biosynthesis was markedly inhibited, which suggests that the site of inhibition is distal to the LH receptor–adenylate cyclase system. A probable site of inhibition appears to be at the biosynthetic step(s) between androgens and their C_{21} precursors, at least in the rat. Ovaries from estrogen-treated intact or hypophysectomized rats responded to dbcAMP stimulation in vitro with increased progesterone but not testosterone production (27). Estrogen pretreatment in vivo of ovaries then incubated with progesterone-4-^{14}C in vitro (28) inhibited the incorporation of radioactivity into several androgens (testosterone, androstenedione, androsterone) and increased incorporation into 3α-OH-5α-pregnan-20-one in an equally marked fashion. Thus estrogen may result in decreased androgen production either by inhibiting the 17α-hydroxylase/$C_{17,20}$-lyase system, or by diverting C_{21} substrates away from this system through stimulation of an alternate pathway of metabolism that leads to 5α-reduced pregnane compounds.

The physiological significance of the intraovarian inhibitory action of estrogen is not known. Stimulation of rat ovaries by LH induces drastic alterations in progesterone metabolism that facilitate the formation of 5α-reduced pregnane compounds with a concomitant decrease in androgen and 5α-reduced androgen production (1). As discussed above, in vivo treatment of immature rats with estradiol induced remarkably similar alterations in progesterone metabolism in the ovary that could not be attributed to alterations in serum LH levels (28). Thus the lowering of androgen production by the effect of LH on progesterone metabolism may, in part at least, be secondary to, and is probably mediated by, a local action of estrogen.

SUMMARY

The pituitary gonadotropic hormones, FSH and LH, are of primary importance in regulating both the steroidogenic and gametogenic functions of the ovary. The ovarian steroids, in turn, exert feedback influences, both negative and positive, in controlling the secretion of the pituitary gonadotropins. Increasing evidence suggests that the ovarian steroids also exert significant actions (perhaps of secondary importance) at the level of the ovarian steroidogenic cells themselves in influencing the type and extent of the responses of these cells to gonadotropic stimulation. Cellular and biochemical sites of some of these intraovarian actions of steroids are summarized in Figure 1.

If normal development of the follicles, including oocyte maturation and the cyclic function of the ovary, depends upon a high degree of coordination among these complex processes, then relatively minor upsets in balances between some of these opposing forces might contribute to such well-known but little understood processes as follicular atresia, refractoriness, or insensitivity to gonadotropins. More complete understanding of these interactions may lead to new ways of approaching fertility regulation, whether the objective be development of alternative forms of contraception, treatment of forms of human infertility, or development of more reliable methods of inducing multiple ovulations for enhancing reproductive performance in domestic animals or endangered wild species.

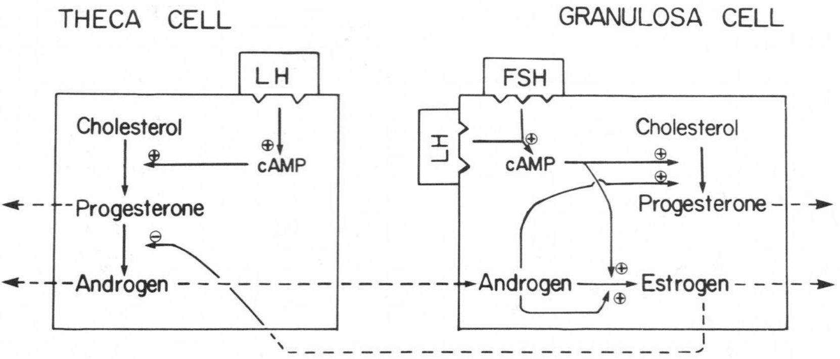

Figure 1 Control of steroidogenesis in the ovarian follicle: cell–cell interactions. Solid lines represent simplified steroidogenic pathways and intraovarian actions of various hormones. ⊕ stimulation, ⊖ inhibition. Dotted lines represent intercellular flow of steroids.

Literature Cited

1. Armstrong, D. T. 1979. Alterations of progesterone metabolism in immature rat ovaries by luteinizing hormone. *Biol. Reprod.* In press
2. Armstrong, D. T., Dorrington, J. H. 1976. Androgens augment FSH-induced progesterone secretion by cultured rat granulosa cells. *Endocrinology* 99:1411–14
3. Armstrong, D. T., Dorrington, J. H. 1977. Estrogen biosynthesis in the ovaries and testes. In *Advances in Sex Hormone Research, Vol. III: Regulatory Mechanisms Affecting Gonadal Hormone Action,* ed. J. A. Thomas, R. L. Singhal, pp. 217–58. Baltimore: University Park Press. 340 pp.
4. Armstrong, D. T., Dorrington, J. H., Robinson, J. 1976. Effects of indomethacin and aminoglutethimide phosphate in vivo on LH-induced alterations of cyclic adenosine monophosphate, PGF, and steroid levels in preovulatory rat ovaries. *Can. J. Biochem.* 54:796–802
5. Armstrong, D. T., Papkoff, H. 1976. Stimulation of aromatization of exogenous and endogenous androgens in ovaries of hypophysectomized rats in vivo by follicle-stimulating hormone. *Endocrinology* 99:1144–51
6. Armstrong, D. T., Weiss, T. J., Seamark, R. F. 1979. Importance of granulosa cells for estradiol-17β secretion by the pre-ovulatory sheep follicle. *Physiol. Can.* 10:10 (Abstr.)
7. Baird, D. T. 1977. Evidence in vivo for the two-cell hypothesis of oestrogen synthesis by the sheep Graafian follicle. *J. Reprod. Fert.* 50:183–85
8. Channing, C. P., Anderson, L. D., Batta, S. K. 1978. Follicular growth and development. *Clin. Obstet. Gynaecol.* 5:375–90
9. Channing, C. P., Coudert, S. P. 1976. Contribution of granulosa cells and follicular fluid to ovarian estrogen secretion in the rhesus monkey in vivo. *Endocrinology* 98:590–97
10. Channing, C. P., Wentz, A. C., Jones, G. S. 1978. Steroid secretion by human and monkey ovarian cell types in vivo and in vitro. In *Endocrinology of the Ovary,* ed. R. Scholler, pp. 71–86. Paris: Editions Sepe
11. Daniel, S. A. J., Armstrong, D. T. 1979. Enhancement of follicle-stimulating hormone–induced aromatase activity by androgens in cultured rat granulosa cells. *Proc. Soc. Study Reprod., 12th Ann. Meet.,* p. 47A. (Abstr.)
12. Dorrington, J. H., Armstrong, D. T. 1979. Effects of FSH on gonadal functions. *Recent Prog. Horm. Res.* In press
13. Dorrington, J. H., Moon, Y. S., Armstrong, D. T. 1975. Estradiol-17β biosynthesis in cultured granulosa cells from hypophysectomized immature rats; stimulation by FSH. *Endocrinology* 97:1328–31
14. Erickson, G. F., Hsueh, A. J. W. 1978. Stimulation of aromatase activity by FSH in rat granulosa cells in vivo and in vitro. *Endocrinology* 102:1275–82
15. Erickson, G. F., Ryan, K. J. 1975. The effect of LH/FSH, dibutyryl cyclic AMP, and prostaglandins on the production of estrogens by rabbit granulosa cells in vitro. *Endocrinology* 97: 108–13
16. Fortune, J. E., Armstrong, D. T. 1977. Androgen production by theca and granulosa isolated from proestrous rat follicles. *Endocrinology* 100:1341–47
17. Fortune, J. E., Armstrong, D. T. 1978. Hormonal control of 17β-estradiol biosynthesis in proestrous rat follicles: estradiol production by isolated theca versus granulosa. *Endocrinology* 102: 227–35
18. Fowler, R. E., Fox, N. L., Edwards, R. G., Walters, D. E., Steptoe, P. C. 1978. Steroidogenesis by cultured granulosa cells aspirated from human follicles using pregnenolone and androgens as precursors. *J. Endocrinol.* 77:171–83
19. Goff, A. K., Leung, P. C. K., Armstrong, D. T. 1979. Stimulatory action of follicle-stimulating hormone and androgens on the responsiveness of rat granulosa cells to gonadotropins in vitro. *Endocrinology* 104:1124–29
20. Hamberger, L., Hillensjö, T., Ahrén, K. 1978. Steroidogenesis in isolated cells of preovulatory rat follicles. *Endocrinology* 103:771–77
21. Haney, A. F., Schomberg, D. W. 1978. Steroidal modulation of progesterone secretion by granulosa cells from large porcine follicles: a role for androgens and estrogens in controlling steroidogenesis. *Biol. Reprod.* 19:242–48
22. Hillensjö, T., Bauminger, S., Ahrén, K. 1976. Effect of LH on the pattern of steroid production by preovulatory follicles of PMSG-injected immature rats. *Endocrinology* 99:996–1002
23. Hillensjö, T., Hamberger, L., Ahrén, K. 1977. Effect of androgens on the biosynthesis of estradiol-17β by isolated periovulatory rat follicles. *Mol. Cell. Endocrinol.* 9:183–93

24. Hillier, S. G., Knazek, R. A., Ross, G. T. 1977. Androgenic stimulation of progesterone production by granulosa cells from preantral ovarian follicles: further in vitro studies using replicate cell cultures. *Endocrinology* 100:1539–49
25. Katz, Y., Armstrong, D. T. 1976. Inhibition of ovarian estradiol-17β secretion by LH in prepubertal, PMS-treated rats. *Endocrinology* 99:1442–47
26. Katz, Y., Leung, P. C. K., Armstrong, D. T. 1979. Testosterone restores ovarian aromatase activity in rats treated with a 17,20-lyase inhibitor. *Mol. Cell. Endocrinol.* 14:37–44
27. Leung, P. C. K., Armstrong, D. T. 1979. Estrogen treatment of immature rats inhibits ovarian androgen production in vitro. *Endocrinology* 104: 1411–17
28. Leung, P. C. K., Armstrong, D. T. 1979. A mechanism for the intraovarian inhibitory action of estrogen on androgen production. *Biol. Reprod.* In press
29. Leung, P. C. K., Goff, A. K., Armstrong, D. T. 1979. Stimulatory action of androgen administration in vivo on ovarian responsiveness to gonadotropins. *Endocrinology* 104:1119–23
30. Leung, P. C. K., Goff, A. K., Kennedy, T. G., Armstrong, D. T. 1978. An intraovarian inhibitory action of estrogen on androgen production in vivo. *Biol. Reprod.* 19:641–47
31. Leung, P. C. K., Henderson, K. M., Armstrong, D. T. 1979. Interactions of estrogen and androgen with gonadotropins on ovarian progesterone production. *Biol. Reprod.* 20:713–18
32. Lucky, A. W., Schreiber, J. R., Hillier, S. G., Schulman, J. D., Ross, G. T. 1977. Progesterone production by cultured preantral rat granulosa cells: stimulation by androgens. *Endocrinology* 100:128–33
33. Makris, A., Ryan, K. J. 1977. Aromatase activity of isolated and recombined hamster granulosa cells and theca. *Steroids* 29:65–72
34. McNatty, K. P., Baird, D. T. 1978. Relationship between FSH, androstenedione and oestradiol in human follicular fluid. *J. Endocrinol.* 76:527–31
35. Moon, Y. S., Tsang, B. K., Simpson, C., Armstrong, D. T. 1978. 17β-Estradiol biosynthesis in cultured granulosa and thecal cells of human ovarian follicles: stimulation by follicle-stimulating hormone. *J. Clin. Endocrinol. Metab.* 47:263–67
36. Moor, R. M. 1977. Sites of steroid production in ovine Graafian follicles in culture. *J. Endocrinol.* 73:143–50
37. Nimrod, A. 1977. Studies on the synergistic effect of androgen on the stimulation of progestin secretion by FSH in cultured rat granulosa cells: progesterone metabolism and the effect of androgens. *Mol. Cell. Endocrinol.* 8:189–99
38. Nimrod, A. 1977. Studies on the synergistic effect of androgen on the stimulation of progestin secretion by FSH in cultured rat granulosa cells: a search for the mechanism of action. *Mol. Cell. Endocrinol.* 8:201–11
39. Nimrod, A., Lindner, H. R. 1976. A synergistic effect of androgen on the stimulation of progesterone secretion by FSH in cultured rat granulosa cells. *Mol. Cell. Endocrinol.* 5:315–20
40. Robson, J. M. 1937. Maintenance by oestrin of the luteal function in hypophysectomized rabbits. *J. Physiol.* 90:435–39
41. Schomberg, D. W., Stouffer, R. L., Tyrey, L. 1976. Modulation of progestin secretion in ovarian cells by 17β-hydroxy-5α-androstan-3-one (dihydrotestosterone): a direct demonstration in monolayer culture. *Biochem. Biophys. Res. Commun.* 68:77–81
42. Schomberg, D. W., Williams, R. F., Tyrey, L., Ulberg, L. C. 1978. Reduction of granulosa cell progesterone secretion in vitro by intraovarian implants of antiandrogen. *Endocrinology* 102:984–87
43. Schreiber, J. R., Ross, G. T. 1976. Further characterization of a rat ovarian testosterone receptor with evidence for nuclear translocation. *Endocrinology* 99:590–96
44. Shemesh, M., Ailenberg, M. 1977. The effect of androstenedione on progesterone accumulation in cultures of bovine ovarian follicles. *Biol. Reprod.* 17:499–505
45. Thanki, K. H., Channing, C. P. 1978. Effects of follicle-stimulating hormone and estradiol upon progesterone secretion by porcine granulosa cells in tissue culture. *Endocrinology* 103:74–80
46. Tsang, B. K., Leung, P. C. K., Armstrong, D. T. 1979. Inhibition by estradiol-17β of porcine thecal androgen production in vitro. *Mol. Cell. Endocrinol.* 14:131–40
47. Tsang, B. K., Moon, Y. S., Simpson, C. W., Armstrong, D. T. 1979. Androgen biosynthesis in human ovarian follicles: cellular source, gonadotropic control and adenosine 3',5'-monophosphate mediation. *J. Clin. Endocrinol. Metab.* 48:153–58

Ann. Rev. Physiol. 1980. 42:83–96

MECHANISM OF ACTION OF PROLACTIN IN THE CONTROL OF MAMMARY GLAND FUNCTION

❖1255

Robert P. C. Shiu[1] *and Henry G. Friesen*

Department of Physiology, Faculty of Medicine, University of Manitoba, Winnipeg, Manitoba, R3E OW3, Canada

INTRODUCTION

Normal growth, differentiation, and function of the mammary gland are under the influence of hormones—insulin, estrogen, progesterone, thyroid hormone as well as growth hormone, prolactin (PRL), and placental lactogens. While some of these hormones may affect primarily growth and development of the mammary gland, others, such as PRL, are of major importance in stimulating mammary gland function. A comprehensive treatment of endocrine influences on the mammary gland may be found in (12). Here we highlight progress in understanding the mechanism of action of PRL on mammary gland function. Since large gaps in this understanding remain, we indicate areas where research may be fruitful.

The role played by PRL on mammary gland function varies from one species to another. For example, lactational changes in the mammary gland can be induced in rabbits by administering PRL alone, while in rats other hormones are required. In the cow the peripartum increase in serum PRL is crucial for successful lactation; but if PRL secretion is inhibited at later periods postpartum, milk secretion is hardly affected. In women, however, inhibition of PRL secretion by similar pharmacological means at any time postpartum causes prompt cessation of lactation. Generalizations and extrapolations from one species to another must thus be made with considerable caution.

The possible role of PRL in the etiology of breast cancer, which is not covered here, has been reviewed extensively (29, 33, 71).

[1]Scholar, Medical Research Council of Canada

0066-4278/80/0315-0083$01.00

INITIATION OF PRL ACTION IN THE MAMMARY GLAND: PROLACTIN RECEPTORS

Prolactin appears to initiate its action by interacting with a specific receptor on the cell surface of the mammary epithelial cell. This mode of action was first suggested by Turkington (62), who showed that PRL covalently linked to Sepharose beads is biologically active in mouse mammary epithelial cells. Because prolactin-sepharose complexes presumably cannot enter the cell, he concluded that PRL initiates its effect by an action on the cell membrane. Subsequent studies, however, suggest that this result might have been due to a slow release of PRL from the Sepharose beads. Microscopic studies (6, 37) have localized ^{125}I-labeled and endogenous PRL on cell membranes of mammary epithelial cells. In the last 6–7 years, much information on PRL receptors in the rabbit and rat mammary gland has accumulated.

The PRL receptors are enriched in plasma membrane fractions derived from pregnant and lactating rabbit mammary glands (53, 54). The same membrane fraction also exhibits the highest specific activity of 5'-nucleotidase, confirming that receptors for PRL are located on the cell membrane. Prolactin receptors are probably lipoprotein complexes: Digestion with proteases and phospholipase C destroys the activity of receptors (54). After solubilization by non-ionic detergents such as Triton X-100, PRL receptors bind to concanavalin A-sepharose column (S. Ohgo, H. G. Friesen, unpublished observation), which indicates that carbohydrate moieties are an intrinsic part of the receptor molecule. Thus the PRL receptor, by analogy with many other membrane proteins, appears to be a glycoprotein with its hydrophobic portion embedded in the lipid bilayer of the plasma membrane and its hydrophilic portion, which contains the carbohydrate moiety, protruding outwards.

The membrane receptor sites for PRL exhibit very high affinity for the hormone, the dissociation constant being in the order of 10^{-10} M (54). Binding of PRL to the receptors occurs readily at physiological concentrations of the hormone; half-saturation of the receptor sites occurs at a hormone concentration of about 7 ng ml^{-1}. The PRL receptor sites in the rabbit mammary gland not only bind PRL but also recognize other lactogenic hormones, such as placental lactogens and human growth hormone [but not nonprimate growth hormone, which is not lactogenic in the rabbit (53)].

In order to demonstrate unequivocally that the membrane receptor sites mediate the lactogenic response of PRL in the mammary gland and that the binding of PRL to membrane receptor indeed represents the first step in the action of hormone, we purified the receptor molecules. The membrane receptors were first solubilized by the non-ionic detergent, Triton X-100.

The soluble receptors (apparent mol wt 220,000) were purified by affinity chromatography (55), and the purified receptors were used to raise antibodies in guinea pigs (56). The antibodies block binding of PRL to its receptors but have no effect on the binding of insulin to its receptors in the rabbit mammary gland (56). Anti-receptor antibodies are also able to block prolactin-mediated incorporation of [^{3}H] leucine into casein and transport of [^{14}C] aminoisobutyric acid but are without effect on insulin-mediated events in explants of rabbit mammary glands maintained in organ culture (57). These findings provide direct evidence for an obligatory functional role of a membrane receptor in mediating the action of a polypeptide hormone. These antibodies to PRL receptors can open up many possibilities for investigation of PRL action. For example, antibodies to rabbit mammary PRL receptors also inhibit the binding of PRL (but not the binding of other hormones such as insulin) to a variety of target organs derived from a number of species—e.g. normal mammary gland and mammary gland tumors from mouse, rat, and human; liver from rat and rabbit; and rat ovary as well as rat prostate (56). These findings suggest that the immunological determinant of the receptor molecule is very similar for tissues derived from both sexes and from different species. Furthermore, when the antibodies were administered to rats in vivo during an estrous cycle the most notable finding was an increase in the number of corpora lutea and an increase in serum PRL level (10). These in vivo results suggest that the antibodies block the luteolytic effect of PRL in the ovary and that deficiency of PRL activates compensatory mechanisms that increase PRL secretion. All these findings demonstrate the usefulness of the anti-receptor antisera for studying the mechanism of action of PRL in various target organs.

Since the prolactin receptors are obligatory for mediating some, if not all, of the actions of the hormone, the receptors may be important in determining the sensitivity of the tissue to the hormone. If this is the case, then physiological factors that affect tissue sensitivity to PRL may also influence the activity of the receptor. Frantz et al (20) first demonstrated that PRL binding activity in lactating rat mammary gland is three times that in pregnant tissue. In rat mammary slices, PRL binding remains low until parturition when a large and sustained (20-fold) increase occurs (23). Receptor content in the mammary glands of the rat and rabbit increases substantially after parturition (9, 15); in the rat this increase is abolished when suckling by pups is prevented. In addition, ergocornine (an inhibitor of PRL secretion) also diminishes this postpartum increase in PRL receptors (9). These findings also suggest that the PRL release caused by suckling increases PRL receptor levels in the rat and rabbit mammary gland. Self-induction of PRL receptor by PRL is also observed in the rat liver (39). Administration of ovine PRL can induce receptors in the rabbit mammary gland, and this effect can be blocked by progesterone (14). This would extend the well-known inhibitory effect of progesterone on lactogenesis to the level of the PRL receptor. (The inhibitory effect of progesterone on milk protein synthesis is discussed below.)

The number of PRL receptors detected in pregnant and lactating mammary glands is subject to underestimation owing to occupancy of receptor by endogenous PRL and placental lactogens. For example, "de-saturation" of receptors by bromocryptine (an ergot derivative that suppresses PRL secretion) raised (above those in untreated animals) estimates of the number of PRL receptors in membrane preparations derived from pregnant and lactating rabbit mammary glands (15). Thus when measuring the number of PRL receptors where circulating levels of the hormone are high or when exogenous hormone is administered, one must recognize that receptor occupancy and self-induction may be operating simultaneously. Moreover, it is worth pointing out that not only the PRL receptor of the mammary gland but also PRL receptors of other organs such as the liver, kidney, ovary, and prostate are regulated by PRL as well as by other hormones. The regulation of PRL receptors in these organs by protein and steroid hormones has been reviewed (67).

The fate of hormones after they have interacted with the cell surface receptors on target cells has received little attention. Immunocytochemical (37) and autoradiographic (2) studies suggest that PRL may be internalized by mammary epithelial cells. Using human mammary tumor cells maintained in long-term culture, we were able to demonstrate for the first time that human mammary tumor lines in culture possess specific PRL receptors and that tumor cells have higher receptor content than a normal human mammary cell line derived from breast milk (58, 59). These human mammary cell lines therefore provide an excellent model in which to examine the fate of PRL in its target cells. We were able to show that more than 95% of receptor-bound ^{125}I-labeled human PRL was released by the cells in 6 hr. Chromatographic analysis of the released radioactive material revealed four radioactive species. Only one species (25% of total radioactivity) represented intact ^{125}I-labeled human PRL; the remaining 75% of radioactivity was associated with three species having molecular weights smaller than PRL. The release of smaller fragments of PRL was prevented if dissociation of ^{125}I-labeled human PRL was carried out in the presence of a metabolic inhibitor such as 2,4-dinitrophenol, the lysosomotropic agent chloroquine, or the protease inhibitor N-α-p-Tosyl-L-lysine-chloro-methyl ketone (TLCK). These findings suggest that in these human breast cancer cells, the receptor-bound PRL is internalized and degraded by lysosomal enzymes, a process similar to that found for some other hormones (1). The physiological significance of the internalization and degradation of PRL by the mammary cells awaits further studies.

THE MECHANISM OF ACTION OF PRL ON MILK PROTEIN SYNTHESIS

Prolactin plays a key role in the induction of milk secretion in the differentiated mammary gland. After priming of the mammary gland by insulin and cortisol, PRL alone can stimulate the synthesis of milk proteins such as casein and α-lactalbumin (27, 60, 61, 63). The exact mechanism by which this is brought about is not clearly understood. We now know that binding of PRL to its cell surface receptor is essential for the subsequent induction of milk protein synthesis (see above). Information regarding the molecular events that take place between the binding of PRL to its receptor and the ultimate stimulation of milk protein synthesis remains fragmentary.

Unlike that of most polypeptide hormones, prolactin's binding to the cell membrane receptor does not lead to the activation of the membrane-bound enzyme, adenylate cyclase (31). Furthermore, neither exogenous adenose 3',5'-cyclic monophosphate (cAMP) nor its analog N^6-2'-O-dibutyryl cAMP mimics the action of PRL in mammary gland explants maintained in organ culture (31). Therefore, cAMP production does not seem to be the rate-limiting step. What then is the second messenger system, if any, for PRL? Rillema and his colleagues suggest that activation by PRL of the membrane-associated enzyme, phospholipase A, may be closely coupled to PRL binding to receptor sites in the mouse mammary gland. Prolactin at concentrations in the μg ml^{-1} range was able to stimulate membrane-associated phospholipase A to release [^{3}H]-arachidonic acid from phosphatidyl choline (49). Bovine growth hormone was without effect. Activation of the enzyme was observed 1 hr after the addition of PRL, and a further increase in activity was seen after 3 hr. Interestingly, the kinetics of prolactin-binding to rabbit mammary membranes were similar to the activation of phospholipase in mouse mammary gland, and bovine growth hormone did not bind to the membranes (53, 54).

Prolactin-stimulated synthesis of milk proteins is preceded temporally by a marked increase in the transcription of ribosomal RNA and messenger RNA (63). The stimulation of milk protein synthesis by PRL is completely prevented by inhibitors of RNA synthesis, such as actinomycin D. Therefore, induction of milk proteins is dependent upon the preceding increase in RNA formation. The action of PRL on early RNA synthesis in mammary gland explants can be mimicked by incubation with phospholipase A and arachidonic acid (41, 47). Since the activation of phospholipase is a key rate-limiting step in prostaglandin synthesis, the above findings suggest that some of the effects of PRL are mediated by prostaglandins. This notion is supported by studies showing that prostaglandins B_2, E_2, and $F_{2\alpha}$ stimulate RNA synthesis in mammary gland explants of mice in a prolactin-like manner (42, 43). These effects are nonadditive to those observed with concentrations of PRL that stimulate the response to a maximal degree. The effects of prostaglandin occur after a period of 2–4 hr, which suggests that their action occurs very early in the chain of events that ultimately leads to the synthesis of RNA and milk proteins. Indomethacin, an inhibitor of prostaglandin synthesis, blocks the stimulatory effect of PRL. Interestingly, the effects of PRL and prostaglandins $F_{2\alpha}$, B_2, and E_2 are abolished by exogenous dibutyryl cAMP or by theophylline, an inhibitor of phosphodiesterase, which elevates the intracellular concentration of cAMP. Moreover, guanosine 3',5'-cyclic monophosphate (cGMP) mimics the early action of PRL on RNA synthesis (43). These observations are compatible with the idea that the action of PRL on RNA synthesis may be mediated by a reduced intracellular concentration of cAMP coupled to an elevated level of cGMP. This hypothesis is further supported by the observation that prostaglandins E_1 and $F_{1\alpha}$, which are known to stimulate adenylate cyclase activity and thus to increase cAMP concentration in rabbit and mouse mammary glands, are able to abolish the effect of PRL (49).

Although prostaglandins B_2, E_2, and $F_{2\alpha}$ stimulate RNA synthesis in a prolactin-like manner, they cannot mimic the effect of PRL on casein synthesis (44). Additional factors are therefore required. A combination of polyamines (e.g. spermidine) and prostaglandins exhibit a prolactin-like effect in stimulating casein synthesis in mouse mammary explants; polyamines by themselves cannot substitute for PRL (45, 48). Methylglyoxal bis-guanyl-hydrazone (methyl GAG), an inhibitor of polyamine synthesis, abolishes the stimulation of casein synthesis by PRL. Addition of exogenous spermidine rescues the effect of PRL from methyl GAG inhibition. Further, PRL stimulates the activity of ornithine decarboxylase, an enzyme involved in the pathway of polyamine biosynthesis (ornithine → putrescine) in mammary gland organ cultures (38, 46). The prolactin-dependent stimulation of ornithine decarboxylase requires newly synthesized RNA (38). The action of PRL on milk protein synthesis in the mammary gland may thus be mediated, at least in part, by polyamines.

Protein phosphorylation has been implicated as an intermediate step of PRL action in the mammary gland (63). In mouse mammary gland organ cultures, PRL induces the appearance of cAMP-dependent protein kinases (63). The increase in enzymatic activity is prevented by the addition of actinomycin D or cycloheximide (63). Thus the induction of kinase enzymes requires concomitant synthesis of RNA and protein. Despite the fact that PRL does not stimulate adenylate cyclase, cAMP may still be essential in mediating some of the hormone's actions. In this case, the rate-limiting factor is the stimulation of cAMP-dependent protein kinases that interact with existing cAMP. Cyclic AMP–dependent protein kinases are stimulated maximally 1 hr after the addition of PRL; maximum phosphorylation of plasma membrane proteins occurs at 8 hr, followed by phosphorylation of ribosomal proteins (16 hr) and nuclear phosphoproteins (24 hr) (63). The nuclear proteins that are phosphorylated are primarily the F_2a_2 and the F_2b histones and all species of acid chromatin proteins (63).

The mechanism of induction of milk proteins by PRL has been studied to some extent in mid-pregnant mouse mammary gland explants maintained in organ culture. In general, priming of mammary tissues with insulin and hydrocortisone is essential for the PRL effect. It is now clear that PRL stimulates the synthesis of milk proteins, possibly at the transcriptional level. Prolactin stimulates the accumulation of messenger RNAs for casein and α-lactalbumin (3, 26, 32, 36). The use of molecular hybridization techniques (32) showed that PRL induces the accumulation of casein mRNA very rapidly (1 hr). Maximum accumulation of casein mRNA is observed 48 hr after the addition of PRL, at which time the level of casein mRNA is 45 times the basal level. The accumulation of casein mRNA precedes that of casein; the latter has a lag time of 6–12 hr, though maximal casein synthesis occurs 48 hr after the addition of PRL. Hydrocortisone potentiates while progesterone inhibits the prolactin-response on the accumulation of casein mRNA and therefore the stimulation of casein synthesis and secretion (26, 32). A similar effect of PRL on mRNA for casein has been observed (26) using rabbit mammary glands. The above studies, however, were not able to differentiate whether PRL directly stimulates the de novo synthesis of casein mRNA or indirectly affects the turnover rate of existing casein mRNA. Posttranscriptional control in the synthesis of α-lactalbumin and casein in lactating rat mammary gland has been suggested (40), but whether PRL is involved in this phenomenon was not studied.

The lactose synthetase system is also unique to the mammary glands (22). This enzyme catalyzes the formation of lactose. It contains two subunits, A and B. The A-protein is a galactosyltransferase, the catalytic subunit; the B-protein is the milk whey protein, α-lactalbumin, the regulatory subunit of lactose synthetase. The functions of this enzyme are also under hormonal control. In the intact mouse the activity of A-protein increases throughout the second half of gestation and remains high during lactation (61). The activity of the B-protein (α-lactalbumin), on the other hand, remains low throughout pregnancy but increases dramatically with the initiation of lactation (61). In experiments using organ cultures PRL stimulated the synthesis of A-protein ten-fold but achieved only a two-fold stimulation of α-lactalbumin (61). In addition, mRNA for α-lactalbumin is low throughout pregnancy in the rat and rises rapidly at the initiation of lactation (36). In a transplantable rat mammary carcinoma (R323OAC) casein mRNA, but not α-lactalbumin mRNA, was stimulated by PRL injection (35). The asynchronous expression of A- and B-proteins of lactose synthetase and of casein appears to reflect the specific functional requirement of the mammary gland during development and lactation. The study of Vonderhaar (65) seems to explain the unresponsiveness of α-lactalbumin production to PRL. Working with mouse mammary gland organ cultures, she found that 3,5,3'-triiodothyronine (T_3) potentiates the effect of PRL in the induction of α-lactalbumin. Thus the study of Turkington et al (61) did not reveal a dramatic effect of PRL because T_3 was not added. In the same study, Vonderhaar (65) observed that progesterone at 1 $\mu g\ ml^{-1}$ blocks the effect of PRL on stimulation of α-lactalbumin. This observation could explain the findings (36, 61) that α-lactalbumin activity in the mammary gland is low throughout pregnancy but will rise at the initiation of lactation. The circulating level of progesterone is high, especially throughout the second half of pregnancy, and then falls abruptly just prior to parturition (34). Presumably the elevated concentrations of progesterone throughout pregnancy would suppress the activity of α-lactalbumin, and this inhibition would be removed when pregnancy is terminated.

These findings suggest the hypothesis that PRL stimulates early RNA synthesis through the participation of membrane receptors and prostaglandins. As a result, "early" RNA synthesis occurs and new protein kinases are formed that then "activate" many functional proteins and gene expression by phosphorylation. Gene expression further results in the expression of "late" RNAs, which may include messenger RNAs for milk proteins.

EFFECT OF PROLACTIN ON LIPID METABOLISM

Triglycerides and phospholipids are important components of milk. Phospholipids are also essential to the functions of the mammary epithelial cells. While the composition of lipids in the milk from many species has been well documented (4), the endocrine control of lipid metabolism in the mammary glands has been neglected. Nevertheless, some data on the effect of PRL and other hormones on milk-fat synthesis are available. Wang et al (66) studied the incorporation of [^{14}C]acetate into fatty acids (F.A.) of pregnant mouse mammary gland explants in organ culture. When tested singly, only insulin stimulates F.A. synthesis; PRL alone has no effect. Prolactin stimulates F.A. synthesis when combined with insulin and hydrocortisone; the effect of PRL could be observed at 10 $ng\ ml^{-1}$ of the hormone. Mainly long-chain F.A. ($C > 14$) are synthesized in the absence of PRL (a pattern of F.A. similar to that found in mouse adipose tissue), while in the presence of PRL, shorter-chain F.A. ($C < 14$) are synthesized. This pattern of F.A. is similar to that found in mouse milk fat.

In mammary explants derived from 16-day pregnant and 11-day pseudopregnant rabbits, PRL alone caused a 15-fold stimulation of F.A. (19). It enhanced primarily synthesis of C_8 and C_{10} F.A., which are characteristic of rabbit milk. When explants are cultured with insulin, corticosterone, and PRL, the rate of F.A. synthesis is increased 42-fold, but both medium- and long-chain F.A.s are synthesized; corticosterone by itself enhances mainly synthesis of long-chain F.A.s. Thus PRL, alone or in combination with insulin and hydrocortisone, stimulates the synthesis of milk fats in the mammary gland.

Fatty acids derived from dietary fat can also be used by lactating mammary gland for synthesis of milk triglyerides (8). The fatty acids are transported in blood as triglycerides in chylomicrons, and their uptake by the mammary gland is regulated by lipoprotein lipase (51). Lipoprotein lipase activity in mammary gland, which is negligible in nonlactating animals, increases 2–3 days before parturition and remains high throughout lactation (21). Hypophysectomy of lactating rats reduces the activity of mammary gland lipoprotein lipase to 1/10 the value observed in sham-operated controls (73). Prolactin injection (0.5 mg, 4 per day) started 2 hr after hypophysectomy restores lipoprotein lipase activity by 48 hr to levels observed in lactating rats. The effect of PRL on lipoprotein lipase activity is not changed significantly by injection of dexamethasone, growth hormone, or thyroxine. Thus the pituitary gland controls lipoprotein lipase activity in the mammary gland and this control is mediated primarily through the secretion of PRL. Prolactin injection into the mammary ducts of rabbits increases lipoprotein lipase activity in the gland (16). The major response occurs on and after the third day of injection of PRL. Simultaneous injection of actinomycin D rapidly leads to inactivation of the enzyme. The prolactin-induced increase in lipoprotein lipase activity in the mammary gland may thus require continued production of a short-lived messenger RNA (16).

The molecular mechanisms by which PRL, acting in concert with other hormones such as insulin and cortisol, stimulates enzymes that participate in the metabolism of lipid in the mammary gland remain to be elucidated.

ACTION OF PRL ON ION FLUXES IN THE MAMMARY GLAND

During milk production the mammary gland transports large volumes of isotonic fluid. The ionic content of this fluid is maintained partially by active transport. The major ions found in milk are Na^+, K^+, and Cl^-. The concentrations of Na^+ and Cl^- in milk are low, that of K^+ high, relative to plasma.

Prolactin may be implicated in maintaining low Na^+ concentrations in milk because this hormone promotes Na^+ retention by the mammary gland, a function that is well-known in lower vertebrates (5).

Prolactin decreases the uptake of $^{22}Na^+$ by rabbit mammary gland slices incubated in vitro (17, 18). Moreover, the amount of Na^+ and Cl^- in tissue slices is reduced by PRL, but that of K^+ is increased (17, 18). Intraductal injection of PRL into rabbit mammary glands in vivo produces a similar effect. Ouabain abolishes the effect of PRL in all cases. These experiments suggested that Na^+ and Cl^- ions enter cells by passive diffusion and that PRL promotes the active transport of these ions out of the tissues, possibly by activating ouabain-sensitive Na^+,K^+-ATPase. These experiments do not indicate clearly the direction of movement of these ions. More elaborate experiments (7) utilized mouse mammary epithelial cells grown on floating collagen gels. Detached gels bearing monolayer cells were placed in Lucite Ussing chambers. The unidirectional transepithelial ionic fluxes were then measured by using $^{22}Na^+$ and $^{36}Cl^-$. Prolactin stimulates 2.5-fold the unidirectional flux of $^{22}Na^+$ from the mucosal to the serosal side of the epithelial monolayer but has no effect on the serosal to mucosal movement of $^{22}Na^+$. No activation by PRL of $^{36}Cl^-$ movement is demonstrable. These results are consistent with the concept that in vivo Na^+ from the milk enters the cells through the mucosal surface and is actively pumped into the blood via the serosal membrane where the Na^+ pump (Na^+,K^+-ATPase) is found. It should be pointed out that in none of the experiments cited above was the effect of PRL on the activity of the Na^+,K^+-ATPase measured. The mechanism of endocrine control of this enzyme should be evaluated in order to delineate the role of prolactin in ion transport in the mammary gland.

ROLE OF PRL IN THE INDUCTION OF THE SECRETORY IMMUNE SYSTEM IN THE MAMMARY GLAND

Antibodies in milk play an important role in the defense of the infant against microbial disease (30). The major class of antibodies found in milk is IgA, which is thought to be derived from local plasma cells and transported across the epithelium into milk. These IgA-bearing plasma cells are derived from the gut-associated lymphoid tissue (30). In the mouse mammary gland both the number of plasma cells synthesizing IgA and the amount of intraepithelial IgA increase dramatically during pregnancy and lactation (68). Hormones have been implicated in promoting the "homing" and retention of the plasma cells by the mammary gland. Use of immunofluorescence techniques demonstrated (69) that PRL injection into virgin female mice increases the number of IgA-bearing plasma cells in the mammary gland 5-fold. Prolactin administration into mice previously treated with estrogen and progesterone further elevates the number of plasma cells to a level found in term pregnant mouse mammary gland. This stimulation of "homing" is specific for IgA-bearing cells; the same hormone regimen does not affect the content of other types of lymphoblasts in the mammary gland. The mechanism by which PRL increases the capacity of the mammary gland to attract and retain IgA-lymphoblasts is not known. Nonetheless, such a role for PRL on mammary gland function is of great interest. Prolactin may promote a receptor-type mechanism that brings about the interaction of plasma cells with the mammary gland.

FUTURE RESEARCH

Investigation of the events immediately following prolactin binding to receptors deserves high priority. The putative second messenger systems for prolactin remain to be delineated. We do not yet understand the molecular mechanisms by which prolactin and its intracellular messenger affect cellular activities (such as gene expression) that may eventually lead to activation of RNA and protein synthesis, enzyme activity, membrane-associated activities, and many other biological functions of the mammary gland. Finally, information is urgently needed concerning the mechanism by which prolactin affects cell proliferation and neoplasia, as in the case of developing mammary gland and growth of breast cancer.

Acknowledgment

We appreciate the secretarial assistance of Miss N. Ryan. This work was supported by Grants from the Medical Research Council of Canada and the National Institutes of Health, U.S.A.

Literature Cited

1. Ascoli, M., Puett, D. 1978. Degradation of receptor-bound human choriogonadotropin by murine Leydig tumor cells. *J. Biol. Chem.* 253:4892–99
2. Aubert, M. L., Suard, Y., Sizonenko, P. C., Krachenbuhl, J. P. 1978. Prolactin receptors: Study with dispersed cells from rabbit mammary gland. *60th Ann. Meet. Endocrine Soc. Progr. Abstr.*, p. 84, Abstr. 19
3. Banerjee, M. R., Terry, P. M., Sakai, S., Lin, F. K., Ganguly, R. 1978. Hormonal regulation of casein messenger RNA. *In Vitro* 14:128–39
4. Bauman, D. E., Davis, C. L. 1974. Biosynthesis of milk fat. In *Lactation: A Comprehensive Treatise*, ed. B. L. Larson, V. R. Smith, 2:66–77. NY: Academic
5. Bern, H. A., Nicoll, C. S. 1968. The comparative endocrinology of prolactin. *Recent Prog. Horm. Res.* 24:681–720
6. Birkinshaw, M., Falconer, I. R. 1972. The localization of prolactin labelled with radioactive iodine in rabbit mammary tissue. *J. Endocrinol.* 55:323–34
7. Bisbee, C. A., Machen, T. E., Bern, H. A. 1979. Mouse mammary epithelial cells on floating collagen gels: transepithelial ion transport and effect of prolactin. *Proc. Natl. Acad. Sci. USA* 76:536–40

8. Bishop, C., Daves, T., Glascock, R. F., Welch, V. A. 1969. Studies on the origin of milk fat, a further study of bovine serum lipoprotein and an estimation of their contribution to milk fat. *Biochem. J.* 113:629–33
9. Bohnet, H., Gomez, F., Friesen, H. G. 1977. Prolactin and estrogen binding sites in the mammary gland of the lactating and non-lactating rat. *Endocrinology* 101:1111–21
10. Bohnet, H. G., Shiu, R. P. C., Grinwich, D., Friesen, H. G. 1978. In vivo effects of antisera to prolactin receptors in female rats. *Endocrinology* 102:1657–61
11. Deleted in proof
12. Cowie, A. T., Tindal, J. S. 1971. *The Physiology Of Lactation.* London: Arnold. 392 pp.
13. Deleted in proof
14. Djiane, J., Durand, P. 1977. Prolactin-progesterone antagonism in self-regulation of prolactin receptors in the mammary gland. *Nature* 266:614–43
15. Djiane, J., Durand, P., Kelly, P. A. 1977. Evolution of prolactin receptors in rabbit mammary gland during pregnancy and lactation. *Endocrinology* 100:1348–56
16. Falconer, I. R., Fiddler, T. J. 1970. Effect of intraductal administration of prolactin, actinomycin D and cycloheximide on lipoprotein lipase activity in the mammary gland of pseudopregnant rabbits. *Biochem. Biophys. Acta.* 218:508–14
17. Falconer, I. R., Rowe, J. M. 1975. Possible mechanism of action of prolactin on mammary cell sodium transport. *Nature* 256:327–28
18. Falconer, I. R., Rowe, J. M. 1977. Effect of prolactin on sodium and potassium concentrations in mammary alveolar tissue. *Endocrinology* 101:181–86
19. Forsyth, I. A., Strong, C. R., Dils, R. 1972. Interaction of insulin, corticosterone and prolactin in promoting milk-fat synthesis by mammary explants from pregnant rabbits. *Biochem. J.* 129:929–35
20. Frantz, W. L., MacIndoe, J. H., Turkington, R. W. 1974. Prolactin receptors: characteristics of the particulate fraction binding activity. *J. Endocrinol.* 60:485–97
21. Hamosh, M., Clary, T. R., Chernick, S. S., Scow, R. O. 1970. Lipoprotein lipase activity of adipose and mammary tissue and plasma triglyceride in pregnant and lactating rats. *Biochim. Biophys. Acta.* 210:473–82
22. Hill, R. L., Brew, K. 1975. Lactose synthetase. *Adv. Enzymol.* 43:411–90
23. Holcomb, H. H., Costlow, M. E., Buschow, R. A., McGuire, W. L. 1976. Prolactin binding in rat mammary gland during pregnancy and lactation. *Biochim. Biophys. Acta.* 428:104–12
24. Deleted in proof
25. Deleted in proof
26. Houdebine, L. M., Gaye, P. 1975. Regulation of casein synthesis in the rabbit mammary gland: titration of mRNA activity for casein under prolactin and progesterone treatments. *Mol. Cell. Endocrinol.* 3:37–55.
27. Juergens, W. G., Stockdale, F. E., Topper, Y. J., Elias, J. J. 1965. Hormone-dependent differentiation of mammary gland in vitro. *Proc. Natl. Acad. Sci. USA* 54:629–34
28. Deleted in proof
29. Kim, V., Furth, J. 1976. The role of prolactin in carcinogenesis. *Vit. Horm.* 34:107–36
30. Lamm, M. E. 1976. Cellular aspects of immunoglobulin A. *Adv. Immunol.* 22:223–90
31. Majumder, G. C., Turkington, R. W. 1971. Adenosine 3',5'-monophosphate-dependent and independent protein phosphokinase isoenzymes from mammary gland. *J. Biol. Chem.* 246:2650–57
32. Matusik, R. J., Rosen, J. M. 1978. Prolactin induction of casein mRNA in organ culture: A model system for studying peptide hormone regulation of gene expression. *J. Biol. Chem.* 253:2343–47
33. McGuire, W. L., Chamness, G. C., Horwitz, K. B., Zava, D. T. 1978. Hormones and their receptors in breast cancer. In *Receptors and Hormone Action II,* ed. B. W. O'Malley, L. Birnbaumer, pp. 401–42. NY: Academic
34. Morishige, W. K., Pepe, G. J., Rothchild, I. 1973. Serum luteinizing hormone, prolactin and progesterone levels during pregnancy in the rat. *Endocrinology* 92:1527–31
35. Nardacci, N. J., McGuire, W. L. 1977. Casein and α-lactalbumin messenger RNA in experimental breast cancer. *Cancer Res.* 27:1186–90
36. Nardacci, N. J., Lee, J. W. C., McGuire, W. L. 1978. Differential regulation of α-lactalbumin and casein messenger RNA's in mammary tissue. *Cancer Res.* 38:2694–99
37. Nolin, J. M., Witorsch, R. J. 1976. Detection of endogenous immunoreactive

prolactin in rat mammory epithelial cells during lactation. *Endocrinology* 99:949–58
38. Oka, T., Perry, J. W. 1976. Studies on regulatory factors of ornithine decarboxylase activity during development of mouse mammary epithelium in vitro. *J. Biol. Chem.* 251:1738–44
39. Posner, B. I., Kelly, P. A., Friesen, H. G. 1975. Prolactin receptors in rat liver: Possible induction by prolactin. *Science* 188:57–59
40. Qasba, P. K., Nakhasi, H. L. 1978. α-Lactalbumin mRNA in 4-day lactating rat mammary gland. *Proc. Natl. Acad. Sci. USA* 75:4739–43
41. Rillema, J. A. 1975. Effect of arachidonic acid on RNA metabolism in mammary gland explants of mice. *Prostaglandins* 10:307–12
42. Rillema, J. A. 1975. Possible role of prostaglandin $F_{2\alpha}$ in mediating effect of prolactin on RNA synthesis in mammary gland explants of mice. *Nature* 253:466–67
43. Rillema, J. A. 1975. Cyclic nucleotides and the effect of prolactin on uridine incorporation into RNA in mammary gland explants of mice. *Horm. Metab. Res.* 7:45–49
44. Rillema, J. A. 1976. Effect of prostaglandins on RNA and casein synthesis in mammary gland explants of mice. *Endocrinology* 99:490–95
45. Rillema, J. A. 1976. Activation of casein synthesis by prostaglandins plus spermidine in mammary gland explants of mice. *Biochem. Biophys. Res. Commun.* 70:45–49
46. Rillema, J. A. 1976. Action of prolactin on ornithine decarboxylase activity in mammary gland explants of mice. *Endocrinol. Res. Commun.* 3:297–305
47. Rillema, J. A., Anderson, L. D. 1976. Phospholipase and the effect of prolactin on uridine incorporation into RNA in mammary gland explants in mice. *Biochem. Biophys. Acta* 428:819–24
48. Rillema, J. A., Linebaugh, B. E., Mulder, J. A. 1977. Regulation of casein synthesis by polyamines in mammary gland explants of mice. *Endocrinology* 100:529–36
49. Rillema, J. A., Wild, E. A. 1977. Prolactin activation of phospholipase A activity in membrane preparations from mammary glands. *Endocrinology* 100:1219–22
50. Deleted in proof
51. Scow, R. O., Hamosh, M., Blanchette-Mackie, E. J., Evans, A. J. 1972. Uptake of blood triglyceride by various tissues. *Lipids* 7:497–505
52. Deleted in proof
53. Shiu, R. P. C., Kelly, P. A., Friesen, H. G. 1973. Radioreceptor assay for prolactin and other lactogenic hormones. *Science* 180:968–71
54. Shiu, R. P. C., Friesen, H. G. 1974. Properties of a prolactin receptor from the rabbit mammary gland. *Biochem. J.* 140:301–11
55. Shiu, R. P. C., Friesen, H. G. 1974. Solubilization and purification of a prolactin receptor from the rabbit mammary gland. *J. Biol. Chem.* 249:7902–11
56. Shiu, R. P. C., Friesen, H. G. 1976. Interaction of cell membrane prolactin receptor with its antibody. *Biochem. J.* 157:619–26
57. Shiu, R. P. C., Friesen, H. G. 1976. Blockade of prolactin action by an antiserum to its receptors. *Science* 192:259–61
58. Shiu, R. P. C. 1979. Prolactin receptors in human breast cancer cells in long term tissue culture. *Cancer Res.* 39:81–86
59. Shiu, R. P. C. 1979. Prolactin binding and processing by human breast cancer cells in long term tissue culture, *Proc. 61st Ann. Meet. Endocrine Soc.,* Abstr. 820, p. 277
60. Topper, Y. J. 1970. Multiple hormone interactions in the development of mammary gland in vitro. *Recent Prog. Horm. Res.* 26:287–303
61. Turkington, R. W., Brew, K., Vanaman, T. C., Hill, R. L. 1968. The hormonal control of lactose synthetase in the developing mouse mammary gland. *J. Biol. Chem.* 243:3382–87
62. Turkington, R. W. 1970. Stimulation of RNA synthesis in isolated mammary cells by insulin and prolactin bound to Sepharose. *Biochem. Biophys. Res. Commun.* 41:1362–67
63. Turkington, R. W., Majumder, G. C., Kadohama, N., MacIndoe, J. H., Frantz, W. L. 1973. Hormonal regulation of gene expression in mammary cells. *Recent Prog. Horm. Res.* 29:417–49
64. Deleted in proof
65. Vonderhaar, B. 1977. Studies on the mechanism by which thyroid hormone enhances α-lactalbumin activity in explants from mouse mammary glands. *Endocrinology* 100:1423–31
66. Wang, D. Y., Hallowes, R. C., Bealing, J., Strong, C. R., Dils, R. 1972. The effect of prolactin and growth hormone

on fatty acid synthesis by pregnant mouse mammary gland in organ culture. *J. Endocrinol.* 53:311–21

67. Waters, M. J., Friesen, H. G., Bohnet, H. G. 1978. Regulation of prolactin receptors by steroid hormones and use of radioligand assays in endocrine research. In *Receptors and Hormone Action III*, ed. B. W. O'Malley, L. Birhbaumer, pp. 457–77. NY: Academic
68. Weisz-Carrington, P., Roux, M. E., Lamm, M. E. 1977. Plasma cells and epithelial immunoglobulins in the mouse mammary gland during pregnancy and lactation. *J. Immunol.* 119: 1306–9
69. Weisz-Carrington, P., Roux, M. E., McWilliams, M., Phillips-Quagliata, J. M., Lamm, M. E. 1978. Hormonal induction of the secretory immune system in the mammary gland. *Proc. Natl. Acad. Sci. USA* 75:2928–32
70. Deleted in proof
71. Welsch, C. W., Nagasawa, H. 1977. Prolactin and murine mammary tumorigenesis: A Review. *Cancer Res.* 37:951–63
72. Deleted in proof
73. Zinder, O., Hamosh, M., Clary-Fleck, T. R., Scow, R. O. 1974. Effect of prolactin on lipoprotein lipase in mammary gland and adipose tissue of rats. *Am. J. Physiol.* 226:744–48

Ann. Rev. Physiol. 1980. 42:97–110

BINDING AND METABOLISM OF SEX STEROIDS BY THE HYPOTHALAMIC-PITUITARY UNIT: PHYSIOLOGICAL IMPLICATIONS

❖1256

Bruce S. McEwen

The Rockefeller University, 1230 York Avenue, New York, NY 10021

INTRODUCTION

During the past decade, putative receptor systems for sex steroid hormones have been identified, characterized, and anatomically mapped in the brains and pituitary glands of representative vertebrate species. This information has been obtained by three techniques: (*a*) steroid autoradiography after in vivo ^{3}H-steroid administration (36, 68), and (*b*) in vitro receptor assays as well as (*c*) in vivo ^{3}H-steroid administration and cell nuclear isolation, both performed on dissected pieces of brain tissue (54). Neural steroid receptors appear to be similar, if not identical, to receptor systems from nonneural target tissues. Their mode of action, implied by their similarity to peripheral receptors, is presumed to be at the level of gene expression and regulation of genomic activity.

Principal interest in these receptors now centers around relating their neuroanatomical location and their occupation by endogenous and exogenous steroids to neuroendocrine and behavioral effects of the hormones. More broadly speaking, research on steroid hormone action in brain and pituitary is now directed toward finding and describing the hormone-initiated chemical and cellular processes that underly these neuroendocrine and behavioral events. The location of steroid receptors is a useful though not infallible guide in deciding where in the brain to look. (Steroid effects may exist that do not involve these receptors. This matter is considered in the Concluding Remarks.) Here I review gonadal steroid metabolism, receptor localization, and approaches to the study of receptor involvement in brain function.

0066-4278/80/0315-0097$01.00

RECEPTOR LOCALIZATION IN RELATION TO STEROID METABOLISM

Androgens

Receptors for androgens have been characterized in rat and mouse brain and pituitary tissue (see 55, 58). The specificity of steroid binding and the physicochemical properties (6–7S in low salt and 3–4S in high ionic strength buffer after sucrose density gradient sedimentation) are similar to those of prostate androgen receptors. Androgen receptors are absent in brain and pituitary tissue of rats and mice bearing the X-linked testicular feminizing (Tfm), or androgen insensitivity, mutation (5, 26, 71). The neuroanatomical distribution of androgen receptors has been characterized for rats and mice by autoradiography (81, 84, 85) and by biochemical analysis (8, 15, 43). Androgen receptors, found throughout the brain, are concentrated in pituitary, hypothalamus (H), septum, preoptic area (P), and amygdala (A). Only one receptor seems able to recognize both testosterone (T) and 5α-dihydrotestosterone (5α-DHT) (27).

Two aspects of T metabolism are crucial to receptor occupation: aromatization to estradiol (44, 72) and Δ 4–5 reduction to 5α- or 5β-DHT and related androstanediols (55). 5α-reductase activity occurs throughout the rat brain and pituitary and does not seem to be a limiting factor in androgen receptor occupation (cf 22, 44). Aromatization is absent from pituitary and from cerebral cortex and is present in H, P, and A (72, 83), where it is capable of supplying estradiol for the occupation of estrogen receptors in these regions (38, 44).

Estrogens

Estrogen receptors have been characterized and mapped in a number of vertebrate species, though most work has been done in rat and mouse (55, 68). The specificity and physicochemical characteristics (8S in low ionic strength buffers and 4S at high ionic strength, with a separate 5S nuclear form) of neural and pituitary receptors resemble properties of uterine estrogen receptors (see 55). Estrogen receptors are found in high concentration in anterior pituitary, where 85% of cells are labeled (89), and in somewhat lower concentrations in basomedial H, P, corticomedial A, and mesencephalic central gray of the rat and mouse (cf 75, 90, 98). A dissection scheme was designed to remove these areas of rat brain (46) and its efficacy was established by in vivo ^{3}H-estradiol uptake and cell nuclear isolation (62). This dissection scheme is being used for a number of studies of estrogen action, including studies (described below) of estrogen induction of progestin receptors.

The estrogen receptor system of the rat brain and pituitary is functionally heterogeneous. This is indicated by the following kinds of information (see

57): (*a*) Aromatization of T is absent from pituitary; it is present at a high level in A and to a somewhat lesser extent in P and H. Within H, P, and A the distribution of aromatase activity is not uniform. That aromatase activity is found in some but not all cells containing estrogen receptors is indicated by the fact that in vivo ^{3}HT labels estrogen receptors with ^{3}H-estradiol in A, P, and H, but not in pituitary (44). (*b*) Estrogen induction of progestin receptors (see next section) is high in pituitary, substantial in H and P, and absent in A. Again the inference is that some, but not all, estrophilic cells have this property. (*c*) Estradiol effects on brain and pituitary enzyme activities [e.g. MAO, tyrosine hydroxylase (TOH), G6PDH, choline acetyltransferase (CAT)] are confined to brain regions containing estrophilic cells, but within any of these regions (H, P, or A) one does not find all of these effects (e.g. TOH activity is down-regulated by estradiol in H; CAT activity is increased by E_2 in P and A). (*d*) In a like manner, estrogen action on pituitary is associated with a variety of cell-specific functions rather than with a function or functions common to all cells (e.g. thyrotroph sensitivity to TRH; formation of preprolactin mRNA; synthesis rates of LH, FSH).

The principal estrogen metabolites of interest for neuroendocrine research are the 2 hydroxylated, or catechol, estrogens. They are formed in brain, especially hypothalamic, tissue (25). They are functionally weak estrogens. So far, little is known about unique nonestrogenic effects of these compounds except for the ability to inhibit catechol-O-methyl transferase activity (for reviews see 25, 58). The functional significance of this inhibition remains to be established.

Progestins

Progestin receptors were once difficult to demonstrate by methods (outlined above) used successfully to reveal estrogen and androgen receptors (e.g. 54, 58). However, there were reports of autoradiographic localization of ^{3}H-progesterone in the hypothalamus of the estrogen-primed guinea pig (80) and biochemical demonstrations of ^{3}H-progesterone binding sites in the hypothalamus and anterior pituitary of estrogen-primed rats (23, 42, 82) and laying hens (32). With the introduction of a synthetic progestin, 17,21-dimethyl-19-norpregna-4,9-diene-3,20-dione (R5020), came more convincing demonstrations of progestin binding sites by autoradiography (99), cell fractionation (11), and cytosol binding assays (30, 49, 51, 65). We can now understand the reasons for the difficulties encountered in earlier studies: (*a*) the small number of binding sites plus the high lipid solubility of progestins, which increased nonspecific uptake in the in vivo studies; (*b*) the lesser affinity and stability of ^{3}H-progesterone-receptor complexes (compared to those with ^{3}H-R5020), which resulted in their dissociation and reduced the sensitivity of binding assays; (*c*) the relatively greater ability of ^{3}H-progesterone (compared to ^{3}H-R5020) to bind to glucocorticoid receptors and transcortin, which further decreases the sensitivity of in vitro assays for specific progestin receptors.

The principle features of progestin receptors demonstrated by ^{3}H-R5020 may be summarized from the references cited above as follows: (*a*) high affinity ($K_d \approx 0.3$nM); (*b*) sedimentation coefficient of ≈7S in low ionic strength buffers and ≈3.6S in high ionic strength buffers; (*c*) specificity for synthetic and natural progestins with practically no affinity for glucocorticoids or testosterone and a low affinity for estradiol. Progesterone has a 10 times lower affinity for the receptor than R5020 and dissociates 6 times faster.

Cell nuclear uptake of ^{3}H-R5020 in vivo in estrogen-primed rats is demonstrable in brain and pituitary, albeit at a low level (see 12, 65), whereas that of ^{3}H-progesterone is not (59). The reasons for the low level of in vivo cell nuclear binding of ^{3}H-R5020 are not clear. It may simply reflect the loss of ^{3}H-R5020 in the lipid fraction of brain tissue at the tracer dose levels used rather than any intrinsic difference in the functioning of these receptors.

Perhaps the most intriguing features of progestin receptor sites are their estrogen-inducibility and their regional distribution in the brain. Induction by estradiol occurs in uterus, pituitary, and brain within 24–48 hr after physiological doses of estradiol (23, 31, 51, 65) and is attenuated by the anti-estrogen CI628 (78). The half-life of the receptors after withdrawal of estradiol is on the order of 24 hr (B. Parsons, B. S. McEwen, in preparation). The receptor induction by estradiol and disappearance of the receptors after estrogen withdrawal is paralleled by the induction and disappearance of the rat's or guinea pig's ability to display feminine sexual behavior [see (9); B. Parsons, B. S. McEwen, in preparation]. Disappearance of progestin receptors is also facilitated by progesterone administration even in the presence of estrogen, and this may explain the refractoriness of the animal to the activation of sexual behavior by a second progesterone injection too soon after the first (10). Progestin receptors are found in all parts of rat and guinea pig brains, including cerebral cortex (see 9, 51), though they are present only in the hypothalamic region of the bonnet monkey (49). In the pituitary and hypothalamic area of all species examined, in the preoptic region in the case of the rat and guinea pig, and in the midbrain of guinea pig, progestin receptors are induced by estradiol. The cerebral cortex is a prime example of a tissue where progestin receptors exist in the relative absence of estrogen receptors. The amygdala, where no induction by estradiol occurs, illustrates that progestin receptor induction is not a universal feature of estrophilic cells. The fact that testosterone induces progestin receptors in H and P (but not A) of rat (L. C. Krey, N. J. MacLusky, B. S. McEwen, unpublished) suggests that some estrophilic cells may combine the ability to aromatize T with progestin receptor induction.

The detailed neuroanatomical pattern of progestin receptors in the rat brain has been revealed by autoradiography after ^{3}H-R5020 administration to estrogen-primed OVX rats (99). The pattern of labeled cells corresponds well to the pattern of estrophilic cells within the medial preoptic (suprachiasmatic, periventricular, and medial P) and basomedial H (arcuate and ventromedial nuclei). After ^{3}H-R5020 treatment, there is a conspicuous absence of labeled cells in the dorsal and lateral P (bed nucleus of stria terminalis) and in A, both of which are regions where estrophilic cells are found. There is also little labeling in cerebral cortex, which must mean that progestin receptors, not inducible by estradiol in this region, are not highly concentrated within a few cells but rather diffusely spread among many.

It is interesting to consider the relationship of progestin receptors to progestin-activated events such as the facilitation of sexual behavior. As noted above, a good correlation in terms of time course and estrogen dose exists between the activation of lordosis behavior and the induction of the progestin receptor, and doses of CI628 that block estrogen activation of lordosis also block progestin receptor induction. The synthetic progestin, R5020, which is a more effective ligand for the receptor, is also a more effective agonist than progesterone in facilitating lordosis behavior (11). While no data directly contradict a role of progestin receptors in activation of lordosis behavior, a few observations remain to be explained within the receptor model. First, some lordosis behavior occurs after only estrogen priming (the higher the estrogen dose the less is the effect of progestin treatment) (e.g. 37). It has been suggested that estradiol at high levels may act as a progestin (37), and indeed estradiol has an affinity for the progestin receptor higher than many nonprogestogenic steroids (51). Second, progestin action can be very rapid, with activation of lordosis behavior commencing 30 min after intravenous administration (39, 64). The rapidity of the progestin effect is difficult, but not impossible, to reconcile with a genomic action: Many genomic effects take hours to be manifested in terms of an overt cellular response, but one effect of glucocorticoids on lymphocyte sugar transport appears within 20 min of steroid application (52). Third, not all intracranial sites where implantation of progestins activates sexual behavior in estrogen-primed rats are sites of estrogen-dependent progestin receptors [see (58) for references]. At this time it is not possible in such studies to rule out diffusion of steroid from such implants to other sites in the brain. On the other hand, progestin receptors not sensitive to estrogen priming may be involved in activation of sexual behavior [see (51) for discussion].

PHYLOGENETIC ASPECTS OF STEROID RECEPTORS IN VERTEBRATE BRAINS

Autoradiographic mapping of estrogen-sensitive cells in representative species of the major vertebrate classes has revealed a remarkable similarity across species in the basic plan. In general, most estrophilic cells are found in the medial P, the tuberal H in specific limbic structures (e.g. the A), and in a specific area of the mesencephalon deep to the tectum (68). Where information is available, the distribution of neurons concentrating ^{3}H-testosterone is similar (though not identical—see below) to that of ^{3}H-estradiol (68), but the significance of this in terms of androgen receptors is in doubt because of the ability of vertebrate brains to aromatize testosterone (see below). More definitive studies of androgen receptors with ^{3}H-5α-dihydrotestosterone have been carried out so far in only a few species: in the reptile, *Anolis carolinensis* (D Crews et al, personal communication), and in the rat (see 43, 81). The pattern of distribution of ^{3}H-DHT neurons is similar to that attained with ^{3}HT and ^{3}H-estradiol (E_2), though the intensity of labelling is lower with ^{3}H-DHT.

Regional distributions of androgen- and estrogen-sensitive neurons parallel each other to a large extent in the brains of vertebrates and show a high degree of similarity across species, but in some species androgen- and estrogen-sensitive neurons are distributed differently in certain brain regions. In a reptile (*Anolis carolinensis*), for example, more estrophilic than androphilic cells are present in the pallium, while androphilic cells are found in the absence of estrophilic cells in the mesencephalon (D. Crews et al, in preparation). In an amphibian (*Xenopis laevis*) where comparisons of ^{3}H-E_2 and ^{3}HT uptake have been carried out, only estrophilic cells are found in torus semicircularis, ventral thalamus, ventral striatum, ventral lateral septum, and rostral A, whereas only androphilic cells are found in the nuclei of the ninth and tenth cranial nerves and in the dorsal tegmental area of the medulla—regions implicated in the control of androgen-dependent mating vocalizations (cf 33, 67). In a bird species (zebra finch, *Poephila guttata*), only androphilic cells are found in brain areas implicated in the control of song (which is activated by androgens): caudal nucleus of the hyperstriatum ventrale, magnocellular nucleus of the anterior neostriatum nucleus intercollicularis of the midbrain, and the tracheasyringeal neurons that innervate the vocal organ or syrinx (cf 3).

The distribution of sex-steroid sensitive neurons in the brain is characteristic of the species and is independent of the genetic sex (cf 34, 68). While qualitative sex differences do not exist, there is at least one quantitative sex difference. In the zebra finch more androgen-concentrating neurons are found in males than in females in two song-control areas: hyperstriatum ventrale pars caudale and magnocellular nucleus of the anterior neostriatum (4). It is unknown whether this finding reflects fewer cells of a particular type or fewer receptors per cell, but the sex difference in number of androphilic cells is in the same direction as the sexual dimorphism in size of the same cell groups (73). It remains to be determined whether similar quantitative sex differences exist in the brain of other vertebrate species.

In connection with the phylogenetic aspects of estrogen and androgen uptake and the ambiguity of interpreting the uptake of ^{3}HT, it is well to consider the phylogenetic distribution of the enzymes that metabolize ^{3}HT —i.e. aromatase and 5α-reductase. Both enzymatic activities have been detected in representative species of all major vertebrate classes, from fish to humans (14). The regional distribution of aromatase activity in brains of representative vertebrate species reveals an interesting but so far unexplained phylogenetic pattern: While aromatase is consistently found in H and P and in the limbic lobe and its homologs of virtually all species examined, there is aromatase activity in the mid- and hindbrain of fish and amphibia that is not present in reptiles, birds, and mammals (14).

ONTOGENY OF NEURAL STEROID RECEPTORS

The appearance and ontogenesis of neural steroid hormone receptors is of considerable interest with respect to understanding the onset of sensitivity of the brain to the influences of the gonadal steroids. This sensitivity takes two forms: (*a*) appearance of the activational influences of these steroids on adult-type behavior and neuroendocrine function; (*b*) sexual differentiation of the brain during an early "critical period" that results in permanent alterations in the behavioral and neuroendocrine responses of the brain to the activating influences of the gonadal steroids in adult life [see (56) for discussion].

In the rat, estrogen and androgen receptors become detectable a few days before birth (6, 29, 48, 50). The increase in estrogen receptor levels is rapid during the first postnatal week of life; the increase of androgen receptors is greatest during the second and third postnatal weeks. Estrogen receptors are present in neonatal rat and mouse cerebral cortex (6, 63, 76), as well as in H, P, and A (6, 48, 50, 63, 86). Cortical estrogen receptors disappear during the third postnatal week.

The appearance of these receptor systems precedes by many days the appearance of activational influences of gonadal steroids on masculine and feminine sexual behavior (see 87, 88) and ovulation [see (56) for references]. Only the negative feedback action of estrogen and androgen may have a relatively early onset [see (56) for references]; these effects may occur at the level of the pituitary (see 38). It is likely that many factors in neural maturation and body growth besides the receptors determine the delayed onset of activational influence of gonadal steroids on the brain. Neurons containing the receptors are probably programmed to respond differently to the hormones during early life. This is apparent for estrogen receptors, which appear to function in neonatal mouse hypothalamus by promoting growth of target neurons (91, 92). The outgrowth phenomenon may be a manifestation of the sexual differentiation of the brain, which occurs in rat and mouse under control of estradiol formed by neural aromatization from testosterone (cf 61). The appearance of neural estrogen receptors at the time of birth in the rat appears to determine the onset of this critical period of brain sexual differentiation (50). It is interesting to note that in the chick embryo, where estrogens may function in an analogous fashion to produce sexual dimorphism of sexual behavior (see 1, 2), the neural estrogen receptors are detected on or about day 10 *in ovo* (53) and hence may subserve a role comparable to that hypothesized for the neonatal rat brain.

CONCLUDING REMARKS: ACTIONS OF GONADAL STEROIDS ON NEURAL AND PITUITARY TISSUE AND THEIR RELATIONSHIP TO RECEPTORS

The steroid receptors are a useful starting point for investigating the cellular and chemical processes that underlie steroid effects on neuroendocrine function and behavior. First, they imply a cellular mechanism—namely, genomic activation—as a basis for steroid effects. Such a mechanism contains certain testable properties: the latency and duration of the effect (on the order of minutes to hours), and the involvement of RNA and protein synthesis (for which there are specific inhibitors). Investigation of these properties has demonstrated that such estrogen effects as activation of sexual behavior and positive and negative feedback in the rat involve genomic activation as implied by the receptor mechanism (see 38, 60). It has also led to a recognition that some steroid effects, such as those on electrical activity following iontophoresis, occur too rapidly to involve the genome (see 35). Other steroid effects, such as those of progestins, occur rapidly, but not too rapidly for a genomic mechanism to be involved (see discussion above). Newly described gonadal steroid effects, such as inhibition by estradiol of dopaminergic activity in corpus striatum (41), must be subjected to the kind of analysis described above.

Steroid receptors also provide a first indication of where in the brain to look for hormone effects. Indeed, estrogen-concentrating regions of the brain like H and P, and no others, are responsive to local estrogen implants in the activation of masculine and feminine sexual behavior (e.g. 7, 16, 18, 19, 21). These same areas show changes in electrical activity acutely and chronically following estrogen treatment (13, 100) and are the sites of chemical changes brought about by estrogen treatment—e.g. progestin receptor induction and changes in various enzyme activities (see 58). Within the developing rodent brain, estrogen-concentrating hypothalamic sites are implicated in brain sexual differentiation by the efficacy of micro-implants of testosterone propionate and estradiol in this region (17, 28, 69, 70) and by the demonstration that neurite outgrowth induced by estradiol in organ cultures of neonatal mouse hypothalamus emanates from estrophilic neurons (92). However, because many neurons project outside their immediate brain region, it is conceivable and in fact likely that some steroid effects may be manifested at the synaptic endings of a nonestrophilic brain area even though the primary site of action is an estrophilic region (60). One example of this is the appearance of estrogen-induced choline acetyl transferase activity in hippocampus as well as in P-septum (47).

Neural and pituitary steroid receptors have also been the subjects of studies seeking to correlate receptor properties (e.g. induction, occupation) and physiologic steroid effects. For example, the process whereby progestin receptors are induced by estradiol and decay following its removal has been correlated positively with induction and decay of lordosis behavior, which is facilitated by progesterone [(9, 10); B. Parsons, B. S. McEwen, in preparation]. Furthermore, the ability of the anti-estrogen CI628 to block estrogen-induced sexual behavior is positively correlated with its ability to block estrogen induction of neural progestin receptors (78). That a synthetic progestin, R5020, activates lordosis behavior more effectively than progesterone itself has been correlated positively with its greater affinity for the progestin receptor (12, 49). In another study, the inhibitory effect of progesterone given concurrently with estradiol on sexual behavior in the rat was shown *not* to result in reduced occupation of estrogen receptors by ^{3}H-estradiol (11, 24, 74).

Other examples of the correlative approach pertain to the actions of estrogen antagonists. The efficacy of CI628 in blocking estrogen-induced lordosis behavior in rats and guinea pigs is correlated with a reduction in the ability of ^{3}H-estradiol to translocate into cell nuclear receptor sites in brain and pituitary (40, 79, 94–97). Likewise, the efficacy of CI628 in blocking negative feedback by ^{3}H-estradiol in the rat is correlated with a reduction of nuclear receptor–bound ^{3}H-estradiol. Furthermore, a "chemical dissection" was accomplished such that the CI628 blockade (but not altered behavior) could be observed when pituitary and not hypothalamic nuclear ^{3}H-estradiol levels were reduced below the threshold for negative feedback. Such results argue for a pituitary site of action (38).

The correlation of receptor occupation and a neuroendocrine effect has been used most effectively, perhaps, in the dissection of pathways of testosterone (T) action during brain development and in adult brain function. Extensive aromatization as well as 5α reduction of T take place in brain. Furthermore, both a specific inhibitor of aromatization, ATD (1,4,6-androstatriene-3,17-dione), and CI628 are available to study estrogen involvement as a product of T metabolism. An androgen antagonist, flutamide, is available to study the involvement of androgen receptors. Moreover, the study of estrogen receptor involvement by an exchange assay permits quantitation of estrogen receptor occupation by endogenous estradiol (77). Using this technique, Krey et al (38) demonstrated androgen- rather than estrogen-receptor involvement in negative feedback by T on LH secretion in rats. At the same time, Morali et al (66) showed that aromatization of T is an important part of T-facilitation of masculine sexual behavior. A similar application of these tools has indicated a significant involvement of aromatization in rat brain sexual differentiation: Both ATD and CI628 in doses that effectively block estrogen receptor occupation by T-derived estradiol result in attenuation or blockade of the defeminizing effects of T in normal males and in T-treated female neonates (20, 45, 61, 93).

Acknowledgments

Research in the author's laboratory is supported by research grant NS 07080 to Dr. McEwen and by an institutional grant for research in reproductive biology, RF 70095, from the Rockefeller Foundation. The author wishes to thank Mrs. Oksana Wengerchuk for editorial assistance and typing of the manuscript.

Literature Cited

1. Adkins, E. K. 1975. Hormonal basis of sexual differentiation in the Japanese quail. *J. Comp. Physiol. Psychol.* 89: 61–71
2. Adkins, E. K. 1976. Embryonic exposure to an antiestrogen masculinizes behavior of female quail. *Physiol. Behav.* 17:357–59
3. Arnold, A. P., Nottebohm, F., Pfaff, D. W. 1976. Hormone concentrating cells in vocal control and other areas of the brain of the Zebra Finch. *J. Comp. Neurol.* 165:487–512
4. Arnold, A. P., Saltiel, A. 1978. Sexual differences in pattern of hormone accumulation in the brain of a song bird. *Ann. Meet. Soc. Neurosci.,* Abstr. #1072
5. Attardi, B., Geller, L. N., Ohno, S. 1976. Androgen and estrogen receptors in brain cytosol from male, female, and testicular feminized (tfm/y o) mice. *Endocrinology* 98:864–74
6. Attardi, B., Ohno, S. 1976. Androgen and estrogen receptors in the developing mouse brain. *Endocrinology* 99: 1279–90
7. Barfield, R. J., Chen, J. J. 1977. Activation of estrous behavior in ovariectomized rats by intracerebral implants of estradiol benzoate. *Endocrinology* 101: 1716–25
8. Barley, J., Ginsburg, M., Greenstein, B. D., MacLusky, N. J., Thomas, P. J. 1975. An androgen receptor in rat brain and pituitary. *Brain Res.* 100:383–93
9. Blaustein, J. D., Feder, H. H. 1979. Cytoplasmic progestin receptors in guinea pig: characteristics and relationship to the induction of sexual behavior. *Brain Res.* 169:481–97
10. Blaustein, J. D., Feder, H. H. 1979. Cytoplasmic progestin receptors in female guinea pig brain and their relationship to refractoriness in expression

of female sexual behavior. *Brain Res.* In press
11. Blaustein, J. D., Wade, G. N. 1977. Concurrent inhibition of sexual behavior, but not brain (^{3}H) estradiol uptake, by progesterone in female rats. *J. Comp. Physiol. Psychol.* 91:742–51
12. Blaustein, J. D., Wade, G. N. 1978. Progestin binding by brain and pituitary cell nuclei and female rat sexual behavior. *Brain Res.* 140:360–67
13. Bueno, J., Pfaff, D. W. 1976. Single unit recording in hypothalamus and preoptic area of estrogen-treated and untreated ovariectomized female rats. *Brain Res.* 101:67–78
14. Callard, G. V., Petro, Z., Ryan, K. J. 1978. Conversion of androgen to estrogen and other steroids in the vertebrate brain. *Am. Zool.* 18:511–23
15. Chamness, G. C., King, T. W., Sheridan, P. J. 1979. Androgen receptor in the rat brain—assays and properties. *Brain Res.* 161:267–76
16. Christensen, L. W., Clemens, L. G. 1974. Intrahypothalamic implants of testosterone or estradiol and resumption of masculine sexual behavior in long-term castrated male rats. *Endocrinology* 95:984–90
17. Christensen, L. W., Gorski, R. A. 1978. Independent masculinization of neuroendocrine systems by intracerebral implants of testosterone or estradiol in the neonatal female rat. *Brain Res.* 146: 325–40
18. Davis, P. G., Barfield, R. J. 1979. Activation of masculine behavior by intracranial estradiol benzoate implants in male rats. *Neuroendocrinology* 28: 217–27
19. Davis, P. G., Barfield, R. J. 1979. Activation of feminine sexual behavior in castrated male rats by intrahypothalamic implants of estradiol benzoate. *Neuroendocrinology* 28:217–27
20. Davis, P. G., Chaptal, C. V., McEwen, B. S. 1979. Independence of the differentiation of masculine and feminine sexual behavior in rats. *Horm. Behav.* 12:12–19
21. Davis, P. G., McEwen, B. S., Pfaff, D. W. 1979. Localized behavioral effects of tritiated estradiol implants on the ventromedial hypothalamus of female rats. *Endocrinology* 104:898–903
22. Denef, C., Magnus, C., McEwen, B. S. 1973. Sex differences and hormonal control of testosterone metabolism in rat pituitary and brain. *J. Endocrinol.* 59:605–21
23. Evans, R. W., Sholiton, L. J., Leavitt, W. W. 1978. Progesterone receptor in the rat anterior pituitary: effect of estrogen priming and adrenalectomy. *Steroids* 31:69–75
24. Feder, H. H., Landau, I. T., Marrone, B. L., Walker, W. A. 1977. Interactions between estrogen and progesterone in neural tissues that mediate sexual behavior of guinea pigs. *Psychoneuroendocrinology* 2:337–47
25. Fishman, J. 1976. The catechol estrogens. *Neuroendocrinology* 22:363–74
26. Fox, T. O. 1975. Androgen- and estrogen-binding macromolecules in developing mouse brain: biochemical and genetic evidence. *Proc. Natl. Acad. Sci. USA* 72:4303–7
27. Ginsburg, M., Shori, D. K. 1978. Are there distinct dihydrotestosterone and testosterone receptors in brain? *J. Steroid Biochem.* 9:437–41
28. Hayashi, S., Gorski, R. A. 1974. Critical exposure time for androgenization by intracranial crystals of testosterone propionate in neonatal female rats. *Endocrinology* 94:1161–67
29. Kato, J. 1976. Ontogeny of 5α-dihydrotestosterone receptors in the hypothalamus of the rat. *Ann. Biol. Anim. Biochem. Biophys.* 16:467–69
30. Kato, J., Onouchi, T. 1977. Specific progesterone receptors in the hypothalamus and anterior hypophysis of the rat. *Endocrinology* 101:920–28
31. Kato, J., Onouchi, T., Okinaga, S. 1978. Hypothalamic and hypophysial progesterone receptors: estrogen-priming effect, differential localization, 5α-dihydroprogesterone binding, and nuclear receptors. *J. Steroid Biochem.* 9:419–27
32. Kawashima, M., Kamiyoshi, M., Tanaka, K. 1978. A cytoplasmic progesterone receptor in hen pituitary and hypothalamic tissues. *Endocrinology* 102:1207–13
33. Kelley, D. B., Morrell, J. I., Pfaff, D. W. 1975. Autoradiographic localization of hormone-concentrating cells in the brain of an amphibian, *Xenopus Laevis.* I. Testosterone. *J. Comp. Neurol.* 164:47–59
34. Kelley, D. B., Pfaff, D. W. 1978. Generalizations from comparative studies on neuroanatomical and endocrine mechanisms of sexual behavior. In *Biological Determinants of Sexual Behavior,* ed. J. B. Hutchison, pp. 225–54. Chichester: John Wiley & Sons
35. Kelly, M. J., Moss, R. L., Dudley, C. A. 1978. The effects of ovariectomy on the responsiveness of preoptic-septal neu-

rons to microelectrophoresed estrogen. *Neuroendocrinology* 25:204–11
36. Kim, Y. S., Stumpf, W. E., Sar, M., Martinez-Vargas, M. C. 1978. Estrogen and androgen target cells in the brain of fishes, reptiles and birds: phylogeny and ontogeny. *Am. Zool.* 18:425–33
37. Kow, L.-M., Pfaff, D. W. 1975. Induction of lordosis in female rats: two modes of estrogen action and the effect of adrenalectomy. *Horm. Behav.* 6: 259–76
38. Krey, L. C., Lieberburg, I., Roy, E., McEwen, B. S. 1979. Estradiol + receptor complexes in the brain and anterior pituitary gland: quantitation and neuroendocrine significance. *J. Steroid Biochem.* 11:279–84
39. Kubli-Garfias, C., Whalen, R. E. 1977. Induction of lordosis behavior in female rats by intravenous administration of progestins. *Horm. Behav.* 9:380–86
40. Landau, I. T. 1977. Relationships between the effects of the antiestrogen, CI628, on sexual behavior, uterine growth, and cell nuclear estrogen retention after estradiol-17β-benzoate administration in the ovariectomized rat. *Brain Res.* 133:119–38
41. Langelier, P., Dankova, J., Boucher, R., Bedard, P. 1978. Steroid hormone and dopaminergic activity in the striatum. *Ann. Meet. Soc. Neurosci.,* Abstr. #1107
42. Leavitt, W. W., Chen, T. J., Allen, T. C. 1977. Regulation of progesterone receptor formation by estrogen action. *Ann. NY Acad. Sci.* 286:210–25
43. Lieberburg, I., MacLusky, N. J., McEwen, B. S. 1977. 5α dihydrotestosterone receptors in rat brain and pituitary cell nuclei. *Endocrinology* 100: 598–607
44. Lieberburg, I., McEwen, B. S. 1977. Brain cell nuclear retention of testosterone metabolites, 5α dihydrotestosterone and estradiol 17β, in adult rats. *Endocrinology* 100:588–97
45. Lieberburg, I., Wallach, G., McEwen, B. S. 1977. The effects of an inhibitor of aromatization (1,4,6-androstatriene-3,17-dione) and an anti-estrogen (CI628) on *in vivo* formed testosterone metabolites recovered from neonatal rat brain tissues and purified cell nuclei. Implications for sexual differentiation of the rat brain. *Brain Res.* 128:176–81
46. Luine, V. N., Khylchevskaya, R. I., McEwen, B. S. 1974. Oestrogen effects on brain and pituitary enzyme activities. *J. Neurochem.* 23:925–34
47. Luine, V. N., Khylchevskaya, R. I., McEwen, B. S. 1975. Effect of gonadal steroids on activities of monoamine oxidase and choline acetylase in rat brain. *Brain Res.* 86:293–306
48. MacLusky, N. J., Chaptal, C., McEwen, B. S. 1979. The development of estrogen receptor systems in the rat brain and pituitary: postnatal development. *Brain Res.* In press
49. MacLusky, N. J., Krey, L., Lieberburg, I., McEwen, B. S. 1978. Estrogen modulation of progestin receptors in the bonnet monkey (*M. Radiata*) and the rat. *Endocrine Soc. 60th Ann. Meet., Miami, 1978,* p. 298, Abstr. 447
50. MacLusky, N. J., Lieberburg, I., McEwen, B. S. 1979. The development of estrogen receptor systems in the rat brain: perinatal development. *Brain Res.* In press
51. MacLusky, N. J., McEwen, B. S. 1978. Oestrogen modulates progestin receptor concentrations in some rat brain regions but not in others. *Nature* 274: 276–78
52. Makman, M. H., Dvorkin, D., White, A. 1971. Evidence for induction by cortisol *in vitro* of a protein inhibitor of transport and phosphorylation processes in rat thymocytes. *Proc. Natl. Acad. Sci. USA* 68:1269–73
53. Martinez-Vargas, M. C., Gibson, D. B., Sar, M., Stumpf, W. 1975. Estrogen target sites in the brain of the chick embryo. *Science* 190:1307–8
54. McEwen, B. S. 1976. Steroid receptors in neuroendocrine tissues: topography, subcellular distribution, and functional implications. In *International Symposium on Subcellular Mechanisms in Reproductive Neuroendocrinology,* ed. F. Naftolin, K. J. Ryan, J. Davies, pp. 277–304. NY: Elsevier
55. McEwen, B. S. 1978. Gonadal steroid receptors in neuroendocrine tissues. In *Hormone Receptors Vol. I, Steroid Hormones.* ed. B. O'Malley, L. Birnbaumer, pp. 353–400. NY: Academic
56. McEwen, B. S., 1978. Sexual maturation and differentiation: the role of the gonadal steroids. *Prog. Brain Res.* 48:291–307
57. McEwen, B. S. 1980. Estrogens, brain cell function, and behavior. In *Biological Regulation and Development,* ed. R. Goldberger. NY: Plenum. In press
58. McEwen, B. S., Davis, P. G., Parsons, B., Pfaff, D. W. 1979. The brain as a target for steroid hormone action. *Ann. Rev. Neurosci.* 2:65–112

59. McEwen, B. S., De Kloet, R., Wallach, G. 1976. Interactions *in vivo* and *in vitro* of corticoids and progesterone with cell nuclei and soluble macromolecules from rat brain regions and pituitary. *Brain Res.* 105:129–36
60. McEwen, B. S., Krey, L. C., Luine, V. N. 1978. Steroid hormone action in the neuroendocrine system: when is the genome involved? In *The Hypothalamus,* ed. S. Reichlin, R. J. Baldessarini, J. B. Martin, pp. 255–68. NY: Raven Press
61. McEwen, B. S., Lieberburg, I., Chaptal, C., Krey, L. C. 1977. Aromatization: Important for sexual differentiation of the neonatal rat brain. *Horm. Behav.* 9:249–63
62. McEwen, B. S., Pfaff, D. W., Chaptal, C., Luine, V. 1975. Brain cell nuclear retention of ^{3}H estradiol doses able to promote lordosis: temporal and regional aspects. *Brain Res.* 86:155–61
63. McEwen, B. S., Plapinger, L., Chaptal, C., Gerlach, J., Wallach, G. 1975. Role of fetoneonatal estrogen binding proteins in the association of estrogen with neonatal brain cell nuclear receptors. *Brain Res.* 96:400–6
64. Meyerson, B. 1972. Latency between intravenous injection of progestins and the appearance of estrous behavior in estrogen-treated ovariectomized rats. *Horm. Behav.* 3:1–10
65. Moguilewsky, M., Raynaud, J.-P. 1977. Progestin binding sites in the rat hypothalamus, pituitary, and uterus. *Steroids* 30:99–109
66. Morali, G., Larsson, K., Beyer, C. 1977. Inhibition of testosterone-induced sexual behavior in the castrated male rat by aromatase blockers. *Horm. Behav.* 9:203–13
67. Morrell, J. I., Kelley, D. B., Pfaff, D. W. 1975. Autoradiographic localization of hormone-concentrating cells in the brain of an amphibian, *Xenopus laevis,* II. Estradiol. *J. Comp. Neurol.* 164: 63–78
68. Morrell, J. I., Pfaff, D. W. 1978. A neuroendocrine approach to brain function: localization of sex steroid concentrating cells in vertebrate brains. *Am. Zool.* 18:447–60
69. Nadler, R. D. 1968. Masculinization of female rats by intracranial implantation of androgen in infancy. *J. Comp. Physiol. Psychol.* 66:157–67
70. Nadler, R. D. 1973. Further evidence on the intrahypothalamic locus for androgenization of female rats. *Neuroendocrinology* 12:110–19
71. Naess, O., Haug, E., Attramadal, A., Aakvaag, A., Hansson, V., French, F. 1976. Androgen receptors in the anterior pituitary and central nervous system of the androgen "insensitive" (Tfm) rat: correlations between receptor binding and effects of androgens on gonadotropin secretion. *Endocrinology* 99: 1295–1303
72. Naftolin, F., Ryan, K. J., Davies, I. J., Reddy, V. V., Flores, F., Petro, Z., Kuhn, M., White, R. J., Takaoka, Y., Wolin, L. 1975. The formation of estrogens by central neuroendocrine tissues, *Recent Prog. Horm. Res.* 31:291–315
73. Nottebohm, F., Arnold, A. P. 1976. Sexual dimorphism in vocal control areas of the songbird brain. *Science* 194:211–13
74. Pavlik, E. J., Coulson, P. B. 1975. Modulation of estrogen receptors in four different target tissues: differential effects of estrogen vs progesterone. *J. Steroid Biochem.* 7:369–76
75. Pfaff, D. W., Keiner, M. 1973. Atlas of estradiol-concentrating cells in the central nervous system of the female rat. *J. Comp. Neurol.* 151:121–58
76. Presl, J., Pospisil, J., Horsky, J. 1971. Autoradiographic localization of radioactivity in female rat neocortex after injection of tritiated estradiol. *Experientia* 27:465–67
77. Roy, E. J., McEwen, B.S. 1977. An exchange assay for estrogen receptors in cell nuclei of the adult rat brain. *Steroids* 30:657–69
78. Roy, E. J., MacLusky, N. J., McEwen, B. S. 1979. Antiestrogen inhibits the induction of progestin receptors by estradiol in the hypothalamus, pituitary, and uterus. *Endocrinology* 104:1333–36
79. Roy, E. J., Wade, G. N. 1977. Binding of (^{3}H) estradiol by brain cell nuclei and female rat sexual behavior: inhibition by antiestrogens. *Brain Res.* 126:73–87
80. Sar, M., Stumpf, W. E. 1973. Neurons of the hypothalamus concentrate ^{3}H-progesterone or its metabolites. *Science* 182:1266–68
81. Sar, M., Stumpf, W. E. 1977. Distribution of androgen target cells in rat forebrain and pituitary after ^{3}H-dihydrotestosterone administration. *J. Steroid Biochem.* 8:1131–35
82. Seiki, K., Haruki, Y., Imanishi, Y., Enomoto, T. 1977. Further evidence of the presence of progesterone-binding proteins in female rat hypothalamus. *Endocrinol. Jpn.* 24:233–38
83. Selmanoff, M. K., Brodkin, L. D., Weiner, R. I., Siiteri, P. K. 1977. Aro-

matization and 5α-reduction of androgens in discrete hypothalamic and limbic regions of the male and female rat. *Endocrinology* 101:841–48

84. Sheridan, P. J. 1978. Localization of androgen- and estrogen-concentrating neurons in the diencephalon and telencephalon of the mouse. *Endocrinology* 103:1328–34
85. Sheridan, P. J. 1979. The nucleus interstitialis striae terminalis and the nucleus amygdaloideus medialis: prime targets for androgen in the rat forebrain. *Endocrinology* 104:130–36
86. Sheridan, P. J., Sar, M., Stumpf, W. E. 1974. Autoradiographic localization of ^{3}H-estradiol or its metabolites in the central nervous system of the developing rat. *Endocrinology* 94:1386–90
87. Södersten, P. 1975. Receptive behavior in developing female rats. *Horm. Behav.* 6:307–17
88. Södersten, P., Damassa, D. A., Smith, E. R. 1977. Sexual behavior in developing male rats. *Horm. Behav.* 8:320–41
89. Stumpf, W. E. 1968. Cellular and subcellular ^{3}H-estradiol localization in the pituitary by autoradiographs. *Z. Zellforsch.* 92:23–33
90. Stumpf, W. E., Sar, M. 1975. Hormone-architecture of the mouse brain with ^{3}H-estradiol. In *Anatomical Neuroendocrinology,* ed. W. E. Stumpf, L. D. Grant, pp. 82–103. Basel: Karger
91. Toran-Allerand, C. D. 1976. Sex steroids and the development of the newborn mouse hypothalamus and preoptic area *in vitro:* implications for sexual differentiation. *Brain Res.* 106:407–12
92. Toran-Allerand, C. D., Gerlach, J. L., McEwen, B. S. 1978. Autoradiographic localization of ^{3}H estradiol in relation to steroid responsiveness in cultures of the hypothalamus/preoptic area. *Soc. Neurosci. Ann. Meet., St. Louis, 1978.* Abstr. 392
93. Vreeburg, J. T. M., van der Vaart, P. D. M., van der Schoot, P. 1977. Prevention of central defeminization but not masculinization in male rats by inhibition neonatally of oestrogen biosynthesis. *J. Endocrinol.* 74:379–82
94. Wade, G. N., Blaustein, J. D. 1978. Effects of an anti-estrogen on neural estradiol binding and on behaviors in female rats. *Endocrinology* 102:245–51
95. Walker, W. A., Feder, H. H. 1977. Anti-estrogen effects on estrogen accumulation in brain cell nuclei: neurochemical correlates of estrogen action on female sexual behavior in guinea pigs. *Brain Res.* 134:467–78
96. Walker, W. A., Feder, H. H. 1977. Inhibitory and facilitatory effects of various anti-estrogens on the induction of female sexual behavior by estradiol benzoate in guinea pigs. *Brain Res.* 134:455–65
97. Walker, W. A., Feder, H. H. 1979. Long-term effects of estrogen action are crucial for the display of lordosis in female guinea pigs: antagonism by antiestrogens and correlations with *in vitro* cytoplasmic binding activity. *Endocrinology* 104:89–96
98. Warembourg, M. 1977. Fixation des steroides au niveau du systeme nerveux central et de l'hypophyse chez differents mammiferes. *Ann. Endocrinol.* 38: 41–54
99. Warembourg, M. 1978. Radioautographic study of the rat brain, uterus, and vagina after (^{3}H) R5020 injection. *Mol. Cell. Endocrinol.* 12:67–79
100. Yagi, K. 1973. Changes in firing rates of single preoptic and hypothalamic units following an intravenous administration of estrogen in the castrated female rat. *Brain Res.* 53:343–52

GASTROINTESTINAL AND NUTRITIONAL PHYSIOLOGY

Ann. Rev. Physiol. 1980. 42:111–26

MECHANISMS OF GASTRIC H^+ AND Cl^- TRANSPORT

❖1257

John G. Forte, Terry E. Machen, and Karl Johan Öbrink[1]

Department of Physiology-Anatomy, University of California, Berkeley, California 94720

INTRODUCTION

Over the past decade the study of gastric HCl secretion has undergone several notable advances. Most of these are the direct result of an increasing awareness of developments in fundamental membrane biology and their application to particular problems surrounding acid secretion, such as secretagogue-receptor activation of the oxyntic cell, membrane transformations and turnover associated with the secretory state, transport and electrophysiological correlations, and analysis of membrane-bound enzyme systems as the putative H^+ pump.

We review recent developments that have come primarily from studies on in vitro preparations, including isolated gastric epithelium, gastric glands, single cells, and various membrane fractions. Our approach largely excludes the voluminous literature on intact animals. Limitations of space have forced us to omit many primary references that have formed the framework of important investigation.

STIMULATORY MECHANISMS

Gastric Secretagogues

The actions and interactions of acetylcholine, gastrin, and histamine are still incompletely understood (e.g. see 68). In vitro tests showed that bullfrog gastric mucosa became refractory to repetitive gastrin and cholinergic stimulation but not to histamine (39), which supported the idea that hista-

[1]Present address: Dept. of Physiology and Biophysics, Uppsala University, Uppsala, Sweden

0066-4278/80/0315-0111$01.00

mine is a common mediator. The effects of H_2-receptor antagonists further substantiated this concept but did not lead to indisputable conclusions (6).

Isolated gastric glands (3) or oxyntic cells (67, 70) have been used in the search for direct effects of gastric stimulants on the oxyntic cell. Where they are used, however, H^+ secretion must be assessed indirectly—e.g. as changes in O_2 consumption or accumulation of a weak base like aminopyrine (3). In such preparations, histamine induced dose-related increases in both these parameters, which could be blocked by H_2-receptor antagonists (1, 67). This agrees with the idea that there are specific histamine (H_2) receptors on oxyntic cells (64).

Carbachol induces a transient atropine-inhibitable rise in O_2 consumption in gastric glands and potentiates histamine stimulation (3). Several studies (e.g. 3, 67) imply that there are specific muscarinic sites on oxyntic cells.

The presence of receptors for gastrin on oxyntic cells has been more controversial (30, 70). In isolated canine oxyntic cells gastrin induced small increases in O_2 consumption that were not blocked by specific H_2 antagonists, and potentiation of histamine's action with gastrin was found when these secretagogues were used in combination with a potent phosphodiesterase inhibitor (67). In contrast, isolated gastric glands were not stimulated by gastrin treatment alone (3), but in combination with a phosphodiesterase inhibitor an increase in aminopyrine uptake did occur. Histamine released by the gastrin was apparently responsible (4). Owing to the dilution of this liberated histamine, no stimulatory effect was observed during control conditions. Thus reports differ about the presence of gastrin receptors on oxyntic cells. In frog gastric mucosa and in isolated rabbit gastric glands it seems likely that most of the gastrin stimulation results from two sequential events: First, gastrin liberates histamine; then histamine activates the oxyntic cells.

Stimulus-Secretion Coupling

It is generally assumed that the secretagogues do not exert their stimulatory effects directly on the H^+ secretion machinery but rather activate intracellular messengers. Cyclic nucleotides and Ca^{2+} have been suspected as playing important roles here, as they do in other secretory systems.

For amphibian gastric mucosa the evidence [with few exceptions; see (8)] is quite convincing that cyclic AMP (cAMP) serves as an intracellular mediator. For example, H^+ secretion was stimulated by phosphodiesterase inhibitors and cAMP, and the secretion rates were correlated to the tissue levels of cAMP (34).

Earlier observations on mammalian stomach were more variable, but adenylate cyclase systems responsive to histamine stimulation have recently been found in a variety of isolated mammalian gastric preparations [(64) and references therein]. In the isolated piglet gastric mucosa, histamine induced a large rapid increase in tissue cAMP content correlated in time with activation of H^+ secretion (14). However, it was also noted that tissue cAMP declined after about 30 min nearly to resting levels despite the continued presence of histamine and ongoing secretion.

We conclude that cAMP is somehow involved as a messenger for histamine-induced H^+ secretion in gastric mucosa but is most likely not the ultimate activator of secretion. Such activation may involve protein kinase and other undefined steps. We should also note that neither pentagastrin nor acetylcholine induces increases in cAMP content of isolated oxyntic cells (69). Lastly, the findings that proton transport occurs in isolated gastric vesicles (see below) without the presence of the usual secretagogues (42), and that acid may be preformed in the unstimulated oxyntic cell (3), may indicate that the secretagogues do not stimulate primarily the proton pump but rather some other event, possibly the morphological transformation of the oxyntic cells from the resting to the secreting state.

MEMBRANE TRANSFORMATIONS OF OXYNTIC CELLS

The general patterns of morphological change associated with HCl secretion are now well established (25, 35, 65). In brief, the apical surface of the nonsecreting oxyntic cell (including the intracellular canaliculus of the mammalian cell) is characterized by relatively short, clubby microvilli; the cytoplasm contains an extensive system of membranes in the form of tubules and vesicles, the so-called tubulovesicles. When these cells are stimulated to secrete HCl, elaborate membrane transformations occur. The tubulovesicles diminish or disappear with a nearly corresponding increase in apical plasma membrane area (35). Morphometric analyses of mammalian oxyntic cells indicate that the apical membrane surface area is increased 6–10-fold during HCl secretion (35, 37, 74). Freeze-fracture studies have shown that both qualitative and quantitative changes occur in the apical plasmalemma structure during the transition from rest to secreting conditions (5).

Withdrawal of the secretory stimulus leads to (*a*) condensation of the elaborate apical membrane projections, (*b*) a cytoplasmic uptake of membrane swirls and pentalaminar membrane structures, and (*c*) restoration of the tubulovesicle population (26, 35). The pattern of change and the relative conservation of membrane surface area form the basis for a membrane recycling hypothesis underlying gastric HCl secretion whereby membrane transport sites are manipulated into place by fusion and withdrawn as secretion is terminated (26). Future work must identify the cellular activating events, the forces of membrane migration, and the specific mechanisms of membrane fusion, and must elucidate the apparent qualitative selectivity in the membrane recycling process.

ION TRANSPORT BY THE GASTRIC EPITHELIUM

In vitro studies of gastric mucosa have often used the approach of assessing active transepithelial ion fluxes during short-circuit current (I_{sc}) conditions (36). Such studies have necessarily treated the mucosa as a uniform sheet, despite the fact that the several different epithelial cell types must have very different transport characteristics. Thus it is well established that oxyntic cells are responsible for H^+ secretion and HCO_3^- absorption (44), but it is not certain which cell type(s) is responsible for Cl^- secretion and Na^+ absorption. The paracellular shunt conductance contributes only a small portion (<25%) to the total tissue conductance (72); therefore, the electrical properties for the fundic gastric mucosa are determined almost exclusively by the properties of the cell membranes.

H^+ and HCO_3^- Transport

H^+ secretion occurs down an electrical gradient but against a huge concentration gradient. This active transport is localized to the apical membranes of oxyntic cells (44), and, as might be expected, the H^+ secretory mechanism is fairly independent of the luminal solution. In contrast, H^+ secretion is exquisitely sensitive to the composition of the serosal (nutrient) solution. The effects of K^+, Na^+, HCO_3^-, and Cl^- have all been studied in detail.

K^+-free serosal solution causes H^+ secretion to decrease to zero if the mucosal solution is also K^+-free; H^+ rates can be maintained at about half of maximal secretory levels with 4 mM K^+ in the mucosal solution and are restored to maximal levels when mucosal [K^+] is increased to about 100mM (62). In K^+-free solutions, tissue K^+ content decreases, but not a great deal, and it has been proposed that only a small fraction of total tissue K^+, in a very critical pool, is involved in the H^+ secretion process (2, 73).

The effects of Na^+-free solutions have been studied by several groups, and widely varying results have emerged. For example, Na^+-free solutions caused complete (46, 59), partial (11), or no (2, 63) reduction in H^+ secretion; the inhibitory effects could be reversed by high [K^+] in one set of experiments (11) but not in others (46). Despite these various effects on H^+ secretion, Na^+-free solutions elicited consistent decreases in I_{sc}, PD, and conductance (46, 59). These data suggest to us that H^+ secretion is not directly dependent on Na^+ but that observed effects of Na^+-free solutions are the result of secondary changes of intracellular milieu (e.g. [K^+], [Ca^{2+}], [HCO_3^-], or pH). On the other hand, current-generating Cl^- transport mechanisms may be directly coupled to the movements of Na^+ across the serosal membrane (see below).

The gastric mucosa normally produces HCO_3^- from the OH^- (consequence of H^+ secretion) and CO_2. Experiments utilizing acetazolamide suggest that the action of carbonic anhydrase is vital for the neutralization of this OH^- and consequent maintenance of cell function and pH in mammalian tissues (12, 44). The uncatalyzed rate of CO_2 hydration is adequate to support lower secretory rates of amphibian gastric mucosa (12). CO_2 requirements have been studied in detail. Maximal secretory rates require a source of exogenous CO_2 (12) or certain specialized conditions (low serosal pH) for a "recycling" of the CO_2 available from respiration (61, 66).

The oxyntic cell eliminates the excess HCO_3^- across the serosal membrane and at the same time accumulates Cl^- to accompany secreted H^+ ions. Rehm has offered convincing evidence for a neutral, nonconductive exchange of HCO_3^- for Cl^- across the serosal membrane (53). This system may be similar to the Cl^--HCO_3^- exchange system of red cells: The well known inhibitors SITS and furosemide (9) cause substantial (30–60%) decreases in H^+ secretion when added to the serosal (but not the mucosal) solution of frog gastric mucosa (E. C. Manning, W. L. McLennan, T. E. Machen, in preparation).

In addition to Cl^--HCO_3^- exchange at the serosal membrane of oxyntic cells, recent evidence indicates that the surface epithelial cells are also capable of transporting HCO_3^- at low ($\leq$10% of maximal H^+ rates) but significant rates (16). In this case, though, HCO_3^- transport is a secretory process, not absorptive, and is sensitive to [HCO_3^-] in the serosal solution (16). Since this HCO_3^- secretion does not generate any I_{sc}, it may be that a HCO_3^--Cl^- exchanger is operable in the surface cells.

H^+ secretion is dependent on the presence of Cl^- in the serosal solution (13, 18), and the Cl^- that accompanies H^+ secretion has been termed "acidic Cl^-". Replacement of Cl^- with more impermeant anions, such as sulfate or isethionate, causes H^+ secretion to decrease by 75% or more (18). This dependency on serosal Cl^- or other halides occurs in a manner resembling Michaelis-Menten kinetics (13), with an apparent $K_{1/2}$ for stimulation of H^+ secretion of about 5 mM Cl^- (13, 18). Since [Cl^-] in the epithelial cells is less than in the serosal solution (33), activation of H^+ secretion at the secretory membrane may occur with a $K_{1/2}$ of 1 mM Cl^- or less.

Electrogenic or Electroneutral H^+ Secretion?

The H^+ secretion mechanism has some characteristics of relatively tight coupling between H^+ and Cl^- transport, perhaps even an *electroneutral* system. For example, during open circuit conditions, equivalent changes of H^+ and Cl^- transport are associated with altered secretory states (stimulation or inhibition) in frog mucosa; neither Na^+ nor K^+ is required in the mucosal fluid. During short-circuit current conditions, stimulation of resting piglet gastric mucosa elicited roughly equivalent increases in H^+ and Cl^- secretion and Cl^--free serosal solutions reduced H^+ secretion to zero (24).

However, the H^+ mechanism also has characteristics of an *electrogenic* pump (i.e. one capable of generating a net current). Passing positive current from serosa to mucosa across dog stomach flap (51) and frog gastric mucosa (10) increased H^+ secretion, while current in the opposite direction reduced secretion. Also, changes in H^+ secretion are usually accompanied by proportional changes in tissue conductance (52, 54). Finally, in Cl^--free solutions, changes in H^+ secretion, as altered by metabolic inhibition, are linearly related to changes in transepithelial PD and resistance (52). Rehm has shown that such a relationship is expected if the inhibitors changed only the resistance and/or electromotive force (emf) of an electrogenic H^+ secretory mechanism (52).

Because the existing experiments are ambiguous, the debate continues over whether the process is electroneutral or electrogenic. More extensive discussion can be found elsewhere (54). At present we conclude that the H^+ secretion mechanism appears to operate in both electroneutral *and* electrogenic modes, depending on the bathing solution employed. A model consistent with the available data is presented below.

"Nonacidic" Cl^- Secretion

In addition to the Cl^- that accompanies H^+ secretion, gastric mucosa can secrete Cl^- in excess of H^+ (36), and Cl^- transport certainly occurs during resting conditions (23, 24, 46). It has been assumed until recently that this active Cl^- secretion involves an electrogenic mechanism, presumably driven by ATP, at the mucosal membrane of gastric epithelial cells (e.g. 17, 18, 33, 62) and that Cl^- is supplied to this apical "pump" by a passive leak from the serosal solution into the cells. However, a number of observations do not fit easily with this model of active Cl^- secretion. For example, no "Cl^- transport enzyme" (e.g. ATPase) has yet been identified in gastric cell fractions. Also, chemical and radioisotopic techniques suggest that [Cl^-] in gastric cells is 30–40 mM (33), and these concentrations are 4–10-fold higher than predicted for passive Cl^- distribution across the serosal membrane (72). High internal [Cl^-] implies an energy-requiring step of Cl^- transport at the serosal membrane. Finally, ouabain, the well-known inhibitor of Na^+,K^+-ATPase, inhibits Cl^- transport (44).

Recent experiments have emphasized the dependency of Cl^- secretion on [Na^+] in the serosal solution (46). When Na^+ was removed from the serosal Ringer's solution of resting frog gastric mucosa, net Cl^- secretion rapidly decreased to zero. This Na^+-free effect was rapidly reversible, even ater 1 hr, so that inhibition did not appear to be caused by simple metabolic inhibition. As [Na^+] was increased in steps back to Ringer's, Cl^- transport also increased in steps back to control levels.

To explain all these data it has been proposed that active Cl^- secretion is generated by a Na^+-dependent step at the *serosal* membrane and that movement of Cl^- across the mucosal membrane into the lumen is passive, down an electrochemical gradient (46). Similar models have been invoked to explain Na^+-dependent anion secretion in other epithelia (27), and one common mechanism may underlie all of these Cl^- secretion systems.

Na^+ Absorption

In mammalian (45) and reptilian (32) preparations, active Na^+ transport is a consistent finding, and a residual Na^+ absorption has even been observed in hypoxic frog gastric mucosa (15). All cells of the gastric epithelium probably have a serosally oriented Na^+ pump at the basolateral membrane, and most of the net active Na^+ absorption is likely accomplished by the surface epithelial cells (44). There are many similarities between the Na^+ transport process in the stomach and that observed in more "classical" Na^+ transport preparations. Thus amiloride specifically inhibits gastric Na^+ transport, with an associated decrease in I_{sc} and transepithelial conductance; ouabain and K^+-free solution reduce Na^+ transport to zero (45).

Given the operation of a Na^+ pump at one epithelial cell surface, the permeability characteristics of the other membrane would serve to regulate whether the system would function in net Na^+ transport or operate as a pump-leak to maintain cellular ionic milieu. In the case of frog stomach, where the apical membrane exhibits very low permeability to Na^+ (46), net Na^+ transport is minimal; perhaps hypoxia causes an increase in Na^+ permeability, thereby allowing access to the Na^+-K^+ pump. For those species where a significant transepithelial Na^+ transport occurs, Na^+ enters the cell via an amiloride-sensitive conductive channel. The Na^+ channel is also blocked by H^+ (45); thus during conditions of low luminal pH, net Na^+ transport is similarly reduced.

ISOLATED MEMBRANE STUDIES

Studies with membrane systems isolated from gastric mucosa have made exciting contributions to the search for the gastric H^+ pump. Kasbekar & Durbin (38) first showed a gastric ATPase with characteristics quite distinct from the Na^+, K^+-ATPase. However, the HCO_3^--stimulated ATPase identified by them and studied further by others (58) has been shown to be largely a mitochondrial contaminating enzyme (28, 71).

K^+-Stimulated ATPase

In a relatively purified preparation of rabbit gastric microsomes, Forte et al (19) observed abundant K^+-stimulated phosphatase activity that was later shown by this group to be a partial reaction for the gastric K^+-stimulated ATPase (20, 28). Interest in the gastric K^+-stimulated ATPase has recently intensified since this enzyme system has been implicated in the process of H^+ secretion. In the developing tadpole stomach, HCl secretion occurs concomitantly with proliferation of the oxyntic cell tubulovesicular system and the appearance of K^+-stimulated phosphatase activity (23, 43). The enzyme system is abundant and peculiar to the acid-secreting portion of gastric mucosa (21). Immunocytochemical studies have localized the enzyme to oxyntic cells (57). Enzyme activity is directly associated with a H^+ pump in the isolated gastric membrane vesicles (see below).

K^+-stimulated ATPase activity is associated with a very light fraction of gastric microsomes prepared by density gradient centrifugation (20, 28) or further purified by free flow electrophoresis (7). In isolation these membranes assume a vesicular form, and freeze fracture images of the vesicles show a highly asymmetric distribution of membrane-associated particles with a general morphological organization similar to that seen for the tubulovesicles of the oxyntic cells (5, 41).

K^+-stimulated ATPase activity of hog gastric microsomes is stimulated 2–5-fold by the addition of K^+ ionophores, e.g. valinomycin, gramidicin, and nigericin (20, 29). Other cations substitute for K^+ with the selectivity $Tl^+ > K^+ > Rb^+ > NH_4^+ > Cs^+$; neither Na^+ nor Li^+ stimulates ATPase activity (21, 50). Procedures that tend to disrupt vesicular integrity enhance the observed stimulation by K^+ while eliminating the stimulating effect of ionophores (29). These observations suggest some internal site for K^+-activation.

The gastric K^+-stimulated ATPase is a complex enzyme whose activity involves several definable steps. ATP is bound to the enzymic site for the transfer of the γ-phosphate through a Mg^{2+}-dependent kinase reaction (50). The resulting phosphoprotein is a high-turnover intermediate whose hydrolysis (phosphatase activity) is stimulated by K^+. The phosphorylated protein is an acid-stable, acyl phosphate complex, probably involving aspartyl or glutamyl residues (50). The K^+-stimulated ATPase, as judged by migration of the phosphointermediate on gel electrophoresis, is a 90,000–100,000 M_r peptide (21, 55). Assuming one phosphate bound per enzyme and that the conditions for assay have preserved the total intermediate, we estimate from data of Ray & Forte (50) that the K^+-ATPase represents at least 10–20% of the total microsomal protein.

H^+ Transport by Gastric Vesicles

Gastric vesicles containing K^+-stimulated ATPase were first shown by Lee, Simpson & Scholes to be capable of H^+ transport (42). In the presence of ATP, Mg^{2+}, and K^+ the bulk medium became alkaline, while the vesicular interior accumulated H^+. They proposed that a H^+/K^+ exchange pump was driven by the K^+-ATPase. Sachs and his co-workers extended these observations in a series of more definitive studies showing the H^+/K^+ exchange mechanism and its correlation to the gastric ATPase (7, 56, 57). For instance, ATPase-dependent efflux of $^{86}Rb^+$ (as K^+ substitute) from gastric vesicles roughly paralleled H^+ uptake. Use of fluorescence intensity of 8-anilinonaphthalene-1-sulfonate (ANS) and the distribution of radiolabeled SCN^- as indexes of membrane potential led to the conclusion that the vesicular H^+/K^+ pump is electroneutral (i.e. 1:1 exchange). Any observed membrane potentials were thought to result from ion gradients and induced conductance pathways, e.g. treatment with valinomycin (56). An intravesicular pH of about 1.7 was estimated, not accounting for internal buffering power (7, 56).

These studies of gastric vesicular H^+ transport employed the relatively insensitive pH electrode method, which monitors changes in the bulk-medium pH. Much more sensitive assays of the development and magnitude of transvesicular pH gradients have monitored the distribution of fluorescent amines, such as acridine orange and 9-aminoacridine (40, 41). With these probes a maximum ATP-generated gradient of about 4 pH units was measured [i.e. the lowest intravesicular pH was about 2.5 (40)].

Both the pH electrode technique and the use of fluorescent amine probes have provided a current picture of the gastric vesicular H^+ pump: (*a*) K^+ is required at some intravesicular or intramembranous site; Mg^{2+} and ATP have external sites, activating H^+ uptake in exchange for K^+ efflux (40, 57). (*b*) Vesicular permeability to K^+ is ordinarily rather low; thus K^+ entry for activation requires either long periods of K^+ preincubation or the addition of a K^+ ionophore—e.g. valinomycin (22, 40). (*c*) The rate of K^+ entry, and hence of H^+ uptake and ATP utilization, is limited by the rate of anion permeation, with the sequence $NO_3^- > Br^- > Cl^- > I^- \gg$ acetate $\approx$ isethionate (41). (*d*) An induced increase in both H^+ and K^+ permeability (e.g. valinomycin plus protonophore or the K^+/H^+ exchange ionophore, nigericin) prevents or immediately abolishes the vesicular pH gradient and relaxes the ATPase requirement for permeable anions (41). In this case the observed stimulation of K^+-ATPase represents an "uncoupled" rate, where ATP hydrolysis is nonproductive in terms of H^+ gradient formation. A schematic representation of the vesicular H^+/K^+ pump and passive permeability pathways is shown in Figure 1 as a pump-leak model. This pump-leak system has been more formally analyzed using Nernst-Planck conditions for ion permeability pathways (H^+, K^+, and anion) and Michaelis-Menten kinetics for the H^+/K^+ pump (41).

Limitations in Applying Isolated Membrane Studies to Intact Secretory Process

Many characteristics of the gastric vesicular K^+-ATPase and H^+ pump suggest its primary role in the fundamental gastric acid secretory machinery. However, a number of problems and questions must still be addressed before such a conclusion can be reached unequivocally:

1. *Maximum vesicular pH gradient (ΔpH).* Is the vesicular pump incapable of generating the maximum ΔpH required for gastric H^+ secretion (i.e. $\Delta pH > 10^6$) or are the isolated vesicles simply too leaky to maintain the pH? Given the conditions of intact gastric tissue, sufficient energy is available to account for H^+ production via ATP hydrolysis if the stoichi-

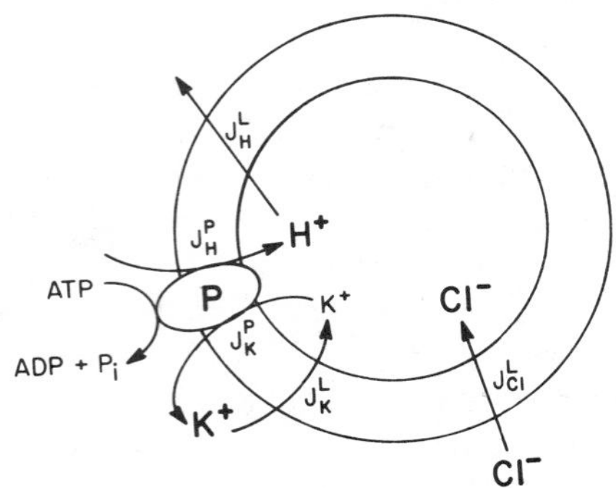

Figure 1 Schematic accounting of ion movements across gastric microsomal vesicles. The J's are ion fluxes with the superscript designating pump flux (P) or leak pathway (L). The model consists of an ATP-driven H^+/K^+ exchange pump, in accord with earlier work (e.g. 40, 42, 56), and the passive leak pathways for the principal ions, H^+, K^+, and Cl^-. [Reproduced from (41), where a more formal analysis of ion movements is given]

ometry at maximum acidity were one H^+ : one ATP (44). Proposed models (48, 60) whereby redox systems are combined with the gastric K^+-ATPase can achieve higher H^+/ATP ratios; however, the appropriate extramitochondrial redox components have yet to be identified. It is apparent that isolated gastric vesicles are very leaky to H^+ (40, 41, 56), which may well account for the inability to produce an intravesicular pH below 2.5. A high proton leak rate is difficult to reconcile with a membrane interface that must sustain large ΔpH; some artifact of H^+ conductance may be introduced in the isolation procedure.

2. *The source of luminal K^+ for the H^+/K^+ exchange pump.* The neutral H^+/K^+ exchange model suggests that K^+ availability at the luminal aspect of the apical plasma membrane would be critical and rate-limiting to gastric H^+ secretion. However, in intact tissue H^+ secretion is not normally dependent on $[K^+]$ in the mucosal solution.

3. *Electrogenicity of the H^+ pump.* For frog gastric mucosa bathed in Cl^--free solutions, passage of electric current from serosa to mucosa was quantitatively more effective in increasing H^+ secretion than elevating mucosal $[K^+]$; Rehm & Sanders (54) reasoned that these data are more consistent with an electrogenic H^+ pump (limited by the return limb of the circuit) than with a neutral H^+/K^+ forced-exchange pump.

Evaluation of the electrical properties of functionally active gastric vesicles is of great importance for detailed interpretation of transport events, but our picture at present is incomplete. Evidence is available to support both a neutral (56) and an electrogenic (31) vesicular H^+ pump. Goodall & Sachs have suggested a specific membrane model that would allow variable electrogenic or neutral exchange behavior depending on chemical interconversions within the ATPase (31, 60).

4. *Elements for control and regulation of the H^+ pump.* The pathways by which secretory control is maintained over gastric ion transport are not known precisely. The coupling process for activation of H^+ secretion has two possible general forms. The first mechanism, called "fusion-activation," would simply require fusion of tubulovesicles to apical plasma membrane for net HCl secretion. In this proposal the H^+ pump is fully "activated" in the resting oxyntic cell; but because the tubulovesicular system is not confluent with the apical surface, the electrochemical gradient for H^+ is maintained in equilibrium with the coupled driving reaction—i.e. ATP $\rightleftharpoons$ ADP + P_i (22, 44). The fusion process would provide a pathway for relaxation of the H^+ gradient, thereby allowing net flow of energy into the new steady secretory state. Such a mechanism predicts regions of high H^+ electrochemical activity (tubulovesicles) consistent with observations of aminopyrine uptake into resting gastric glands (3).

The alternative mechanism requires that some specific functional aspect of the pump be activated by the secretagogue-induced reaction sequence—i.e. "pump-activation." Chemical activators for the gastric ATPase have been reported. In fact, K^+-ionophores serve as effective activators; however, we do not know whether a natural counterpart exists to facilitate the local supply and recycling of K^+. Ca^{2+} ($\approx$10 μm) has been reported to produce stimulatory effects on gastric K^+-ATPase similar to those of gramicidin (47). Ray has found that a soluble proteic component of rabbit gastric homogenates will serve to stimulate K^+-phosphatase and K^+-ATPase activities (49). Such studies must be pursued in greater depth to provide specific mechanistic detail for the putative activation processes. Whether the initiation of HCl secretion occurs by pump-activation, fusion-activation, or some combination of events, represents a problem of immediate importance in elucidating the biochemical basis for control and regulation.

SUMMARY

Significant advances in the study of gastric secretory systems have realigned our views regarding the specific modes of transport of both H^+ and Cl^-. We summarize one conception of the ion transporting gastric epithelium in Figure 2. In this schematic represenation, the ATP-driven H^+/K^+ exchange pump is shown at the apical surface. To fit with observations made with intact and isolated membrane preparations the specific detail postulates a recycling of K^+ between cytoplasm and membrane phase to supply the H^+/K^+ pump. The role for Cl at the apical surface would be to provide for the return limb of the circuit, thus permitting net flow of HCl.

Cl^- movement at the serosal surface would occur by (*a*) Cl^-/HCO_3^- exchange, (*b*) coupled NaCl entry, and (*c*) a Cl^- conductive pathway (not shown). All of these would not necessarily be on the same cell type of the histologically complex gastric epithelium.

The model, clearly an oversimplified view, serves to highlight important questions for future research. Details for the recycling of K^+, and the distinctive contributions of H^+, K^+, and Cl^- to the apical cell membrane potential, must be established. The relative contributions of fusion-activation and pump-activation toward the stimulation of secretion must be defined. The nature of the interdependency between Na^+ and Cl^- movements must be elucidated further. This will require analysis of flux characteristics and their electrochemical driving forces. The study of gastric HCl secretion can now be approached in the context of modern membrane biology.

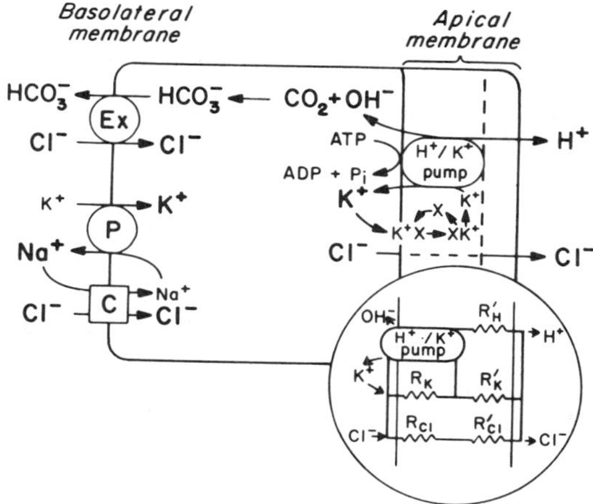

Figure 2 Schematic representation of gastric epithelial transport processes. An ATP-driven H^+/K^+ exchange pump is shown at the apical membrane. In order to fit with observed conditions for K^+ activation in both intact preparations and isolated vesicles a modification from Figure 1 is proposed: that K^+ is largely recycled within the membrane phase. An ad hoc postulate is introduced whereby K^+ movement with the membrane phase is facilitated by a specific channel or carrier (X), which has not yet been identified. (Perhaps it has been removed by vesicle preparation or requires a particular activating reaction—e.g. pump activation.) The equivalent circuit, in which resistance to K^+ movement might be different in the inner and outer membrane region ($R'_K > R_K$), is shown in the inset. The recycling of K^+, coupled to the H^+/K^+ exchange, would provide the basis for an electrogenic pump that would be especially apparent in Cl^--free solutions. Cl^- at the apical surface would provide the return limb of the circuit, thus permitting the net flow of HCl, which might appear tightly coupled on open circuit. Under conditions of active HCl secretion Cl^- entry into the oxyntic cell would be provided by the neutral Cl^-/HCO_3^- exchanger (Ex) at the basolateral surface. The Na^+ pump (P) at that same surface would serve to maintain the cellular ionic milieu and K^+ balance. The Na^+ gradient, serosa to cell, could provide the driving force for moving Cl^-, via a coupled NaCl entry (C), into the cell against its electrochemical potential gradient. If the permeability of the apical membrane to Na^+ and K^+ were very low, we would not expect this system to provide significant net transepithelial ion flow; however, under short-circuit conditions there would be an associated Cl^- current. This same serosal Na^+ pump system could provide for net K^+ secretion or net Na^+ absorption, depending upon the permeability of the apical membrane to these ions. At rest the membrane potential would largely be the summation of a K^+ concentration emf across the serosal surface and a Cl^- concentration emf across the mucosal surface. When secreting HC1 there would be the additional emf associated with current flow through the H^+ and K^+ limbs at the apical surface. This highly simplified representation does not account for the different cell types of the gastric epithelium, nor for the membrane transformation known to be associated with secretion.

Literature Cited

1. Berglindh, T. 1977. Effects of common inhibitors of gastric acid secretion on secretagogue-induced respiration and aminopyrine accumulation in isolated gastric glands. *Biochim. Biophys. Acta* 464:217–33
2. Berglindh, T. 1978. The effects of K^+ and Na^+ on acid formation in isolated gastric glands. *Acta Physiol. Scand.* (Spec. Suppl.) pp. 55–68
3. Berglindh, T., Helander, H. F., Öbrink, K. J. 1976. Effects of secretagogues on oxygen consumption, aminopyrine accumulation and morphology in isolated gastric glands. *Acta Physiol. Scand.* 97:401–14
4. Bergquist, E., Öbrink, K. J. 1979. Gastrin-histamine as a normal sequence in gastric acid stimulation in rabbit. *Uppsala J. Med. Sci.* 84:145–54
5. Black, J. A., Forte, T. M., Forte, J. G. 1978. Changes in membrane-associated particle distribution in resting and stimulated oxyntic cells. *J. Cell Biol.* 79:A375 (Abstr.)
6. Black, J. W. 1973. Speculation about the nature of the antagonism between metiamide and pentagastrin. In *International Symposium on Histamine H_2-Receptor Antagonists,* ed. C. F. Wood, M. A. Simkins, pp. 219–24. London: Smith, Kline & French
7. Chang, H., Saccomani, G., Rabon, E., Schackmann, R., Sachs, G. 1977. Proton transport by gastric membrane vesicles. *Biochim. Biophys. Acta* 464: 313–27
8. Chew, C. S., Hersey, S. J. 1978. Dissociation between oxyntic cell cAMP formation and HCl secretion in bullfrog gastric mucosa. *Am. J. Physiol.* 235:E140–49
9. Cousin, J. L., Motais, R. 1976. The role of carbonic anhydrase inhibitors on anion permeability into ox red blood cells. *J. Physiol. London* 256:61–80
10. Crane, E. E., Davies, R. E., Longmuir, N. M. 1948. The effect of electric current on hydrochloric acid secretion by isolated frog gastric mucosa. *Biochem. J.* 43:321–36
11. Davenport, H. W. 1963. Sodium space and acid secretion in frog gastric mucosa. *Am. J. Physiol.* 204:214–16
12. Davies, R. E. 1948. Hydrochloric acid production by isolated gastric mucosa. *Biochem. J.* 42:609–21
13. Durbin, R. P. 1964. Anion requirements for gastric acid secretion. *J. Gen. Physiol.* 4:735–48
14. Ekblad, E. B. M., Machen, T. E., Licko, V., Rutten, M. J. 1978. Histamine, cyclic AMP and the secretory response of piglet gastric mucosa. *Acta Physiol. Scand.* (Spec. Suppl.) pp. 69–80
15. Flemstrom, G. 1971. Na^+ transport and impedence properties of the isolated frog gastric mucosa at different O_2 tensions. *Biochim. Biophys. Acta* 225: 35–45
16. Flemstrom, G. 1977. Active alkalinization by amphibian gastric fundic mucosa in vitro. *Am. J. Physiol.* 233: El–12
17. Forte, J. G. 1969. Studies on three components of Cl^- flux across isolated bullfrog gastric mucosa. *Am. J. Physiol.* 216:167–74
18. Forte, J. G., Adams, P. H., Davies, R. E. 1963. The source of the gastric mucosal potential difference. *Nature* 197:874–76
19. Forte, J. G., Forte, G. M., Saltman, P. 1967. K^+-stimulated phosphatase of microsomes from gastric mucosa. *J. Cell Physiol.* 69:293–304
20. Forte, J. G., Ganser, A., Beesley, R., Forte, T. M. 1975. Unique enzymes of purified microsomes from pig fundic mucosa. *Gastroenterology* 69:175–89
21. Forte, J. G., Ganser, A. L., Ray, T. K. 1976. The K^+-stimulated ATPase from oxyntic glands of gastric mucosa. In *Gastric Secretion,* ed. D. K. Kasbekar, G. Sachs, W. Rehm, 13:302–30. NY: Marcel Dekker
22. Forte, J. G., Lee, H. C. 1977. Gastric adenosine triphosphatases: A review of their possible role in HCl secretion. *Gastroenterology* 73:921–26
23. Forte, J. G., Limlomwongse, L., Kasbekar, D. K. 1969. Ion transport and the development of hydrogen ion secretion in the stomach of the metamorphosing bullfrog tadpole. *J. Gen. Physiol.* 54:76–95
24. Forte, J. G., Machen, T. E. 1975. Transport and electrical phenomena in resting and secreting piglet gastric mucosa. *J. Physiol. London* 244:33–51
25. Forte, T. M., Machen, T. E., Forte, J. G. 1975. Ultrastructural and physiological changes in piglet oxyntic cells during histamine stimulation and metabolic inhibition. *Gastroenterology* 69: 1208–22
26. Forte, T. M., Machen, T. E., Forte, J. G. 1977. Ultrastructural changes in oxyntic cells associated with secretory function: a membrane recycling hypothesis. *Gastroenterology* 73:941–55

27. Frizzell, R. A., Field, M., Schultz, S. G. 1979. Sodium-coupled chloride transport in epithelial tissues. *Am. J. Physiol.* 236:F1–8
28. Ganser, A. L., Forte, J. G. 1973. K^+-stimulated ATPase in purified microsomes of bullfrog oxyntic cells. *Biochim. Biophys. Acta* 307:169–80
29. Ganser, A. L., Forte, J. G. 1973. Ionophoretic stimulation of K^+-ATPase of oxyntic cell microsomes. *Biochem. Biophys. Res. Commun.* 54:690–96
30. Gardner, J. 1979. Receptors for gastrointestinal hormones. *Gastroenterology* 76:202–14
31. Goodall, M. C., Sachs, G. 1977. Reconstitution of a proton pump from gastric mucosa. *J. Membr. Biol.* 35:285–301
32. Hansen, T., Slegers, J. F. G., Bonting, S. L. 1975. Gastric acid secretion in the lizard. Ionic requirements and effects of inhibitors. *Biochim. Biophys. Acta* 382:590–608
33. Harris, J. B., Edelman, I. S. 1964. Chemical concentration gradients and electrical properties of gastric mucosa. *Am. J. Physiol.* 206:769–82
34. Harris, J. B., Nigon, K., Alonso, D. 1969. Adenosine-3'5' monophosphate; intracellular mediator for methyl xanthine stimulation of gastric secretion. *Gastroenterology* 57:377–84
35. Helander, H. F., Hirschowitz, B. I. 1972. Quantitative ultrastructural studies on gastric parietal cells. *Gastroenterology* 63:951–61
36. Hogben, C. A. M. 1955. Active transport of chloride by isolated frog gastric epithelium. Origin of the gastric mucosal potential. *Am. J. Physiol.* 180: 641–49
37. Ito, S., Schofield, G. C. 1974. Studies on the depletion and accumulation of microvilli and in the tubulovesicular compartment of mouse parietal cells in relation to gastric acid secretion. *J. Cell. Biol.* 63:364–82
38. Kasbekar, D. K., Durbin, R. P. 1965. An adenosine triphophatase from frog gastric mucosa. *Biochim. Biophys. Acta* 105:472–82
39. Kasbekar, D. K., Ridley, H. A., Forte, J. G. 1969. Pentagastrin and acetylcholine relation to histamine in H^+ secretion by gastric mucosa. *Am. J. Physiol.* 216:961–67
40. Lee, H. C., Forte, J. G. 1978. A study of H^+ transport in gastric microsomal vesicles using fluorescent probes. *Biochim. Biophys. Acta* 508:339–56
41. Lee, H. C., Breitbart, H., Berman, M., Forte, J. G. 1979. Potassium stimulated ATPase activity and H^+ transport in gastric microsomal vesicles. *Biochim. Biophys. Acta* 553:107–31
42. Lee, J., Simpson, G., Scholes, P. 1974. An ATPase from dog gastric mucosa; changes of outer pH in suspensions of membrane vesicles accompanying ATP hydrolysis. *Biochem. Biophys. Res. Commun.* 60:835–32
43. Limlomwongse, L., Forte, J. G. 1970. Developmental changes of ATPase and K^+-stimulated phosphatase in microsomes of tadpole gastric mucosa. *Am. J. Physiol.* 219:1717–22
44. Machen, T. E., Forte, J. G. 1979. Gastric secretion. In *Handbook of Transport, Vol. IVB, Transport Organs,* ed. G. Giebisch, D. C. Tosteson, H. H. Ussing. Berlin: Springer. 13:693–747
45. Machen, T. E., Silen, W., Forte, J. G. 1978. Na^+ transport by mammalian stomach. *Am. J. Physiol.* 234:228–35
46. Machen, T. E., McLennan, W. L. 1980. Na^+-dependent H^+ and Cl^- secretion in in vitro frog gastric mucosa. *Am. J. Physiol.* In press
47. Proverbio, F., Michelangeli, F. 1978. Effect of calcium on the H^+/K^+ ATPase of hog gastric microsomes. *J. Membr. Biol.* 42:301–15
48. Rabon, E. C., Sarau, H. M., Rehm, W. S., Sachs, G. 1977. Redox involvement in acid secretion in the amphibian gastric mucosa. *J. Membr. Biol.* 35:189–204
49. Ray, T. K. 1978. Gastric K^+-stimulated adenosine triphosphatase. Demonstration of an endogeneous activator. *FEBS Lett.* 92:49–52
50. Ray, T. K., Forte, J. G. 1976. Studies on the phosphorylated intermediates of a K^+-stimulated ATPase from rabbit gastric mucosa. *Biochim. Biophys. Acta* 443:451–67
51. Rehm, W. S. 1956. Effect of electric current on gastric hydrogen ion and chloride ion secretion. *Am. J. Physiol.* 185:325–31
52. Rehm, W. S., Lefevre, M. E. 1965. Effect of dinitrophenol on potential, resistance, and H^+ rate of frog stomach. *Am. J. Physiol.* 208:922–30
53. Rehm, W. S., Sanders, S. S. 1975. Implications of the neutral carrier Cl^--HCO_3^- exchange mechanism in gastric mucosa. *Ann. NY Acad. Sci.* 264:442–55
54. Rehm, W. S., Sanders, S. S. 1977. Electrical events during activation and inhibition of gastric HCl secretion. *Gastroenterology* 73:959–69

55. Saccomani, G., Shah, G., Spenney, J. G., Sachs, G. 1975. Characterization of gastric mucosal membrane. VIII. Localization of peptides by iodination and phosphorylation. *J. Biol. Chem.* 250: 4802–9
56. Sachs, G., Chang, H. H., Rabon, E., Schackmann, R., Lewin, M., Saccomani, G. 1976. A nonelectrogenic H^+ pump in plasma membranes of hog stomach. *J. Biol. Chem.* 251:7690–98
57. Sachs, G., Chang, H., Rabon, E., Schackmann, R., Sarau, H. M., Saccomani, G. 1977. Metabolic and membrane aspects of gastric H^+ transport. *Gastroenterology* 73:931–40
58. Sachs, G., Shah, G., Strych, A., Cline, G., Hirschowitz, B. I. 1972. Properties of ATPase of gastric mucosa. III. Distribution of HCO_3^--stimulated ATPase in gastric mucosa. *Biochim. Biophys. Acta* 266:625–38
59. Sachs, G., Shoemaker, R. L., Hirschowitz, B. I. 1966. Effects of sodium removal on acid secretion by frog gastric mucosa. *Proc. Soc. Exp. Biol. Med.* 123:47–52
60. Sachs, G., Spenney, J. G., Lewin, M. 1978. H^+ transport: Regulation and mechanism in gastric mucosa and membrane vesicles. *Physiol. Rev.* 58:106–73
61. Sanders, S. S., Hayne, V. B., Rehm, W. S. 1973. Normal H^+ rates in frog stomach in absence of exogenous CO_2 and a note on pH stat method. *Am. J. Physiol.* 225:1311–21
62. Sanders, S. S., Noyes, D. H., Spangler, S. G., Rehm, W. S. 1973. Demonstration of a barium-potassium antagonism on lumen side of in vitro frog stomach. *Am. J. Physiol.* 224:1254–59
63. Sanders, S. S., Pirkle, J. A., Rehm, W. S. 1978. Analysis of a Na^+ specific model for Cl^--HCO_3^- exchange in the in vitro frog gastric mucosa. *Fed. Proc.* 37:651 (Abstr.)
64. Scholes, P., Cooper, A., Jones, D., Major, J., Walters, M., Wilde, C. 1976. Characterization of an adenylate cyclase system sensitive to histamine H_2-receptor excitation in cells from dog gastric mucosa. *Agents and Actions* 6:677–82
65. Sedar, A. W. 1965. Fine structure of the stimulated oxyntic cell. *Fed. Proc.* 24:1360–67
66. Silen, W., Machen, T. E., Forte, J. G. 1975. Acid base balance in amphibian gastric mucosa. *Am. J. Physiol.* 229:721–30
67. Soll, A. H. 1978. The interaction of histamine with gastrin and carbomylcholine on oxygen uptake by isolated mammalian parietal cells. *J. Clin. Invest.* 61:381–89
68. Soll, A. H., Walsh, J. H. 1979. Regulation of gastric acid secretion. *Ann. Rev. Physiol.* 41:35–53
69. Soll, A. H., Wollin, A. 1979. Histamine and cyclic AMP in isolated canine parietal cells. *Am. J. Physiol.* In press
70. Soumarmon, A., Cheret, A. M., Lewin, M. J. M. 1977. Localization of gastrin receptors in intact isolated separated rat fundic cells. *Gastroenterology* 73:900–3
71. Soumarmon, A., Lewin, M., Cheret, A. M., Bonfils, S. 1974. Gastric HCl_3^--stimulated ATPase: evidence against its microsomal localization in rat fundus mucosa. *Biochim. Biophys. Acta* 339: 403–14
72. Spenney, J. G., Shoemaker, R. L., Sachs, G. 1974. Microelectrode studies of fundic gastric mucosa: cellular coupling and shunt conductance. *J. Membr. Biol.* 19:105–28
73. Takeguchi, N., Horikoshi, I., Hattori, M. 1977. Uptake of K^+ by frog gastric mucosa from submucosal side and acid secretory rate. *Am. J. Physiol.* 232: E294–97
74. Zalewsky, C. A., Moody, F. G. 1977. Stereological analysis of the parietal cell during acid secretion and inhibition. *Gastroenterology* 73:66–74

Ann. Rev. Physiol. 1980. 42:127–56

THE EXOCRINE PANCREAS: THE ROLE OF SECRETAGOGUES, CYCLIC NUCLEOTIDES, AND CALCIUM IN ENZYME SECRETION

❖1258

Irene Schulz and Hans H. Stolze

Max-Planck-Institut für Biophysik, Kennedyallee 70,
6000 Frankfurt am Main 70, West Germany

INTRODUCTION

This review summarizes recently acquired knowledge about early events in enzyme secretion from the exocrine pancreas. We emphasize processes that comprise (*a*) hormone-receptor interaction, (*b*) simultaneous or subsequent release of secondary messengers, such as free calcium and cyclic nucleotides, and (*c*) subsequent alterations of the cell membrane involving passive and active transport processes. These events have been investigated more thoroughly than those that govern enzyme release from the cell at the luminal cell side—i.e. the fusion of zymogen granules with the luminal cell membrane and subsequent exocytosis of proteins.

Calcium has a central role in the secretory process. It is the trigger, promoter, and modulator at different levels of events leading to enzyme secretion. Determination of single steps in cellular events studied at the cellular and subcellular levels is probably arbitrary and academic. When the cell is stimulated to secrete, multiple responses with interwoven relations lead both to forward-directed events, which result in enzyme release, and to backward-directed events, which modify (either inhibit or enhance) the original stimulus. Such regulatory mechanisms have been discussed as "open-loop" and "closed-loop" control systems (116); they comprise the mutual influences of processes at the cell membrane and within the cell. Isolated systems developed during the past decade—e.g. the artificially perfused or superfused pancreas (18, 126) and isolated cells (2) and mem-

0066-4278/80/0315-0127$01.00

brane vesicles (99)—make it possible to recognize physiological mechanisms that could not be investigated directly with classical in vivo procedures.

We do not review here the literature on synthesis, storage, intracellular transport, and exocytosis of enzymes (see 16, 71, 95), nor do we discuss the mechanism of bicarbonate and fluid secretion. The latter takes place in the pancreatic duct system and its cellular basis is quite different from enzyme secretion (reviewed in 135).

SECRETAGOGUES OF ENZYME SECRETION

Physiological stimulants of enzyme secretion from the acini are the neurotransmitter acetylcholine and the oligopeptide pancreozymin (CCK-PZ). Recently, butyryl derivatives of guanosine 3',5'-monophosphate (cGMP) have been found to antagonize competitively the action of pancreozymin (103a, 107b). Atropine blocks the response to acetylcholine but not to pancreozymin. Gastrin, which consists of 17 amino acids and is similar to pancreozymin in its C-terminal amino acid sequence (Figure 1), also stimulates enzyme secretion (55). Among the variety of peptidic secretagogues described recently, some are similar in structure and amino acid sequence to pancreozymin and others are totally different (Figure 1). Like pancreozymin and acetylcholine (26), they stimulate enzyme secretion and increase cellular cGMP and calcium efflux from pancreatic fragments and dispersed acinar cells (Table 1) (37, 93). The pancreozymin-like peptides include the decapeptide caerulein, isolated from the skin of the Australian amphibian *Hyla caerulea* (3). The secretagogues with structures unlike that of pancreozymin include (*a*) bombesin, litorin, and physalaemin, which are peptides extracted and purified from amphibian skin, and (*b*) eledoisin, which has been isolated from the posterior salivary gland of a Mediterranean octopod (for review see 44, 45). Moreover, secretin and vasoactive intestinal polypeptide (VIP), which exert their primary actions on fluid secretion in the pancreatic duct system, have been shown to stimulate amylase release in some animal species (34, 52). They increase cellular adenosine 3',5'-monophosphate (cAMP) (120) but do not change calcium fluxes or cellular cGMP levels (Table 2) (26, 51). Furthermore, they potentiate the response of pancreozymin, the C-terminal octapeptide of pancreozymin-cholestystokinin (CCK-OP), acetylcholine (carbamylcholine), and dibutyryl cyclic GMP (dbcGMP) (52).

The observations that the secretin effect on fluid secretion can be potentiated by pancreozymin, and that the pancreozymin effect on enzyme secretion is potentiated by secretin have led to the assumption that the hormones interact closely in the same cell (48, 55b).

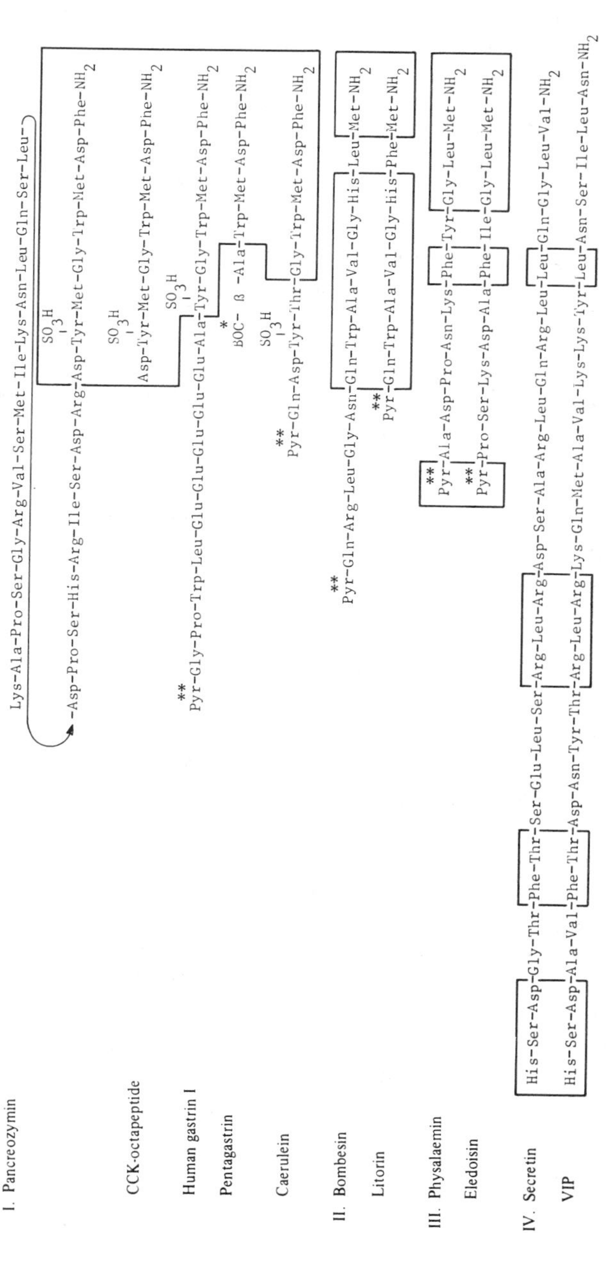

Figure 1 **Amino acid sequence for pancreatic secretagogues of enzyme secretion. BOC* = tert-butyloxycarbonyl residue; Pyr** = pyroglutamyl residue.**

Table 1 Effects of secretagogues of enzyme secretion on adenylate cyclase activity (AC) in isolated membranes, on the intracellular cAMP and cGMP levels, and on Ca^{2+} fluxes of pancreatic acinar cells.

Secretagogue	AC	cAMP level	cGMP level	Ca^{2+} fluxes
1. Pancreozymin (and caerulein, CCK-OP)	increases	no effect	increases	increases
2. Acetylcholine	no effect	no effect	increases	increases
3. Bombesin, litorin	no effect	no effect	increases	increases
4. Eledoisin, physalaemin	no effect	no effect	increases	increases
5. Secretin and VIP	increases	increases	no effect	no effect

Secretagogues of enzyme secretion to which a physiological action cannot be ascribed are the calcium ionophore A 23187 (43) and the compounds catharanthine (146) and phorbol myristate acetate (5). These substances have been used to obtain insight into the mechanism of enzyme secretion since they seem to act by changing intracellular Ca^{2+} levels.

STUDIES OF HORMONE-BINDING AND THE RELATION BETWEEN HORMONE STRUCTURE AND ACTIVITY

Pancreozymin, Caerulein

The specific binding of the ^{3}H-octapeptide of pancreozymin to a plasma membrane fraction from cat pancreas correlated closely with the dose-response curve for adenylate cyclase activity. Half-maximal binding of the hormone occurred at a concentration of 3×10^{-8} M, whereas the apparent K_m value for adenylate cyclase activation was 2×10^{-8} M (101). Pentagastrin, a weak agonist of adenylate cyclase activity (79, 121), competed with the ^{3}H-octapeptide of pancreozymin for binding sites (101) and inhibited the effect of pancreozymin on the adenylate cyclase activity at high concentrations (79). These effects can be explained by the C-terminal tetrapeptide common to pentagastrin, pancreozymin, and the octapeptide molecule. In contrast, secretagogues of pancreatic fluid secretion, secretin and VIP, were ineffective in displacing the ^{3}H-octapeptide (101).

A similar conclusion about the nature of the pancreozymin receptor was derived from data on the interaction of the pancreozymin analog caerulein with the rat pancreas (27, 36, 121). The apparent K_d value of 1.8×10^{-8} M for binding of caerulein to a high-affinity site on pancreatic plasma membranes (36) corresponded well to that for binding of CCK-OP (101). CCK-OP also displaced ^{3}H-caerulein from its binding site. Moreover, both secretagogues stimulated adenylate cyclase in isolated membranes and stimulated $^{45}Ca^{2+}$ efflux and amylase release from dispersed acinar cells with the same potency and efficacy (121). Taken together these findings suggest that both secretagogues act on the same receptor. In addition, the binding of ^{3}H-caerulein is characterized by a negative cooperativity. Thus in acinar cells a single class of caerulein binding sites may exist in two states: one with high affinity and another with low affinity. The high-affinity state of the receptor is interpreted to be associated with a calcium ionophore-like effector system, whereas the low-affinity state of the receptor (resulting from a high degree of caerulein occupancy) may be necessary for full adenylate cyclase activation. Using caerulein analogs, these authors concluded (121) that the C-terminal tetrapeptide of caerulein (Table 1) is sufficient for binding and for evoking such biological activities as calcium outflux from isolated acinar cells, amylase secretion, and adenylate cyclase activity.

However, the presence of a tyrosyl sulfated residue in position 7 from the C-terminal end increases the affinity for the peptide substantially and is necessary for full activation of adenylate cyclase activity. This observation is in agreement with the finding (89) that, in addition to sulfated tyrosine in the proper position, full adenylate cyclase activation requires the presence of the negatively charged aspartic acid in position 2 from the C-terminal end of CCK-OP. If aspartic acid was replaced by alanine (alanine^{32} CCK-OP) only a poor agonist efficacy of adenylate cyclase activity remained. CCK-OP stimulated adenylate cyclase in homogenates of acinar cells from guinea pig pancreas; this effect, however, was strongly inhibited by Ala^{32} CCK-OP.

Bombesin, Litorin, Physalaemin, Eledoisin

In a study on binding characteristics of nonmammalian peptides using ^{125}I-labelled [Tyr^{4}]-bombesin in which leucine in position 4 was replaced by thyrosine, only one class of receptors that interacts with [Tyr^{4}]-bombesin, bombesin, and litorin was found on dispersed acini from guinea pig pancreas (74). There was a close correlation between the relative potency of bombesin and litorin for inhibition of [Tyr^{4}]-bombesin binding and that for stimulation of amylase secretion. For a given peptide, however, a 10-fold higher concentration was required for half-maximal inhibition of binding than for half-maximal stimulation of amylase secretion, calcium outflux, or cGMP accumulation. At concentrations higher than 0.1 M, pancreozymin and caerulein each caused a small reduction in binding of labelled [Tyr^{4}]-bombesin. Since eledoisin, physalaemin, gastrin, carbachol, secretin, and VIP did not interact with bombesin binding sites, acinar cells may possess a class of receptors specific for bombesin and litorin.

Insulin

The finding of a high- and a low-affinity site for insulin in binding studies using biologically active ^{125}I-insulin suggests that insulin may directly regulate specific functions in the exocrine pancreas (84). Studies employing either intact, perfused, or fragmented pancreas have suggested that insulin may regulate glucose oxidation (30) and amylase secretion and synthesis (77, 138). Uptake of the glucose analog 2-deoxy-D-glucose was stimulated by insulin in isolated acini (84). However, the relation of insulin binding to stimulus-secretion coupling is not clear yet.

Secretin and VIP

In isolated acinar cells, binding of ^{125}I-secretin and ^{125}I-VIP (a hormone similar to secretin in structure and function) and stimulation of adenylate cyclase are intimately correlated (25, 100). The dissociation constant of secretin binding (3.7×10^{-9} M) was found to be in the same concentration range as the apparent K_m value for adenylate cyclase stimulation (8.4×10^{-9} M) in cell membranes from cat pancreas (100). Since acinar cells make up about 95% of total tissue, the secretin binding in these studies can be assumed to be located on acinar cells.

Data on ^{125}I-VIP binding on isolated acinar cells demonstrate two classes of receptors that interact with both VIP and secretin. One receptor has a high affinity for VIP and a low affinity for secretin. The other receptor has a low affinity for VIP and a high affinity for secretin (25). The half-maximal secretin concentration for VIP displacement from its low-affinity site (high-affinity secretin site) compares very well with the secretin binding data in isolated membranes (100). Compared to the above-described K_m value of secretin for adenylate cyclase stimulation in acinar cells, half-maximal secretin concentration for adenylate cyclase stimulation in *duct cells* is lower (8×10^{-10} M) (101). This finding may reflect the higher secretin sensitivity of the bicarbonate-secreting duct cells, which require 3×10^{-10} M of secretin for half-maximal stimulation of bicarbonate and fluid secretion in the intact organ (149).

Further insight into the nature of receptor complexes came from studies with synthetic structural analogs of both secretin and VIP (102, 149). Three secretin analogs were used (see Figure 1): (*a*) glucagon-secretin (aspartic acid in position 3 was exchanged for glutamic acid, which yielded the same 1–5 amino acid sequence as in glucagon); (*b*) VIP-secretin (exchange of the amino acids in positions 4 and 5 of secretin for alanine and valine resulted in the 1–5 sequence of VIP); and (*c*) GIP-secretin (exchange of the 1–3 amino acids of secretin for tyrosine, alanine, and glutamic acid produced the 1–4 sequence of the gastric inhibitor protein). All three secretin analogs were assayed for their potency in stimulating adenylate cyclase in isolated pancreatic plasma membranes and in evoking fluid secretion in the artificially perfused organ (102, 149). The results showed that replacement of the hydrophilic dipeptide sequence glycyl-threonine in positions 4–5 by the hydrophobic alanyl-valine sequence in VIP-secretin (analog *b*) reduced the biological activity only slightly. Substitution in GIP-secretin (analog *c*) of the hydrophilic and basic histidyl-serine portion by the more lipophilic and slightly more acid tyrosyl-alanine sequence, with concomitant exchange of aspartic acid in position 3 for its higher homolog glutamic acid, decreased strongly the ability to stimulate both adenylate cyclase and secretion of fluid. Simply substituting the side-chain carboxylate anion of aspartic acid in position 3 of secretin with the neutral and less hydrophobic carboxamide of glutamine (glucagon-secretin) resulted in a remarkable loss of biological activity—i.e. the K_m value decreased by a factor of 10. Similar studies (49) used four secretin analogs, each with tyrosine instead of leucine in position 10. In one of these analogs glycine in position 4 had been exchanged for alanine; in two others aspartic acid in position 3 had been replaced by either glutamic acid or glutamine. These analogs were tested for their ability to interact with the high-affinity secretin receptor to increase cellular accumulation of cAMP in dispersed acinar cells. In terms of the apparent receptor affinity, the experiments established the following order: Tyr^{10}-secretin > $Ala^{4}Tyr^{10}$-secretin > $Glu^{3}Tyr^{10}$-secretin = $Gln^{3}Tyr^{10}$-secretin.

Taken together these findings indicate that the carboxylic group of aspartic acid (position 3) may be critically involved in the hormone-receptor binding process of secretin and possibly VIP. In addition, Bodanszky's finding that deletion of histidine in position 1 of secretin causes almost complete loss of activity (14) indicates that for the maximum receptor affinity and biological activity the full 5-unit sequence of the first amino acids with position 3 occupied by the carboxyl side-chain of the aspartyl residue is required. A secretin fragment missing the first four amino acids (5–27 secretin) is also recognized by secretin and VIP receptors (25, 50, 54); however, it stimulates much less cAMP production in pancreatic acini (54) (only 2% of that stimulated by secretin) and little pancreatic fluid secretion (91).

In summary, binding studies with secretagogues whose relation with stimulus-secretion coupling has been established, have demonstrated the presence of different classes of binding sites on pancreatic acinar cells: (*a*) the receptor of the pancreozymin family, which interacts with CCK-OP and with the decapeptide caerulein at higher affinity than with the physiological pancreozymin containing 33 amino acids; it has a low affinity for pentagastrin, which has the same C-terminal tetrapeptide as pancreozymin; (*b*) the single class of receptors that recognizes bombesin and litorin; (*c*) the secretin receptor with high affinity for secretin and low affinity for its homolog, VIP; and (*d*) the VIP receptor with a high affinity for VIP and a low affinity for secretin. The binding characteristics of other secretagogues —e.g. (*e*) acetylcholine to its muscarinic receptor, and (*f*) the amphibian peptides eledoisin and physalaemin—have not been established yet. Although insulin binds to acini, evidence for its function in enzyme secretion is weak.

HORMONE RECEPTORS AND THEIR RELATION TO ADENYLATE CYCLASE

The first event in a hormone's action is its binding to a specific receptor at the cell surface. In many cases this involves activation of an adenylate cyclase at the plasma membrane (122). This enzyme is viewed as a distinct protein at the inner side of the plasma membrane (123), while the receptor proteins are thought to float within the outer leaflet of lipid bilayer that forms the surface cell membrane (28, 29). The "transduction" or "coupling process" that translates hormone-to-receptor binding into activation of adenylate cyclase was illuminated by the discovery in adenylate cyclase systems of a component that binds guanosine triphosphate (GTP) (107a, 124, 125). Hormonal occupation of receptors does not lead to activation of adenylate cyclase unless this nucleotide regulatory component is present and occupied by GTP (81, 124). The view that GTP is hydrolyzed by a GTPase associated with the GTP binding component was supported by the finding that analogs of GTP that are poor substrates for GTPase yield a persistent state of adenylate cyclase activity (19, 88, 139). A model for the role of guanyl nucleotides in activation by hormones (118) involves three states in which a low-activity adenylate cyclase is converted to a higher activity state by either GTP or the analog guanylyl imidodiphosphate [Gpp(NH)p]. Transition to the highest activity state is accelerated by association with the hormone-receptor complex. In the absence of hormone the conversion to the highest activity state is a slow process.

A similar mechanism for adenylate cyclase activation has been found for the pancreas (33, 142). GTP and particularly Gpp(NH)p stimulate pancreatic adenylate cyclase activity. The stimulatory effect of the GTP analog was higher than that of fluoride, an ubiquitous activator of membrane-bound adenylate cyclases in animal cells (104), and higher than the effects of secretin or the octapeptide of pancreozymin. Gpp(HN)p in combination with secretin, with CCK-OP, or with both hormones either had the same effect as Gpp(NH)p alone (33) or was twice as potent (142). Since cholera toxin inhibits the breakdown of GTP bound to the regulatory protein (19), its effect on pancreatic function is of special interest. In the perfused pancreas it activates adenylate cyclase with a rise of the intracellular cAMP level but does not stimulate enzyme secretion in cat and rat (80, 137). In dispersed acini from guinea pig pancreas, however, cholera toxin increases cellular cAMP and amylase release; half-maximal concentrations of cholera toxin correlate closely with the effect on both cAMP level and amylase release (53). These results should be expected since both secretin and VIP also increase cellular cAMP and stimulate enzyme secretion (52, 120). Furthermore, amylase release from guinea pig pancreas can be increased by dbcAMP (52), which suggests that the effect of secretin and VIP on amylase release is mediated by cAMP. This conclusion has also been derived by correlating secretin-stimulated adenylate cyclase activity and secretin-evoked enzyme secretion in various animal species (34).

POSSIBLE ROLE OF CYCLIC NUCLEOTIDES

Although cyclic nucleotides have often been implicated as intracellular mediators of enzyme secretion, the evidence for a direct role of these substances in stimulus-secretion coupling is weak.

Stimulation of enzyme secretion by pancreozymin or its analogs or by bombesin, litorin, physalaemin, or eledoisin is accompanied by a rise of intracellular cGMP but not of cAMP (26, 37, 93). In cells that release amylase in response to secretin or VIP (52), however, increased levels of cAMP (120) but not of cGMP (26) have been observed. Enzyme secretion is poorly elicited by cyclic nucleotides or their dibutyryl or 8-bromo derivatives (for review see 16). However, the effect of cyclic nucleotide derivatives on enzyme secretion is potentiated when they are given together with calcium (58, 133) or when dbcAMP is given together with either CCK-OP or carbamylcholine (52, 58). Known actions of pancreozymin and acetylcholine—e.g. Ca^{2+} release from intracellular stores (51, 117, 140), or depolarization of the acinar cell membrane (105)—are not mimicked by cyclic nucleotides or their analogs. It should be mentioned, however, that the effects of cyclic nucleotide derivatives are hard to interpret and are not necessarily physiologic. As mentioned already, dbcGMP has been found to be a competitive antagonist of pancreozymin (103a, 107b). The effect of dbcGMP in potentiating amylase release in response to secretin or VIP (52) could not be confirmed (103a). The effect of 8-bromo-cGMP in increasing pancreatic enzyme secretion (53a) now appears due to its ability to mimic endogenous cAMP (53a, 103a). Direct measurements of cGMP levels did not clarify its role in pancreatic acinar cell function. Incubation of guinea pig pancreatic lobules in calcium-free medium containing 10^{-3} M EGTA for 60 min was followed by a severe reduction of carbachol-stimulated enzyme secretion, whereas the tissue response of cGMP remained largely intact (129). Nitrosourea compounds increase pancreatic cGMP levels, but fail to affect enzyme secretion (55a). Depolarization of the acinar cell membrane by elevated KC1 concentrations in the incubation medium in the presence of atropine caused enzyme release but did not elevate cGMP levels (130). Thus cGMP does not appear to be involved in the sequence of events following hormone stimulation and leading to enzyme release. However, cyclic nucleotides might be located in intracellular compartments that form only a small fraction of the total cell volume, so that the "active pool" of cyclic nucleotides could be increased without any detectable elevation in the total cell content. The location of such a "trigger pool" and the action of cyclic nucleotides in stimulus-secretion coupling remain undecided.

Cyclic nucleotides stimulate protein kinases (86), which, by phosphorylating membrane-bound or soluble proteins, may activate processes that lead to the physiological response. In the pancreas, both cAMP- and cGMP-dependent protein kinases have been found (73, 145). Also, pancreozymin and caerulein have been shown to stimulate phosphorylation of proteins in pancreas fragments preincubated in the presence of hormones (85). However, the exact location and functional role of such phosphorylated proteins remain unknown.

CA^{2+} AS REGULATOR OF INTRACELLULAR cAMP AND cGMP

In isolated pancreatic acinar membranes, adenylate cyclase can be activated by secretagogues of both group 1 (pancreozymin and caerulein) and group 5 (secretin and VIP) (Table 1). However, in the intact acinar cell only the latter group increases cAMP levels (120).

Ca^{2+} and Adenylate Cyclase—cAMP

The lack of cAMP rise in the intact pancreas in response to pancreozymin could be due to processes activated either concomitantly with hormone-receptor interaction or secondarily by an intracellular mediator. An important component in regulation of adenylate cyclase may be the intracellular calcium concentration (11, 115). In some tissues calcium can activate cAMP synthesis; in others it can inhibit (116). In analogy to fly salivary gland, where 5-hydroxytryptamine stimulates adenylate cyclase activity (with cAMP production) and Ca^{2+} release (11), the group 1 secretagogues (Table 1) stimulate adenylate cyclase activity (without a rise of intracellular cAMP), Ca^{2+} release from intracellular stores, and Ca^{2+} influx into the cell. The latter events presumably result in increased cytoplasmic Ca^{2+} concentration, which could then secondarily inhibit the pancreatic adenylate cyclase activity. Such inhibitory effect of calcium on adenylate cyclase has been observed in the heart (42), the renal cortex (141), the liver (112), and in isolated membranes of the pancreas of the rat (127). A definite shortcoming of this explanation for the missing cAMP response to the group 1 secretagogues, however, is the fact that calcium concentrations required for adenylate cyclase inhibition in vitro (127) are higher than estimates of free calcium concentrations in the cell (13).

Ca^{2+} and Guanylate Cyclase—cGMP

Pancreatic secretagogues, whose action is currently explained by the fact that they increase the cytosolic free Ca^{2+} concentration (groups 1–4, Table 1), also increase cGMP levels in pancreatic tissue (1, 26, 57). The rise of cGMP does not seem to depend on the presence of extracellular calcium but is thought to occur following Ca^{2+} release from intracellular stores (26).

However, following vigorous calcium withdrawal from pancreatic lobules, either by calcium washout or EGTA treatment, cGMP response to either carbamylcholine or pancreozymin stimulation remained largely intact (129, 130). Stimulation of enzyme secretion, however, was nearly abolished. Although Ca^{2+} fluxes were not measured in the latter studies, the authors thought that these experimental conditions eliminated the movement of large quantities of calcium across the plasma membrane and the internal cell membranes. They concluded that guanylate cyclase stimulation is independent of calcium translocation but follows closely hormone–receptor interaction (129, 130). Furthermore, they suggested that two distinct pathways are involved in carbachol- or pancreozymin-induced enzyme secretion. One pathway involves release of Ca^{2+} from intracellular stores and is *independent* of medium calcium. The other pathway, which is determined by events in the plasma membrane, depends on medium calcium. The second pathway of enzyme secretion is obviously involved if enzyme secretion is stimulated by depolarization of the cell membrane with elevated KC1 concentrations of the medium in the presence of atropine (130). This second pathway could be mimicked by a combination of the calcium ionophore A 23187 and calcium when pancreatic tissue was preincubated in the presence of only the ionophore for 20 min before calcium was added to the incubation medium. In contrast to the current opinion that (*a*) intracellular synthesis of cGMP is stimulated by increased free cytosolic Ca^{2+}, which activates guanylate cyclase (132), and (*b*) the rise of cGMP in the pancreas occurs following release of Ca^{2+} from intracellular stores (26), Scheele & Haymovits suggest that under physiological stimulation with acetylcholine or pancreozymin most of the cGMP rise is independent of the translocation of calcium. They propose that the cGMP increase is tightly coupled to secretagogue-receptor interaction at the cell membrane. Their demonstration of the direct effect of potassium on the discharge of secretory proteins from acinar cells in pancreatic lobules (130) contradicts previous observations that membrane depolarization of acinar cells is not sufficient to initiate secretion (4, 10, 114). Scheele and Haymovits explain the discrepancy on technical grounds and maintain that their preparation of isolated pancreatic lobules is more viable than that of isolated cells. Their assertion that sustained secretion (pathway II) requires Ca^{2+} influx agrees with the report of

Petersen & Iwatsuki (106) and Schreurs et al (131a) that Ca^{2+} influx into the cell is necessary for maintaining secretion after an initial extracellular calcium-independent burst of secretion evoked by secretagogues.

Ca^{2+} and Cyclic Nucleotide Phosphodiesterases

Another possible mechanism for regulation of cyclic nucleotide levels involves the activity of phosphodiesterase, the enzyme that inactivates cAMP and cGMP by cleaving the cyclic 3',5'-phosphodiester bond to give the corresponding 5'-nucleotide (122). Although careful studies on the characteristics of the pancreatic phosphodiesterase have been performed (128, 143, 144), interpretation of its importance in the regulation of secretory processes remains difficult owing to the multiple forms of the enzyme. From studies on more fully investigated organs, this enzyme appears to vary with respect to molecular weight, kinetic properties, and tissue localization. It likely exists simultaneously in several associated and dissociated states, which are interconvertible (108, 109). Furthermore, activity and substrate affinity of the enzyme appear to be modulated by its state of aggregation. Thus the dissociated form was shown to have a lower affinity and a higher specific activity for cAMP than the associated form (109), whereas the reverse holds for cGMP (108).

An endogenous calcium-dependent protein that activates one of the major forms of phosphodiesterase was described for brain and heart (24, 75). This protein was also found in the cytoplasm of the exocrine pancreas (144). In the presence of free Ca^{2+} ions, the lowest-molecular-weight (P3) form of phosphodiesterase was stimulated by this protein with cGMP but not with cAMP as substrate. The other two phosphodiesterases present in the organ were not stimulated by this activator. Since secretagogues of enzyme secretion release Ca^{2+} from intracellular stores and raise cellular cGMP levels (26), the observed *transient* elevation of cGMP concentration in response to the secretagogues carbamylcholine or pancreozymin was believed to result from a sequential stimulation of guanylate cyclase and the Ca^{2+}-dependent cGMP phosphodiesterase. Thus the latter enzyme regulates the pancreatic concentration of cGMP by returning the elevated level of cGMP to its prestimulation level (144).

SECRETAGOGUE-EVOKED FUNCTIONAL CHANGES AT THE PLASMA MEMBRANE

Secretagogue-Induced Changes of the Electrical Parameters of Acinar Cells

Secretagogues of enzyme secretion cause marked membrane potential and resistance changes. Brief exposure of the superfused mouse pancreas to acetylcholine, pancreozymin, gastrin, caerulein, or bombesin resulted in a short-term depolarization of the acinar cells from a resting potential of about –40 mV to about –20 mV. All these stimulants had the same action with an equilibrium potential of about –15 mV (67, 68). Atropine blocked the depolarizing action of cholinergic stimulants but not that of hormones, whereas dbcGMP blocked the effect of pancreozymin (107b). A detailed analysis of the electrical events revealed that acetylcholine-induced depolarization coincides with a reduction of input resistance caused by an increased conduction of the plasma membrane to Na^+, K^+, and Cl^-, resulting in an uptake of Na^+ and Cl^- into the acinar cells and a small efflux of K^+ (66, 67).

Membrane depolarization and resistance reduction in response to maximal stimulation were largely independent of the presence of Ca^{2+} in the extracellular fluid (103). Extracellular Ca^{2+} is important, however, in maintaining both high resting membrane potential and resistance. Reducing extracellular calcium concentration to near zero caused depolarization and resistance reduction that were fully reversible following readmission of Ca^{2+}. Admission of Mg^{2+} or Mn^{2+} to Ca^{2+}-free solution also increased cell potential and resistance (107). Although membrane depolarization and resistance reduction in response to maximal stimulation with acetylcholine were largely independent of the presence of extracellular Ca^{2+}, responses to barely suprathreshold acetylcholine pulses gradually disappeared after the start of exposure to Ca^{2+}-free solution containing EGTA. The authors interpreted these findings as due to an effect of extracellular Ca^{2+} concentration on the Na^+ permeability in the sense of "stabilizing" the membrane (107) rather than to an acetylcholine-evoked movement of calcium into the cell (66).

In the intact superfused mouse pancreas, the Ca^{2+} ionophore A 23187 caused a $[Ca^{2+}]_o$-dependent depolarization of the acinar cell membrane, but only in the presence of Na^+. Substitution of Na^+ by $Tris^+$ abolished the depolarization (113). Since it was supposed that a rise in intracellular Ca^{2+} exerted this effect, the effect of intracellular Ca^{2+} on membrane properties was tested by intracellular iontophoretic Ca^{2+} injections. Indeed, increasing the free calcium concentration in the acinar cell in this way caused surface cell membrane depolarization and resistance reduction similar to those evoked by acetylcholine. This suggests that the acetylcholine effect is caused by a rise of cytosolic intracellular free Ca^{2+}, which in turn influences the Na^+ permeability (65). Furthermore, the Ca^{2+}-injected cell, like cells stimulated with acetylcholine, CCK-Pz, or bombesin, was almost completely uncoupled electrically from the neighboring cells. These experiments showed that intracellular Ca^{2+} admission can qualitatively mimic the effects of extracellular acetylcholine, CCK-Pz, or bombesin stimulation on resistance reduction and depolarization of surface cell membranes and on the electrical uncoupling of neighboring cells.

Effect of Ca^{2+} on Na^+ Permeability

Experiments in isolated membrane vesicles from pancreas have shown that Ca^{2+} increased Na^+ permeability when applied from the inside of the cell membrane vesicle but decreased it when applied from the outside (134). These effects of Ca_i^{2+} on Na^+ permeability observed in isolated organelles are in agreement with those observed in intact tissue by means of electrical recordings (65, 113).

Effect of Secretagogues on Membrane Phospholipids

Phosphatidylinositols have a high affinity for Ca^{2+} ions (56) and are therefore possible candidates for membrane calcium storage sites. It has been suggested that activation of muscarinic receptors leads to hydrolysis of phosphatidylinositol in plasma membranes and thus directly or indirectly to Ca^{2+} release from the membrane (98). In most systems the effects of hormones on inositol metabolism are independent of extracellular calcium. In the pancreas the increased turnover of phosphatidylinositol in the presence of acetylcholine or pancreozymin was first described by Hokin & Hokin (62, 63) and since then has been amply confirmed (8, 9, 64). Since phosphatidylinositol breakdown depends only weakly on extracellular calcium (61) its role in stimulus-secretion coupling may be either the intracellular liberation of membrane-bound Ca^{2+} or the opening of Ca^{2+} gates (98). The increased ^{32}P-phosphatidylinositol turnover seems to correlate with Ca^{2+}-mediated secretory steps. In the rat parotid gland only the Ca^{2+}-mediated α-adrenergic or cholinergic response was associated with increased incorporation of ^{32}P into phosphatidylinositols, while isoproterenol (which stimulates enzyme secretion independently of extracellular Ca^{2+}) did not lead to increased ^{32}P turnover (136).

Further evidence links calcium entry to phosphatidylinositol breakdown: In the blowfly salivary gland, a decrease in 5-hydroxytryptamine–stimulated calcium influx into cells was related to a net decrease in phosphatidylinositol. After a 2 hr exposure to 5-hydroxytryptamine there was a net loss of 80% of the labeled phosphatidylinositol (46), and the ability of 5-hydroxytryptamine to increase calcium flux was markedly reduced (12). If the glands were washed free of 5-hydroxytryptamine and incubated in the presence of 2 mM inositol for 1 hr, the increase in calcium transport caused by 5-hydroxytryptamine was restored. Little recovery occurred in the absence of inositol. The authors concluded that breakdown of phosphatidylinositol by 5-hydroxytryptamine is involved in the gating of calcium. The similarity of the action of 5-hydroxytryptamine (which activates both adenylate cyclase activity and Ca^{2+} influx into the cell of fly salivary gland) to that of pancreozymin in the pancreas is striking. Although direct evidence that the phosphatidylinositol breakdown in response to hormones is located in the plasma membranes of the pancreas has not yet been obtained, the model proposed by Berridge & Fain (12) remains an attractive hypothesis for the link between hormone-receptor interaction and release and/or influx of Ca^{2+} into the acinar cell.

THE ROLE OF CALCIUM IN THE STIMULATORY PROCESS

Dependence of Enzyme Secretion on Extracellular Calcium

The importance of calcium in intracellular processes that initiate secretion became apparent from studies on nerve terminals (78), adrenal medulla (39, 41), and the posterior pituitary (40). In contrast to these observations, however, in which dependence of secretagogue-induced secretion on extracellular calcium was clearly established, in the pancreas an immediate cessation of stimulated secretion in the absence of extracellular calcium could not be observed. Only prolonged preincubation or perfusion (30–60 min) of the pancreas in the absence of calcium and with EGTA was found to markedly diminish (107, 119) or abolish (4, 17, 58, 61, 76) enzyme secretion.

Controversial findings should be evaluated in terms of the experimental conditions and the definitions of "calcium-free medium" employed. The membrane surface can act as a calcium pool that equilibrates with the calcium concentration of the medium and thus buffers sudden changes in extracellular free calcium. Following reduction of extracellular calcium, the time necessary to empty this pool depends on the use of chelators, their concentrations, the contact time, and the presence or absence of stirring. Thus Williams & Chandler (147) observed only 50% depression of bethanechol-stimulated secretion from mouse pancreatic fragments after 30–90 min of preincubation in a Ca^{2+}-free medium without any chelator. In contrast, Hokin (61) found a complete loss of the acetylcholine response in pigeon pancreas slices "presoaked" in a Ca^{2+}-free NaCl saline containing 0.72 mM EDTA and further incubated for 40 min in a Krebs-Ringer bicarbonate saline without calcium. The significance of these observations is difficult to assess. On the one hand, extracellular calcium might be involved in the stimulation of enzyme secretion, and the negative observations or the lack of immediate effects of calcium omission might result from insufficient calcium removal. On the other hand, complete and prolonged removal of extracellular calcium might provoke unspecific damage or other secondary effects (e.g. decrease in intracellular calcium) that might be responsible for the missing response.

A study on superfused mouse pancreatic fragments (107) showed that amylase secretion in response to short pulses of acetylcholine stimulation at half-hour intervals was little affected by prolonged exposure to Ca^{2+}-free solution even when the Ca^{2+}-chelating agent EGTA was present. However, in Ca^{2+}-free solution containing EGTA, sustained acetylcholine stimulation (normally causing sustained enzyme secretion) or addition of caerulein or of bombesin resulted in only a short burst of secretion (106, 131a). Readmission of Ca^{2+} to the bathing fluid during continued maximal stimulation with any of the three secretagogues resulted in an immediate and sustained secretory response. Removal of Ca^{2+} during sustained stimulation abolished the stimulant-evoked secretion immediately (106, 131a). The authors concluded that secretion evoked by a short-pulse stimulation is triggered by Ca^{2+} ions released from the plasma membrane by the interaction of secretagogues with specific receptor sites on the cell surface. This would lead to an increase in Ca^{2+} conductance with a consequent Ca^{2+} influx from the medium into the cell, which then would be the trigger for secretion under sustained stimulation. That amylase release is independent of extracellular calcium during the first minutes of secretion and is later dependent on extracellular calcium agrees with the results from Ca^{2+} flux measurements (reported below) that show a net efflux during onset of stimulation and a net influx during sustained secretion.

Secretagogue-Induced Ca^{2+} Fluxes

All secretagogues of enzyme secretion, including pancreozymin, its analogs CCK-OP and caerulein (37, 51), the peptides isolated from amphibia [i.e. bombesin, litorin, physalaemin, eledoisin (37, 93)], acetylcholine (51), and compounds like A 23187 (26), catharantine (146), and phorbol myristate acetate (5), stimulate enzyme secretion with a concomitant effect on Ca^{2+} fluxes.

Calcium movements have been measured in pancreatic fragments, superfused tissue, and isolated acinar cells using $^{45}Ca^{2+}$. In pancreas fragments and superfused intact tissue an increased $^{45}Ca^{2+}$ influx after addition of secretagogues could be observed only by Heisler & Grondin (59) using the "lanthanum method." All other investigators observed increased $^{45}Ca^{2+}$ efflux from $^{45}Ca^{2+}$ preloaded tissue and were not able to detect any effect on $^{45}Ca^{2+}$ influx (17, 20, 37, 92). Similarly, using enzymatically dissociated dispersed acinar cells, an increased $^{45}Ca^{2+}$ efflux from $^{45}Ca^{2+}$-preloaded cells has been observed in a number of studies (26, 51, 83). Except Kondo & Schulz (82, 83), who actually measured tracer Ca^{2+} exchange at zero Ca^{2+} net flux, all investigators used conditions under which they assumed that the movement of $^{45}Ca^{2+}$ indicated Ca^{2+} net fluxes. The experimental protocol using intact pancreas or fragments was usually as follows: Tissue was preloaded with $^{45}Ca^{2+}$ until a quasi-steady state was reached and then superfused with tracer-free media without calcium or of identical calcium concentration. After addition of secretagogues the $^{45}Ca^{2+}$ release into the medium per time was measured and compared to controls (17, 20, 90). In several studies, however, after preloading with $^{45}Ca^{2+}$ the cellular $^{45}Ca^{2+}$ was measured without removing $^{45}Ca^{2+}$ from the incubation medium (37, 51, 117). Since under these conditions one might assume that a stationary state for the tracer is reached and that the specific activity of $^{45}Ca^{2+}$ is the same in all readily exchangeable cell compartments, the rate of $^{45}Ca^{2+}$ flux can be taken to indicate Ca^{2+} net flux. Acute addition of secretagogue to pancreas fragments or cells showed that the $^{45}Ca^{2+}$ stationary state with zero net flux was not maintained, but a net outflux of Ca^{2+} resulted (Figure 2, phase 1). This quick Ca^{2+} release was followed by a slower Ca^{2+} reuptake (Figure 2, phase 2). The $^{45}Ca^{2+}$ flux measurements of Kondo & Schulz (82, 83), however, were performed at quasi-stationary state conditions with zero net flux of Ca^{2+}, in the absence or presence of secretagogues added to the incubation medium (1.25 mM Ca^{2+}) 30 min before adding the Ca^{2+} tracer. Under these conditions, the initial tracer uptake does not indicate net fluxes but the unidirectional $^{45}Ca^{2+}$ flux. The increased uptake of $^{45}Ca^{2+}$ in the presence of secretagogues in the experiments of Kondo & Schulz (82) shows an increased Ca^{2+} exchange at stationary state. Assuming increased cyto-

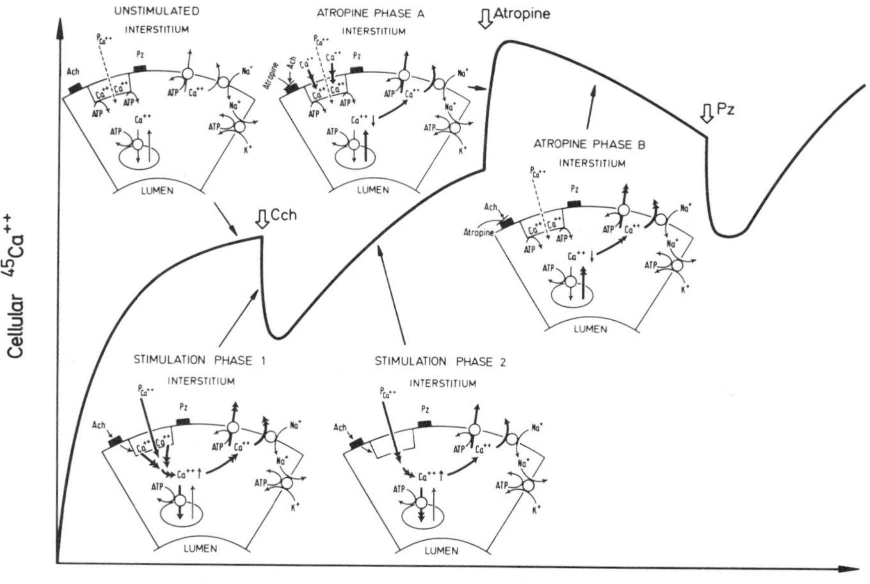

Figure 2 Synopsis of changes in cellular Ca^{2+} content during secretagogue-induced stimulation in the pancreatic acinar cell (for explanation see text). Double arrows indicate routes of net flux. Events at the luminal membrane concerned with exocytosis of zymogens are not shown.

plasmic free Ca^{2+} concentration under these conditions, this finding indicates that the Ca^{2+} permeability of the membrane or/and the Ca^{2+}-pump activity is augmented. Since increase in the Ca^{2+}-pump activity would lead to a decrease rather than to an increase in the cytoplasmic Ca^{2+} concentration, it is more probable that the secretagogues increase the Ca^{2+} permeability of the membrane.

Inhibitors as Tools in the Analysis of Calcium Transport Mechanisms Across the Cell Membrane

Following secretagogue stimulation of pancreatic acinar cells a change of active Ca^{2+} transport is postulated to occur not only across the plasma membrane but also in mitochondria and endoplasmic reticulum (21, 21a, 33, 140). The redox inhibitor antimycin A inhibits the aerobic ATP production in mitochrondia and leads to ATP depletion of the cells, thereby influencing not only the Ca^{2+} pump of mitochondria but also other ATP-driven pumps. ATP-consuming primary active Ca^{2+} transport in microsomes from pancreas, consisting probably of vesicles from both plasma membrane and endoplasmic reticulum, has been reported (6, 90, 112a). This active Ca^{2+} transport was not inhibited by mitochondrial inhibitors such as antimycin A, azide, oligomycin, or carbonylcyanide-p-trifluoromethoxyphenylhydrazone (CFCCP). A Ca^{2+} ATPase present in pancreatic membranes could be distinguished from the mitochondrial Ca^{2+},Mg^{2+}-ATPase by its insensitivity to mitochondrial inhibitors (6, 87). In an attempt to clarify further the nature of calcium transport steps, Stolze & Schulz (140) reinvestigated Ca^{2+} fluxes in isolated acinar cells; centrifugation through silicone oil was employed to obtain a quick removal of extracellular medium without washing the cells. If in $^{45}Ca^{2+}$ preloaded isolated acinar cells antimycin A was given, Ca^{2+} release similar to that of phase 1 in Figure 2 was observed. It was not followed, however, by reuptake as seen with secretagogues (phase 2 in Figure 2). This suggests that the Ca^{2+} extrusion mechanism at the plasma membrane was still intact and that antimycin A had released calcium from intracellular stores which was readily extruded from the cell. If, however, a subsequent low dose of A 23187 (0.1 μg mg^{-1} cell protein) was given, fast reuptake of $^{45}Ca^{2+}$ occurred. The Ca^{2+} pump of the plasma membrane had apparently been overcome by an increased Ca^{2+} permeability, which resulted in net Ca^{2+} influx into the cell.

Besides a Ca^{2+} ATPase, however, another Ca^{2+} extrusion mechanism involving Ca^{2+}/Na^{+} countertransport must be considered (140). It was first observed in squid axon and heart (for review see 13), where Ca^{2+}-dependent cell responses are stimulated when the Na^{+}-coupled Ca^{2+} extrusion mechanism is blocked following ouabain administration or after replacing Na^{+} of the extracellular medium with Li^{+}. In both cases the inwardly directed

Na^+ concentration gradient is reduced or abolished. Consequently the driving force for Ca^{2+} efflux in the postulated Na^+/Ca^{2+} countertransport system is diminished. Reduction of Ca^{2+} efflux then results in increased cytoplasmic Ca^{2+} levels, which exert their specific effects. Although in the isolated perfused pancreas (I. Schulz, unpublished) as well as in the uncinate pancreas of baby rats ouabain does not elicit enzyme secretion (17), evidence for the existence of a Na^+/Ca^{2+} countertransport mechanism in the plasma cell membrane has been obtained from Ca^{2+} flux studies in isolated acinar cells. In ouabain-pretreated cells the carbamylcholine-induced sudden loss of cellular $^{45}Ca^{2+}$ (phase 1 in Figure 2) was blocked by about 60%. The following reuptake of $^{45}Ca^{2+}$ (phase 2 in Figure 2) was completely abolished (140). Thus Ca^{2+} extrusion (phase 1 in Figure 2) may be partially achieved by a Na^+/Ca^{2+} countertransport mechanism. The missing reuptake in phase 2 (Figure 2) might be explained by reduced Ca^{2+} uptake into mitochondria in the presence of increased cytoplasmic Na^+ concentrations (15).

Inhibitors as Tools in the Analysis of Intracellular Calcium Pools

It appears that the calcium net fluxes during secretagogue-stimulated enzyme secretion are biphasic, first exhibiting efflux and later influx (26, 51, 117), with net accumulation of calcium due to the increased permeability of the cell membrane to calcium (82, 140). The interpretation of the underlying mechanisms resulting in calcium redistribution, however, remains discrepant. Cell fractionation studies report that enhanced Ca^{2+} release in response to secretagogues occurs from mitochondria (27a) and from membranes present in a microsomal fraction (33). Fluorometry of dissociated pancreatic acini preloaded with the fluorescent probe chlorotetracycline (CTC) showed that application of the acetylcholine analog bethanechol, of caerulein, and of the mitochondrial inhibitors antimycin A, NaCN, rotenone carbonyl cyanide m-chlorophenylhydrazone or of the divalent cation ionophore A23187 decreased the fluorescence of acini. This indicated release of Ca^{2+} from acini. Since the effects of both bethanechol and mitochondrial inhibitors were not additive, the authors concluded that bethanechol and mitochondrial inhibitors release calcium from the same intracellular site. This could be either mitochondria or another organelle that requires ATP to sequester calcium (21, 21a). We used atropine, antimycin A, and A 23187 to analyze further secretagogue-induced $^{45}Ca^{2+}$ fluxes and to get insight into the nature and location of intracellular calcium pools (140). Sudden addition of carbamylcholine to cells in stationary state for $^{45}Ca^{2+}$ (so that the tracer flux indicates net Ca^{2+} fluxes) resulted in the same instantaneous loss of $^{45}Ca^{2+}$ followed by a fast reuptake as has been observed by Gardner et al (51) and Renckens et al (117). Sudden addition of atropine to cells prestimulated with carbamylcholine and preloaded with $^{45}Ca^{2+}$ resulted in a transient increase in cellular $^{45}Ca^{2+}$ (Figure 2, phase A) followed by a slow decrease to a steady-state value (Figure 2, phase B), whereas atropine added to control cells had no effect (40). A net uptake of calcium by atropine in carbamylcholine-prestimulated cells suggests that the pool from which carbamylcholine had released calcium is refilled by blocking the cholinergic stimulant with atropine. This assumption received further support when, after carbamylcholine-induced calcium release, a second release could be evoked by pancreozymin after an interposed step of atropine administration (140). Without atropine neither carbamylcholine nor pancreozymin (or its octapeptide) would induce Ca^{2+} release a second time (51, 140). Addition of the Ca^{2+} ionophore, A 23187, or the mitochondrial inhibitor of oxidative phosphorylation, antimycin A, resulted in a fast decrease followed by a further slower decrease in cellular $^{45}Ca^{2+}$. When A 23187 or antimycin A was given to cells pretreated with carbamylcholine, however, they induced only a slow decrease in $^{45}Ca^{2+}$ without the preceding quick $^{45}Ca^{2+}$ release seen in cells without carbamylcholine. These data suggest that carbamylcholine, A 23187, and antimycin A act on the same Ca^{2+} pool from which Ca^{2+} is released quickly (140). A similar conclusion was reached by Chandler & Williams (21a, 22).

The effect of A 23187 on the Ca^{2+} fluxes depended very much on the concentration used. At concentrations lower than 0.2 μg of ionophore per mg cell protein a quick Ca^{2+} release without a following Ca^{2+} reuptake was observed. At 1 $\mu g\ mg^{-1}$ cell protein, however, the amount of Ca^{2+} accumulated in the cell exceeded 10 times the control value (140). These data suggest that at low concentrations the ionophore empties an intracellular calcium pool from which Ca^{2+} is released; Ca^{2+} efflux is observed because the Ca^{2+} extrusion mechanism located in the plasma membrane is not yet sufficiently bypassed by the ionophore. At higher concentrations, however, the ionophore-induced increase in the plasma membrane permeability predominates over the active transport process, and Ca^{2+} influx rather than Ca^{2+} efflux is the consequence. A similar conclusion was derived from studies of calcium fluxes in bovine sperm and rat hepatocytes (7, 23).

Increasing concentrations of antimycin A from 10^{-7} M to 10^{-5} M and of A 23187 from 0.02 $\mu g\ mg^{-1}$ cell protein to 0.1 $\mu g\ mg^{-1}$ cell protein increased fast $^{45}Ca^{2+}$ release from a pool that was not additive to the pool emptied by hormones (140). Thus a subsequent maximal dose of carbamylcholine in cells pretreated with antimycin A (10^{-5} M) or A 23187 (0.1 $\mu g\ mg^{-1}$ protein) did not lower cellular calcium further. This indicates that antimycin A and A 23187 act on the same calcium pool that can be emptied by hormone stimulation. If either A 23187 or antimycin A was given following carbamylcholine stimulation, fast Ca^{2+} efflux was not seen. This indicates that during phase 2 (Figure 2) a calcium pool had been filled different from the one that can be emptied by carbamylcholine, antimycin A, and A 23187. Further support for this conclusion is the observation that neither carbamylcholine nor CCK-OP elicits a second $^{45}Ca^{2+}$ release from cells preincubated for 60 min with the respective secretagogue (51). Atropine, however, enables the refilling of the first Ca^{2+} pool, which can then be emptied by carbamylcholine, A 23187, or antimycin A a second time (140).

Figure 2 summarizes our hypothesis. The pool from which "trigger calcium" is released by hormone-receptor interaction is located in the cell membrane. At rest, Ca^{2+} is bound to phosphatidylinositols formed from cytidin diphosphate glycerides and inositols. Energy-rich phosphates such as ATP and CTP are used for hydrolysis and resynthesis of phosphatidylinositol in a closed cycle of reactions. Release of bound calcium is induced by phosphatidylinositol breakdown as a consequence of receptor activation, which then leads to increased Ca^{2+} permeability of the plasma membrane. The calcium released from phosphatidylinositols into the cytosol is extruded from the cell by Ca^{2+} pumps which can be either primary active (driven by ATP) or secondary active (via a Ca^{2+}/Na^{+} countertransport) (stimulation, phase 1, Figure 2). Owing to the increased Ca^{2+} permeability of the plasma cell membrane a persisting Ca^{2+} influx occurs; Ca^{2+} is taken up actively from the cytosol into an intracellular pool (supposedly mitochondria), which now causes the reuptake phase (stimulation, phase 2, Figure 2). Atropine blocks the acetylcholine effect and causes refilling of the "trigger calcium pool" (resynthesis of phosphatidylinositol and its Ca^{2+} binding) and return of the increased Ca^{2+} permeability of the plasma membrane back to the unstimulated state. Antimycin also causes Ca^{2+} release from the Ca^{2+} pool in the plasma membrane since ATP production, which is necessary for resynthesis of phosphatidylinositols, is diminished. However, enough ATP remains to run the Ca^{2+} pumps so that Ca^{2+} can be extruded. Reuptake does not occur since the Ca^{2+} permeability is not increased. A 23187 at low concentrations causes release of Ca^{2+} from hydrophobic regions in the plasma membranous calcium pool to which A 23187 has access (110). At low A 23187 concentrations release without reuptake is observed; release followed by Ca^{2+} reuptake is observed at higher A 23187 concentrations, when the Ca^{2+} permeability of the plasma membrane is greater. At highest A 23187 concentrations the Ca^{2+} pumps are bypassed and Ca^{2+} overflows the cell.

It is still possible that the "trigger Ca^{2+} pool" is located in the cell interior, either connected with the plasma membrane or separate. In the latter case, however, an intracellular mediator of hormone action must be postulated. At present no second messenger is known to release Ca^{2+} from intracellular stores.

MORPHOLOGICAL CHANGES AT THE PLASMA MEMBRANE

The baso-lateral and the luminal cell sides of pancreatic acinar cells differ in structural and functional properties as well as in protein and lipid composition (31, 32, 47). The sites where this transition occurs are supposedly the circumferential tight junctions or zonula occludens. Detailed investigations of structure of tight junctions in acinar cells (96, 97) found that incubation of pancreatic lobules in Ca^{2+}-free Krebs-Ringer bicarbonate medium containing EGTA in low concentration resulted in the progressive disassembly of the tight junction. The elaborated meshwork of intramembrane fibrils first became disordered and then fragmented into numerous small strands, which spread in both the lateral and luminal portion of the plasmalemma. At this stage the architecture of the acini appeared altered: Most of the cells were no longer joined together by a continuous belt-like structure but only by numerous spot-like junctions. Concomitantly, the intramembrane particles in these cells, which in untreated cells were distributed uniformly in the basal and lateral plasma membrane but were selectively excluded from the luminal surface, were homogeneously distributed in both the luminal and lateral regions (97). Readmission of Ca^{2+} in the incubation medium resulted in rapid reformation of the tight junctions in the same location as in the intact cell. The density of the particles in the luminal plasmalemma remained high for at least 2 hr. After treatment with colchicine, the reassembly but not the disassembly in Ca^{2+}-free EGTA medium was missing (96).

The interruption of the continuity of zona occludens correlates with the loss of heterogeneity in the density of intramembranous particles in the luminal and contraluminal membrane. Thus in the pancreas, as in other tissues (111), zona occludens are responsible for the segregation of the extracellular space and also act as mechanical barriers against the intermixing of membrane components of the luminal and lateral regions of the plasma membrane. This fact has methodological implications: In the dissociation procedure used to obtain isolated acinar cells for biochemical studies (2) an EGTA step is interposed. In such cells the distribution of various sugar residues as revealed by the binding of specific lectins is uniform over the entire cell surface, which suggests intermixing of plasma membrane components (94). Therefore, a method that obtains functionally intact acini (148) in which 3–5 acinar cells remain associated would probably offer an advantage (with respect to physiological integrity of the secretory function) over isolated acinar cells.

Whether the morphological phenomena observed in tight junctions in the absence of Ca^{2+} have any implication for stimulus-secretion coupling cannot be decided yet. Although the importance of Ca^{2+} in the assembly of the occluding junctions has been demonstrated, it is not yet clear whether

Ca^{2+} acts directly on the junctional components or indirectly on either the organization of the plasma membrane or the intracellular components (96). Likewise it remains undecided whether there exists some correlation between the phenomena occurring at the tight junctions and the cellular events following stimulation of enzyme secretion. The transepithelial pathway in isolated superfused rabbit pancreas is permeable to divalent cations and mannitol; its permeability can be increased by carbachol (131). In the same system, the permeation of molecules decreases with increase in their molecular size (72). Stimulants of enzyme secretion increase the permeability of this pathway. The authors conclude from these findings that the transepithelial pathway for the tested substances is the paracellular route through the tight junctions, a conclusion also derived from measurements (38) of the permeation of nonelectrolytes of different molecular size.

The presence of gap junctions between neighboring cell pairs has also been demonstrated in lateral regions of acinar plasma membranes using freeze-fracture techniques (97). In experiments that demonstrated electrical coupling of neighboring acinar cells (65, 69, 105), intracellular Ca^{2+} injections caused electrical uncoupling, thus mimicking the effect of secretagogues of enzyme secretion. Cells within pancreatic acini thus communicate electrically via low-resistance gap junctions through which molecules up to a certain size can flow freely (70). So far, however, the physiological implications of the change in lateral communications of acinar cells after excessive stimulation with secretagogues are not clear.

CONCLUSIONS

Enzyme secretion from the exocrine pancreas can be elicited by four classes of hormones: (*a*) cholinergic stimulants; (*b*) hormones belonging to the family of pancreozymin; (*c*) those belonging to the family of bombesin; and (*d*) the amphibian peptides eledoisin and physalaemin. Secretin and VIP stimulate enzyme release, but their mechanism involves cAMP and is probably entirely different from that of the other secretagogues. The four classes of hormones listed above seem to use common pathways in stimulus-secretion coupling, involving Ca^{2+} as intracellular messenger and probably cGMP as modulator of their action (Table 1). Their effects can be described in two pathways. One pathway involves release of Ca^{2+} from an intracellular store, which is most likely located in the plasma membrane. Augmented cytosolic free calcium concentration increases the plasma membrane permeability for Na^+, Cl^-, and K^+, which leads to depolarization of the cell. This pathway is independent of extracellular Ca^{2+} and leads to a rise in cGMP. The other pathway is characterized by an increased permeability of the plasma membrane for Ca^{2+}, which is necessary for sustained secretion.

The increase in intracellular free calcium concentration leads to uncoupling of neighboring acinar cells, probably by a direct effect on gap junctions. Whether increased intracellular Ca^{2+} concentration is also responsible for the effects on tight junctions (as observed by means of freeze-fracture electronmicroscopy and by measuring the secretion properties of molecules of different sizes through paracellular pathways) remains open. Ca^{2+} seems to be the second messenger for enzyme secretion—i.e. it is either directly involved in fusion of zymogen granules with the luminal cell membrane, or it triggers events that lead to exocytosis.

Acknowledgments

We wish to thank Prof. K. J. Ullrich, Prof. E. Frömter, and Dr. J. J. H. H. M. de Pont for helpful suggestions and discussions during preparation of the manuscript. We are also indebted to Dr. F. Simon for looking through the final version. Many thanks are due to all of our colleagues who sent us reprints and manuscripts of their unpublished work.

Literature Cited

1. Albano, J., Bhoola, K. D., Harvey, R. F. 1976. Intracellular messenger role of cyclic GMP in exocrine pancreas. *Nature* 262:404–6
2. Amsterdam, A., Jamieson, J. D. 1972. Structural and functional characterization of isolated pancreatic exocrine cells. *Proc. Natl. Acad. Sci. USA* 69:3028–32
3. Anastasi, A., Erspamer, V., Endean, R. 1967. Isolation and structure of caerulein, an active decapeptide from the skin of Hyla caerulea. *Experientia* 23:699–700
4. Argent, B. E., Case, R. M., Scratcherd, T. 1973. Amylase secretion by the perfused cat pancreas in relation to the secretion of calcium and other electrolytes and as influenced by the external ionic environment. *J. Physiol. London* 230:575–93
5. Argent, B. E., Case, R. M., Hirst, F. C. 1978. The effect of phorbol myristate acetate on amylase secretion and ^{45}Ca efflux from rat pancreas. *J. Physiol. London* 285:33P
6. Argent, B. E., Smith, R. K., Case, R. M. 1975. The distribution of bivalent-cation-stimulated adenosine triphosphate hydrolysis and calcium accumulation in subcellular fractions of rat pancreas. *Biochem. Soc. Trans.* 3:713–14
7. Babcock, D. F., First, N. L., Lardy, H. A. 1976. Action of ionophore A23187 at the cellular level. Separation of effects at the plasma and mitochondrial membranes. *J. Biol. Chem.* 251:3881–86
8. Bauduin, H., Cantraine, F. 1972. "Phospholipid effect" and secretion in the rat pancreas. *Biochim. Biophys. Acta* 270:248–53
9. Bauduin, H., Rochus, L., Vincent, D., Dumont, J. E. 1971. Role of cyclic 3',5'-AMP in the action of physiological secretagogues on the metabolism of rat pancreas in vitro. *Biochim. Biophys. Acta* 252:171–83
10. Benz, L., Eckstein, B., Matthews, E. K., Williams, J. A. 1972. Control of pancreatic amylase release *in vitro:* effects of ions, cyclic AMP and colchicine. *Brit. J. Pharmacol.* 46:66–77
11. Berridge, M. J. 1975. The interaction of cyclic nucleotides and calcium in the control of cellular activity. *Adv. Cyclic Nucleotide Res.* 6:1–98
12. Berridge, M. J., Fain, J. N. 1979. Inhibition of phosphatidylinositol synthesis and the inactivation of calcium entry after prolonged exposure of the blowfly salivary gland to 5-hydroxytryptamine. *Biochem. J.* 178:59–69
13. Blaustein, M. P. 1974. The interrelationship between sodium and calcium fluxes across cell membranes. *Rev. Physiol. Biochem. Pharmacol.* 70:33–82
14. Bodanszky, M. 1974. Gastrointestinal hormones, family of oligoelectrolytes. In *Endocrinology of the Gut,* ed. W. Y.

Chey, F. P. Brooks, pp. 3–13. Thorofare, NJ: Slack
15. Carafoli, E., Malmström, K., Capano, M., Sigel, E., Crompton, M. 1975. Mitochondria and the regulation of cell calcium. In *Calcium Transport in Contraction and Secretion,* ed. E. Carafoli, F. Clementi, W. Dabrikowski, A. Margreth, pp. 53–64. Amsterdam: North Holland. 588 pp.
16. Case, R. M. 1978. Synthesis, intracellular transport and discharge of exportable proteins in the pancreatic acinar cell and other cells. *Biol. Rev.* 53:211–354
17. Case, R. M., Clausen, T. 1973. The relationship between calcium exchange and enzyme secretion in the isolated rat pancreas. *J. Physiol. London* 235:75–102
18. Case, R. M., Harper, A. A., Scratcherd, T. 1968. Water and electrolyte secretion by the perfused pancreas of the cat. *J. Physiol. London* 196:133–49
19. Cassel, D., Selinger, Z. 1977. Mechanism of adenylate cyclase activation by cholera toxin: Inhibition of GTP hydrolysis at the regulatory site. *Proc. Natl. Acad. Sci. USA* 74:3307–11
20. Chandler, D. E., Williams, J. A. 1974. Pancreatic acinar cells: Effects of lanthanum ions on amylase release and calcium ion fluxes. *J. Physiol. London* 243:831–46
21. Chandler, D. E., Williams, J. A. 1978. Intracellular divalent cation release in pancreatic acinar cells during stimulus-secretion coupling. I. Use of chlorotetracycline as fluorescent probe. *J. Cell Biol.* 76:371–85
21a. Chandler, D. E., Williams, J. A. 1978. Intracellular divalent cation release in pancreatic acinar cells during stimulus-secretion coupling. II. Subcellular localization of the fluorescent probe chlorotetracycline. *J. Cell Biol.* 76:386–99
22. Chandler, D. E., Williams, J. A. 1977. Fluorescent probe detects redistribution of cell calcium during stimulus-secretion coupling. *Nature* 268:659–60
23. Chen, J.-L. J., Babcock, D. F., Lardy, H. A. 1978. Norepinephrine, vasopressin, glucagon, and A23187 induce efflux of calcium from an exchangeable pool in isolated rat hepatocytes. *Proc. Natl. Acad. Sci. USA* 75:2234–38
24. Cheung, W. Y. 1971. Cyclic 3',5'-nucleotide phosphodiesterase: Evidence for and properties of a protein activator. *J. Biol. Chem.* 246:2859–69
25. Christophe, J. P., Conlon, T. P., Gardner, J. D. 1976. Interaction of porcine vasoactive intestinal peptide with dispersed pancreatic acinar cells from the guinea pig. Binding of radioiodinated peptide. *J. Biol. Chem.* 251:4629–34
26. Christophe, J. P., Frandsen, E. K., Conlon, T. P., Krishna, G., Gardner, J. D. 1976. Action of cholecystokinin, cholinergic agents, and A-23187 on accumulation of guanosine 3' : 5'-monophosphate in dispersed guinea pig pancreatic acinar cells. *J. Biol. Chem.* 251:4640–45
27. Christophe, J., De Neef, P., Deschodt-Lanckman, M., Robberecht, P. 1978. The interaction of caerulein with the rat pancreas. 2. Specific binding of [^{3}H] caerulein on dispersed acinar cells. *Eur. J. Biochem.* 91:31–38
27a. Clemente, F., Meldolesi, J. 1975. Calcium and pancreatic secretion-dynamics of subcellular calcium pools in resting and stimulated acinar cells. *Br. J. Pharmacol.* 55:369–79
28. Cuatrecasas, P. 1974. Membrane receptors. *Ann. Rev. Biochem.* 43:169–214
29. Cuatrecasas, P., Hollenberg, M. D., Chang, K. J., Bennett, V. 1975. Hormone receptor complexes and their modulation of membrane function. *Rec. Prog. Hormone Res.* 31:37–94
30. Danielsson, A., Sehlin, J. 1974. Transport and oxidation of amino acids and glucose in the isolated exocrine mouse pancreas: Effects of insulin and pancreozymin. *Acta Physiol. Scand.* 91: 557–65
31. De Camilli, P., Peluchetti, D., Meldolesi, J. 1974. Structural difference between luminal and lateral plasmalemma in pancreatic acinar cells. *Nature* 248:245–47
32. De Camilli, P., Peluchetti, D., Meldolesi, J. 1976. Dynamic changes of the luminal plasmalemma in stimulated parotid acinar cells. A freeze-fracture study. *J. Cell Biol.* 70:59–74
33. De Pont, J. J. H. H. M., Kempen, H. J. M., Bonting, S. L. 1977. Hormonal activation of adenylate cyclase and its effects in exocrine pancreatic function. In *Hormonal Receptors in Digestive Tract Physiology, INSERM Symp. No. 3,* ed. S. Bonfils, P. Fromageot, G. Rosselin, pp. 289–300. Amsterdam: Elsevier/North-Holland. 514 pp.
34. De Pont, J. J. H. H. M., Luyben, D., Bonting, S. L. 1979. Rat pancreas adenylate cyclase. VI. Role of the enzyme in secretin stimulated enzyme secretion. *Biochim. Biophys. Acta.* In press
35. Deleted in proof
36. Deschodt-Lanckman, M., Robberecht, P., Camus, J., Christophe, J. 1978. The interaction of caerulein with the rat pancreas. 1. Specific binding of [^{3}H] ca-

erulein on plasma membranes and evidence for negative cooperativity. *Eur. J. Biochem.* 91:21–29

37. Deschodt-Lanckman, M., Robberecht, P., De Neef, P., Lammens, M., Christophe, J. 1976. In vitro action of bombesin and bombesin-like peptides on amylase secretion, calcium efflux, and adenylate cyclase activity in the rat pancreas. A comparison with other secretagogues. *J. Clin. Invest.* 58:891–98
38. Dewhurst, D. G., Hadi, N. A., Hutson, D., Scratcherd, T. 1978. The permeability of the secretin stimulated exocrine pancreas to non-electrolytes. *J. Physiol. London* 277:103–14
39. Dormer, R. L., Williams, J. A. 1978. Stimulation of pancreatic enzyme secretion results in intracellular redistribution of calcium. *J. Cell Biol.* 79:383a
40. Douglas, W. W., Poisner, A. M. 1964. Stimulus-secretion coupling in a neurosecretory organ: The role of calcium in the release of vasopressin from the neurohypophysis. *J. Physiol. London* 172:1–18
41. Deleted in proof
42. Drummond, G. I., Duncan, L. 1970. Adenyl cyclase in cardiac tissue. *J. Biol. Chem.* 245:976–83
43. Eimerl, S., Savion, N., Heichal, O., Selinger, Z. 1974. Induction of enzyme secretion in rat pancreatic slices using the ionophore A-23187 and calcium. *J. Biol. Chem.* 249:3991–93
44. Erspamer, V., Melchiorri, P. 1973. Active polypeptides of the amphibian skin and their synthetic analogs. *Pure Appl. Chem.* 35:463–94
45. Erspamer, V., Melchiorri, P. 1975. Actions of bombesin on secretions and motility of the gastrointestinal tract. In *Gastrointestinal Hormones,* ed. J. C. Thompson, pp. 575–89. Austin, Tex: Univ. Texas Press. 666 pp.
46. Fain, J. N., Berridge, M. J. 1979. Relationship between hormonal activation of phosphatidylinositol hydrolysis, fluid secretion and calcium flux in the blowfly salivary gland. *Biochem. J.* 178:45–58
47. Farquhar, M. G., Bergeron, J. J. M., Palade, G. E. 1974. Cytochemistry of Golgi fractions prepared from rat liver. *J. Cell Biol.* 60:8–25
48. Fölsch, U. R., Wormsley, K. G. 1973. Pancreatic enzyme response to secretin and cholecystokinin-pancreozymin in the rat. *J. Physiol. London* 234:79–94
49. Gardner, J. D., Conlon, T. P., Beyerman, H. C., Van Zon, A. 1977. Interaction of synthetic 10-tyrosyl analogues of secretin with hormone receptors on pancreatic acinar cells. *Gastroenterology* 73:52–56
50. Gardner, J. D., Conlon, T. P., Fink, M. L., Bodanszky, M. 1976. Interaction of peptides related to secretin with hormone receptors on pancreatic acinar cells. *Gastroenterology* 71:965–70
51. Gardner, J. D., Conlon, T. P., Klaeveman, H. L., Adams, T. D., Ondetti, M. A. 1975. Action of cholecystokinin and cholinergic agents on calcium transport in isolated pancreatic acinar cells. *J. Clin. Invest.* 56:366–75
52. Gardner, J. D., Jackson, M. J. 1977. Regulation of amylase release from dispersed pancreatic acinar cells. *J. Physiol. London* 270:439–54
53. Gardner, J. D., Rottman, A. J. 1979. Action of cholera toxin on dispersed acini from guinea pig pancreas. In press

53a. Gardner, J. D., Rottman, A. J. 1980. Evidence against cyclic GMP as a mediator of the actions of secretagogues on amylase release from guinea pig pancreas. *Biochim. Biophys. Acta.* In press

54. Gardner, J. D., Rottman, A. J., Natarajan, S., Bodanszky, M. 1979. Interaction of secretin 5–27 and its analogues with hormone receptors on pancreatic acini. *Biochim. Biophys. Acta.* In press
55. Gregory, R. A., Tracy, H. J. 1964. The constitution and properties of two gastrins extracted from hog antral mucosa. *Gut* 5:103–17

55a. Gunther, G. R., Jamieson, J. D. 1977. Secretion by pancreatic acinar cells is not caused by an increase in intracellular cGMP. *J. Cell Biol.* 75:415a

55b. Harper, A. A. 1972. The control of pancreatic secretion. *Gut* 13:308–17

56. Hauser, H., Dawson, R. M. C. 1967. The binding of calcium at lipid-water interfaces. *Eur. J. Biochem.* 1:61–69
57. Haymovits, A., Scheele, G. A. 1976. Cellular cyclic nucleotides and enzyme secretion in the pancreatic acinar cell. *Proc. Natl. Acad. Sci. USA* 73:156–60
58. Heisler, S., Fast, D., Tenenhouse, A. 1972. Role of Ca^{2+} and cyclic AMP in protein secretion from rat exocrine pancreas. *Biochim. Biophys. Acta* 279: 561–72
59. Heisler, S., Grondin, G. 1973. Effect of lanthanum on ^{45}Ca flux and secretion of protein from rat exocrine pancreas. *Life Sci.* 13:783–94
60. Heisler, S., Lambert, M. 1978. Dissociation of cyclic GMP synthesis from cholinergic-stimulated secretion of protein from rat exocrine pancreas. *Can. J. Physiol. Pharmacol.* 56:395–99

61. Hokin, L. E. 1966. Effects of calcium omission on acetylcholine-stimulated amylase secretion and phospholipid synthesis in pigeon pancreas slices. *Biochim. Biophys. Acta* 115:219–21
62. Hokin, L. E., Hokin, M. R. 1955. Effects of acetylcholine on the turnover of phosphoryl units in individual phospholipids of pancreas slices and brain cortex slices. *Biochim. Biophys. Acta* 18:102–10
63. Hokin, L. E., Hokin, M. R. 1956. The actions of pancreozymin in pancreas slices and the role of phospholipids in enzyme secretion. *J. Physiol. London* 132:442–53
64. Hokin, M. R. 1974. Breakdown of phosphatidylinositol in the pancreas in response to pancreozymin and acetylcholine. In *Secretory Mechanisms of Exocrine Glands,* ed. N. A. Thorn, O. H. Petersen, pp. 101–12. Copenhagen: Munksgaard. 645 pp.
65. Iwatsuki, N., Petersen, O. H. 1977. Acetylcholine-like effects of intracellular calcium application in pancreatic acinar cells. *Nature* 268:147–49
66. Iwatsuki, N., Petersen, O. H. 1977. Pancreatic acinar cells: Localisation of acetylcholine receptors and the importance of chloride and calcium for acetylcholine-evoked depolarization. *J. Physiol. London* 269:723–33
67. Iwatsuki, N., Petersen, O. H. 1977. Pancreatic acinar cells: The acetylcholine equilibrium potential and its ionic dependency. *J. Physiol. London* 269: 735–51
68. Iwatsuki, N., Petersen, O. H. 1978. In vitro action of bombesin on amylase secretion, membrane potential and membrane resistance in rat and mouse pancreatic acinar cells. A comparison with other secretagogues. *J. Clin. Invest.* 61:41–46
69. Iwatsuki, N., Petersen, O. H. 1978. Pancreatic acinar cells: acetylcholine evoked electrical uncoupling and its ionic dependency. *J. Physiol. London* 274:81–96
70. Iwatsuki, N., Petersen, O. H. 1979. Direct visualization of cell to cell coupling: Transfer of fluorescent probes in living mammalian pancreatic acini. *Pflügers Arch.* 380:277–81
71. Jamieson, J. D. 1978. Processing of exportable proteins: structure-function correlates and role of cellular membranes. In *Physiology of Membrane Disorders,* ed. T. E. Andreoli, J. F. Hoffman, D. D. Fanestil, pp. 447–58. NY, London: Plenum. 1122 pp.
72. Jansen, J. W. C. M., De Pont, J. J. H. H. M., Bonting, S. L. 1979. Transepithelial permeability in the rabbit pancreas. *Biochim. Biophys. Acta.* 551:95–108
73. Jensen, R. T., Gardner, J. D. 1978. Cyclic nucleotide-dependent protein kinase activity in acinar cells from guinea pig pancreas. *Gastroenterology* 75:806–17
74. Jensen, R. T., Moody, T., Pert, C., Rivier, J. E., Gardner, J. D. 1978. Interaction of bombesin and litorin with specific membrane receptors on pancreatic acinar cells. *Proc. Natl. Acad. Sci. USA* 75:6139–43
75. Kakiuchi, S., Yamazaki, R., Nakajima, H. 1970. Properties of a heat-stable phosphodiesterase activating factor isolated from brain extract. *Proc. Jpn. Acad.* 46:587–92
76. Kanno, T. 1972. Calcium-dependent amylase release and electrophysiological measurements in cells of the pancreas. *J. Physiol. London* 226:353–71
77. Kanno, T., Saito, A. 1976. The potentiating influences of insulin on pancreozymin-induced hyperpolarization and amylase release in the pancreatic acinar cell. *J. Physiol. London* 261: 505–21
78. Katz, B., Miledi, R. 1967. The timing of calcium action during neuromuscular transmission. *J. Physiol. London* 189: 535–44
79. Kempen, H. J. M. 1976. *Role of cyclic AMP in exocrine pancreatic secretion.* Thesis. Catholic Univ., Nijmegen. 180 pp.
80. Kempen, H. J. M., De Pont, J. J. H. H. M., Bonting, S. L. 1975. Rat pancreas adenylate cyclase. III. Its role in pancreatic secretion assessed by means of cholera toxin. *Biochim. Biophys. Acta* 392:276–87
81. Kimura, N., Nagata, N. 1977. The requirement of guanine nucleotides for glucagon stimulation of adenylate cyclase in rat liver plasma membranes. *J. Biol. Chem.* 252:3829–35
82. Kondo, S., Schulz, I. 1976. Calcium ion uptake in isolated pancreas cells induced by secretagogues. *Biochim. Biophys. Acta* 419:76–92
83. Kondo, S., Schulz, I. 1976. Ca^{2+} fluxes in isolated cells of rat pancreas. Effect of secretagogues and different Ca^{2+} concentrations. *J. Membrane Biol.* 29:185–203
84. Korc, M., Sankaran, H., Wong, K. Y., Williams, J. A., Goldfine, I. D. 1978. Insulin receptors in isolated mouse pan-

creatic acini. *Biochem. Biophys. Res. Commun.* 84:293–99

85. Lambert, M., Camus, J., Christophe, J. 1973. Pancreozymin and caerulein stimulate in vitro protein phosphorylation in the rat. *Biochem. Biophys. Res. Commun.* 52:935–42
86. Langan, T. A. 1973. Protein kinases and protein kinase substrates. *Adv. Cyclic Nucleotide Res.* 3:99–153
87. Löffler, G., Lucas, M., Schmid, G. 1977. Calcium binding and calcium ATPase in a microsomal fraction from guinea pig pancreas. *Hoppe-Seyler's Z. Physiol. Chem.* 358:271 (Abstr.)
88. Londos, C., Lin, M. C., Welton, A. F., Lad, P. M., Rodbell, M. 1977. Reversible activation of hepatic adenylate cyclase by guanyl-5'-yl-(α,β-methylene)-diphosphonate and guanyl-5'-yl-imido diphosphate. *J. Biol. Chem.* 252: 5180–82
89. Long, B. W., Gardner, J. D. 1977. Effects of cholecystokinin on adenylate cyclase activity in dispersed pancreatic acinar cells. *Gastroenterology* 73: 1008–14
90. Lucas, M., Schmid, G., Kromas, R., Löffler, G. 1978. Calcium metabolism and enzyme secretion in guinea pig pancreas. Uptake, storage and release of calcium in whole cells and mitochondrial and microsomal fractions. *Eur. J. Biochem.* 85:609–19
91. Makhlouf, G. M., Bodanszky, M., Fink, M. L., Schebalin, M. 1978. Pancreatic secretory activity of secretin$_{5-27}$ and substituted analogues. *Gastroenterology* 75:244–48
92. Matthews, E. K., Petersen, O. H., Williams, J. A. 1973. Pancreatic acinar cells: Acetylcholine-induced membrane depolarization, calcium efflux and amylase release. *J. Physiol. London* 234: 689–701
93. May, R. J., Conlon, T. P., Erspamer, V., Gardner, J. D. 1978. Actions of peptides isolated from amphibian skin on pancreatic acinar cells. *Am. J. Physiol.* 235:E112–18
94. Maylié-Pfenninger, M.-F., Jamieson, J. D. 1979. Distribution of cell surface saccharides on pancreatic cells. II. Lectin-labeling patterns on mature guinea pig and rat pancreatic cells. *J. Cell Biol.* 80:77–95
95. Meldolesi, J., Borgese, N., De Camilli, P., Ceccarelli, B. 1978. Cytoplasmic membranes and the secretory processes. In *Membrane Fusion,* ed. G. Poste, G. L. Nicolson, pp. 509–627. Amsterdam: Elsevier/North-Holland. 862 pp.
96. Meldolesi, J., Castiglioni, G., Parma, R., Nassivera, N., De Camilli, P. 1978. Ca^{++}-dependent disassembly and reassembly of occluding junctions in guinea pig pancreatic acinar cells. Effect of drugs. *J. Cell Biol.* 79:156–72
97. Meldolesi, J., De Camilli, P., Brenna, A. 1977. The topology of plasma membrane in pancreatic acinar cells. See Ref. 33, pp. 203–12
98. Michell, R. H. 1975. Inositol phospholipids and cell surface receptor function. *Biochim. Biophys. Acta* 415:81–147
99. Milutinović, S., Sachs, G., Haase, W., Schulz, I. 1977. Studies on isolated subcellular components of cat pancreas. I. Isolation and enzymatic characterization. *J. Membrane Biol.* 36:253–79
100. Milutinović, S., Schulz, I., Rosselin, G. 1976. The interaction of secretin with pancreatic membranes. *Biochim. Biophys. Acta* 436:113–27
101. Milutinović, S., Schulz, I., Rosselin, G., Fasold, H. 1977. The interaction of pancreatic secretagogues with pancreatic plasma membranes. See Ref. 33, pp. 213–26
102. Moroder, L., Jaeger, E., Drees, F., Gemeinar, M., Knof, S., Stelzel, H.-P., Thamm, P., Bataille, D., Domschke, S., Schlegel, W., Schulz, I., Wünsch, E. 1979. Structure-function studies on gastrointestinal hormones. I. Synthesis of secretin analogues and their biological and immunological properties. *Bioorganic Chem.* In press
103. Nishiyama, A., Petersen, O. H. 1975. Pancreatic acinar cells: Ionic dependency of acetylcholine-induced membrane potential and resistance change. *J. Physiol. London* 244:431–65

103a. Peikin, S. R., Costenbader, C. L., Gardner, J. D. 1980. Actions of derivatives of cyclic nucleotides on dispersed acini from guinea pig pancreas: Discovery of a competitive antagonist of the action of cholecystokinin. *J. Biol. Chem.* In press

104. Perkins, J. P. 1973. Adenyl cyclase. *Adv. Cyclic Nucleotide Res.* 3:1–64
105. Petersen, O. H. 1976. Electrophysiology of mammalian gland cells. *Physiol. Rev.* 56:535–77
106. Petersen, O. H., Iwatsuki, N. 1978. The role of calcium in pancreatic acinar cell stimulus-secretion coupling: an electrophysiological approach. *Ann. NY Acad. Sci.* 307:599–617
107. Petersen, O. H., Ueda, N. 1976. Pancreatic acinar cells: the role of calcium

in stimulus-secretion coupling. *J. Physiol. London* 254:583–606

107a. Pfeuffer, T. 1977. GTP-binding protein in membrane and the control of adenylate cyclase activity. *J. Biol. Chem.* 252:7224–34

107b. Philpott, H. G., Petersen, O. H. 1980. Separate activation sites for cholecystokinin and bombesin on pancreatic acini. An electrophysiological study employing a competitive antagonist for the action of CCK. *Pflügers Arch.* In press

108. Pichard, A.-L., Cheung, W. Y. 1976. Cyclic 3':5'-nucleotide phosphodiesterase. Interconvertible multiple forms and their effects on enzyme activity and kinetics. *J. Biol. Chem.* 251:5726–37

109. Pichard, A.-L., Kaplan, J.-C. 1975. Interconvertibilité des formes moléculaires de l'AMP 3'-5' cyclique phosphodiestérase des plaquettes humaines. *C. R. Acad. Sci. Paris Ser. D* 280: 673–76

110. Pick, U., Racker, E. 1979. Inhibition of the (Ca^{2+})ATPase from sarcoplasmic reticulum by dicyclohexylcarbodiimide: Evidence for location of the Ca^{2+} binding site in a hydrophobic region. *Biochemistry* 18:108–13

111. Pisam, M., Ripoche, P. 1976. Redistribution of surface macromolecules in dissociated epithelial cells. *J. Cell Biol.* 71:907–20

112. Pointer, R. H., Butcher, F. R., Fain, J. N. 1976. Studies on the role of cyclic guanosine 3':5'-monophosphate and extracellular Ca^{2+} in the regulation of glycogenolysis in rat liver cells. *J. Biol. Chem.* 251:2987–92

112a. Ponnappa, B. C., Dormer, R. L., Williams, J. A. 1979. Energy dependent calcium sequestration activity in pancreatic microsomes. *Fed. Proc.* 38:1039

113. Poulsen, J. H., Williams, J. A. 1977. Effect of the calcium ionophore A 23187 on pancreatic acinar cell membrane potentials and amylase release. *J. Physiol. London* 264:323–39

114. Poulsen, J. H., Williams, J. A. 1977. Effect of extracellular K^+ concentration on resting potential, caerulein-induced depolarization and amylase release from mouse pancreatic acinar cells. *Pflügers Arch.* 370:173–77

115. Rasmussen, H. 1970. Cell communication, calcium ion, and cyclic adenosine monophosphate. *Science* 170:404–12

116. Rasmussen, H., Goodman, D. B. P. 1977. Relationships between calcium and cyclic nucleotides in cell activation. *Physiol. Rev.* 57:421–509

117. Renckens, B. A. M., Schrijen, J. J., Swarts, H. G. P., De Pont, J. J. H. H. M., Bonting, S. L. 1978. Role of calcium in exocrine pancreatic secretion. IV. Calcium movements in isolated acinar cells of rabbit pancreas. *Biochim. Biophys. Acta* 544:338–50

118. Rendell, M., Salomon, Y., Lin, M.C., Rodbell, M., Berman, M. 1975. The hepatic adenylate cyclase system. III. A mathematical model for the steady state kinetics of catalysis and nucleotide regulation. *J. Biol. Chem.* 250:4253–60

119. Robberecht, P., Christophe, J. 1971. Secretion of hydrolases by perfused fragments of rat pancreas: effect of calcium. *Am. J. Physiol.* 220:911–17

120. Robberecht, P., Conlon, T. P., Gardner, J. D. 1976. Interaction of porcine vasoactive intestinal peptide with dispersed pancreatic acinar cells from the guinea pig. *J. Biol. Chem.* 251:4635–39

121. Robberecht, P., Deschodt-Lanckman, M., Morgat, J.-L., Christophe, J. 1978. The interaction of caerulein with the rat pancreas. 3. Structural requirements for in vitro binding of caerulein-like peptides and its relationship to increased calcium outflux, adenylate cyclase activation, and secretion. *Eur. J. Biochem.* 91:39–48

122. Robison, G. A., Butcher, R. W., Sutherland, E. W. 1971. *Cyclic AMP.* NY: Academic. 531 pp.

123. Rodbell, M., Birnbaumer, L., Pohl, S. L. 1970. Adenyl cyclase in fat cells. III. Stimulation by secretin and the effects of trypsin on the receptors for lipolytic hormones. *J. Biol. Chem.* 245:718–22

124. Rodbell, M., Birnbaumer, L., Pohl, S. L., Krans, H. M. J. 1971. The glucagon-sensitive adenyl cyclase system in plasma membranes of rat liver. V. An obligatory role of guanyl nucleotides in glucagon action. *J. Biol. Chem.* 246:1877–82

125. Rodbell, M., Lin, M. C., Salomon, Y., Londos, C., Harwood, J. P., Martin, B. R. 1975. Role of adenine and guanine nucleotides in the activity and response of adenylate cyclase systems to hormones: Evidence for multisite transition states. *Adv. Cyclic Nucleotide Res.* 5:3–29

126. Rothman, S. S. 1964. Exocrine secretion from the isolated rabbit pancreas. *Nature* 204:84–85

127. Rutten, W. J., De Pont, J. J. H. H. M., Bonting, S. L. 1972. Adenylate cyclase in the rat pancreas. Properties and stimulation by hormones. *Biochim. Biophys. Acta* 274:201–13

128. Rutten, W. J., Schoot, B. M., De Pont, J. J. H. H. M., Bonting, S. L. 1973. Adenosine 3',5'-monophosphate phosphodiesterase in rat pancreas. *Biochim. Biophys. Acta* 315:384–93

129. Scheele, G., Haymovits, A. 1979. Cholinergic and peptide stimulated discharge of secretory protein in guinea pig pancreatic lobules: Role of intracellular and extracellular calcium. *J. Biol. Chem.* In press

130. Scheele, G., Haymovits, A. 1979. Potassium and ionophore A 23187 induced discharge of secretory protein in guinea pig pancreatic lobules: Role of extracellular calcium. *J. Biol. Chem.* In press

131. Schreurs, V. V. A. M., Swarts, H. G. P., De Pont, J. J. H. H. M., Bonting, S. L. 1975. Role of calcium in exocrine pancreatic secretion. I. Calcium movements in the rabbit pancreas. *Biochim. Biophys. Acta* 404:257–67

131a. Schreurs, V. V. A. M., Swarts, H. G. P., De Pont, J. J. H. H. M., Bonting, S. L. 1976. Role of calcium in exocrine pancreatic secretion. II. Comparison of the effects of carbachol and the ionophore A-23187 on enzyme secretion and calcium movements in rabbit pancreas. *Biochim. Biophys. Acta* 419: 320–30

132. Schultz, G., Hardman, J. G., Schultz, K., Baird, C. E., Sutherland, E. W. 1973. The importance of calcium ions for the regulation of guanosine 3':5' cyclic monophosphate levels. *Proc. Natl. Acad. Sci. USA* 3889–93

133. Schulz, I. 1975. The role of extracellular Ca^{++} and cyclic nucleotides in the mechanism of enzyme secretion from cat pancreas. *Pflügers Arch.* 360:165–81

134. Schulz, I., Heil, K. 1979. Ca^{2+} control of electrolyte permeability in plasma membrane vesicles from cat pancreas. *J. Membr. Biol.* 46: In press

135. Schulz, I., Ullrich, K. J. 1978. Transport processes in the exocrine pancreas. In *Membrane Transport in Biology, Vol. IVB,* ed. G. Giebisch, pp. 811–52. New York: Springer. 939 pp.

136. Selinger, Z. 1974. Discussion remark. See Ref. 64, p. 114

137. Smith, P. A., Case, R. M. 1975. Effects of cholera toxin on cyclic adenosine 3',5'-monophosphate concentration and secretory processes in the exocrine pancreas. *Biochim. Biophys. Acta* 399: 277–90

138. Söling, H. D., Unger, K. O. 1972. The role of insulin in the regulation of α-amylase synthesis in the rat pancreas. *Eur. J. Clin. Invest.* 2:199–212

139. Spiegel, A. M., Downs, R. W. Jr., Aurbach, G. D. 1977. Guanosine 5',α-β-methylene-triphosphate, a novel GTP analog, causes persistent activation of adenylate cyclase: Evidence against pyrophosphorylation mechanism. *Biochem. Biophys. Res. Commun.* 76: 758–64

140. Stolze, H., Schulz, I. 1979. Effect of atropine, ouabain, antimycin A, and A 23187 on the "trigger Ca^{2+} pool" in the exocrine pancreas. *Am. J. Physiol.* Submitted

141. Streeto, J. M. 1969. Renal cortical adenyl cyclase: effect of parathyroid hormone and calcium. *Metabolism* 18: 968–73

142. Svoboda, M., Robberecht, P., Camus, J., Deschodt-Lanckman, M., Christophe, J. 1978. Association of binding sites for guanine nucleotides with adenylate cyclase activation in rat pancreatic plasma membranes. Interaction of gastrointestinal hormones. *Eur. J. Biochem.* 83:287–97

143. Terai, M., Furihata, C., Matsushima, T., Sugimura, T. 1976. Partial purification of adenosine 3',5'-cyclic monophosphate phosphodiesterases from rat pancreas in the presence of excess protease inhibitors. *Arch. Biochem. Biophys.* 176:621–29

144. Vandermeers, A., Vandermeers-Piret, M.-C., Rathé, J., Kutzner, R., Delforge, A., Christophe, J. 1977. A calcium-dependent protein activator of guanosine 3':5'-monophosphate phosphodiesterase in bovine and rat pancreas. Isolation, properties and levels in vivo. *Eur. J. Biochem.* 81:379–86

145. Van Leemput-Coutrez, M., Camus, J., Christophe, J. 1973. Cyclic nucleotide–dependent protein kinases of the rat pancreas. *Biochem. Biophys. Res. Commun.* 54:182–90

146. Williams, J. A. 1978. Catharanthine: a novel stimulator of pancreatic enzyme release. *Cell Tissue Res.* 192:277–84

147. Williams, J. A., Chandler, D. 1975. Ca^{++} and pancreatic amylase release. *Am. J. Physiol.* 228:1729–32

148. Williams, J. A., Korc, M., Dormer, R. L. 1978. Action of secretagogues on a new preparation of functionally intact, isolated pancreatic acini. *Am. J. Physiol.* 235:E517–24

149. Wünsch, E., Jaeger, E., Moroder, L., Schulz, I. 1977. Progress in the problem of structure activity relations of gastrointestinal hormones. See Ref. 33, pp. 19–27

Ann. Rev. Physiol. 1980. 42:157–71

WATER-SOLUBLE VITAMIN ABSORPTION IN INTESTINE

❖1259

Richard C. Rose[1]

Departments of Physiology and Surgery, The Milton S. Hershey Medical Center, The Pennsylvania State University, Hershey, Pennsylvania 17033

INTRODUCTION

Few topics in gastrointestinal physiology are more in need of a comprehensive review than the mechanism by which the small intestine handles water-soluble vitamins. Early reports attributed vitamin[2] absorption primarily to simple diffusion; evidence in favor of specialized transport processes was frequently obscured because investigators used either (*a*) a concentration of vitamin in the bathing solution far in excess of the K_m for carrier-mediated absorption; (*b*) too long an in vitro incubation for the tissue to remain viable; (*c*) bathing media that lacked certain metabolic substrates necessary to maintain tissue viability; (*d*) a molecular form of the vitamin that is not absorbed by a specific transport mechanism; and/or (*e*) relatively insensitive microbiological assays for the vitamin.

Because of the conclusions reached from the early studies, the burden of proof recently has been on the investigator whose results suggest that vitamins are absorbed by a process other than simple diffusion. Considerable progress has been made, however. The reader familiar with textbook accounts of vitamin absorption may be surprised to find that evidence now exists in favor of a specialized transport mechanism for nearly all vitamins that have been studied in detail (Table 1). The present article does not discuss vitamin B_{12}, which has been reviewed adequately elsewhere. Here I focus on the most carefully executed studies of other water-soluble vitamins. (This literature search was completed in March, 1979.)

[1]Work related to this review was supported by USPHS Grant AM 19119.
[2]The term "vitamin" in this text refers to water-soluble vitamins.

0066-4278/80/0315-0157$01.00

Table 1 Properties of vitamin transport in small intestine

Vitamin	MW	Species	Site of absorption in small intestine	Mechanism of transport	K_m	Other properties[a]
Ascorbic acid	176	man	ileum	active transport		1
		guinea pig	ileum	active transport	1.0 mM	1
p-Aminobenzoic acid	137	rat, hamster	no preference	simple diffusion	none	
Biotin	244	hamster	proximal	active transport	1.0 mM	1
Choline	121	guinea pig	jejunum	facilitated transport	0.6 mM	4
		chick	?	facilitated transport	0.1 mM	1
		hamster	ileum	facilitated transport	0.2 mM	
Folic acid (pteroylglutamic acid)	441	rat	jejunum	facilitated transport	1.6 μM	1,4
5-MTHF[b]	488	rat	jejunum	simple diffusion	none	
Nicotinic acid	123	bullfrog	proximal	active transport		1
		rat	jejunum	carrier mediated	1.0 mM	1
Pyridoxine	206	rat, hamster	no known preference	simple diffusion	none	3
Riboflavin	376	man	proximal	facilitated transport		2
		rat	jejunum	carrier mediated	3.0 μM	1
Thiamine	337	rat	jejunum	active transport	0.2–0.6 μM	1,3

[a]Other properties: 1 = Na-dependent; 2 = bile salt–dependent; 3 = phosphorylated; 4 = metabolized other than by phosphorylation
[b]5-MTHF: 5-methyltetrahydrofolic acid

L-ASCORBIC ACID (VITAMIN C)

Animals requiring dietary ascorbic acid (primates and guinea pig) absorb it by an intestinal transport process more complex than that of animals synthesizing it from glucose and absorbing it from the intestinal lumen only by simple diffusion. In humans and guinea pigs, the transport rate is most rapid in the ileum. Studies in vitro (61, 62) have demonstrated clearly that the vitamin moves from the mucosal to the serosal solution against a concentration gradient and also accumulates in the cellular fluid at a concentration higher than is present in the luminal fluid. This concentrating ability of the intestinal mucosa is lost under anaerobic conditions or following exposure of the tissue to metabolic poisons.

Influx of ascorbic acid across the brush border of guinea pig ileum from low concentrations of ascorbic acid (<6 mM) in the luminal solution follows saturation kinetics and is specific for the L stereoisomer [(37), Figure 1]. Ascorbic acid influx is reduced 67% by the presence in the mucosal solution of L-dehydroascorbic acid, a naturally occurring ascorbic acid analog. These observations indicate that a carrier-mediated mechanism at the brush border is involved in absorption of the vitamin. Because recently absorbed ascorbic acid is present in the cell in free form, it is concluded that ascorbic acid is actively transported across the mucosal membrane into epithelial cells of the ileum.

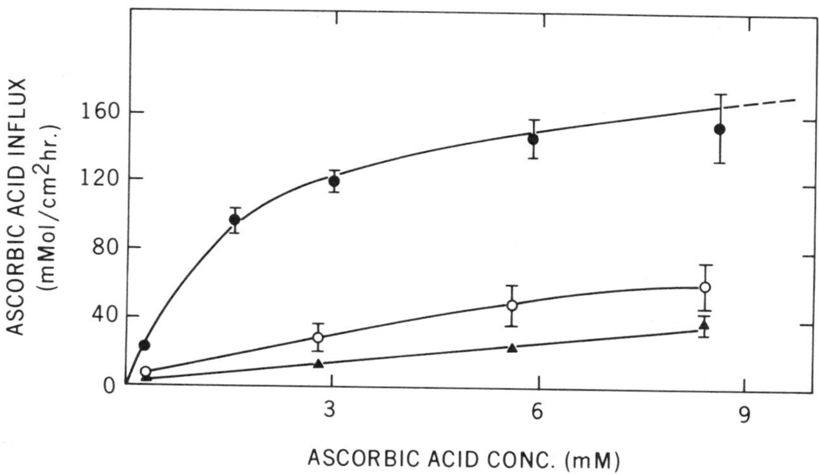

Figure 1 Ascorbic acid influx into guinea pig ileal mucosa from mucosal ascorbic acid concentrations of 0.28–8.6 mM. Exposure times were 5 min. Test solution contained Na = 140 (●), 50 (○), or 0 (▲) mEq l^{-1}. Dashed line extends toward data points at ascorbic acid concentrations of 14.2 and 28.2 mM and has a slope of 7.2×10^{-3} cm h^{-1}. [Mellors, Nahrwold & Rose (37), Published by permission of *The American Journal of Physiology.*]

Influx of ascorbic acid is highly dependent on the presence of Na in the luminal bathing solution (37). Complete substitution of either K or choline for Na reduces the entry rate by 70–80% and prevents the tissue/medium ratio from exceeding unity. On the basis of electrical measurements it appears that Na from the mucosal solution is co-transported into the intestinal transport cells with ascorbic acid.

The information available on ascorbic acid transport in primate and guinea pig intestine is accommodated by a model of transport quite similar to the Na-gradient hypothesis (9) that describes sugar and amino acid transport in small intestine. Ascorbic acid and Na are envisioned to bind to a carrier molecule in the brush-border membrane that translocates them into the cell. When the Na concentration in luminal fluid is 140 mEq l^{-1}, the intracellular Na concentration is maintained relatively low (about 70 mEq l^{-1}) because an energy-dependent active transport mechanism at the basolateral membrane "pumps" Na toward the serosal bathing solution. Sodium dissociates from the carrier mechanism at the inner side of the mucosal membrane, and the vitamin moves into the free solution of the cell. The carrier may then assume its original orientation with its binding sites exposed to the luminal solution, and the process is repeated.

Ascorbic acid influx in the absence of extracellular Na is linearly related to the vitamin's concentration in the mucosal solution; the slope of the relationship is similar to the slope observed at Na = 140 mEq l^{-1} when ascorbic acid is present at concentrations from 6 to 28 times the K_m. This suggests that ascorbic acid influx proceeds at a low rate by simple diffusion in addition to carrier-mediated influx. This interpretation leads to the conclusion that the brush-border mechanism for ascorbic acid transport is quite similar to that for glucose transport—i.e. the carrier molecule cannot translocate substrate across the membrane in the absence of Na, and removal of Na from the bathing media is kinetically equivalent to addition of a noncompetitive inhibitor. Although the transport process for ascorbic acid appears to be generally similar to that for actively transported sugars and amino acids, the carrier mechanisms involved are not shared by the three types of solutes: Glucose, alanine, and ascorbic acid do not compete for transport.

p-AMINOBENZOIC ACID

The most instructive work on absorption of para-aminobenzoic acid (PABA) demonstrated that everted sacs of mouse and flying squirrel small intestine (but not rat and hamster intestine) concentrate this vitamin in the serosal solution against a chemical gradient (59). The PABA-carboxyl-C^{14} absorbed from the mucosal solution (10^{-5} M, initial concentration) appeared to be chemically unaltered according to chromatographic analysis.

In addition, there was no $C^{14}O_2$ formation. A specialized mechanism of PABA absorption is not necessarily indicated from the study, however, because the effects of an existing transepithelial electrical gradient must also be considered. Under the experimental conditions, the serosal surface of mouse and flying squirrel intestine was 5–10 mV positive with respect to the mucosal surface. Such an electrical driving force would be capable of accumulating the negatively charged vitamin in the serosal bathing solution in excess of the ratio observed. Anionic analogs of PABA (benzoic acid, p-chlorobenzoic acid, and p-methoxybenzoic acid) were absorbed to the same extent as PABA. Thus, even though the study (59) was carefully executed it did not provide firm evidence of a specialized mechanism of PABA absorption. A recent study (1) on PABA transport in rat intestine does not yield additional useful information because the vitamin was investigated over the range 1.0–50 mM. The observed results, which were characteristic of simple diffusion, are expected whenever a nutrient is investigated at luminal concentrations grossly above the physiological range.

BIOTIN

Significant variation among species has been observed in intestinal absorption of biotin. Transmural transport against a concentration gradient was demonstrated in everted sacs of small intestine in hamster, mouse, chinchilla, gerbil, and squirrel, but not in the rat, rabbit, guinea pig, ferret, or carp (58). Biotin is required in the diets of rats and rabbits and in the diets of hamsters and monkeys; thus no strong correlation exists between these species' need for the vitamin and the ability of the intestine to absorb it by active transport. Transport of biotin from the luminal solution into mucosal cells of hamster small intestine follows saturation kinetics with a K_m of 1.0 mM and V_{max} of 2.2×10^{-2} micromoles min^{-1} ml^{-1} tissue water (2).

Elimination of Na from the solution bathing the mucosal surface (choline substitution) reduced biotin uptake by increasing the K_m without affecting the V_{max}. Biotin uptake was essentially eliminated when K completely replaced Na. Because biotin uptake was not reduced by partial depletion of intracellular Na, it was concluded that extracellular Na is necessary for formation of a ternary carrier-biotin-Na complex. The inhibitory effects of several biotin analogs on biotin uptake suggest that the free carboxyl group of the side chain participates in the carrier-substrate interaction.

CHOLINE

Experiments performed on everted sacs of rat and hamster ileum and jejunum with choline concentrations below 8 $mM\,l^{-1}$ provided evidence of a saturable uptake of the vitamin. This was interpreted to indicate that choline absorption takes place by a specific transport mechanism in addition to simple diffusion (51). Segments of chick intestine were incubated in buffer, and the absorption rate of [^{14}C] choline was determined (20). Absorption followed saturation kinetics and was reduced by structural analogs. Because of the incubation technique used, however, the results of these experiments cannot be attributed specifically to transport events at either the mucosal or the serosal cell membrane. Examination of choline influx across the brush-border membrane of guinea pig jejunum (30) identified a Na-independent, carrier-mediated transport process at this site. Choline appears to be the only vitamin absorbed in mammalian intestine by a carrier-mediated process not dependent on mucosal Na. Choline influx into colon showed characteristics of simple diffusion.

A clear indication of active transport of choline from mucosa to serosa could not be obtained in hamster intestine because a substantial fraction of transported choline reached the serosal solution as a metabolite (51), probably betaine (13). Thus, it appears that choline is absorbed in mammalian small intestine by a facilitated transport process not dependent on cellular metabolic energy. A coenzyme form of choline, citidine diphosphate choline, is degraded in the intestine prior to absorption of the components (70).

FOLIC ACID

Folic acid is the parent compound of a family of pteroylpolyglutamates having one to six molecules of L-glutamic acid linked by gamma peptide bonds to pteroylglutamic acid (PGA). Plasma folate is usually the monoglutamate compound. Cleavage of polyglutamates occurs during absorption. Studies with the jejunal perfusion technique in human subjects demonstrated that hydrolysis of dietary pteroylheptaglutamate occurs during absorption, but it does not take place within the intestinal lumen (15). Pteroylheptaglutamate appears to be absorbed across the mucosal cell membrane prior to hydrolysis by the intracellular λ-carboxypeptidase, folate conjugase (17, 21). Folate conjugase is highly active in the lysosomal fractions of rat and guinea pig small intestine but not in the brush-border membrane (17, 21, 49).

It is apparent that folic acid is absorbed in the intestine of the rat, guinea pig, dog, and human by a process more specialized than simple diffusion. Studies on proximal rat intestine in vivo and in vitro suggest that at low luminal concentrations PGA is absorbed by means of a saturable mechanism (4, 10, 16, 18, 24, 47, 55). The uptake of PGA by the gut wall of rat is susceptible to competition by folate analogs (10, 18, 47, 55). In addition, the unidirectional influx of PGA across the mucosal border of hamster intestine follows saturation kinetics and is reduced by structural analogs of folic acid or by replacement of Na in the bathing solution by K or Tris (47). It therefore appears that a brush-border carrier mechanism is involved in folate absorption. Clinical observations have been made of patients with a specific intestinal defect in absorption of folate; this supports the concept of a specialized transport process for this vitamin (52). Is metabolic energy required in the transport process? Does PGA accumulate against an electrochemical gradient? One problem in evaluating the mechanism of intestinal transport of this vitamin is its substantial modification during absorption. The claim of active transport in human and rat intestine in situ (8, 18, 19) is not convincing because folic acid is quite rapidly metabolized to 5-methyltetrahydrofolic acid; thus a concentration gradient of PGA between plasma and intestinal lumen was probably not established. The strongest indication of active transport of PGA comes from studies in vitro on rings of rat jejunum that appeared to concentrate the vitamin in the intracellular fluid by a process dependent on metabolic energy (3, 10). Confirmation and elaboration of these results (which appeared as abstracts) will help to settle the issue.

Another explanation for the saturable uptake of PGA has been suggested (4, 5, 31, 33, 34, 55) that is based on the solubility properties of folic acid in the acid microclimate at the mucosal surface of small intestine. The existence of the acid microclimate was predicted by Hogben et al (22) and measured with pH-sensitive microelectrodes by Lucas et al (31, 33, 35), who found that this region of pH 6.3 is dependent on Na and glucose in the bathing solution. Folic acid exists as a neutral species at a low pH, and absorption of the neutral species by simple diffusion is likely to be proportional to its concentration at the mucosal surface. Thus, an increase in the folic acid concentration within the acid microclimate at the mucosal membrane might result in a proportionate increase in the absorption rate until the neutral species approaches its saturation concentration, and saturation kinetics of absorption would be expected.

This model of folic acid transport was evaluated in several ways by measuring PGA influx across the brush-border membrane of rat intestine (47):

1. In rat duodenum in vitro, cellular metabolism of glucose is necessary to maintain the acid microclimate (34). Removal of Na from the bathing solution is thought to reduce availability of luminal glucose for cellular metabolism and thereby limit folic acid transport because the acid microclimate is not maintained. Therefore, a Na-free bathing solution should not inhibit folic acid transport into glucose-depleted tissue. However, a pronounced (95%) inhibition of PGA influx due to Na removal is seen under glucose-free conditions.

2. Intraperitoneal injection of methotrexate 24 hr before sacrifice of a rat increases the microclimate pH by approximately 0.35 units (31), which is

a loss of 58% of the normal H^+ ion gradient between the microclimate and the bulk bathing solution. Under these conditions, folic acid influx should be much less Na-dependent than normal because Na removal is also predicted to reduce influx through an effect on eliminating the acid microclimate. However, PGA influx 24 hr after methotrexate injection is highly (88%) dependent on Na.

3. In rat jejunum, the pH gradient between the microclimate and bulk bathing solution becomes diminished as the bathing solution is progressively acidified; at approximately pH 5.8 the gradient is abolished (31). Under these conditions, Na removal should have no inhibitory effect on folic acid influx because cellular metabolism is not maintaining a distinct acid microclimate. However, at pH 5.8 influx is reduced by 50% when Na in the bathing solution is lowered to 30 mM.

4. Exposure of rat jejunum to ouabain reduces the pH gradient between the microclimate and the bathing solution (34). Thus, folic acid influx into tissue incubated in media with ouabain and glucose would not be expected to be Na-dependent. However, influx is reduced by 75% when Na is removed from the bathing solution of tissue preincubated with glucose and ouabain.

Thus, the results of influx studies offer no support for the mechanism of PGA transport suggested by Blair et al but are consistent with a model of carrier-mediated transport across the brush-border membrane. The results of a study on absorption of the PGA analog, methotrexate, may also be used to evaluate the importance of nonionic diffusion in folate transport (64). Methotrexate and PGA both have peak rates of transport when the bathing solution pH is 6.0, though the two compounds differ in values of pk_a by 2.6 units (56). This comparison indicates that absorption of PGA and methotrexate proceed by transport events that are similarly affected by pH (such as a common carrier mechanism) rather than by nonionic diffusion. Also of interest is the recent conclusion (25) that influxes of a variety of weak acids and bases into rat small intestine are not influenced by a microclimate of distinctive pH at the epithelial surface.

5-Methyltetrahydrofolic acid (5MTHF) is another important form of folate in man's diet. Found in human red cells and plasma, it originates, in part, from metabolism of dietary nonmethylated folic acid in intestinal cells. 5MTHF is absorbed in rat jejunum by a nonsaturable transport mechanism, probably simple diffusion (6, 65).

NICOTINIC ACID

The most thorough study of nicotinic acid absorption was performed in vitro on bullfrog proximal small intestine (14). At initial concentrations of

2.0×10^{-3} M and below, a net flux of nicotinic acid in the direction of absorption was demonstrated. Thus it appears that this vitamin is absorbed by active transport in bullfrog intestine, but the details of this process were not elucidated. Influx of nicotinic acid across the mucosal membrane of rat jejunum includes a component that is saturable, Na-dependent, and reduced by the presence of structural analogs (L. A. Myers, D. L. Nahrwold, R. C. Rose, unpublished observations). Thus the few data available suggest that a specific carrier-mediated mechanism in the brush-border membrane brings nicotinic acid into the cell.

A specialized transport process could not be detected by measurement of transepithelial nicotinic acid fluxes (67), perhaps because the experiments were discontinued before the isotopic tracer techniques could give meaningful results. Thus it is not known whether or not any mammalian intestine actively transports nicotinic acid.

PYRIDOXINE AND RELATED COMPOUNDS (VITAMIN B_6)

Experiments in vitro and in vivo with rat and hamster small intestine have provided no evidence of active transport of pyridoxine (7, 38, 54, 66). Uptake into everted sacs of rat jejunum over the vitamin concentration range 0.01 μM–10 mM did not show saturation kinetics and was not inhibited by anoxia, metabolic poisons, Na-free media, ouabain, or the presence of a structural analog, 4-deoxypyridoxine. Pyridoxine uptake between 0° and 37°C had a Q_{10} value of only 1.3. Thus absorption of this vitamin into the tissues investigated appears to proceed by simple diffusion.

It has recently been shown in rat jejunum in vivo and in vitro that phosphorylation of pyridoxine is saturable but that this process has no effect on tissue uptake of the vitamin from the luminal fluid (39, 40). Phosphorylation is presumed to be mediated by pyridoxal kinase, a cytoplasmic enzyme of the small intestine. Because the normal occurrence of phosphorylation results in a decreased rate of transmural absorption whereas uptake is unaffected, the primary effect of phosphorylation must be one of reducing efflux of absorbed vitamin from the mucosal cells. The biologic significance of this phosphorylation and subsequent dephosphorylation is not clear; it might serve to control the intracellular level of pyridoxal phosphate, which participates in the absorption of other nutrients.

RIBOFLAVIN

Our understanding of intestinal transport of riboflavin in humans is based on several indirect observations. Rapid absorption in the proximal intestine is suggested because orally administered riboflavin appears at a peak concentration in the plasma and urine within 2 hr after ingestion (36, 41). A maximum absorption of riboflavin (10–18 mg) from a single dose of the vitamin suggests that a saturable mechanism participates in absorption (32, 50, 63). A saturable mechanism was also suggested because plasma concentration plateaued at high oral doses of the vitamin (63). No evidence has been presented, however, that allows one to evaluate whether or not riboflavin is actively transported by human intestine.

Controversy exists in the literature concerning the mechanism of riboflavin absorption in experimental animals: Two groups (60, 68) reported that absorption in everted sacs of rat and hamster intestine proceeds by simple diffusion, whereas Rivier (46) favored a saturable, Na-dependent mechanism. Because the former investigators failed to identify a specialized transport mechanism for most of the other water-soluble vitamins (57, 60, 68), it appears likely that the conclusions of the latter are more accurate. It would be worthwhile, nonetheless, to confirm these observations and to explore further the details of the riboflavin transport process.

The presence of bile salts in the intestinal lumen enhances riboflavin absorption in humans and dogs (36, 42). A role of bile salts is also indicated by the impaired absorption in cases of biliary obstruction (27). The means by which bile salts increase absorption has not been determined. They may function through an effect on membrane permeability, on vitamin solubility in the lumen, or on intestinal transit time.

The phosphorylated form of the vitamin in the diet is rapidly dephosphorylated in the intestinal lumen, which suggests that the free form of the vitamin is absorbed (26). Once within the mucosal cells the vitamin may undergo phosphorylation, which probably accounts for the high concentration of this form of the vitamin reaching the portal blood in studies in vivo or the serosal bath in studies in vitro (42). In rabbits, phosphorylation of riboflavin appears unnecessary for absorption since the rate of absorption and the degree of phosphorylation along the intestine are not correlated (71).

THIAMINE

In contrast to earlier studies, which favored simple diffusion, recent evidence from several laboratories indicates that thiamine is absorbed by one or more specific transport mechanisms (23, 28, 45, 53). In humans and rats, absorption is most rapid in the proximal small intestine. Studies in vivo on intact loops of rat small intestine revealed saturation kinetics for thiamine absorption over the concentration range 0.06–1.5 μM (23). At higher concentrations (2–560 μM) absorption was linearly related to the luminal vitamin concentration. In studies in vitro on everted sacts of jejunum, thiamine accumulated in the serosal bathing solution at a concentration higher than in the mucosal solution (23, 53). The underlying active transport mechanism appears to be directed into the cell, as indicated by an ability of rat small intestine to accumulate free thiamine in the cell in excess of the extracellular concentration (28). Transport is reduced by metabolic inhibitors, anaerobic conditions, low temperatures, and Na-free conditions. Additional evidence for a carrier-mediated process comes from countertransport (or substrate-counterflow) studies in which the presence of a structural analog of thiamine, pyrithiamine, in the bathing solution greatly accelerated the efflux of thiamine from tissue preloaded with the vitamin (45).

Dietary thiamine undergoes phosphorylation either in the intestinal lumen or within the intestinal cells (11). A close relationship between thiamine transport and phosphorylation appeared likely because only the structural analogs of thiamine that inhibit thiamine phosphorylation are effective in inhibiting its intestinal transport (44). Also, the kinetics of thiamine phosphorylation and transport by intestinal sacs of rats indicate that these processes have similar K_m values (69). Thus, it was concluded that thiamine pyrophosphokinase, the enzyme catalyzing thiamine phosphorylation, is the carrier involved. This conclusion appeared to be supported by recent work (43) showing that human jejunum in vitro accumulates thiamine in the phosphorylated form.

However, a role of phosphorylation in thiamine transport is doubted by other investigators because (*a*) the distribution of thiamine pyrophosphokinase along the intestine does not correlate well with the rate of thiamine uptake into rat intestine (28); (*b*) although chloroethylthiamine, a thiamine analog, does not inhibit thiamine pyrophosphokinase, it reduces uptake of thiamine into chick intestine (29); (*c*) thiamine pyrophosphokinase activity is localized mainly in the soluble cell fraction rather than in the microvillus membrane (28); (*d*) lack of Na in the mucosal solution markedly reduces net thiamine transport but affects thiamine phosphorylation much less (12); and (*e*) free thiamine accumulates in rat (but not human) mucosa against a gradient (11, 28). Thus, the role of phosphorylation in thiamine transport has not been clarified.

CONCLUSION

Most water-soluble vitamins are absorbed in the intestine as a consequence of intricate metabolic and transport phenomena. Movement of several vitamins across the luminal membrane into absorptive cells is characterized by saturation kinetics and stereospecificity, which suggests that specific "carriers" are operative. Inhibition of this step in transport by the presence of structural analogs of individual vitamins in the luminal solution substantiates this conclusion. In the case of ascorbic acid, folic acid, nicotinic acid, biotin, and thiamine this step in absorption is dependent on the presence of Na in the solution bathing the luminal surface.

Although no single transport model is likely to describe accurately the absorptive properties of such a structurally diverse group of nutrients, it appears that several vitamins are absorbed by a process similar to the Na-gradient hypothesis formulated for sugar and amino acid transport in intestine. However, evidence in support of such a model is still incomplete. For instance, it has not yet been determined whether most of the vitamins accumulate in the cell water of the intestinal mucosa at a concentration higher than that present in the extracellular fluid (or bathing solution). This is more difficult to assess for vitamins than for sugars and amino acids, since the latter have been shown to be present in an osmotically active form and are therefore presumably free in solution. The molar quantity of any vitamin within the cell is likely to be no more than 4% of the cellular concentration of alanine when each solute is available at concentrations resembling that found in situ. Thus it is exceedingly difficult to use osmotic evidence to demonstrate that the absorbed vitamin is present in free form.

In addition, the Na-gradient hypothesis predicts that Na enters the cell across the mucosal membrane in association with the organic substrate. This has been shown convincingly to be the case for amino acid influx. However, because only a small amount of Na appears to enter the cells in association with even the most rapidly transported vitamin (ascorbic acid), direct measurement has been obscured by the more prominent solute-independent Na influx. An attempt to estimate by electrical parameters whether or not Na influx is coupled to ascorbic acid influx has given an affirmative answer, but the result is not decisive because a wide variety of factors influence the electrical potential profile of small intestine. Additional techniques must be devised to evaluate the interdependence of vitamin and Na uptake by intestinal mucosa.

An alternate model of cellular vitamin accumulation has been evaluated which suggests that absorption of weak organic bases may be accelerated due to the presence of an acid microclimate at the brush border; several lines of evidence indicate that folic acid is not absorbed by this mechanism. Convincing evidence of some form of a specialized mechanism of transport is lacking for only two vitamins (p-aminobenzoic acid and pyridoxine); in these cases absorption by simple diffusion is therefore presumed. However, this presumption is based on only one or two reports; more careful scrutiny of these processes may reveal specialized transport mechanisms. It is also possible that the electrical potential profile of small intestine contributes significantly to vitamin distribution; serosa-positive PDs of 3–10 mV could account for substantial net mucosa-to-serosa fluxes of anionic vitamins.

Information about the basic mechanism of vitamin absorption will ultimately find clinical applications. For instance, because several vitamins are absorbed primarily by means of a carrier-mediated mechanism at low luminal vitamin concentrations, and only a slightly greater rate of absorption proceeds by simple diffusion at high luminal concentrations, mega-vitamin therapy may be wasteful and ineffective. In addition, a recent finding indicates that long-term high oral doses or IM injections of ascorbic acid result in a decreased ability of the ileal transport mechanism in guinea pig to absorb this vitamin (48). Thus, mega-vitamin therapy in humans may have the net result of reducing the intestinal transport capacity for absorbing vitamins. An individual who alternately consumes very high and low doses of a vitamin may therefore be predisposed to vitamin deficiency. A more complete knowledge of the details of vitamin absorption is likely to promote our understanding of clinical vitamin deficiency resulting from malabsorption due to disease, genetic defects, or oral drug administration.

Literature Cited

1. Arvanitakis, C., Longnecker, M. P., Folscroft, J. 1978. Characterization of p-aminobenzoic acid transport across the rat intestine. *J. Lab. Clin. Med.* 91:467–72
2. Berger, E., Long, E., Semenza, G. 1972. The sodium activation of biotin absorption in hamster small intestine in vitro. *Biochim. Biophys. Acta* 255:873–87
3. Binder, H. J., Whiting, D. 1975. Active pteroylmonoglutamate transport by jejunal mucosa. *Clin. Res.* 23:391A (Abstr.)
4. Blair, J. A., Johnson, I. T., Matty, A. J. 1974. Absorption of folic acid by everted segments of rat jejunum. *J. Physiol. London* 236:653–61
5. Blair, J. A., Johnson, I. T., Matty, A. J. 1976. Aspects of intestinal folate transport in the rat. *J. Physiol. London* 256:197–208
6. Blair, J. A., Matty, A. J., Razzaque, A. 1975. Uptake of 5-methyltetrahydrofolic acid by the rat jejunum. *J. Physiol. London* 250:221–30
7. Booth, C., Brain, M. 1962. The absorption of tritium-labelled pyridoxine hydrochloride in the rat. *J. Physiol. London* 164:282–94
8. Burgen, A. S. V., Goldberg, N. J. 1962. Absorption of folic acid from the small intestine of the rat. *Brit. J. Pharmacol.* 19:313–20
9. Crane, R. K. 1962. Hypothesis for mechanism of intestinal active transport of sugars. *Fed. Proc.* 21:891 (Abstr.)
10. Dhar, G. J., Selhub, J., Gay, C., Rosenberg, I. 1977. Characterization of the individual components of intestinal folate transport. *Gastroenterology* 72: 1049 (Abstr.)
11. Ferrari, G., Sciorelli, G., Del Poggio, P., Ventura, U., Rindi, G. 1975. Free thiamine as the likely precursor of endocellular thiamine phosphates in everted rings of rat jejunum. *Pflügers Arch.* 356:111–20
12. Ferrari, G., Ventura, U., Rindi, G. 1971. The Na^+-dependence of thiamine intestinal transport in vitro. *Life Sci.* 10:67–75
13. Flower, R. J., Pollitt, R. J., Sanford, P. A., Smyth, D. H. 1972. The metabolite formed during choline transfer by the intestine. *J. Physiol. London* 222:146P–147P
14. Fox, K., Hogben, C. 1974. Nicotinic acid active transport by in vitro bullfrog small intestine. *Biochim. Biophys. Acta* 332:336–40
15. Halsted, C. H., Baugh, C. M., Butterworth, C. E. Jr. 1975. Jejunal perfusion of simple and conjugated folates in man. *Gastroenterology* 68:261–69
16. Halsted, C. H., Bhanthumnavin, K., Mezey, E. 1974. Jejunal uptake of tri-

tiated folic acid in the rat studied by in vivo perfusion. *J. Nutr.* 104:1674–80
17. Halsted, C. H., Reisenauer, A., Back, C., Gotterer, G. S. 1976. In vitro uptake and metabolism of pteroylpolyglutamate by rat small intestine. *J. Nutr.* 106:485–92
18. Hepner, G. W. 1969. The absorption of pteroylglutamic (folic) acid in rats. *Brit. J. Haematol.* 16:241–49
19. Hepner, G. W., Booth, C. C., Hoffbrand, A. V., Cowan, J., Mollin, D. L. 1968. Absorption of crystalline folic acid in man. *Lancet* 2:302–6
20. Herzberg, G. R., Lerner, J. 1973. Intestinal absorption of choline in the chick. *Biochim. Biophys. Acta* 307:234–42
21. Hoffbrand, A. V., Peters, T. J. 1969. Subcellular localization of folate conjugase in guinea pig intestinal mucosa. *Biochem. Biophys. Acta* 192:479–85
22. Hogben, C. A. M., Tocco, D., Brodie, B. B., Shanker, L. 1959. On the mechanism of intestinal absorption of drugs. *J. Pharmacol. Exp. Ther.* 125:275–82
23. Hoyumpa, A. M., Middleton, H. M., Wilson, F. A., Schenker, S. 1975. Thiamine transport across the rat intestine. I. Normal characteristics. *Gastroenterology* 68:1218–27
24. Izak, G., Galevski, K., Grossowicz, N., Jablonska, M., Rachmilewitz, M. 1972. Studies on folic acid absorption in the rat. *Am. J. Dig. Dis.* 17:591–98
25. Jackson, M. J., Williamson, A. M., Dombrowski, W. A., Garner, D. E. 1978. Intestinal transport of weak electrolytes: Determinants of influx at the luminal surface. *J. Gen. Physiol.* 71: 301–27
26. Jusko, W. J., Levy, G. 1967. Absorption, metabolism and excretion of riboflavin-5'-phosphate in man. *J. Pharmacol. Sci.* 56:58–62
27. Jusko, W. J., Levy, G., Yaffe, S. J., Allen, J. E. 1971. Riboflavin absorption in children with biliary obstruction. *Am. J. Dis. Child.* 121:48–52
28. Komai, T., Kawai, K., Shindo, H. 1974. Active transport of thiamine from rat small intestine. *J. Nutr. Sci. Vitaminol.* 20:163–77
29. Komai, T., Shindo, H. 1972. Metabolic fate and mechanism of action of chloroethylthiamine. III. Active transport of thiamine from chick intestine and competitive inhibition by chloroethylthiamine. *J. Vitaminol.* 18:55–62
30. Kuczler, F. J., Nahrwold, D. L., Rose, R. C. 1977. Choline influx across the brush border of guinea pig jejunum. *Biochim. Biophys. Acta* 465:131–37
31. Lei, F. H., Lucas, M. L., Blair, J. A. 1977. The influence of pH, low sodium ion concentration and methotrexate on the jejunal-surface pH: a model for folic acid transfer. *Biochem. Soc. Trans., 566th Meet. Cambridge* 5:149–52
32. Levy, G., Jusko, W. J. 1966. Factors affecting the absorption of riboflavin in man. *J. Pharm. Sci.* 55:285–89
33. Lucas, M. L., Blair, J. A. 1978. The magnitude and distribution of the acid microclimate in proximal jejunum and its relation to luminal acidification. *Proc. R. Soc. London Ser. A* 200:27–41
34. Lucas, M. L., Blair, J. A., Cooper, B. T., Cooke, W. T. 1976. Relationship of the acid micro-climate in rat and human intestine to malabsorption. *Biochem. Soc. Trans., 560th Meet. Oxford* 4:154–56
35. Lucas, M. L., Schneider, W., Haberich, F. J., Blair, J. A. 1975. Direct measurement by pH-microelectrode of the pH microclimate in rat proximal jejunum. *Proc. R. Soc. London Ser. B* 192:39–48
36. Mayersohn, M., Feldman, S., Gibaldi, M. 1969. Bile salt enhancement of riboflavin and flavin mononucleotide absorption in man. *J. Nutr.* 98:288–96
37. Mellors, A. J., Nahrwold, D. L., Rose, R. C. 1977. Ascorbic acid flux across the mucosal border of guinea pig and human ileum. *Am. J. Physiol.* 233: E374–79
38. Middleton, H. M. III. 1977. Uptake of pyridoxine hydrochloride by the rat jejunal mucosa in vitro. *J. Nutr.* 107:126–31
39. Middleton, H. M. III. 1978. Jejunal phosphorylation and dephosphorylation of absorbed pyridoxine · HCl in vitro. *Am. J. Physiol.* 235:E272–78
40. Middleton, H. M. III. 1979. In vivo absorption and phosphorylation of pyridoxine: HCl in rat jejunum. *Gastroenterology* 76:43–49
41. Morrison, A. B., Campbell, J. A. 1960. Vitamin absorption studies. I. Factors influencing the excretion of oral test doses of thiamine and riboflavin by human subjects. *J. Nutr.* 72:435–40
42. Onishi, N. 1956. Effect of ursodesoxycholic acid and adenosine on the intestinal absorption of riboflavin. *Vitamins* 11:479–81
43. Rindi, G., Ferrari, G. 1977. Thiamine transport by human intestine in vitro. *Experientia* 33:211–13
44. Rindi, G., Ventura, U. 1967. Phosphorylation and uphill intestinal transport of thiamine in vitro. *Experientia* 23:175–76

45. Rindi, G., Ventura, U. 1969. Thiamine countertransport in rat small intestine. *Pflügers Arch.* 310:185–88
46. Rivier, D. A. 1973. Kinetics and Na-dependence of riboflavin absorption by intestine in vivo. *Experientia* 29: 1443–46
47. Rose, R. C., Koch, M. J., Nahrwold, D. L. 1978. Folic acid transport by mammalian small intestine. *Am. J. Physiol.* 4:E678–85
48. Rose, R. C., Nahrwold, D. L. 1978. Intestinal ascorbic acid transport following diets of high or low ascorbic acid content. *Int. J. Vit. Nutr. Res.* 48: 382–86
49. Rosenberg, I. H., Godwin, H. A. 1971. The digestion and absorption of dietary folate. *Gastroenterology* 60:445–63
50. Ryu, Y. W., Kim, E. S., Song, C. S. 1968. Riboflavin and thiamine absorption. *Yonsei Med. J.* 9:11–13
51. Sanford, P. A., Smyth, D. H. 1971. Intestinal transfer of choline in rat and hamster. *J. Physiol. London* 215:769–88
52. Santiago-Borrero, P. J., Santini, R., Perez-Santiago, E. Maldonado, N., Millan, S., Coll-Camalez, G. 1973. Congenital isolated defect of folic acid absorption. *J. Ped.* 82:450–55
53. Schaller, K., Holler, H. 1974. Thiamine absorption in the rat. I. Intestinal permeability and active transport of thiamine; passage and cleavage of thiamine pyrophosphate in vitro. *Int. J. Vit. Nutr. Res.* 44:443–50
54. Serebro, H. A., Solomon, H. M., Johnson, J. H., Hendrix, T. R. 1966. The intestinal absorption of vitamin B_6 compounds by the rat and hamster. *Bull. Johns Hopkins Hosp.* 119:166–71
55. Smith, M. E. 1973. The uptake of pteroylglutamic acid by the rat jejunum. *Biochim. Biophys. Acta* 298:124–29
56. Smith, M. E., Matty, A. J., Blair, J. A. 1970. The transport of pteroylglutamic acid across the small intestine of rat. *Biochim. Biophys. Acta* 219:37–46
57. Spencer, R. P., Bow, T. M. 1964. In vitro transport of radiolabeled vitamins by the small intestine. *J. Nucl. Med.* 5:251–58
58. Spencer, R. P., Brody, K. R. 1964. Biotin transport by small intestine of rat, hamster and other species. *Am. J. Physiol.* 206:653–57
59. Spencer, R. P., Brody, K. R., Vishno, F. 1966. Species differences in the intestinal transport of p-aminobenzoic acid. *Comp. Biochim. Physiol.* 17:883–89
60. Spencer, R. P., Zamcheck, N. 1961. Intestinal absorption of riboflavin by rat and hamster. *Gastroenterology* 40: 794–97
61. Stevenson, N. R. 1974. Active transport of L-ascorbic acid in the human ileum. *Gastroenterology* 67:952–56
62. Stevenson, N. R., Brush, M. K. 1969. Existence and characteristics of Na^+-dependent active transport of ascorbic acid in guinea pig. *Am. J. Clin. Nutr.* 22:318–26
63. Stripp, B. 1965. Intestinal absorption of riboflavin by man. *Acta Pharmacol. Toxicol.* 22:353–62
64. Strum, W. B. 1977. A pH-dependent, carrier-mediated transport system for the folate analog, amethopterin, in rat jejunum. *J. Pharmacol. Exp. Ther.* 203:640–45
65. Strum, W. B., Nixon, P. F., Bertino, J. B., Binder, H. J. 1971. Intestinal folate absorption. I. 5-methyltetrahydrofolic acid. *J. Clin. Invest.* 50:1910–16
66. Tsuji, T., Yamada, R., Nose, Y. 1973. Intestinal absorption of vitamin B_6. I. Pyridoxol uptake by rat intestinal tissue. *J. Nutr. Sci. Vitaminol.* 19:401–17
67. Turner, J. B. 1959. *The mechanism of absorption of vitamins from the intestines of small laboratory animals.* PhD Thesis. Queen's College, Univ. Oxford, England
68. Turner, J. B., Hughes, D. E. 1962. The absorption of some B-group vitamins by surviving rat intestine preparations. *Q. J. Exp. Physiol.* 47:107–23
69. Ventura, U., Ferrari, G., Tagliabue, R., Rindi, G. 1969. A kinetical study of thiamine intestinal transport in vitro. *Life Sci.* 8:699–705
70. Yashima, K., Takamatsu, M., Okuda, K. 1975. Intestinal absorption of cytidine diphosphate choline and its changes in the digestive tract. *J. Nutr. Sci. Vitaminol.* 21:49–60
71. Yoshihara, S. 1954. Studies on the mechanisms of riboflavin absorption. I. Distribution and absorption of riboflavin in digestive tracts of normal rabbits. *Vitamins* 7:763–67

RESPIRATORY PHYSIOLOGY

RESPIRATORY PHYSIOLOGY

Introduction, Alfred P. Fishman, *Section Editor*

> ... for by careful investigation I have discovered that the whole mass of the lung to which are attached the excurrent vessels, is an aggregate of very thin fine membranes which, stretched and folded, form an almost infinite number of orbicular bladders just as we see formed by wax plates in the walls of the honeycomb cells of beehives. These have such partition and connection that passage is provided from the trachea into them.
>
> Malpighi, M. First letter to Borelli, *Duae Epistolae de Pulmonibus,* 1661 (4)

> [Peering at a] dried lung of a frog ... by the help of our more perfect [magnifying] glass, there met the eye ... vessels joined together in a ring-like fashion. And such is the wandering about of these vessels, as they proceed on this side from the vein and on the other side from the artery, that the vessels no longer maintain a straight direction, but there appears a network made up of the articulations of the two vessels. ... Hence it was clear to the senses that the blood flowed away along tortuous vessels and was not poured into spaces, but was always contained within tubules [capillaries] ...
>
> Malpighi, M. Second letter to Borelli, *Duae Epistolae de Pulmonibus,* 1661 (4)

That air and blood go their separate ways within the lungs was shown by Malpighi more than 300 years ago (4). At that time the function of the lungs was not understood. Therefore, the purpose served by the juxtaposition of alveoli and capillaries was perplexing. Did respiration serve primarily to propel blood in the lungs? Or to stir it? Once the idea surfaced that the primary business of the lungs is gas exchange (3), arrangements of air sacs and blood vessels within the substance of the lungs took on special meaning. The mechanisms that controlled the distribution of air and blood to the alveolar-capillary interfaces were recognized to be important for proper gas exchange.

Sooner or later, anyone concerned with the control of the pulmonary circulation has to face up to the troublesome question of how to distinguish between mechanical and vasomotor effects. To envisage the problem, one has only to examine the cut surface of the air-filled lung—as Malpighi did, but from a somewhat different perspective. Fine vessels and air spaces are everywhere, now and then penetrated by larger conduits for air and blood and partitioned at intervals by struts of supporting tissue that extend in all directions. How does one sort out passive changes in vascular dimensions caused by pushes and pulls generated in the airways or at the pleural surfaces from active constriction or dilatation (2)?

One traditional experimental refuge is to control everything imaginable but the mechanism in question (1). This strategy has uncovered much of the pulmonary circulation's regulatory equipment. But such a procedure risks obscuring both (*a*) the importance of the mechanism under more natural conditions and (*b*) its interplay with other influences that may, depending on the circumstance, override, enhance, or temper it.

A closer approach to physiologic conditions is offered by the use of intact experimental animals. Here the major problem is one of species variation. The lung of one species contains many mast cells, which are sparse in the lungs of another; the bronchial circulation is well developed in one species and virtually absent in another; muscular development and architecture in the pulmonary circulation vary from species to species. Since the fundamental equipment for control may differ, it is not surprising that the contribution of different mechanisms may vary from species to species.

The use of anesthesia in the intact animal can, per se, modify control mechanisms. Moreover, changes in vascular calibers are often inferred from occasional determinations of changes in calculated pulmonary vascular resistance. Pressure-flow curves provide greater reliability in interpretation, particularly when changes in the course of the experiment affect both blood pressure and flow.

These considerations apply to the following six papers, which describe a variety of observations and conclusions from experiments concerned with the control of the pulmonary circulation. The papers fall into two large categories: (*a*) mechanical factors that influence the pulmonary circulation [Gil; Butler]; (*b*) the control of the pulmonary circulation by nerves, vasoactive agents, and chemical stimuli [Fishman; Downing; Butler], and the implications of what this control accomplishes with respect to ventilation-perfusion relationships (Wagner).

Both categories are time-honored in physiology. How the mechanics of breathing affect pulmonary blood flow began to be explored more than two centuries ago (4). About a century ago, the role of the sympathetic nerves was under investigation (1). On the other hand, the classical experiments on the chemical control of the pulmonary circulation are of more recent vintage: Not until 1946 did Von Euler & Liljestrand point out that the respiratory gases could play an important role in regulation of the pulmo-

Table 1 Zones of the lung[a]

Zone	Pressures[b]	Behavior of capillary	Depends on
I	$P_{ALV} > P_{PA} > P_{PV}$	Collapsed	No flow[c]
II	$P_{PA} > P_{ALV} > P_{PV}$	Starling resistor	P_{PA}-P_{ALV}
III	$P_{PA} > P_{PV} > P_{ALV}$	Open or distended	P_{PA}-P_{PV}

[a] After West et al (5)

[b] P_{ALV} = Alveolar Pressure; P_{PA} = Pulmonary Artery Pressure; P_{PV} = Pulmonary Venous Pressure.

[c] Except for flow through corner vessels.

nary circulation and suggest how they might help to match pulmonary blood flow to alveolar ventilation (1).

Why an update on these ageless questions at this time? Because the last few years have gone a long way both in providing, and in pointing the way to, answers. Quantitative anatomy, applied to lungs in carefully monitored physiological preparations, has helped to unravel the functional anatomy of the pulmonary microcirculation and the surrounding interstitium. The effects of gravity on the distribution of pulmonary blood flow have been sorted out according to driving pressures in different zones (see Table 1) of the lungs (5). Sophisticated physiological techniques have helped to explain the connections and the function of the extrapulmonary nerves. Receptor mechanisms in the pulmonary circulation have been identified and are being explored. A wide assortment of humoral and neurohumoral substances—some released within the lungs and others delivered from afar—have been shown to be processed by the lungs to different degrees and to be capable of influencing vascular tone. The effects of hypoxia on the pulmonary circulation are being examined to determine whether it acts by means of mediators or has a direct effect on smooth muscle. The process of distinguishing between what agents *can* do to the pulmonary circulation and what they *actually* do under natural conditions is now under way. The next six chapters summarize our present understanding of the control of the pulmonary circulation and indicate the directions from which new information and insights can be anticipated.

Literature Cited

1. Cournand, A. 1964. Air and blood. In *Circulation of the Blood. Men and Ideas,* ed. A. P. Fishman, D. W. Richards, pp. 3–70. NY: Oxford Univ. Press
2. Lai-Fook, S. J. 1979. A continuum mechanics analysis of pulmonary vascular interdependence in isolated dog lobes. *J. Appl. Physiol.* 46:419–28
3. Lower, R. 1932. Tractatus de Corde. Transl. K. J. Franklin. In *Early Science in Oxford,* ed. R. T. Gunther. Oxford: Clarendon Press. Vol. IX
4. Perkins, J. F. Jr. 1964. Historical development of respiratory physiology. In *Handbook of Physiology, Section 3. Respiration,* ed. W. O. Fenn, H. Rahn, 1:12, 13. Washington, DC: Am. Physiol. Soc.
5. West, J. B. 1977. *Regional Differences in the Lung.* NY: Academic

Ann. Rev. Physiol. 1980. 42:177–86

ORGANIZATION OF MICROCIRCULATION IN THE LUNG

❖1260

Joan Gil

Departments of Medicine and Anatomy, Hospital of the University of Pennsylvania, Philadelphia, Pennsylvania 19104

INTRODUCTION

During the last few years, attempts have continued to ground physiologic concepts of the circulations of the lung into anatomic realities. The most exciting single development has been with respect to changes in configuration and dimensions in the alveolar microvascular bed. In this review, only the capillary network of the pulmonary circulation is considered; lymphatics are not discussed (for review see 21).

CAPILLARY NETWORK

The capillaries of a human lung are found to have a total volume of 213 ml and an endothelial surface of 126 m^2 (12). Weibel (36) has provided a morphometric description of the capillary bed based on the observation that alveolar capillaries are arranged in a hexagonal array of wedged tubes. Before discussing the capillaries it is necessary to deal with the extra-alveolar vessels, which behave differently from pulmonary capillaries.

Extra-Alveolar Vessels

The concept of extra-alveolar vessels originated in the physiological literature; the definition of such vessels has remained purely operational, not anatomic. According to West (34) "extra-alveolar vessels are those which are not exposed to alveolar pressure and which are found to expand with lung inflation" (in contrast to the alveolar capillaries, which are compressed when alveolar pressure rises). They include such anatomically diverse entities as veins, venules, arteries, and precapillaries. The key to the behavior

0066-4278/80/0315-0177$01.00

of these vessels seems to be the existence of a connective tissue sheath around them; this sheath is also all they have in common. Their functional significance is reviewed in detail elsewhere in this volume by Butler.

Fixation Techniques

Critical in studies of configurations of the alveolar capillary network are (*a*) the selection of a fixation procedure (chemical fixatives or rapid freezing?; if chemical fixatives are used, what route of administration, airways or blood vessels?) and (*b*) an appraisal of how the findings relate to the method of fixation. Use of the following methods has been reported:

1. Instillation or filling of the airways with fixative at pressure after pneumothorax results in excellent tissue preservation. This easy and reliable fixation technique has been used by many authors. The common textbook representation of the lung is based on lungs fixed by this or a similar procedure.

2. Vascular perfusion of fixatives (preferably isotonic, buffered 1% OsO_4 with macromolecules added) into the pulmonary artery with a peristaltic pump has been described (15, 16). Preservation of structures for light and electron microscopy is good, though the capillaries are flushed out. The danger of edema formation must be avoided by strict control of inflow pressures and oncotic and osmotic pressures of the perfusates. This more demanding technique fixes rapidly at any desired level of inflation without disturbing the original air-tissue or air-fluid interface. Because the physical properties of the fixatives are different from those of blood, computation of the effective intracapillary distending pressure is difficult. If one perfuses an aldehyde, flow resistance rises rapidly after the onset of the perfusion; if one perfuses OsO_4, however, no substantial change of flow resistance at constant flow can be sensed. Hence there is little reason to believe that osmium changes the original architecture. As for the glutaraldehyde, most of the increase in flow resistance is probably due to constriction of the muscular vessels.

3. Fung & Sobin (8, 9, 30, 31) injected a silicone elastomer into the pulmonary artery, inflated the lung at pressure, embedded it in paraffin or gelatin, and made thick histological sections. What they observed gave rise to the theory of the sheet flow. This method is a combination of a microvascular cast followed by introduction of fixatives into the air spaces after polymerization of the cast. The preparation of very thick sections is suited for the type of morphometric analysis intended by the authors (31).

4. Finally, rapid freezing methods have been applied to the study of the alveolar microcirculation by several authors, particularly by Glazier et al (17). The method includes quenching of the lung by spraying liquid Freon, transferring to liquid nitrogen, freeze-drying, embedding, and sectioning.

The advantages of this approach are well-known. From the histological point of view, however, rapid freezing yields results of modest quality and resolution. Furthermore, formation of ice crystals can be prevented only in the subpleural area, and the method is not well suited for electron microscopy. Improvements are conceivable. For instance, attempts are under way to extend freezing methods to electron microscopy by replacing freeze-drying with a freeze-substitution technique (22). Workers using this technique are usually concerned that the subpleural region accessible to them might not be representative of the parenchyma as a whole. Except in the case of the first row of alveoli, which are directly anchored to the pleura, this is not a serious problem (15). Finally, one must consider the dangers of too slow a freezing rate and possible shrinkage during fixation and embedding.

Morphometry

Different laboratories have used different approaches to examine lungs fixed for various purposes, thereby complicating a meaningful comparison of data.

Some workers have adapted for their own purposes the type of comprehensive morphometry pioneered by Weibel. This approach rests on a probabilistic basis derived from notions of integral geometry and geometrical probability. Experience is required to ensure proper choice of parameters. Intuitive approaches to study morphological features that intrigue an investigator sometimes lack a theoretical basis and may undermine quantitative morphology. The major studies reported have been along the following lines:

1. Data on capillary volume and endothelial surface have been obtained in lungs fixed by filling the airways with fixatives [several species (5, 11, 28) including man (12)]. Blood volumes were computed by a point counting procedure, the capillary surface by counting intersections of the endothelial boundary line with test lines. These studies sought to estimate what Weibel (37–39) calls the "structural diffusing capacity" and how it adapts to different conditions. The same type of morphometry has been applied to lungs fixed by vascular perfusion (1, 16, 40).

2. Fung & Sobin (8) described the morphometric basis of their sheet flow concept of the pulmonary microcirculation (8) and presented a morphometric method that involves two steps, both carried out on thick sections examined in an elaborate stage of a modified microscope (31). Septum thickness was measured with an image-shearing eyepiece; the "vascular-space-tissue ratio" or VSTR, defined as the ratio of the vascular luminal volume to the circumscribing tissue volume, was determined by planimetry of a tracing of flat views of the alveolar wall. They also measured the post

diameter and the interpost distance. The notion of posts in the sheet flow theory is discussed below.

3. Glazier et al (17) and Warrell et al (33) studied embedded sections of frozen and freeze-dried lungs. They counted erythrocytes inside the vessels (this value is related to the blood volume) in lungs perfused with normal and hardened erythrocytes and measured diameters of capillary profiles. More recently Mazzone et al (22) reported measurements of the depth of profiles of alveolar folds in electron microscopic specimens.

4. A little-known method for estimating capillary loading was introduced by Butler & Kleinerman (4). This is an estimate of how many capillary segments are present per volume or alveolar surface unit of the lung. On flat views of thick sections (200–400 μm), intersections of capillary segments with a straight line of known length are counted and related to the alveolar diameter measured on the same specimen. This allows one to estimate an index of capillary loading per alveolar volume under the assumption that all capillaries are of the same diameter and that all alveoli are symmetric figures with constant shape. Since morphometric estimation of capillary volume by point counting procedures at the light microscopy level is impossible because of insufficient resolution, Weibel (38) attempted to use the notion of capillary loading to obtain an estimate of capillary volume, which he proposed to relate to the alveolar surface rather than to the alveolar diameter.

Corner Vessels

This term was introduced by Glazier et al (17) and used later by Rosenzweig et al (27). The latter group reported that blood still flowed in the pulmonary circulation after the transpulmonary pressure exceeded the arterial pressure by 10 cm H_2O. Histological examination of frozen lungs fixed under these conditions and perfused with India ink revealed accumulations of stain in alveolar "corners"—i.e. in places where three alveoli met. These areas were interpreted as arterio-venous anastomoses. The corner vessels would evidently be protected against high alveolar pressures. Anatomical identification of these structures was difficult. They could not be identical with the extra-alveolar vessels, which are surrounded by connective tissue, but on the other hand corner vessels were not a part of the commonly described lung anatomy. Gil (13, 14) showed that the corner vessels appear to be located inside the pleats of the alveolar walls that had been described by Gil & Weibel (16). The specimens of Gil & Weibel were fixed by vascular perfusion of OsO_4 and embedded in epoxy resins that were cut for light microscopy and offered excellent resolution. Both rapid freezing and vascular perfusion are techniques more likely to preserve the original pulmonary structure than is conventional filling of the alveoli with fluids.

Functional Issues

RECRUITMENT VS DISTENSION That the extensive alveolar network is uniquely adaptable is shown by the fact that it presents itself in different forms depending on the fixation technique used. Glazier et al (17) reported histological observations and measurements made on isolated lungs of greyhound dogs perfused in closed circuit with previously removed blood and fixed by rapid freezing. They counted the number of red blood cells per 10 μm of alveolar septum, the mean width of capillaries, and the percentage of septum occupied by red blood cells. Groups of lungs were fixed under conditions of alveolar and vascular pressures apt to reproduce the flow patterns existing in the three-zone model. Under Zone I conditions few capillaries were open and most alveolar walls were thin. They found only one erythrocyte per 100 μm of septum, mostly in corner areas. Zone II lungs showed more red blood cells, but the filling of the septa was patchy: Some alveolar walls contained strings of erythrocytes, others contained only closed capillaries. The capillary width also increased down Zone II. The alveolar walls under Zone III conditions contained still more erythrocytes. The capillary width increased again very substantially. The authors concluded that their preparations showed both recruitment and distension of capillary segments.

Warrell et al (33) followed up on the problem of recruitment versus distension using similar methods. They ruled out the possibility of recruitment at the level of arterioles or small arteries on the basis that the patchy appearance would have been different. They concluded that both recruitment and distension at the capillary level were the dominant factors in controlling pulmonary vascular resistance. Capillary volume increased by means of recruitment in Zone II but mostly by dilation in Zone III.

In an attempt to study the effect of pressure increases on a network, West et al (35) analyzed a computer simulation composed of 50 interconnected elements arranged in two different configurations. The two models were planar. One had two independent, low-resistance lines (across the arterial and venular end but not along the flow axis); the other had none. Recruitment over a large range of pressures, as well as intermittent flow and flow reversal in individual segments, were observed. From these studies one must conclude that no simple relationship exists between the transmural pressures and the histological picture: The corner vessels stay open despite high air pressures, and recruitment of capillaries requires high intravascular opening pressures.

Gil (13) introduced an anatomic model that may be relevant to this type of functional problem. First, he suggested the existence of low-resistance lines ("preferential paths") along the longitudinal axis of the flow which could change with the degree of tension of the wall. Second, one should distinguish between primary and secondary septa: Primary septa are those alveolar walls separating neighboring alveolar ducts; secondary septa are the walls between alveoli open to the same duct. In this model the capillaries of the secondary walls had to be regarded as collaterals; the main thoroughfares were inside the primary septa, which are in the longitudinal axis from the conducting airways to the pleural surface. Finally, the corner vessels were regarded by Gil as periodically placed areas of drainage into the veins (13).

Sheet flow A different interpretation is that of the sheet flow theory (8). In the plan view, the sheet flow model does not differ much from the traditional cylindrical tube model; in the cross section, however, the alveolar vascular space is a broad sheet lined on both sides by endothelium with regularly arranged obstructions—the posts. The authors compare the vascular space with a parking garage with cylindrical columns. In the plan view, the sheet may be divided into a network of hexagons with a circular post at the center of each hexagon, but no part of it can be regarded as an individual capillary segment. The model is characterized by three parameters: length of each side of the hexagon, height or thickness of the sheet, and diameter of the posts. Electron microscopic studies (30) demonstrated an internal structure of the posts, which would be responsible for the unusual compliance of the microvascular blood spaces. Fung & Sobin (9) also devised experiments that showed an extraordinary elasticity of the vascular sheet: Within a physiological range of positive transmural pressures, sheet thickness varied linearly with the pressure.

The contrast with the notions of West et al (35), for whom capillary distension is only relatively marginal, is striking. In the sheet model, there is no space for capillary recruitment. The theory equally fails to account for items such as corner vessels and areas of patchy filling. These difficulties, however, do not invalidate the sheet flow notion, whose main significance (as Fung & Sobin emphasized) is more fluid-mechanical than geometric. Whether we have sheet flow or tube flow, the Poiseuillian formula cannot be applied to the relationship between pressure gradient and blood flow because the whole microvascular bed is under "entry" or "end" effects due to the short length of the capillary segments. The only anatomical observation that would upset the hydrodynamic considerations of Fung & Sobin would be the demonstration of long, cylindrical segments in the capillary network of the alveolar wall, where Poiseuille flow could occur. Such cylinders do not seem to exist. Recently Fung & Sobin (10) have published a detailed review of their notions. Moreover, Kapanci et al (20) have reported that many interstitial cells contain contractile filaments. This could give a new dimension to the "posts" by making them capable of regulatory activity. Assimacopoulos et al (1) examined lungs fixed by vascular perfusion and interpreted their findings as support for the sheet flow theory.

CAPILLARY CHANGES WITH LUNG VOLUME Gil and co-workers (15, 16, 38) have been concerned with (*a*) alveolar events related to changes in pulmonary volume and (*b*) a morphometric definition of alveolar surface-to-volume relationships. They fixed lungs by vascular perfusion of osmium tetroxide and found septal pleats in alveolar corners formed by varying degrees of folding of the alveolar walls. These pleats were reversible features of variable size. Electron micrographs revealed that the pleats enclosed gaps continuous with the alveolar spaces and filled with free fluid. The lower the lung volume, the more pleats were present. In edematous or flooded lungs (14, 15) these pleats were absent; all capillaries were full and bulged into the alveolar space.

Weibel et al (40) described different types of folds on the alveolar surface: Some affect only a small portion of a thin barrier, others form a deeper cleft associated with collagen, and still others result in plication of the whole septum giving rise to a pleat. Therefore, there are more folds than pleats and the two notions are not identical. Weibel et al also showed that capillary volume in low-inflation lungs increased inversely to total lung volume owing to the fact that capillaries in the pleated areas are wide open with a circumferential perimeter.

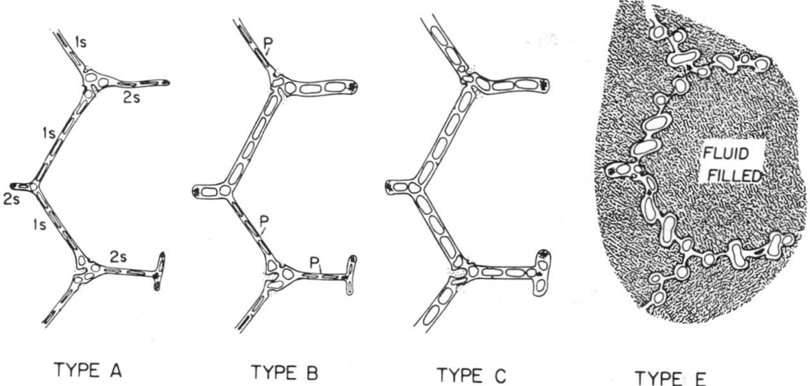

Figure 1 Simplified schemes of four types of capillary configurations described in the literature (see Conclusions). As shown on type A, 1s are primary septa, placed between different ducts; 2s are secondary septa placed between alveoli open to the same duct. On type B,P points at patches of closed septal capillaries. Corner pleats in real histological specimens are usually larger. At this magnification level, the smoothness of the alveolar surface (particularly on type C) is exaggerated. Air-filled surfaces show no bumps except under connective-tissue condensations, but gentle changes of curvature can occur. Type E is the configuration seen in flooded alveoli.

CONCLUSIONS

In 1963 Weibel (36) modeled the alveolar capillaries as wedged cylinders arranged in predominantly hexagonal arrays, an interpretation buttressed by substantial morphometric information. At that time this anatomic structure was regarded as stable, but recent studies have shown the extraordinary adaptability of this network. The network is a part of the alveolar wall, which itself undergoes adaptations. The wall and the vascular spaces are inseparable and share many constraints. The limited number of capillary configurations that have been shown to be possible are depicted in Figure 1. These different configurations were brought about by the various manipulations to which different workers submitted the lungs before histological fixation. The most important factor in determining these configurations is the transmural balance of forces, but it is open for discussion what else may also play a role. In the view of this reviewer configuration A is what Rosenzweig et al (27) showed in lungs with intra-alveolar pressures higher than arterial pressures, and is also what Glazier et al (17) described for Zone I. The "corner vessels," the only conspicuously open parts of the capillary network, are placed inside the septal pleats described by Gil & Weibel (16). Configuration B differs mostly in that some of the septal capillaries are filled, while patches of capillaries remain closed. The overall alveolar surface is smooth; corner vessels persist, though they are not the only open components. All corners need not be pleated. This seems to be what Glazier et al described as Zone II. Configuration C is characterized by the filling of all capillaries while the surface remains smooth. Septa are thick and

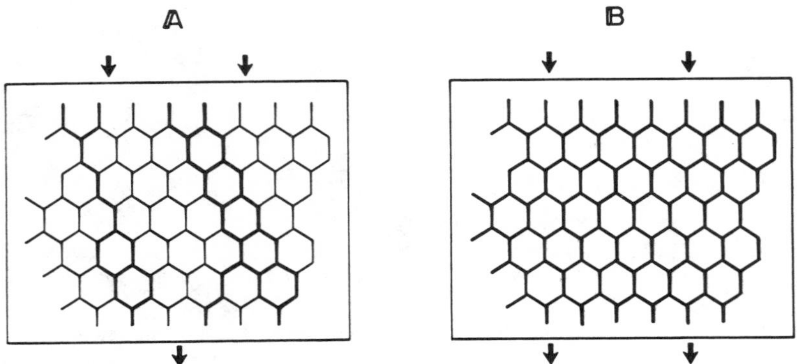

Figure 2 Planar view of a hexagonal capillary network similar to that seen inside alveolar walls. Open segments are shown with thick lines, closed segments are thin. Panel A shows only preferential paths open; it is suggested that this is the case with configuration types A and B shown in Figure 1. In Panel B all segments are open, as in configurations C and E.

corner vessels are hardly noticeable. This is very similar to the Zone III situation described by Glazier et al, but also best fits the sheet flow model of Fung & Sobin (8). According to recent studies (14, 15), when the alveolar space is flooded (configuration E) the septum falls back to the original all-open capillary model of Weibel; capillaries continuously cross the connective tissue midplane, the epithelial surface is very irregular, and the pleats (and the corner vessels) are completely unraveled.

Figure 2 shows how the capillary network must be regarded on a plan view. On the left only parts of the hexagonal network (preferential or throughfares) are open as in configurations A and B. This is shown by thickened lines. On the right all the capillaries are open, something that configurations C and E have in common. One should attempt to extrapolate the hexagonal network of Figure 2 into Figure 1. The main difference between the computer simulation of West et al and the preferential-path notion suggested by Gil is that, in the latter, deformability of the alveolar wall may open a longitudinal path of low resistance. The blood might be steered into preferential paths by small folds of the alveolar surface. A distinction between primary and secondary septa is made because capillaries of both cannot be represented in the same plane.

Literature Cited

1. Assimacopoulos, A., Guggenheim, R., Kapanci, Y. 1976. Changes in alveolar capillary configuration at different levels of lung inflation in the rat: An ultrastructural and morphometric study. *Lab. Invest.* 34:10–22
2. Boyd, R. B. 1975. A gross and microscopic study of the respiratory anatomy of the antarctic Weddell Seal, *Leptonychotes weddelli. J. Morphol.* 147:309–36
3. Burri, P. H., Dbaly, J., Weibel, E. R. 1974. The postnatal growth of the rat lung. I. Morphometry. *Anat. Rec.* 178:711–30
4. Butler, C., Kleinerman, J. 1970. Capillary density: alveolar diameter, a morphometry approach to ventilation and perfusion. *Am. Rev. Respir. Dis.* 102:886–94
5. Burri, P., Weibel, E. R. 1971. Morphometric estimation of pulmonary diffusion capacity. II. Effect of environmental PO_2 on the growing lung. *Respir. Physiol.* 11:247–64
6. Elliott, F. M., Reid, L. 1965. Some new facts about the pulmonary artery and its branching pattern. *Clin. Radiol.* 16:193–98
7. Fiebiger, F. J. 1916. Über Eigentümlichkeiten im Aufbau der Delphinlunge und ihre physiologishe Bedeutung. *Anat. Anz.* 48:540–65
8. Fung, Y. C., Sobin, S. S. 1969. Theory of sheet flow in lung alveoli. *J. Appl. Physiol.* 26:472–88
9. Fung, Y. C., Sobin, S. S. 1972. Elasticity of the pulmonary alveolar sheet. *Circ. Res.* 30:451–69
10. Fung, Y. C., Sobin, S. S. 1977. Pulmonary alveolar blood flow. In *Bioengineering Aspects of the Lung,* ed. J. B. West, pp. 267–359. NY: M. Dekker
11. Geelhaar, A., Weibel, E. R. 1971. Morphometric estimation of pulmonary diffusion capacity. III. The effect of increased oxygen consumption in Japanese waltzing mice. *Respir. Physiol.* 11:357–66
12. Gehr, P., Bachofen, M., Weibel, E. R. 1978. The normal human lung: ultrastructure and morphometric estimation of diffusion capacity. *Respir. Physiol.* 32:121–40
13. Gil, J. 1978. Morphologic aspects of alveolar microcirculation. *Fed. Proc.* 37:2462–65
14. Gil, J. 1979. Influence of surface forces on pulmonary circulation. In *Pulmonary Edema,* ed. A. P. Fishman, E. M. Renkin, pp. 53–64. Bethesda, Md: Am. Physiol. Soc.

15. Gil, J., Bachofen, H., Gehr, P., Weibel, E. R. 1979. The alveolar volume to surface area relationship in air and saline filled lungs fixed by vascular perfusion. *J. Appl. Physiol.: Respir. Environ. Exercise Physiol.* In press
16. Gil, J., Weibel, E. R. 1972. Morphological study of pressure-volume hysteresis in rat lungs fixed by vascular perfusion. *Respir. Physiol.* 15:190–213
17. Glazier, J. B., Hughes, J. M. B., Maloney, J. E., West, J. B. 1969. Measurements of capillary dimensions and blood volume in rapidly frozen lungs. *J. Appl. Physiol.* 26:65–76
18. Hislop, A., Reid, L. 1978. Normal structure and dimensions of the pulmonary arteries in the rat. *J. Anat.* 175:71–84
19. Horsfield, K. 1978. Morphometry of the small pulmonary arteries in man. *Circ. Res.* 42:593–97
20. Kapanci, Y., Assimacopoulos, A., Irle, C., Zwahlen, A., Gabbiani, G. 1974. Contractile interstitial cells in pulmonary alveolar septa: a possible regulator of ventilation/perfusion ratio? *J. Cell Biol.* 60:375–92
21. Lauweryns, J. M., Baert, J. H. 1977. Alveolar clearance and the role of the pulmonary lymphatics. *Am. Rev. Respir. Dis.* 115:625–83
22. Mazzone, R. W., Durand, C. M., West, J. B. 1978. Electron microscopy of lung rapidly frozen under controlled physiological conditions. *J. Appl. Physiol.: Respir. Environ. Exercise Physiol.* 45:325–33
23. Meyrick, B., Reid, L. 1979. Ultrastructural features of the distended pulmonary arteries of the normal rat. *Anat. Rec.* 193:71–98
24. Pietra, G. G., Magno, M., Johns, L., Fishman, A. P. 1979. Bronchial veins and pulmonary edema. See Ref. 14, pp. 195–206
25. Pietra, G. G., Szidon, J. P., Carpenter, H. A., Fishman, A. P. 1974. Bronchial venular leakage during endotoxin shock. *Am. J. Pathol.* 77:387–406
26. Pietra, G. G., Szidon, J. P., Leventhal, M. M., Fishman, A. P. 1971. Histamine and interstitial pulmonary edema in the dog. *Circ. Res.* 29:323–37
27. Rosenzweig, D. Y., Hughes, J. M. B., Glazier, J. B. 1970. Effects of transpulmonary and vascular pressure on pulmonary blood volume in isolated lung. *J. Appl. Physiol.* 28:553–60
28. Siegwart, B., Gehr, P., Gil, J., Weibel, E. R. 1971. Morphometric estimation of pulmonary diffusion capacity: IV. The normal dog lung. *Respir. Physiol.* 13:141–59
29. Singhal, S., Henderson, R., Horsfield, K., Harding, K., Cumming, G. 1973. Morphometry of the human pulmonary arterial tree. *Circ. Res.* 33:190-97
30. Sobin, S. S., Fung, Y. C., Tremer, H. M., Rosenquist, T. H. 1972. Elasticity of the pulmonary alveolar microvascular sheet in the cat. *Circ. Res.* 30:440–50
31. Sobin, S. S., Tremer, H. M., Fung, Y. C. 1970. Morphometric basis of the sheet flow concept of the pulmonary alveolar microcirculation in the cat. *Circ. Res.* 26:397–414
32. Wagner, P., McRae, J., Read, J. 1967. Stratified distribution of blood flow in secondary lobule of the rat. *J. Appl. Physiol.* 22:1115–23
33. Warrell, D. A., Evans, J. W., Clarke, R. O., Kingaby, G. P., West, J. B. 1972. Pattern of filling in the pulmonary capillary bed. *J. Appl. Physiol.* 32:346–56
34. West, J. B. 1977. Blood flow. In *Regional Differences in the Lung,* ed. J. B. West, pp. 85–165. NY: Academic
35. West, J. B., Schneider, A. M., Mitchell, M. M. 1975. Recruitment in networks of pulmonary capillaries. *J. Appl. Physiol.* 39:976–84
36. Weibel, E. R. 1963. *Morphometry of the Human Lung.* NY: Academic
37. Weibel, E. R. 1970. Morphometric estimation of pulmonary diffusion capacity I. Model and method. *Respir. Physiol.* 11:54–75
38. Weibel, E. R. 1973. A simplified morphometric method for estimating diffusing capacity in normal and emphysematous human lungs. *Am. Rev. Respir. Dis.* 107:579–88
39. Weibel, E. R., Gil, J. 1977. Structure-function relationships at the alveolar level. See Ref. 10, pp. 1–81
40. Weibel, E. R., Untersee, P., Gil, J., Zulauf, M. 1973. Morphometric estimation of pulmonary diffusion capacity. IV. Effect of varying positive pressure inflation of air spaces. *Respir. Physiol.* 18:235–308

Ann. Rev. Physiol. 1980. 42:187–98

MECHANICAL INFLUENCES ON THE PULMONARY MICROCIRCULATION ❖1261

Bruce H. Culver and John Butler

Division of Respiratory Diseases, Department of Medicine, University of Washington, Seattle, Washington 98195

> The similarity between the arteries and airways is a beautiful feature of lung function which is not always clearly recognized and appreciated.
>
> C. C. Macklin (25)

The investigator seeking to understand the pulmonary circulation is confronted by awesome problems: a system of collapsible tubes, of variable number, parts of which narrow while others expand with lung inflation, suspended in an air-filled organ and perfused in a pulsatile fashion with a fluid whose viscosity changes with flow rate, the whole system being subjected to cyclical changes of pressure and volume during breathing (15). This chapter considers some of these mechanical factors in the light of the intriguing new information that has become available in recent years. We build from a consideration of the pulmonary circulation at a horizontal level into the effects of stacking different levels of perfusion in the vertical lung. Separate consideration of extra-alveolar vessels and alveolar vessels (made up of mural and corner vessels) is warranted because these segments are affected in different ways by changes of lung volume and other mechanical influences.

There have been several major landmarks in our understanding of the pulmonary circulation during the last few decades: cardiac catheterization, the concept of the the sluice or waterfall, and the vertical zones of perfusion in the air-filled lung. Recently, an equally great advance has been made in understanding the morphology of the vessels, particularly the alveolar microvessels, using the newer techniques of vascular or quick-freeze fixation reviewed by Gil in this volume.

0066-4278/80/0315-0187$01.00

Unlike the airways, which do not narrow much beyond the acinar level, the arterial blood vessels continue to narrow at each division as far as the capillaries. Horsfield (17), Cumming, and their colleagues, who deserve credit for creating order out of chaos by extolling the geophysical Strahler system of numbering branches from the smallest to the largest instead of vice versa, found that the total cross-sectional area increases like the bell of a trumpet, though less strikingly than that of the airways (Figure 1). In a system of branching tubes, however, it is possible for resistance per unit length through the combined pathway to increase even though total cross-sectional area increases, depending on the ratio of parent to daughter radii (a/b) and the number of daughters per generation (n). Total cross-sectional area increases with branching if $n > (a/b)^2$, but a decrease in resistance occurs only if $n > (a/b)^4$ (15). The latter occurs in the smaller airways but

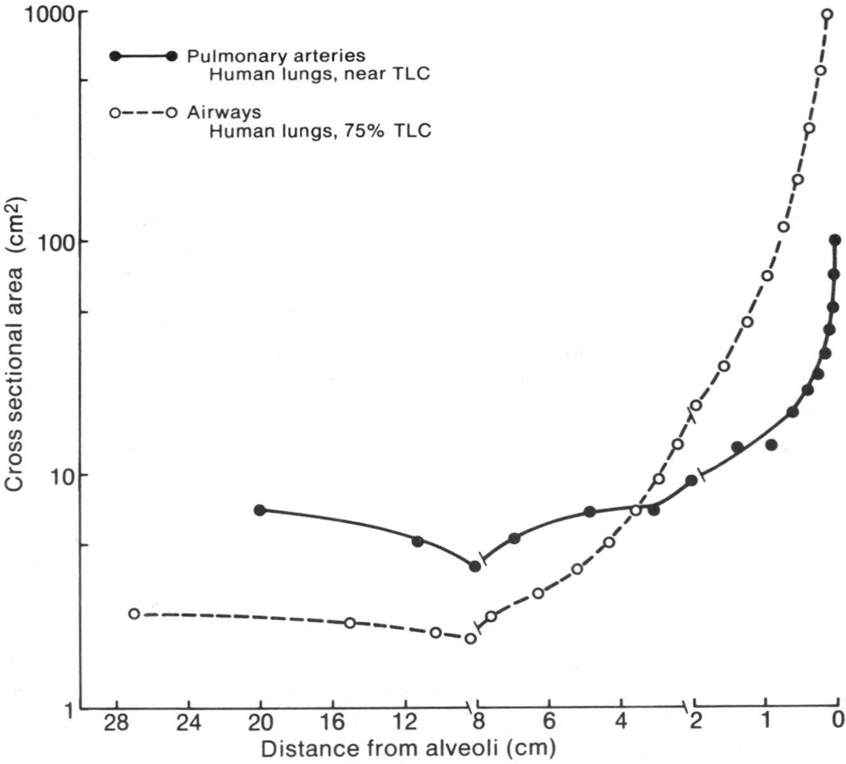

Figure 1 Cross sectional area of the pulmonary arterial tree (17) and airways (39) plotted vs distance proximal to the precapillary vessels or alveolar ducts. Although both increase markedly towards the alveoli the effect on flow resistance is quite different (as discussed in the text). (Note log scale ordinate and breaks in abscissa scale.)

not in the arterial tree, so resistance increases in the smaller arteries. The capillary bed is composed of a network of short tubes when undistended but when distended looks and works like a sheet of blood interrupted by an array of posts (11). The veins originate from groups of capillaries in acini and run around the lobule in the interlobular area where they may be exposed to somewhat different stresses than the arteries. The distensibility of the vessels varies along their course. The large arteries are elastic, allowing continuous expansion as the systolic distending pressure increases. The smaller arteries and veins are less compliant, especially at higher physiologic pressures (8). The large vein walls are nondistensible but can undergo large volume changes by collapsing (4).

The vessels of the pulmonary circulation are subjected to markedly different perivascular pressures in their course from mediastinum through lung parenchyma to the alveolar air spaces and back. Extra-alveolar vessels include the arteries and veins, both outside and inside the lungs, not directly influenced by alveolar pressure. Alveolar vessels are influenced by alveolar pressure. This is a functional, not an anatomic definition. The microvessels in alveolar "corners" have a physiologic similarity to extra-alveolar vessels because they are less affected by alveolar pressure than other alveolar vessels. However we have chosen to consider these corner vessels as a type of alveolar vessel.

EXTRA-ALVEOLAR VESSELS

The *heart* and *extrapulmonary* vessels are influenced by mediastinal pressures. The pressure around the airways in the mediastinum in the dog becomes positive relative to subcostal pleural pressures as the chest is inflated (36). This may be due to the pattern of expansion of the lungs, which are fixed together at the hilum and tend to press against each other as they distend above the functional residual capacity (FRC). Similarly, the pericardial and perivascular pressures may fall less than subcostal pleural pressure (9, 28). An apparent increase in left atrial transmural pressure, calculated from subcostal rather than measured peri-atrial pressure, has been assumed to indicate left ventricular dysfunction with lung inflation. However, it and the bigger pulse swing observed even in the open chest may be due to this compressive effect on the heart by the tense surface of the inflated lung (41). The main pulmonary artery distends with inspiration (15) since its intravascular pressure rises relative to mediastinal pressure. In contrast, left atrial and pulmonary venous pressures fall with the surrounding pressure.

The *intrapulmonary* arteries and veins lengthen as lung volume increases. The behavior of elastic tubes suggests that these vessels might narrow when stretched, but excised intrapulmonary artery segments up to 6 cm long do not narrow appreciably with lengthening in the physiologic range (22a).

Vessel diameter is influenced by transmural pressure; since intravascular pressures are low in the pulmonary circulation, the perivascular pressure can have considerable effect. That lung inflation tends to expand extra-alveolar vessels has been recognized for some time (18, 25), but the degree of change depends on the initial distention of the vessels in relation to that of the lungs. At high vascular pressures the vessels are more rigid so there is less influence of lung volume. Conversely, at high transpulmonary pressures the lungs are stiff so there is less change with vascular pressure (3, 21). In post-mortem human lungs, expansion of the extra-alveolar vessels with lung inflation occurs only if vascular pressures are very low; at physiologic vascular pressures the diameter seems to decrease (20). Thus, the old credo that extra-alveolar vessels are dilated as lung volume increases may not always apply.

An increase in vessel diameter with lung inflation at the same intravascular pressure implies a decrease in the perivascular pressure. In an unusual approach, Lai-Fook et al (22) observed the effect of the surrounding parenchyma on cylindrical holes bored in excised dog lungs. A blood vessel lying in the hole would be subjected to perivascular pressures depending on the relation of the vessel to the hole diameter. Then, from the pressure-diameter behavior of vessels in other intact lobes at different transpulmonary pressures it was possible to calculate the perivascular pressure (21). The estimated perivascular pressures from this and another set of experiments are summarized in Table 1. They vary with transpulmonary pressure more closely than lung volume, are more negative around arteries than veins, and are more negative with lower intravascular pressures. Howell et al (18) dramatically demonstrated that, in the extreme case with the pulmonary vasculature emptied, full inflation of a dog lung can suck fluid into the arteries from 30 cm below the hilum.

Technical advances, together with unusual care and persistence, are yielding preliminary data for perivascular fluid pressures directly measured with a wick technique around the larger extra-alveolar vessels in the dog lung (14, 19). These pressures also consistently become negative to pleural pressure as the lung expands, particularly at low vascular pressures (Table 1).

As lung volume decreases below FRC, the small arteries and veins tend to close. An elegant analysis of this phenomenon (24) suggested that it occurs when they are narrowed below a critical diameter. Such a critical closure could arise from the active tension in the vessel wall. Lai-Fook (21) found that vessels were often irregular and partially collapsed when estimated transmural pressure was zero after decreasing vascular pressures at low lung volumes; however, the caliber did not decrease further, perhaps because the surrounding parenchyma would not allow it. Burton & Patel (6) still provide the only morphologic data on extra-alveolar vessel

Table 1 Perivascular pressure in isolated dog lungs. The pressure (cm water, relative to pleural pressure) outside pulmonary arteries and veins at different vascular and transpulmonary pressures

Estimated pressure[a]										References
Pulmonary arteries						Pulmonary veins				
Ppa	Ptp	4	12	25	Ppv	Ptp	4	12	25	
25		−1	−7	−15	10		0	−3	−8	(21)
10		−3	−10	−17	0		−1	−5	−10	
	Ptp	5	15	30		Ptp	5	15	30	
25		+2	0	−2	12.5		+1	0	−2	(29, 35)
5		−1	−5	−11	2.5		−1	−3	−6	

Measured pressure									
Pulmonary arteries									
Ppa	Ptp	0	5	10	15	20	25	30	
25			−2	−3	−5		−8		(14)
10			−3	−5	−7		−11		
0		−3		−15		−28		−41	(19)

[a]Ppa, pulmonary artery pressure; Ppv, pulmonary vein pressure; Ptp, transpulmonary pressure

changes at very low lung volumes. The incidence of "gnarliness" (how contorted and grooved arterial casts were) was markedly increased when lung volume was small. The distribution of resistance, determined by following the driving pressure as an injected bolus of low viscosity fluid moves through a perfused lung, shows that the site of maximum resistance moves from the midpoint of the total lung blood volume (presumably in alveolar capillaries) to a more proximal position in the arterial tree as the lungs are deflated (10). However, it is possible that this narrowing also reflects vasospasm, not so much due to a venomotor reflex (6) as to hypoxia (30), since alveolar oxygen may well be very low in the poorly expanded regions.

ALVEOLAR VESSELS

Our understanding of what happens to the alveolar vessels with changing lung volume may have been postponed by years because of the misleading morphology provided by fixation techniques that required drying of the lungs or filling of the alveoli with fluid. Who would not have been impressed by the bulging of the capillaries into the alveolar lumen in the fluid-filled lung illustrated by Gil? (See page 183.) How difficult it was to understand why, since surface tension should flatten out vascular bulges, perfusion was facilitated (5, 23) rather than obstructed when surface tension was increased. Now we know: The capillaries do not bulge into the air-filled lung. Another discrepancy, that between the high morphometric estimates and low measured diffusing capacity values for the pulmonary capillary blood volume, also seems to have been due to the histological fixation with fluid filling, which opens alveolar folds and capillaries to an unphysiologic extent.

Mural Vessels

The diaphanous alveolar walls are made up of a sheet of capillaries interlaced with connective tissue fibers. These are coiled like springs at resting volumes, but stretched straight at higher volumes (12). When lung volume decreases, the alveolar walls may fold, with the structural elements and cell bodies moving centrally and the capillaries still lying on the surface. The capillary wall can also crumple, forming pleats protruding into the capillary lumen (26). When the lung expands, the alveolar walls gradually unfold. To the extent that alveolar surface is recruited with lung inflation by unfolding of pleats or completely collapsed alveoli, the mural capillaries need not be stretched. Indeed, capillary wall thickness is not reduced at high levels in the lung despite marked flattening of the lumen as alveolar pressure exceeds perfusion pressure (26). The capillaries behave as though their walls are plastic, rather than elastic.

Corner Vessels

It is possible to perfuse the lungs slowly even when alveolar pressure exceeds pulmonary artery pressure right to the bottom of the lungs (5, 23, 33). The vessels in the corners of the alveoli are open when alveolar exceeds plumonary arterial pressure by 10 cm H_2O (33). Recent studies suggest that these corner vessels are in a pleated zone beneath the more sharply curved corner areas of the alveolar fluid film. Surface tension along a curved air-fluid interface creates a force vector pointing toward the center of curvature. This increases as the radius of curvature decreases. In alveolar corners this force opposes alveolar pressure; thus alveolar corner vessels are protected and less compressed than alveolar mural vessels. Careful inspection of photomicrographs of distended, perfusion-fixed lungs shows that the vessels in the septa close to the corners are also open. Indeed, some of these mural vessels appear to be wedge-shaped, with the wider end of the wedge beneath the more curved alveolar surface. In the succulent living lung, tissue fluids and the subphase of the alveolar fluid film tend to accumulate where the interstitial pressure is most reduced by abrupt curvatures of the overlying film. The more each alveolus tends to be given a spherical shape by increasing the radius of the corners, the greater the proportion of capillaries protected by the surface tension, though the smaller the vector opposing alveolar pressure.

The perivascular pressure in the alveolar walls, though probably reduced by surface tension, may remain close to alveolar pressure as the lung expands. On the other hand, the perivascular pressure around the extra-alveolar vessels is less than alveolar pressure and falls below pleural pressure at higher lung volumes (Table 1). Thus, the pressure gradient between the alveolar and extra-alveolar interstitium increases with lung volume, tending to shift fluids away from alveoli.

EFFECT OF LUNG HEIGHT

In the normal lung, horizontal slices of the circulation lie one above the other to a height of about 25 cm (30 cm at total lung capacity). Some 15 cm lie above the left atrium and about 10 cm below. At FRC, the normal mean pulmonary artery pressure (Ppa) at the left atrial level is 12–15 cm H_2O and the left atrial pressure (Pla) is about 7 cm H_2O. Thus there is a zone of less than 3 cm (1, 7) at the top of the lung where mean pulmonary artery pressure may be inadequate for steady perfusion but capillaries may blink open with the systolic pulse. Below this zone 1, zone 2 (driving pressure Ppa – Palv) stretches for the next 5–8 cm (7) and shows a regular increase of flow with distance down the lung (1). Below this again, venous exceeds alveolar pressure in the high-flow zone 3 (driving pressure Ppa – Pla) where flow increases downward, but may decrease near the base (zone 4). West (40) found this decrease to be exaggerated by edematous cuffing of the extra-alveolar vessels, but Ritchie et al (32) could find no vascular obstructions due to edema. Nevertheless, it seems possible that the narrowing of extra-alveolar vessels in the relaxed basal lung tissues is consideerably worsened by even minimal perivascular edema.

VASCULAR RESISTANCES

The most surprising feature of the pulmonary circulation is that driving pressures between pulmonary artery and left atrium of only 6 or 7 cm H_2O cause flow rates of 6 l min^{-1} in man. During exercise, the pulmonary artery pressure goes up, and so does the left atrial pressure (sometimes to 20 cm H_2O). Thus driving pressures of only 10–15 cm H_2O may be associated with flow rates up to 20 l min^{-1}! The pulmonary artery pressure itself seems to be influenced by flow, lung volume, volume history, transpulmonary pressure, blood viscosity, and surface tension (2). The pressure in the alveolar vessels, which is very difficult to measure directly, has been assumed to equal the pressure in the left atrium plus a proportion, depending on the upstream resistance, of the pressure difference between pulmonary artery and left atrium. The 40% proportion often used is based on only a few studies in excised lungs. A capillary pressure almost exactly halfway between pulmonary artery and left atrial pressure has been determined in a living zone-3 dog lobe (13). Estimates of capillary pressure are more difficult if zone-2 conditions exist where the left atrial pressure may not affect capillary pressure.

Understanding resistance calculations is challenging in a vertical lung when the effective driving pressure may be either the difference between pulmonary artery and alveolar pressure (zone 2) or pulmonary artery and left atrial pressure (zone 3). Flow resistance, measured overall as (Ppa − Pla)/Q, tends to fall with increasing rates of flow, though this effect is not so dramatic as was first thought (15). More flow causes pulmonary artery pressure and pulmonary venous pressure to increase; resistance falls because the extent of the low resistance zone 3 rises at the expense of the medium resistance zone 2, which, in turn, encroaches on the extremely high resistance of zone 1. Also, the increased pressure in distensible vessels increases their caliber and leads to vascular recruitment. Isolated lung experiments show that the perfusion pressure changes with time after lung inflation because of stress relaxation in both the lung and the vessels (2). This may be the cause of the remarkable pressure decay in the pulmonary artery after a rise due to an abrupt increase of flow (15). The opposite occurs when flow suddenly declines. It is surprising that these important time-dependent effects are still not evaluated or even recognized in otherwise elegant studies.

Resistance is normally lowest at about FRC (7), an efficient arrangement; it rises at higher and lower lung volumes and transpulmonary pressures. To what extent one would expect the alveolar and extra-alveolar vessels to be independently influenced by the lung volume or the transpulmonary pressure change depends upon the relevance of one's model of lung-vessel interaction (Figure 2). According to the "grape" model, the interstitial space and vessel caliber between abutting acini would tend to increase as lung volume increases but would hardly be modified by changes in lung recoil at the same volume. On the other hand, the model used to illustrate lung interdependence (27) suggests that the increasing lung recoil at higher volumes affects the vessels and that a change of transpulmonary pressure at the same lung volume might markedly alter vessel caliber. Both models may be applicable, depending on the circumstances, but it is impossible to predict even how changes in the caliber of the vessel affect its resistance because of associated alterations in length and angles of branching.

The *perfusion of excised lungs* allows the pressure volume hysteresis of the lungs to be used to separate pressure from volume effects by getting two transpulmonary pressures at each volume during an inflation-deflation cycle. "Negative pressure inflation" with vascular pressures constant relative to alveolar pressure has been espoused by some as most relevant to physi-

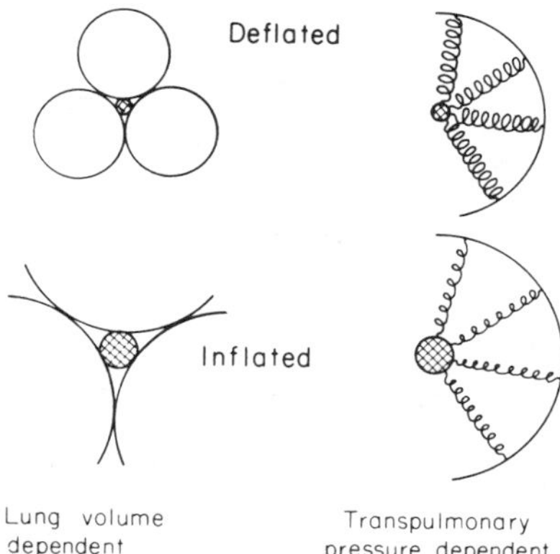

Figure 2 Two models of the effect of lung parenchymal expansion on an extra-alveolar vessel. (*left*) The perivascular pressure is related to the lung volume changes in this "grape" model. (*right*) The distending force on the vessel is related to transpulmonary pressure in this model.

ologic conditions (6). Others (41) feel that "positive pressure" inflation with vascular pressures constant relative to pleural pressure is a better model. Permutt (29) has pointed out, with an edifying diagram (Figure 3) that should be used by anyone reading a lung perfusion paper, that the best model uses parts of each. With natural inspiration, the pulmonary artery pressure rises relative to pleural pressure so that it keeps its relation to alveolar pressure (as in "negative pressure inflation"); however, left atrial pressure falls with pleural pressure (as in "positive pressure inflation"). This discussion has been going on for over a century now. It is salutary to find that in 1871 Quincke & Pfeiffer (31) apparently reached the same conclusion as Permutt regarding the best model.

Other problems in interpreting data from these studies are that the lungs tend to develop edema and that the usual excised lung preparation is distended by the same transpulmonary pressure throughout. In the chest, the lung is surrounded by a gradient of pleural pressure depending on thoracic shape, with more negative pressures and more distended alveoli in its upper than in its lower part. The greater tissue traction of the normal upper lung partially compensates the extra-alveolar vessels for the hydrostatic disadvantage of their height (1).

"Positive pressure" studies in which perfusion pressure falls relative to alveolar pressure show a slight, if any, increase in resistance below FRC and a dramatic rise above it (41). The sharp rise closely follows alveolar pressure (41), which suggests that the falling transmural pressure and narrowing of alveolar capillaries is the key factor. "Negative pressure" studies (6, 37) show a small increase in resistance below FRC consistent with a narrowing of the arteries and veins. Above FRC, resistance rises moderately, possibly

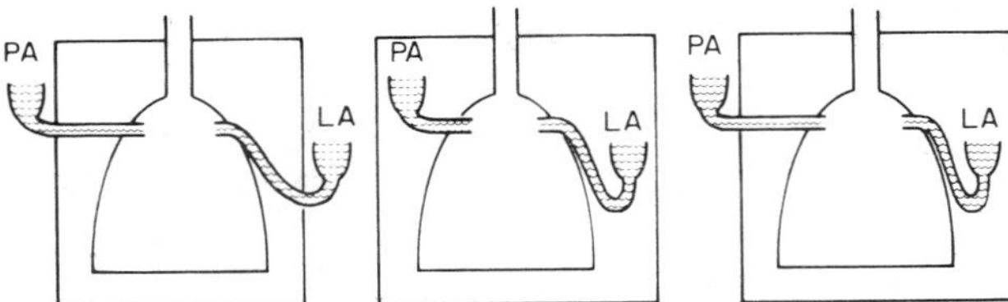

Figure 3 Three excised lung perfusion methods. Alveolar pressure is atmospheric and the lung is inflated by negative chamber pressure in each case but the location of the pulmonary arterial (PA) and left atrial (LA) reservoirs is shifted. (*left*) Perfusion pressures are related to alveolar (atmospheric) pressure in this typical "negative pressure inflation" model. (*center*) Perfusion pressures are related to pleural pressure and fall relative to alveolar pressure with lung inflation in this model equivalent to "positive pressure inflation". (*right*) Pulmonary artery pressure is maintained relative to alveolar pressure while left atrial pressure follows pleural pressure in this more physiologic model. [Adapted from Permutt (29) by permission of the author and publisher.]

owing to lengthening of all the vessels since Thomas (37) found it to vary with lung volume rather than transpulmonary pressure. Thus both transpulmonary pressure and lung volume appear to have important independent effects on the vessels (5). In the vertical lung, vascular resistance depends on the relationship of vascular to transpulmonary pressure insofar as this fixes the extent of the three zones of perfusion and resistance.

TAKING A DEEP BREATH

These mechanical factors can be integrated into a speculative picture of breathing. As inspiration begins, the fall in pleural pressure results in an increase in venous return to the right atrium. However, this return is flow-limited; if intrapleural pressures fall further, a waterfall effect occurs owing to collapse of the veins just before they enter the thorax. Capillary blood flow increases considerably at the start of inhalation but tends to fall as inhalation proceeds (38) because vascular impedance is increasing with lung volume. Pulmonary artery pressure, maintaining its relation to alveolar pressure, rises in relation to pleural pressure. Left atrial pressure falls, so the extent of zone 2 increases. Zone 3 is preserved as the lower lobe expands downwards; the human lung is relatively fixed at the hilar region and, although the heart moves down with inspiration, most of the increase in vertical height due to diaphragmatic motion takes place below the hilum. Emptying of intrapulmonary veins appears to be limited by a pulmonary venous waterfall where the veins exit from the lungs (34), but the larger downstream veins have a reservoir function and flatten when left atrial inflow increases (4).

During exhalation, increases in pleural pressure impede systemic venous return, tending to diminish pulmonary blood flow. The arteries are subject to somewhat the same influences as the airways, the resistance of which becomes almost infinitely high as residual volume is approached. The extra-alveolar vessels may be sequentially affected by critical closure at increasing levels up the lung during exhalation, leading to an effect similar to the closing volume in the airways. The rise in pericardial relative to atmospheric pressure increases the pressure around the left ventricle pushing up the systemic arterial pressure. This contributes to the "paradoxical pulse," or increased systemic pressure during exhalation and decreased pressure during inhalation that becomes more evident with the big pleural pressure transients of obstructive airway disease.

Our understanding of the dynamic events occurring during breathing is still rudimentary. For instance, mechanically determined changes in the pulsatile alveolar capillary volume and flow are undoubtedly important in gas exchange (16). More information is needed about these and many other interactions between the lung and the plumonary circulation.

ACKNOWLEDGMENTS

The critical review of the manuscript by Dr. Jack Hildebrandt is very much appreciated. This work was supported, in part, by Public Health Service Grants HL-00248, HL-07287, and HL-20690.

Literature Cited

1. Anthonisen, N. R., Milic-Emili, J. 1966. Distribution of pulmonary perfusion in erect man. *J. Appl. Physiol.* 21:760–66
2. Beck, K., Hildebrandt, J. 1979. Hysteresis in the pulmonary circulation. *Fed. Proc.* 38:1336 (Abstr.)
3. Benjamin, J. J., Murtagh, P. S., Proctor, D. F., Menkes, H. A., Permutt, S. 1974. Pulmonary vascular interdependence in excised dog lobes. *J. Appl. Physiol.* 37:887–94
4. Bertram, C. D., Lee, G. deJ., Rajagopalan, B., Stallard, T. 1977. Measurement of the dimension of the extraparenchymal pulmonary veins in dogs. *J. Physiol. London* 272:101
5. Bruderman, I., Somers, K., Hamilton, W. K., Tooley, W. H., Butler, J. 1964. Effect of surface tension on circulation in the excised lung of the dog. *J. Appl. Physiol.* 19:707–12
6. Burton, A. C., Patel, D. J. 1958. Effect on pulmonary vascular resistance of inflation of the rabbit lung. *J. Appl. Physiol.* 12:239–46
7. Butler, J., Paley, H. W. 1962. Lung volume and pulmonary circulation. *Med. Thorac.* 19:261–67
8. Caro, C. G., Saffman, T. G. 1965. Extensibility of blood vessels in isolated rabbit lungs. *J. Physiol. London* 178: 193–210
9. Culver, B., Marini, J., Butler, J. 1978. Ventricular function with PEEP; separation of pleural pressure and lung volume effect. *Am. Rev. Respir. Dis.* 117:325 (Abstr.)
10. Dawson, C. A., Grimm, D. J., Linehan, J. H. 1977. Effects of lung inflation on longitudinal distribution of pulmonary vascular resistance. *J. Appl. Physiol.* 43:1089–92
11. Fung, Y. C. B., Sobin, S. S. 1969. Theory of sheet flow in lung alveoli. *J. Appl. Physiol.* 45:545–50
12. Fung, Y. C. B., Sobin, S. S., Lindal, R. G., Tremer, H. M., Bernick, S., Wall, R., Karspeck, M. 1979. The connective tissue of the interalveolar wall. *Fed. Proc.* 38:1235 (Abstr.)
13. Gabel, J., Drake, R. E. 1978. Pulmonary capillary pressure in intact dog lungs. *Am. J. Physiol.* 235:569–73
14. Goshy, M., Lai-Fook, S. J., Hyatt, R. E. 1979. Perivascular pressure measurements by the wick-catheter technique in

isolated dog lobes. *J. Appl. Physiol.* 46:950–55

15. Harris, P., Heath, D. 1977. *The Human Circulation.* Edinburgh: Churchill-Livingstone. 2nd ed.
16. Hlastala, M. P. 1972. A model of fluctuating alveolar gas exchange during the respiratory cycle. *Respir. Physiol.* 15:214–32
17. Horsfield, K. 1978. Morphometry of the small pulmonary arteries in man. *Circ. Res.* 42:593–97
18. Howell, J. B. L., Permutt, S., Proctor, D. F., Riley, R. L. 1961. Effect of inflation of the lung on different parts of the vascular bed. *J. Appl. Physiol.* 16:71–76
19. Inoue, H., Inoue, C., Hildebrandt, J. 1979. Interstitial fluid pressure [P X (f)] gradients along bronchi in excised dog lobes. *Fed. Proc.* 38(3):1265 (Abstr.)
20. Kalk, J., Benjamin, J. J., Comite, H., Hutchins, G., Traystman, R., Menkes, H. A. 1975. Vascular interdependence in postmortem human lungs. *Am. Rev. Respir. Dis.* 112:505–11
21. Lai-Fook, S. J. 1979. A continuum mechanics analysis of pulmonary vascular interdependence in isolated dog lobes. *J. Appl. Physiol.* 46:419–29
22. Lai-Fook, S. J., Hyatt, R. E., Rodarte, J. R., Wilson, T. A. 1977. Behavior of artificially produced holes in lung parenchyma. *J. Appl. Physiol.* 43: 648–55

22a. Lai-Fook, S. J., Hyatt, R. E. 1979. Effect of parenchyma and length changes on vessel pressure-diameter behavior in pig lungs. *J. Appl. Physiol.* 47:666–69

23. Lloyd, T. C., Wright, G. W. 1960. Pulmonary vascular resistance and vascular transmural gradient. *J. Appl. Physiol.* 15:241–45
24. Lopez-Muniz, R., Stephens, N. L., Bromberger-Barnea, B., Permutt, S., Riley, R. L. 1968. Critical closure of pulmonary vessels analyzed in terms of Starling resistor model. *J. Appl. Physiol.* 24:625–35
25. Macklin, C. C. 1946. Evidence of increase in the capacity of the pulmonary arteries and veins of dogs, cats and rabbits during inflation of the freshly excised lung. *Rev. Can. Biol.* 5:199–232
26. Mazzone, R. W., Durand, C. M., West, J. B. 1978. Electron microscopy of lung rapidly frozen under controlled physiological conditions. *J. Appl. Physiol.* 45:325–33
27. Mead, J., Takishima, T., Leith, D. 1970. Stress distribution in lungs. A model of pulmonary elasticity. *J. Appl. Physiol.* 28:596–608
28. Menkes, H. A., Forster, J., Griffith, L., Summer, W. 1974. Interdependence of the heart and surrounding structures. *Fed. Proc.* 33:448 (Abstr.)
29. Permutt, S. 1979. Mechanical influences on water accumulation in the lungs. In *Pulmonary Edema,* ed. A. Fishman, E. M. Renkin, pp. 175–94. Bethesda, Md: Am. Physiol. Soc.
30. Quebbeman, E. J., Dawson, C. A. 1977. Effect of lung inflation and hypoxia on pulmonary arterial blood volume. *J. Appl. Physiol.* 43:8–13
31. Quincke, H., Pfeiffer, E. 1871. *Arch. Anat. Physiol. Wissensch. Med.* 90–116
32. Ritchie, B. C., Shauberger, G., Staub, N. C. 1969. Inadequacy of perivascular edema hypothesis to account for the distribution of pulmonary blood flow in lung edema. *Circ. Res.* 24:807–14
33. Rosenzweig, D. Y., Hughes, J. M. B., Glazier, J. B. 1970. Effects of transpulmonary and vascular pressure on the pulmonary blood volume in the isolated lung. *J. Appl. Physiol.* 28:553–60
34. Smith, H. C., Butler, J. 1975. Pulmonary venous waterfall and perivenous pressure in the living dog. *J. Appl. Physiol.* 38:304–8
35. Smith, J. C., Mitzner, W. A., Proctor, D. F. 1977. Interdependence of extra-alveolar blood vessels and lung parenchyma in excised dog lobes. *Fed. Proc.* 36:493 (Abstr.)
36. Spiro, S. G., Culver, B. H., Butler, J. 1978. Pressure outside the extrapulmonary airway in dogs. *J. Appl. Physiol.* 45:437–41
37. Thomas, L. J., Griffo, Z. J., Roos, A. 1961. Effect of negative pressure inflation of the lung on pulmonary vascular resistance. *J. Appl. Physiol.* 16:451–56
38. Vermeire, P., Butler, J. 1968. Effect of respiration on pulmonary capillary blood flow in man. *Circ. Res.* 22:299–303
39. Weibel, E. R. 1963. *Morphometry of the Human Lung.* NY: Academic
40. West, J. B., Dollery, C. T., Hurd, B. E. 1965. Increased pulmonary vascular resistance in the dependent zone of the isolated dog lung caused by perivascular edema. *Circ. Res.* 17:191–206
41. Whittenberger, J. L., McGregor, M., Berglund, E., Borst, H. G. 1960. Influence of state of inflation of the lung on pulmonary vascular resistance. *J. Appl. Physiol.* 15:878–82

Ann. Rev. Physiol. 1980. 42:199–210

NERVOUS CONTROL OF THE PULMONARY CIRCULATION

❖1262

S. Evans Downing and John C. Lee

Department of Pathology, Yale University School of Medicine, New Haven, Connecticut 06510

> The question was decided by Führer and Starling (1913), who showed that adrenaline constricts the branches of the pulmonary artery, so that the sympathetic sends vasoconstrictor fibres to them.
>
> Sir William Bayliss (1923)

Dr. Bayliss' statement implied that responses to adrenaline may be taken as sufficient evidence for sympathetic innervation and hence for autonomic control of the pulmonary vessels. In the ensuing decades detailed anatomical studies of the pulmonary nerve supply clearly demonstrated that the pulmonary vascular bed is indeed well innervated by a variety of fiber types. But their contribution, if any, to regulation of blood flow through the lungs has proved difficult to establish. Even more elusive has been convincing evidence for neural control during normal physiological adjustments. Sensory systems that might be involved in any postulated feedback system have been difficult to identify.

INNERVATION OF THE PULMONARY VESSELS

The early anatomists recognized that the lungs are innervated primarily from the anterior and posterior pulmonary plexi (41). The latter are formed by a commingling of fibers from the sympathetic trunks and the vagi. From this network the major pulmonary arteries receive a plexus of large nerve trunks coursing within the adventitial layer (36). Many of these trunks are myelinated; others are composed of fine nonmyelinated fibers (50). After multiple branchings, terminal twigs pass to the region of smooth muscle

0066-4278/80/0315-0199$01.00

cells of the media of both the large elastic arteries and smallest muscular arteriols. The muscular arteries are exclusively supplied by fine fibers (59). Relatively few nerve fibers are associated with the pulmonary veins when contrasted with the arterial network (22).

The nature and potential physiological significance of neural structures were illuminated by reliable histochemical staining techniques and by application of improved ultrastructural methodology. The use of Richardson's silver stain confirmed the presence of networks of nerve fibers accompanied by Schwann-cell nuclei. These surround branches of the pulmonary arteries and extend to those as small as 30 μm in diameter (22). Muscle cells are normally absent from vessels of smaller caliber. The innervation is relatively sparse, however, and most fibers are located 5–10 μm from the medial smooth muscle layer. Axons with vesicle-rich segments are present but usually separated from muscle cells by the external elastic lamina and fibrocyte processes. Muscle cells frequently extend processes rich in pinocytotic vesicles across the external elastic lamina toward a vesicle-rich axon,

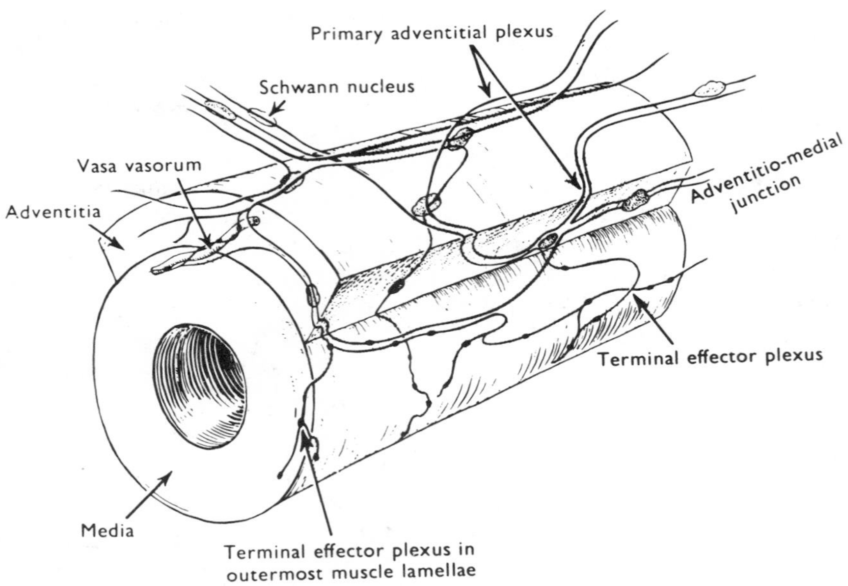

Figure 1 Schematic representation of the neural organization of the pulmonary artery. Postganglionic sympathetic fibres of the recurrent cardiac nerve ramify in the adventitia to form the primary plexus. This plexus of unmyelinated nerves contains numerous Schwann-cell nuclei. The terminal effector plexus, essentially limited to the adventitio-medial junction, is the terminal continuation of the primary plexus. There is focal superficial penetration of the media in the perivasal plexus. The nodal specializations of axoplasm represent bare nerve terminal areas containing accumulations of granular vesicles. [From (57) with permission]

providing a nerve-muscle gap of 100 nm. Two classes of vesicles have been identified: a uniformly sized (45–50 nm), generally agranular species; and a larger class, often containing cores of variable electon density (22). In the region of the effector plexus most vesicles are granular and vary in size and shape (59). These findings are consistent with the view that smooth muscle activation is achieved by transmitter diffusion from specialized regions in the axon (54).

Application of catecholamine histofluorescent methods has been of great value in identification and classification of the pulmonary vascular nerve supply (22, 55). Fluorescent nerve fibers are readily identified in the adventitia of the pulmonary arteries and larger veins (28). In the larger elastic arteries fluorescent fibers penetrate the outer third of the media. In the smaller muscular arteries, however, the fibers remain external to the medial coat. No fibers are present in vessels smaller than 30 μm diameter. These observations appear consistent with the finding that stimulation of sympathetic fibers causes vasoconstriction in isolated segments of the larger pulmonary vessels but not of those less than 0.6 mm in diameter (55). It is of interest that in 1958 von Euler and Lishajko reported that the norepinephrine concentration in bovine pulmonary arteries greater than 2 mm diameter is 10 times that of more peripheral vessels (60). They interpreted this to mean that the larger vessels are richly innervated with adrenergic vasomotor fibers but the small pulmonary vessels are poorly innervated.

Cholinesterase staining techniques have revealed in most species the presence of a network of fibers surrounding the pulmonary arteries on the outer surface of the media (28). Intralobar pulmonary veins are probably devoid of parasympathetic fibers (22, 28). Indeed, the total innervation of the pulmonary veins is sparse in most species. However, fine (as small as 30 μm diameter) presumably motor fibers have been described supplying human pulmonary veins (50). Interestingly, the calf manifests a rather striking sympathetic innervation of the pulmonary veins, while the arteries are poorly innervated (28).

Despite this species variability, rather definite patterns of pulmonary vascular innervation emerge. Both sympathetic and parasympathetic fibers are found in close association with the pulmonary vessels (61). The pulmonary vascular innervation is in most species relatively sparse when compared with bronchial or other systemic arteries. The distribution of fibers is most intense in the larger elastic vessels, less in the muscular arteries, and absent in vessels smaller than 30 μm. This suggests a system that might alter wall stiffness but have less capacity to influence resistance to blood flow at the arteriolar level. Especially dense innervation of a population of arterioles arising at right angles from larger pulmonary arteries (22, 28) may be important in regulating the distribution of blood flow within the lungs. It is noteworthy that both adrenergic and cholinergic fibers innervate these side-branch arterioles. Finally, most morphological studies have suggested that the intrapulmonary veins and venules are devoid of appreciable autonomic motor innervation.

NEURAL INFLUENCES ON THE FETAL PULMONARY CIRCULATION

The possibility exists that autonomic control of the pulmonary circulation is much greater in the fetus than in the adult. The pulmonary vascular bed of the unexpanded fetal lung possesses a high level of vasomotor tone, and these vessels are remarkably sensitive to autonomic agonists. In most respects, pulmonary vascular responses closely resemble those of the systemic vasculature (6, 42). Injection of small doses of acetylcholine into the pulmonary artery of the fetal lamb elicits pronounced vasodilatation (7, 17, 18, 42); this effect has been observed as early as mid-gestation (6, 42). In the fetus, blood flow after ACh may increase six-fold, much more than is observed in 2–3 month old lambs (17) or adults of other species. Electrical stimulation of the distal cut end of the vagus nerve also causes striking vasodilatation of the ipsilateral lung vessels (7, 17); this response, as well as those to acetylcholine, is abolished by atropine. The magnitude of the acetylcholine response increases progressively with gestational age; this has been ascribed to maturation of the effector system rather than the vascular receptors (42). In contrast to the powerful vasodilatory effects of cholinergic stimulation, fetal pulmonary vessels exhibit negligible parasympathetic tonic activity: Bilaterial vagotomy does not alter plumonary vascular resistance in the exteriorized (17) or chronically instrumented fetus in utero (49). Once the fetal lungs are expanded by ventilation with air, the dilator response to acetylcholine is markedly attenuated (17, 18). Moreover, in the newborn puppy breathing air, paradoxical responses sometimes occur: Acetylcholine occasionally elicits a transient increase rather than a decrease in pulmonary vascular resistance, and this response is reversed during acute hypoxia (49).

The fetal pulmonary bed responds as well to adrenergic stimulation as to cholinergic stimulation. Moreover, experiments involving a variety of agonists and antagonists (see chapter by Bergofsky) indicate that both α and β adrenergic receptors are plentiful (6, 17, 42).

Electrical stimulation of sympathetic fibers to the fetal lung elicits pronounced vasoconstriction, with pulmonary flow occasionally falling more than 70% (7, 17). These large responses, which are substantially greater than those in adults of most species, have been ascribed to the initially higher tone of the fetal pulmonary vessels. In the exteriorized fetal lamb, bilateral sympathectomy (T 1–8) causes pulmonary vasodilatation, implying the presence of sympathetic vasoconstrictor tone (7). However, this observation could not be confirmed while the fetus remained in utero (49). Neither did β-blockade with propranalol nor α-blockade with phentolamine or dibenzyline alter pulmonary arterial pressure or flow in the undisturbed fetus. Thus it appears that whereas the pulmonary vasculature of the unexpanded fetal lung is exquisitely sensitive to both parasympathetic and sympathetic neural stimulation and to their respective agonists, there is no evidence that either neurotransmitter is tonically released in the unstimulated state. The normally high resistance of the fetus must be ascribed to factors other than sympathetic neural activity, or for that matter, circulating adrenal medullary hormones.

RESPONSES OF THE ADULT PULMONARY CIRCULATION TO AUTONOMIC NERVE STIMULATION

Electrical stimulation of the autonomic nerve supply to the lungs has been used extensively to identify and characterize neuroeffector responses that may contribute to regulation of pulmonary blood flow in the adult mammal. However, inferences drawn from this approach may not apply to regulation under more natural conditions.

Interpretation of in vivo hemodynamic changes in terms of changes in pulmonary vascular tone is no simple matter. For example, calculated values for pulmonary vascular resistance decline progressively as blood flow increases over a broad range (25, 46, 49, 58). This is presumably a consequence of passive dilatation of the pulmonary vasculature (9, 23). It is equally clear that alterations in left atrial pressure exert a pronounced influence on the pulmonary vessels and calculated resistance values (4, 5, 35, 58). Indeed, changes in the inotropic state of the left heart, which occur with catecholamine stimulation, may sharply alter pressure gradient patterns and confound interpretation of pulmonary vascular responses from hemodynamic measurements (58).

Daly and his associates attempted to circumvent this problem by devising a canine preparation in which virtually all complicating influences could be separately regulated or assessed (8, 9, 12–15). They demonstrated that electrical stimulation of either the upper thoracic sympathetic chain, the stellate or middle cervical ganglia, or thoracic vagosympathetic branches consistently elicits a rise in pulmonary arterial pressure when pulmonary blood flow is held constant. This pressure rise is not large, averaging 10–15% of resting pressure, and usually less than 5 mm Hg. However, if pulmonary arterial pressure is held constant and flow allowed to vary, stimulation of the same nerve structures causes as much as a 30% fall in blood flow (13). Occasionally the responses are biphasic or dilator, especially during stimulation of the left sympathetic chain. Stimulation of the distal cervical vagosympathetic trunk causes pulmonary vasodilatation (15), presumably due to predominance of the parasympathetic effect; atropine abolishes the vasodilatation and evokes a constrictor response, indicating that this trunk contains sympathetic as well as parasympathetic fibers that innervate the pulmonary vessels. Whether the dominant dilatator response to stimulation of the trunk reflects a larger number of cholinergic fibers or greater neuroeffector sensitivity to cholinergic stimulation is not clear.

The larger pulmonary vessels appear more richly innervated than those of smaller caliber. In the rabbit an abundant adrenergic nerve supply is evident from catecholamine histofluorescence studies and measurements of neuronal uptake of norepinephrine (54). When isolated segments of arteries greater than 0.6 mm in diameter are subjected to transmural electrical stimulation these nerves release sufficient transmitter to cause vasoconstriction (55). Nerve stimulation or the application of norepinephrine to segments from vessels smaller than 0.6 mm in diameter elicits small responses, or none at all.

These observations appear consistent with the earlier physiological studies in the dog (31), which showed that sympathetic stimulation increases the stiffness of the larger lobar arteries but has little effect on calculated pulmonary vascular resistance. To a lesser extent reduced distensibility of the smaller vessels of the precapillary bed occur as well. Phenoxybenzamine elicits opposite responses, indicating that the effects are largely due to stimulation of alpha adrenergic receptors. In contrast with nerve stimulation, injection of norepinephrine causes an increase in calculated resistance, as well as reduced compliance, of the larger pulmonary arteries and precapillary bed, though the latter effects are less pronounced than with sympathetic stimulation. These authors (31) ascribed the resistance changes reported by earlier workers to the use of nonpulsatile, low-flow pulmonary perfusion systems that might exaggerate viscosity effects at low shear rates.

Recent reexaminations of this problem (32, 33) used constant, physiological blood flow levels and a cannulation technique likely to avoid damage to the pulmonary vascular innervation. In these canine preparations left atrial pressure was held constant and the influences of respiratory activity, bronchomotor tone, and bronchial flow could be ruled out. Increasing frequency of stellate ganglion stimulation was associated with frequency-related increases of pulmonary vascular resistance and input impedance. Similar responses were observed with norepinephrine infusion, and both modes of stimulation were largely blocked by phentolamine. The maximal increase of resistance with stellate stimulation was approximately 25% at 30 Hz and was distributed across the entire vascular bed. These findings have recently been confirmed in a similar investigation (26).

The conclusion appears inescapable that stellate ganglion stimulation over a broad range of frequencies increases both pulmonary vascular impedance and calculated resistance, though the latter is smaller and somewhat less consistent (43, 45). Propranalol, given during stellate stimulation, did not blunt the increases in pulmonary vascular impedance. These findings may therefore be attributed to arterial stiffening. The average characteristic impedance increased 76% during stellate stimulation at 20 Hz. This evidence for arterial stiffening is consistent with earlier evidence that the volume distensibility of the main pulmonary artery is reduced and the dynamic modulus is considerably increased during stimulation (30).

Thus a major effect of sympathetic activation in the dog is to increase the stiffness of the large pulmonary arteries. This augments the hydraulic load on the right ventricle and increases the fraction of total hydraulic power associated with pressure oscillations (45). Similar findings have been reported in the feline preparation (46), in which, however, pulmonary vascular resistance (PVR) increased about 30% during sympathetic stimulation —somewhat more than has been found in similar canine preparations. Although a species difference may exist, it is noteworthy that the ratio of pulsatile to total hydraulic power in the cat increases some 40% during stimulation, indicating a relatively greater effect on impedance than on resistance (46). Finally, the dynamic characteristics of isolated perfused lung preparations generally may differ from those in which blood is supplied by the right ventricle. For example, mechanically perfused vessels exhibit relatively greater changes in resistance with respect to impedance during sympathetic stimulation (12). Moreover, removal of the stellate ganglia in these preparations causes a fall in PVR of as much as 63% from control values (20). Changes of this magnitude are unlikely to occur in the intact animal (49).

NEURAL REFLEX EFFECTS ON THE PULMONARY CIRCULATION

The many nerve stimulation studies have firmly established the presence of efferent sympathetic pathways that might participate in neural regulation of the pulmonary vessels. However, the relative intensities of the neuroeffector response in various segments of the vascular tree are still not fully resolved. Having established the autonomic innervation of the pulmonary circulation, investigators began to examine systematically whether afferent and/or central pathways existed that could be shown capable of modulating the sympathetic discharge prerequisite for reflex regulation of the pulmonary circulation.

A contribution by central mechanisms was suggested by the demonstration that electrical stimulation of the hypothalamic integrative area for defense reaction in the cat causes an increase of calculated PVR along with a host of rather large hemodynamic changes (1). In the intact animal, however, pulmonary arterial pressure and flow both increased, and resistance calculations were based on nonsteady-state measurements.

A second approach was to examine the cephalic ischemia response, which elicits an intense sympathetic discharge to the cardiovascular system (19). In this feline preparation pulmonary arterial (PA) and left atrial (LA) pressures were measured at several levels of constant pulmonary flow (provided by the right ventricle); responses to intermittent cephalic ischemia were compared with control values at comparable flows (25). Systolic PA pressure increased as much as 11 mm Hg, but mean PA pressure remained unchanged as did the PA-LA gradient and the calculated pulmonary vascular resistance (PVR). These findings are consistent with studies of ganglionic stimulation in which the primary effect was a reduction in vascular compliance with limited changes in PVR (30, 31, 43, 45, 46, 56). A similar approach to the cephalic ischemia response in the dog, where sympathetic activation was achieved by increasing intracranial pressure, also yielded no evidence for autonomically mediated augmentation of PVR (37). In a recent report more moderate and sustained increases of intracranial pressure did lead to an increase of PVR (38). However, the discrepancy may be related to the appearance of pulmonary edema and hypoxemia in the latter experiments. Thus sympathetic discharge evoked by cephalic ischemia decreases vascular compliance but has little or no effect on pulmonary vascular resistance.

The foregoing observations are difficult to meld with suggestions that the baroreceptor (10, 16) and chemoreceptor (2, 11, 16, 51, 53) sensory systems reflexly modulate pulmonary vascular tone through sympathetic pathways. Recent work has cast doubt on a role for the baroreceptors in pulmonary vascular regulation (44) even though earlier studies had shown that injection of nicotine into the aortic root to stimulate aortic chemoreceptors caused a rapid rise in PA pressure (within 2–3 seconds) while flow fell (53). Both increased PA-LA gradient and calculated PVR. Aortic chemoreceptor denervation, vagotomy, or sympathetic blockade eliminate these responses. The studies involving nicotine and aortic chemoreceptors suggest an important reflex pathway for chemoreflex control of pulmonary vascular tone, but evidence is unavailable that this system responds to physiological stimuli—i.e. altered arterial gas tensions and pH. Perhaps relevant are recent observations that systemic hypoxia may reflexly increase pulmonary vascular tone (62). In these experiments the systemic and pulmonary vascular beds were independently perfused with two pump-oxygenator systems at constant rates of flow. Desaturation of the systemic bed while the pulmonary perfusate was fully oxygenated caused a rise in PA pressure of up to 5 mm Hg. This response was attributed to systemic chemoreceptor stimulation, though no attempt was made to identify the receptor system or efferent pathways.

It is noteworthy that, in contrast with the response of aortic chemoreceptors, pulmonary vasoconstriction is not elicited by stimulation of the *carotid* chemoreceptors with nicotine (53). This finding is at variance with earlier work (2) suggesting that pulmonary vasoconstrictor response during hypoxia can be ascribed to carotid chemoreceptor activation. It is also inconsistent with the observations of Daly et al, who could only demonstrate this effect while the bronchial arterial blood supply was interrupted (11). At present the role of the peripheral chemoreceptors in the reflex regulation of the pulmonary vessels is unsettled.

Further evidence favoring an autonomic contribution to regulation of pulmonary flow during hypoxia was provided by studies involving unilateral hypoxia. In anaesthetized dogs, each lung was independently ventilated; one lung was exposed to gases with low O_2 content, while the other was ventilated with high O_2 mixtures (34). Blood flow to the hypoxic lung fell by 33%, while that to the other lung increased. Mean PA pressure remained unchanged. Bilaterial cervical vagotomy was without effect, but removal of the stellate ganglia reduced the magnitude of the flow reduction in the hypoxic lung to 11%. Thus, two thirds of the hypoxic response could be attributed to sympathetic ganglionic activity and the remainder to local effects. These findings are inconsistent with those (39) showing that the sharp elevation in PVR (about 70%) after 10 min of hypoxia was unaltered by beta blockade with propranalol or alpha blockade with phentolamine in a canine preparation in which ventilation and arterial PCO_2 and pH were carefully controlled. Nor did hypercapnic acidosis seem to involve adrenergic mechanisms in the pressor response (40) even though both alpha and beta receptors apparently contribute to resting PVR. Despite this exception, the weight of evidence strongly suggests that adrenergic receptors in the pulmonary vessels are involved in local responses to hypoxia and hypercapnia (3, 47, 48). The nature of their role is not entirely clear. At present it is uncertain that autonomic reflexes influence PVR through alterations in discharge intensity to the pulmonary resistance vessels. On firmer ground is the evidence that centrally mediated adrenergic reflexes serve to reduce vascular compliance (2, 25, 26, 31, 46). This decrease in distensibility serves to reduce the dilatation of the pulmonary vascular tree during the increase in cardiac output that usually accompanies an increase in adrenergic activity.

ACKNOWLEDGMENTS

This review was supported in part by grants HL-08659, HL20401, and HD-07276 from the National Institutes of Health. We are grateful to Miss Patricia Parker for her secretarial and editorial assistance.

Literature Cited

1. Anderson, F. L., Brown, A. M. 1967. Pulmonary vasoconstriction elicited by stimulation or hypothalamic integrative area for the defense reaction. *Circ. Res.* 21:747–56
2. Aviado, D. M., Ling, J. S., Schmidt, C. F. 1957. Effects of anoxia on the pulmonary circulation: reflex pulmonary vasoconstriction. *Am. J. Physiol.* 189: 253–62
3. Bergofsky, E. H. 1974. Mechanisms underlying vasomotor regulation or regional pulmonary blood flow in normal and disease states. *Am. J. Med.* 57: 378–94
4. Borst, H. G., McGregor, M., Whittenberger, J. L., Berglund, E. 1956. Influence of pulmonary arterial and left atrial pressures on pulmonary vascular resistance. Cir. Res. 4:393–99
5. Carill, S. D., Duke, H. N. 1956. Pulmonary vascular changes in response to variations in left auricular pressure. *J. Physiol. London* 133:275–86
6. Cassin, S., Dawes, G. S., Ross, B. B. 1964. Pulmonary blood flow and vascular resistance in immature feotal lambs. *J. Physiol. London* 171:80–89
7. Colebatch, H. J. H., Dawes, G. S., Goodwin, J. W., Nadeau, R. A. 1965. The nervous control of the circulation in the foetal and newly expanded lungs of the lamb. *J. Physiol. London* 178: 544–62
8. Daly, I. de B. 1958. Intrinsic mechanisms of the lung. *Q. J. Exp. Physiol.* 43:2–26
9. Daly, I. de B. 1961. Analysis of active and passive effects on the pulmonary vascular bed in response to pulmonary nerve stimulation. *Q. J. Exp. Physiol.* 46:257–71
10. Daly, I. de B., Daly, M. de B. 1959. The effects of stimulation of the carotid sinus baroreceptors on the pulmonary vascular bed in the dog. *J. Physiol. London* 148:220–26
11. Daly, I. de B., Daly, M. de B. 1959. The effects of stimulation of the carotid body chemoreceptors on the pulmonary vascular bed in the dog: the vasosensory controlled perfused living animal preparation. *J. Physiol. London* 148:201–19
12. Daly, I. de B., Daly, M. de B. 1973. Sympathetic nerve control of pulmonary vascular resistance and impedance in isolated perfused lungs of the dog. *J. Physiol. London* 234:106P–8
13. Daly, I. de B., Duke, H., Hebb, C. O., Weatheral, J. 1948. Pulmonary vasometer fibres in the sympathetic chain and its associated ganglia in the dog. *Q. J. Exp. Physiol.* 34:285–313
14. Daly, I. de B., Duke, H. N., Linzell, J. L., Weatheral, J. 1952. Pulmonary vasomotor nerve activity. *Q. J. Exp. Physiol.* 37:149–62
15. Daly, I. de B., Hebb, C. 1952. Pulmonary vasomotor fibres in the cervical vagosympathetic nerve of the dog. *Q. J. Exp. Physiol.* 37:19–43
16. Daly, I. de B., Hebb, C. O. 1967. *Pulmonary and Bronchial Vascular Systems.* Baltimore: Williams and Wilkins
17. Dawes, G. S. 1966. Pulmonary circulation in the feotus and new-born. *Br. Med. Bull.* 22:61–65
18. Dawes, G. S., Mott, J. C. 1962. The vascular tone of the foetal lung. *J. Physiol. London* 164:465–77
19. Downing, S. E., Gardner, T. H. 1968. Cephalic and carotid reflex influences on cardiac function. *Am. J. Physiol.* 215:1192–99
20. Duke, H. N., Stedeford, R. D. 1959. Pulmonary vasoconstrictor fibres in the stellate ganglion of the cat. *J. Physiol. London* 16P–17P
21. Fanburg, B. L., Mieszala, J. R., Levine, H. J. 1977. Absence of a role for angiotensin II in the pulmonary vascular response to hypoxia in the intact dog. *Cardiovasc. Med.* 39:1023–29
22. Fillenz, M. B. 1970. Innervation of pulmonary and bronchial blood vessels of the dog. *J. Anat.* 106:449–61
23. Fishman, A. P. 1961. Respiratory gases in the regulation of the pulmonary circulation. *Ann. Rev. Physiol.* 41:214–80
24. Gilbert, R. D., Hessler, J. R., Eitzman, D. V., Cassin, S. 1972. Site of pulmonary vascular resistance in fetal goats. *J. Appl. Physiol.* 32:47–53

25. Grand, G. M., Downing, S. E. 1970. Metabolic and reflex influences on pulmonary vasomotion. *Am. J. Physiol.* 218:654–61
26. Hakim, T. S., Dawson, C. A. 1979. Sympathetic nerve stimulation and vascular resistance in a pump-perfused dog lung lobe. *Proc. Soc. Exp. Biol. Med.* 160:38–41
27. Hauge, A., Lunde, P. K. M., Waaler, B. A. 1967. Effects of catecholamines on pulmonary blood volume. *Acta Physiol. Scand.* 70:323–33
28. Hebb, C. 1969. Motor innervation of the pulmonary blood vessles of mammals. In *The Pulmonary Circulation and Interstitial Space,* ed. A. P. Fishman, H. H. Hecht, p. 195. Chicago: Univ. Chicago Press
29. Hung, K. S., Hertweck, M. S., Hardy, J. D., Loosli, C. G. 1967. Innervation of pulmonary alveoli of the mouse lung: an electron microscopic study. *Am. J. Anat.* 135:477–96
30. Ingram, R. H., Szidon, J. P., Fishman, A. P. 1970. Response of the main pulmonary artery of dogs to neuronally released versus blood-borne norepinephrine. *Circ. Res.* 26:249–69
31. Ingram, R. H., Szidon, J. P., Skalak, R., Fishman, A. P. 1968. Effects of sympathetic nerve stimulation of the pulmonary arterial tree of the isolated lobe perfused in situ. *Circ. Res.* 22:801–15
32. Kadowitz, P. J., Hyman, A. L. 1973. Effect of sympathetic nerve stimulation on pulmonary vascular resistance in the dog. *Circ. Res.* 32:221–27
33. Kadowitz, P. J., Joiner, P. D., Hyman, A. L. 1974. Effect of sympathetic nerve stimulation on pulmonary vascular resistance in the intact spontaneously breathing dog. *Proc. Soc. Exp. Biol. Med.* 147:68–71
34. Kazemi, H., Bruecke, P. E., Parsons, E. F. 1972. Role of autonomic nervous system in the hypoxic response of the pulmonary vascular bed. *Res. Physiol.* 15:245–54
35. Kuramoto, K., Bodbard, S. 1962. Effects of blood flow and left atrial pressure on pulmonary venous resistance. *Circ. Res.* 11:240–46
36. Larsell, O. 1922. Ganglia, plexuses and nerve terminations of the mammalian lung and pleura pulmonalis. *J. Comp. Neurol.* 35:97–132
37. Lloyd, T. C. 1973. Effect of increased intracranial pressure on pulmonary vascular resistance. *J. Appl. Physiol.* 35: 332–35
38. Malik, A. B. 1977. Pulmonary vascular response to increase in intracranial pressure: role of sympathetic mechanisms. *J. Appl. Physiol.* 42:335–43
39. Malik, A. B., Kidd, B. S. L. 1973. Adrenergic blockade on the pulmonary vascular response to hypoxia. *Res. Physiol.* 19:96–106
40. Malik, A. B., Newmark, J. M. 1976. Adrenergic mechanisms and the pulmonary vascular response to respiratory acidosis. *Respiration* 33:179–87
41. Nagaishi, C. 1972. *Functional Anatomy and Histology of the Lung.* Baltimore: University Park Press. pp. 180–234
42. Nuwayhid, B., Brinkman, C. R., Su, C., Bevan, J. A., Assali, N. S. 1975. Systemic and pulmonary hemodynamic responses to adrenergic and cholinergic during fetal development. *Biol. Neonate* 26:301–7
43. Pace, J. B. 1971. Sympathetic control of pulmonary vascular impedance in anesthetized dogs. *Circ. Res.* 29:555–68
44. Pace, J. B. 1978. Influence of carotid occlusion on pulmonary vascular resistance in anesthetized dog. *Proc. Soc. Exp. Biol. Med.* 158:215–19
45. Pace, J. B., Cox, R. H., Alvarez-Vara, F., Karreman, G. 1972. Influence of sympathetic nerve stimulation on pulmonary hydraulic input power. *Am. J. Physiol.* 222:196–201
46. Piene, H. 1976. The influence of pulmonary blood flow rate on vascular input impedance and hydraulic power in the sympathetically and noradrenaline stimulated cat lung. *Acta Physiol. Scand.* 98:44–53
47. Porcelli, R. J., Bergofsky, E. H. 1973. Adrenergic receptors in pulmonary vasoconstrictor responses to hypoxia and humoral agents. *J. Appl. Physiol.* 34:483–88
48. Porcelli, R. J., Viau, A. T., Naftchi, N. E., Bergofsky, E. H. 1977. β-Receptor influence on lung vasoconstrictor responses to hypoxia and humoral agents. *J. Appl. Physiol.* 43:612–16
49. Rudolph, A. M. 1977. Fetal and neonatal pulmonary circulations. *Ann. Rev. Respir. Dis.* 115:11–18
50. Spencer, H., Leof, D. 1964. The innervation of the human lung. *J. Anat.* 98:559–609
51. Stern, S., Braun, K. 1966. Effect of chemoreceptor stimulation on the pulmonary veins. *Am. J. Physiol.* 210: 535–39
52. Stern, S., Braun, K. 1970. Pulmonary arterial and venous response to cooling:

role of alpha-adrenergic receptors. *Am. J. Physiol.* 219:982–85

53. Stern, S., Ferguson, R. E., Rapaport, E. 1964. Reflex pulmonary vasoconstriction due to stimulation of the aortic body by nicotine. *Am. J. Physiol.* 206:1189–95
54. Su, C., Bevan, J. A. 1976. Pharmacology of pulmonary blood vessels. *Pharmacol. Ther.* B2:275–88
55. Su, C., Bevan, R. D., Duckles, S. P., Bevan, J. A. 1978. Functional studies of the small pulmonary arteries. *Microvasc. Res.* 15:37–44
56. Szidon, J. P., Fishman, A. P. 1969. Autonomic control of the pulmonary circulation. In *The Pulmonary Circulation and Interstitial Space,* ed. A. P. Fishman, H. H. Hecht, p. 239–68. Chicago: Univ. Chicago Press
57. Szidon, J. P., Fishman, A. P. 1971. Participation of pulmonary circulation in the defense reaction. *Am. J. Physiol.* 220:364–70
58. Taylor, J. F. N., Lee, J. C., Downing, S. E. 1975. Effects of acidosis, catechols, and atrial function on pulmonary pressure gradients. *J. Surg. Res.* 18:587–96
59. Verity, M. A., Bevan, J. A. 1968. Fine structural study of the terminal effector plexus, neuromuscular and intermuscular relationships in the pulmonary artery. *J. Anat.* 103:49–63
60. von Euler, U. S., Lishajko, F. 1958. Catechol amines in the vascular wall. *Acta Physiol. Scand.* 42:333–44
61. Waaler, B. A. 1971. Physiology of the pulmonary circulation. *Angiologica* 8:266–84
62. Wilcox, B. R., Austin, W. G., Bender, H. W. 1964. Effect of hypoxia on pulmonary artery pressure of dogs. *Am. J. Physiol.* 207:1314–18

Ann. Rev. Physiol. 1980. 42:211–20

VASOMOTOR REGULATION OF THE PULMONARY CIRCULATION ❖1263

Alfred P. Fishman

Cardiovascular-Pulmonary Division, Department of Medicine, University of Pennsylvania School of Medicine, Philadelphia, Pennsylvania 19104

INTRODUCTION

Three separate mechanisms could be responsible for contraction or dilatation of pulmonary vessels: (*a*) the vagus and sympathetic nerves acting as the efferent limbs of reflex pathways, (*b*) humoral agents, such as the catecholamines, that are brought to the pulmonary vessels from afar via the blood stream, and (*c*) local effects that begin and end within the lungs (22). Under experimental conditions each of these is usually tested singly; under more natural circumstances they are apt to act in concert. Separate chapters in this volume deal extensively with the first two of these mechanisms (see chapters by Bergofsky and by Culver & Butler). This chapter focuses on the local effects.

Four vasoregulatory systems known to be operative in the systemic circulation have been sought in the pulmonary circulation: vasomotor critical closure of small muscular arteries, axon reflexes, reactive hyperemia, and baroreceptor reflexes. None of these could be shown to be involved in local vasomotor regulation in the lungs. On the other hand, the respiratory gases prove to be of paramount importance. A decrease in the oxygen tension of inspired gas proved remarkably effective in evoking pulmonary vasoconstriction. Hypercapnia, which seems to act by producing acidosis locally (5, 66), was not quite as effective; somehow, however, it potentiated the hypoxic pressor response (33, 52). Alkalosis generally depressed the hypoxic response (63). A large literature points out the importance of this local control by respiratory gases in lung disease, where it constitutes an important mechanism for readjusting blood flow to well ventilated parts of the lungs (21, 33). Because of the wealth of experimental information about

0066-4278/80/0315-0211$01.00

the pulmonary vasomotor effects of hypoxia, and because a drive is now under way to uncover the site and mechanism of its action (23), the remainder of this chapter appraises the effects of hypoxia on the pulmonary circulation.

ACUTE HYPOXIA

The repeated demonstration that acute hypoxia causes pulmonary vasoconstriction in the isolated perfused lung (devoid of extrapulmonary nerves, humors, and collateral circulation) has settled beyond further debate that a large part of the hypoxic pressor response begins and ends within the lungs. The response is predominantly due to precapillary vasoconstriction, not to any component of blood. But it has also become clear that this local response is not the complete story. Modulating influences must also be taken into account: (*a*) The intensity of the local response is importantly influenced by the tone of the vessels before the hypoxic stimulus is applied ["initial tone"] (7, 23, 29); and (*b*) extrapulmonary influences often contribute to and, in some situations, determine the vigor of the response. It is likely that variations in initial tone and in the participation of extrapulmonary influences contribute significantly to the familiar differences in pulmonary pressor response among species and experimental situations.

Initial Tone

Two important determinants of initial tone are the muscle mass in the small pulmonary arteries and the level of the pulmonary artery pressure. Hypertrophied vascular muscle operates at a greater mechanical advantage and is capable of more vigorous vasomotor response than normal muscle (24, 54, 76). For example, the fetal pulmonary circulation constricts more vigorously during hypoxia and dilates more fully when exposed to bradykinin than does the adult pulmonary circulation (23). Also, the muscular fetal pulmonary circulation displays reactive hyperemia whereas the adult pulmonary circulation does not (17). Similarly, the hypertrophied pulmonary circulation of certain high-altitude dwellers shows a brisk pressor response to hypoxia. Initial tone is also set by humoral or neurohumoral substances either released locally or carried to the pulmonary vessels via the blood stream; among these are the catecholamines, histamine, angiotensin, and serotonin. All of these substances but serotonin seem to compete for adrenergic receptor sites in pulmonary vascular smooth muscle (60). Whether other nonadrenergic receptors are involved with other humoral agents is unclear.

It has been suggested that hypoxia somehow operates through the adrenergic system (See Bergofsky's chapter in this volume). Therefore, with respect to initial tone, the extent to which certain receptor sites are preoccupied by catecholamines (5) or angiotensin (9) or other factors as yet unknown (16) may shape the pulmonary pressor response to hypoxia.

Extrapulmonary Influences

Easier to prove and to quantify than initial tone is the participation of extrapulmonary mechanisms in the hypoxic pressor response. The role of the nerves is a classical question (14). Twenty years ago two groups of investigators (3, 15) demonstrated that stimulation of the systemic chemoreceptors by hypoxia could elicit pulmonary vasoconstriction by way of sympathetic efferent pathways. But interpretation of this system under more natural conditions was complicated by the complexity of the preparations. Since then the role of the sympathetic nerves has been assessed in a variety of ways (4, 32, 46, 51, 65, 72). Most impressive was the demonstration about ten years ago of the interplay between systemic chemoreceptors and the pulmonary circulation in the fetal lamb (12). The two lungs were separated using an airway divider so that each lung could be ventilated separately. Systemic asphyxia produced pulmonary vasoconstriction in the well-ventilated lung, a result that could only be attributed to a systemic chemoreflex that affected the pulmonary circulation. In contrast to these observations on the fetus, the adult pulmonary circulation showed little if any effect of a systemic chemoreflex on the hypoxic response of the pulmonary resistance vessels. Instead, the following dichotomy emerged for the hypoxic pressor response of the adult pulmonary circulation (62, 70, 71): (*a*) The systemic chemoreflex, operating by way of the aortic bodies, affects predominantly the large pulmonary arteries, causing them to stiffen [decrease compliance] (40) and thereby enhancing hemodynamic interplay between the two ventricles and the pulmonary circulation during times of stress and heightened sympathetic activity. (*b*) Alveolar hypoxia increases predominantly the resistance of the small pulmonary arteries, an effect that is not influenced by sympathectomy (49, 66, 71). The results also indicate that the contribution of the systemic chemoreflex diminishes from fetal life to adulthood. Although the sympathetic contribution to the increase in pulmonary vascular resistance seen in the adult is small, the local response may be reinforced somewhat by sympathetic activity (12, 45, 71).

Mechanisms for the Local Pulmonary Pressor Response to Hypoxia

Most of the pulmonary pressor response to hypoxia begins and ends within the lungs. How this local response is effected remains unclear. Experimental inquiry into mechanisms is currently proceeding along two separate lines:

On one hand is the view that hypoxia causes pulmonary vasoconstriction by the local release of chemical mediators; on the other is the view that the hypoxic pressor response is an expression of an inherent property of pulmonary vascular smooth muscle when exposed to hypoxia.

Intrapulmonary Chemical Mediators

Several lines of evidence have encouraged the search for a unique chemical intermediary: (*a*) Unless an isolated pulmonary artery is encased in a cuff of parenchyma, hypoxia fails to cause it to constrict (50). (*b*) Cells within the lungs contain vasoactive substances; the most evident of these are the mast cells, some of which are disposed periarterially, immediately adjacent to the adventitia, in guinea pigs, rats, and cattle (30), and which usually contain histamine, serotonin, adenosine, triphosphate, slow-reacting substance, and occasionally dopamine (38), and which degranulate [in the rat and guinea pig during hypoxia (30)]. (*c*) The effects of hypoxia on systemic and pulmonary muscular arteries are diametric; since the direct effect of hypoxia on systemic arteries causes relaxation, the pulmonary vasoconstriction can be construed as support for the existence of an overriding pressor mechanism in the lung, i.e. the release of chemical mediators. (*d*) Certain pharmacologic agents block the pressor response to hypoxia and to the mediator in question (35). (*e*) During acute hypoxia the concentration of a suspected mediator in the pulmonary venous effluent increases (30). (*f*) Antihistamines blunt the hypoxic pressor response in the isolated perfused lung (35), and histaminase inhibitors potentiate it (1, 36, 37, 68).

Unfortunately, neither the evidence for the existence of a unique chemical mediator nor its identification as histamine is entirely convincing (23, 43, 44). Of the agents that have been proposed—histamine (31, 35), prostaglandins (75), circulating catecholamines (27), arachidonic acid (25), serotonin (58), and angiotensin (9)—histamine has the strongest experimental support. However, histamine has not been as interspecifically consistent as hypoxia in causing pulmonary vasoconstriction (67, 74); and in a single species, the cat, the more abnormal the preparation, the more likely is histamine to simulate the pressor response to hypoxia (39). Other inconsistencies also await resolution: The concentration of histamine in the pulmonary venous effluent increases during acute hypoxia, but the histamine content of the lungs—where the histamine presumably originates—does not (44). In contrast to hypoxia, which exerts its predominant vasomotor effects on precapillary pulmonary vessels, histamine often appears to constrict pulmonary veins rather than pulmonary arteries (11, 26). Moreover, most evidence for histamine mediation derives from the rat (34–36), a species that manifests a poor pulmonary response to hypoxia.

Nor is the relationship between histamine and mast cells on the one hand, and hypoxia on the other, entirely clear (28, 55). Why do mast cells degranulate so slowly whereas the hypoxic response is abrupt (44)? What accounts for the lack of correlation between mast cell concentration in the lungs of various species and the vigor of the pulmonary pressor response (54)? Finally, the inconsistency of antihistamines in blocking the hypoxic pressor response is worrisome.

In the face of these misgivings, interest in histamine as the mediator began to wane (39); but it was recently rekindled on two accounts: (*a*) Two types of histamine receptors were identified in the pulmonary circulation: one, vasoconstrictor (H-1) and the other, vasodilator (H-2), each responsive to its own set of selective inhibitors. This led to the idea that histamine may be a moderator rather than the activator of the pressor response (74). (*b*) It is possible that extraordinarily high concentrations of histamine are released locally in the lungs during hypoxia and that quantities of antihistamines to match these levels cannot be administered experimentally without severely deranging or killing the animal (see Bergofsky's chapter in this volume). Like Antaeus, histamine has rebounded as the leading contender for *involvement* in the pulmonary vasomotor response caused by hypoxia, but not necessarily as the *unique activator* of the hypoxic vasoconstriction.

Direct Action of Hypoxia on Pulmonary Vascular Smooth Muscle

Inability to pinpoint a unique chemical substance as the mediator of the pulmonary pressor response to acute hypoxia has strengthened the case for a direct effect (10, 23). In keeping with current concepts of smooth muscle contraction, there are at least three frameworks within which the mechanism for the pressor response to hypoxia can be sought: the cell surface, the energetics of muscular contraction, or the contractile machinery per se (10, 41). Since there are no experimental data to suggest an effect of hypoxia directly on the contractile proteins, only the first two categories are considered here.

The Cell Surface

In this context, hypoxia could influence the transmembrane flow of ions to initiate pulmonary vasoconstriction by decreasing the supply of energy to the Na^+-K^+ pump in the membrane (6, 8). In keeping with this proposition is the enhancement of the hypoxic pressor response by ouabain (30). Unfortunately, conflicting evidence exists about the role of the potassium ion that would be involved in this mechanism. Another flaw in the argument is that the effects of ouabain are not confined to inhibition of the Na^+-K^+ pump (13). Other mechanisms for the transmembrane flux of ions in smooth muscle have not yet been tested with respect to the effects of hypoxia on pulmonary vascular smooth muscle (2).

Much easier to envisage is the possibility that hypoxia directly increases permeability of the plasma membrane to ionized calcium so that more ionized calcium is delivered to the sarcoplasm (10, 18, 28, 53). Evidence from other types of smooth muscle is consistent with this hypothesis (10). Whether hypoxia also mobilizes calcium ions from depots within the cell, i.e. sarcoplasmic reticulum, mitochondria, and the plasma membrane per se, is unclear.

Energetics of Muscular Contraction

According to current concepts, hypoxia could modify the availability of chemical energy for transduction into the mechanical response (10, 41, 59). However, data about the metabolic changes in pulmonary vascular smooth muscle induced by hypoxia are sparse. For example, in the aorta, anaerobic conditions relax vessels by decreasing energy production [and aerobic phosphorylation], but exposure of the pulmonary artery to hypoxia [for ten hours or more] enhances the energy production by glycolytic processes (10). This observation is of particular interest in view of the opposite vasomotor effects of hypoxia on systemic and pulmonary arteries (73). The relevance of this observation on prolonged hypoxia to the brisk rise in pulmonary vascular resistance that acute hypoxia elicits within minutes is unclear.

Other sporadic observations about energetics and the pulmonary pressor response are available. Almost 30 years ago, Duke & Killick tested the effects of a variety of metabolic inhibitors on the pressor response to acute hypoxia (20). All blocked or blunted the pressor response. Among these was azide, which decreases oxidative phosphorylation. More recently, dinitrophenol, which also inhibits oxidative phosphorylation, augmented rather than decreased the pressor response (19). This inconsistency remains to be resolved. Attempts to implicate either adenosine or AMP in the pressor response (42) were unsuccessful (56). Nor has the proposition that intracellular lactic acid is the mediator of the pressor response been substantiated (48).

Carbon monoxide was one of the agents tested by Duke & Killick (20). It too blunted the pressor response. Recent experiments have confirmed and extended these observations and attempted to unravel the underlying mechanism (69). The results suggested that the blunting effect is due to the reaction of carbon monoxide [like that of oxygen] with the heme iron of a metalloporphyrin in the lungs. Hemoglobin, myoglobin, and cytochrome oxidases were discounted on experimental grounds as the metalloporphyrin in question. Conversely, use of the competing agent, metaphrone, suggested that cytochrome P-450 is involved and that its desaturation, probably by a change in molecular configuration, is responsible for the pressor response to acute hypoxia. Where in the lungs the metalloporphyrin is lodged is an open question. It is also uncertain if other metalloporphyrins, particularly the cytochrome oxidases, have been entirely excluded. Observations on carbon monoxide will trigger a renaissance of interest in the hypothesis that the hypoxic pressor effect is the result of a direct effect on pulmonary vascular smooth muscle.

In summary, advocates of a direct vasoconstrictor effect of hypoxia on pulmonary vascular smooth muscle are now attempting to settle whether it occurs because hypoxia affects the permeability of the muscle cell to ions [particularly calcium], depresses the rate of oxidative phosphorylation, or affects a metalloporphyrin [particularly cytochrome P-450].

CHRONIC HYPOXIA

Studies of chronic alveolar hypoxia (54, 57, 61), in which intact animals are usually exposed to long-term hypobaria, have enlarged the scope of the observations made during acute hypoxia, which are generally performed under more artificial experimental conditions. For example, the long-term experiments have disclosed genetic differences in the vigor of the hypoxic pressor response: Some animals are hyporesponders; others are hyperresponders (64). Exposure of the hyperresponders to cold (0 to –5° for two days) enhances the pressor response to acute hypoxia; the hyporesponders do not show this potentiation. The mechanism of enhancement appears to be a large sympathetic discharge (39, 77). Also, chronically hypoxic rats manifest a blunted pulmonary pressor response to acute hypoxia even though the number of perivascular cells in the lungs is greater than at sea level and the pulmonary pressor response to a variety of pharmacologic agents is well preserved (54). Occasional observations along lines of special interest, such as relief of chronic hypoxic pulmonary hypertension in the rat by blocking the converting enzyme in the lungs (78), remain to be reconciled with the results of similar blockade during acute hypoxia (47). They also raise the prospect that in the process of adapting to prolonged hypoxia, the mechanisms responsible for maintaining pulmonary hypertension need not be the same, nor in the same proportions, as those operative during acute hypoxia.

Literature Cited

1. Altura, B. M., Zweifach, B. W. 1965. Pharmacologic properties of antihistamines in relation to vascular reactivity. *Am. J. Physiol.* 209:550–56
2. Anderson, D. K. 1976. Cell potential and the sodium-potassium pump in vascular smooth muscle. *Fed. Proc.* 35: 1294–97
3. Aviado, D. M., Ling, J. S., Schmidt, C. F. 1957. Effect of anoxia on pulmonary circulation: reflex pulmonary vasoconstriction. *Am. J. Physiol.* 189:253–62
4. Badder, E., Magill, T., Gump, F. E. 1973. Regional alpha-adrenergic blockade and the pulmonary pressor response to hypoxia. *Surgery* 74:555–61
5. Barer, G. R., McCurrie, J. R., Shaw, J. W. 1971. Effect of changes in blood pH on the vascular resistance in the normal and hypoxic cat lung. *Cardiovasc. Res.* 5:490–97
6. Bergofsky, E. H. 1969. Ions and membrane permeability in the regulation of the pulmonary circulation. In *The Pulmonary Circulation and Interstitial Space,* ed. A. P. Fishman, H. H. Hecht, pp. 269–92. Chicago: Univ. Chicago Press
7. Bergofsky, E. H. 1974. Mechanisms underlying vasomotor regulation of regional pulmonary blood flow in normal and disease states. *Am. J. Med.* 57: 378–94
8. Bergofsky, E. H., Holtzman, S. 1967. A study of the mechanisms involved in the pulmonary arterial pressor response to hypoxia. *Circ. Res.* 20:506–19
9. Berkov, S. 1974. Hypoxic pulmonary vasoconstriction in the rat. The necessary role of angiotensin II. *Circ. Res.* 35:257–61
10. Bohr, D. F. 1977. The pulmonary hypoxic response. *Chest* 71: (Suppl.) 244–46
11. Brody, J. S., Stemmler, E. J., DuBois, A. B. 1968. Longitudinal distribution of vascular resistance in the pulmonary arteries, capillaries and veins. *J. Clin. Invest.* 47:783–99
12. Campbell, A. G. M., Cockburn, F., Dawes, G. S., Milligan, J. E. 1967. Pulmonary vasoconstriction in asphyxia during cross-circulation between twin foetal lambs. *J. Physiol. London* 192: 111–21
13. Casteels, R., Raeymaekers, L. 1976. L'action de l'oubaine sur la distribution du calcium dans les fibres lisses. *J. Physiol. Paris* 72:3A
14. Cournand, A. 1964. Air and blood. In *Circulation of the Blood. Men and Ideas,* ed. A. P. Fishman, D. W. Richards, pp. 3–70. NY: Oxford Univ. Press
15. Daly, I. de B., Daly, M. de B. 1959. The effects of stimulation of the carotid body chemoreceptors on the pulmonary vascular bed in the dog: the vasosensory controlled perfused living animal preparation. *J. Physiol. London* 148:201–19
16. Daly, I. de B., Michel, C. C., Ramsay, D. J., Waaler, B. A. 1968. Conditions governing the pulmonary vascular response to ventilation hypoxia and hypoxaemia in the dog. *J. Physiol. London* 196:351–79
17. Dawes, G. S., Mott, J. C. 1962. The vascular tone of the foetal lung. *J. Physiol. London* 164:465–77
18. Detar, R., Gellai, M. 1971. Oxygen and isolated vascular smooth muscle from the main pulmonary artery of the rabbit. *Am. J. Physiol.* 221:1791–94
19. Doekel, R. C., Weir, E. K., Looga, R., Grover, R. F., Reeves, J. T. 1978. Potentiation of hypoxic pulmonary vasoconstriction by ethyl alcohol in dogs. *J. Appl. Physiol.* 44:76–80
20. Duke, H. N., Killick, E. M. 1952. Pulmonary vasomotor responses of isolated perfused cat lungs to anoxia. *J. Physiol. London* 117:303–16
21. Euler, U.S. von, Liljestrand, G. 1946. Observations on the pulmonary arterial blood pressure in the cat. *Acta Physiol. Scand.* 12:301–20
22. Fishman, A. P. 1963. Dynamics of the pulmonary circulation. In *Handbook of Physiology, Section 2: Circulation,* 2:1667–743. Washington DC: Am. Physiol. Soc.
23. Fishman, A. P. 1976. Hypoxia on the pulmonary circulation. How and where it acts. *Circ. Res.* 38:221–31
24. Folkow, B. 1971. The hemodynamic consequences of adaptive structural changes of the resistance vessels in hypertension. *Clin. Sci.* 4:1–12
25. Glazier, J. B., Murray, J. F. 1971. Sites of pulmonary vasomotor reactivity in the dog during alveolar hypoxia and serotonin and histamine infusion. *J. Clin. Invest.* 50:2550–58
26. Goldring, R. A., Turino, G. M., Cohen, G., Jameson, A. G., Bass, B. G., Fishman, A. P. 1964. The catecholamines in the pulmonary arterial pressor response to acute hypoxia. *J. Clin. Invest.* 41:1211–20
27. Haack, D. W., Abel, J. H., Jaenke, R. S. 1975. Effects of hypoxia on the distribution of calcium in arterial smooth mus-

cle cells of rats and swine. *Cell Tissue Res.* 157:125–40

28. Haas, F., Bergofsky, E. H. 1972. Role of the mast cell in the pulmonary pressor response to hypoxia. *J. Clin. Invest.* 51:3154–62
29. Haas, F., Foster, W. M., Bergofsky, E. H. 1975. Direct effects of ouabain on the pulmonary vasculature and its enhancement of the vasoconstrictor response to hypoxia. *Prog. Respir. Res.* 9:273–84
30. Hales, C. A., Kazemi, H. 1975. Role of histamine in the hypoxic vascular response of the lung. *Respir. Physiol.* 24:81–88
31. Hales, C. A., Rouse, E., Buchwald, I. A., Kazemi, H. 1977. Role of prostaglandins in alveolar hypoxic vasoconstriction. *Respir. Physiol.* 29:151–62
32. Hales, C. A., Westphal, D. M. 1979. Pulmonary hypoxic vasoconstriction: not affected by chemical sympathectomy. *J. Appl. Physiol.* 46:529–33
33. Harvey, R. M., Enson, Y., Betti, R., Lewis, M. L., Rochester, D. F., Ferrer, M. I. 1967. Further observations on the effect of hydrogen ion on the pulmonary circulation. *Circulation* 35:1019–27
34. Hauge, A. 1968. Conditions governing the pressor response to ventilation hypoxia in isolated perfused rat lungs. *Acta Physiol. Scand.* 72:33–44
35. Hauge, A. 1968. Role of histamine in hypoxic pulmonary hypertension in the rat. I. Blockade or potentiation of endogenous amines, kinins, and ATP. *Circ. Res.* 22:371–83
36. Hauge, A., Melmon, K. L. 1968. Role of histamine in hypoxic pulmonary hypertension in the rat. II. Depletion of histamine, serotonin and catecholamines. *Circ. Res.* 22:385–92
37. Hauge, A., Staub, N. C. 1969. Prevention of hypoxic vasoconstriction in cat lung by histamine-releasing agent 48/80. *J. Appl. Physiol.* 26:693–99
38. Hebb, C. 1969. Motor innervation of the pulmonary blood vessels of mammals. In *The Pulmonary Circulation and Interstitial Space,* ed. A. P. Fishman, H. H. Hecht, pp. 195–222. Chicago: Univ. Chicago Press
39. Hoffman, E. A., Munroe, M. L., Tucker, A., Reeves, J. T. 1977. Histamine H-1 and H-2 receptors in the cat and their roles during alveolar hypoxia. *Resp. Physiol.* 29:255–64
40. Ingram, R. H., Szidon, J. P., Skalak, R., Fishman, A. P. 1968. Effects of sympathetic nerve stimulation on the pulmonary arterial tree of the isolated lobe perfused in situ. *Circ. Res.* 22:801–15
41. Johansson, B. 1974. Determinants of vascular reactivity. *Fed. Proc.* 33: 121–26
42. Kaukel, E., Siemssen, S., Völkel, N., Sill, V. 1975. cAMP dependent and cAMP independent alterations of lung hemodynamic in the pig. *Biochem. Pharmacol.* 24:2159–62
43. Kay, J. M., Grover, R. F. 1975. Lung mast cells and hypoxic pulmonary hypertension. *Prog. Respir. Res.* 9:157–64
44. Kay, J. M., Waymire, J. C., Grover, R. F. 1974. Lung mast cell hyperplasia and pulmonary histamine-forming capacity in hypoxic rats. *Am. J. Physiol.* 226: 178–84
45. Kazemi, H., Bruecke, P., Parsons, E. 1972. Role of the autonomic nervous system in the hypoxic response of the pulmonary vascular bed. *Respir. Physiol.* 15:245–54
46. Korner, P. I., White, S. W. 1966. Circulatory control in hypoxia by sympathetic nerves and adrenal medulla. *J. Physiol. London* 184:272–90
47. Leuenberger, P. J., Stalcup, S. A., Mellins, R. B., Greenbaum, L. M., Turino, G. M. 1978. Decrease in angiotensin I conversion by acute hypoxia in dogs. *Proc. Soc. Exp. Biol. Med.* 158:586–89
48. Liljestrand, G. 1958. Chemical control of distribution of pulmonary blood flow. *Acta Physiol. Scand.* 44:216–40
49. Lloyd, T. C. Jr. 1966. Role of nerve pathways in the hypoxic vasoconstriction of lung. *J. Appl. Physiol.* 21: 1351–55
50. Lloyd, T. C. Jr. 1968. Hypoxic pulmonary vasoconstriction: role of perivascular tissue. *J. Appl. Physiol.* 25:560–65
51. Malik, A. B., Kidd, B. S. L. 1973. Adrenergic blockade and the pulmonary vascular response to hypoxia. *Respir. Physiol.* 19:96–106
52. Malik, A. B., Kidd, B. S. L. 1973. Independent effects of changes in H^+ and CO_2 concentrations on hypoxic pulmonary vasoconstriction. *J. Appl. Physiol.* 34:318–24
53. McMurtry, I. F., Davidson, A. B., Reeves, J. T., Grover, R. F. 1976. Inhibition of hypoxic pulmonary vasoconstriction by calcium antagonists in isolated rat lungs. *Circ. Res.* 38:99–104
54. McMurtry, I. F., Petrun, M. D., Reeves, J. T. 1978. Lungs from chronically hypoxic rats have decreased pressor response to acute hypoxia. *Am. J. Physiol.* 235:H104–9
55. Martin, L. F., Tucker, A., Monroe, M. L., Reeves, J. T. 1978. Lung mast cells

and hypoxic pulmonary vasoconstriction in cats. *Respiration* 35:73–77

56. Mentzer, R. M. Jr., Rubio, R., Berne, R. M. 1975. Release of adenosine by hypoxic canine lung tissue and its possible role in the pulmonary circulation. *Am. J. Physiol.* 229:1625–31
57. Moret, P., Covarrubias, E., Coudert, J., Duchosal, F. 1972. Cardiocirculatory adaptation to chronic hypoxia. *Acta Cardiol. (Brux.)* 27:596–619
58. Nayar, H. S., Mathur, R. M., Ranade, V. V. 1972. The role of serotonin (5-hydroxytryptamine) in the pulmonary arterial pressor response during acute hypoxia. *Ind. J. Med. Res.* 60:1665–73
59. Peterson, J. W., Paul, R. J. 1974. Aerobic glycolysis in vascular smooth muscle: relation to isometric tension. *Biochem. Biophys. Acta* 357:167–76
60. Porcelli, R. J., Bergofsky, E. H. 1973. Adrenergic receptors in pulmonary vasoconstrictor responses to gaseous and humoral agents. *J. Appl. Physiol.* 34:483–88
61. Rabinovitch, M., Gamble, W., Nadas, A. S., Miettinen, O. S., Reid, L. 1979. Rat pulmonary circulation after chronic hypoxia: hemodynamic and structural features. *Am. J. Physiol.* 236:H818–27
62. Reuben, S. R., Swadling, J. P., Gersh, B. J., Lee, G. de J. 1971. Impedance and transmission properties of the pulmonary arterial system. *Cardiovasc. Res.* 5:1–9
63. Rudolph, A. M., Yuan, S. 1966. Response of the pulmonary vasculature to hypoxia and H^+ion concentration changes. *J. Clin. Invest.* 45:399–411
64. Ruiz, A. V., Bisgard, G. E., Will, J. A. 1973. Hemodynamic responses to hypoxia and hyperoxia in calves at sea level and altitude. *Pfluegers Arch.* 344: 275–86
65. Silove, E. D., Grover, R. F. 1968. Effects of alpha adrenergic blockade and tissue catecholamine depletion on pulmonary vascular responses to hypoxia. *J. Clin. Invest.* 47:274–85
66. Silove, E. D., Inoue, T., Grover, R. F. 1968. Comparison of hypoxia, pH and sympathomimetic drugs on bovine pulmonary vasculature. *J. Appl. Physiol.* 24:355–65
67. Silove, E. D., Simcha, A. J. 1973. Histamine-induced pulmonary vasodilatation in the calf; relationship to hypoxia. *J. Appl. Physiol.* 35(6):830–36
68. Susmano, A., Carleton, R. A. 1971. Prevention of hypoxic pulmonary hypertension by chlorpheniramine. *J. Appl. Physiol.* 31:531–35
69. Sylvester, J. T., McGowan, C. 1978. The effects of agents that bind to cytochrome P-450 on hypoxic pulmonary vasoconstriction. *Circ. Res.* 43:429–37
70. Szidon, J. P., Fishman, A. P. 1969. Autonomic control of the pulmonary circulation. In *The Pulmonary Circulation and Interstitial Space,* ed. A. P. Fishman, H. H. Hecht, pp. 239–68. Chicago: Univ. Chicago Press
71. Szidon, J. P., Flint, J. F. 1977. Significance of sympathetic innervation of pulmonary vessels in response to acute hypoxia. *J. Appl. Physiol. Respir. Environ. Exer. Physiol.* 43:65–71
72. Thilenius, O. G., Candiolo, B. M., Beug, J. I. 1967. Effect of adrenergic blockade on hypoxia induced pulmonary vasoconstriction in awake dogs. *Am. J. Physiol.* 213:990–98
73. Traystman, R. J., Fitzgerald, R. S., Loscutoff, S. C. 1978. Cerebral circulatory responses to arterial hypoxia in normal and chemodenervated dogs. *Circ. Res.* 42:649–57
74. Tucker, A., Weir, E. K., Reeves, J. T., Grover, R. F. 1975. Histamine H-1 and H-2 receptors in the pulmonary and systemic vasculature of the dog. *Am. J. Physiol.* 229:1008–13
75. Vaage, J., Hauge, A. 1975. Prostaglandins and the pulmonary vasoconstrictor response to alveolar hypoxia. *Science* 189:899–900
76. Weir, E. K., Will, D. H., Alexander, A. F., McMurtry, I. F., Looga, R., Reeves, J. T., Grover, R. F. 1979. Vessel hypertrophy, not prostaglandins, determine pulmonary vasoreactivity in cattle. *J. Appl. Physiol.* 46:517–21
77. Will, D. H., McMurtry, I. F., Reeves, J. T., Grover, R. F. 1978. Cold-induced pulmonary hypertension in cattle. *J. Appl. Physiol. Respir. Environ. Exer. Physiol.* 45(3):469–73
78. Zakheim, R. M., Mattioli, L., Molteni, A., Mullis, K. B., Bartley, J. 1975. Prevention of pulmonary vascular changes of chronic alveolar hypoxia by inhibition of angiotensin I-converting enzyme in the rat. *Lab. Invest.* 33:57–61

Ann. Rev. Physiol. 1980. 42:221–33

HUMORAL CONTROL OF THE PULMONARY CIRCULATION

❖1264

Edward H. Bergofsky

Pulmonary Disease Division, Department of Medicine,
State University of New York, Stony Brook, New York 11794

INTRODUCTION

During the last several years many studies have attempted to describe the action of vasoactive substances on the pulmonary vascular bed, to characterize the humoral receptors of its smooth muscle receptors, and to determine the make-up of the "cascades" of activation and release of agents that may mediate the pulmonary vascular responses to their major regulators, i.e. the levels of O_2 and CO_2.

VASOACTIVE AMINES AND THEIR PULMONARY CIRCULATORY EFFECTS

Pulmonary Vasoconstrictors

CATECHOLAMINES The naturally occurring catecholamines, epinephrine and norepinephrine, are dependable and consistent vasoconstrictors in a wide variety of pulmonary circulatory preparations and species. The most definitive experiments to characterize the action of these two agents have been performed in the perfused, but intact, lung preparation with constant blood flow and outflow pressures, since use of these agents in the intact animal or human is complicated by extraordinary changes in cardiac output and systemic arterial and left ventricular pressures. In this preparation, intravenous infusions of 10^{-5} g kg^{-1} over 1 min of either agent elicits at least a 50% rise in pulmonary vascular resistance. Dose-response curves, to the extent they can be carried out, suggest a linear relation between dose and degree of rise in pulmonary vascular resistance (37c); the paradoxical vasodilation seen with certain doses of epinephrine in the systemic circula-

0066-4278/80/0315-0221$01.00

tion is not readily discernible in the lung. A similar pattern occurs with the isolated pulmonary arterial smooth muscle strip; epinephrine or norepinephrine in the water bath at concentrations of 10^{-5} g ml^{-1} causes sustained contractions greater in amplitude than those elicited by supramaximal electrical stimulation. In a few studies in the intact human, these two catecholamines have elicited pulmonary vasoconstriction independent of the host of other hemodynamic changes; usually this approach has utilized single injections of agent into the pulmonary artery with continuous measurements of pulmonary vascular and left atrial pressures (4b). The relation of these two agents to normal control of the pulmonary circulation, to the adrenergic receptors of the vascular smooth muscle, and to cyclic nucleotide generation is discussed below.

HISTAMINE As with the catecholamines, the effects of histamine are also best demonstrated in the perfused lung preparation or isolated vascular smooth muscle (23), rather than in the whole animal or human (22). In such preparations in the cat, dog, and rodent at sea level (5), the preponderant result is brisk vasoconstriction coincident with infusion of the agent in doses as small as 10^{-5} g kg^{-1}. In certain animals, or at high altitude, the result may sometimes be pulmonary vasodilation (44). The isolated pulmonary blood vessel between 200 and 2000 μm in diameter also undergoes contraction in response to concentrations of histamine of 10^{-6} to 10^{-7} g ml^{-1} of bath solution. Systemic vessels of similar size appear to relax in response to histamine (2,4b). This paradox may be explicable on the basis of the number of histaminic constrictor and dilator receptors, which are discussed below.

The effect of histamine has been assessed on the three major divisions of the pulmonary vascular bed: arterial, capillary, and venous. The most definitive studies have used simultaneous measurements of the volumes of each of these. Table 1 shows the relative responses of lung arteries and veins to histamine and other vasoconstrictors.

Although the net pulmonary vasoconstrictor effect of histamine will be resolved into its vasoconstrictor and vasodilator components when histamine receptors are discussed below, it is pertinent to emphasize the sources giving rise to the histamine influencing the pulmonary vascular bed. Circulating levels in mixed venous blood range from 50–200 μM ml^{-1}, but at least 80% of this is contained in the white blood cell population; the remainder available to affect the pulmonary circulation may result from release from organs such as the gastrointestinal tract (41). Another, more important source is the lung itself, where mast cells in the peribronchial region serve as excellent depots from which histamine and other vasoactive agents may be released in bronchial asthma and possibly as a normal regulator of bronchial tone. Periarterial mast cells have been discovered in the lungs of several species—e.g. rats, guinea pigs, and cats. They are distributed singly and in clusters and are often located immediately adjacent to the adventitia. It is possible that these cells may also serve as depots for vasoactive agents for a variety of regulatory functions (19). One such function is the regulation of local pulmonary perfusion during regional alveolar hypoxia [(6, 13); see also Fishman's review in this volume]. These depots containing vasoconstrictors are admirably situated to release histamine or other agents immediately adjacent to the media of the pulmonary arteries.

SEROTONIN This circulating agent bears many similarities to histamine. It is a powerful vasoconstrictor to the pulmonary circulation (while at the same time a systemic vasodilator), is housed in the mast cell of some animals, and is metabolized by the endothelial cell of the lung by amine oxidases (4a, 16). Several important differences also exist: (*a*) Serotonin does not occur in the pulmonary mast cell of all animals—e.g. probably not in that of the human (41); (*b*) serotonin seems mainly a constrictor of the pulmonary arterial segment, whereas histamine affects both arterial and venous segments of the pulmonary vascular tree (11, 17); and (*c*) as will be indicated below, no system of constrictor and dilator receptors like that for histamine has yet been discovered for serotonin, though specific inhibitors of serotonin responses, both pulmonary and systemic, are available in the form of lysergic acid analogs such as methysergide (30).

In addition, serotonin is contained in circulating platelets, which are good sources of serotonin in disease states where platelet aggregation in the pulmonary vascular bed is important (12). In such cases a combination of serotonin release and an endothelium incapable of metabolizing the released serotonin may provide levels high enough to cause significant pulmonary arterial constriction. However, serotonin infusion itself produces pulmonary vasoconstriction and no platelet aggregation (32).

Pulmonary Vasodilators

Several vasoactive amines elicit either modest pulmonary vasodilation in the normal circulation or considerable dilation in the pulmonary hypertensive state. Isoproterenol relaxes strips of pulmonary arterial muscle in the normal cat, dog, rat, and guinea pig. In the intact normal pulmonary circulation (4b), the modest (1–3 mm Hg) dilation may be attributable either to the small number of beta receptors (see the section below on Pulmonary Vascular Receptor Systems) or to the relatively flaccid state in this circulation. In the patient with pulmonary hypertension, isoproterenol (42), dopamine (45), hydralazine (39), diazoxide (48), phentolamine, and tolazoline (28, 31) all produce similar hemodynamic changes: marked vasodilation, as indicated by a fall in pulmonary vascular resistance; rise in cardiac output; and only a modest fall in pulmonary arterial pressure.

ACETYLCHOLINE Acetylcholine has one of the most perplexing effects on the pulmonary circulation (4c). In the intact pulmonary circulation of both humans and animals, infusion of this agent produces slight vasodilation in the normal situation. Vasodilation is more apparent when the pulmonary circulation is artificially constricted by induced alveolar hypoxia, by serotonin, or during the pulmonary vasoconstriction observed in chronic obstructive lung disease, primary pulmonary hypertension, and mitral stenosis (15). Acetylcholine infusion is thus similar to vagal stimulation. In some animals atropine blocks effects (9).

The mechanism underlying this vasodilation is unclear, since most isolated strips of vascular smooth muscle, including pulmonary strips, constrict when bathed in acetylcholine. Several explanations may be advanced to explain the disparity. Acetylcholine in vivo may cause release of a dilating agent from sympathetic endings or from mast cells that does not occur in the isolated muscle strip; it may provoke a reflex by preferential stimulation of sympathetic ganglia; or it may have a dose-dependent response related to the numbers of and affinity to separate vasodilator and vasoconstrictor forms of postganglionic parasympathetic fibers or of vascular receptors.

Pulmonary Vascular Receptor Systems for Vasoactive Amines

An adrenergic receptor system, complete with alpha constrictor and beta dilator divisions, has now been positively identified in the pulmonary vascular bed (37a). This system has been characterized by (*a*) use of pharmacologic blocking agents specific for one or the other receptor and (*b*) selective adjustment of alpha or beta adrenergic activity by generation of pulmonary vascular cyclic nucleotides. The two alpha receptor blockers, phenoxybenzamine and phentolamine, are capable of completely blocking the pulmonary vasoconstrictor effects of norephinephrine and of converting the vasoconstriction due to epinephrine to vasodilation. These effects are achieved in the constantly perfused lung of the cat and dog, and in the pulmonary vascular smooth muscle strip of the cat, rat, and guinea pig. Although studies in the intact animal have wider variations because of alterations in cardiac output and systemic arterial pressure, the intact calf behaves similarly (43). The beta adrenergic blocker, propranolol, greatly enhances the pulmonary vasoconstrictor responses to epinephrine and norepinephrine in the perfused lung and pulmonary vascular smooth muscle strip (37a, d); but the effect of this agent in the intact animal has not readily lent itself to testing, since the infused catecholamines produce extraordinary increases in systemic arterial and left-heart pressures under this circumstance. Dose-response curves are incomplete, but, as a general rule, equimolar doses of the blocking agents, i.e. 0.5×10^{-4} g kg^{-1}, elicit almost maximal alterations in the responses to the two catechols at doses of 10^{-5} g kg^{-1}: Propranolol at least doubles the pulmonary pressure response to the catecholes, epinephrine and norepinephrine, in the perfused lung; phentolamine abolishes the pulmonary vasoconstriction (or converts to a vasodilation) with these two agents (see Figure 1). In accord with this behavior, the modest pulmonary vasodilation in the normal perfused lung to isoproterenol is also abolished by phentolamine. A good correlation also exists between pulmonary lobar tissue cyclic adenosine monophosphate (cAMP) levels and the pulmonary vasoconstrictor response to catecholamines. When repeated doses of epinephrine raise the cAMP tissue level (as manifested by an increment in pulmonary venous over arterial concentrations by 200–300 pM ml^{-1}), selective abolition of vasoconstrictor responses to catecholamines occurs, even though the responses to other vasoconstrictors, such as serotonin or vasopressin, are unaltered (37c).

Such data indicate that the pulmonary smooth muscle is equipped with a functioning alpha and beta adrenergic system. The balance between these two appears to favor vasoconstriction in response to agents such as epinephrine. Thus alpha receptors in the pulmonary circulation greatly predominate over beta receptors. This predominance in the pulmonary circulation is similar to that in the circulations of the kidney, muscle, and gut. The precise functions of this adrenergic system must still be worked out. That they function as terminal receptors for autonomic nerve terminals at the level of the pulmonary resistance vessels seems uncertain. Although direct stimulation of the feline stellate ganglion or autonomic nuclei in the brain elicits clear-cut adrenergic-mediated pulmonary vasoconstriction (see chapter by Downing), a normal physiologic function for the sympathetic ner-

Table 1 Relative activity of pulmonary vasoconstrictors to produce a doubling of pulmonary vascular resistance[a]

	Dose	Artery	Vein
Epinephrine	1×10^{-5} g kg^{-1}	++	+
Norepinephrine	1×10^{-5} g kg^{-1}	++	+
Histamine	1×10^{-4} g kg^{-1}	+	+
Serotonin	1×10^{-5} g kg^{-1}	++	0
Hypoxia	$PAO_2 = 60$ mm Hg	++	0
Hypercapnic acidosis	$pH_s = 7.20$	++	0
PGE_2	3×10^{-6} g kg^{-1}	+	++
$PGF_{2\alpha}$	1×10^{-6} g kg^{-1}	++	++
Bradykinin	1×10^{-4} g kg^{-1}	?	?
Angiotensin II	10×10^{-4} g kg^{-1}	?	?
Vasopressin	3×10^{-4} g kg^{-1}	?	?

[a]In either an isolated perfused lung/lobe or intact lung in which blood flow is virtually constant (see text); PAO_2 = alveolar O_2 tension; pH_s = serum pH.

vous system in local or generalized circulatory regulation has been difficult to adduce.

Pulmonary vascular alpha and beta receptors appear to have functions independent of their available autonomic nerve endings. The strongest support for this deduction comes from experiments with adrenergic blockade in perfused lungs or lobes, or in isolated pulmonary vascular smooth muscle strips. These preparations are bereft of autonomic innervation but presumably not of pharmacologic receptors (37d). In the perfused lobe where circulating catecholamines diffuse into tissues, alpha blockade by phentolamine causes modest vasodilation, and beta blockade by propranolol causes a similar degree of vasoconstriction. In the pulmonary vascular smooth muscle strip, where circulating, and presumably tissue, catecholamines are absent, these blocking agents have no effect. The two observations thus indicate that (*a*) these blocking agents are not themselves constrictors or dilators of pulmonary vascular smooth muscle; (*b*) they act through blockade of the alpha and beta agonist function of catecholamines; and (*c*) in the intact animal the pulmonary vascular smooth muscle tone is set in part through action on alpha and beta receptors by tissue catecholamines either locally released or diffusing in from the circulating blood. (In the case of the perfused lung with all nervous connections cut, catecholamines and similar agents from the circulation seem the only ones to set tone.)

The adrenergic receptors of pulmonary vascular smooth muscle may have other functions. It has been suggested that they play a part in mediating some or most of the vasoconstrictor effects of alveolar hypoxia, hypercapnic acidosis, and histamine. The degree to which adrenergic blockade effects hypoxic vasoconstriction has depended on the experimental preparation used (26). As Figure 1 indicates, for perfused lung preparations, alpha blockade on the average abolishes 60% of the vasoconstrictor response to hypoxia. In this preparation the effects of two other vasoconstrictors, hypercapnic acidosis and histamine, are almost but not quite abolished by alpha blockade, and the effects of all three agents are greatly enhanced by beta blockade. In other studies alpha adrenergic blockade has been far less effective in blocking the pulmonary vasoconstrictor effects of histamine (23, 26); but these studies used pentobarbital anesthesia, which has itself been shown to abolish the vasoconstrictor effects of histamine.

Alterations of vasoconstrictor responses by adrenergic blockade are not based on mediation of these responses by released catecholamines. The evidence includes studies that deplete catecholamines from nerve endings beforehand by means of reserpine, as well as measurements of an index of catecholamine release from autonomic nerve endings—i.e. dopamine beta hydroxylase. Pulmonary vascular responses to hypoxia, hypercapnia, and histamine are undisturbed after reserpine, and no dopamine beta hydroxylase is released during these responses (37c). But the adrenergic receptor

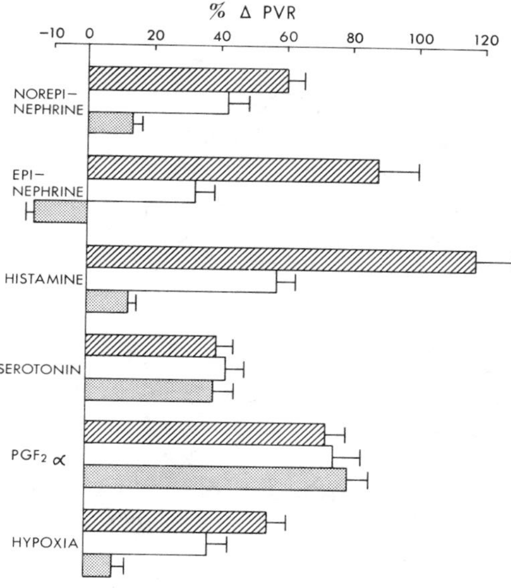

Figure 1 The changes in pulmonary vascular resistance elicited by a variety of vasoactive agents in the perfused lung of the cat during a control situation (clear histogram in the middle of each group), during beta blockade with propranolol (cross-hatched histogram at the top of a group), and during alpha blockade (stippled histogram at the bottom of each group). Doses were: vasoactive amines = 10^{-5} g kg^{-1}; serotonin, 10^{-4} g kg^{-1}; prostaglandins = 10^{-6} g kg^{-1}; hypoxia = PA_{O_2} of 50 mm Hg; hypercapnic acidosis = pH of 7.20.

mechanisms are not universal receptors for other types of humoral agents or even for all vasoactive amines. For instance, alpha and beta blockade, or beta receptor enhancement by stimulation of adenylcyclase, does not alter the potent pulmonary vasoactive responses of serotonin, vasopressin, prostaglandins, bradykinin, or angiotensin II (37*a*), 49).

Despite the great sensitivity of the pulmonary vasoactive effects of histamine to blockade by typical adrenergic blocking agents, a separate set of selective inhibitors of the vasoactive effects of histamine have been identified. These appear to mediate vasoconstrictor and vasodilator effects of histamine and are thus identical or analogous to H-1 and H-2 receptors identified elsewhere in the body. Chlorpheniramine in a dose of 10^{-3} g kg^{-1} will antagonize all the pulmonary vasoconstrictor effects of histamine in doses of 10^{-5} g kg^{-1} and occasionally convert the responses to vasodilation (50); in the cat and rat, similar responses to similar doses of agonist and antagonist were reported (23, 24). Thus pulmonary vasoconstriction by histamine is considered mediated by an H-1 receptor. Metiamide in doses of 25–70 mg kg^{-1} enhances the vasoconstrictor effects of 10 μg kg^{-1} doses of histamine in the perfused lobe of the cat (37b) and, in intact animals, not only enhances the pulmonary vasoconstrictor effect of histamine, but also prevents the usual rise in cardiac output (50). Thus virtually all pulmonary vasoconstrictor activity induced by exogenously administered histamine is blocked by chlorphenamine in doses 100-fold higher than those of histamine. However, if a ratio of 100:1 of antagonist to agonist is needed for blockade when both are exogenously infused, it is possible that endogenous histamine, released at the adventitia a few microns from the vascular smooth muscle by pulmonary periarterial mast cells, cannot be antagonized by the doses of exogenously administered chlorphenamine that are feasible in the intact animal: The local tissue concentrations of histamine at the adventitia may be as much as 10^{-12} μg μm^{-3}, whereas the tissue concentrations of chlorpheniramine, administered as a dose of 1 mg kg^{-1}, could only be equal to that amount, not 100-fold higher.

These relationships may explain why decreased effects of histamine on the pulmonary vascular bed are observed when a mast cell stabilizing agent such as disodium cromoglycate is infused, rather than when H-1 blocking agents are used: Disodium cromoglycate, and not H-1 blocking agents, decreases pulmonary vascular resistance; it also appears selectively to make available the H-1 constrictor receptor, in that, after disodium cromoglycate is administered, infused histamine calls forth a greater constrictor response than usual (37b). Such a hypothesis suggests different rates of agonist activity at H-1 and H-2 sites between acutely infused and steady-state endogenous histamine, perhaps based on relative reaction rates or binding. This hypothesis would also explain the different pulmonary vasoactive effects of infused histamine when either dose or species is varied (26); although vasoconstriction is the predominant response, the occasional incidence of vasodilation varies with the species and varies indirectly with the dose.

Thus two apparently separate receptor systems for pulmonary vascular smooth muscle appear to have a close, but not interchangeable, relation to each other. Both the adrenergic and histaminic receptors appear able to function independent of postganglionic autonomic or other nervous innervation; they appear to moderate tone in the pulmonary vascular bed; and they may play a part in mediating some or most of the pulmonary vasoconstrictor effects of hypoxia and hypercapnia. The ability of adrenergic blocking agents markedly to affect vasoactive responses to histamine, but the inability of histamine blocking agents to affect at all the vasoactive role of adrenergic agents, suggests at least (*a*) that histaminic reception requires a second step through the adrenergic receptor mechanism prior to mechanocontraction, or (*b*) that the adrenergic and histaminic receptor mechanisms are stereologically amalgamated to the extent that some blocking agents (i.e. the adrenergics) fit well enough to block both catecholamines and histamine, whereas others (i.e. the antihistamines) fit well enough to block only their specific agonists.

VASOACTIVE POLYPEPTIDES

Angiotensin and bradykinin are natural substances capable of altering pulmonary vascular tone.

Angiotensin

Angiotensin II, the octapeptide formed from the decapeptide angiotensin I by endothelial cell–converting enzyme (16, 35), is a consistent pulmonary vasoconstrictor (4a). In a dose-response curve it exceeds by several orders of magnitude the effects of angiotensin I. Unlike histamine and serotonin, however, angiotensin II is as consistently vasoconstrictive in the systemic circulation as it is in the pulmonary vasculature. Slips of vascular smooth muscle from the large vessels of virtually all vascular beds contract in response to this agent. The magnitude of the vasoconstrictor effects of angiotensin II is best seen in the perfused lung of the cat, where without the drawbacks of fluctuating systemic pressure angiotensin II on a molar basis is at least an order of magnitude more effective than histamine or serotonin in evoking pulmonary vasoconstriction (23, 37c).

In the unanesthetized human, during infusions of angiotensin II in small enough doses (3×10^{-7} kg min^{-1}) to minimize the potent systemic pressor effects, the pulmonary circulation still reacts with considerable vasoconstriction (37a). Because of its consistency in all vascular beds, the vasoconstrictor effect of angiotensin II on all vascular smooth muscle has been assumed to be "direct," perhaps using a single common receptor; neither release of intermediate substances nor use of the alpha adrenergic system, which is highly variable from bed to bed, has been invoked. However, the two adrenergic receptors may play some role in the vascular response to angiotensin II, though not a dominant one; alpha and beta blockade can increase and decrease, respectively, the pulmonary vasoconstrictor effects of angiotensin II, but not nearly to the same degree as with histamine, or, of course, epinephrine. Thus angiotensin II may use alpha receptors for part of its vasoconstrictor effect, or it may, like tyramine and other pharmacologic agents, release norepinephrine at sympathetic endings close to the pulmonary resistance vessels (35). Angiotensin II was once thought to be a humoral agent "necessary" for the pulmonary vasoconstrictor response to hypoxia (8), though not the direct mediator. Experiments using an analog octapeptide, saralasin, which acts as a competitive inhibitor of angiotensin II and abolishes all its cardiovascular effects, have not supported this hypothesis (1, 21).

Bradykinin and the Kallidins

These agents comprise a system of polypeptides requiring activation by plasma factors called kallikreins. Their function in the normal pulmonary circulation is uncertain. Although bradykinin is considered a systemic vasodilator (33) in all species, and in humans with pulmonary hypertension (14), in the rat it appears to be a pulmonary vasoconstrictor (23). A relatively high dose of 10^{-4} g kg^{-1} is required to double pulmonary vascular resistance (see Table 1). Moreover, its vasoconstrictor effect appears to be blocked by aspirin. Its vasoconstrictor effect (when it occurs) may therefore be largely mediated by release of vasoconstrictor prostaglandins, such as PGE_2 and $PGF_{2\alpha}$ (36). In other species bradykinin is a pulmonary vasodilator. Differences in the concentrations of these mediating prostaglandins may account for the variation in the pulmonary vasoactive response to bradykinin.

PROSTAGLANDINS AND PRECURSORS

A major precursor of prostaglandins, arachidonic acid, is an active pulmonary vasoconstrictor (10^{-3} g kg^{-1}) when infused into the intact animal or isolated lobe (27, 34, 49). Its effects are completely inhibited by aspirin, a synthetase inhibitor, and its metabolites are therefore presumed in the net to result in the vasoconstrictor effect, despite the fact that a combination of constrictor and dilator prostaglandins are formed from arachidonic acid (25).

Of these bisenoic metabolites, two have been well characterized and appear to have consistent effects (7). The first is $PGF_{2\alpha}$, which in virtually every variety of preparation in the rodent, cat, dog, and primate is a pulmonary vasoconstrictor (34, 49). In doses of 1–3 μg kg^{-1} min^{-1}, it will produce sustained elevations of pulmonary vascular resistance at least twice normal. These effects are not affected by prostaglandin synthetase inhibition. In women in the first trimester of pregnancy the same doses cause 50% increments in pulmonary vascular resistance with no alterations in cardiac output (40). The mechanisms of action of $PGF_{2\alpha}$ have not all been defined, but, at least in the rodent, the excitatory action of this agent is associated with depolarization and reduction of smooth muscle cell membrane resistance (29).

The two prostaglandins of the E series have different pulmonary vascular effects. Although PGE_1 and PGE_2 seem both to be peripheral vasodilators, only PGE_1 is still a vasodilator in the lung (27). PGE_2 seems to be a consistent vasoconstrictor with about the same, or slightly lower, potency as $PGF_{2\alpha}$; it vasoconstricts in the perfused lung, the intact animal, and isolated vessel strip. Where attempts to differentiate between arterial and venous effects have been made, PGE_2 is effective on the canine artery and vein but only on the artery in swine and lamb (27). The intermediate metabolites between arachidonic acid and the bisenoic prostaglandins are so shortlived (thromboxane $A_2 = 30$ sec and endoperoxides ≈ 5 min) that few have been tested for their pulmonary vascular effects. One perhaps representative intermediate is PGH_2, for which a stable epoxymethano analog is available. This analog is a potent constrictor of pulmonary arterial and venous strips from rabbit, cow, and dog lung (18).

The interrelations between the prostaglandins and other pulmonary vasoactive phenomena have not been fully worked out. For instance, the important role of prostaglandins in mediating the pulmonary vasoconstrictor response of injected endotoxin seems now well established (36). Synthetase inhibitors are potent inhibitors of this and other effects of endotoxin. In addition, measured levels of $PGF_{2\alpha}$ have been elevated in the pulmonary venous effluent blood after endotoxin injection, and this elevation has been suppressed by indomethacin (3). On the other hand, a role of prostaglandins in mediating the pulmonary vasoconstrictor response to alveolar hypoxia has been suggested (38) but not substantiated (20, 47). However, the opposite may be the case: In the special instance of the perfused lung, the spontaneous elaboration of PGE_1 may prevent the hypoxic pulmonary vasoconstrictor response, and this inhibition may be overcome by aspirin (47).

A precise physiological role in the normal regulation of the pulmonary circulation is difficult to assign at the present to the prostaglandins: Mediation of the pulmonary effects of endotoxin is not physiologic in the same sense as mediation of the vasoconstrictor effect of localized alveolar hypoxia. Thus although prostaglandin release and metabolism in the lung occur at easily discernible levels in a variety of states [e.g. mechanical perturbation (38)], their significance in normal regulation of the pulmonary circulation has yet to be realized.

Literature Cited

1. Alexander, J. M., Nyby, M. D., Jasberg, L. A. 1976. Effect of angiotensin on hypoxic pulmonary vasoconstriction in isolated dog lung. *J. Appl. Physiol.* 41:184–88
2. Altura, B. M., Altura, B. T. 1974. Effects of local anesthetics, antihistamines and glucocorticoids on peripheral blood flow and vascular smooth muscle. *Anesthesiology* 41:197–214
3. Anderson, F. L., Tsagaris, T. J., Jubiz, W., Kuida, H. 1975. Prostaglandin F and E levels during endotoxin-induced pulmonary hypertension in calves. *Am. J. Physiol.* 228:1479–82

4a. Aviado, D. M. 1960. Pulmonary venular responses to anoxia, 5-hydroxy-tryptamine and histamine. *Am. J. Physiol.* 198:1032–36

4b. Aviado, D. M. 1965. *The Lung Circulation,* Vol. 1, Ch. 5. London: Pergamon

4c. Aviado, D. M. 1965. *The Lung Circulation,* Vol. 1, Ch. 6. London: Pergamon

5. Aviado, D. M., Samaneck, M., Folle, L. E. 1966. Cardiopulmonary effects of tobacco and related substances. I. The release of histamine during inhalation of cigarette smoke and anoxemia in the heart-lung and intact dog preparation. *Arch. Env. Health* 12:705–11
6. Bergofsky, E. H. 1974. Mechanisms underlying vasomotor regulation of regional pulmonary blood flow in normal and disease states. *Am. J. Med.* 57:378–94
7. Bergstrom, S., Carlson, L. A., Weeks, S. R. 1968. Prostaglandins. *Pharmacol. Rev.* 20:1–37
8. Berkov, S. 1974. Hypoxic pulmonary vasoconstriction in the rat; the necessary role of angiotensin II. *Circ. Res.* 35:257–61
9. Bianchi, A., Vleeschower, G. R. de. 1962. Effect of various pharmacological compounds on the vagal induced lung constriction. *Arch. Int. Pharmacodyn.* 135:472–80
10. Bisgard, G. E., Will, J. A. 1972. Glucagon and aminophylline as pulmonary vasodilators in the calf with hypoxic pulmonary hypertension. *Chest* 71:2 Suppl. 263–65
11. Brody, J. S., Stemmler, E. J., DuBois, A. B. 1968. Longitudinal distribution of vascular resistance in the pulmonary arterial capillaries and veins. *J. Clin. Invest.* 47:783–89
12. Daicoff, G. R., Chavez, F. R., Anton, A. H., Swenson, E. W. 1968. Serotonin-induced pulmonary venous hypertension in pulmonary embolism. *J. Thorac. Cardiovasc. Surg.* 56:810–16
13. Fishman, A. P. 1976. Hypoxia on the pulmonary circulation: How and where it acts. *Circ. Res.* 38:221–31
14. Freitas, F. M. de, Faraco, E. Z., Azevedo, D. F. de, Lewin, I. 1966. Action of bradykinin on human pulmonary circulation. Observations in patients with mitral valvular disease. *Circulation* 34:385–90
15. Fritts, H. W. Jr., Harris, P., Clauss, R. H., Odell, J. E., Cournand, A. 1958. The effect of acetylcholine on the human pulmonary circulation under normal and hypoxic conditions. *J. Clin. Invest.* 37:99–108
16. Gillis, C. N. 1973. Metabolism of vasoactive hormones by lung. *Anesthesiology* 39:626–32
17. Glazier, J. B., Murray, J. F. 1971. Sites of pulmonary vasomotor reactivity in the dog during alveolar hypoxia and serotonin and histamine infusion. *J. Clin. Invest.* 50:2250–57
18. Gruetter, C. A., McNamara, D. B., Hyman, A. L., Kadowitz, P. J. 1978. Contractile responses of intrapulmonary vessels from three species to arachidonic acid and an epoxymethano analog of PGH2. *Can. J. Physiol. Pharmacol.* 56:206–15
19. Haas, F., Bergofsky, E. H. 1972. Role of the mast cell in the pulmonary pressor response to hypoxia. *J. Clin. Invest.* 51:3154–62
20. Hales, C. A., Rouse, E. Buchwald, I. A., Kazemi, H. 1977. Role of prostaglandins in alveolar hypoxic vasoconstriction. *Respir. Physiol.* 29:151–62
21. Hales, C. A., Rouse, E. T., Kazemi, H. 1977. Failure of saralasin acetate, a competitive inhibitor of angiotensin II, to diminish alveolar hypoxic vasoconstriction in the dog. *Cardiovasc. Res.* 11:541–46
22. Harris, P., Heath, S. 1977. *The Human Pulmonary Circulation,* Ch. 9. Baltimore: Williams and Wilkins
23. Hauge, A. 1968. Role of histamine in hypoxic pulmonary hypertension in the rat. I. Blockade or potentiation of endogenous amines, kinins, and ATP. *Circ. Res.* 23:371–83
24. Hauge, A., Melmon, K. L. 1968. Role of histamine in hypoxic pulmonary hypertension in the rat. II. Depletion of histamine, serotonin, and catecholamines. *Circ. Res.* 22:385–92
25. Horton, E. W. 1969. Hypotheses on physiological role of prostaglandins. *Physiol. Rev.* 49:122–41
26. Howard, P., Barer, G. R., Thompson, B., Warren, P. M., Abbott, C. J., Mungall, I. P. R. 1975. Factors causing and reversing vasoconstriction in the unventilated lung. *Resp. Physiol.* 24:325–45
27. Kadowitz, P. J., Joiner, P. D., Hyman, A. L. 195. Effect of prostaglandin E_2 on pulmonary vascular resistance in intact dog, swine and lamb. *Eur. J. Pharmacol.* 31:72–80
28. Kelminson, L. L., Cotton, E. K., Vogel, J. H. 1967. The reversibility of pulmonary hypertension in patients with cystic fibrosis. Observations on the effects of tolazoline hydrochloride. *Pediatrics* 39:2–35
29. Kitamura, K., Suzuki, H., Kuriyama, H. 1976. Prostaglandin action on the main pulmonary artery and portal vein of the rabbit. *Jpn. J. Physiol.* 26:4, 681–92
30. Kusajima, K., Ozdemir, I. A., Webb, W. R., Wax, S. D., Parker, F. B. Jr. 1974. Role of serotonin and serotonin antagonist on pulmonary hemodynam-

ics and microcirculation in hemorrhagic shock. *J. Thorac. Cardiovasc. Surg.* 67:908–14

31. Levy, R. J., Rosenthal, A., Freed, M. D., Smith, C. D., Eraklis, A., Nadas, A. S. 1977. Persistent pulmonary hypertension in a newborn with congenital diaphragmatic hernia: Successful management with tolazoline. *Pediatrics* 60:740–42
32. Levy, S. E., Simmons, D. H., Assali, N. S. 1971. Serotonin, pulmonary hypertension, and airway constriction in the anesthetized dog. *Proc. Soc. Exp. Biol. Med.* 138:365–68
33. Maxwell, G. M., Elliott, R. B., Kneebone, G. M. 1962. Effects of bradykinin on the systemic and coronary vascular bed of the intact dog. *Circ. Res.* 10:359–63
34. Okpako, D. T. 1972. The actions of histamine and prostaglandins F_2 and E_2 on pulmonary vascular resistance of the lung of the guinea pig. *J. Pharm. Pharmacol.* 24:40–50
35. Palaic, D. 1971. Effect of angiotensin on noradrenaline—^{3}H accumulation and synthesis in vivo. *Can. J. Physiol. Pharmacol.* 49:495–501
36. Parratt, J. R., Sturgess, R. M. 1975. Evidence that prostaglandin release mediates pulmonary vasoconstriction induced by *E. coli* endotoxin. *J. Physiol. London* 246:79–80

37a. Porcelli, R. J., Bergofsky, E. H. 1973. Adrenergic receptors in pulmonary vasoconstrictor responses to gaseous and humoral agents. *J. Appl. Physiol.* 34:483–88

37b. Porcelli, R. J., Bergofsky, E. H. 1977. Histamine regulation by the lung. *Physiologist* 20(4):75

37c. Porcelli, R. J., Viau, A. T., Naftchi, N. E., Bergofsky, E. H. 1977. B-receptor influence on lung vasoconstrictor responses to hypoxia and humoral agents. *J. Appl. Physiol.* 43:612–16

37d. Porcelli, R. J., Mahoney, W. A., Shukla, L. S., Bergofsky, E. H. 1978. Role of pulmonary adrenergic mechanisms in regulating pulmonary vascular tone. *Physiologist* 22(4):78

38. Said, S. I., Kitamura, S., Vreim, C. 1972. Prostaglandins: release from the lung during mechanical ventilation at larger tidal volumes. *J. Clin. Invest.* 51:83a
39. Satyanarayana Rao, B. N., Moller, J. H., Edwards, J. E. 1969. Primary pulmonary hypertension in a child. Response to pharmacologic agents. *Circulation* 40:583–87
40. Secher, N. J., Andersen, L. H. 1977. Changes in the pattern of regional pulmonary blood flow after PGF_2 alpha infusion in pregnant women. *Cardiovasc. Res.* 11:26–30
41. Selye, H. 1965. *The Mast Cells.* Washington DC: Butterworth
42. Shettigar, U. R., Hultgren, H. N., Specter, M., Martin, R., Davies, D. H. 1976. Primary pulmonary hypertension: favorable effect of isoproterenol. *N. Engl. J. Med.* 295:(25) 1414–15
43. Silove, E. D., Grover, R. F. 1968. Effects of alpha adrenergic blockade and tissue catecholamine depletion on pulmonary vascular response to hypoxia. *J. Clin. Invest.* 47:274–85
44. Silove, E. D., Simcha, A. J. 1973. Histamine-induced vasodilation in the calf: relationship to hypoxia. *J. Appl. Physiol.* 35:830–36
45. Suggett, A. J., Herget, J. 1977. Effect of alpha-methyldopa on the pulmonary vascular changes induced by chronic hypoxia in rats. *Clin. Sci. Mol. Med.* 53:397–400
46. Tucker, A., Weir, E. K., Reeves, J. T., Grover, R. F. 1975. Histamine H-1 and H-2 receptors in the pulmonary and systemic vasculature of the dog. *Am. J. Physiol.* 229:1008–13
47. Vaage, J., Bjertnaes, L., Hauge, A. 1975. The pulmonary vasoconstriction response to hypoxia: effects of inhibitors of prostaglandin biosynthesis. *Acta Physiol. Scand.* 95:95–1001
48. Wang, S. W., Pohl, J. E., Rowlands, D. J., Wade, E. G. 1978. Diazoxide in treatment of primary pulmonary hypertension. *Br. Heart J.* 40:572–74
49. Wicks, T. C., Rose, J. C., Johnson, M., Ramwell, P. W., Kot, P. A. 1976. Vascular response to arachidonic acid in the perfused canine lung. *Circ. Res.* 38:167–71
50. Woods, J. R. Jr., Brinkman, C. R., Dandavino, A., Murayama, K., Assali, N. S. 1977. Action of histamine and H-1 and H-2 blockers on the cardiopulmonary circulation. *Am. J. Physiol.* 232:73–78

Ann. Rev. Physiol. 1980. 42:235–47

VENTILATION-PERFUSION RELATIONSHIPS

❖1265

Peter D. Wagner

Department of Medicine, University of California, San Diego, La Jolla, California 92093

INTRODUCTION

This chapter aims to give the reader a balanced perspective on recent developments in the field of ventilation-perfusion ($\dot{V}_A/\dot{Q}$) relationships. Knowledge in this area has grown in a series of leaps interspersed with relatively dormant periods. While the important aspects are certainly physiological, the leaps in understanding $\dot{V}_A/\dot{Q}$ relationships are tied to advances in the ability to devise and apply mathematical tools (54). Thus during the first half of this century, without much use of mathematics, maldistribution of ventilation and bloodflow was merely recognized as a barrier to gas exchange (16, 24). Only rudimentary work was done in the field, and some important conceptual errors were made (16). After World War II came the first major advances (14, 36–38). These were the result of ingenious graphic approaches to the mathematical problems associated with $\dot{V}_A/\dot{Q}$ relationships, and they have provided the basis of our current understanding of how Po_2 and Pco_2 in the lung are determined by its ventilation and bloodflow. Indeed the clinical tests of gas exchange in patients with lung disease used widely today stem directly from this early work.

The problems still to be solved can be stated as follows: (*a*) The major cause of hypoxemia in lung disease is an abnormal ventilation-perfusion relationship. Thus *quantitation of the degree of $\dot{V}_A/\dot{Q}$ mismatching* has been a constant goal ever since the initial three-compartment analysis of Riley and coworkers (38). (*b*) $\dot{V}_A/\dot{Q}$ maldistribution cannot be considered in isolation: Gas exchange depends not only on $\dot{V}_A/\dot{Q}$ mismatching but also on factors such as the overall level of ventilation and pulmonary bloodflow,

0066-4278/80/0315-0235$01.00

and of oxygen consumption and CO_2 production; the acid/base status of the blood; the hemoglobin concentration; and the inspired P_{O_2}. Interpretation of indexes of $\dot{V}_A/\dot{Q}$ mismatching (such as the arterial P_{O_2}, the alveolar-arterial P_{O_2} difference, and the amount of venous admixture) is difficult because so many factors affect arterial P_{O_2}. Thus we seek an *orderly way of understanding these complex relationships.* Recent progress in both areas is described below, commencing with the latter.

MATHEMATICAL MODELING OF VENTILATION-PERFUSION INEQUALITY

The first major breakthrough was the development of digital computer algorithms for the oxygen and carbon dioxide dissociation curves (21, 22, 29). While these routines themselves were modest accomplishments, their significance for the study of ventilation-perfusion relationships was (and remains) great. The principal barrier to further understanding of gas exchange in the lung had been the numerical difficulties in solving the mass balance equations of Rahn and of Riley, whose graphic methods were fundamental to the advancement of the basic concept of how $\dot{V}_A/\dot{Q}$ maldistribution affected gas exchange but were poorly suited to systematic exploration of the two types of problems outlined above. Soon computer programs were published (23, 30, 51) that used the dissociation-curve subroutines together with the original mass balance equations to compute the relationships between alveolar P_{O_2} and P_{CO_2} and the ratio of ventilation to bloodflow. [For details see (31, 55).] These programs opened the door to previously infeasible analyses of gas exchange in the presence of $\dot{V}_A/\dot{Q}$ inequality. Of particular importance was the development of the notion of a *distribution* of lung units. Previously most workers had recognized the complexity of gas exchange but had simply characterized the lung by two or three virtual compartments. While this approach continues to be useful at the clinical level, the real lung is a collection of many alveoli and capillaries. It is thus more appropriate (if more difficult) to think of the lung as consisting of many units of different $\dot{V}_A/\dot{Q}$ ratios—i.e. as a distribution. Central to the understanding of gas exchange is the quantitative allocation of bloodflow and ventilation to all of these lung units of different $\dot{V}_A/\dot{Q}$. In Figure 1A, only units of $\dot{V}_A/\dot{Q}$ between 0.3 and 3.0 are present, and between these limits two populations or modes are evident. Figure 1B shows a single mode; it is much broader than the distribution of Figure 1A, encompassing $\dot{V}_A/\dot{Q}$ ratios from about 0.03 to 30.0. Picturing the lung in this way gives insight and information not apparent from the two- or three-compartment approaches.

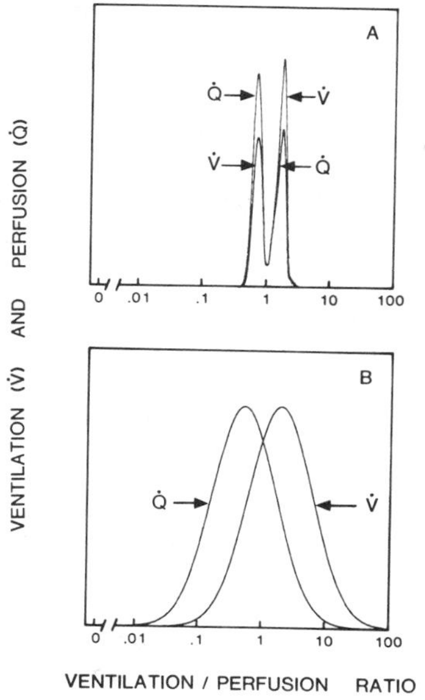

Figure 1 Distribution of ventilation-perfusion ratios, defined as the plot of compartmental ventilation and perfusion against compartmental ventilation/perfusion ratio. Two hypothetical examples illustrate the ratios of shape, position, dispersion, and modality of distributions.

By means of these programs, the effect of maldistribution of $\dot{V}_A/\dot{Q}$ on pulmonary exchange of O_2, CO_2, and a variety of "inert" gases has been explored at great length (2, 4, 10, 12, 39, 51–53, 57). From these studies (some numerical, using the above algorithms; some analytical, using algebraic methods), several concepts emerge:

1. The presence of $\dot{V}_A/\dot{Q}$ inequality [no matter what the shape, position, or dispersion of the distribution (Figure 1)] results in an interference with the uptake (or elimination) of all gases under essentially all physiological conditions (2, 10, 39, 51). Evans and coworkers (10) rigidly defined the conditions under which $\dot{V}_A/\dot{Q}$ inequality might enhance gas exchange. In humans such enhanced gas exchange is possible only during the induction of anesthesia with nitrous oxide [where the alveolar Po_2 of low $\dot{V}_A/\dot{Q}$ units is greatly elevated by the volume shrinkage caused by N_2O uptake (12)].

2. In general, the solubility (in blood) of a gas is the principal determinant of how much interference with gas exchange takes place in the presence of a given distribution of $\dot{V}_A/\dot{Q}$ (2, 52). Gases of very low and very high solubility (e.g. helium and ether, respectively) are not affected as much as gases of medium solubility (e.g. C_2H_2 and N_2O).

3. If a distribution of $\dot{V}_A/\dot{Q}$ contains areas of low and (near) normal $\dot{V}_A/\dot{Q}$ but not of high $\dot{V}_A/\dot{Q}$, less soluble gases will be interfered with to a greater extent and more soluble gases to a lesser extent (39, 43). Such is the case in asthma (47), in interstitial disease (46), and in some patients with COPD (45). Conversely, a distribution containing units of high and (near) normal $\dot{V}_A/\dot{Q}$ but not of low $\dot{V}_A/\dot{Q}$ preferentially interferes with gases of higher solubility [pulmonary embolism (5), some patients with COPD (45), PEEP ventilation (7)].

4. While one cannot strictly discuss O_2 and CO_2 in the above terms, the nonlinearity of their dissociation curves is of secondary importance (43, 52). Therefore, if an average "solubility" is calculated using the average slope of their dissociation curves, both O_2 and CO_2 fit the above concept well (43). Oxygen can be regarded as a gas of medium solubility [(arterio-venous content)/(partial pressure differences) gives a value of (20–15)/(100–40) or 0.083 ml O_2/100 ml blood/torr] while CO_2 can be regarded as a gas of rather high solubility [(48–52)/(40–45) or 0.8 ml CO_2/100 ml blood/torr]. These values can be compared to those of helium (0.001), N_2O (0.066), C_2H_2 (0.12), and ether (1.75).

5. For a given gas and a given distribution of ventilation-perfusion ratios, the *boundary conditions* can be of extreme importance in determining the overall pattern of gas exchange. In other words, the composition of the mixed venous blood and the inspired gas entering the lungs can greatly affect gas transfer. This is especially true for oxygen. A recent review (54) illustrated the dependence of alveolar and end-capillary P_{O_2} and O_2 content on both mixed venous and inspired P_{O_2}. These relationships are further illustrated in Figure 2. It is evident that (*a*) in lung regions of very low $\dot{V}_A/\dot{Q}$, alveolar (and end-capillary) P_{O_2} and O_2 content are tied closely to mixed venous values, especially breathing room air; (*b*) in lung regions of very high $\dot{V}_A/\dot{Q}$, alveolar (and end-capillary) P_{O_2} and O_2 content are tied closely to inspired values irrespective of mixed venous P_{O_2}; and (*c*) in lung units of intermediate $\dot{V}_A/\dot{Q}$, the alveolar (and end-capillary) P_{O_2} and O_2 content have intermediate values dependent on both inspired and mixed venous values. Thus the arterial P_{O_2} that results from a particular pattern of $\dot{V}_A/\dot{Q}$ maldistribution depends on mixed venous and inspired P_{O_2} values in complex but logical ways.

While these concepts are widely known, they have often been ignored in the clinical evaluation of patients with cardiopulmonary disease. Calculations that illustrate these concepts in the clinical setting are therefore of extreme importance in the understanding of lung disease. Pontoppidan (34) was among the first to show by calculation that during 100% breathing, the arterial P_{O_2} corresponding to a given value of right-to-left shunt was highly dependent on the mixed venous P_{O_2} (which in turn closely reflects cardiac output). For example, when cardiac output is normal and the arterio-venous O_2 content difference is 5 ml O_2/100 ml blood, arterial Po_2 would be about 270 torr for a 20% shunt. However, if cardiac output is high (due to fever, overtransfusion, etc), the arterial Po_2 could be as high as 500 torr and if low (due to shock, etc) could be well under 100 torr even with the shunt remaining at 20% of the cardiac output. While Pontoppidan was concerned primarily with patients under intensive care with respiratory distress syndromes, the effect is seen in many areas—e.g. asthmatic subjects may have unduly high cardiac output levels (due to both endogenous and exogenous sympathetic overstimulation) so that their arterial Po_2 is higher than otherwise expected for the degree of $\dot{V}_A/\dot{Q}$ mismatch (47). In contrast, following a myocardial infarct, patients may have severe hypoxemia (48) out of proportion to the amount of $\dot{V}_A/\dot{Q}$ mismatch because of their lower than normal cardiac output levels.

6. Computer modeling has also explained another important manifestation of $\dot{V}_A/\dot{Q}$ mismatching: discordant behavior of arterial Po_2 and Pco_2. Patients with $\dot{V}_A/\dot{Q}$ mismatching most often exhibit hypoxemia and normocapnia (or even hypocapnia). Such a picture was formerly taken as evidence that $\dot{V}_A/\dot{Q}$ inequality affected O_2 and not CO_2, but now it has been shown repeatedly (52, 55) that the alinearity of the O_2 dissociation curve explains the findings. Thus with $\dot{V}_A/\dot{Q}$ mismatching both O_2 and CO_2 transfer are impaired (52, 55), resulting initially in hypoxemia and (at least transiently) hypercapnia. Chemoreceptor response to these changes results

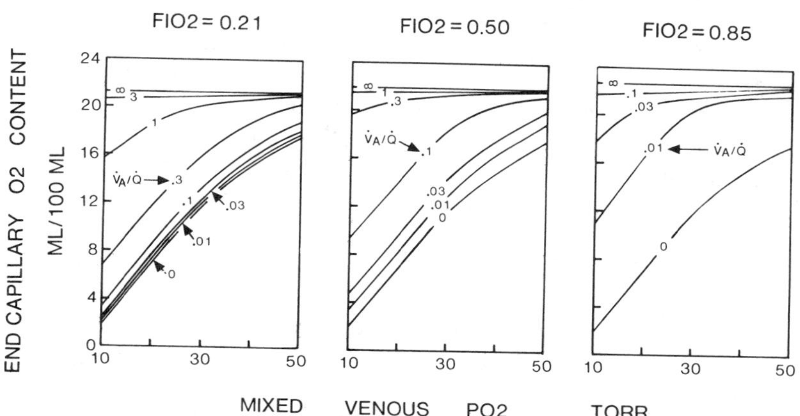

Figure 2 End-capillary O_2 content in lung units of the specified $\dot{V}_A/\dot{Q}$ ratios, shown as a function of both inspired and mixed venous Po_2. For $FIo_2 = 0.21$ and units of low $\dot{V}_A/\dot{Q}$, O_2 content is determined by mixed venous values while in units of high $\dot{V}_A/\dot{Q}$ it follows O_2 content computed for the given inspired Po_2. As FIo_2 is increased, units of moderately low $\dot{V}_A/\dot{Q}$ (e.g. 0.1) tend to follow inspired rather than mixed venous levels.

in hyperventilation, which more easily returns P_{CO_2} than P_{O_2} to its normal value because of the differences in the shape of the two dissociation curves.

7. Finally, computer modeling has shown that even if the assumption of a parallel arrangement of gas exchange units is not valid, other configurations of lung units produce gas exchange that can be interpreted in terms of parallel models (8, 15, 49, 57). Such configurations include series gas exchange units (8, 49), units having different hematocrit (57), and re-inspiration of deadspace gas that is common to many units (15). While these perturbations are thought by many investigators to exist in the real lung, their experimental measurement is currently infeasible. Computer modeling obviates such measurements: The simple parallel model is robust enough to be useful in characterizing gas exchange abnormalities despite peturbations.

QUANTITATION OF $\dot{V}_A/\dot{Q}$ MISMATCHING

As with the lung modeling described above, there are two main approaches to estimating the extent of $\dot{V}_A/\dot{Q}$ maldistribution. One uses a model containing only two or three parameters—e.g. (*a*) Riley's original ideal alveolar air-physiologic deadspace-venous admixture compartmentalization (36), (*b*) Briscoe's two-compartment model (1), (c) Farhi & Yokoyama's two-compartment model based on simultaneous elimination of three inert gases (11, 13, 56), and (*d*) parameterization methods for matching (lognormal) distributions to an appropriate set of gas exchange data (17, 40). All such approaches are here called "parametric" methods to distinguish them from methods involving description of the lung by a much larger number of variables—e.g. the multiple inert gas elimination approach (6, 9) or the corresponding method for analyzing the multibreath N_2 washout (26). These are here called "multicompartmental" approaches.

The remainder of this review evaluates both types of approach in an effort to resolve what appear to be differences of opinion in the literature.

The Parametric Approach

The parametric approach attempts to obtain experimentally exactly as many data as there are unknown parameters to be determined—no more and no fewer. The simplest example of this kind of logic is the Riley venous admixture analysis (36). The data for this analysis come from the arterial P_{O_2} (converted by calculation into O_2 content), while the parameter to be determined is the virtual shunt (i.e. venous admixture expressed as a fraction of cardiac output) necessary to account for the measured arterial P_{O_2}. As is well known, a simple mixing equation leads to the solution of this problem:

$$C_{aO_2} * \dot{Q}_T = C_{iO_2} * (\dot{Q}_T - \dot{Q}_S) + C_{\bar{v}O_2} * \dot{Q}_S \qquad 1.$$

where $\dot{Q}_T$ is cardiac output, $\dot{Q}_S$ is that portion of $\dot{Q}_T$ flowing through the virtual shunt, and CaO_2, CiO_2, and $C\bar{v}O_2$ are, respectively, O_2 contents of arterial blood, end-capillary blood in the ideal compartment, and mixed venous blood.

Rearrangement of this expression gives the well-known relationship:

$$\frac{\dot{Q}_S}{\dot{Q}_T} = \frac{CiO_2 - CaO_2}{CiO_2 - C\bar{v}O_2} \qquad 2.$$

In this expression, one piece of measured information, CaO_2, coupled with an assumed (or better, measured) value of $C\bar{v}O_2$ and a calculated value of CiO_2 leads to a *unique* answer for $\dot{Q}_S/\dot{Q}_T$, the virtual shunt fraction. That only one value of $\dot{Q}_S/\dot{Q}_T$ can explain the measured value of CaO_2 is the advantage of such an approach. Such an advantage also holds true for the other parametric methods listed above. However, a major disadvantage has generally been overlooked in the application of such methods. Equation 1 can just as easily be restated as follows:

$$CaO_2 * \dot{Q}_T = CiO_2 * (\dot{Q}_T - \dot{Q}_b) + CbO_2 * \dot{Q}_b, \qquad 3.$$

where a hypothetical lung unit of $\dot{V}_A/\dot{Q} > O$ is substituted for the compartment having $\dot{V}_A/\dot{Q} = O$ as in equation 1. In equation 3, the low $\dot{V}_A/\dot{Q}$ compartment b is specified with bloodflow $\dot{Q}_b$ and end-capillary O_2 content CbO_2 ($CbO_2 > C\bar{v}O_2$ since $\dot{V}_A/\dot{Q} > O$), instead of a shunt compartment. Rearrangement yields:

$$\frac{\dot{Q}_b}{\dot{Q}_T} = \frac{CiO_2 - CaO_2}{CiO_2 - CbO_2}. \qquad 4.$$

In other words, there exists a *unique* value of bloodflow, $\dot{Q}_b$, such that the measured arterial Po_2 is precisely explained by the two-compartment model consisting of compartment b and the ideal compartment.

The conclusion from this analysis is that while the parametric approach gives a unique solution, the basic parametric model itself is not unique. Many different models (in fact, an infinite number) can equally well explain the given data. The reader is referred to two recent descriptions of this problem (31, 41).

The danger in accepting a unique parametric description of a nonunique model is that the user may interpret the parametric uniqueness as imparting validity to the model. Moreover, this kind of approach uses the measured data "as is," without regard for experimental error. Since parametric representations by their formulation result in an exact solution (that is, a value of $\dot{Q}_S/\dot{Q}_T$ exists that exactly fits equation 2), the effects of experimental error are difficult to allow for. Finally, even when these limitations are properly considered, the parameter values obtained depend on the boundary conditions. In other words, parameters such as physiologic deadspace and venous admixture change with changes in inspired gas and venous blood composition even when the extent of $\dot{V}_A/\dot{Q}$ mismatching in the lung itself remains unchanged (51). However, if these limitations are understood and allowed for, the parameters are useful in clinical situations.

The Multicompartmental Approach

Multicompartment approaches only make sense when many data are available. Thus a multicompartmental equivalent to the Riley model for venous admixture, while technically feasible, would be of little practical use owing to the very problem of "model nonuniqueness" referred to above: So many multicompartmental arrangements (i.e. $\dot{V}_A/\dot{Q}$ distributions) would be equally compatible with the given single measured arterial P_{O_2} that no one such arrangement would, with any confidence, reflect the features of the true $\dot{V}_A/\dot{Q}$ distribution in the lung.

The essential logic of the multicompartment approach is as follows: Given sufficient data, a general model of the lung consisting of a large number of compartments is specified. The task is to fit (by least squares criteria) the given data by a distribution of perfusion and ventilation (6, 9). By proper choice of this general lung model, the problems of model nonuniqueness are largely overcome. There is sufficient flexibility to accommodate the potential existence of virtually all models, so that the artificiality of constraining the parametric model to, for example, "virtual shunt" is unnecessary. Thus, in the multicompartment approach, the least squares analysis results in a fit to the data that may include bloodflow to unventilated lung (shunt), to poorly ventilated lung (low $\dot{V}_A/\dot{Q}$), or both, as the data decree. The important consideration in specifying a general model on the basis of limited data is that, mathematically speaking, the problem is underdetermined. In contrast to the parametric approach, the data are (much) fewer than the compartments in the model. Underdetermination results in a least squares fit to the data that is nonunique: Many different multicompartment distributions of $\dot{V}_A/\dot{Q}$ are compatible with a given set of data.

At first sight, both the parametric and multicompartment approaches seem unsatisfactory. The former gives a reasonably reliable numerical estimate for a model that may be entirely fictitious; the latter gives a numerical estimate that is not unique for a model that is entirely reasonable. No approach yet devised can determine exactly the shape, position, and dispersion of the real $\dot{V}_A/\dot{Q}$ distribution, and we must make the best of what is available.

Recent advances in understanding $\dot{V}_A/\dot{Q}$ relationships have emerged from the heated arguments in the literature regarding the fundamental relationships between observable patterns of gas exchange and the responsible $\dot{V}_A/\dot{Q}$ distribution.

Information Content of Methods for Measuring $\dot{V}_A/\dot{Q}$ Maldistribution

About this complex subject several points may be made at the outset:

1. All methods for evaluating $\dot{V}_A/\dot{Q}$ mismatching acknowledge that complete specification of the $\dot{V}_A/\dot{Q}$ distribution is beyond reach (9, 28).
2. The greater the number (and quality) of data, the more can be said about the $\dot{V}_A/\dot{Q}$ distribution in a given case (41).
3. Just how much can be said about the details of a $\dot{V}_A/\dot{Q}$ distribution from analysis of a given set of data depends on the data themselves. If the distribution actually present in the lungs is simple, existing methods may be able to describe it in some detail; but if the distribution is complex, relatively little detail about its shape, position, and dispersion may be forthcoming from a similar analysis (41).
4. The mathematical approach used in analyzing the data is also important in determining how much can be said about the $\dot{V}_A/\dot{Q}$ distribution in a given case. Thus in the multicompartment approach based on inert gas elimination, failure to ensure a nonnegativity constraint on the perfusion distribution found to fit the data (33) greatly reduces the utility of the method: If a fit to the data is permitted using negative values of bloodflow in some compartment, the physiological meaning of the entire result is indeterminate. Alternatively, fitting inert gas data with a parametric approach (using, for example, a single lognormal mode of $\dot{V}_A/\dot{Q}$ ratios in which the parameters to be determined are the mean and standard deviation of the mode) may be a good approach for cases in which the distribution is in fact lognormal but may be entirely inadequate if the distribution is skewed or composed of more than one mode.
5. Certain experimental approaches offer more information than others. Thus using a N_2 washout and measuring also the rate of rise of arterial Po_2 (25) gives less resolution in most instances than does the multiple inert gas elimination technique (32). The latter employs gases that, because of widely different solubilities, afford resolution in all regions of the $\dot{V}_A/\dot{Q}$ spectrum whereas for O_2, units of normal and high $\dot{V}_A/\dot{Q}$ are difficult to resolve because of the shallow slope of the O_2 dissociation curve.

A number of investigators have contributed to our further understanding of $\dot{V}_A/\dot{Q}$ relationships through studies of one or more of the above points. After the initial attempt to measure multicompartment $\dot{V}_A/\dot{Q}$ distributions (25) was criticized on grounds of nonuniqueness (32), another approach using inert gases was published (6, 9, 50). A number of workers responded to this method also by pointing out the nonunique solutions afforded by the method. Olszowka gave a clear-cut example of a complex distribution in which the uncertainty was sufficiently great that no useful result could be obtained (28). Other counter-examples have been given in which considerable definition of detail of the distribution is possible (41, 45, 47), thus highlighting point 3, above. Jaliwala and co-workers (20) drew attention to experimental errors (see also 6, 9, 41). Neufeld and co-workers decided that the problems in attempting to specify distributions outweighed their advantages and have proposed a method for determining parameters directly from the inert gas data (27). Their approach involves a critical examination of alveolar-arterial inert gas differences as a function of solubility of the gas. Its results are just as uncertain as those from an approach that uses inert gas data to specify $\dot{V}_A/\dot{Q}$ distributions. The methods of Zwart (58) and of Hlastala & Robertson (18) also prefer to evaluate directly the inert gas retention and excretion data curves themselves.

What is clearly required is a *general and rigorous approach to the interpretation of data used for assessing* $\dot{V}_A/\dot{Q}$ *maldistribution.* None of the above methods provides such an approach; each provides a single method for describing $\dot{V}_A/\dot{Q}$ mismatching by either a form of parametric representation or a form of $\dot{V}_A/\dot{Q}$ distribution. Techniques of linear programming, on the other hand, can be used to analyze a measured set of data and provide these rigorous and general statements (9, 19, 41, 44). Such methods place rigid bounds (or envelopes) on distributions compatible with a given set of data and can answer specific important questions that arise from the execution of any of the above described approaches. In this way the variability among different distributions compatible with a given data set can be satisfactorily investigated and their physiologically important common features can be identified. For example, the presence or absence of perfusion in a particular region of the $\dot{V}_A/\dot{Q}$ spectrum can be stated with certainty; the existence of more than one mode of $\dot{V}_A/\dot{Q}$ can usually be determined. Linear programming uses considerably more computer time than the various methods that provide single estimates of $\dot{V}_A/\dot{Q}$ mismatching. Details of how linear programming works and how it is applied have been published elsewhere (3, 31, 42, 44).

SUMMARY

Recent developments in understanding $\dot{V}_A/\dot{Q}$ relationships have been closely tied to advances in mathematical techniques and computer technology. Two general areas of interest have been identified: (*a*) theoretical computer modeling of gas exchange, performed in order to better understand the complex interrelationships among many factors that affect gas transfer, and (*b*) development of methods for experimental measurement of $\dot{V}_A/\dot{Q}$ mismatching. In both areas, the concept of a distribution of lung units (as opposed to earlier representation of the lung by two or three lumped parameters) has been important to the development of ideas and methods. Most recent work has sought to develop methods for measuring $\dot{V}_A/\dot{Q}$ mismatching. The fundamental problem is that there can never be enough data to allow exact determination of the $\dot{V}_A/\dot{Q}$ distribution. There has been much discussion concerning just how much information actually exists in available data and consequently just how close to the exact $\dot{V}_A/\dot{Q}$ distribution one can come in practice. Unfortunately, there is no simple answer to this important question; it is clear from reviewing recent literature that each set of data must be analyzed individually. The most promising approach appears to be the application of linear programming to the evaluation of variability among distributions that differ but are compatible with a given set of data.

Acknowledgment

This research has been supported by Grants HL 17731 and HL 00111 from the National Institutes of Health.

Literature Cited

1. Briscoe, W. A. 1959. A method for dealing with data concerning uneven ventilation of the lung and its effects on blood gas transfer. *J. Appl. Physiol.* 14:291–98
2. Colburn, W. E., Evans, J. W., West, J. B. 1974. Analysis of the effect of the solubility on gas exchange in nonhomogeneous lungs. *J. Appl. Physiol.* 37: 547–51
3. Dantzig, G. B. 1963. *Linear Programming and Extensions.* Princeton, NJ: Princeton Univ. Press. pp. 94–108
4. Dantzker, D. R., Wagner, P. D., West, J. B. 1975. Instability of lung units with low $\dot{V}_A/\dot{Q}$ ratios during O_2 breathing. *J. Appl. Physiol.* 38:886–95
5. Dantzker, D. R., Wagner, P. D., Tornabene, V. W., Alazaraki, N. P., West, J. B. 1978. Gas exchange after pulmonary thromboembolization in dogs. *Circ. Res.* 42:92–103
6. Dawson, S. V., Butler, J. P., Reeds, J. 1978. Indirect estimation of physiological distribution functions. *Fed. Proc.* 37:2803–10
7. Dueck, R., Wagner, P. D., West, J. B. 1977. Effects of PEEP on gas exchange in dogs with normal and edematous lungs. *Anesthesiology* 47:359–66
8. Evans, J. W., Cantor, D. G. 1970. A correction for the effect of the dead space in pulmonary gas washout studies. *Bull. Math. Biophys.* 32:215–18
9. Evans, J. W., Wagner, P. D. 1977. Limits on $\dot{V}_A/\dot{Q}$ distributions from analysis of experimental inert gas elimination. *J. Appl. Physiol.* 42:889–98
10. Evans, J. W., Wagner, P. D., West, J. B. 1974. Conditions for reduction of pulmonary gas transfer by ventilation-perfusion inequality. *J. Appl. Physiol.* 36: 533–67
11. Farhi, L. E. 1967. Elimination of inert gas by the lung. *Resp. Physiol.* 3:1–11
12. Farhi, L. E., Olszowka, A. J. 1968. Analysis of alveolar gas exchange in the presence of soluble inert gases. *Resp. Physiol.* 5:53–67
13. Farhi, L. E., Yokoyama, T. 1967. Effects of ventilation-perfusion inequality on elimination of inert gases. *Resp. Physiol.* 3:12–20
14. Fenn, W. O., Rahn, H., Otis, A. B. 1946. A theoretical study of the composition of alveolar air at altitude. *Am. J. Physiol.* 146:637–53
15. Fortune, J. B., Wagner, P. D. 1979. Effect of reinspired common deadspace on pulmonary gas exchange. *Fed. Proc.* 38:949
16. Haldane, J. S. 1922. *Respiration.* New Haven, Conn: Yale Univ. Press
17. Hendricks, F. F. A. 1979. *Pulmonary gas exchange during myocardial ischaemia.* PhD thesis. State University at Leiden, Netherlands
18. Hlastala, M. P., Robertson, H. T. 1978. Inert gas elimination characteristics of the normal and abnormal lung. *J. Appl. Physiol.* 44:258–66

19. Howard, R. D., Bradner, H. 1977. The $\dot{V}_A/\dot{Q}$ resolution of inert gas data. *Bull. Math. Biol.* 39:87–98
20. Jaliwala, S. A., Mates, R. E., Klocke, F. J. 1975. An efficient optimization technique for recovering ventilation-perfusion distributions from inert gas data. Effects of random experimental error. *J. Clin. Invest.* 55:188–92
21. Kelman, G. R. 1966. Digital computer subroutine for the conversion of oxygen tension into saturation. *J. Appl. Physiol.* 21:1375–76
22. Kelman, G. R. 1967. Digital computer procedure for the conversion of P_{CO_2} into blood CO_2 content. *Resp. Physiol.* 3:111–15
23. Kelman, G. R. 1968. Computer program for the production of O_2–CO_2 diagrams. *Resp. Physiol.* 4:260–69
24. Krogh, A., Lindhard, J. 1917. The volume of the dead space in breathing and the mixing of gases in the lungs of man. *J. Physiol. London* 51:59–90
25. Lenfant, C., Okubo, T. 1968. Distribution function of pulmonary blood flow and ventilation-perfusion ratio in man. *J. Appl. Physiol.* 24:668–77
26. Lewis, S. M., Evans, J. W., Jalowayski, A. A. 1978. Continuous distributions of specific ventilation recovered from inert gas washout. *J. Appl. Physiol.* 44: 416–23
27. Neufeld, G. R., Williams, J. J., Klineberg, P. L., Marshall, B. E. 1978. Inert gas a-A differences: a direct reflection of $\dot{V}/\dot{Q}$ distribution. *J. Appl. Physiol.* 44:277–83
28. Olszowka, A. J. 1975. Can $\dot{V}_A/\dot{Q}$ distributions in the lung be recovered from inert gas retention data? *Resp. Physiol.* 25:191–98
29. Olszowka, A. J., Farhi, L. E. 1968. A system of digital computer sub-routines for blood gas calculation. *Resp. Physiol.* 4:270–80
30. Olszowka, A. J., Farhi, L. E. 1969. A digital computer program for constructing ventilation-perfusion lines. *J. Appl. Physiol.* 26:141–46
31. Olszowska, A. J., Wagner, P. D. 1979. Numerical analysis in gas exchange. In *Pulmonary Gas Exchange,* ed. J. B. West. Academic. In press
32. Peslin, R., Dawson, S., Mead, J. 1971. Analysis of multicomponent exponential curves by the Post-Widder's equation. *J. Appl. Physiol.* 30:462–72
33. Pimmel, R. L., Tsai, M. J., Bromberg, P. A. 1977. Estimating $\dot{V}/\dot{Q}$ distributions from inert gas data with an enforced smoothing algorithm. *J. Appl. Physiol.* 43:1106–10
34. Pontoppidan, H., Geffin, B., Lowenstein, E. 1973. *Acute Respiratory Failure in the Adult.* Boston: Little, Brown and Co.
35. Rahn, H., Fenn, W. O. 1955. *A Graphical Analysis of the Respiratory Gas Exchange.* Washington DC: Am. Physiol. Soc.
36. Riley, R. L., Cournand, A. 1949. 'Ideal' alveolar air and the analysis of ventilation-perfusion relationships in the lungs. *J. Appl. Physiol.* 1:825–47
37. Riley, R. L., Cournand, A. 1951. Analysis of factors affecting partial pressures of oxygen and carbon dioxide in gas and blood of lungs: Theory. *J. Appl. Physiol.* 4:77–101
38. Riley, R. L., Cournand, A., Donald, K. W. 1951. Analysis of factors affecting partial pressures of oxygen and carbon dioxide in gas and blood of lungs: Methods. *J. Apply. Physiol.* 4:102–20
39. Scrimshire, D. A. 1977. Theoretical analysis of independent $\dot{V}_A$ and $\dot{Q}$ inequalities upon pulmonary gas exchange. *Resp. Physiol.* 29:163–78
40. Tham, M. K. 1975. Letter to the editor. *J. Appl. Physiol.* 38:950
41. Wagner, P. D. 1977. A general approach to the evaluation of ventilation-perfusion ratios in normal and abnormal lungs. *Physiologist* 20:18–25
42. Wagner, P. D. 1978. Measurement of the distribution of ventilation-perfusion ratios. In *Regulation of Ventilation and Gas Exchange,* ed. D. G. Davies, C. D. Barnes, p. 217–60. NY: Academic
43. Wagner, P. D. 1979. Susceptibility of different gases to ventilation-perfusion inequality. *J. Appl. Physiol.* 46:372–86
44. Wagner, P. D. 1979. Information content of the multibreath nitrogen washout. *J. Appl. Physiol.* 46:579–87
45. Wagner, P. D., Dantzker, D. R., Dueck, R., Clausen, J. L., West, J. B. 1977. Ventilation-perfusion inequality in chronic obstructive pulmonary disease. *J. Clin. Invest.* 59:203–16
46. Wagner, P. D., Dantzker, D. R., Dueck, R., dePolo, J. L., Wasserman, K., West, J. B. 1976. Distribution of ventilation-perfusion ratios in patients with interstitial lung disease. *Chest* 69:256
47. Wagner, P. D., Dantzker, D. R., Iacovoni, V. E., Tomlin, W. C., West, J. B. 1978. Ventilation-perfusion inequality in asymptomatic asthma. *Am. Rev. Resp. Dis.* 118:511–24

48. Wagner, P. D., Dantzker, D. R., Tornabene, V. W., Le Winter, M. M., West, J. B. 1976. Effect of $\dot{V}_A/\dot{Q}$ inequality on arterial P_{O_2} following acute myocardial infarction. *Clin. Res.* 24:160A (Abstr.)
49. Wagner, P. D., Evans, J. W. 1977. Conditions of equivalence for gas exchange in series and parallel models of the lung. *Resp. Physiol.* 31:117–38
50. Wagner, P. D., Saltzman, H. A., West, J. B. 1974. Measurement of continuous distributions of ventilation-perfusion ratios: theory. *J. Appl. Physiol.* 36: 588–99
51. West, J. B. 1969. Ventilation-perfusion inequality and overall gas exchange in computer models of the lung. *Resp. Physiol.* 7:88–110
52. West, J. B. 1969. Effect of slope and shape of dissociation curve on pulmonary gas exchange. *Resp. Physiol.* 8: 66–85
53. West, J. B. 1971. Gas exchange when one lung region inspires from another. *J. Appl. Physiol.* 30:479–87
54. West, J. B. 1977. State of the art—ventilation-perfusion relationships. *Am. Rev. Resp. Dis.* 116:919–43
55. West, J. B., Wagner, P. D. 1977. Pulmonary gas exchange. In *Bioengineering Aspects of the Lung,* ed. J. B. West. NY: Marcel Dekker
56. Yokoyama, T., Farhi, L. E. 1967. Study of ventilation-perfusion ratio distribution in the anesthetized dog by multiple inert gas washout. *Resp. Physiol.* 3: 166–76
57. Young, I. H., Wagner, P. D. 1979. Effect of intrapulmonary hematocrit maldistribution on O_2, CO_2, and inert gas exchange. *J. Appl. Physiol.* 46:240–48
58. Zwart, A., Luijendijk, S. C. M., van Dieren, A., Wesseling, K. H., Erturk, F. 1976. Ventilation-perfusion distributions in the lung: Measurement and estimation. In *Progress Report 5.* Da Costakade 45, Utrecht, Netherlands: Inst. Med. Phys. pp. 73–80

CELL AND MEMBRANE PHYSIOLOGY

Ann. Rev. Physiol. 1980. 42:249–59

CO- AND COUNTER-TRANSPORT MECHANISMS IN CELL MEMBRANES

❖1266

Robert B. Gunn

Department of Pharmacological and Physiological Sciences,
University of Chicago, Chicago, Illinois 60637

INTRODUCTION

The relations between lipid solubility and membrane permeability are often the starting point in texts dealing with transport. The lipid core of the membrane forms the primary barrier for molecular diffusion, but most biologically important small molecules, particularly ions, have specific transport mechanisms in cell membranes, and the impermeability of the lipid bilayer only emphasizes the control these specific pathways have on transport between the interior of cells and their environment. This review concerns only the specific transport mechanisms that permit the coupling of transport between molecules. In most cases this coupling does not result from the formation of direct complexes in solution between the various transported molecules but rather requires a membrane component to form binary complexes (ping pong mechanisms) or tertiary or higher order complexes (sequential or simultaneous mechanisms) with the transported molecules. In other words, these are cases of facilitated transport. In other cases the coupling is the result of direct complexation (e.g. ion pair formation) that occurs in solution to form a complex more permeant than perhaps either component but certainly more permeant than one of the components alone. Facilitated transport involves at least three conceptually separate steps: (*a*) complexation of the transported molecules to the membrane component; (*b*) the transport step, in which access of the complex to one solution is occluded while access to the opposite solution is created; and (*c*) the decomplexation of the transported molecules from the membrane component into the opposite solution. Enzymologists working in a homoge-

0066-4278/80/0315-0249$01.00

neous phase have an extensive nomenclature dealing with the first and last of these steps (10); it only partially meets the needs of a transport physiologist, whose focus is on the middle or transport step. For example, a *bi-bi-ping-pong mechanism* refers to two substrates and two products that react alternately with two forms of the enzyme. In transport terms, a mobile carrier that performs the obligatory exchange of one molecule from one solution with one molecule from the other solution has these kinetics. The bi-bi-ping-pong terminology is not explicit for the central notion for transport—i.e. that only binary complexes are formed one at a time between a substrate molecule and a carrier.

In principle, other selective transport mechanisms exist that do not allow coupling of transport. These are not considered here, except to give two examples: (*a*) channels specific for a single nonelectrolyte; and (*b*) ion-specific channels that contribute negligibly to the total membrane conductance and therefore cannot significantly alter the membrane potential by opening or closing. There may be many such mechanisms, but here I review only co- and countertransport mechanisms.

NOMENCLATURE

Cotransport of molecular species *A* and *B* is the coupled transport of *A* and *B* in the same direction across the membrane. The term does not imply a specific stoichiometry between the number of type *A* molecules that travel with a type *B* molecule. Cotransport refers to phenomenology and not to any particular molecular mechanism, and it does not imply that *A* and *B* are physically joined by covalent or electrostatic forces *nor* that the detailed transport pathway for the two molecules is the same across the rate-limiting or other lesser barriers in the membrane. A cotransport mechanism is indicated experimentally when the transport of *B* is stimulated by *A* and the transport of *A* is stimulated by *B* on the same side of the membrane. This categorization is strengthened if there is no transport of *A* without *B* and no transport of *B* without *A* in the same solutions. This phenomenology is necessary but not sufficient. For example, *A* may be a necessary component for a separate *B* transport mechanism while it is not itself cotransported on the same mechanism but has its own parallel pathway. Two such parallel mechanisms for *A* and *B* would have variable stoichiometry (Flux-of-B/Flux-of-$A \neq$ constant) since only catalytic amounts of *A* would be needed for the *B* transport system, which would then function independently of further increases in the concentration of *A*. In transport studies it is difficult to distinguish between (*a*) activation due to complexation at a transport site, with concomitant transport of the activator molecule, and (*b*) activation due to complexation at a nontransport site, where activation is unrelated to the transport of the activator molecule. It is often assumed in the case of small molecules (not ATP) that activation is at a transport site for the activator, but this may not be true.

Countertransport of the molecular species A and B is the coupled transport of A and B in opposite directions. The two components are not necessarily transported simultaneously but may be coupled by some regular alternation between transport of A in one direction and then B in the opposite direction. Again, the reciprocal activation of the flux in one direction by the addition of the second molecular species to the other solution is necessary but not sufficient, since activation on the other side may not be related to the transport of the stimulator.

The terms symport and antiport are frequently used, particularly in bacterial and mitochondrial transport studies, to mean cotransport and countertransport.

THEORY

Coupling of two fluxes can be described phenomenologically (45) without any appeal to reasonable mechanistic notions. Irreversible thermodynamics describes the unknown internal workings of a membrane system as a black box through which the flows of the different molecules can be measured. The conjugate forces on these molecules can be determined from the outside. In a simple system in which there are two transported species, A and B, their fluxes, J_A and J_B, can be described in terms of their conjugate forces, X_A and X_B, by the following linear equations:

$$J_A = L_{AA}X_A + L_{AB}X_B \quad 1.$$

$$J_B = L_{BA}X_A + L_{BB}X_B \quad 2.$$

A sufficient condition for the coupling of the fluxes is that the cross coefficients L_{BA} and L_{AB} (which are equal if the system is well behaved) are not zero. If $L_{AB} > 0$ the electrochemical gradient of species B reflected in X_B will promote the flux of A in the same direction as that of B. This behaves like cotransport. However B may be transported without an A molecule in the system, nor is the coupling ratio necessarily fixed—i.e. J_B is not necessarily a fixed proportion of J_A. If $L_{AB} < 0$, the electrochemical gradient of species B reflected in X_B will promote the flux of A in the direction opposite from that of B. This system then behaves like countertransport, but again the coupling is neither obligatory nor stoichiometrically fixed. Therefore, the phenomenological coupling of fluxes does not constitute co- or countertransport as we have defined them, and we must open the black box and consider specific molecular mechanisms within the membrane.

The mechanism of coupling between the fluxes of co- and countertransport systems must be through a limited number of specific membrane sites. In other words co- and countertransport are characteristics of facilitated transport systems and are often used as criteria for the presence of such systems in biological membranes.

The simplest facilitated system has the characteristics of countertransport but not cotransport. This is a mechanism involving a single site with reciprocating access to the two bathing solutions on opposite sides of the membrane. The membrane site, *C*, can complex with a molecule of either *A* or *B* on the outside (*o*), then facilitate *A's* or *B's* transmembrane movement and will then dissociate from it on the inside (*i*). The inside membrane site can complex another *A* or *B* molecule and reverse the process. If *A* and *B* are otherwise impermeant, and if *C* may only move from (*o*) to (*i*) with a molecule of *A* or *B* attached, the sum of the net steady-state fluxes of *A* and *B* must be zero; the individual net fluxes are opposite and equal, or both zero. This simple countertransport system has ping-pong kinetics (10); even in this simple pine-pong transport system these kinetics are complex. For example, if initially there is only *A* on the outside and *B* on the inside of the membrane, the initial flux of *A* is

$$J_A = (V_{\text{max-out}} A_o)(K_{½\text{-out}} + A_o)^{-1}, \tag{3.}$$

where A_o is the concentration of *A* on the outside and $V_{\text{max-out}}$ and $K_{½\text{-out}}$ are parameters of the system dependent on B_i, the inside concentration of *B*.

$$\text{V}_{\text{max-out}} = (V^{\text{max}}_{\text{max}} B_i)(K^{\text{max}}_{½\text{-in}} + B_i)^{-1}, \tag{4.}$$

and

$$K_{½\text{-out}} = (K^{\text{max}}_{½\text{-out}} B_i)(K^{\text{max}}_{½\text{-in}} + B_i)^{-1}. \tag{5.}$$

The initial flux J_A is a hyperbolic function of the concentration of *A* and obeys Michaelis-Menten kinetics. But $V_{\text{max-out}}$ and $K_{½\text{-out}}$ are also hyperbolic functions of the *B* concentration inside. Intuitively and mathematically one can see that an increase in B_i promotes the flux of *A* toward the inside by providing more complexes returning to the outside to complex with *A* molecules. Symmetrical equations describe the flux of *B*, J_B. Even in a passive system that requires no metabolic energy there is no requirement that $K_{½\text{-out}}$ and $K_{½\text{-in}}$ should be equal or that $V_{\text{max-in}}$ equal $V_{\text{max-out}}$, neither in general nor if *A* and *B* are the same chemical species. This simple ping-pong system has a coupling coefficient of unity.

The statements above only apply if the empty carrier cannot move between the two solutions. If this restriction is waived, the kinetics for the transport of A become a complicated combination of (a) net transport (conductance, if A is charged) involving the return of the empty carrier and (b) exchange transport involving the return of B (electro-neutral transport, if the valence of A and B is the same).

Facilitated transport systems that mediate cotransport are more complicated. The requirement that three reactants (two transported molecules from the same solution and the carrier) must form a tertiary complex allows both ordered and random loading and unloading on each side of the membrane. In a simple cotransport of two molecules, A and B, in an ordered reaction (first A then B) scheme where A and B are otherwise impermeant and no net A or B transport occurs because C may only move when doubly loaded with an A and a B molecule attached, the unidirectional (tracer) flux of A or B is

$$J_A = J_B = (\mathrm{D}_1 A_i A_o B_i B_o)[(\mathrm{D}_2 A_i B_i B_o + \mathrm{D}_3 B_o + \mathrm{D}_4 A_i B_o + \mathrm{D}_5 A_i B_i) A_o + \mathrm{D}_6 A_i B_i]^{-1}, \qquad 6.$$

where the Ds are constants, and A_i equals the concentration of A on the inside, etc. Less restricted conditions yield more complex equations (52), but the essential feature of this simple case is that all four concentrations of the two substrates on the two sides are important in the flux. Only in the Na-K cotransport system of human red cells have all four dependences been demonstrated (57).

PROBLEMS

The molecular mechanism of facilitated transport is unknown. Our understanding of the mechanisms of co- and countertransport systems is at the level of trying to state the components of the transport complex and its effective charge. For countertransport, binary complexes between the transported species and the membrane carrier are a minimum requirement; for cotransport, tertiary complexes seem to be required. A system in which transport of one substrate leaves the system in a conformation that can only transport the second substrate in the same direction might be considered to use an ordered sequence of binary transport complexes. If the transport complex, which alters the access of the substrates to the solutions on either side of the membrane, has a net charge then the transport step will move charge through an electric field, and this movement will be influenced by the membrane potential difference. The extent of influence will be a function of the sign and magnitude of the net charge on the transferred complex, the fraction of the field through which the charge moves, and any degree of charge or dipole rearrangement that accompanies the conformational shift altering the access of the molecule from one solution to the other. Even when overall transport is electrically silent (as in the obligatory exchange of monovalent anions in red blood cell membranes) the individual steps in the complexation and conformational changes may be dependent on the transmembrane electrochemical potential difference. In the analysis by Geck & Heinz (18) of the expected behavior of cotransport systems having a charged complex, the effects of an electrical potential driving force ($\Delta\psi$) were not the same as a thermodynamically equivalent concentration driving force. The results depend on whether the ternary complex or the empty carrier is charged and whether the mechanism is of the affinity or velocity type. These two types are defined (18) to distinguish transport mechanisms in which the complexation reactions or the translocation reactions are rate limiting. If the empty carrier is slowly transported, $\Delta\psi$ mostly affected the $K_{1/2}$ when the ternary complex was charged but mostly affected J_{max} if the empty carrier was ionic.

The theoretical possibilities far exceed the experimental techniques available to extract the data necessary for intelligent choices between them. The sometimes wild manipulations of biological membranes by means of ionophores, whose functions are as poorly understood as the membrane systems themselves, has led to a profusion of papers whose validity may be surprisingly low. For example, the addition of valinomycin to a system is assumed to bring the membrane potential toward E_K, the equilibrium potential for potassium; but it may lead to quite a different result and bring the potential toward E_{Na}, if the membrane has voltage-dependent channels selective for sodium. A careful approach is needed that addresses problems on a molecular basis instead of focusing on phenomenology and epiphenomenology.

The central problem in studies on facilitated transport is determining how a conformational change of a binding site alters the access of the site to the solutes in the solutions on opposite sides of the membrane. The central problem for cotransport systems is determining how the binding of a second substrate allows the conformational change. The solution of these problems is far off. The more immediate goals for those interested in the molecular mechanisms of these transport systems include: (*a*) determination of whether both substrates of a countertransport system are simultaneously transported using two binding sites or whether one transport step follows the other using only one binding site; (*b*) determination of the order of addition of the two substrates of a cotransport system; (*c*) the reconstitution of a purified, functional, transport system in a planar thin lipid membrane for detailed evaluation of its electrical properties, lipid requirements, and functional asymmetry.

The present state of studies on co- and countertransport systems must be considered rudimentary. Most of the systems identified to date are based on incomplete information. First, new efforts should be made to distinguish binding from transport. Second, a transport system whose activity is enhanced by increasing the concentration gradient of another molecule should not be automatically labeled a cotransport system. Nor should the inhibition of transport by similar manipulations be considered sufficient proof. Third, the observation of transient accumulation of a compound after it has been added to a cell suspension should not be considered sufficient evidence for a countertransport system for the compounds even if the peak amount accumulated is enhanced by preloading a second compound. The use of these phenomena as the sole criteria for labeling the mechanism results in unjustified categorization and consequently in preconceptions about how the transport system should behave under other experimental conditions.

SYSTEMS OF CO- AND COUNTERTRANSPORT

A number of co- and countertransport systems have been studied with varying success. A brief review of some of these systems follows. The hexose system and Na^+-K^+ pump of red cells have been omitted.

Monovalent Inorganic Anion Exchange in Red Blood Cells

Halides, bicarbonate, NO_3^-, phosphate, and sulfate are carried by a common system (21) that obligatorily exchanges (countertransports) one monovalent anion for another (25, 26) in an electrically silent 1 : 1 exchange. Protons are cotransported with sulfate in exchange for chloride (28) and may also be cotransported with chloride at a very low rate (22, 29). The exchange and the conductance of anions (30) are irreversibly inhibited by 4,4'-diisothiocyano-2,2'-stilbene disulfonic acid [DIDS (7)]. The uninhibited conductance is 10^{-5} to 10^{-6} times the exchange of chloride (34). The kinetics appear to be bi-bi-ping-pong for chloride and bromide (23), but deviations are apparent when slower anions such as dithionite are studied (44). This process appears to be mediated by band 3 protein (51), which spans the erythrocyte membrane at least once (6).

Proton Cotransport with Cell Nutrients

The specific translocation of amino acids and sugars across plasma membranes of microorganisms and yeast is coupled to H^+ cotransport (24, 31, 37, 49, 55). The stoichiometries of H^+/sugar and H^+/amino acid cotransport appear to be fixed at 1.0 for H^+/lactose transport (56) and at 2.0 for H^+/succinate transport (20) in *E. coli,* at 0.8–1.4 for H^+/glucose in *N. crassa* (50), and at 1.0 for H^+/xylose in *R. graules* (*glutines*) (24). This constancy of stoichiometry under different rates of transport is strong evidence for cotransport. Variable stoichiometries have also been observed both in bacteria (19) and in mammalian cells (9). The evidence for electrogenicity in some of these systems is suggestive but not conclusive since the ΔpH and $\Delta\psi$ are inferred from distribution studies and from the effect of K^+-valinomycin, both of which have been characterized inadequately (32). A possible mechanistic role of the membrane potential has been discussed (48). Surprisingly, the M protein of *E. coli* mediates H^+/lactose transport with qualitatively symmetrical kinetics when studied in inside-out and normally oriented membranes (33).

Sodium Cotransport with Cell Nutrients

Sodium cotransport with sugars and amino acids (8) is commonly found in vertebrates but is also known in *E. coli* (36, 53) and yeast (42). The absolute need for Na^+ in sugar transport in intestine was well known (12) before the kinetics demonstrated the existence of cotransport with amino acids and sugars (15). These kinetic characteristics are preserved in brush-border membrane vesicles from the intestine (35), and there appears to be sufficient energy in the Na^+ gradient to move the cotransported species uphill into the cells (13, 18, 27, 47). Similiar mechanisms of sodium cotransport with sugars and amino acids have been shown in nucleated erythrocytes (9, 54). The cotransport of sodium and glycine (G) in mucosal cells of marine shrimp epithelium has a stoichiometry of 1 : 1 at low Na^+ concentration and of 2 : 1 at high concentrations, which suggested that not only NaCG was a transported complex but also Na_2CG (1). Other sodium co- and countertransport systems in vesicles derived from intestinal cells include Na-phosphate cotransport and sodium-proton countertransport. (3, 39)

Ion Pairs with Carbonate

Na^+, Li^+, and H^+ can form monovalent anions by ion pair formation with carbonate. $NaCO_3^-$, $LiCO_3^-$, and HCO_3^- can all be transported by the erythrocyte anion countertransporter (16, 17). In general, ion pair formation (e.g. protons with weak acids), which promotes the transport of the neutral species, is not considered cotransport since there is no specific membrane facilitation; however, in the case above, ion pair formation provides a substrate for a specific coupled exchange mechanism.

Sodium-Potassium Cotransport in Red Blood Cells

Na^+-K^+ cotransport in erythrocytes was first suggested by the work of Sachs (43), who reported that K_o^+ increased the ouabain-insensitive Na^+ influx into human red blood cells. Sachs used furosemide as an inhibitor of the system. Na_o^+-dependent K^+ influx was described in detail by Beauge & Adragna (2). Wiley & Cooper (57) confirmed these co-ion dependences and used furosemide as a tool to inhibit the mutually stimulated cation fluxes that were ouabain-insensitive. Schmidt & McManus (46) demonstrated a hyperbolic functional dependence of ouabain-insensitive unidirectional sodium influx on K_o^+ and of rubidium influx on Na_o^+ in duck red cells. Furosemide is an inhibitor of these stimulated cation fluxes of Na and K (Rb) but is not a specific inhibitor of cation fluxes (5).

Sodium-Calcium Countertransport

Countertransport of Ca^{2+} and Na^+ has been suggested in dog red cells by Parker (40), who showed: (*a*) ^{45}Ca influx was enhanced by Ca_o^{2+} and Na_i^+ but inhibited by Na_o^+; (*b*) ^{45}Ca efflux was enhanced by Ca_o^{2+} and Na_o^+, but their effects were exclusive and not additive; (*c*) stoichiometry between ^{45}Ca influx and Ca^{2+}-dependent Na^+ efflux varied from 0.02 to 2.2 under different experimental conditions, perhaps owing to the inconstant contribution of the Ca^{2+}-efflux pump to the ^{45}Ca influx determination.

Calcium-sodium countertransport in heart muscle (41) and squid axons (4, 38) have been reported. The fractional internal activation with Ca^{2+} does not affect the $K_{½\text{-Na}}^{\text{out}}$ but does alter $V_{\text{max-Na}}^{\text{out}}$. This is characteristic of a sequential (simultaneous) mechanism and not a ping-pong mechanism. However, the converse kinetics of external Ca^{2+} and internal Na^+ have not been examined in detail, and internal ATP appears to reduce $K_{½}$ for Ca^{2+} on the inside and for Na^+ on the outside. This suggests a more complicated mechanism (4). Mitochondrial membranes also have important interrelations between Na^+ and Ca^{2+} transport (14).

ACKNOWLEDGMENT

I wish to thank Dr. O. Fröhlich for his helpful discussions. Partial support came from a Career Development Award, USPHS HL-00208, and from research grants HL-20365 and HL-20725.

Literature Cited

1. Ahearn, G. A. 1976. Co-transport of glycine and sodium across the mucosal border of the midgut epithelium in the marine shrimp, *Penaeus marginatus*. *J. Physiol. London* 258:499–520
2. Beauge, L. A., Adragna, N. 1971. The kinetics of ouabain inhibition and the partition of rubidium influx in human red cells. *J. Gen. Physiol.* 57:576–92
3. Berner, W., Kinne, R., Murer, H. 1976. Phosphate transport into brush-border membrane vesicles isolated from rat small intestine. *Biochem. J.* 160:467–74
4. Blaustein, M. P., Santiago, E. M. 1977. Effects of internal and external cations and of ATP on sodium-calcium and calcium-calcium exchange in squid axons. *Biophys. J.* 20:79–111
5. Brazy, P. C., Gunn, R. B. 1976. Furosemide inhibition of chloride transport in human red blood cells. *J. Gen. Physiol.* 68:583–99
6. Bretscher, M. S. 1973. Membrane structure: Some general principles. *Science* 181:622–29
7. Cabantchik, Z. I., Rothstein, A. 1974. Membrane proteins related to anion

permeability of human red blood cells. I. Localization of disulfonic stilbene binding sites in proteins involved in permeation. *J. Membr. Biol.* 15:207–26
8. Christensen, H. N., Riggs, T. R., Fischer, H., Palatine, I. M. 1952. Amino acid concentration by a free cell neoplasm: Relations among amino acids. *J. Biol. Chem.* 198:1–25
9. Christensen, H. N. 1972. In *Na-linked Transport of Organic Solutes,* ed. E. Heinz, pp. 161–68. Berlin: Springer
10. Cleland, W. W. 1963. The kinetics of enzyme-catalysed reactions with two or more substrates or products. I. Nomenclature and rate equations. *Biochim. Biophys. Acta* 67:104–37
11. Cockburn, M., Earnshaw, P., Eddy, A. A. 1975. The stoicheiometry of the absorption of protons with phosphate and *L*-glutamate by yeast of the genus *Saccharomyces. Biochem. J.* 146:705–12
12. Crane, R. K. 1960. Intestinal absorption of sugars. *Physiol. Rev.* 40:789–824
13. Crane, R. K. 1962. Hypothesis for mechanism of intestine active transport of sugars. *Fed. Proc.* 71:891–95
14. Crompton, M., Moser, R., Ludi, H., Carafoli, E. 1978. The interrelations between the transport of sodium and calcium in mitochondria of various mammalian tissues. *Eur. J. Biochem.* 82: 25–31
15. Curran, P. F., Schultz, S. G., Chez, R. A., Fuisz, R. E. 1967. Kinetic relations of the Na–amino acid interaction at the mucosal border of the intestine. *J. Gen. Physiol.* 50:1261–86
16. Duhm, J., Becker, B. F. 1977. Studies on the lithium transport across the red cell membrane. IV. Interindividual variations in the Na^+-dependent Li^+ countertransport system of human erythrocytes. *Pfluegers Arch.* 370:211–19
17. Funder, J., Tosteson, D. C., Wieth, J. O. 1978. Effects of bicarbonate on lithium transport in human red cells. *J. Gen. Physiol.* 71:721–46
18. Geck, P., Heinz, E. 1976. Coupling in secondary transport. Effect of electrical potentials on the kinetics of ion linked co-transport. *Biochim. Biophys. Acta* 443:49–63
19. Grüneberg, A., Kormor, E. 1976. Different proton-sugar stoichiometries for the uptake of glucose analogues by *Chlorella vulgaris.* Evidence for sugar-dependent proton uptake without concomitant sugar uptake by the proton-sugar symport system. *Biochim. Biophys. Acta* 448:133–42
20. Gutowski, S. F., Rosenberg, G. 1975. Succinate uptake and related proton movements in *Escherichia coli* K12. *Biochem. J.* 152:647–54
21. Gunn, R. B. 1972. A titratable carrier model for both mono- and divalent anion transport in human red blood cells. In *Oxygen Affinity of Hemoglobin and Red Cell Acid-Base States,* ed. M. Rø rth, W. Astrup, pp. 823–27. Copenhagen: Munksgaard
22. Gunn, R. B., Wieth, J. O., Tosteson, D. C. 1975. Some effects of low pH on chloride exchange in human red blood cells. *J. Gen. Physiol.* 65:731–49
23. Gunn, R. B., Fröhlich, O. 1979. Asymmetry in the mechanism for anion exchange in human red cell membranes: Evidence for reciprocating sites that react with one transported anion at a time. *J. Gen. Physiol.* 74:351–74
24. Höfer, M., Misra, P. C. 1978. Evidence for a proton/sugar symport in the yeast *Rhodontorula gracilis* (*glutinis*). *Biochem. J.* 172:15–22
25. Hunter, M. J. 1971. A quantitative estimate of the non-exchange-restricted chloride permeability of the human red cell. *J. Physiol. London* 218:498–509
26. Hunter, M. J. 1977. Human erythrocyte anion permeabilities measured under conditions of net charge transfer. *J. Physiol. London* 268:35–49
27. Jacquez, J. A. 1972. Models of ion and substrate cotransport and the effect of membrane potential. *Math. Biosci.* 13:71–93
28. Jennings, M. L. 1976. Proton fluxes associated with erythrocyte membrane anion exchange. *J. Membr. Biol.* 28: 187–205
29. Jennings, M. L. 1978. Characteristics of CO_2-independent pH equilibration in human red blood cells. *J. Membr. Biol.* 40:365
30. Knauf, P. A., Fuhrmann, G. F., Rothstein, S., Rothstein, A. 1977. The relationship between anion exchange and net anion flux across the human red blood cell membrane. *J. Gen. Physiol.* 69:363–86
31. Kormor, E., Tanner, W. 1974. The hexose-proton cotransport system of *Chlorella:* pH dependent change in Km values and translocation constants of the uptake. *J. Gen. Physiol.* 64:568–81
32. Lagarde, A. 1977. Evidence for an electrogenic 3-deoxy-2-oxo-d-gluconate-proton co-transport driven by the protonmotive force in *Escherichia coli* K12. *Biochem. J.* 168:211–21

33. Lancaster, J. R. Jr., Hinkle, P. C. 1977. Studies of the beta-galactoside transporter in inverted membrane vesicles of *Escherichia coli.* I. Symmetrical facilitated diffusion and proton gradient-coupled transport. *J. Biol. Chem.* 252: 7657–61
34. Lassen, U. V., Pape, L., Vestergaard-Bogind, B. 1978. Chloride conductance of Amphiuma red cell membrane. *J. Membr. Biol.* 39:27–48
35. Lucke, H., Haase, W., Murer, H. 1977. Amino acid transport in brush-border-membrane vesicles isolated from human small intestine. *Biochem. J.* 168:529–32
36. MacDonald, R. E., Lanyi, J. K., Greene, R. V. 1977. Sodium-stimulated glutamate uptake in membrane vesicles of *Escherichia coli:* The role of ion gradients. *Proc. Natl. Acad. Sci. USA* 74:3167–70
37. Misra, R. C., Höfer, M. 1975. An energy-linked proton-extrusion across the cell membrane *Rhodotorula gracilis. FEBS Lett.* 52:95–99
38. Mullins, L. J. 1979. Transport across axon membranes. In *Membrane Transport in Biology. II. Transport Across Single Biological Membranes,* ed. D. C. Tosteson, pp. 161–210. Berlin: Springer
39. Murer, H., Höpfer, U., Kinne, R. 1976. Sodium/proton antiport in brush-border-membrane vesicles isolated from rat small intestine and kidney. *Biochem. J.* 154:597–604
40. Parker, J. C. 1978. Sodium and calcium movements in dog red blood cells. *J. Gen. Physiol.* 71:1–17
41. Reuter, H., Seitz, N. 1968. The dependence of calcium efflux from cardiac muscle on temperature and external ion composition. *J. Physiol. London* 195: 451–70
42. Roomans, G. M., Blasco, F., Gurst-Pauwels, G. W. 1977. Cotransport of phosphate and sodium by yeast. *Biochim. Biophys. Acta* 467:65–71
43. Sachs, J. R. 1971. Ouabain insensitive sodium movements in the human red blood cell. *J. Gen. Physiol.* 57:259–82
44. Salhany, J. M., Swanson, J. C. 1978. Kinetics of passive anion transport across the human erythrocyte membrane. *Biochemistry* 17:3354–62
45. Sauer, F. A. 1975. In *Intestinal Permeation,* ed. M. Kramer, F. Lauterbach, pp. 320–31. Amsterdam: Excerpta Medica
46. Schmidt, W. F., McManus, T. J. 1977. Ouabain-insensitive salt and water movements in duck red cells. II. Norepinephrine stimulation of sodium plus potassium cotransport. *J. Gen. Physiol.* 70:81–97
47. Schultz, S. G. 1977. Sodium-coupled solute transport of small intestine: A status report. *Am. J. Physiol.* 233: E249–54
48. Schwab, W. G., Komor, E. 1978. A possible mechanistic role of the membrane potential in proton-sugar cotransport of chlorella. *FEBS Lett.* 87:157–60
49. Seaston, A., Inkson, C., Eddy, A. A. 1973. The absorption of protons with specific amino acids and carbohydrates by yeast. *Biochem. J.* 134:1031–43
50. Slayman, C. L., Slayman, C. W. 1974. Depolarization of the plasma membrane of *Neurospora* during active transport of glucose: Evidence for a proton dependent cotransport system. *Proc. Natl. Acad. Sci. USA* 71:1935–39
51. Steck, T. L. 1974. The organization of proteins in the human red blood cell membrane. *J. Cell Biol.* 62:1–19
52. Stein, W. D. 1976. An algorithm for writing down equations for carrier kinetics, and its application to co-transport. *J. Theor. Biol.* 62:467–78
53. Tsuchiya, T., Raven, J., Wilson, T. H. 1977. Co-transport of Na^+ and methyl-beta-d-thiogalactopyranoside mediated by the melibiose transport system of *Escherichia coli. Biochem. Biophys. Res. Commun.* 76:26–31
54. Vidaver, G. A., Shepherd, S. L. 1968. Transport of glycine by hemolyzed and restored pigeon red blood cells. *J. Biol. Chem.* 243:6140–50
55. West, I. C., Mitchell, P. 1972. Proton-coupled beta galactoside translocation in non-metabolizing *Escherichia coli. J. Bioenerg.* 3:445–62
56. West, I. C., Mitchell, P. 1973. Stoicheiometry of lactose-protein [sic] symport across the plasma membrane of *Escherichia coli. Biochem. J.* 132:587–92
57. Wiley, J. S., Cooper, R. A. 1974. A furosemide sensitive cotransport of sodium plus potassium in human red cell. *J. Clin. Invest.* 53:745–55

Ann. Rev. Physiol. 1980. 42:261–73

SPLIT MEMBRANE ANALYSIS ❖1267

Knute A. Fisher

Cardiovascular Research Institute and Department of Biochemistry and Biophysics, University of California, San Francisco, California 94143

INTRODUCTION[1]

The classical distinctions between morphology and physiology tend to break down at the molecular level. In fact contemporary discussions of membrane functions are often meaningful only if a detailed knowledge of the molecular architecture of the membrane is at hand. For instance, in order to determine the mechanism by which an ion could pass through a biological membrane, one would first have to identify the molecules involved and then determine whether the carrier system was, for example, either a lipid-soluble ionophore or a membrane-spanning polypeptide. Awareness of the fact that the structural properties of the molecule are intimately related to its function explains the presence of this brief article on the molecular composition and topography of membranes in a physiological review.

In this article I discuss one recently developed approach to investigating membrane structure: membrane analysis by bilayer splitting. This approach represents a logical extension of conventional freeze-fracture technique and is based on the observation that the bilayer splits during this process (2, 47). Freeze-fracture images of biological membranes are often given molecular interpretations (6, 7, 43, 45) despite a paucity of direct physical-chemical studies on the processes of freezing and fracturing. Thus I here review the recent use of freeze-fracturing as a tool to separate the membrane bilayer into its constituent monolayers for subsequent chemical and physical analysis. Because an overview of the methods used to produce and analyze split

[1]List of abbreviations: IMPs = intramembrane particles; MONOFARG = monolayer freeze-fracture autoradiography; PAS = periodic acid Schiff's reagent; PL = poly-L-lysine; RBCs = red blood cells; SDS = sodium dodecyl sulfate.

0066-4278/80/0315-0261$01.00

membrane lipids and polypeptides, especially of the electron-microscopic aspects, has recently been published (21), those methods are not discussed in detail here. This review focuses on the two major classes of molecules that are components of biomembranes—lipids and polypeptides, including the glycosylated derivatives of the latter. Those two classes are further categorized according to their in-plane (within the plane of the split membrane monolayer) or transmembrane (across the plane of the bilayer) distribution.

FREEZE-FRACTURE, "BULK" SPLITTING, AND MONOFARG

In conventional freeze-fracturing, microliter volumes of tissues or isolated membranes are usually fixed and/or cryoprotected, frozen in bulk, and fractured with a razor blade. A replica is then made of the fractured sample by vacuum deposition of platinum-carbon (22). Several experimental approaches have been taken [many recently reviewed in (5, 7, 53)] to alter the microscopic appearance of the split membrane fracture faces. Smooth regions are thought to represent lipids, and the intramembrane particles (IMPs) are believed to represent integral membrane proteins with, perhaps, some lipid molecules attached. Correlation of fracture face structure with surface markers revealed by etching has been one of the most profitable cytochemical approaches. Numerous ferritin derivatives have been used to probe the antigenic as well as the charge properties of membrane surfaces (48–51).

In "bulk" splitting, membrane "halves" are produced in quantities suitable for direct biochemical and biophysical analysis. This has been achieved using planar monolayers as shown in Figure 1. "Bulk" is in quotation marks to indicate that microgram, or smaller, quantities are produced; "halves," to indicate that the split membrane portions are not necessarily identical (17). The rationale behind flattening the cell membrane to a planar surface was the expectation that such surfaces would fracture in preference to those more randomly oriented. That "half" membranes are indeed left on the polylysine (PL) glass surface has been verified by electron microscopy (12, 13, 16–20). About 90% of bound and flattened erythrocytes do indeed fracture to produce two portions, one enriched in outer "half" membranes (the PL-glass side) and one enriched in inner "half" membranes. Both erythrocyte lipids (18) and polypeptides [(12, 13); K. A. Fisher, unpublished observations] and purple membrane polypeptides (20, 23, 25) have been examined using this approach.

MONOFARG is an acronym for monolayer freeze-fracture autoradiography, a combination of the previously described planar monolayer method and electron-microscopic autoradiography (19, 21). Following fracturing the isotopically labeled split membranes are shadowed with platinum-carbon; replicas are then coated with photographic emulsion, exposed, and developed. The position and number of silver grains overlying split membranes when compared to intact membrane controls indicate both the in-plane and transmembrane concentrations of the radioisotope. The potential (but untested) limit of resolution is probably about 100 nm. Because only membrane bound isotope lies between the PL-glass and the extracellular "half" membrane, all developed silver grains can with confidence be assigned to that membrane "half," tabulated, and statistically evaluated.

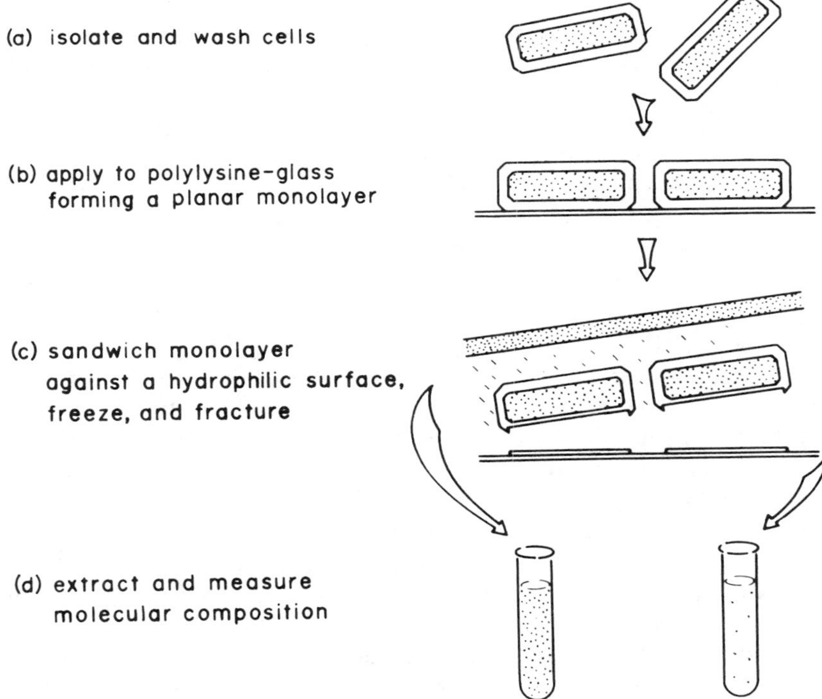

Figure 1 Steps involved in "bulk" splitting. (*a*) Cells or isolated membranes are washed to remove soluble proteins. (*b*) Membranes are applied to a polylysine-treated planar surface (e.g. PL-glass) to form a closely packed monolayer. (*c*) The hydrated monolayer is placed against a hydrophilic surface, rapidly frozen, and fractured. (*d*) The two split portions are extracted with solvents; e.g. chloroform-methanol for lipids, sodium dodecyl sulfate for polypeptides. Alternatively the fractured surfaces in (*c*) can be etched in vacuo and shadowed with platinum-carbon to produce replicas for electron microscopy and EM autoradiography (MONOFARG). The transmembrane and in-plane distributions of both lipids and polypeptides can be examined with these methods.

Other advantages (and disadvantages) of the technique have been summarized recently (21). Although this technique is currently in an early stage of development, it clearly offers the unique opportunity to investigate both the in-plane and the transmembrane distribution of diffusible radioisotopes and of radioisotopic probes in general.

MEMBRANE LIPIDS

In-Plane Distribution

The forte of conventional freeze-fracture is that it can distinguish structural features in the plane of the split membrane as well as along the etched surface. Recent reviews have discussed experimental and interpretive aspects of freeze-fracture images (5, 7, 11, 53). In certain model-bilayer, mixed-lipid systems, the temperature-dependent presence of separate phases in the plane of the monolayer can be readily distinguished by characteristic morphologies (28, 58) that have been given molecular interpretations (10, 29). The arrangements of IMPs can also be influenced by the state of packing of the lipids. For example, linear, reticular, or aggregated arrays of particles can be generated in both model (8, 42) and native membranes (30, 38, 41, 54) simply by varying the temperature. Methods using saponins and polyene antibiotics for labeling split membranes have been examined recently to determine their suitability for lipid cytochemistry (14, 15, 26). These studies suggest that the lipid composition of contiguous areas of the plasma membrane may be compositionally distinct. For example, filipin, a polyene antibiotic, interacts with membrane sterols to produce complexes that are visible as pits and protuberances in freeze-fractured membranes (15, 26, 57). These structures are found only in specific cellular membrane fractions and/or specific regions within single membranes (26).

MONOFARG (19, 21) can also be used to determine the in-plane distribution of radioisotopic lipids. In one preliminary study (19), intact human erythrocytes were pulse-labeled at low temperature with tritiated cholesterol. MONOFARG was used to evaluate the concentration of tritium (number of silver grains) within split membrane areas, as a function of the size of the area. Areas from about 1 to 50 μm^2 produced a straight-line plot. This suggested that the tritiated cholesterol was homogeneously distributed in the plane of the extracellular "half" membrane at least to a resolution of a few μm^2 [(21); K. A. Fisher, unpublished observations].

Transmembrane Distribution

Of the three splitting methods only "bulk" splitting and MONOFARG have been directly applied to an examination of the transmembrane distribution of native and tritiated lipids, respectively (16–19). Analysis of transmembrane concentrations of lipids using "bulk" splitting methods should in principle be simpler than the analysis of polypeptides. Separation of the lipid bilayer into two monolayer portions by fracturing would not be expected to cleave covalent bonds. For certain lipids, however, analysis might be complicated. For example, lipids that reside on the extracellular side of the bilayer, tightly bound to transmembrane polypeptides, could partition to the cytoplasmic side upon freeze-fracturing.

Accurate quantitation is required for all analyses of the distribution of lipids using "bulk" splitting (16–18, 21). To achieve this, several categories of data are needed. One must determine: (*a*) the fraction of membrane fractured per cell; (*b*) the total number of cells fractured (percentage of total area); (*c*) the concentration of lipids in each split portion; and (*d*) the concentration of total lipid in unsplit matching controls. Given these four quantities, one can readily analyze the distribution of specific lipids in terms of their concentration in each monolayer of the bilayer (18).

"Bulk" splitting currently permits evaluation only of major classes of lipids. A lipid such as cholesterol, present in large quantities in the erythrocyte plasma membrane, still produces only nanogram amounts from single coverglasses in planar monolayer splitting experiments (18). Nevertheless these levels can be detected and quantified by minor modifications of thin-layer chromatographic techniques coupled with charring and microdensitometry (16, 18). In such studies cholesterol was found to be asymmetrically distributed across the human erythrocyte bilayer; higher concentrations were found in the outer monolayer, lower ones in the inner monolayer (see Figure 2). Investigations of the compositionally minor but functionally important lipids will require the development of quantitative assays of greater sensitivity.

MONOFARG can also be used to evaluate the transmembrane distribution of radioisotopic probes (19, 21). The approach is similar to "bulk" splitting except that concentration analysis is derived from electron-microscopic tabulation of silver grains overlying either intact membranes or split membrane "halves." A preliminary examination of red blood cells (RBCs) labeled at low temperature with tritiated cholesterol of high specific activity revealed that all developable silver grains could be assigned to the outer monolayer. The conclusion was that under special conditions just the outer monolayer (and/or outer surface) of the RBC membrane is labeled (19).

MONOFARG has the special advantage of being a way to determine directly whether or not a radioisotopic hydrophobic or amphiphilic molecule resides in or on the extracellular monolayer of the bilayer. Its current disadvantage is that, like most electron-microscopic autoradiographic techniques, for accurate statistical analysis it is tedious, requiring long exposures and numerous micrographs.

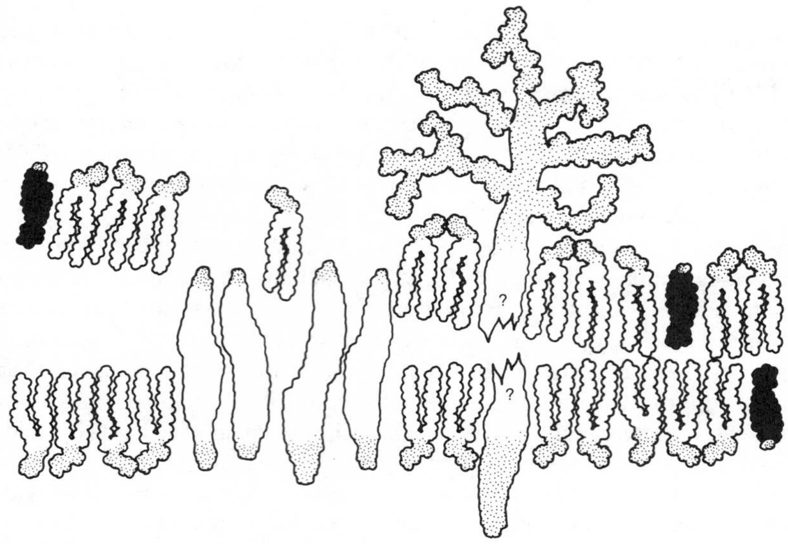

Figure 2 Membrane splitting: a molecular synopsis. The split propagates from left to right between monolayers of the lipid bilayer. The transmembrane concentration of certain lipids (e.g. erythrocyte cholesterol) is asymmetric. Two types of transmembrane polypeptides are shown. (*left*) Helices unmodified by freeze-fracturing partition to the cytoplasmic side of the membrane; deviation of the plane of fracture around the integral membrane polypeptide appears to be the general case. (*right*) A glycosylated transmembrane protein (with carbohydrate "tree") showing the quantitatively minor event of polypeptide cleavage proposed by Edwards et al (13). Whether or not lipids also partition with the particles is currently unknown. Peripheral polypeptides (located at membrane surfaces) are not included but would be expected to partition unmodified to their appropriate side. The lipids and carbohydrate chains are projections of space-filling molecular models; polypeptide helices are derived from the 3-D model of bacteriorhodopsin (33) matched in scale to the lipids. Hydrophilic regions are stippled, hydrophobic regions solid white or black (cholesterol).

MEMBRANE PROTEINS

In-Plane Distribution

All three methods of membrane splitting have been applied to the analysis of membrane proteins. In conventional freeze-fracture, several investigations, especially reconstitution studies (27, 34, 42, 52, 58), conclusively established that IMPs were formed by integral membrane proteins (amphiphilic polypeptides that penetrate the membrane's hydrophobic interior). More detailed analyses of the number of polypeptides per IMP have often involved correlation. The number of particles per unit area of split membrane is determined and compared to the bulk composition of lipids and protein (52, 59). A limitation to such an approach is the requirement for two, often tacit, assumptions: that all protein resides in the particle, and that all lipid resides in the bilayer. In many *other* biological studies particle sizes have been measured to determine whether or not the IMP is large enough to accommodate one or more proteins of a particular molecular weight. Again such calculations require too many assumptions (such as partial specific volume, or spatial characteristies of the protein) to be very helpful. Nevertheless, based on such approaches membrane particles are currently thought to be composed of relatively few polypeptides.

Part of the difficulty in the analysis of in-plane polypeptide distribution lies in the general absence of detailed information about transmembrane polypeptide structure in vivo. Such information, however, has recently become available for bacteriorhodopsin through the electron-microscopic and diffraction studies of Unwin & Henderson (33, 56). Bacteriorhodopsin is the exclusive protein component of the purple membrane, a fraction isolated from the plasma membrane of certain halophilic bacteria. The molecule is elongated and contains seven helical segments, each spanning the 40–50 Å thickness of the bilayer. In the purple membrane, bacteriorhodopsin is closely packed, forming a lattice of well-defined dimensions (1, 32, 56). Because purple membranes produced IMPs upon freezing and fracturing (1), IMP dimensions could be directly compared to high-resolution diffraction data (20, 23). Comparison was made by means of optical diffraction of fractured planar monolayers of purple membranes (23). The lattice dimensions derived from the study of the frozen replicated samples were in remarkably close agreement with those derived from measurements of hydrated (1, 32), glucose-embedded (33, 56), or lipid-coated (31) membranes. Direct measurement of particle sizes on micrographs of fractured purple membranes shows a mean width of about 120 Å, large enough to accommodate four 63 Å unit cells each containing three proteins. The conclusion is that a single 120 Å particle contains an average of twelve bacteriorhodopsin molecules. Since each molecule is composed of seven helical segments, a single freeze-fractured purple membrane particle must contain 84 transmembrane helices (23). Thus its structure is a full order of magnitude more complex than that commonly assumed for a "typical" IMP. Whether or not this complexity is a general feature of large particles or is in fact exclusive to purple membrane awaits further direct correlations between high-resolution structural techniques and freeze-fractured samples.

Transmembrane Distribution

The greatest interest and the most difficult data to analyze arise from questions such as "What happens to the membrane proteins during freeze-fracture? Are covalent bonds broken?" We can derive only limited answers from conventional freeze-fracture. For example, more IMPs are consistently found on the cytoplasmic fracture face of the split membrane than on the luminal or extracellular fracture face (3, 4, 45). If IMPs represent membrane-spanning proteins as shown for rhodopsin (34), RBC band 3 polypeptides (59), and bacteriorhodopsin (23), then do the particles contain polypeptides that have partitioned to one fracture face but are otherwise unmodified? Present data suggest that at least two types of transmembrane proteins exist: those that are not modified by freeze-fracturing—the dominant class—and those that are modified.

Direct, albeit qualitative, evidence that covalent bonds of transmembrane polypeptides are not cleaved during freeze-fracture was obtained during studies of purple membranes. Isolated membranes attached to PL-glass by their cytoplasmic surfaces (25) were frozen, fractured, scrubbed with SDS solutions, concentrated, and run on polyacrylamide gels (23). Parallel samples examined by electron microscopy showed that between 25% and 50% of all membranes were fractured (23, 25). The Coomassie-stained band of bacteriorhodopsin derived from split membranes lay at the same position as that of the unfractured controls, which indicated that no major fragment had been split off. However, small differences in molecular weights would not have been detected in these experiments. Moreover, the percentage of total membrane fractured was variable and unpredictable, which made an accurate assessment of the total amount of fractured membrane questionable. In addition, bacteriorhodopsin is a highly specialized transmembrane polypeptide both structurally (1,23) and functionally (25), and thus it might be expected to behave in a unique way during freeze-fracture (20,23).

In contrast to the single protein found in purple membrane the varied polypeptide composition of human RBC membranes offers a special advantage. The membrane contains both peripheral and integral proteins, including well-documented transmembrane proteins band 3 and the glycosylated PAS staining bands (44, 55). The carbohydrate-bearing polypeptides are of particular interest. One might expect the hydrophilic carbohydrate portion of the molecule to be strongly anchored in an eutectic mixture at the frozen surface of the membrane. Such anchorage could influence the partitioning of that polypeptide during freeze-fracture. If the glycoprotein also spanned the membrane and were additionally attached through ionic or stronger bonds to cytoplasmic or peripheral membrane molecules, then the polypeptide backbone might be broken during freeze-fracture.

Evidence for cleavage of human erythrocyte sialoglycoproteins has recently been presented by Edwards et al (12, 13). Using monolayer freeze-fracture they examined both Coomassie staining patterns and autoradiographs of fractured membrane from cells labeled either by periodate oxidation followed by NaB^3H_4 reduction or by lactoperoxidase-catalyzed iodination. Autoradiography clearly showed the presence of additional bands, which were interpreted as cleavage fragments of the sialoglycoproteins (Figure 2). Although such cleavage is plausible, the degree to which it occurs is uncertain. We have examined the polypeptide profile of "bulk" fractured RBC ghost membranes (K. A. Fisher, unpublished observations) and observed Coomassie staining patterns similar to those reported by Edwards et al (13). Unfortunately, both studies, besides being preliminary, have the disadvantage of being qualitative and must in addition deal with the ever present threat of endogenous proteases.

Can one generalize about covalent bond cleavage? In the radioisotopic study cited above, judging from the relative intensity of the autoradiographs (13) and the fact that the PL-glass samples required four to nine times the exposure of the complementary copper side, covalent cleavage is probably a minor event. Moreover, the position of band 3 is unaltered, although the band 3 material does appear to partition preferentially to the cytoplasmic side after fracturing. Recall, too, that in the human erythrocyte membrane most classes of membrane polypeptides (especially peripheral proteins) do not span the lipid bilayer (44, 55). Thus one would not expect their covalent bonds to be cleaved by freezing and fracturing. Again, final analysis of the splitting data awaits a careful quantitative assessment of the amount of fracture and techniques that insure total recovery of all membrane components.

CONCLUSIONS AND FUTURE DIRECTIONS

Split membrane analysis is still in its infancy. Although freeze-fracture is in its second decade, only in the past few years have methods become available to initiate a chemical analysis of the split "half" membranes. Two techniques based on planar monolayer freeze-fracture are currently being used to produce membrane halves in quantities suitable for "bulk" or autoradiographic analysis. The yields of "half" membrane components are of the order of micrograms or nanograms, but modern instrumentation and an increasing number of sensitive fluorescent and radioisotopic techniques can easily analyze such quantities.

Both split membrane lipids and split membrane polypeptides can be analyzed in terms of their in-plane and transmembrane distributions. MONOFARG can give information about the in-plane localization of radioisotopically labeled molecules as well as their transmembrane distribution. "Bulk" splitting can be used to examine the transmembrane concentrations of native molecules, such as cholesterol, not amenable to conventional membrane labeling techniques. Bacteriorhodopsin and human erythrocyte membrane polypeptides have been examined with the qualitative findings that the dominant proportion of polypeptides are not modified by freeze-fracturing but simply partition to the cytoplasmic side of the membrane.

Although the feasibility of both in-plane and transmembrane analyses of membrane lipids and proteins and their glycosylated derivatives has been demonstrated, only a few molecules of two membrane systems have been examined in any detail. Many other isolated cell or membrane fractions will have to be examined before convincing generalizations can be made. To be meaningful in molecular terms those examinations should be based on a quantitative format, where at the very least the sum of the fractured samples matches the whole of the intact control. Because small quantities of sample are produced by the planar monolayer approach, only the most sensitive assays can be utilized. In the future more sensitive assays and/or scaling-up of the bulk fracture process will be required.

First steps toward fracturing membrane with larger yields have been taken (37, 46). Polylysine-coated beads have been produced (9, 35–37, 39) in an effort to increase the total surface area of bound membrane for fracturing (35, 37). In addition, a fluorescent energy transfer assay has been proposed to evaluate the amount of membrane splitting (40). No further progress along these lines has been reported. Such projects could allow the use of more standard chemical and physical assays of membrane molecules and could provide the opportunity to examine quantitatively minor components of the membrane.

In principle, monolayer splitting can be used to monitor the kinetics of transmembrane events. For example, a cell could be pulsed with a radioisotopic probe and the transmembrane distribution of the isotope could be monitored as a function of time by MONOFARG. To make the technique more generally useful and perhaps even of diagnostic value, quantification of membrane splitting should be made more rapid. If sensitive marker molecules could be developed to label the cytoplasmic and extracellular surfaces of the membrane, the splitting methods would become generally useful. For any new membrane system, however, electron microscopy should also be used to verify that the fracturing pattern is as anticipated.

In the future, planar monolayer freeze-fracture will undoubtedly be used to examine the more interesting physiological aspects of split membranes. For example, it should be possible to determine the sidedness and movement of isotopic pharmaceuticals across the plane of the membrane, or to determine whether or not receptor and effector functions reside in two molecules located on opposite sides of the membrane or are part of one transmembrane molecule.

ACKNOWLEDGMENTS

This research was supported by a Program Project Grant from the US Public Health Service, HL 06285, and was done during the tenure of an Established Investigatorship from the American Heart Association and with funds contributed in part by the American Heart Association, California Affiliate.

Literature Cited

1. Blaurock, A. E., Stoeckenius, W. 1971. Structure of the purple membrane. *Nature* 233:152–54
2. Branton, D. 1966. Fracture faces of frozen membranes. *Proc. Natl. Acad. Sci. USA* 55:1048–56
3. Branton, D. 1969. Membrane structure. *Ann. Rev. Plant Physiol.* 20:209–38
4. Branton, D. 1971. Freeze-etching studies of membrane structure. *Philos. Trans. R. Soc. London Ser. B* 261: 133–38
5. Branton, D., Kirchanski, S. 1977. Interpreting the results of freeze-etching. *J. Microsc. Oxford* 111:117–24
6. Bullivant, S. 1974. Freeze-etching studies on membranes and junctions. *Proc. 8th Int. Congr. Elect. Microsc., Canberra,* 2:192–93. Canberra: Austr. Acad. Sci.
7. Bullivant, S. 1977. Evaluation of membrane structure facts and artefacts produced during freeze-fracturing. *J. Microsc. Oxford* 111:101–16
8. Chen, Y. S., Hubbell, W. L. 1973. Temperature and light dependent structural changes in rhodopsin-lipid membranes. *Exp. Eye Res.* 17:517–32
9. Cohen, C. M., Kalish, D. I., Jacobson, B. S., Branton, D. 1977. Membrane isolation on polylysine-coated beads. *J. Cell Biol.* 75:119–34
10. Costello, M. J., Gulik-Krzywicki, T. 1976. Correlated X-ray diffraction and freeze-fracture studies on membrane model systems. Perturbations induced by freeze-fracture preparative procedures. *Biochim. Biophys. Acta* 455: 412–32
11. Deamer, D. W., Leonard, R. 1972. Freeze-etch images of an ion transporting membrane. In *The Role of Membranes in Metabolic Regulation,* ed. M. A. Mehlman, R. W. Hanson, pp. 17–31. NY: Academic
12. Edwards, H. H., Mueller, T. J., Morrison, M. 1978. Fractionation of membrane polypeptides by freeze fracture. *J. Cell Biol.* 79:226 (Abstr.)
13. Edwards, H. H., Mueller, T. J., Morrison, M. 1979. Distribution of transmembrane polypeptides in freeze fracture. *Science* 203:1343–46
14. Elias, P. M., Friend, D. S., Goerke, J. 1978. Freeze-fracture localization of cholesterol in cell and liposome membranes with saponin and filipin. *J. Cell Biol.* 79:232 (Abstr.)
15. Elias, P. M., Goerke, J., Friend, D. S. 1978. Freeze-fracture identification of sterol-digitonin complexes in cell and liposome membranes. *J. Cell Biol.* 78: 577–96
16. Fisher, K. A. 1974. Analysis of cholesterol distribution in bound erythrocyte membranes. *J. Cell Biol.* 63:100 (Abstr.)
17. Fisher, K. A. 1975. "Half" membrane enrichment: verification by electron microscopy. *Science* 190:983–85
18. Fisher, K. A. 1976. Analysis of membrane halves: cholesterol. *Proc. Natl. Acad. Sci. USA* 73:173–77
19. Fisher, K. A. 1976. Autoradiography of membrane "halves": ^{3}H-cholesterol labeled erythrocytes. *J. Cell Biol.* 70:218 (Abstr.)
20. Fisher, K. A. 1977. Protein content of a freeze-fractured membrane particle. *J. Elect. Microsc.* 26:171 (Abstr.)
21. Fisher, K. A. 1978. Split membrane lipids and polypeptides. In *Electron Microscopy 1978,* ed. J. M. Sturgess, pp. 521–32. *Proc. 9th Int. Congr. Elect. Microsc., Toronto.* Toronto: Microsc. Soc. Can.
22. Fisher, K., Branton, D. 1974. Application of the freeze-fracture technique to natural membranes. *Methods Enzymol.* 32:35–44
23. Fisher, K. A., Stoeckenius, W. 1977. Freeze-fractured purple membrane particles: protein content. *Science* 197: 72–74
24. Fisher, K. A., Yanagimoto, K., Stoeckenius, W. 1977. Purple membrane bound to polylysine glass: effects of pH and light. *J. Cell Biol.* 75:220 (Abstr.)

25. Fisher, K. A., Yanagimoto, K., Stoeckenius, W. 1978. Oriented adsorption of purple membrane to cationic surfaces. *J. Cell Biol.* 77:611-21
26. Friend, D. S., Elias, P. M. 1978. Heterogeneity of filipin-sterol complexes in the guinea pig sperm plasma membrane. *J. Cell Biol.* 79:216 (Abstr.)
27. Grant, C. W. M., McConnell, H. M. 1974. Glycophorin in lipid bilayers. *Proc. Natl. Acad. Sci. USA* 71:4653–57
28. Grant, C. W. M., Wu, S. H., McConnell, H. M. 1974. Lateral phase separations in binary lipid mixtures: correlation between spin label and freeze-fracture electron microscopic studies. *Biochim. Biophys. Acta* 363:151–58
29. Gulik-Krzywicki, T., Costello, M. J. 1978. The use of low temperature X-ray diffraction to evaluate freezing methods used in freeze-fracture electron microscopy. *J. Microsc. Oxford* 112:103–13
30. Haest, C. W. M., Verkleij, A. J., De Gier, J., Scheek, R., Ververgaert, P. H. J. Th., Van Deenen, L. L. M. 1974. The effect of lipid phase transitions on the architecture of bacterial membranes. *Biochim. Biophys. Acta* 356:17–26
31. Hayward, S. B., Grano, D. A., Glaeser, R. M., Fisher, K. A. 1978. Molecular orientation of bacteriorhodopsin within the purple membrane of *Halobacterium halobium. Proc. Natl. Acad. Sci. USA* 75:4320–24
32. Henderson, R. 1975. The structure of the purple membrane from *Halobacterium halobium:* analysis of the X-ray diffraction pattern. *J. Mol. Biol.* 93: 123–38
33. Henderson, R., Unwin, P. N. T. 1975. Three-dimensional model of purple membrane obtained by electron microscopy. *Nature* 257:28–32
34. Hong, K., Hubbell, W. L. 1972. Preparation and properties of phospholipid bilayers containing rhodopsin. *Proc. Natl. Acad. Sci. USA* 69:2617–21
35. Jacobson, B. S., Branton, D. 1977. Plasma membrane: rapid isolation and exposure of the cytoplasmic surface by use of positively charged beads. *Science* 195:302–4
36. Jacobson, B. S., Cronin, J., Branton, D. 1978. Coupling polylysine to glass beads for plasma membrane isolation. *Biochim. Biophys. Acta 506:81–96*
37. Jacobson, B. S., Welt, M., Branton, D. 1974. Purification of half-membranes by bulk freeze-fracturing. *J. Cell Biol.* 63:153 (Abstr.)
38. James, R., Branton, D. 1973. Lipid- and temperature-dependent structural changes in *Acholeplasma laidlawii* cell membranes. *Biochim. Biophys. Acta* 323:378–90
39. Kalish, D. I., Cohen, C. M., Jacobson, B. S., Branton, D. 1978. Membrane isolation on polylysine-coated glass beads: asymmetry of bound membrane. *Biochim. Biophys. Acta* 506:97–110
40. Kirchanski, S., Branton, D. 1977. Fluorescent energy transfer measurement of frozen membrane fracture. *J. Cell Biol.* 75:216 (Abstr.)
41. Kleemann, W., McConnell, H. M. 1974. Lateral phase separations in *Escherichia coli* membranes. *Biochim. Biophys. Acta* 345:220–30
42. Kleemann, W., McConnell, H. M. 1976. Interactions of proteins and cholesterol with lipids in bilayer membranes. *Biochim. Biophys. Acta* 419: 206–22
43. Malan, N. T., Sabbadini, R., Scales, D., Inesi, G. 1975. Functional and structural roles of sarcoplasmic reticulum protein components. *FEBS Lett.* 60: 122–25
44. Marchesi, V. T., Furthmayr, H., Tomita, M. 1976. The red cell membrane. *Ann. Rev. Biochem.* 45:667–98
45. Meyer, H. W., Winkelmann, H. 1969. Die Gefrieratzung und die Struktur biologischer Membranen. *Photoplasma* 68:253–70
46. Park, R. B., Pfeifhofer, A. 1974. Chemical composition of fractured membrane halves. In *Membrane Proteins in Transport and Phosphorylation,* ed. G. F. Azzone, M. E. Klingenberg, E. Quagliariello, N. Siliprandi, pp. 97–102. Amsterdam: North-Holland
47. Pinto da Silva, P., Branton, D. 1970. Membrane splitting in freeze-etching. Covalently bound ferritin as a membrane marker. *J. Cell Biol.* 45:598–605
48. Pinto da Silva, P., Martinez-Palomo, A. 1974. Induced redistribution of membrane particles, anionic sites and Con A receptors in *Entamoeba histolytica. Nature* 249:170–71
49. Pinto da Silva, P., Nicolson, G. L. 1974. Freeze-etch localization of Concanavalin A receptors to the membrane intercalated particles of human erythrocyte ghost membranes. *Biochim. Biophys. Acta* 363:311–19
50. Pinto da Silva, P., Douglas, S. D., Branton, D. 1971. Localization of A antigen sites on human erythrocyte ghosts. *Nature* 232:194–96
51. Pinto da Silva, P., Moss, P. S., Fudenberg, H. H. 1973. Anionic sites on the membrane intercalated particles of hu-

man erythrocyte ghost membranes. Freeze-etch localization. *Exp. Cell Res.* 81:127–38
52. Segrest, J. P., Gulik-Krzywicki, T., Sardet, C. 1974. Association of the membrane-penetrating polypeptide segment of the human erythrocyte MN-glycoprotein with phospholipid bilayers. I. Formation of freeze-etch intramembranous particles. *Proc. Natl. Acad. Sci. USA* 71:3294–98
53. Sleytr, U. B., Robards, A. W. 1977. Freeze-fracturing: a review of methods and results. *J. Microsc. Oxford* 111:77–100
54. Speth, V., Wunderlich, F. 1973. Membranes of *Tetrahymena.* II. Direct visualization of reversible transitions in biomembrane structure induced by temperature. *Biochim. Biophys. Acta* 291:621–28
55. Steck, T. L. 1974. The organization of proteins in the human red blood cell membrane. *J. Cell Biol.* 62:1–19
56. Unwin, P. N. T., Henderson, R. 1975. Molecular structure determination by electron microscopy of unstained crystalline specimens. *J. Mol. Biol.* 94:425–40
57. Verkleij, A. J., De Kruijff, B., Gerritsen, W. F., Demel, R. A., Van Deenen, L. L. M., Ververgaert, P. H. J. Th. 1973. Freeze-etch electron microscopy of erythrocytes, *Acholeplasma laidlawii* cells and liposomal membranes after the action of filipin and amphotericin B. *Biochim. Biophys. Acta* 291:577–81
58. Ververgaert, P. H. J. Th., Verkleij, A. J., Elbers, P. F., Van Deenen, L. L. M. 1973. Analysis of the crystallization process in lecithin liposomes: a freeze-etch study. *Biochim. Biophys. Acta* 311:320–29
59. Yu, J., Branton, D. 1976. Reconstitution of intramembrane particles in recombinants of erythrocyte protein Band 3 and lipid: effects of spectrin-actin association. *Proc. Natl. Acad. Sci. USA* 73:3891–95

Ann. Rev. Physiol. 1980. 42:275–92

PHOSPHORYLATION OF THE MYOFIBRILLAR PROTEINS ❖1268

Michael Bárány and Kate Bárány

Departments of Biological Chemistry, and Physiology and Biophysics, University of Illinois at the Medical Center, Chicago, Illinois 60612

INTRODUCTION

In muscle, protein phosphorylation takes place in both the sarcoplasm and the myofibrils. This review deals only with those myofibrillar proteins that can be phosphorylated—i.e. myosin light chain and in a few cases the heavy chain, the inhibitory and tropomyosin-binding subunits of troponin, and tropomyosin. Although research on this topic began as recently as 1972, several interesting results have been accumulated (for reviews, see 86–88, 114, 116).

GENERAL

The protein phosphorylation and dephosphorylation reactions discussed in this review are shown in the following two equations:[1]

$$\text{Protein-OH} + [\gamma\text{-}^{32}\text{P}]\text{ATP} \xrightarrow{\text{protein kinase}} \text{Protein-O-}^{32}\text{PO}_3\text{H}_2 + \text{ADP} \qquad 1.$$

$$\text{Protein-O-}^{32}\text{PO}_3\text{H}_2 + \text{H}_2\text{O} \xrightarrow{\text{phosphoprotein phosphatase}} \text{Protein-OH} + \text{H}_3{}^{32}\text{PO}_4 \qquad 2.$$

The protein hydroxyl group that accepts the terminal phosphate of labeled ATP usually belongs to a serine residue; threonine has been identified only in exceptional cases (87). Phosphoserine residues in proteins are essen-

[1]The reactions catalyzed by the protein kinase and phosphoprotein phosphatase are partially reversible in vitro (59); however, under conditions of living cells, these reactions are irreversible (114).

0066-4278/80/0315-0275$01.00

tially ionized at physiological pH; thus serine phosphorylation and dephosphorylation changes the net negative charge of proteins.

For in vitro experiments [γ-^{32}P]ATP of high specific radioactivity is available commercially, or it may be synthesized (e.g. 40). In vivo, ATP is synthesized via oxidative phosphorylation or glycolysis. The label is from [^{32}P] orthophosphate, which is injected into a live animal or added into an incubation medium. In live muscle the γ-phosphate of ATP is completely labeled within a few hours, the β-phosphate is the next one labeled, and the labeling of the α-phosphate takes about a day. The specific activity of the [γ^{32}P] of ATP is used as a standard for the calculation of the [^{32}P] phosphate content of proteins, and several methods have been described for these determinations (12, 32, 39).

The protein kinases that catalyze the phosphorylation of myofibrillar proteins are either Ca^{2+} or cAMP activated. Only the myosin light chain kinase has been shown to be protein substrate–specific (89, 90). Very little is known about the phosphoprotein phosphatases; an exception is the myosin light chain phosphatase that has been purified from rabbit skeletal muscle (79).

It is generally believed that incorporation of ^{32}P from [γ-^{32}P]ATP into proteins corresponds to true protein phosphorylation. However, isolated protein mixtures or even purified proteins may contain nucleic acids and phospholipids as contaminants; these may also be labeled, especially in vivo. Removal of nucleic acids by "hot acid extraction" for phosphoprotein determination (56) may lead to a greatly reduced phosphoprotein content, since under these conditions not only nucleic acids but also the phosphoproteins themselves are hydrolyzed; trichloroacetic acid soluble ^{32}P-labeled phosphopeptides are taken up in the supernatant along with ^{32}P-labeled hydrolytic products of nucleic acids. Therefore, diethylaminoethyl-[DEAE]-cellulose chromatography or digestions of the proteins with RNAse and DNAse are suggested as preferred approaches to the removal of contaminant nucleic acids. On the other hand, the acid chloroform-methanol extraction recommended to remove phospholipids (56) works well. In the authors' laboratory, phospholipids are separated from proteins by polyacrylamide gel electrophoresis in Na-dod-SO_4 and urea (10, 13).

The ultimate proof for true protein phosphorylation must come from the isolation and identification of the phosphorylated amino acid. The relative instability of protein-bound serine phosphate in 6.0 N HCl, 108°C (conditions for protein hydrolysis) presents a problem; thus, as much as 65% of the phosphate from serine is released within 5 hr (13). Enzymic proteolysis of phosphoproteins appears to be the correct procedure. This has the advantage that in addition to the phosphorylated residue the sequence around it may also be determined.

Protein phosphorylation is routinely measured by ^{32}P-incorporation because of the high sensitivity of this technique. In case the protein substrate is already partially phosphorylated, the radioactive method underestimates the protein-bound phosphate. Therefore, analytical phosphate determination should also be carried out whenever possible. Malachite green, a phosphate reagent, is sensitive in the nanomolar range; its proper use has been recently described (112).

PHOSPHORYLATION OF MYOSIN LIGHT CHAINS

In Vitro

Since the discovery (84) that the 18,000 dalton light chain of rabbit skeletal myosin is phosphorylated, studies on the overall topic of light chain phosphorylation have become extremely popular. In vitro phosphorylation of light chains, $M_r \sim$ 18–20,000, has been reported in myosin from slow skeletal muscle (35), from heart (35, 98), and from smooth muscle (4, 19, 27, 36, 109). Similar phosphorylation was described in myoblast myosin (104) and in nonmuscle myosins from platelets (2), fibroblasts (80), and neuroglial cells (106). It seems appropriate to designate the light chains that can undergo phosphorylation in these widely divergent myosins as "P-light chains," following the nomenclature in (35).

LIGHT CHAIN KINASE Myosin light chain kinase from rabbit fast skeletal muscle has been purified to homogeneity, as judged by polyacrylamide gel electrophoresis (89). The enzyme exists as a monomer of 77,000 daltons. It is highly specific for the P-light chain of rabbit fast skeletal muscle, but the light chains of slow skeletal, cardiac, and smooth muscle are also effective substrates. On the other hand, the enzyme is inactive toward the most common substrates of protein kinases—i.e. casein and histones. Myosin light chain kinase has an absolute requirement for Ca^{2+}. In the presence of physiological Mg^{2+} concentrations (12.5 mM), 1 μM Ca^{2+} fully activates the enzyme. Although light chain kinase is isolated from the sarcoplasmic fraction of muscle it has a high affinity to myosin. As a matter of fact, in the pilot studies freeze dried myosin was used as a source of the enzyme (90).

Pure myosin light chain kinase was also isolated from human blood platelets (25). The molecular weight of this kinase, 83,000, is similar to that of its skeletal muscle counterpart. Rabbit and human skeletal and cardiac myosins are not substrates, but the 20,000 dalton light chains of chicken gizzard and fibroblast myosin are phosphorylated by the platelet enzyme to a small extent. Platelet myosin light chain kinase activity is not affected by the removal of trace Ca^{2+}. Ca^{2+}-independent light chain kinases were also described in dog heart (98) and proliferative rat myoblasts (105).

It is well established that smooth muscle light chain kinase is under Ca^{2+} control (4, 19, 27, 36, 41, 108, 109). This kinase was purified from chicken gizzard and was shown to be composed of two subunits of approximately 105,000 and 17,000 daltons (23). Subsequent work by the same authors (24) identified the 17,000-dalton component as the Ca^{2+}-dependent modulator protein. Gizzard myosin light chain kinase is phosphorylated by the catalytic subunit of cAMP-dependent protein kinase (3), resulting in a two-fold decrease in the rate at which the enzyme phosphorylated the 20,000 dalton light chain of gizzard myosin. These authors postulate the following series of events for smooth muscle contraction: The intracellular free Ca^{2+} interacts with the modulator protein to activate the phosphodiesterase, which lowers the cAMP level. The decreased level of cAMP leads to an increase in the dephosphorylated (more active) form of light chain kinase, thus resulting in an increase of phosphorylated myosin, which is a prerequisite for actin-activation of smooth muscle myosin ATPase.

The Ca^{2+}-binding subunit of the skeletal muscle light chain kinase has also been identified as the modulator protein (15, 123), and homogeneous modulator protein has been isolated from rabbit skeletal muscle (125). With a modulator-deficient light chain kinase the Japanese workers clearly demonstrated that both the modulator protein and Ca^{2+} are necessary for kinase activity (124). These results have been confirmed (81).

A further development in this field has been the purification (118) of another protein kinase from rabbit skeletal muscle that depends on both Ca^{2+} and the modulator protein. Myosin light chains and phosphorylase kinase were substrates for the protein kinase. The Ca^{2+}-dependent modulator protein has been identified (20) as the fourth subunit of rabbit skeletal muscle phosphorylase kinase. It has been suggested that all Ca^{2+}-dependent protein kinases are activated by the same mechanism (59, 118):

$$Ca^{2+} + MP \rightleftharpoons Ca^{2+} - MP \rightleftharpoons Ca^{2+} - MP^* \qquad 3.$$

$$PK + Ca^{2+} - MP^* \rightleftharpoons Ca^{2+} - MP^* - PK \rightleftharpoons Ca^{2+} - MP^* - PK^*. \qquad 4.$$

where MP, MP*, PK, and PK* correspond to modulator protein, activated modulator protein, kinase, and its activated form, respectively. This scheme assumes that the 17,000-dalton modulator protein possesses recognition sites for several enzymes.

SITE OF PHOSPHORYLATION The serine residue phosphorylated by the light chain kinases has been located near the N-terminus of rabbit and chicken skeletal and chicken gizzard light chains (22, 54, 71). This region of the light chain is rich in basic residues, thus fulfilling the requirement for a cationic site around the phosphorylation site, a general rule in substrates of intracellular protein kinases (121). The sequences around the phosphoserine residue in both skeletal and smooth muscle light chains are similar; they differ from those of troponin-I, troponin-T, or phosphorylase *a* (87).

LIGHT CHAIN PHOSPHATASE Light chain phosphorylation is reversed by a specific enzyme, light chain phosphatase, purified about 10,000-fold from rabbit skeletal muscle (79). The enzyme migrated as a single component on electrophoresis in SDS polyacrylamide gels with an apparent mol wt of 70,000. It was inactive when tested in the absence of added bivalent cations. Light chain phosphatases, crude or partially purified, have been identified in various smooth muscles (19, 36, 53, 74, 108).

EFFECT OF PHOSPHORYLATION ON BIOLOGICAL ACTIVITIES OF MYOSIN The existence of light chain phosphorylating-dephosphorylating enzymes in muscle suggests a physiological role for light chain phosphorylation. Efforts to find such a role in vitro were most successful in the cases of smooth muscle myosin and myosin from nonmuscle cells. Thus, the finding that phosphorylation of platelet myosin increases its actin-activated ATPase activity (1) was rapidly followed by the demonstration of the same phenomenon with myosins from fowl gizzard (41), guinea pig vas deferens (19), pig stomach (108), and rat myoblasts (104). Moreover, it was suggested that Ca^{2+} regulation in smooth muscle actomyosin is mediated through the phosphorylation of myosin (4, 107, 108). However, an opposing conclusion was reached (48, 74) using the superprecipitation of actomyosin from chicken gizzard or aorta as an index of contractility. Phosphorylation and dephosphorylation of myosin light chain were found to have no appreciable effect. Instead, the leiotonin system, a mixture of 80,000- and 18,000-dalton proteins (75), and tropomyosin are believed to be involved in the regulation. On the other hand, it was shown that the superprecipitation of gizzard actomyosin depends on light chain phosphorylation (53). Furthermore, phosphorylation was also shown to be required for the superprecipitation of actomyosin from human blood platelets and, even more importantly, the maximum isometric tension development of threads from this actomyosin was also phosphorylation-dependent (65). Finally, recent reports show an increase in the actin-activated ATPase activity of phosphorylated rabbit skeletal and rat heart myosin, in comparison to controls (83, 97), though no significant changes had been found in previous studies (79).

EFFECT OF PHOSPHORYLATION ON THE STRUCTURE AND CALCIUM-BINDING OF LIGHT CHAIN Physical chemical techniques such as intrinsic fluorescence, circular dichroism, proton magnetic resonance, and gel filtration have indicated subtle differences between the structures of phosphorylated and dephosphorylated rabbit skeletal muscle light chains (5). The addition of calcium was found to lead to a considerable change in the characteristic parameters of both phosphorylated and unphosphorylated light chains. For instance, the circular dichroism change was consistent with an increase in α-helix content of about 5% upon addition of Ca^{2+}. Surprisingly, phosphorylation decreased the binding constant for Ca^{2+} by almost an order of magnitude. Previously, comparison of ESR spectra of spin-labeled light chain (82) had shown that phosphorylation reduces the Ca^{2+} affinity by a factor of 10,000. These results are at variance with those obtained by equilibrium dialysis, which indicate no effect of phosphorylation on the Ca^{2+} binding of either isolated light chains or myosin (49, 62).

In Vivo, Skeletal Muscle

Techniques have been developed in our laboratory for measuring protein phosphorylation in contracting live muscle (9, 10, 12, 101) by injecting live frogs, in their dorsal lymph sacs or intraperitoneally, with carrier-free [^{32}P]-orthophosphate. Analysis of the muscles of frogs kept at 25°C for 2–3 days after the injection shows the same specific radioactivity in all the water soluble phosphates—i.e. inorganic phosphate, the sugar phosphates, phosphocreatine, and the α-, β-, and γ-phosphate groups of ATP, indicating a full equilibrium between injected ^{32}P and the phosphate metabolites. Since over this time period the muscle proteins are only partially labeled through the protein kinase catalyzed transfer of the terminal phosphate of ATP, any additional change in the radioactivity of phosphoproteins caused by the stimulation of muscle is directly related to a protein phosphorylation or dephosphorylation reaction rather than to changes in the turnover of phosphate metabolites. The change in phosphoprotein concentration as a result of muscle contraction is measured as the difference in the [^{32}P] phosphate content of a given protein derived from both resting and contracting muscle. Therefore, it is important that the unstimulated left and right leg muscles of the frog should possess identical radioactivities. This is assured by injecting the ^{32}P in a relatively large volume, 0.5–0.7 ml, so that it should be evenly dispersed in the blood and lymph system before penetrating through the muscle membrane.

We have identified three ^{32}P-labeled myofibrillar proteins in live frog muscle: the α-component of tropomyosin, the tropomyosin-binding subunit of troponin, and the 18,000 dalton light chain of myosin (10). Only the light chain exhibited a change in the [^{32}P] phosphate content upon tetanic stimulation. We have found 0.35–0.4 mole of [^{32}P] phosphate incorporated per mole of light chain during a 20–30 sec tetanus of frog muscle at 25°C (9,

10). Similarly, a 0.4 mole phosphate increment in the light chain of rabbit gracilis muscle frozen after a 15 sec tetanus has been reported (113). At the same time, the phosphate content of troponin-tropomyosin fraction did not change (113).

We have followed light chain phosphorylation-dephosphorylation during the entire contraction-relaxation cycle of frog muscle (10). The extent of phosphorylation paralleled the development of tension, whereas that of dephosphorylation approximated the return of tension to zero. Phosphorylation was also observed in stimulated semitendinosus muscles that were stretched to 3.9 μm sarcomere length so that the muscles did not produce active tension. This indicated that the stimulus per se and not the mechanical event initiates the phosphorylation. We were also able to demonstrate light chain phosphorylation in caffeine-treated muscles. This suggested, based on the commonly known fact that caffeine releases Ca^{2+} from the sarcoplasmic reticulum, that the increased Ca^{2+} concentration in the sarcoplasm resulting from an electrical stimulus activates the myosin light chain kinase, which then phosphorylates the P-light chain (9, 10). The finding that phosphorylation is concurrent with the activation phase of contraction suggested that this reaction is correlated with the swinging of the crossbridges. Since phosphorylation of the light chain increases the negative charge of the myosin head, it appeared that phosphorylation provides the driving force that moves the bridges away from the negatively charged backbone of the thick filaments toward the vicinity of the actin filaments upon activation of the muscle (10). However, fluorescence depolarization experiments revealed no difference between the rotary mobility of phosphorylated myosin heads in synthetic thick filaments and that of unphosphorylated heads (R. A. Mendelson, M. Bárány, unpublished results). This implies that phosphorylation upon activation of muscle does not serve to move the bridges.

Phosphorylation of light chains is apparently involved in the formation of noncovalent bonds between myosin and actin in live muscle (11). The phosphoryl group attached to the myosin head forms a chelate with the actin-bound calcium. The affinity constant for this binding is greater than that of Ca^{2+} for EDTA, since EDTA could not dissociate the complex. Accordingly, the physiological role of light chain phosphorylation could be to increase the rate of combination of the crossbridges with the actin filaments.

The reported increase in the actin-activated ATPase activity of myosin due to phosphorylation (83, 97) might improve the efficiency of the mechanochemical coupling. The energy requirement for the phosphorylation is rather low; even if all the myosin heads were phosphorylated simultaneously only 0.28 μmole ATP would be utilized per gram of muscle.

During a tetanic contraction, phosphorylation takes place only once, at the start of the series; ATP hydrolysis at the crossbridges, on the other hand, occurs during each contractile cycle.

In Vivo, Heart and Smooth Muscle

Light chain phosphorylation has also been observed in hearts of dogs injected with [^{32}P] orthophosphate (73), in perfused rabbit heart (37), in perfused rat heart (57), and in cat ventricular papillary muscles (66). Correlation between myocardial function and light chain phosphorylation has not been established. In case of rabbit heart, adrenaline was first reported to decrease the phosphate content of the P-light chain (37), whereas in a subsequent series of experiments no change in the phosphorylation was found (88). In contrast, an increase in the [^{32}P] phosphate content of the light chain of papillary muscle stimulated by norepinephrine was noted (66).

The 20,000 dalton light chain of smooth muscle myosin was shown to be phosphorylated in rat myometrial strips incubated in [^{32}P] phosphate-containing saline solution (55). Contractions induced by oxytocin, carbachol, or KCl increased the phosphorylation markedly. The light chain of arterial smooth muscle also incorporated [^{32}P] phosphate (14). Furthermore, we have found a significant increase in phosphorylation when the muscle strips produced tension upon addition of norepinephrine or KCl (14).

PHOSPHORYLATION OF MYOSIN HEAVY CHAINS

The phosphorylation of the 140,000 dalton heavy chain in *Acanthamoeba* myosin I appears to be complementary to light chain phosphorylation in smooth muscle myosin, since the actin-activated Mg^{2+}-ATPase activity of phosphorylated *Acanthamoeba* myosin I was increased over 10-fold (69). Furthermore, no phosphorylation of the light chain of *Acanthamoeba* myosin was detected under these conditions. The novel myosin heavy chain kinase was Ca^{2+}-independent. This enzyme also phosphorylated the 125,000 dalton heavy chain of *Acanthamoeba* myosin IB, which is an absolute requirement for the actin- and Mg^{2+}-activated ATPase activity of this myosin (70). After treatment of *Acanthamoeba* myosin IB with 2 M LiCl more than 90% of its 27,000 dalton light chain could be removed, and the isolated heavy chain retained all the characteristic ATPase activities of myosin. This result shows for the first time that a myosin can have full enzymic activity in the absence of light chains.

Evidence has been presented (80) for the phosphorylation, without any activator, of the heavy chains of fibroblast myosin. In contrast, the phosphorylation of heavy chains in retinal myosin (47) and *Dictyostelium discoideum* was shown to be induced by cAMP (92). When *Dictyostelium* was grown in a medium containing [^{32}P] phosphate both the 210,000 dalton heavy and the 18,000 dalton light chain of its myosin became labeled (E. R. Kuczmarski, J. A. Spudich, personal communication). These workers have also separated both the heavy and light chain kinase activities of the amoeba.

In vivo phosphorylation of myosin heavy chain in dog hearts was first reported by McPherson et al (73). These investigators found 4.5 moles of phosphate per mole heavy chain. In our laboratory we did not observe any significant incorporation of [^{32}P] phosphate into myosin heavy chain either in perfused rat heart or in skeletal muscle of ^{32}P-injected frog.

PHOSPHORYLATION OF TROPONIN

The Inhibitory Subunit from Skeletal Muscle

Skeletal TN-I[2] can be phosphorylated by two different enzymes, namely the cAMP-dependent protein kinase (6) and the Ca^{2+}-dependent phosphorylase kinase (115). Sequence studies (51, 78) have shown that the principal sites of phosphorylation by these two enzymes are different. The threonine residue at position 11 was identified as the main site of phosphorylation by phosphorylase kinase, while serine 117 is a minor site. The amino acid sequence around the phosphorylated threonine residue of TN-I, ALA-ILE-THR-ALA-ARG, is similar to that surrounding the phosphorylated serine in phosphorylase *a*, GLN-ILE-SER-VAL-ARG (51, 78). However, the sequence surrounding serine 117 (42), whose phosphorylation is catalyzed by cAMP-dependent kinase, ARG-MET-SER-ALA-ASP, is not at all homologous. A detailed comparison of the phosphorylation sites of various myofibrillar proteins is given in Table IV of (88). Phosphorylation of both threonine 11 and serine 117 was found to be strongly inhibited by TN-C (21, 85). Phosphorylase kinase activity with TN-I as a substrate was relatively low; the V_{max} for TN-I phosphorylation was only 1/15 of that for phosphorylation of phosphorylase *b* (115).

Phosphorylase phosphatase from rabbit skeletal muscle, purified 700-fold, dephosphorylates TN-I at a rate four times that with its natural substrate, phosphorylase *a* (33). In rat skeletal muscle two phosphoprotein phosphatases, clearly distinguishable from phosphorylase phosphatase, have been identified. They showed activity mainly with TN-I as the substrate (95).

Skeletal muscle TN-I was not found to be phosphorylated in muscles of live frogs incubated with ^{32}P for several days (101). This observation suggests that in the resting frog muscle TN-I is complexed with TN-C, since,

[2]Abbreviations used: TN-C, TN-I, and TN-T = Ca^{2+}-binding, actomyosin ATPase inhibitory, and tropomyosin-binding subunits of troponin, respectively.

as mentioned before, in vitro studies showed that TN-C blocks phosphorylation of TN-I (21, 85). Furthermore, skeletal muscle TN-I could not be phosphorylated in response to tetanic contractions (12, 101, 111), or to isoproterenol treatment (111), indicating that neither phosphorylase kinase nor the cAMP-dependent kinase can transfer phosphate to TN-I in contracting muscle. Thus, negative results on the physiological role of TN-I phosphorylation in skeletal muscle suggest that TN-I and TN-C are combined in both the resting and contracting states.

The Inhibitory Subunit from Cardiac Muscle

Cardiac TN-I, like the skeletal one, is phosphorylated by phosphorylase kinase (21), the cAMP-dependent kinase (8, 21, 31, 96, 99, 112), the cAMP-independent kinase (96), and in addition by a cGMP-dependent protein kinase (17, 67). Of these enzymes, the cardiac cAMP dependent kinase is the most significant, since its activity, unlike that of phosphorylase kinase, is not inhibited by TN-C (21). Cardiac TN-I possesses 26 more amino acid residues at the N-terminus than skeletal TN-I (43). This N-terminal portion of the molecule contains a serine at position 20, which is rapidly phosphorylated by the cAMP-dependent kinase both in vitro (76) and in vivo (110).

A correlation between an increase in the contractile force of perfused hearts and the phosphorylation of TN-I has been studied in several laboratories. Phosphorylation has been shown to parallel roughly the increase in contraction induced by catecholamines (29–31, 34, 57, 110). Similarly, when an ionophore (RO2–2985) was used to activate contraction, the increase in force generation and the phosphate content of TN-I were found to be correlated (34). On the other hand, neither ouabain, increased frequency of stimulation, nor an increased Ca^{2+} concentration (all of which significantly augmented contractility) produced any increase in phosphorylation of TN-I (34). In experiments where hearts were treated with glucagon or acetylcholine no relationship existed between force generation and TN-I phosphorylation (30).

A hypothesis to explain increased cardiac contractility on the basis of TN-I phosphorylation would require modification of the cardiac actomyosin ATPase by phosphoryl-TN-I. Several workers have recently shown that when TN-I is phosphorylated, higher than normal Ca^{2+} concentrations are required to activate the ATPase (8, 94, 122). These results contradict previous reports that either showed increased Ca^{2+} sensitivity (103) or indicated that the Ca^{2+} dependence was the same (87). Ray & England (94) pointed out that the in vitro and in vivo results were "in the opposite direction" since TN-I phosphorylation is maximal with increased contractility of the heart. Bailin (8) suggested that the decreased Ca^{2+} sensitivity may "facilitate the relaxation process in cardiac muscle." The finding (18) that phosphorylation of cardiac TN-I had no effect on either the affinity or the amount of Ca^{2+} bound to cardiac troponin-tropomyosin is difficult to reconcile with the idea that phosphorylation changes the Ca^{2+} sensitivity of cardiac actomyosin.

The Tropomyosin-Binding Subunit

Phosphorylation of rabbit skeletal TN-T is catalyzed by phosphorylase kinase (77, 85), but bovine cAMP-dependent protein kinase has no significant effect on the process (77, 91). Phosphorylase kinase appears to have two different catalytic centers: one for phosphorylase *b* and another for TN-T. This conclusion was reached on the basis of the difference in the inhibition pattern of phosphorylation of both substrates by antibodies against phosphorylase kinase (26). On the other hand, the "40 P" fraction of extracts from skeletal muscle of mice carrying the phosphorylase kinase deficiency gene showed a Ca^{2+}-dependent phosphorylation of troponin B (a mixture of TN-I and TN-T). This same fraction showed little or no activity with phosphorylase *b* as a substrate (46). The latter observation is consistent with the possibility that phosphorylase kinase preparations contain a trace of another kinase specific for TN-T. Indeed, TN-T kinase has been purified recently from rabbit skeletal muscle (28, 61). This enzyme is not stimulated by cyclic nucleotides or divalent metal ions.

Three major phosphorylation sites were identified in TN-T from rabbit skeletal muscle (77). The first site is the N-terminal serine; the other two sites, Ser-149 or -150, and Ser-156 or -157, are in the middle of the molecule. Troponin C decreases the extent of phosphorylation of the three sites to 29, 19, and 5%, respectively, of the values obtained in the absence of TN-C (77). However, Ser-1 is phosphorylated in vivo as evidenced from the phosphate analysis of the N-terminal peptide. Thus TN-C is not blocking this phosphorylation site in live muscle. Troponin-T isolated from ^{32}P-injected frogs is substantially phosphorylated (10).

A possible involvement of TN-T phosphorylation in the regulation of actomyosin ATPase has been thoroughly investigated (7, 63, 85, 91). All experiments failed to show a significant effect, thus leaving the significance of TN-T phosphorylation open for future studies.

Information on the phosphorylation of cardiac TN-T is very limited. A part of the protein-bound phosphate in isolated troponin has been reported to be associated with the TN-T subunit (21, 112).

PHOSPHORYLATION OF TROPOMYOSIN

Tropomyosin is the newest member of the list of myofibrillar proteins known to be phosphorylated. Phosphoryl-tropomyosin was discovered not through any in vitro enzymic studies but rather in the course of identification of the ^{32}P-labeled proteins in live frog muscle (100). Of the two components of tropomyosin, α and β, only the former is labeled (68). A single phosphorylation site has been found in frog α-tropomyosin; it is located at Ser-283 (the penultimate residue at the C-terminal end). When proper precautions are taken to inhibit the phosphoprotein phosphatase, this site is completely phosphorylated in frog muscle. The same phosphorylated peptide was recovered, in low yields, from both rabbit skeletal α and cardiac tropomyosin (68). A few years ago we showed ^{32}P-incorporation into tropomyosin in slices of normal and dystrophic chicken muscles (12). Therefore it appears that phosphorylation of tropomyosin in vertebrate skeletal muscle is a general phenomenon.

The finding that in the frog or rabbit only α tropomyosin is phosphorylated, while the β component is not, is somewhat surprising since the amino acid sequences of these two tropomyosins are so similar. If one compares the C-terminal regions of α and β tropomyosins, in the sequence of 16 amino acids there are only three differences (68). Two of these are conservative: Met-281 is replaced by isoleucine, and Ile-284 is replaced by leucine in β tropomyosin. The only significant substitution, a charge change, is the replacement of His-276 by asparagine. This may account for the selective phosphorylation of α tropomyosin, although the positively charged histidine residue is separated by several residues from the phosphate acceptor Ser-283. The sequence of the phosphorylation site of α-tropomyosin is not similar to any other known phosphorylation site in myofibrillar proteins. This is consistent with data showing that tropomyosin is not phosphorylated by either phosphorylase kinase or cAMP-dependent protein kinase (87, 91, 112).

Mak et al (68) speculated on the physiological role of tropomyosin-bound phosphate. It was suggested that in the head to tail polymerization of tropomyosin, one P-Ser-283 in one molecule in the overlapping structure could form a salt bridge to the ϵ-NH_2 group of Lys-12, while the other P-Ser-283 could form a similar salt linkage with ϵ-NH_2 group of Lys-6.

CONCLUSIONS AND FUTURE SUGGESTIONS

Within the last six years several myofibrillar proteins have been shown to be phosphorylated, in both in vitro and in vivo systems. Considerable progress has been made in identifying and characterizing the enzyme systems that mediate the phosphorylation-dephosphorylation mechanisms; further delineation of the specific enzymes involved may be expected in the future.

What is the functional significance of each of the reported phosphorylations? In the case of skeletal myosin light chains, a clear correlation has been established between phosphorylation and contraction. A probable physiological role of light chain phosphorylation is to increase the rate of combination of actin and myosin filaments in the contracting phase of the mechanical activity. Light chain phosphorylation in heart and smooth muscle occurs at a rate equal to that in skeletal muscle. Preliminary studies suggest that in smooth muscle the peak of phosphorylation coincides with the maximal tension, just as it does in skeletal muscle. The phosphorylation of light chain in smooth muscle raises experimental prospects for studying the effects of various hormones and drugs on this reaction.

Of the thin filament proteins, only TN-I is a candidate for a functional relationship. The fact that TN-I phosphorylation is restricted to heart is intriguing and requires further elucidation. The precise timing of TN-I phosphorylation in the cardiac cycle must be known in order to understand its relationship to the decreased Ca^{2+}-sensitivity of phosphorylated actomyosin.

Tropomyosin phosphorylation in various muscles apparently plays a structural role in the assembly of the coiled coil chains. In contrast, the physiological significance of TN-T phosphorylation is obscure. The bound phosphate of this protein may stabilize its three dimensional structure, or it may participate in protein interactions not detectable by current techniques. Phosphorylation may also be a signal for the synthesis or degradation of myofibrillar proteins. A study of the correlation between protein turnover and phosphate incorporation may help to clarify the latter possibility.

Acknowledgments

The writing of this article and the work described from the authors' laboratory were supported by Grant NS-12172 from the United States National Institute of Health and by the Muscular Dystrophy Association.

We are grateful to Mrs. Barbara Rogowski for her typing the manuscript.

Literature Cited

1. Adelstein, R. S., Conti, M. A. 1975. Phosphorylation of platelet myosin increases actin-activated myosin ATPase activity. *Nature* 256:597–98
2. Adelstein, R. S., Conti, M. A., Anderson, W. Jr. 1973. Phosphorylation of human platelet myosin. *Proc. Natl. Acad. Sci. USA* 70:3115–19
3. Adelstein, R. S., Conti, M. A., Hathaway, D. R. 1978. Phosphorylation of smooth muscle myosin light chain kinase by the catalytic subunit of adenosine 3':5'-monophosphate-dependent protein kinase. *J. Biol. Chem.* 253: 8347–50
4. Aksoy, M. O., Williams, D., Sharkey, E. M., Hartshorne, D. J. 1976. A relationship between Ca^{2+} sensitivity and phosphorylation of gizzard actomyosin. *Biochem. Biophys. Res. Commun.* 69: 35–41
5. Alexis, M. N., Gratzer, W. B. 1978. Interaction of skeletal myosin light chains with calcium ions. *Biochemistry* 17: 2319–25
6. Bailey, C., Villar-Palasi, C. 1971. Cyclic AMP dependent phosphorylation of troponin. *Fed. Proc.* 30:1147
7. Bailin, G. 1977. Phosphorylation of an actin-tropomyosin-troponin complex from human skeletal muscle. *Biochim. Biophys. Acta* 462:689–99
8. Bailin, G. 1979. Phosphorylation of a bovine cardiac actin complex. *Am. J. Physiol.* 236:C41–46
9. Bárány, K., Bárány, M. 1977. Phosphorylation of the 18,000-dalton light chain of myosin during a single tetanus of frog muscle. *J. Biol. Chem.* 252:4752–54
10. Bárány, K., Bárány, M., Gillis, J. M., Kushmerick, M. 1979. Phosphorylation-dephosphorylation of the 18,000-dalton light chain of myosin during the contraction-relaxation cycle of frog muscle. *J. Biol. Chem.* 254:3617–23
11. Bárány, M., Bárány, K. 1979. Effect of phosphorylation of myosin light chain in intact frog muscle on the bound calcium of actin. *Biophys. J.* 25 (2):74a
12. Bárány, M., Bárány, K., Gaetjens, E., Horvath, B. Z. 1974. Studies on the phosphorylation-dephosphorylation of troponin-tropomyosin during muscle contraction and applications as a probe of dystrophic chicken muscle. In *Exploratory Concepts in Muscular Dystrophy,* ed. A. T. Milhorat, 2:451–62. Amsterdam: Excerpta Medica
13. Bárány, M., Bárány, K., Gaetjens, E., Steinschneider, A. 1977. Isolation of phosphorylated acid chloroform/methanol-soluble proteins from live frog muscle. *Biochim. Biophys. Acta* 491: 387–97
14. Barron, J. T., Bárány, M. Bárány, K. 1979. Phosphorylation of the 20,000-dalton light chain of myosin of intact arterial smooth muscle in rest and contraction. *J. Biol. Chem.* 254:4954–56
15. Barylko, B., Kuznicki, J., Drabikowski, W. 1978. Identification of Ca^{2+}-binding subunit of myosin light chain kinase from skeletal muscle with modulator protein. *FEBS Lett.* 90:301–4
16. Deleted in proof
17. Blumenthal, D. K., Stull, J. T., Gill, G. N. 1978. Phosphorylation of cardiac troponin by guanosine 3':5'-monophosphate-dependent protein kinase. *J. Biol. Chem.* 253:334–36
18. Buss, J. E., Stull, J. T. 1977. Calcium binding to cardiac troponin and the effect of cyclic AMP–dependent protein kinase. *FEBS Lett.* 73:101–4
19. Chacko, S., Conti, M. A., Adelstein, R. S. 1977. Effect of phosphorylation of smooth muscle myosin on actin activation and Ca^{2+} regulation. *Proc. Natl. Acad. Sci. USA* 74:129–33
20. Cohen, P., Burchell, A., Foulkes, J. G., Cohen, P. T. W., Vanaman, T. C., Nairn, A. C. 1978. Identification of the Ca^{2+}-dependent modulator protein as the fourth subunit of rabbit skeletal muscle phosphorylase kinase. *FEBS Lett.* 92:287–93
21. Cole, H. A., Perry, S. V. 1975. The phosphorylation of troponin I from cardiac muscle. *Biochem. J.* 149:525–33
22. Collins, J. H. 1976. Homology of myosin DTNB light chain with alkali light chains, troponin C and parvalbumin. *Nature* 259:699–700
23. Dabrowska, R., Aromatorio, D., Sherry, J. M. F., Hartshorne, D. J. 1977. Composition of the myosin light chain kinase from chicken gizzard. *Biochem. Biophys. Res. Commun.* 78: 1263–72
24. Dabrowska, R., Sherry, J. M. F., Aromatorio, D. K., Hartshorne, D. J. 1978. Modulator protein as a component of the myosin light chain kinase from chicken gizzard. *Biochemistry* 17:253–58
25. Daniel, J. L., Adelstein, R. S. 1976. Isolation and properties of platelet myosin light chain kinase. *Biochemistry* 15: 2370–77
26. Dickneite, G., Jennissen, H. P., Heilmeyer, L. M. G. Jr. 1978. Differentiation of two catalytic sites on phosphorylase kinase for phosphorylase *b* and

troponin-T phosphorylation. *FEBS Lett.* 87:297–302

27. DiSalvo, J., Gruenstein, E., Silver, P. 1978. Ca^{++} dependent phosphorylation of bovine aortic actomyosin. *Proc. Soc. Exp. Biol. Med.* 158:410–14
28. Dobrovol'skii, A. B., Gusev, V. B., Martynov, A. V., Severin, S. E. 1976. The search for a troponin-T specific protein kinase. *Biokhimiya* 41:1291–96
29. England, P. J. 1975. Correlation between contraction and phosphorylation of the inhibitory subunit of troponin in perfused rat heart. *FEBS Lett.* 50: 57–60
30. England, P. J. 1976. Studies on the phosphorylation of the inhibitory subunit of troponin during modification of contraction in perfused rat heart. *Biochem. J.* 160:295–304
31. England, P. J. 1977. Phosphorylation of the inhibitory subunit of troponin in perfused hearts of mice deficient in phosphorylase kinase. *Biochem. J.* 168:307–10
32. England, P. J., Walsh, D. A. 1976. A rapid method for the measurement of $[\gamma\text{-}^{32}P]$ATP specific radioactivity in tissue extracts and its application to the study of $^{32}P_i$ uptake in perfused rat heart. *Anal. Biochem.* 75:429–35
33. England, P. J., Stull, J. T., Krebs, E. G. 1972. Dephosphorylation of the inhibitory component of troponin by phosphorylase phosphatase. *J. Biol. Chem.* 247:5275–77
34. Ezrailson, E. G., Potter, J. D., Michael, L., Schwartz, A. 1977. Positive inotropy induced by ouabain, by increased frequency, by X537A (RO2–2985), by calcium and by isoproterenol: The lack of correlation with phosphorylation of TnI. *J. Mol. Cell. Cardiol.* 9:693–98
35. Frearson, N., Perry, S. V. 1975. Phosphorylation of the light-chain components of myosin from cardiac and red skeletal muscle. *Biochem. J.* 151:99–107
36. Frearson, N., Focant, B. W. W., Perry, S. V. 1976. Phosphorylation of a light chain component of myosin from smooth muscle. *FEBS Lett.* 63:27–32
37. Frearson, N., Solaro, R. J., Perry, S. V. 1976. Changes in phosphorylation of P light chain of myosin in perfused rabbit heart. *Nature* 264:801–2
38. Deleted in proof
39. Glass, D. B., Masaracchia, R. A., Feramisco, J. R., Kemp, B. E. 1978. Isolation of phosphorylated peptides and proteins on ion exchange papers. *Anal. Biochem.* 87:566–75
40. Glynn, I. M., Chappel, J. B. 1964. A simple method for the preparation of ^{32}P-labelled adenosine triphosphate of high specific activity. *Biochem. J.* 90:147–49
41. Gorecka, A., Aksoy, M. O., Hartshorne, D. J. 1976. The effect of phosphorylation of gizzard myosin on actin activation. *Biochem. Biophys. Res. Commun.* 71:325–31
42. Grand, R. J. A., Wilkinson, J. M. 1977. The amino acid sequence of rabbit slow-muscle troponin I. *Biochem. J.* 167: 183–92
43. Grand, R. J., Wilkinson, J. M., Mole, L. E. 1976. The amino acid sequence of rabbit cardiac troponin I. *Biochem. J.* 159:633–41
44. Deleted in proof
45. Deleted in proof
46. Gross, S. R., Mayer, S. E. 1973. The phosphorylation of troponin B by phosphorylase *b* kinase in skeletal muscle of mice carrying the phosphorylase *b* kinase deficiency gene. *Biochem. Biophys. Res. Commun.* 54:823–30
47. Hesketh, J. E., Virmaux, N., Mandel, P. 1978. Evidence for a cyclic nucleotide-dependent phosphorylation of retinal myosin. *FEBS Lett.* 94:357–360
48. Hirata, M., Mikawa, T., Nonomura, Y., Ebashi, S. 1977. Ca^{2+} regulation in vascular smooth muscle. *J. Biochem. (Tokyo)* 82:1793–96
49. Holroyde, M. J., Potter, J. D., Solaro, R. J. 1979. The calcium binding properties of phosphorylated and unphosphorylated cardiac and skeletal myosins. *J. Biol. Chem.* 254:6478–82
50. Deleted in proof
51. Huang, T. S., Bylund, D. B., Stull, J. T., Krebs, E. G. 1974. The amino acid sequences of the phosphorylated sites in troponin-I from rabbit skeletal muscle. *FEBS Lett.* 42:249–52
52. Deleted in proof
53. Ikebe, M., Aiba, T., Onishi, H., Watanabe, S. 1978. Calcium sensitivity of contractile proteins from chicken gizzard muscle. *J. Biochem.* (*Tokyo*) 83:1643–55
54. Jakes, R., Northrop, F., Kendrick-Jones, J. 1976. Calcium binding regions of myosin regulatory light chains. *FEBS Lett.* 70:229–34
55. Janis, R. A., Gualteri, R. T. 1978. Contraction of intact smooth muscle is associated with the phosphorylation of a 20,000 dalton protein. *The Physiologist* 21:59
56. Kleinsmith, L. J., Allfrey, V. G., Mirsky, A. E. 1966. Phosphoprotein

metabolism in isolated lymphocyte nuclei. *Proc. Natl. Acad. Sci. USA* 55:1182–89
57. Kopp, S. J., Bárány, M. 1979. Influence of positive and negative inotropic agents on incorporation of [^{32}P] orthophosphate into myofibrillar proteins of perfused rat heart. *Biophys. J.* 25 (2):121a
58. Deleted in proof
59. Krebs, E. G., Beavo, J. A. 1979. Phosphorylation-dephosphorylation of enzymes. *Ann. Rev. Biochem.* 48:923–59
60. Deleted in proof
61. Kumon, A., Villar-Palasi, C. 1978. Skeletal muscle troponin-T kinase. *The Physiologist* 21:69
62. Kuwayama, H., Yagi, K. 1979. Ca^{2+} bindings of pig cardiac myosin, subfragment-1 and g_2 light chain. *J. Biochem. (Tokyo)* 85:1245–55
63. Lallemant, C., Seraydarian, K., Mommaerts, W. F. H. M., Suh, M. 1975. A survey of the regulatory activity of some phosphorylated and dephosphorylated forms of troponin. *Arch. Biochem. Biophys.* 169:367–71
64. Deleted in proof
65. Lebowitz, E. A., Cooke, R. 1978. Contractile properties of actomyosin from human blood platelets. *J. Biol. Chem.* 253:5443–47
66. Lebowitz, E. A., Thibault, L. E., Adelstein, R. S. 1976. Phosphorylation of cat myocardial myosin and M-line-protein and enhancement by norepinephrine. *Circulation* 54 (2):113
67. Lincoln, T. M., Corbin, J. D. 1978. Purified cyclic GMP-dependent protein kinase catalyzes the phosphorylation of cardiac troponin inhibitory subunit (TN-I). *J. Biol. Chem.* 253:337–39
68. Mak, A., Smillie, L. B., Bárány, M. 1978. Specific phosphorylation at serine-283 of α tropomyosin from frog skeletal and rabbit skeletal and cardiac muscle. *Proc. Natl. Acad. Sci. USA* 75:3588–92
69. Maruta, H., Korn, E. D. 1977. *Acanthamoeba* cofactor protein is a heavy chain kinase required for actin activation of the Mg^{2+}-ATPase activity of *Acanthamoeba* myosin I. *J. Biol. Chem.* 252:8329–32
70. Maruta, H., Gadasi, H., Collins, J. H., Korn, E. D. 1978. The isolated heavy chain of an *Acanthamoeba* myosin contains full enzymatic activity. *J. Biol. Chem.* 253:6297–300
71. Matsuda, G., Suzuyama, Y., Maita, T., Umegane, T. 1977. The L-2 light chain of chicken skeletal muscle myosin. *FEBS Lett.* 84:53–56
72. Deleted in proof
73. McPherson, J., Fenner, C., Smith, A., Mason, D. T., Wikman-Coffelt, J. 1974. Identification of in vivo phosphorylated myosin subunits. *FEBS Lett.* 47:149–54
74. Mikawa, T., Nonomura, Y., Ebashi, S. 1977. Does phosphorylation of myosin light chain have direct relation to regulation in smooth muscle? *J. Biochem. (Tokyo)* 82:1789–91
75. Mikawa, T., Nonomura, Y., Hirata, M., Ebashi, S., Kakiuchi, S. 1978. Involvement of an acidic protein in regulation of smooth muscle contraction by the tropomyosin-leiotonin system. *J. Biochem. (Tokyo)* 84:1633–36
76. Moir, A. J. G., Perry, S. V. 1977. The sites of phosphorylation of rabbit cardiac troponin I by adenosine 3':5'-cyclic monophosphate-dependent protein kinase. *Biochem. J.* 167:333–43
77. Moir, A. J. G., Cole, H. A., Perry, S. V. 1977. The phosphorylation sites of troponin T from white skeletal muscle and the effects of interaction with troponin C on their phosphorylation by phosphorylase kinase. *Biochem. J.* 161: 371–82
78. Moir, A. J. G., Wilkinson, J. M., Perry, S. V. 1974. The phosphorylation sites of troponin I from white skeletal muscle of the rabbit. *FEBS Lett.* 42:253–56
79. Morgan, M., Perry, S. V., Ottaway, J. 1976. Myosin light-chain phosphatase. *Biochem. J.* 157:687–97
80. Muhlrad, A., Oplatka, A. 1977. Phosphorylation of fibroblast myosin. *FEBS Lett.* 77:37–40
81. Nairn, A. C., Perry, S. V. 1979. Calmodulin and myosin light chain kinase of rabbit fast skeletal muscle. *Biochem. J.* 179:89–97
82. Okamoto, Y., Yagi, K. 1976. Ca^{2+}-induced conformational changes of spin-labeled g_2 chain bound to myosin and the effect of phosphorylation. *J. Biochem.* 80:111–20
83. Pemrick, S. 1978. Phosphorylation of skeletal myosin enchances interaction with actin. *Circulation* 58 (2):73
84. Perrie, W. T., Smillie, L. B., Perry, S. V. 1972. A phosphorylated light-chain component of myosin. *Biochem. J.* 128:105–6P
85. Perry, S. V., Cole, H. A. 1974. Phosphorylation of troponin and the effects of interactions between the components of the complex. *Biochem. J.* 141:733–43
86. Perry, S. V. 1979. The regulation of contractile activity in muscle. *Biochem. Soc. Trans.* 7:596–617

87. Perry, S. V., Cole, H. A., Morgan, M., Moir, A. J. G., Pires, E. 1975. Phosphorylation of the proteins of the myofibril. *Proc. 9th Meet. Fed. Eur. Biochem. Soc.* Amsterdam: North-Holland. pp. 163–76
88. Perry, S. V., Cole, H. A., Frearson, N., Moir, A. J. G., Nairn, A. C., Solaro, R. J. 1979. Phosphorylation of the myofibrillar proteins. In *Proc. 12th Meet. Fed. Eur. Biochem. Soc.*, Vol. 54. Cyclic Nucleotides and Protein Phosphorylation in Cell Regulation, ed. A. Wollenberger, E. G. Krause, L. Pinna, pp. 147–59. NY: Pergamon
89. Pires, E. M. V., Perry, S. V. 1977. Purification and properties of myosin light-chain kinase from fast skeletal muscle. *Biochem. J.* 167:137–46
90. Pires, E., Perry, S. V., Thomas, M. A. W. 1974. Myosin light-chain kinase, a new enzyme from striated muscle. *FEBS Lett.* 41:292–96
91. Pratje, E., Heilmeyer, L. M. G. Jr. 1972. Phosphorylation of rabbit muscle troponin and actin by a 3',5'-cAMP-dependent protein kinase. *FEBS Lett.* 27:89–93
92. Rahmsdorf, H. J., Malchow, D., Gerisch, G. 1978. Cyclic AMP-induced phosphorylation in *Dictyostelium* of a polypeptide comigrating with myosin heavy chains. *FEBS Lett.* 88:322–26
93. Deleted in proof
94. Ray, K. P., England, P. J. 1976. Phosphorylation of the inhibitory subunit of troponin and its effect on the calcium dependence of cardiac myofibril adenosine triphosphatase. *FEBS Lett.* 70:11–16
95. Ray, K. P., England, P. J. 1976. The identification and properties of phosphatases in skeletal muscle with activity towards the inhibitory subunit of troponin, and their relationship to other phosphoprotein phosphatases. *Biochem. J.* 159:369–80
96. Reddy, Y. S. 1976. Phosphorylation of cardiac regulatory proteins by cyclic AMP-dependent protein kinase. *Am. J. Physiol.* 231:1330–36
97. Reddy, Y. S., Wyborny, L. E. 1978. Phosphorylation and ATPase activity of cardiac and skeletal myosins. *The Physiologist* 21:97
98. Reddy, Y. S., Pitts, B. J. R., Schwartz, A. 1977. Cyclic AMP-dependent and independent protein kinase phosphorylation of canine cardiac myosin light chains. *J. Mol. Cell. Cardiol.* 9:501–13
99. Reddy, Y. S., Ballard, D., Giri, N.Y., Schwartz, A. 1973. Phosphorylation of cardiac native tropomyosin and troponin: Inhibitory effect of actomyosin and possible presence of endogeneous myofibrillar-located cyclic AMP-dependent protein kinase. *J. Mol. Cell. Cardiol.* 5:461–71
100. Ribolow, H., Bárány, M. 1977. Phosphorylation of tropomyosin in live frog muscle. *Arch. Biochem. Biophys.* 179: 718–20
101. Ribolow, H., Bárány, K., Steinschneider, A., Bárány, M. 1977. Lack of phosphate incorporation into TN-I in live frog muscle. *Arch. Biochem. Biophys.* 179:81–85
102. Deleted in proof
103. Rubio, R., Bailey, C., Villar-Palasi, C. 1975. Effects of cyclic-AMP dependent protein kinase on cardiac actomyosin: increase in Ca^{2+} sensitivity and possible phosphorylation of troponin I. *J. Cyclic Nucl. Res.* 1:143–50
104. Scordilis, S. P., Adelstein, R. S. 1977. Myoblast myosin phosphorylation is a prerequisite for actin-activation. *Nature* 268:558–60
105. Scordilis, S. P., Adelstein, R. S. 1978. A comparative study of the myosin light chain kinases from myoblast and muscle sources. *J. Biol. Chem.* 253:9041–48
106. Scordilis, S. P., Anderson, J. L., Pollack, R., Adelstein, R. S. 1977. Characterization of the myosin-phosphorylating system in normal murine astrocytes and derivative SV40 wild-type and A-mutant transformants. *J. Cell. Biol* 74:940–49
107. Sherry, J. M. F., Gorecka, A., Aksoy, M. O., Dabrowska, R., Hartshorne, D. J. 1978. Roles of calcium and phosphorylation in the regulation of the activity of gizzard myosin. *Biochemistry* 17: 4411–18
108. Small, J. V., Sobieszek, A. 1977. Ca-regulation of mammalian smooth muscle actomyosin *via* a kinase-phosphatase-dependent phosphorylation and dephosphorylation of the 20,000 M_r light chain of myosin. *Eur. J. Biochem.* 76:521–30
109. Sobieszek, A. 1977. Ca-linked phosphorylation of a light chain of vertebrate smooth-muscle myosin. *Eur. J. Biochem.* 73:477–83
110. Solaro, R. J., Moir, A. J. G., Perry, S. V. 1976. Phosphorylation of troponin I and the inotropic effect of adrenaline in the perfused rabbit heart. *Nature* 262:615–17
111. Stull, J. T. 1975. Phosphorylation of skeletal muscle troponin in vivo. *Pharmacologist* 17:234

112. Stull, J. T., Buss, J. E. 1977. Phosphorylation of cardiac troponin by cyclic adenosine 3':5'-monophosphate-dependent protein kinase. *J. Biol. Chem.* 252:851–57
113. Stull, J. T., High, C. W. 1977. Phosphorylation of skeletal muscle contractile proteins in vivo. *Biochem. Biophys. Res. Commun.* 77:1078–83
114. Stull, J. T., Mayer, S. E. 1979. Biochemical mechanisms of adrenergic and cholinergic regulation of myocardial contractility. In *Handbook of Physiology: The Cardiovascular System,* ed. R. M. Berne, N. Sperelakis, pp. 741–74. Bethesda, Md: Am. Physiol. Soc.
115. Stull, J. T., Brostrom, C. O., Krebs, E. G. 1972. Phosphorylation of the inhibitor component of troponin by phosphorylase kinase. *J. Biol. Chem.* 247:5272–74
116. Stull, J. T., Blumenthal, D. K., deLanerolle, P., High, C. W., Manning, D. R. 1978. Phosphorylation and regulation of contractile proteins. In *Advances in Pharmacology and Therapeutics,* ed. J. R. Boissier, P. Lechat, J. Fichelle, pp. 171–80. NY: Pergamon Press
117. Deleted in proof
118. Waisman, D. M., Singh, T. J., Wang, J. H. 1978. The modulator-dependent protein kinase. A multifunctional protein kinase activatable by the Ca^{2+}-dependent modulator protein of the cyclic nucleotide system. *J. Biol. Chem.* 253:3387–90
119. Deleted in proof
120. Walsh, D. A., Perkins, J. P., Krebs, E. G. 1968. An adenosine 3',5'-monophosphate dependent protein kinase from rabbit skeletal muscle. *J. Biol. Chem.* 243:3763–74
121. Williams, R. E. 1976. Phosphorylated sites in substrates of intracellular protein kinases: A common feature in amino acid sequences. *Science* 192: 473–74
122. Wyborny, L. E., Reddy, Y. S. 1978. Phosphorylated cardiac myofibrils and their effect on ATPase activity. *Biochem. Biophys. Res. Commun.* 81: 1175–79
123. Yagi, K., Yazawa, M. 1978. Identification of an activator protein for myosin light chain kinase as the Ca^{2+}-dependent modulator protein. *J. Biol. Chem.* 253:1338–40
124. Yazawa, M., Yagi, K. 1978. Purification of modulator-deficient myosin light-chain kinase by modulator protein-Sepharose affinity chromatography. *J. Biochem.* (*Tokyo*) 84:1259–65
125. Yazawa, M., Kuwayama, H., Yagi, K. 1978. Modulator protein as a Ca^{2+}-dependent activator of rabbit skeletal myosin light-chain kinase. *J. Biochem.* (*Tokyo*) 84:1253–58

Ann. Rev. Physiol. 1980.42:293–309

THE RELATION OF MUSCLE BIOCHEMISTRY TO MUSCLE PHYSIOLOGY

❖1269

Evan Eisenberg and Lois E. Greene

Laboratory of Cell Biology, National Heart, Lung, and Blood Institute, National Institutes of Health, Bethesda, Maryland 20205

INTRODUCTION

During the last several years, the major challenge in the field of muscle contraction has been to develop a detailed theory explaining how muscle develops force and produces work. There is now general agreement that the overall mechanism of muscle contraction involves the sliding of the thick myosin filaments past the thin actin filaments, a process driven by the hydrolysis of ATP (29, 31). Most workers also agree that this sliding process is caused by a cyclic interaction of the actin filaments with cross-bridges extending from the myosin filament (28, 29, 31). However, the details of this cyclic interaction remain elusive.

The cyclic interaction of the myosin cross-bridges with the actin filaments has been investigated from structural, physiological, and biochemical viewpoints. This review discusses how these three viewpoints might be united in a single view of cross-bridge action. Rather than attempt an exhaustive review of the literature, we focus on various biochemical models proposed for the actomyosin ATPase and how they relate to the mechanism of muscle contraction. In addition, a new model of cross-bridge action in vivo is presented, based on a biochemical model that appears to fit best the current biochemical data.

EARLY BIOCHEMICAL AND CROSS-BRIDGE MODELS

The Biochemical and Cross-Bridge Models of Eisenberg & Moos

Figure 1 summarizes the kinetic models of the actomyosin ATPase that have been presented during the last ten years. These models are all based

0066-4278/80/0315-0293$01.00

on steady-state and pre-steady-state kinetic data obtained using the soluble proteolytic fragments of myosin, the two-headed heavy meromyosin (HMM), and the single-headed subfragment-one (S-1) (32). They are soluble at low ionic strength where marked actin-activation of the myosin ATPase occurs. Furthermore, they retain the ATP and actin binding sites of the parent myosin molecule (8, 14, 33, 36, 41).

The major steady-state kinetic result that must be explained by the models shown in Figure 1 is the linear double reciprocal plot of ATPase vs actin concentration (13, 15, 16, 51). The intercepts of this double reciprocal plot yield values for V_{max}, the maximum actin activated ATPase rate, and K_{app}, the actin concentration required for half maximal ATPase activity. The linear double reciprocal plot was the stimulus for the kinetic model shown in Figure 1A. This model, proposed by Eisenberg & Moos in 1968 (13), suggested that each myosin head contained a separate ATP and actin binding site. The binding of ATP weakened the binding of actin and at the same time the binding of actin activated the myosin ATPase activity. This kinetic model was proposed at about the same time that structural studies (44, 45) showed that in the absence of ATP, the myosin cross-bridges were attached to actin filaments at a 45° angle, while in relaxed muscle the detached cross-bridges extended from the myosin filament at a 90° angle. Thus Eisenberg and his coworkers (16) proposed the simple cross-bridge model shown in Figure 2A. The cross-bridge with bound ATP was attached to actin at a 90° angle, while following hydrolysis of ATP the cross-bridge was attached at a 45° angle. Work was done when the cross-bridge changed its angle of attachment to actin. One of the interesting features of this cross-bridge model was that different biochemical states had different angles of attachment to actin. However, the model was naive because no attempt had been made to combine this biochemical concept with the physiological concept, first suggested by A. F. Huxley in 1957 (28), that the cross-bridge is an elastic structure.

The Biochemical and Cross-Bridge Models of Lymn & Taylor

The cross-bridge model of Eisenberg et al (16) had other problems. First, it appeared that this model would only work if, during each cycle of ATP hydrolysis, the binding of ATP caused the cross-bridge to detach from actin before the attached cross-bridge returned to a 90° angle; otherwise it seemed that the attached cross-bridge would oscillate between 90° and 45° without doing useful work. Yet the biochemical model on which this cross-bridge model was based provided no mechanism for the binding of ATP to detach the myosin from actin during each cycle of ATP hydrolysis. Second, the work of Tonomura and his colleagues (52) and Taylor and his colleagues (34, 35) had shown that ATP, after it binds to myosin, is hydrolyzed to form bound ADP and Pi on the surface of the enzyme much more rapidly than the ADP and Pi are subsequently released to the medium. This rapid hydrolysis of ATP, called the "initial Pi burst,"

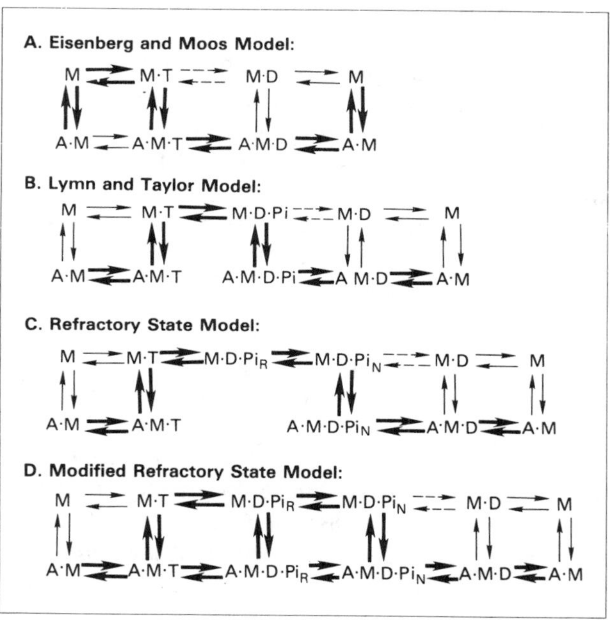

Figure 1 Kinetic schemes for the hydrolysis of ATP by myosin and actomyosin. These schemes are for the Eisenberg & Moos model (13), Lymn & Taylor model (35), refractory state model (5), and modified refractory state model (50). The predominant pathway for the actomyosin ATPase cycle in each scheme is shown by the heavy solid lines. The dashed arrows indicate the rate-limiting steps in the myosin ATPase cycles in the absence of actin. M = a single myosin cross-bridge head (S-1 in vitro); A = an actin monomer in F-actin filament; T = ATP; D = ADP; and the R and N subscripts indicate the refractory and nonrefractory states, respectively. In these schemes * and ‡ superscripts, which have been used in the past to indicate conformational changes in the myosin molecule (2, 5), have been omitted for reasons of clarity. In addition, it is likely that all of the steps involving the binding or release of ATP, ADP, and Pi in these schemes are, in fact, at least two-step processes consisting of formation of a collision intermediate followed by a conformational change (2). For simplicity, in the present schemes all of these two-step processes have been shown as single steps. Finally, in one version of the original refractory state model (5) state $M \cdot D \cdot Pi_R$ was shown as transforming to state $M \cdot D \cdot Pi_N$ in the actomyosin ATPase cycle, while in the myosin ATPase cycle state $M \cdot D \cdot Pi_R$ transformed directly to state $M \cdot D$ as originally proposed by Bagshaw et al (2). In the present scheme, for uniformity, no branches have been shown; state $M \cdot D \cdot Pi_N$ occurs in both the myosin and actomyosin ATPase cycles.

which became an important phenomenon in the mechanism of the myosin ATPase, was not incorporated in the biochemical or cross-bridge models of Eisenberg & Moos.

The classic pre-steady-state kinetic studies of Lymn & Taylor (35) provided a possible solution to both of these problems. Lymn & Taylor found that, at low actin concentration, the rate of dissociation of acto·HMM by ATP was much faster than the rate of ATP hydrolysis in the initial Pi burst, a result since confirmed by Sleep & Taylor (49). On this basis they proposed the kinetic model shown in Figure 1B. Here dissociation of the acto·HMM complex by ATP precedes hydrolysis of the ATP on the HMM in the initial Pi burst. Following the hydrolysis step the HMM·product complex reassociates with actin and the actin causes rapid release of the products. On the basis of this kinetic model, Lymn & Taylor proposed the cross-bridge model shown in Figure 2B (35), involving a mandatory dissociation step which seemed to fulfill the requirements of a cyclic model of cross-bridge action.

The Refractory State Biochemical Model

The Lymn-Taylor kinetic model was based on pre-steady-state kinetic data, but, of course, it also had to explain the steady-state kinetic results of Eisenberg & Moos. Since the rate of the initial Pi burst appeared to be considerably faster than the maximum actin-activated steady-state ATPase rate, Lymn & Taylor suggested that the rate-limiting step in the ATPase cycle was the release of products that occurred after the myosin-product complex rebound to actin (35). However, as pointed out by these authors, such a slow step occurring with the myosin attached to actin was difficult to reconcile with the brief time a cross-bridge spends attached to actin in

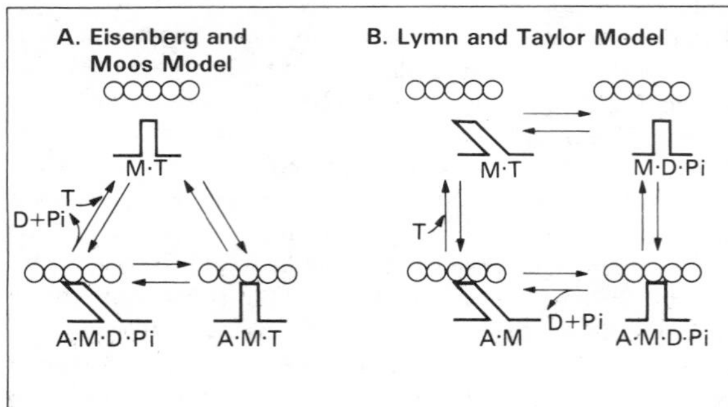

Figure 2 Cross-bridge models of muscle contraction. A schematic representation of the cross-bridge cycle in muscle proposed by Eisenberg & Moos (Figure 2A) and Lymn & Taylor (Figure 2B). These cycles are based on the kinetic schemes shown in Figures 1A and 1B, respectively.

a rapidly shortening muscle. The Lymn-Taylor model also led to the prediction that if in vitro the initial Pi burst is fast compared to V_{max}, then almost all of the HMM or S-1 will be complexed with actin when the ATPase is close to V_{max} (since in any ATPase cycle the dominant species occurs just before the rate-limiting step). However, contrary to this prediction, Eisenberg and his co-workers found that a large fraction of the HMM or S-1 was dissociated from actin when the ATPase was close to V_{max} (5, 9, 12, 19, 40). On this basis they proposed the refractory state model shown in Figure 1C (5, 12). This model was identical with the Lymn-Taylor model except that an additional step, the transition from the refractory to the nonrefractory state, was added following the initial Pi burst. Like the initial Pi burst, this step could only occur when the S-1 was detached from actin. In addition, however, it was the slowest step in the kinetic cycle. Thus this model explained why, when the ATPase was close to V_{max}, the dominant S-1 species present was not attached to actin.

From the point of view of developing a cross-bridge model, the refractory state kinetic model had several advantages. First, since a slow rate-limiting step occurred before the S-1 reattached to actin, it provided a possible biochemical explanation for a suggestion in A. F. Huxley's 1957 model of cross-bridge action (28). He had suggested that the rate constant for attachment of the cross-bridge to actin, "*f*", was quite slow. This relatively slow rate of attachment of the cross-bridge was important both in determining a large part of the force-velocity curve and in explaining the levelling off of the ATP turnover rate at high velocity. The slow transition from the refractory to the nonrefractory state could explain slow attachment of the cross-bridge in vivo. Second, in the refractory state model the rate of product release, which occurred after S-1 reattached to actin, was quite rapid. This was consistent with the brief time a cross-bridge spends attached to actin in a rapidly shortening muscle (29). It was also, at least superficially, consistent with the suggestion of Huxley & Simmons (30) that after the cross-bridge attached to actin at a 90° angle it rapidly rotated through a series of states to a 45° angle. Fast rates of transition between these attached states were postulated to explain the rapid force recovery that occurred when a muscle in the isometric state was suddenly shortened (isometric transient).

The Location of the Cross-Bridge Elasticity

Before a complete cross-bridge model could be developed a major change had to be made in the way a cross-bridge biochemical state was described. The idea that a cross-bridge attached to actin can exist in several different states comes naturally from the biochemical data. However, in physiological experiments on whole muscle fibers, different attached cross-bridge states are never directly observed. Rather, the studies of Ford, Huxley, & Simmons (18) on the response of muscle fibers subjected to sudden changes in length suggest that the cross-bridge has elastic properties. These studies on the isometric transient confirmed earlier studies (6) suggesting that the cross-bridge is an elastic structure operating over a range of about 50–100 Å. To develop a complete cross-bridge model, the concepts of cross-bridge elasticity and multiple biochemical states must be combined.

The first approach to this problem came from Huxley & Simmons (30) in explanation of their isometric transient data. They speculated that the rapid changes in force observed experimentally might be caused by the presence of both a force generator and an elastic element in the attached cross-bridge. Therefore, they suggested that the cross-bridge contained an independent elastic element, as in the 1957 model of A. F. Huxley (28), and that rapid time-dependent transitions occurring elsewhere in the cross-bridge (e.g. a ratchet-like rotation of the head on the actin filament) indirectly changed the length of this elastic element. Because the behavior of this elastic element was totally mechanical—i.e. its elastic properties were not directly affected by the time-dependent transitions—this model had the predictive advantage of being quite restrictive in its choice of rate constants. As yet, however, it has not been shown that such a model can quantitatively explain both the transient and steady-state physiological properties of intact muscle fibers. Furthermore, the time-dependent transitions occurring in the cross-bridge in this model have never been related to the biochemical states observed in solution.

Eisenberg & Hill (10) suggested an elastic cross-bridge model that was less restrictive in its choice of rate constants. The important studies of T. L. Hill (25, 26) had provided a theoretical formalism which enabled free energy changes and rate constants determined in biochemical studies to be related to force, velocity, and elasticity measurements determined in physiological studies. This formalism, therefore, made it possible to integrate biochemistry with physiology in a complete cross-bridge model. Like Huxley & Simmons, Eisenberg & Hill used the cross-bridge structure proposed by H. Huxley (31), where two flexible hinges attach the myosin head to the myosin filament. In addition, Eisenberg & Hill proposed that changes in the biochemical state of the cross-bridge are directly related to changes in its elastic properties. As in the previous models shown, the cross-bridge can occur in a 90° or 45° state. However, here the cross-bridge is able to rotate on the actin so that the "90° state" or the "45° state" do not exist at just the single angles 90° and 45°, respectively. Rather, in the 90° and 45° states the cross-bridges prefer being at 90° and 45° angles, respectively, but can rotate to higher angles, where they exert positive force, and lower angles, where they exert negative force. The key point in this model is that the elastic properties of the cross-bridge states do not determine the rate constants between these states. Therefore, the rate constants between the 90° and 45° states do not depend on thermal motion to stretch an elastic element as in the Huxley-Simmons model. Eisenberg, Hill & Chen (11) have pointed out that, although in the original description of this model the S-1 is rigid and all of the elasticity occurs at the S-1-actin junction, the basic properties of the model would be the same if the S-1 portion of the HMM were flexible and both the angle of attachment and the shape of the S-1 changed as the filaments slid past each other. Recent evidence suggesting that the two HMM heads simultaneously bind strongly to adjacent actin sites in vitro (24) supports the idea that the HMM heads themselves are flexible (24, 42).

COMPLETE CROSS-BRIDGE MODELS

The Cross-Bridge Model of Eisenberg, Hill & Chen

The idea that the rate constants between the 90° and 45° cross-bridge states do not depend on the elasticity of the cross-bridge allowed Eisenberg, Hill & Chen (11) enough freedom to develop a complete quantitative cross-bridge model based on the earlier qualitative cross-bridge model of Eisenberg & Hill (10). The kinetic cycle shown in Figure 1C (6) formed the biochemical basis for this model. In muscle two unattached states, the refractory and nonrefractory state, and two attached states, $A \cdot M \cdot D \cdot Pi_N$ and $A \cdot M \cdot D$, were assumed to occur in significant concentration; the other states were assumed to be transient intermediates. $A \cdot M \cdot D \cdot Pi_N$ and $A \cdot M \cdot D$ were assumed to be the 90° and 45° attached states, respectively; qualitatively they had the elastic properties of the attached cross-bridge states proposed by Eisenberg & Hill (10).

Cross-bridge states in solution always exist at their minimum free energy levels; but in muscle, attached cross-bridge states have variable free energy levels because the cross-bridge is elastic (25, 26). The free energy profile in Figure 3 shows the basic free energy of the four cross-bridge states in the model of Eisenberg, Hill & Chen as a function of x. The variable x is a measure of the position of the actin site relative to the cross-bridge. With the cross-bridge structure of Eisenberg & Hill, the value of x is directly related to the angle of the attached cross-bridge—e.g. when the attached cross-bridge is at a 90° angle, $x = 80$Å, and when the attached cross-bridge is at a 45° angle, $x = 0$. Because the free energies of the unattached cross-bridge states are independent of the position of the actin site, the free energies of the refractory ($M \cdot D \cdot Pi_R$) and nonrefractory ($M \cdot D \cdot Pi_N$) states are independent of x. On the other hand, because the attached cross-bridge is elastic, the free energies of the 90° and 45° states depend on x. The slope of the free energy curve for an attached state, at any value of x, is equal to the force exerted by that cross-bridge state at that value of x (10, 25). Of course, at the minimum of the free energy curve, the attached state exerts zero force.

The free energy profile shown in Figure 3 relates a chemical parameter (free energy) to physiological parameters (the position of the attached cross-bridge, x, and the mechanical force). Therefore, this free energy profile is based on both chemical and physiological data. The shapes of the free energy curves are based on the elastic properties of the cross-bridge which, in turn, are given by the isometric transient data of Ford, Huxley & Simmons (18). Because cross-bridge states are at their minimum free energy levels in solution, the relative vertical positions of the minima of the free energy curves in Figure 3 are based on the equilibrium constants between cross-bridge states in solution (11).

To match the high efficiency of muscle contraction, Eisenberg, Hill & Chen assumed that, at $x = 0$, the binding constant of actin to the nucleotide-free cross-bridge was about equal to the binding constant of ATP to

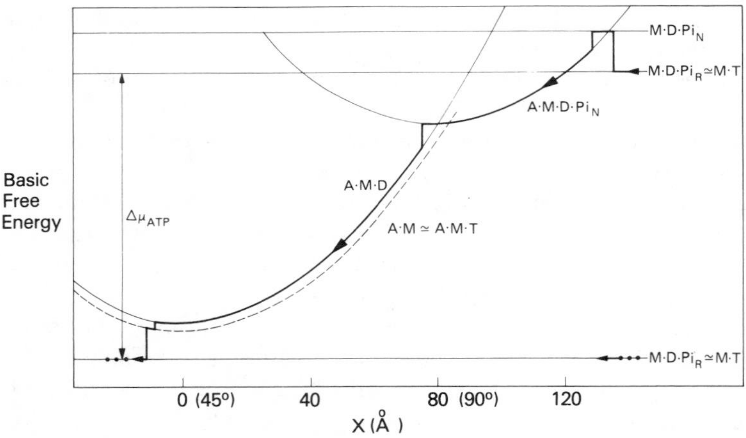

Figure 3 Basic free energy profile for the Eisenberg, Hill & Chen (11) cross-bridge model. The abscissa, x, shows the axial position of the attached cross-bridge with reference to its position when the 45° state (A·M·D) is at its minimum free energy. The angle of the attached cross-bridge to actin at $x = 0$, and $x = 80$Å is indicated in parentheses. The ordinate shows the relative basic free energy of the cross-bridge states. The profile repeats indefinitely above and below, with one ATP being hydrolyzed during each cycle. The new cycle is shown to start again in the lower right hand corner with the dotted arrow (←····). The heavy solid line represents the path of a nearly optimal cross-bridge cycle during an isotonic contraction (see text). A·M and A·M·T are shown as a dashed curve because they are assumed to be transient intermediates in this model.

the unattached cross-bridge. This assumption guaranteed that, at $x = 0$, only a small drop in free energy occurred when the cross-bridge in the 45° state detached to form the refractory state. If actin bound much weaker than ATP, a large drop in free energy would occur when the cross-bridge detached; if actin bound much more strongly than ATP, the cross-bridge would not detach at all. Since the work of Trentham and his collaborators (2, 3), Goody and his collaborators (21), and Wolcott & Boyer (55) suggested that the binding constant of ATP to myosin is about 10^{11} M^{-1} and the ATP concentration in vivo is about 10^{-3} M (7), the binding constant of actin to the cross-bridge at $x = 0$ should be about 10^8. [Note the absence of units: The binding of the cross-bridge to actin in vivo is a first-order process (10, 25).] Since the binding constant of actin to S-1 in vitro is about 10^7 M^{-1}, this model predicted that the "effective actin concentration" in vivo is about 10 M, a very high concentration.

A complete cross-bridge model must specify not only the free energy profile but also the rate constants between the states. Because there are four states in the model of Eisenberg, Hill & Chen, there are four pairs of rate constants in this model. The ratio of the forward and reverse rate constants between any two states is determined by the free energy difference between the two states (10, 25). If the free energy difference is a function of x, as it will be if one or both of the states are attached to actin, one or both of the rate constants between the two states will also be a function of x. However, the value of individual rate constants is not determined by the free energy curves. Like the free energy curves themselves, the values of these rate constants were chosen to be consistent with both biochemical and physiological data.

In addition the rate constants in this model were chosen to be consistent with the high efficiency (~50%) of muscle contraction (54). This is illustrated by the heavy solid line in Figure 3, which shows the optimal sequence of transitions that a cross-bridge might follow as an actin site makes a single "pass" by it during an isotonic contraction. Each vertical line along this path represents a transition between two states. No work is done by the cross-bridge during these transitions; work is only done when the cross-bridge in an attached state moves along x while its free energy simultaneously decreases (10, 25). Therefore, to make this cross-bridge model efficient within the limits imposed by the experimental data, the rate constants were chosen to minimize the free energy loss during transitions between states.

The key values of the rate constants in the model of Eisenberg, Hill & Chen can be discussed in terms of the path the cross-bridge follows along the heavy solid line in Figure 3. The cross-bridge first makes the transition from the refractory to the nonrefractory state ($M \cdot D \cdot Pi_R \rightarrow M \cdot D \cdot Pi_N$). The rate constant for this transition was based on the maximum actin-activated ATPase rate determined in biochemical experiments (17) and is similar to "f" in the 1957 model of A. F. Huxley (28). Following a very rapid attachment step ($M \cdot D \cdot Pi_N \rightarrow A \cdot M \cdot D \cdot Pi_N$), the cross-bridge undergoes the transition from the 90° state ($A \cdot M \cdot D \cdot Pi_N$) to the 45° state ($A \cdot M \cdot D$). The rate constants for this transition were based on the rate of recovery of force in the isometric transient as a function of the amount of release on stretch (18).

The rate of detachment of the cross-bridge from actin in this model was assumed to depend on the rate of ADP release; the subsequent rebinding of ATP and detachment of the cross-bridge were assumed to be rapid. For this reason, states $A \cdot M \cdot T$ and $A \cdot M$ (dashed curve in Figure 3) were transient intermediates in this model. To keep the cross-bridge attached throughout its power-stroke, Eisenberg, Hill & Chen assumed that the rate of ADP release from state $A \cdot M \cdot D$ was slow until the cross-bridge reached its minimum free energy at $x = 0$. At $x \leqslant 0$, the rate of ADP release was assumed to become rapid, as it is in solution. Thus the dependence of the rate of ADP release on x was similar to the x-dependence of the detachment rate constant, "g," in the 1957 cross-bridge model of A. F. Huxley (28).

Following detachment of the cross-bridge, the cross-bridge again is in the refractory state ($M \cdot D \cdot Pi_R$) ready to begin another cycle. This new cycle begins on the right side of Figure 3 as another actin site becomes available for attachment. Since one ATP molecule has been hydrolyzed, the free energy level of this new cycle is $\Delta \mu_T$ (chemical potential of ATP hydrolysis in vivo) below the first cycle shown.

The cross-bridge model of Eisenberg, Hill & Chen was reasonably successful in quantitatively matching the isometric transient data of Ford, Huxley & Simmons by assuming that the recovery of force in the isometric transient was due to the transition from the 90° to the 45° state. It also provided an explanation for the well-established relationship between the velocity of muscle contraction and the actomyosin ATPase (4): The rate-limiting transition from the refractory to the nonrefractory state determined both V_{max} of the double reciprocal plot of ATPase vs actin and a large part of the force-velocity curve.

Recent Biochemical Data

A key assumption of the cross-bridge model of Eisenberg, Hill & Chen is that, at $x = 0$, $M \cdot T$ binds very weakly to actin; this assumption is necessary to make state $A \cdot M \cdot T$ a transient intermediate, thereby enabling the cross-bridge to detach rapidly from actin. By detailed balance this assumption leads to the prediction that ATP should bind weakly to actomyosin in vitro ($K \simeq 1 \times 10^2\ M^{-1}$). Recently, this prediction has been tested by Stein et al

(50). They found that, in fact, $K \simeq 1 \times 10^7 M^{-1}$ in solution. In the same series of experiments they found that several major aspects of the Lymn-Taylor model (Figure 1B) and the refractory state model (Figure 1C) were incorrect. Most important, they found that hydrolysis of ATP in the initial Pi burst seemed to occur at about the same rate whether or not the S-1 was bound to actin. They also found that the refractory state ($M \cdot D \cdot Pi_R$), like M·T, bound weakly to actin, and the transition from the refractory to the nonrefractory state ($M \cdot D \cdot Pi_R \rightarrow M \cdot D \cdot Pi_N$) occurred at about the same rate whether or not the S-1 was bound to actin. These data led to the biochemical model shown in Figure 1D (50). The key points of this model are: First, all of the myosin states with bound phosphate (M·T, $M \cdot D \cdot Pi_R$ and $M \cdot D \cdot Pi_N$) are in rapid equilibrium with their respective actin bound states (A·M·T, $A \cdot M \cdot D \cdot Pi_R$, and $A \cdot M \cdot D \cdot Pi_N$); second, ATP hydrolysis can occur without detachment of the myosin from actin; third, a large free energy drop occurs when ATP binds to actomyosin; and fourth, as in the original refractory state model, a slow rate-limiting transition occurs after the initial Pi burst. However, in contrast to the original refractory state model, this rate-limiting step not only occurs when the S-1 is unattached to actin, but also when it is attached to actin.

The recent biochemical data of Sleep and his collaborators (47, 48) are consistent with the biochemical model shown in Figure 1D. The detailed properties of each of the steps in this model as well as controversies concerning the existence of several of the steps are discussed in a separate review focusing on the biochemical aspects of the actin-myosin interaction and its regulation (1). In the present review, we discuss the possible implications of this new biochemical model for the mechanism of cross-bridge action in vivo.

A New Cross-Bridge Model

A cross bridge model based on the biochemical scheme in Figure 1D must provide a mechanism for cyclic detachment of the cross-bridge in vivo as the muscle shortens, though ATP hydrolysis can occur in vitro with or without detachment of S-1 from actin. The cross-bridge model must also explain how the large decrease in free energy associated with ATP binding to actomyosin in vitro is utilized in vivo. A possible solution to these problems may come from data obtained with the ATP analog, 5'-adenylyl imidodiphosphate (AMP-PNP) (56), both in solution and with muscle fibers. In solution, work from many laboratories has shown that like ATP, AMP-PNP weakens the binding constant of S-1 to actin (22, 27, 37, 38). Greene & Eisenberg (23) compared the ability of AMP-PNP, ADP, and PPi to weaken the binding of S-1 to actin. They found that ADP weakened the binding about 30-fold, while PPi and AMP-PNP weakened the binding about 400-fold. Similar results for the weakening of acto·S-1 by AMP-PNP and ADP were obtained by Marston et al (39). Since Stein et al (50) found that ATP weakened the binding of S-1 to actin about 5000-fold, AMP-PNP appears to be intermediate between ATP and ADP in its ability to dissociate the acto·S-1 complex.

In their effect on the X-ray pattern in vivo AMP-PNP and PPi also appear to be intermediate between ATP and ADP (20). AMP-PNP and PPi have a marked effect on the equatorial X-ray pattern, an effect considerably greater than that of ADP but less than that of ATP. Recent work of Marston et al (38, 39) has suggested that much of this effect may be due to a change in cross-bridge angle. Their stiffness measurements suggest that, at saturating levels of AMP-PNP, most of the cross-bridges remain attached to actin. Their experiments also show that AMP-PNP causes the muscle fiber to lengthen significantly, an effect that also occurs with ADP but to a lesser extent than with AMP-PNP (38). On the basis of these data, Marston et al (39) have suggested that the X-ray pattern induced by AMP-PNP may be caused by an increase in the preferred angle of the attached cross-bridge from the 45° angle occurring in rigor to an angle closer to 90°.

Since ATP, like AMP-PNP, weakens the binding of S-1 to actin, it is possible that, like AMP-PNP, ATP also increases the preferred angle of the attached cross-bridge. However, just as ATP binds much more strongly to myosin than AMP-PNP (21, 23, 46, 53, 55), it may change the preferred angle of the cross-bridge much more than AMP-PNP—e.g. ATP may increase the preferred angle to 90°, while AMP-PNP only increases the preferred angle to about 55°. Such a small change in the preferred angle of the cross-bridge by AMP-PNP would be consistent with the data of Marston et al (39) that AMP-PNP tends to lengthen single muscle fibers only about 20 Å per half sarcomere.

Figure 4 shows a new cross-bridge model based on the biochemical scheme of Stein et al (50). The major assumption of this model is that the conformational change associated with the binding of ATP to actomyosin not only weakens the binding of actin, but also changes the preferred angle of the attached cross-bridge from 45° back to 90°. Thus, as shown in Figure 4, the free energy change associated with the binding of ATP to actomyosin is a function of x—i.e. it is sensitive to the angle of attachment of the cross-bridge. In this model the minimum free energy level of A·M·T (lower curve A·M·T in Figure 4) is markedly lower than the minimum free energy of A·M. This is consistent with the marked decrease in free energy that occurs when ATP binds to acto·S-1 in solution. In contrast, at $x = 0$ where the cross-bridge is attached at a 45° angle, there is no change in free energy when ATP binds to actomyosin. Rather, the cross-bridge in state A·M·T at a 45° angle is at a relatively high free energy—in fact, as high as the free energy of state M·T. Thus although the attached cross-bridge in state A·M·T is exerting negative force at $x = 0$, it will do so only for a brief time before it detaches from actin to form state M·T.

It is easy to see from Figure 4 that if A·M and A·M·T both had a preferred angle of 45°, a large loss of free energy would occur when ATP bound to actomyosin at $x = 0$ because a large free energy drop would occur during the change in state. By assuming that A·M·T has a preferred angle of 90°, this loss of free energy is avoided. This loss could also have been avoided by assuming that A·M·T has a preferred angle much less than 45°—e.g. 20°. However, based on the ability of AMP-PNP to cause muscle fibers to lengthen slightly by increasing the preferred angle of the cross-bridge (39), it seems more likely that ATP would increase rather than decrease the preferred angle of the cross-bridge.

The cross-bridge model shown qualitatively in Figure 4 may appear quite different from the model of Eisenberg, Hill & Chen (11) shown in Figure 3, but in fact the two models are quite similar. The heavy solid line in Figure

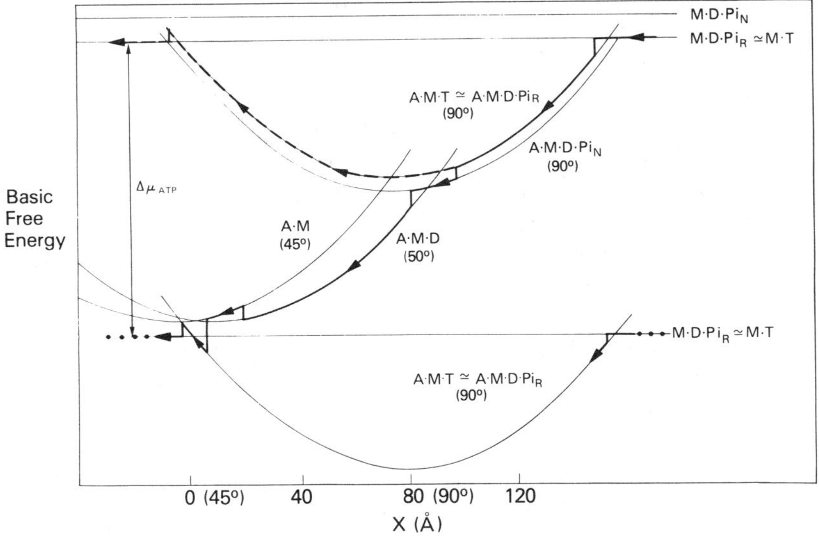

Figure 4 Basic free energy profile for the new cross-bridge model. The relative basic free energies of the cross-bridge states are plotted as a function of their axial position, x. The angle of the attached cross-bridge to actin at $x = 0$ and $x = 80$Å is indicated in parentheses on the abscissa. The preferred angles of the different cross-bridge states proposed in this model are shown beneath the given states. The heavy solid line represents the path of a nearly optimal cross-bridge cycle during an isotonic contraction. The new cycle is shown to start again in the lower right hand corner with the dotted arrow (←•••). The heavy dashed line shows the path of the cross-bridge if it does not make the transition A·M·D·Pi$_R$ → A·M·D·Pi$_N$ (see text).

4 shows the more or less optimal sequence of transitions that a cross-bridge might follow as an actin site makes a single "pass" by it during an isotonic contraction. The cross-bridge in the refractory state rapidly attaches to actin in a region where it exerts positive force; the cross-bridge then makes the slow rate-limiting transition to the nonrefractory state. Following this transition, the conformational change associated with Pi release occurs rapidly at about $x \approx 80$Å. Just as the conformational change induced by ATP changes the preferred angle of the cross-bridge from 45° to 90°, so conversely the conformational changes associated with Pi and ADP release return the cross-bridge to a preferred angle of 45°. The step involving release of Pi could be fast and could thus account for the isometric transient data (18), just as it does in the model of Eisenberg, Hill & Chen (11).

Since the data of Marston et al (38) suggest that ADP lengthens the muscle fiber, although to a lesser extent than AMP-PNP, we have suggested in this model that the release of Pi returns the preferred angle of the cross-bridge to only about 50°. ADP release is then necessary before the cross-bridge returns all the way to a preferred angle of 45°. This means that state A·M·D is more stable than state A·M until the cross-bridge rotates over to about $x \simeq 0$. In regions of x where state A·M·D is more stable than state A·M, ADP might well be slow to detach from the cross-bridge. Thus the ability of ADP to increase slightly the preferred angle of the cross-bridge may provide a mechanism for keeping the cross-bridge attached to actin until it has nearly completed its power-stroke.

Following release of ADP, the cross-bridge rebinds ATP to form state A·M·T with a preferred angle of 90°. However, the cross-bridge in state A·M·T exerts negative force only briefly before it detaches and is ready to begin a new cross-bridge cycle. The occurrence of rapid equilibria between weakly attached and unattached states in vitro supports the possibility that, in vivo, the attached cross-bridge in state A·M·T will rapidly detach from actin when its free energy exceeds that of the unattached cross-bridge in state M·T. However, this detachment will only occur when the muscle is shortening. In the isometric state the cross-bridge will not detach as it hydrolyzes ATP. It will oscillate between the various attached states and at $x < 80$ Å will spend most of its time in state A·M·D exerting positive force.

Note that if the attached cross-bridge does not make the transition from the refractory to the nonrefractory state ($\mathrm{A{\cdot}M{\cdot}D{\cdot}Pi_R} \rightarrow \mathrm{A{\cdot}M{\cdot}D{\cdot}Pi_N}$), which is the rate-limiting step in the cycle, it will remain attached to actin as it rotates all the way to $x = 0$ (heavy dashed line). It will then rapidly detach from actin just as M·T rapidly detaches from actin in the lower part of the cycle. Since the cross-bridge will rapidly detach without having hydrolyzed ATP or performed net work, the net effect will be the same as if the cross-bridge had never attached to actin at all. Thus, as in the model of Eisenberg, Hill & Chen (11), the rate-limiting transition from the refractory to the nonrefractory state will be a major determinant of the velocity of muscle contraction because it controls the ability of the cross-bridge to go through a complete work cycle. However, the model of Eisenberg, Hill & Chen predicted that the number of attached cross-bridges will decrease markedly as the shortening velocity increases. In contrast, with the new model the number of attached cross-bridges will probably not change much as the shortening velocity increases because the refractory state is weakly attached to actin. Therefore, the new model may be more consistent with X-ray measurements on contracting frog muscle, which suggest that there is little, if any, change in the number of attached cross-bridges as the velocity increases (43).

CONCLUSION

Kinetic models have become increasingly complex, and biochemists have become more sophisticated in their understanding of how cross-bridge elasticity may be related to the biochemical kinetic models. Paradoxically, the recent model of Stein et al (50) is similar to the earlier model of Eisenberg et al (16) in that the cross-bridge is not required to detach from actin during the hydrolysis of ATP. However, we now understand that the presence of cross-bridge elasticity in combination with the x-dependence of the rate constants and rapid equilibria between attached and detached states could explain cross-bridge detachment during muscle shortening without a mandatory detachment step. Perhaps the biochemical concept of rapid equilibria combined with the physiological concept of cross-bridge elasticity will prove to be useful in understanding the mechanism of cross-bridge action.

ACKNOWLEDGMENT

We would like to thank Dr. Terrell Hill for many helpful discussions—in particular, regarding the new cross-bridge model presented in this review.

Literature Cited

1. Adelstein, R. S., Eisenberg, E. 1980. *Ann. Rev. Biochem.* In press
2. Bagshaw, C. R., Eccleston, J. F. Eckstein, F., Goody, R. S., Gutfreund, H., Trentham, D. R. 1974. Two-step process of adenosine triphosphate association and adenosine diphosphate dissociation. *Biochem. J.* 141:351–64
3. Bagshaw, C. R., Trentham, D. R. 1973. The reversibility of ATP cleavage by myosin. *Biochem. J.* 133:323–28
4. Bárány, M. 1967. ATPase activity of myosin correlated with speed of muscle shortening. In *The Contractile Process,* pp. 197–216. Boston: Little, Brown & Company. 299 pp.
5. Chock, S. P., Chock, P. B., Eisenberg, E. 1976. Pre-steady-state kinetic evidence for a cyclic interaction of myosin subfragment one with actin during the hydrolysis of ATP. *Biochemistry* 15: 3244–53
6. Civan, M. M., Podolsky, R. J. 1966. Contraction kinetics of striated muscle fibers following quick changes in load. *J. Physiol. London* 184:511–34
7. Dawson, M. J., Gadian, P. G., Wilkie, D. R. 1978. Muscular fatigue investigated by phosphorus nuclear magnetic resonance. *Nature* 274:861–66
8. Eisenberg, E., Dobkin, L., Kielley, W. W. 1972. Binding of actin to heavy meromyosin in the absence of ATP. *Biochemistry* 11:4657–60
9. Eisenberg, E., Dobkin, L., Kielley, W. W. 1972. Heavy meromyosin: evidence for a refractory state unable to bind to actin in the presence of ATP. *Proc. Natl. Acad. Sci. USA* 69:667–71
10. Eisenberg, E., Hill, T. L. 1978. A cross-bridge model of muscle contraction. *Prog. Biophys. Mol. Biol.* 33:55–82
11. Eisenberg, E., Hill, T. L., Chen, Y. 1980. *Biophys. J.* In press
12. Eisenberg, E., Kielley, W. W. 1972. Evidence for a refractory state of HMM and S-1 unable to bind to actin in the presence of ATP. *Cold Spring Harbor Symp. Quant. Biol.* 37:145–52
13. Eisenberg, E., Moos, C. 1968. The ATPase activity of acto-heavy meromyosin. A kinetic analysis of actin activation. *Biochemistry* 7:1486–89
14. Eisenberg, E., Moos, C. 1970. Binding of adenosine triphosphate to myosin, heavy myosin, and subfragment 1. *Biochemistry* 9:4106–10
15. Eisenberg, E., Moos, C. 1970. Actin activation of heavy meromyosin adenosine triphosphatase. *J. Biol. Chem.* 245:2451–56
16. Eisenberg, E., Zobel, C. R., Moos, C. 1968. Subfragment 1 of myosin: adenosine triphosphatase activation by actin. *Biochemistry* 7:3186–94
17. Ferenczi, M., Homsher, E., Trentham, D. R., Weeds, A. G. 1978. Preparation and characterization of frog muscle myosin subfragment-1 and actin. *Biochem. J.* 171:155–62
18. Ford, L. E., Huxley, A. F., Simmons, R. M. 1977. Tension responses to sudden length change in stimulated frog muscle fibres near slack length. *J. Physiol.* 269:441–515
19. Fraser, A. B., Eisenberg, E., Kielley, W. W., Carlson, F. D. 1975. The interaction of heavy meromyosin and subfragment 1 with actin. Physical measurements in the presence and absence of adenosine triphosphate. *Biochemistry* 14:2207–13
20. Goody, R. S., Barrington-Leigh, J., Mannherz, H. G., Tregear, R. T., Rosenbaum, G. 1976. X-ray titration of binding of β-α-imido-ATP to myosin in insect flight muscle. *Nature* 262:613–15
21. Goody, R. S., Hofmann, W., Mannherz, H. G. 1977. The binding constant of ATP to myosin S1 fragment. *Eur. J. Biochem.* 78:317–24
22. Greene, L. E., Eisenberg, E. 1978. Formation of a ternary complex: actin, 5'-adenylyl imidodiphosphate, and the subfragments of myosin. *Proc. Natl. Acad. Sci. USA* 75:54–58
23. Greene, L. E., Eisenberg, E. 1980. Dissociation of the actin subfragment-one complex by 5'-adenylyl imidodiphosphate, ADP, and PP_i. *J. Biol. Chem.* In press
24. Greene, L. E., Eisenberg, E. 1980. The binding of heavy meromyosin to F-actin. *J. Biol. Chem.* In press
25. Hill, T. L. 1974. Theoretical formalism for the sliding filament model of contraction of striated muscle. Part I. *Prog. Biophys. Mol. Biol.* 28:267–340
26. Hill, T. L. 1977. *Free Energy Transduction in Biology.* NY: Academic Press. 229 pp.
27. Hofmann, W., Goody, R. S. 1978. The ternary complex formed between actin, myosin subfragment 1 and ACT (β,γ -NH). *FEBS Lett.* 89:169–72
28. Huxley, A. F. 1957. Muscle structure and theories of contraction. *Prog. Biophys. Biophys. Chem.* 7:255–318
29. Huxley, A. F. 1974. Muscular contraction. *J. Physiol. London* 243:1–43
30. Huxley, A. F., Simmons, R. M. 1971. Proposed mechanism of force genera-

tion in striated muscle. *Nature* 233: 533–38

31. Huxley, H. E. 1969. The mechanism of muscular contraction. *Science* 164: 1356–66
32. Lowey, S., Slayter, H. S., Weeds, A., Baker, H. 1969. Substructure of the myosin molecule I. Subfragments of myosin by enzymatic degradation. *J. Mol. Biol.* 42:1–29
33. Lowey, S., Luck, S. M. 1969. Equilibrium binding of ADP to myosin. *Biochemistry* 8:3195–99
34. Lymn, R. W., Taylor, E. W. 1970. Transient state phosphate production in the hydrolysis of nucleoside triphosphates my myosin. *Biochemistry* 9: 2975–83
35. Lymn, R. W., Taylor, E. W. 1971. Mechanism of adenosine triphosphate hydrolysis by actomyosin. *Biochemistry* 10:4617–24
36. Margossian, S. S., Lowey, S. 1973. Substructure of the myosin molecule IV. Interactions of myosin and its subfragments with adenosine triphosphate and F-actin. *J. Mol. Biol.* 74:313–30
37. Margossian, S. S., Lowey, S. 1978. Interaction of myosin subfragments with F-actin. *Biochemistry* 17:5431–39
38. Marston, S. B., Rodger, C. D., Tregear, R. T. 1976. Changes in muscle crossbridges when β,γ-imido-ATP binds to myosin. *J. Mol. Biol.* 104:263–76
39. Marston, S. B., Tregear, R. T., Rodger, C. D., Clarke, M. L. 1978. Coupling between the enzymatic site and the mechanical output of muscle. *J. Mol. Biol.* 128:111–26
40. Mulhern, S. A., Eisenberg, E. 1976. Further studies on the interaction of actin with heavy meromyosin and subfragment 1 in the presence of ATP. *Biochemistry* 15:5702–8
41. Nauss, K. M., Kitagawa, S., Gergely, J. 1969. Pyrophosphate binding to and adenosine triphosphatase activity of myosin and its proteolytic fragments. *J. Biol. Chem.* 244:755–65
42. Offer, G., Elliott, A. 1978. Can a myosin molecule bind to two actin filaments? *Nature* 271:325–29
43. Podolsky, R. J., St. Onge, R., Yu, L., Lymn, R. W. 1976. X-ray diffraction of actively shortening muscle. *Proc. Natl. Acad. Sci. USA* 64:504–8
44. Reedy, M. K. 1967. Cross-bridges and periods in insect flight muscle. *Am. Zool.* 7:465–81
45. Reedy, M. K., Holmes, K. C., Tregear, R. T. 1965. Induced changes in orientation of the cross-bridges of glycerinated insect flight muscle. *Nature* 207: 1276–80
46. Schliselfeld, L. H. 1974. Binding of adenylyl imidodiphosphate, an analog of adenosine triphosphate, to myosin and heavy meromyosin. *J. Biol. Chem.* 249:4985–89
47. Sleep, J. A., Boyer, P. D. 1978. Effect of actin concentration on the intermediate oxygen of myosin; relation to the refractory state and the mechanism of exchange. *Biochemistry* 17:5417–22
48. Sleep, J. A., Hutton, R. L. 1978. Actin mediated release of ATP from a myosin-ATP complex. *Biochemistry* 17: 5423–30
49. Sleep, J. A., Taylor, E. W. 1976. Intermediate states of actomyosin adenosine triphosphatase. *Biochemistry* 15: 5813–17
50. Stein, L. A., Schwarz, R., Chock, P. B., Eisenberg, E. 1979. The mechanism of the actomyosin ATPase: evidence that ATP hydrolysis can occur without dissociation of the actomyosin complex. *Biochemistry* 18:3895–909
51. Szentkirályi, E. M., Oplatka, A. 1969. On the formation and stability of the enzymically active complexes of heavy meromyosin with actin. *J. Mol. Biol.* 43:551–66
52. Tokiwa, T., Tonomura, Y. 1965. The pre-steady state of the myosin adenosine triphosphate system. *J. Biochem. Tokyo* 57:616–23
53. Wagner, P. D., Yount, R. G. 1975. The covalent modification of myosin's proteolytic fragments by a purine disulfide analog of adenosine triphosphate. Reaction at a binding site other than the active site. *Biochemistry* 14: 5156–62
54. Wilkie, D. R. 1975. Muscle as a thermodynamic machine. *Ciba Found. Symp.* 31 (NS): 327–35
55. Wolcott, R. G., Boyer, P. D. 1974. The reversal of the myosin and actomyosin ATPase reactions and the free energy of ATP binding to myosin. *Biochem. Biophys. Res. Commun.* 57:709–16
56. Yount, R. G., Ojala, D., Babcock, D. 1971. Interaction of P-N-P and P-C-P analogs of adenosine triphosphate with heavy meromyosin, myosin, and actomyosin. *Biochemistry* 10:2490–95

CARDIOVASCULAR PHYSIOLOGY

Ann. Rev. Physiol. 1980. 42:311–24

RHEOLOGY AND HEMODYNAMICS

❖1270

Giles R. Cokelet

Department of Radiation Biology and Biophysics, School of Medicine and Dentistry, University of Rochester, Rochester, New York 14642

INTRODUCTION

Much of the Third International Congress of Biorheology in La Jolla, California (1978) was devoted to blood rheology and hemodynamics. The dynamic, time-dependent rheological properties of blood and the unsteady flow of blood were among the most active topics of interest. Consequently, the blood rheology portion of this review is devoted to those topics.

Uncertainty still exists in the methods for making predictions of actual blood flow behavior from macroscopic rheological parameters. This is especially true for microvascular vessels and networks of vessels. The hemodynamics section here centers on that topic.

BLOOD RHEOLOGY

The steady-flow rheological properties of blood are generally well-understood, in terms of both numerical values and flow mechanisms. However, the in vivo flow is unsteady, both because the heart forces the flow in an unsteady manner and because a volumetric element of blood travels through a complex network of vessels of varying geometric qualities (lumen shape, diameter, single vessels, bifurcations, valves, etc) and so sees constantly varying conditions. Can the unsteady blood flow be predicted by solution of equations of motion that utilize steady-flow rheological relationships?

The unsteady flow will not be predictable from steady rheological data if (*a*) the characteristic time for the variations in the flow are comparable

0066-4278/80/0315-0311$01.00

to or smaller than the time constants of the molecular or particulate processes that occur during flow, and/or (*b*) the fluid is significantly elastic.

Two relevant flow processes occur in blood: deformation of blood cells, and red cell aggregation. The time constants of these processes can be characterized from more-or-less direct observations. Micropipette tests on individual red cells (24, 63) and observation of microcirculatory blood flow (49) indicate that the characteristic erythrocyte deformation time is very short: For normal human red cells this seems to be 0.06 sec or less.

The aggregation-disaggregation process is probably not symmetrical. The factors that influence the rate of buildup of cellular aggregates include cell and aggregate collision frequency (itself a function of hematocrit and shear rate), ionic and macromolecular content of the plasma, and, to a lesser degree, such red cell parameters as shape, deformability, and surface charge. On the other hand, disaggregation depends not so much on particle collision frequency as on the rate of buildup of local stresses on the aggregates during changing flow conditions, and the shear rate.

A measure of light transmission through sheared layers of red cell suspensions (about 100 μm thick), as well as direct observation, has been used to study red cell aggregation and deformation in sheared red cell suspensions (29, 45, 46). For normal bloods, upon suddenly decreasing the shear rate from 460 sec^{-1} (where all cells are dispersed) to zero, the initial rate of aggregation is exponential with a half-time of about 3.6 sec (shorter for more strongly aggregating bloods), though the complete aggregation process takes perhaps 7–12 sec. When the shear rate is suddenly decreased from 460 sec^{-1} to 7 sec^{-1}, normal bloods show a total aggregation time of about 5–7 sec. (However, pathological bloods may show much longer aggregation times under the same conditions.)

The dynamics of red cell aggregation have also been studied by microphotographing a 10 μm layer of sheared, normal, human blood in a modified Rheogoniometer (7). In steady shear rate studies, the red cells were dispersed by shearing at 1000 sec^{-1}, and then suddenly the shear rate was decreased to a steady value between zero and 10 sec^{-1}. Again, the time required to reach a steady state of aggregation from a completely dispersed state depends on the shear rate: For stasis, several minutes are required; as shear rate increases, the required time is shortened to less than 30 sec (the minimum elapsed time between microphotographs) for shear rates of 1.0 and 10.0 sec^{-1}. These workers also observed red cell aggregation during oscillatory flow (61), in the same flow channel; at the observation point, the amplitude of the oscillatory displacement of the moving channel wall was ± 7.8 μm and frequencies varied from zero (stasis) to 10.0 Hz. From a dispersed state, most of the aggregation seems to take less than 30 sec in all cases of motion, though the nature of the aggregates seems to change slowly for times up to 1–2 min. These times may be longer than those required in bulk blood flow since only a single layer of cells is observed in this flow channel, which causes cell collision frequency to be much lower than in bulk blood.

In summary, the aggregation process for red cells in normal blood seems relatively slow. While the time required for a blood to change between aggregation states may depend in a nonsimple way on the magnitude of the shear rate change (39) and the shear rates, this process seems to take on the order of a few seconds in normal bloods.

The kinetics of disaggregation of red cells has not been as well studied. Preliminary observations (H. Schmid-Schoenbein, personal communication) indicate that disaggregation in normal blood takes place almost instantaneously when a low shear rate is suddenly increased; in pathological bloods, disaggregation times are longer.

It therefore appears that when red cell aggregation can occur, its characteristic time constant of several seconds is the governing factor in time-dependent flows; otherwise, where aggregation does not occur, the blood's characteristic time constant is governed by the cell deformation time, and normally is about 0.06 sec or less for red cells.

These times must be compared with the characteristic time constants of the unsteady, in vivo blood flow. For large variations in flow conditions, the time constants are ≈0.33–2 sec, owing to heart pulsations, but are ≈0.02–12 sec for residence times between bifurcations in microvascular vessels (19, 36). Smaller perturbations in the flow due to local variations in vessel lumen shape, lumen dimensions, and pressure probably have shorter characteristic times. The ratio of characteristic times of cell deformation and aggregation processes to characteristic times of in vivo flow conditions (a Deborah number) is large enough to raise questions, within the in vivo blood flow framework, about the utility of the often-successful engineering procedure of using steady rheological data to predict unsteady fluid flows.

If we consider a viscoelastic fluid to be one from which we can recover some of the mechanical energy put into the fluid to cause its flow, then blood has two flow mechanisms that can "store" mechanical energy during flow and release some of it when the flow-forcing mechanism is removed: (*a*) the cell aggregation process, since the dispersed state must be a higher energy state than the aggregated state, and (*b*) the cell deformation process, since the red cell membrane is known to have elastic properties [see (13) for an excellent review on red cell membrane mechanics; see (3) for some recent experimental findings]. The question is not whether or not the blood is viscoelastic, but rather whether or not the elastic contribution is significant enough for inclusion in flow models.

Even if blood could be treated (for practical purposes) as a purely viscous fluid, its rheological properties may depend not only on instantaneous values of flow parameters but also on the flow history of the blood.

Experimental Rheological Measurements

While time-constants for flow-mechanism processes can be estimated from steady flow experiments [e.g. see (11)], dynamic flows are generally more useful for getting time-dependent and/or viscoelastic rheological information. In addition to all the experimental problems associated with steady-flow rheological measurements (such as those due to capillary tube entrance lengths, fluid acceleration and red cell radial migration, sedimentation at low shear rates, and syneresis of red cells at low shear rates that causes two-phase flow in the viscometric device), difficulties arise when considering unsteady flows. In addition to obvious problems, such as those due to equipment limitations (compliance of equipment components, response characteristics of measuring elements, backlash in oscillatory devices, etc) and problems of technique (e.g. removal of invisible gas bubbles from the system), there are new problems. As an example, in oscillatory flow in capillary devices, "new" fluid is brought into the capillary from the reservoirs serving the capillary, on both the forward and back stroke; if the fluid has property time constants comparable to (or longer than) the "new" fluid residence time in the capillary, and if the volume of "new" fluid drawn into the capillary is a sizeable fraction of the total capillary volume, then it may be difficult to calculate rheological parameters for the fluid from the experimental data. Instruments that endeavor to subject all of the fluid sample simultaneously to the same flow conditions have an advantage.

Certain methods of data analysis can lead to unsatisfactory calculations of rheological properties. Assumptions about what kind of fluid blood is (e.g. a linear viscoelastic fluid) are convenient because they permit the development of equations describing the fluid-instrument behavior, even when inertial factors are significant; but they are nevertheless assumptions that must be verified. The key question with this type of assumption is whether or not the calculated rheological data can be used to describe flow in nonviscometric (or different viscometric) flows. Inertial effects are always of concern.

Thurston's experimental data on blood viscoelasticity have usually been obtained by forced oscillatory volumetric flow of fluid between two unstirred reservoirs joined by a test section consisting of 1–80 parallel vertical tubes (52, 56). The effective lengths of the tubes are determined from tests with Newtonian fluids (52), and corrections for compliance effects of instrument components are made (56). Test vessels have ranged in diameter from about 0.0440 cm to 0.70 cm. The entire hematocrit range has been covered, as well as the frequency range of 0.2–200 Hz and the root mean squared volumetric flow velocity range of about 10^{-6}–10^{-1} cm^3 sec^{-1}. The method of theoretical analysis of the data is available in several places (51, 52, 56). Pulsatile flow has also been studied (55).

In all reported studies, Thurston has detected no elastic component in the rheological properties of plasma; he reports plasma to be Newtonian fluid (54, 60).

Thurston's steady flow data for blood (54, 55, 59) show a linear (proportional) relationship between pressure drop per unit length of vessel and the volumetric flow rate for wall shear rates of less than about 1 sec^{-1}, the proportionality constant decreasing with vessel diameter. An approximate analysis (59) supports the model of two-phase flow under such conditions: a core fluid consisting of relatively undisturbed aggregates of red cells in plasma, and a wall zone where viscous flow disturbs the aggregates (not necessarily of a different hematocrit from the core blood). This is the same flow range in which the pressure-drop–flow-rate relationship for steady blood flow through horizontal tubes (of diameter 288–850 μm) depended on tube diameter (40) [an effect shown (38) to be due to red cell sedimentation], and where red cell syneresis away from surfaces occurs in viscometers (4). If syneresis of red cells is playing a role here, the red cell–poor wall layer would, on the basis of Thurston's data (59), be only about 15 μm thick, independent of tube diameter, when the overall hematocrit is 59%. Thurston (59) has extended the two-phase fluid flow model to oscillatory blood flow in tubes (both the core fluid and the boundary layer fluid are taken to be viscoelastic).

Thurston has shown (54) that, in the absence of inertial effects, the in-phase and out-of-phase (relative to the forcing volumetric flow) components of the complex shear stress are linear functions of the mean velocity gradient when the values of the velocity gradient are low; the critical gradient value depends on oscillatory frequency, increasing roughly with the square root of the frequency. In this linear region, the viscous component of the complex viscosity slowly decreases with increasing frequency; the elastic component shows complicated behavior, first increasing and then decreasing with increasing frequency. The phase angle of the complex viscosity undergoes a similar complicated behavior. Thurston has extended the linear viscoelastic model to oscillatory flow where inertial effects may be significant (56). Again, for the flow region where behavior is linear, the blood data agree with the earlier findings. A single set of relations between viscosity and frequency, and between phase angle and frequency, for flow in the linear region was used to predict the impedance and impedance angle for blood oscillatory flow in tubes with diameters of 0.094–0.70 cm; for smaller tubes, the viscosity had to be reduced (greater reduction for smaller tube) to get agreement with experimental data. The critical shear rate for the onset of nonlinearity of tube impedance occurred at approximately the same value for all tubes. The impedance phase angle was negative at low frequencies, and increased as frequency increased. Since a homogeneous, purely viscous fluid could not have negative angles, this behavior is given as strong evidence that blood is viscoelastic.

Thurston's study of pulsatile blood flow showed that the effects of steady and oscillatory flow do not combine in a linear fashion, except at very low flow rates (55). The elastic component of the oscillatory motion seems to be reduced by the steady flow. This is consistent with a flow model that gives the major mechanistic source of the elastic component of the complex viscosity to the aggregates of red cells formed at low shear rates.

Thurston has also presented studies of the role of viscoelasticity in wave propagation in the circulation (57), the effect of hematocrit variations on the linear viscoelastic parameters of blood (60), and flow mechanisms in pulsatile flow (58).

Other studies of oscillatory blood flow in tubes (8, 31, 47, 48) have reported impedance-frequency curves (31) similar to those of Thurston (56). Originally (31), the data were compared to Womersley's theory for oscillatory flow of a Newtonian fluid in a tube. The experimental hydraulic reactance agreed fairly well with the predictions for a viscous fluid of viscosity of 4 centipoise. This is not surprising: Under the flow conditions used, inertial effects dominate any reactance term. The Newtonian fluid viscosities calculated from the experimental hydraulic resistance part of the impedance varied with volumetric flow amplitude, reflecting the non-Newtonianism of blood. This practice of calculating an "equivalent viscosity" for blood (the viscosity of a Newtonian fluid that gives the same magnitude for the impedance under the same oscillatory conditions) is followed in subsequent studies (8, 47), in which the flow amplitude was held constant while the frequency was increased. Again the hydraulic reactance was predictable, but the equivalent viscosity increased with frequency. The latter finding conflicts with those of Thurston. These authors have also compared their data to a Kline-Allen fluid flow model (47, 48).

Experimental oscillatory measurements have also been made in nontubular instruments. An oscillatory concentric-cylinder viscometer was used (33) to obtain the relaxation spectrum of bloods. From the relaxation spectrum, the dynamic elastic modulus of the bloods was calculated as a function of oscillatory frequency. Red cell aggregation processes in oscillatory blood flow have time constants of about 0.8 sec or less, and blood's dynamic elastic modulus is negligible below a frequency of 1.3 rads sec^{-1}. Differences between normal and patients' bloods were judged insignificant.

Oscillatory blood flow was studied (2) in a modified Weissenberg Rheogoniometer (cone-and-plate geometry) operating at frequencies between 6×10^{-4} and 60 Hz (approximate shear rate amplitude range of of 4×10^{-3}–400 sec^{-1}). Hematocrit was varied between 45% and 95% for two types of suspensions: (*a*) red cells suspended in plasma, and (*b*) washed red cells suspended in isotonic buffered saline containing 0.5% albumin. In the former suspensions, red cell aggregation is possible at low shear rates; in the latter, aggregation does not occur at any shear rate. The viscous (in-phase) and elastic (out-of-phase) components of the complex viscosity are reported. Among the interesting findings are the following: (*a*) For hematocrits above about 80%, the elastic component of the viscosity was the same for both types of suspensions, indicating that red cell deformation in this crowded environment is the source of this elastic behavior; (*b*) at lower hematocrits, the elastic components were lower in the albumin-saline suspension (at 45% hematocrit, the ratio of values was 1:6), indicating that red cell aggregation is the more important elastic mechanism in blood at lower hematocrits and low shear rates; (*c*) for the 45% hematocrit suspensions, the elastic component of the complex viscosity of the red-cell–albumin-saline suspensions was not a function of frequency, while that of the red-cell–plasma suspension decreased with increasing frequency, apparently converging with that of the other type suspension at a frequency corresponding to a shear rate amplitude close to the critical shear rate for red cell aggregation found in steady flow viscometric studies.

A number of studies have started with a proposed constitutive equation to describe blood's rheological behavior and then have proceeded to evaluate experimentally the parameters that appear in such equations. A six-parameter, time-dependent viscous model was proposed (25, 26) for the description of thixotropic fluids. By means of a modified Weissenberg Rheogoniometer, data were obtained on torque decay with time (at a constant low shear rate) and shear-stress–shear-rate hysteresis. These were used to evaluate the parameters in the constitutive equation. Such a procedure ignores the observations that at low shear rates, red cell syneresis causes the fluid near the viscometer surfaces to become, with time, mainly plasma. An Oldroyd-type constitutive equation has been proposed (9, 10, 42) and the parameters in it have been evaluated by determining the conditions under which Taylor vortices are formed in a concentric-cylinder viscometer. Predicted steady and oscillatory viscometric behavior for blood was then compared with experimental data: The predicted and experimental behaviors are qualitatively similar. Their use (9) of their constitutive equation to predict torque-time behavior of blood in suddenly started Couette viscometers at very low shear rates is not proof of its validity: Red cell syneresis under these conditions will give the same behavior (4).

Summary

The mechanisms of red cell aggregation and cell deformation can impart viscoelastic behavior to blood: At very high hematocrits, the cell deformation mechanism dominates; at physiological and low hematocrits, red cell aggregation dominates at low shear rates. At physiological hematocrits, the viscoelastic behavior may be linear at low shear rates, where the elastic component of the complex viscosity may be comparable in magnitude to the viscous component; in the higher shear rate region, where red cell aggregation is less extensive or absent, blood behavior is nonlinear, and the elastic component becomes less significant. The nonadditivity of steady and oscillatory flow data for prediction of pulsatile flow behavior is indicative of the importance of the mean shear rate and the kinetics of the red cell aggregation-disaggregation processes in governing pulsatile blood flow. While oscillatory measurements will be useful in assessing rheological parameters that may give insight into the fundamental aspects of flow of normal and pathological bloods, it is not clear that the elastic component of the complex viscosity of blood will be of significance in physiological pulsatile flow. Many interesting questions remain to be answered, such as the question raised by the finding (6) that normal stress differences were not detectable for blood under low shear rates. Judging from the number of papers presented at the Third International Congress of Biorheology,[1] we can look forward to considerable activity in this area.

HEMODYNAMICS

We hope to be able eventually to predict local and overall (organ) blood flow parameters through a network analysis. Such analyses have been attempted, based on limited information, and have been qualitatively successful (14, 21, 35, 36). However, the pieces of the puzzle remain incompletely understood.

Blood Flow in Single Vessels

One of the most important parameters governing blood flow in small vessels is the hematocrit of the blood in the vessel (H_T). Considerable experimental work has been done to determine how H_T varies with vessel diameter. Recent work on this problem (1, 16–18, 23) has extended the information

[1]Abstracts may be found in *Biorheology* 15(5/G):447–96.

to tubes with dimensions comparable to in vivo capillaries but has not resolved differences among reported results.

Steady red cell suspension flow in tubes 3.3–95 μm in diameter has been studied recently (15–18). Among the variables measured were the average hematocrits of the blood in the feed reservoir (H_F), in the tube (H_T), and flowing out the tube exit (H_D); tube dimensions; blood flow rates and pressures. Two hematocrit ratios are of interest: H_D/H_F, because it is an indication of red cell screening at the tube entrance, and H_T/H_D, because it is a measure of vessel hematocrit reduction due to differences in average red cell and plasma velocities (Fahraeus effect). Figure 1 summarizes data (16) for red cells suspended in Ringers-Tyrode solution and not only indicates the type of data obtained but, by a comparison with similar data obtained for red-cell–plasma suspensions (5), shows the range of apparent differences in data found by various investigators. Different values of H_T/H_D have been obtained by various investigators for a given tube diameter, and measures of the dependency of these values on blood velocity in the tube are markedly different. Some of these differences may be easy to explain. For example, because of the technique used to measure H_T in the 23 and 15 μm micron tubes, our values of H_T/H_D for these two sizes of tube may be slightly low. On the other hand, the failure of Gaehtgens and co-workers to find a flow rate dependency in tubes with diameters below 15

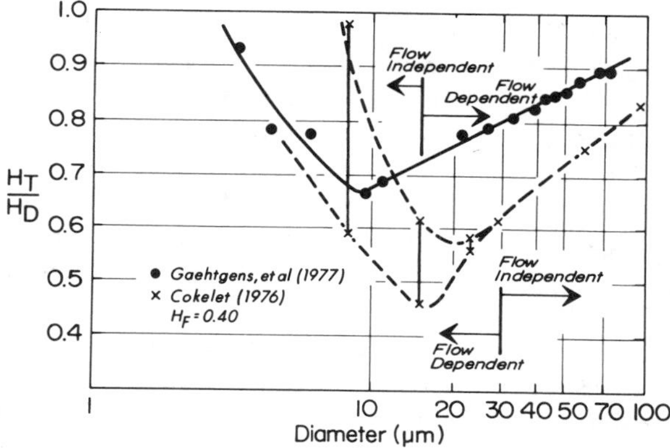

Figure 1 A comparison of data: the ratio of the average hematocrit of the red cell suspension in the tube to the average hematocrit of the suspension flowing out of the tube as a function of tube diameter. Note the differences in dependency on suspension velocity. The vertical lines connecting the crosses for small tubes show H_T/H_D as a function of blood velocity; the upper crosses are for low velocities (where H_T/H_D becomes insensitive to velocity decreases) and the lower crosses are for high velocities (where H_T/H_D becomes insensitive to velocity increases).

μm microns (15, 16) may be a matter of the velocity levels used in the experiments: At high flow rates, the red cells cannot deform further with increasing flow rate, and so H_T/H_D would be independent of velocity; whereas at low flow rates, where cell shape depends on velocity, H_T/H_D would be expected to increase as velocity slows. Other differences may be due to the use of different techniques and to differences in suspensions, flow conditions, and conditions around the tube entrance. Gaehtgens et al found that in suspensions of nonaggregating red cells, H_T/H_D (in tubes with diameters above 15 μm) increases with increasing blood velocity, but in suspensions of aggregating red cells, H_T/H_D is a maximum for a given tube at a blood flow rate of about 200 tube diameters per second. The influence of velocity is largest at lower velocities, but at higher flow rates the influence of velocity is similar to that found for nonaggregating suspensions (because aggregates are not present at high flow rates in either suspension). They have also investigated the influence of flow conditions at the tube entrance. The blood velocity in the feed reservoir also exerts an influence on conditions in the tube, especially in the cases of suspensions in which red cell aggregation can occur (16). These types of measurements are performed to help establish hematocrit relationships between vessels in the microcirculation [most likely applicable to the "capillary–thoroughfare channel" situation described by Johnson (28) rather than to the "capillary-capillary" bifurcation arrangement] and to determine how the pressure-flow relationship for blood in small vessels can be predicted.

Yen & Fung (66) have studied the same problem in a scaled-up model in which they attempted to make the values of all pertinent dimensionless groups comparable to in vivo capillary flow values. In agreement with the findings mentioned above, H_T was found to be a function of flow conditions at the tube entrance. However, the screening effect (H_D/H_F) was not a monotonic function of fluid velocity in the tube, and the H_T/H_D ratio is higher than expected from the work done with real red cells. Perhaps this partly reflects differences in the nature of deformation and aggregation of real red cells and model "cells."

Krishnakumar et al (30) have recently studied pulsatile blood flow in 65 and 78 μm tubes. Their results can be interpreted to mean that in pulsatile flow (under their experimental conditions) the time-averaged hematocrit parameters are the same as the steady flow values for the same mean flow velocities.

These studies have considered only the red cell aspects of flow in single vessels. In the microcirculation, the white cells, being larger and less deformable than the red cells, can exert an influence on blood flow that is much out of proportion to their number. Schmid-Schoenbein and co-workers (44) have been studying white and red cell flow interactions in rabbit ear chambers and in large-scale models of a capillary-postcapillary venule system. Because the white cells travel more slowly through capillaries than red cells, red cells accumulate on the upstream side of white cells in capillaries; downstream from the white cells, red cells are depleted. When the white cell enters the postcapillary venule and the vessel diameter expands so that a red cell can squeeze past the white cell, the white cell is displaced to the venule wall (and kept there) by the hydrodynamic action of the passing red cells. Measurements of pressure drops, velocities, and other parameters are being made; such information is needed. Recent discussions of leukocyte flow behavior in the microcirculation can be found in (37) and (43).

A recent in vivo finding (H. H. Lipowsky, S. Usami, S. Chien, unpublished manuscript) is that in 25–47 μm diameter vessels, the pressure-flow relationship can be predicted from in vitro rheological data, provided the actual in vivo vessel hematocrit is used as the pertinent hematocrit variable. The range of utility of this finding must be established, but the finding gives significant support to the use of predictive flow relations based on in vitro work.

Mathematical models of blood flow in microvascular-size single vessels continue to be made more realistic, though the older models (e.g. 50) continue to be useful. Models of capillary flow of red cells have been reported recently (22, 68) in which the axially symmetrical shape of the red cells is developed during computer-solution of the equations of motion. Additional aspects of single vessel flow of particle suspensions, such as the hydrodynamic development of "trains" of particles (41), are being developed.

Blood Flow through Bifurcations

The importance of blood flow through bifurcations is great in terms not only of red cell distribution but also of pressure-flow rate-time (unsteady) relations (20, 21, 27); but little quantitative information is available on the details of such flows. The flow paths of individual cells are complicated, certainly for venous (converging-flow) bifurcations (12, 34).

Model studies (64, 65, 67) have demonstrated that the most important parameters governing red cell distribution at an arterial bifurcation are the diameter ratio of the cells and vessels, the shape and deformability of the cells, the hematocrit in the main feeder vessel, and the ratio of the flow velocities in the two downstream vessels. In the case where the two downstream vessels are of equal diameter, the ratio of hematocrits in the two downstream vessels is a linear function of the ratio of the two blood velocities, up to a critical velocity ratio, above which essentially all the cells are swept into the vessel with the higher velocity. These models are applicable to Johnson's "capillary-capillary" bifurcations (28) and to the sheet-bifurcations of the alveolar circulation.

Mathematical models, such as those for pressure losses across bifurcations (62) and those on the concept of a "zone-of-influence" (32), are helpful.

Acknowledgment

The author's work has been partially supported by a research grant (HL23355) from the National Heart, Lung, and Blood Institute, NIH, and partially performed under contract with the U.S. Department of Energy at the University of Rochester Department of Radiation Biology and Biophysics. It has been assigned Report No. UR-3490-1634.

Literature Cited

1. Azelvandre, F., Oiknine, C. 1976. Effect Fahraeus et effect Fahraeus-Lindquist: Resultats experimentaux et modeles theoriques. *Biorheology* 13:325–35
2. Chien, S., King, R. G., Skalak, R., Usami, S., Copley, A. L. 1975. Viscoelastic properties of human blood and red cell suspensions. *Biorheology* 12: 341–46
3. Chien, S., Sung, K.-I. P., Skalak, R., Usami, S., Tozeren, A. 1978. Theoretical and experimental studies on viscoelastic properties of erythrocyte membrane. *Biophys. J.* 24:463–87
4. Cokelet, G. R. 1972. In *Biomechanics: Its Foundations and Objectives,* ed. Y. C. Fung, N. Perrone, M. Anliker, pp. 63–103. Englewood Cliffs, NJ: Prentice-Hall. 641 pp.
5. Cokelet, G. R. 1976. In *Microcirculation,* ed. J. Grayson, W. Zingg, 1:9–31. NY: Plenum. 420 pp.
6. Copley, A. L., King, R. G. 1975. On the viscoelasticity of anticoagulated whole human blood in steady shear as tested by rheogoniometric measurements of normal forces. *Biorheology* 12:5–10
7. Copley, A. L., King, R. G., Chien, S., Usami, S., Skalak, R., Huang, C. R. 1975. Microscopic observations of viscoelasticity of human blood in steady and oscillatory shear. *Biorheology* 12:257–63
8. Coulter, N. A. Jr., Singh, M. 1971. Frequency dependence of blood viscosity in oscillatory flow. *Biorheology* 8:115–24
9. Deutsch, S., Phillips, W. M. 1976. An interpretation of low strain rate blood viscosity measurements: a continuum approach. *Biorheology* 13:297–307
10. Deutsch, S., Phillips, W. M. 1977. The use of the Taylor-Couette stability problem to validate a constitutive equation for blood. *Biorheology* 14:253–66
11. Elbirli, B., Shaw, M. T. 1978. Time constants from shear viscosity data. *J. Rheol.* 22(5):561–70
12. El Masry, O. A., Feuerstein, I. A., Round, G. F. 1978. Experimental evaluation of streamline patterns and separated flows in a series of branching vessels with implications for atherosclerosis and thrombosis. *Circ. Res.* 43(4):608–18
13. Evans, E. A., Hochmuth, R. M. 1978. In *Current Topics in Membranes and Transport,* ed. F. Bronner, A. Kleinzeller, 10:1–63. NY: Academic
14. Fletcher, J. E. 1978. Mathematical modeling of the microcirculation. *Math. Biosci.* 38:159–202
15. Gaehtgens, P. 1978. *Proc. Third Int. Congr. Biorheol.,* La Jolla, p. 70. (Abstr.)
16. Gaehtgens, P., Albrecht, K. H., Kreutz, F. 1977. Capillary hematocrit as a function of screening and Fahraeus effect. Presented at Ann. Meet. Am. Inst. Chem. Eng., 70th, New York
17. Gaehtgens, P., Albrecht, K. H., Kreutz, F. 1978. Fahraeus effect and cell screening during tube flow of human blood. I. Effect of variation of flow rate. *Biorheology* 15:147–54
18. Gaehtgens, P., Kreutz, F., Albrecht, K. H. 1978. Fahraeus effect and cell screening during tube flow of human

blood. II. Effect of dextran-induced cell aggregation. *Biorheology* 15:155–61

19. Gaehtgens, P., Meiselman, H. J., Wayland, H. 1970. Erythrocyte flow velocities in mesenteria microvessels of the cat. *Microvasc. Res.* 2(2):151–62
20. Gross, J. F. 1978. The significance of pulsatile microhemodynamics. In *Microcirculation,* ed. G. Kaley, B. M. Altura, I:365–90. Baltimore: University Park Press. 528 pp.
21. Gross, J. F., Intaglietta, M. 1973. Effects of morphology and structural properties on microvascular hemodynamics. *Bibl. Anat.* 11:532–39
22. Gupta, B. B., Natarajan, R., Seshadri, V. 1976. Analysis of blood flow in capillaries by finite element method. *Microvasc. Res.* 12:91–100
23. Gupta, B. B., Seshadri, V. 1977. Flow of red blood cell suspensions through narrow tubes. *Biorheology* 14:133–43
24. Hochmuth, R. M., Worthy, P. R., Evans, E. A. 1979. Red cell extensional recovery and the determination of membrane viscosity. *Biophys. J.* 26(1): 101–14
25. Huang, C. R., Fabisiak, W. 1976. Viscosity and viscoelasticity of blood systems. *Thromb. Res.* 8:(Suppl. II) 1–8
26. Huang, C. R., Siskovic, N., Robertson, R. W., Fabisiak, W., Smitherberg, E. H., Copley, A. L. 1975. Quantitative characterization of thixotropy of whole human blood. *Biorheology* 12:279–82
27. Intaglietta, M. 1976. Pressure-flow relationships in the *in-vivo* microcirculation. In *Microcirculation,* ed. J. Grayson, W. Zingg, 1:71–76. NY: Plenum
28. Johnson, P. C. 1971. Red cell separation in the mesenteric capillary network. *Am. J. Physiol.* 221(1):99–104
29. Klose, H. J., Volger, E., Brechtelsbauer, H., Heinich, L., Schmid-Schoenbein, H. 1972. Microrheology and light transmission of blood. I. The photometric effects of red cell aggregation and red cell orientation. *Pflügers Arch.* 333: 126–39
30. Krishnakumar, C. K., Rovick, A. A., Lavan, Z. 1978. The effect of pressure pulsations on the Fahraeus-Lindquist effect. *Microvasc. Res.* 15:245–49
31. Kung, A. L., Coulter, N. A. Jr. 1967. Non-Newtonian behavior of blood in oscillatory flow. *Biophys. J.* 7:25–36
32. Lefort, M., Stoltz, J. F., Larcan, A. 1974. Etude des embranchements du lit vasculaire premiere approche a l'aide de la zone d'influence. *Biorheology* 11: 79–86
33. Lessner, A., Zahavi, J., Silberberg, A., Frei, E. H., Dreyfus, F. 1971. The viscoelastic properties of whole blood. In *Theoretical and Clinical Hemorheology,* ed. H. H. Hartert, A. L. Copley, pp. 194–205. NY: Springer. 411 pp.
34. Levine, R., Goldsmith, H. 1977. Particle behavior in flow through small bifurcations. *Microvasc. Res.* 14:319–44
35. Lipowsky, H. H., Zweifach, B. W. 1974. Network analysis of microcirculation of cat mesentery. *Microvasc. Res.* 7:73–83
36. Mayrovitz, H. N., Wiedeman, M. P., Noordergraaf, A. 1975. Microvascular hemodynamic variations accompanying microvessel dimensional changes. *Microvasc. Res.* 10(3):322–39
37. Mayrovitz, H. N., Weideman, M. P., Tuma, R. F. 1977. Factors influencing leukocyte adherence in microvessels. *Thromb. Haemostas. Stuttg.* 38:823–30
38. Meiselman, H. J. 1965. *Some physical and rheological properties of human blood.* ScD thesis. Mass. Inst. Technol., Cambridge, Mass. 328 pp.
39. Mercer, H. A., Weymann, H. D. 1974. Structure of thixotropic suspensions in shear flow. III. Time-dependent behavior. *Trans. Soc. Rheol.* 18(2):199–218
40. Merrill, E. W., Benis, A. M., Gilliland, E. R., Sherwood, T. K., Salzman, E. W. 1965. Pressure-flow relations of human blood in hollow fibers at low flow rates. *J. Appl. Physiol.* 20(5):954–67
41. Perlin, A., Hung, T.-K. 1978. Flow development of a train of particles in capillaries. *J. Eng. Mech. Div., Am. Soc. Civil Eng.* 104 (Em 1):49–66
42. Phillips, W. M., Deutsch, S. 1975. Toward a constitutive equation for blood. *Biorheology* 12:383–89
43. Schmid-Schoenbein, G. W., Fung, Y. C., Zweifach, B. W. 1975. Vascular endothelium-leukocyte interaction. *Circ. Res.* 36:173
44. Schmid-Schoenbein, G. W., Usami, S., Chien, S. 1978. *Proc. Third Int. Congr. of Biorheol.,* La Jolla, p. 136. (Abstr.)
45. Schmid-Schoenbein, H. 1976. In *Cardiovascular Physiology II,* ed. A. C. Guyton, A. W. Cowley Jr., pp. 1–62. Baltimore: University Park Press. 393 pp.
46. Schmid-Schoenbein, H., Volger, E., Klose, H. J. 1972. Microrheology and light transmission of blood. II. The photometric quantification of red cell aggregation formation and dispersion in flow. *Pflügers Arch.* 333:140–55
47. Singh, M., Balakrishman, S. 1974. Viscosity of oscillating non-Newtonian fluids—an empirical approach as ap-

plied to blood. *Biorheology* 11:351–53
48. Singh, M., Coulter, N. A. Jr. 1974. Frequency invariance of constitutive parameters of blood in oscillatory flow. *Biorheology* 11:51–59
49. Skalak, R., Branemark, P.-I. 1969. Deformation of red blood cells in capillaries. *Science* 164:717–19
50. Skalak, R., Chen, P. H., Chein, S. 1972. Effect of hematocrit and rouleaux on apparent viscosity in capillaries. *Biorheology* 9:67–82
51. Thurston, G. B. 1960. Theory of oscillation of a viscoelastic fluid in a circular tube. *J. Acoust. Soc. Am.* 32:210–13
52. Thurston, G. B. 1961. Measurement of the acoustic impedance of a viscoelastic fluid in a circular tube. *J. Acoust. Soc. Am.* 33:1091–95
53. Thurston, G. B. 1972. Viscoelasticity of human blood. *Biophys. J.* 12:1205–17
54. Thurston, G. B. 1973. Frequency and shear rate dependence of viscoelasticity of human blood. *Biorheology* 10:375–81
55. Thurston, G. B. 1975. Elastic effects in pulsatile blood flow. *Microvasc. Res.* 9:145–57
56. Thurston, G. B. 1976. The effects of frequency of oscillatory flow on the impedance of rigid, blood-filled tubes. *Biorheology* 13:191–99
57. Thurston, G. B. 1976. Effects of viscoelasticity of blood on wave propagation in the circulation. *J. Biomech.* 9:13–20
58. Thurston, G. B. 1976. Blood viscoelasticity and the vessel wall in pulsatile flow. In *Blood Vessels: Problems Arising at the Borders of Natural and Artificial Blood Vessels,* ed. S. Effert, J. D. Meyer-Erkelenz, pp. 105–11. Berlin: Springer
59. Thurston, G. B. 1976. The viscosity and viscoelasticity of blood in small diameter tubes. *Microvasc. Res.* 11:133–46
60. Thurston, G. B. 1978. Effects of hematocrit on blood viscoelasticity and in establishing normal values. *Biorheology* 15:239–49
61. Usami, S., King, R. G., Chien, S., Skalak, R., Huang, C. R., Copley, A. L. 1975. Microcinephotographic studies on red cell aggregation in steady and oscillatory shear—a note. *Biorheology* 12:323–25
62. Vawter, D., Fung, Y. C., Zweifach, B. 1974. Distribution of blood flow and pressure from a microvessel into a branch. *Microvasc. Res.* 8:44–52
63. Waugh, R., Evans, E. A. 1976. Viscoelastic properties of erythrocyte membranes of different vertebrate animals. *Microvasc. Res.* 12:291–304
64. Yen, R. T. 1978. Effect of blood rheology on hematocrit distribution in pulmonary sheet flow. *Biorheology* 15: 523–31
65. Yen, R. T., Fung, Y.-C. 1973. Model experiments on apparent blood viscosity and hematocrit in pulmonary alveoli. *J. Appl. Physiol.* 35(4):510–17
66. Yen, R. T., Fung, Y.-C. 1977. Inversion of Fahraeus effect and effect of mainstream flow on capillary hematocrit. *J. Appl. Physiol.* 42(4):578–86
67. Yen, R. T., Fung, Y.-C. 1978. Effect of velocity distribution on red cell distribution in capillary blood vessels. *Am. J. Physiol.* 235(2):H251–57
68. Zarda, P. R., Chien, S., Skalak, R. 1977. Interaction of viscous incompressible fluid with an elastic body. In *Computational Methods for Fluid–Structure Interaction Problems—AMD Vol. 26,* ed. T. Belytschko, T. L. Geers, pp. 65–82. NY: Am. Soc. Mech. Eng.

Ann. Rev. Physiol. 1980. 42:325–36

TRANSPORT PATHWAYS IN CAPILLARIES—IN SEARCH OF PORES

❖1271

Magnus Bundgaard

Institute of Medical Physiology, Department A, University of Copenhagen, The Panum Institute, DK-2200 Copenhagen N, Denmark

INTRODUCTION

The existence of minute pores in the capillary wall was deduced from experimental results with low molecular weight probes of various sizes (46). It was not expected that they would be demonstrable in morphological studies. The situation changed completely when ultrastructural studies of the capillary wall permitted a theoretical resolution down to less than 10 Å. However, no perforations uniformly distributed with the appropriate density of 10 μm^{-2} and diameters of 70–90 Å could be seen. A long and cumbersome series of attempts to identify the pores (or slits) has examined (*a*) the junctions between endothelial cells, (*b*) transcellular channels, (*c*) fenestrae, (*d*) transporting vesicles, and (*e*) leaks. That the pores might be found in structurally poorly defined regions such as the endocapillary layer and basement membrane has been submitted to serious investigation only in the capillaries of the kidney glomerulus (15, 51), where it turns out that the size-discriminating structure lies outside the capillary wall.

This critical overview of the data and opinions from recent years emphasizes the evaluation of ultrastructural data. The simplicity of the Pappenheimer pore theory (46) challenges morphologists to identify the structural equivalents of the hypothetical small and large pores.

The numerous problems of ultrastructural studies should be known to physiologists so that they will not extrapolate too far from the persuasive pictures the morphologists produce. This stresses the several explanations of solute transport plausible from the structure as we know it today. The matter is not simple. Endotheliology shares the status of epitheliology,

0066-4278/80/0315-0325$01.00

where fundamental problems in explaining solute-solvent transport in terms of cells and junctions persist (20).

GENERAL PROBLEMS

Permeability varies along the microvasculature (34, 60). Thus precise knowledge of the site of specimen sampling is indispensible. In fact, however, the topographical localization of the various capillary sections between the arteriole and the venule has in most cases been unknown.

Since pore equivalents are structures the size of the smaller macromolecules, the methods of preparing the tissue for microscopy are obviously critical (denaturing of proteins, extraction of lipids and water, etc). Sjöstrand (62) found that conventional procedures gave a thickness for the mitochondrial membrane of 60 Å, while a technique minimizing denaturing and extraction gave 150 Å.

The pore equivalents may follow a tortuous path through the endothelium. Because the section thickness is 500–800 Å, tortuousity can take parts of the porous path out of the plane of section. The solution to this problem is serial sectioning, which has been used in surprisingly few instances (3).

The electron-dense markers present some methodological problems. They look convincing in pictures; but it must be remembered that in the ill-defined period between tracer administration and definitive fixation of the tissue, the tracer may diffuse by routes that are not necessarily visualized in the tissue section (38). A real problem is hidden when, for example, vesicles in the abluminal half of the endothelial cell are labelled at the same time as the pericapillary space. In immersion-fixation, the commonly used technique, an unspecified delay occurs between the administration of the fixative and the definitive fixation. The distribution of capillaries at various depths from the tissue surface adds another uncertainty to accurate timing. The study of concentration profiles of electron-dense tracers is therefore a hazardous undertaking, and a critical attitude toward such information is important. For example, within 1 sec of its exit from a pore mouth a concentration profile or front of myoglobin will have moved 1–5 μm (57); this distance can be fully covered only by at least 40 thin sections, and only one of these will actually show the pore opening.

Little attention has been paid to the purity and binding to plasma proteins of the electronmicroscopic proteinaceous tracers. Conclusions are usually based on the assumption that these circulate as monomers. However, although a highly purified microperoxidase does circulate as a monomer (58), the commercially available microperoxidase (Sigma Chemical Co.) binds heavily to plasma proteins (10).

JUNCTIONS

Following the first detailed studies (42, 45) the capillary junctions were classed as *zonulae occludentes.* Luft (37), however, demonstrated patent pathways in muscle endothelium by means of ruthenium red. The presence of this tracer even in the supposed zone of fusion suggested that the endothelial junctions were zones of contact between cell coats rather than zones of membrane fusion. Karnovsky (29, 30, 31) advocated the view that the junctions are *maculae occludentes,* with gaps about 40 Å wide between the maculae. The latter proposal has been taken seriously by several physiologists, who have made quantitative calculations of the permeability of the small pore system based on this geometry (25, 35, 47, 75).

In frog mesenteric capillaries the total cleft length has been found to be 2400 Å μm^{-2}. To explain the potassium permeability obtained on these capillaries by an intercellular passage, 58% of the cleft would have to be open with an average width of 134 Å (5).

Generalizations are hindered by the undefined localization of most of the published sections. This is particularly serious after the demonstration (54) that the structure of the junction varies systematically along the length of the microvasculature, with the junctions in the arterial end being closed and the junctions in the venular end being opener and more permeable to macromolecules. Freeze-fracture studies have shown only a few discontinuous "strands" in the pericytic venules from the rat omentum and mesentery. This breakthrough in the study of endothelial junctions was followed (60, 61) by a study of capillaries in the mouse diaphragm, where again the pericytic venules had completely open junctions in about a third of the cases, with gap sizes of 30–60 Å. As before, the arterial end showed closed junctions. The authors were very reluctant to extrapolate from their morphological findings to the functional implications, particularly since the "strands" are situated not between the endothelial cells but within the cell membranes proper. (The plane of cleavage in freeze-fracture studies lies within the unit membrane.) Whether the number of "strands" in a junction reflects the tightness is debated. The originally simple conclusion that tight epithelia had many "strands" while leaky epithelia had only a few is apparently an oversimplification (41). The "strands" may even be formed and eliminated during the fixation procedure (68).

Simionescu et al (57, 58) have not been able to reproduce Karnovsky's finding that 40 Å gaps are present in the capillary junctions. In muscle capillaries the junctions were impermeable to myoglobin and microperoxidase (with diameters of 33 and 20 Å, respectively). Wissig (71) arrived at the opposite conclusion with microperoxidase. He regularly observed a decline in the tracer concentration in the junctions from lumen to tissue side

—sometimes in a stepwise fashion that indicated tortuous pathways (a kind of labyrinth structure) within the junction. The vessels were classified as capillaries when only a single erythrocyte could be accommodated in their lumen. Since competent research groups have opposite views, one must conclude that the situation with respect to the permeability of the junctional zones between endothelial cells is still unclear. Thus, although it would be satisfyingly simple for physiologists to see the endothelial junctional region as the equivalent of the small pore system, the matter remains unsettled. This is interesting, since in studies of transepithelial transport the junctional zone is definitely regarded as a permeable region that allows osmotic water transport as well as solute transport (24, 74).

In this context junctions of brain capillaries are unique, since studies using various tracers have indicated unequivocally that they are very tight (50, 67). This also applies to brain capillaries in lower vertebrates (6).

TRANSENDOTHELIAL CHANNELS

Because the junctions in capillaries appeared to be mostly of the zonula occludens type, Bruns & Palade (3) suggested that the small pore equivalents were to be found in transendothelial channels created by chains of fused vesicles. This required the demonstration of a continuity of the plasma membrane all the way through the structure. Various groups have, in fact, observed such continuous systems (7, 27, 58, 60, 72, 73, 76). The inner diameter of a vesicle is about 700 Å but strictures with dimensions down to 200 Å are found where two vesicles join and where a vesicle opens to the surface. Since the strictures are often provided with a diaphragm structurally identical to the fenestral diaphragm, the possibility exists that a molecular sieving system is interposed in the channel.

A serious problem with this proposal is, however, the rarity with which the continuous channels can be demonstrated. According to most physiological calculations, a density of 10 μm^{-2} is expected, so that a capillary cross-section with a thickness of 0.05 μm should contain 5–10 channels. So many have never been observed. However, a tortuous channel could leave the plane of section (in cases where it is composed of several vesicles). Thus the scarcity of continuous channels is not a watertight counter-argument. Some workers have not been able to find any continuous channels at all (14, 31, 71). This may reflect use of different techniques. The technical details are crucial to an interpretation of many of the results obtained with electron microscopy.

In a study of 700 sections of frog mesenteric capillaries Bundgaard et al (7) could not find any vesicular channels, even in the very thin peripheral zones of the endothelium (thickness 0.1 μm). In a few cases they were found in venules.

From the beginning it was realized that an overlap of two neighboring, but not fused, vesicles might appear as one continuous channel. Simionescu et al (58) tilted their specimens 23° to look for cytoplasmic processes between two vesicles that appeared to be fused. This method may not be sensitive enough. In some cases, the interspace between apparently fused vesicles would be visualized only after 40–60° of tilting, and investigations at these high angles are desirable. A further complication stems from the fact that channels are most often demonstrated with reaction product from peroxidase tracers present. This tends to blur the lining of the system so that one cannot be certain of a continuity of plasma membrane.

VESICULAR TRANSPORT

As described above, many workers find the plasmalemmal vesicles in the endothelial cytoplasm an equally likely candidate for the large pore system. This point of view, of course, implies that the vesicles move freely from side to side and fuse with the plasma membrane, carrying with them a sample of either plasma or interstitial fluid. The strongest support for vesicular transport came from the studies of Bruns & Palade (4), who showed that ferritin was incorporated into the vesicles. Since the tracer appeared on the tissue front, and since it seemed inconceivable that molecules with a size of 110 Å could have passed through the junctions, vesicular transport was an almost unavoidable explanation. Vesicles were, in fact, regarded as the equivalent of the large pore system, though many features of macromolecular transport cannot be reconciled with a mechanism decisively bidirectional (2, 43).

Simionescu et al (57, 58, 60) realized that to demonstrate vesicular transport very short periods of observation were needed; they sampled specimens 30–60 sec after the macromolecular tracer had been injected. Vesicles were seen to have unloaded their contents on the tissue side after 45–60 seconds. There were problems with the interpretation however, since the tissue space could have been filled with tracer via other routes—especially in sections of venous capillaries (60). Since fixation may not be rapid enough to "freeze" the diffusion profile outside a discharging vesicle, one cannot safely judge whether the material is entering the vesicle or whether the vesicle is unloading.

The many calculations on vesicle turnover (11, 12, 26, 53, 64) rest on the premise that vesicles move freely and stochastically. The average rate with which the vesicle traverses the cytoplasm is derived from backward calculations starting with the actual rate of macromolecular transport. The fact that tracers of different molecular dimensions appear on the tissue side with variable delays suggests diffusion rather than vesicular transport, which should result in more equal transport rates. Ferritin appears after 10 min (4), horseradish peroxidase after 5–16 min (29, 69). Smaller tracers such as myoglobin, cytochrome c, and microperoxidase appear after 0.5–1 min (31, 57, 58, 71).

Hesitation in accepting the theory of vesicular transport has occasionally been expressed (21, 38). Florey (21) observed that the labeling of vesicles was unaffected by anoxia or metabolic poisons, a finding corroborated on isolated capillaries (70). Energy-independent fusion and fission is hardly possible.

Recently, a new theory of vesicular organization has been advanced (8), according to which vesicles are permanent structures that together constitute a more or less elaborate system of invaginations from the endothelial cell surface into the interior. This view was based on observations on mesenteric capillaries treated with tannic acid to increase membrane contrast, after aldehyde and osmium fixation (59, 66). Occasionally tannic acid acted as an extracellular tracer, and vesicles communicating with the pericapillary space, often as elements in complex invaginations, were labelled. Half of the vesicles apparently communicate with one surface and the other half with the other (23). The existence of a few free vesicles is not denied. In accordance with this view, Wolff (73) found that in capillaries perfused with fixative at high pressure, vesicles in the luminal half of the cytoplasm were cleared of protein. Additions of tracers to fixed capillaries in heart and striated muscle gave pictures surprisingly similar to those found when tracers were administered to live animals (30, 32). Pietra et al (48), working with perfused lungs and hemoglobin as tracer, could not demonstrate hemoglobin in the perivascular space even after 20 min. With increased perfusion pressure, interstitial labelling occurred, apparently via the interendothelial clefts. Practically all vesicles were labelled, those facing the tissue front having the same concentration as the interstitium. Similar observations have been made on muscle and lung capillaries studied with different tracers (49, 69). At short times only the luminally placed vesicles are labelled. This picture is stationary until tracer concentration in the interstitium begins to increase. Then all vesicles are labelled, the abluminal with the same tracer concentration as in the interstitium. During ferritin labelling (from either blood or tissue side) the vesicles along the side with label have the highest concentration of ferritin; with increasing distance from the surface, tracer concentration decreases (17, 28). This finding fits well with diffusion in a cisternal system.

The conclusion that vesicles are sessile structures not involved in macromolecular transport may appear drastic. However, similar conclusions have recently been reached by purely indirect reasoning (52). The existence of a permanent system of invaginations does not exclude the existence of transendothelial channels. The close approach of two invaginations might sometimes lead to fusion of neighboring, centrally located vesicles, thus creating a transcellular channel.

FENESTRAE

The diameter of fenestrae is 400–600 Å; they could serve as large pores. They occur in very thin and probably very permeable endothelia associated with transporting epithelia (kidney tubules, intestine, glands, choroid plexus, etc). Horseradish peroxidase permeates the entire population of fenestrae (16). Simionescu et al (56) reported that only a portion of the fenestrae were permeable to large tracers such as ferritin, dextrans, and glycogens. The properties of the diaphragm are important but at present unknown. The diaphragm may comprise specialized cell membrane found by elimination of the lipids. It may consist of proteoglycans (16, 38).

Fenestrae have given their name to a special category of capillaries. The distinction between fenestrated and nonfenestrated capillaries may not be as sharp as originally supposed, since they are occasionally found in continuous capillaries (9, 18, 33). Whether they might be the structural equivalent of large pores cannot be decided. They occur with a frequency of 1 per 60 cross sections in rat diaphragm (33), which is a higher frequency than expected for large pores. If colloid osmotic pressures can develop across them (13) they are not likely to have characteristics corresponding to those deduced for large pores (permeable to proteins).

LEAKS

The rarity of the large pores makes it rather unlikely that they could be systematically found and identified, and the odds are that this system may well remain unidentifiable.

Large gaps (several thousand angstroms) between endothelial cells are found in the venular end of the microcirculation in response to inflammation (1, 63) or after treatment with histamin (22), snake venom (65), serotonin (61), bradykinin, and prostaglandin (63). The burning question is whether they occur as normal phenomena or only in response to extreme stimuli. Majno (39) proposed that they occur where junctions are mechanically weak, when endothelial contraction is induced by various transmitters and other chemicals. It has been suggested that junctions in postcapillary venules constitute an additional pathway belonging to the small pore system (61) because they are permeable to horseradish peroxidase but not to ferritin.

THE ENDOCAPILLARY LAYER

The glycocalyx lines the surface of the capillaries (37). It appears in unstained preparations as a several-hundred-angstrom thick fuzzy layer that can be visualized by means of ruthenium red, alcian blue, and ionic lanthanum. The fact that it binds cations can be explained by the presence of polyelectrolytes (acidic glycoproteins). They probably form a network upon which serum proteins are adsorbed. None of the cationic stains that precipitate polyelectrolytes has adequate specificity to determine which compound is present within the intercellular spaces. The endocapillary layer probably continues down through the intercellular junction. If so, it will affect the junctional permeability.

Writing about junctions between epithelial cells, Oschman (44) revives the earlier term *intercellular cement* (cf Figure 1). It has been suggested that hyaluronic acid is the intercellular cement (40) because of its high affinity for calcium. The interaction with proteins is incompletely understood. It is likely that further studies of the material in the junctions may lead to

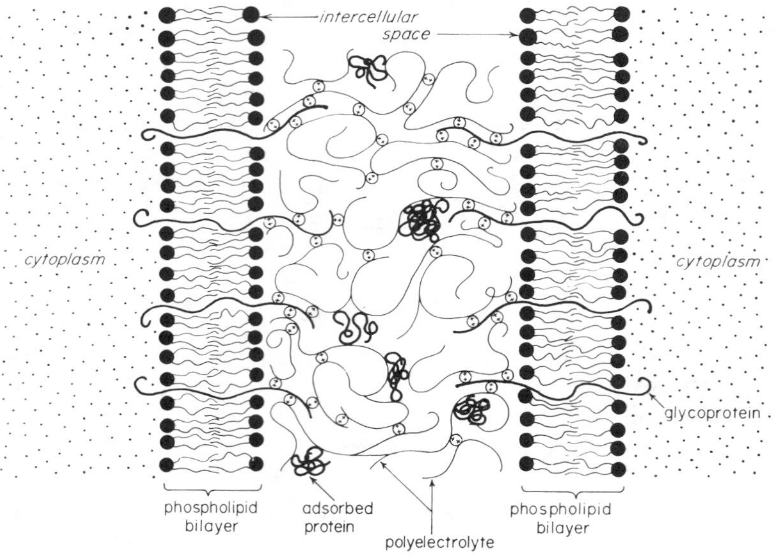

Figure 1 Model of intercellular diffusion pathway of vascular and epithelial tissues based on knowledge of membrane structure, properties of extracellular macromolecules, cell–cell adhesion, and physiological characteristics of pericellular shunt. Firmly anchored in the lipid bilayer are glycoproteins bearing negatively charged sialic residues cross-linked to soluble polyelectrolyte molecules. [After (44), reproduced with kind permission of the author and the publisher, Springer Verlag]

changing views of their hydraulic conductivity. If a fixed matrix exists between cells, Poiseuillean flow is not likely to occur; instead one expects the different type of flow that occurs in chromatographic columns. This possibility has far-reaching consequences. The finding that D- and L-glucose permeate muscle capillaries at slightly different rates might indicate that chromatographic separation takes place in the junctions (19).

The slow labelling of surface-bound vesicles with ferritin (36) might be due to the endocapillary layer. The observation that the net charge of the tracer affects the labelling of vesicles is also indicative of restriction by the endocapillary layer (55).

CONCLUSION

The *junctions* were once the obvious candidates for the small pore system, with the *vesicles* the equivalents of the large pores. It is now proposed that structures not clearly visible in the electron microscope are the structures that discriminate between small solutes of various sizes. If the large pore system comprises rare gaps in the venular ends, the pores may never be identifiable. If the further possibility is considered that, because of the structure of the interendothelial junction, "plug" flow rather than Poiseuillean flow occurs during filtration, then several fundamental problems face the experimentalist.

Since crucial information about structure and chemical composition of cell coat, diaphragms, and junctions has been unobtainable with current techniques, new approaches seem necessary to clarify the structural basis of transcapillary exchange. The use of electronmicroscopic tracers with high specificity for chemical groups assumed to form part of the permeability-related structures (immunocytochemistry) may significantly influence future developments in this field.

Literature Cited

1. Arfors, K.-E., Rutili, G., Svensjö, E. 1979. Microvascular transport of macromolecules in normal and inflammatory conditions. *Acta Physiol. Scand.* Suppl. 463
2. Bill, A. 1977. Plasma protein dynamics: Albumin and IgG capillary permeability, extravascular movement and regional blood flow in unanesthetized rabbits. *Acta Physiol. Scand.* 101:28–42
3. Bruns, R. R., Palade, G. E. 1968. Studies on blood capillaries. I. General organization of blood capillaries in muscle. *J. Cell Biol.* 37:244–76
4. Bruns, R. R., Palade, G. E. 1968. Studies on blood capillaries. II. Transport of ferritin molecules across the wall of muscle capillaries. *J. Cell Biol.* 37:277–99
5. Bundgaard, M., Frøkjær-Jensen, J., Crone, C. 1979. Determination of the interendothelial cleft length in the frog mesenteric capillary. *Acta Physiol. Scand.* 105:3A–4A
6. Bundgaard, M., Cserr, H. F., Murray, M. 1979. Impermeability of hagfish cerebral capillaries to horseradish peroxidase. An ultrastructural study. *Cell. Tiss. Res.* 198:65–77
7. Bundgaard, M., Frøkjær-Jensen, J., Crone, C. 1979. Extreme rarity of transendothelial channels in the frog me-

senteric capillary. *J. Physiol. London* 291:38P

8. Bundgaard, M., Frøkjær-Jensen, J., Crone, C. 1979. Endothelial plasmalemmal vesicles as elements in a system of branching invaginations from the cell surface. *Proc. Natl. Acad. Sci. USA* 76:6439–42
9. Bundgaard, M., Frøkjær-Jensen, J. 1979. Does perfusion of single capillaries with high K^+ solutions affect the morphology of the capillary wall? *Microvasc. Res.* 17:S7
10. Bundgaard, M., Møller, M. 1980. Horseradish peroxidase and microperoxidase, their purity and binding to plasma protein. *J. Histochem. & Cytochem.* Submitted
11. Carter, R. D., Joyner, W. L., Renkin, E. M. 1974. Effects of histamine and some other substances on molecular selectivity of the capillary wall to plasma proteins and dextran. *Microvasc. Res.* 7:31–48
12. Casley-Smith, J. R. 1969. The dimensions and numbers of small vesicles in cells, endothelial and mesothelial, and the significance of these for endothelial permeability. *J. Microsc.* 90:251–68
13. Casley-Smith, J. R., Bolton, T. 1973. The presence of large effective colloidal osmotic pressures across large pores. *Microvasc. Res.* 5:213–16
14. Casley-Smith, J. R. 1979. Freeze-substitution of capillary endothelium: the passage of ions and the artefactual nature of "thoroughfare channels." *Microvasc. Res.* 17:S8
15. Caulfield, J. P., Farquhar, M. G. 1974. The permeability of glomerular capillaries to graded dextrans. Identification of the basement membrane as the primary filtration barrier. *J. Cell Biol.* 63:883–903
16. Clementi, F., Palade, G. E. 1969. Intestinal capillaries. I. Permeability to peroxidase and ferritin. *J. Cell Biol.* 41:33–58
17. Clough, G., Michel, C. C. 1979. The sequence of labelling of endothelial cell vesicles with ferritin in the frog. *J. Physiol. London* 292:61–62P
18. Collin, H. B. 1969. Ultrastructure of fenestrated blood capillaries in extraocular muscles. *Exp. Eye Res.* 8:16–20
19. Crone, C. 1973. Transcapillary transport of D- and L-glucose in isolated skeletal muscle. *Acta Physiol. Scand.* 87:138–44
20. Diamond, J. M. 1974. Tight and leaky junctions of epithelia: A perspective on kisses in the dark. *Fed. Proc.* 33:2220–24
21. Florey, H. W. 1964. The transport of materials across the capillary wall. *Q. J. Exp. Med.* 49:117–28
22. Fox, J., Galey, F., Wayland, H. 1979. Action of histamine on the mesenteric microvasculature. *Microvasc. Res.* Submitted
23. Frøkjær-Jensen, J., Bundgaard, M. 1979. Sessile vesicle "clusters" in frog mesenteric capillaries. A new concept of vesicular organization in the endothelial cell. *Microvasc. Res.* In press
24. Frömter, E., Diamond, J. 1972. Route of passive ion permeation in epithelia. *Nature New Biol.* 235:9–13
25. Gosselin, R. E., Stibitz, G. R. 1977. The diffusive conductance of slits between endothelial cells in muscle capillaries. *Microvasc. Res.* 14:363–82
26. Green, H. S., Casley-Smith, J. R. 1972. Calculations on the passage of small vesicles across endothelial cells by Brownian motion. *J. Theor. Biol.* 35:103–11
27. Hashimoto, P. H. 1972. Intracellular channels as a route for protein passage in the capillary endothelium of the shark brain. *Am. J. Anat.* 134:41–58
28. Johansson, B. R. 1978. Permeability of muscle capillaries to interstitially microinjected ferritin. *Microvasc. Res.* 16:362–68
29. Karnovsky, M. J. 1967. The ultrastructural basis of capillary permeability studied with peroxidase as a tracer. *J. Cell Biol.* 35:213–36
30. Karnovsky, M. J. 1968. The ultrastructural basis of transcapillary exchanges. *J. Gen. Physiol.* 52:64s–93s
31. Karnovsky, M. J. 1970. Morphology of capillaries with special reference to muscle capillaries. In *Capillary Permeability,* ed. C. Crone, N. A. Lassen, p. 681. NY: Academic
32. Kobayashi, S. 1970. Ferritin labeling in the fixed muscle capillary. A doubt on the tracer-experiments as the basis for the vesicular transport theory. *Arch. Histol. Jpn.* 32:81–86
33. Korneliussen, H. 1975. Fenestrated blood capillaries and lymphatic capillaries in rat skeletal muscle. *Cell Tiss. Res.* 163:169–74
34. Landis, E. M. 1964. Heteroporosity of the capillary wall indicated by cinematographic analysis of the passage of dyes. *Ann. NY Acad. Sci.* 116:765–73
35. Lassen, N. A., Trap-Jensen, J. 1970. Estimation of the fraction of the interendothelial slit which must be open in

order to account for the observed transcapillary exchange of small hydrophilic molecules in skeletal muscle in man. See Ref. 31, pp. 647–53

36. Loudon, M. F., Michel, C. C., White, I. F. 1975. Some observations upon the rate of labelling of endothelial cell vesicles with ferritin in frog mesenteric capillaries. *J. Physiol. London* 252:79–80P
37. Luft, J. H. 1966. Fine structure of capillary and endocapillary layer as revealed by ruthenium red. *Fed. Proc.* 25:1773–83
38. Luft, J. H. 1973. Capillary permeability. I. Structural considerations. In *The Inflammatory Process,* ed. B. W. Zweifach, L. Grant, R. T. McCluskey, 2:47–93. NY: Academic
39. Majno, G., Shea, S. M., Leventhal, M. 1969. Endothelial contraction induced by histamine-type mediators. An electron microscopic study. *J. Cell. Biol.* 42:647–72
40. Manery, J. F. 1966. Connective tissue electrolytes. *Fed. Proc.* 25:1799–1803
41. Martinez-Palomo, A., Erlij, D. 1975. Structure of tight junctions in epithelia with different permeability. *Proc. Natl. Acad. Sci. USA* 72:4487–91
42. Muir, A. R., Peters, A. 1962. Quintuple-layered membrane junctions at terminal bars between endothelial cells. *J. Cell Biol.* 12:443–48
43. Noer, I., Lassen, N. A. 1978. Evidence of active transport (filtration?) of plasma proteins across the capillary walls in muscle and subcutis. *Lymphology* 11:133–37
44. Oschman, J. L. 1978. Morphological correlates of transport. In *Membrane Transport in Biology,* ed. G. Giebisch, D. C. Tosteson, 3:55–93. Heidelberg: Springer
45. Palade, G. E., Bruns, R. R. 1964. Structure and function in normal muscle capillaries. In *Small Blood Vessels Involvement in Diabetes Mellitus,* ed. M. D. Siperstein, A. R. Colwell Sr., K. Meyer, pp. 39–49. Washington, DC: Am. Inst. Biol. Sci.
46. Pappenheimer, J. R. 1953. Passage of molecules through capillary walls. *Physiol. Rev.* 33:387–423
47. Perl, W. 1973. A friction coefficient, series-parallel channel model for transcapillary flux of nonelectrolytes and water. *Microvasc. Res.* 6:169–93
48. Pietra, G. G., Szidon, J. P., Leventhal, M. M., Fishman, A. P. 1969. Hemoglobin as a tracer in hemodynamic pulmonary edema. *Science* 166:1643–46
49. Pietra, G. G., Spagnoli, L. G., Fishman, A. P. 1977. Permeability of pulmonary and muscle capillaries to lipid-insoluble macromolecules. In *Respiratory Adaptations, Capillary Exchange and Reflex Mechanisms,* ed. A. S. Paintal, P. Gill-Kumar, pp. 145–52. New Delhi: Navchetan Press
50. Reese, T. S., Karnovsky, M. J. 1967. Fine structural localization of a blood-brain barrier to exogenous peroxidase. *J. Cell Biol.* 34:207–17
51. Rennke, H. G., Cotran, R. S., Venkatachalam, M. A. 1975. Role of molecular charge in glomerular permeability. Tracer studies with cationized ferritins. *J. Cell Biol.* 67:638–46
52. Rippe, B., Kamiya, A., Folkow, B. 1979. Transcapillary passage of albumin, effects of tissue cooling and of increases in filtration and plasma colloid osmotic pressure. *Acta Physiol. Scand.* 105:171–87
53. Shea, S. M., Bossert, W. H. 1973. Vesicular transport across endothelium: A generalized diffusion model. *Microvasc. Res.* 6:305–15
54. Simionescu, M., Simionescu, N., Palade, G. E. 1975. Segmental differentiations of cell junctions in the vascular endothelium. The microvasculature. *J. Cell Biol.* 67:863–85
55. Simionescu, M., Simionescu, N. 1978. Constitutive endocytosis of the endothelial cell. *J. Cell Biol.* 79:381a
56. Simionescu, N., Simionescu, M., Palade, G. E. 1972. Permeability of intestinal capillaries. Pathway followed by dextrans and glycogens. *J. Cell Biol.* 53:365–92
57. Simionescu, N., Simionescu, M., Palade, G. E. 1973. Permeability of muscle capillaries to exogenous myoglobin. *J. Cell Biol.* 57:424–52
58. Simionescu, N., Simionescu, M., Palade, G. E. 1975. Permeability of muscle capillaries to small hemepeptides. Evidence for the existence of patent transendothelial channels. *J. Cell Biol.* 64:586–607
59. Simionescu, N., Simionescu, M. 1976. Galloylglucoses of low molecular weight as mordant in electron microscopy. *J. Cell Biol.* 70:608–33
60. Simionescu, N., Simionescu, M., Palade, G. E. 1978. Structural basis of permeability in sequential segments of the microvasculature of the diaphragm. II. Pathways followed by microperoxidase across the endothelium. *Microvasc. Res.* 15:17–36

61. Simionescu, N., Simionescu, M., Palade, G. E. 1978. Open junctions in the endothelium of the postcapillary venules of the diaphragm. *J. Cell Biol.* 79:27–44
62. Sjøstrand, F. S. 1978. The structure of mitochondrial membranes: A new concept. *J. Ultrastruct. Res.* 64:217–45
63. Svensjö, E. 1978. *Characterization of leakage of macromolecules in postcapillary venules.* PhD thesis. Univ. Uppsala, Sweden. 41 pp.
64. Tomlin, S. G. 1969. Vesicular transport across endothelial cells. *Biochem. Biophys. Acta* 183:559–64
65. Tsuchiya, M., Oshio, C., Ohashi, M., Ohsaka, A., Fujishiro, Y. 1975. Electron microscopical study of the hemorrhage induced by the venom of *Trimeresurus flavoviridis. Bibl. Anat.* 13:190–91
66. Wagner, R. C. 1976. The effect of tannic acid on electron images of capillary endothelial cell membranes. *J. Ultrastruct. Res.* 57:132–39
67. van Deurs, B., Amtorp, O. 1978. Blood-brain barrier in rats to the hemepeptide microperoxidase. *Neuroscience* 3: 737–48
68. van Deurs, B., Luft, J. H. 1979. Effects of glutaraldehyde fixation on the structure of tight junctions. A quantitative freeze-fracture analysis. *J. Ultrastruct. Res.* In press
69. Williams, M. C., Wissig, S. L. 1975. The permeability of muscle capillaries to horseradish peroxidase. *J. Cell Biol.* 66:531–55
70. Williams, S. K., Matthews, M. A., Wagner, R. C., Andrews, S. B. 1977. Capillary endothelial metabolism and micropinocytic ingestion. *J. Cell Biol.* 75:364a
71. Wissig, S. L., Williams, M. C. 1978. Permeability of muscle capillaries to microperoxidase. *J. Cell Biol.* 76: 341–59
72. Wolff, J. R. 1966. Elektronenmikroskopische Untersuchungen über die Vesikulation in Kapillarendothel. Lokalisation, Variation und Fusion der Vesikel. *Z. Zellforsch.* 73:143–64
73. Wolff, J. R. 1977. Ultrastructure of the terminal vascular bed as related to function. In *Microcirculation,* ed. G. Kaley, B. M. Altura, 1:95–130. Baltimore: University Park Press
74. Wright, E. M. 1977. Passive water transport across epithelia. In *Water Relations in Membrane Transport in Plants and Animals,* ed. A. M. Jungreis, T. K. Hodges, A. Kleinzeller, S. G. Schultz, pp. 199–213. NY: Academic
75. Yablonski, M. E., Levitt, D. G. 1973. Relationship between capillary wall structure and "effective" transcapillary osmotic pressure. *Microvasc. Res.* 5: 97–99
76. Zweifach, B. W. 1972. Capillary filtration and mechanisms of edema formation. *Pflügers Arch.* 336:S81–S95

Ann. Rev. Physiol. 1980. 42:337–57

FLUID EXCHANGE ACROSS SINGLE CAPILLARIES[1]

❖1272

Robert W. Gore

Department of Physiology, College of Medicine, University of Arizona, Tucson, Arizona 85724

Paul F. McDonagh

Department of Cardiothoracic Surgery, Yale University School of Medicine, New Haven, Connecticut 06510

INTRODUCTION

All major organisms must establish and maintain proper water balance between the blood and interstitium. In 1896, Ernest Starling (61) presented the first modern description of the major forces governing fluid exchange across capillaries. His ideas were later confirmed by Landis (26–28). Although many details have since been added to our knowledge of transcapillary fluid exchange, Starling's fundamental assertions and Landis' observations still represent the foundations of our present understanding. Most studies of transcapillary fluid exchange have been done on either single capillaries or isolated whole organs. Single capillary studies date from the work of Landis, while modern whole-organ studies began with the classic experiments of Pappenheimer & Soto-Rivera (53). In the last decade, renewed interest in the study of single capillaries has produced many experiments designed to examine the biophysical and structural nature of the exchange barrier and the interstitium. This review discusses fluid exchange across single capillaries, with only a few references to whole organ-studies. Comprehensive reviews of the general subject of transcapillary exchange are available (21, 25, 40, 57). Crone & Christensen's recent review (6) is especially good. Brief treatments of specific aspects of fluid exchange are recom-

[1]Supported in part by NIH Grants HL-13437 & HL-17421.

0066-4278/80/0315-0337$01.00

mended for supplemental reading (4, 20, 23, 44, 45, 48, 55, 56). Reviews are available of mathematical models and biophysical aspects of fluid exchange (1, 7, 10, 18, 51), and of fluid exchange in the kidney (3), the GI tract (64), skin and skeletal muscle (21), adipose tissue (35), the lungs (54, 62), and the lymphatics and interstitium (19, 50, 63, 70, 74).

REVIEW OF SINGLE CAPILLARY METHODS AND ANALYTICAL MODELS

The relationships among the factors governing passive transvascular fluid exchange are often described by the expression:

$$J_v = \dot{V}/S_f = L_p\,[(P_c - P_t) - \sigma(\Pi_c - \Pi_t)] \qquad 1.$$

where $J_v = \dot{V}/S_f$ is the fluid flux at any point along the capillary, or the volume rate of flow across the endothelium per unit functional surface area; L_p is the average hydraulic conductivity; P_c and P_t are the capillary and tissue hydrostatic pressures; Π_c and Π_t are the capillary and tissue colloid osmotic pressures; and σ is the average colloid osmotic reflection coefficient. All the studies of fluid exchange across single capillaries have been designed to measure or calculate one or more of the terms in equation 1. Most of the procedures developed to measure J_v, L_p, and σ in single capillaries are based on Landis' original *occlusion method* (27). Indeed, the current concepts of fluid exchange across single capillaries have evolved in conjunction with modifications and adaptations of the Landis method and the introduction of more sophisticated, but not necessarily better, analytical models.

Figure 1 summarizes the Landis method (27). The mesentery of a frog was exposed and viewed under a microscope. A single capillary was then occluded with a glass microprobe (Figure 1a) and the distance (l) between an erythrocyte trapped in the capillary and the occluding probe was measured as a function of time (t). It was assumed that the red blood cell (RBC) movement was a direct measure of axial plasma fluid movement. The diameter (D) of the capillary was also measured. The occluding probe was left in place and the mean *occluded* capillary pressure (Figure 1b, P_c') was then measured directly with a micropipette using the micro-injection method (26). The distance (l) was graphed as a function of time and the initial cell velocity $(dl/dt)_0$ was estimated from a tangent drawn by eye through the data at $t = 0$ (Figure 1c). The initial fluid flux ($J_{v,0}$) was then calculated from the relationship:

$$J_{v,0} = -(D/4l_0)\,(dl/dt)_0 \qquad 2.$$

where l_0 was the initial distance between the marker erythrocyte and the occluding probe at the moment of occlusion (t = 0). This procedure was repeated on many different capillaries, both arterial and venous. Finally, the values for $J_{v,0}$ were graphed as a function of P_c', and the slope of a least squares fit through the data (Figure 1d) gave a single value for the hydraulic conductivity for all capillaries studied. The X-intercept (Figure 1d) was an estimate of the algebraic sum of the unmeasured transmural pressures in the occluded capillaries. We will refer to this as the *Landis occluded effective pressure* [$P_L' = P_t + \sigma(\Pi_c - \Pi_t)$]. It includes the reflection coefficient, and equals P_c' when $J_{v,0} = 0$. Landis measured a value for L_p of 56 X 10^{-4} $\mu m \cdot sec^{-1} \cdot cmH_2O^{-1}$ from 70 capillaries in 11 frogs, although he reported it as the inverse ($1/L_p$)—see legend, Figure 10 in (27). He also reported a value for P_L' of 11.5 cmH_2O but referred to it as the "effective osmotic pressure of the plasma proteins." He apparently assumed that P_t and Π_t were zero, but this assumption was not a necessary part of the analysis and did not influence the numerical values of L_p and P_L'. The graphical analysis (Figure 1d) assumes only that σ, P_t, and Π_t are constants. The disadvantages of the Landis method are that it requires cannulation of the capillaries, so it is limited to use in animals that have large capillaries (i.d. $\geqslant$ 10 μm).

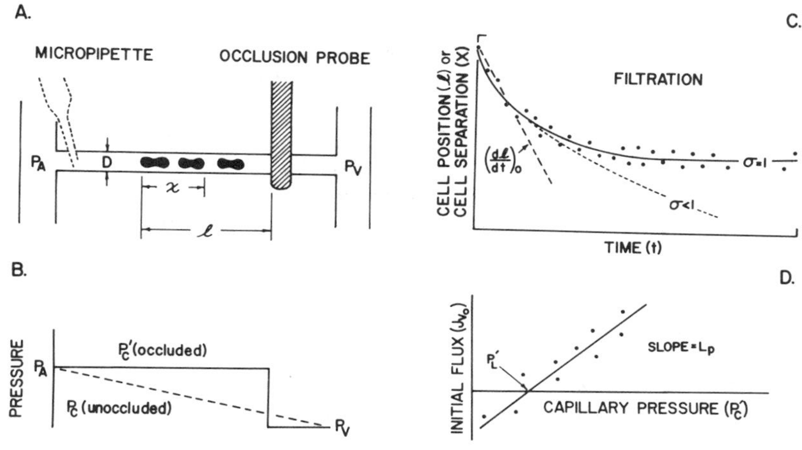

Figure 1 Landis occluded capillary experiment: *A:* Diagram of occluded capillary with trapped cells. Capillary diameter (D), cell position relative to occluding probe (l), marker cell separation (x), arteriolar pressure (P_A), venular pressure P_V. *B:* Hydrostatic pressure distribution in occluded (P_c') and unoccluded (P_c) capillary. *C:* Typical curve of marker cell position or separation vs time following occlusion. Solid line depicts fit of Lee model (30) to data. Dashed straight line $(dl/dt)_0$ represents tangent drawn by eye at t = 0. *D:* Landis graphical method for obtaining value for L_p and occluded effective pressure (P_L') from calculated fluxes and measured occluded hydrostatic pressures.

Also, only one value for L_p and P_L' can be obtained from all capillaries studied. Thus, differences in L_p and P_L' among capillaries in the same tissue cannot be deduced easily, and axial gradients in L_p along single capillaries cannot be quantitated without modifying the method or making additional assumptions. Finally, multiple curve fitting procedures are involved in the analysis. The important advantage of the Landis occlusion technique and graphical analysis over other methods is that it requires the least number of assumptions to obtain absolute values for L_p and P_L'. It is not necessary to assume that $\sigma = 1$ or to know the exact relationship between the concentration of plasma proteins and Π_c.

In 1937, Wind (72) used the Landis techniques to measure L_p's in toad mesentery but modified the analysis. He assumed that Π_c was 10 cmH_2O and divided the calculated fluxes of each capillary by $(P_c' - \Pi_c)$ to obtain a value of L_p for each capillary studied. He thereby estimated the variability in L_p among different capillaries in the same tissue. Because he did not do Landis' graphical analysis (Figure 1d) of the flux data, the assumptions that $P_t = 0$, $\Pi_t = 0$ and $\sigma = 1$ were automatically introduced into the final calculations and affected the numerical results. The range of L_p's for 28 capillaries was $14–470 \times 10^{-4} \mu m \cdot sec^{-1} \cdot cmH_2O^{-1}$.

Nearly 30 years passed before subsequent major studies on single capillaries were reported, but between 1966 and 1977 there was a veritable explosion in this area of study. Several modifications and improvements in the Landis occlusion method were introduced by Intaglietta, Zweifach, and Smaje (22, 24, 59, 60, 73) and Michel et al (47). Wiederhielm (67, 68) developed a densitometric method. Ten years later Levick & Michel (33) suggested two additional densitometric procedures. Wayland, Fox & Elmore (66) introduced a fluorescence technique. Finally, two clever and useful analytical models were developed. The Lee, Smaje, & Zweifach model (30) is particularly useful because it is the only experimentally proven model that can be applied to studies of fluid exchange across single capillaries in a variety of tissues other than mesentery, omentum, and cremaster muscle without excessive manipulation and damage to the tissues. The Blake-Gross model (2) is more sophisticated and potentially more versatile, but it has not yet been implemented and tested experimentally. The various available methods and analytical models with their advantages, disadvantages, and principle assumptions are discussed below. Representative data from studies employing them are summarized in Table 1.

The changes that Zweifach & Intaglietta (24, 73) made in the Landis method eliminated the need to cannulate the capillaries. Hence, separate values of L_p and effective pressure could be obtained from each capillary examined. Differences between the arterial and venous ends within a single vessel could be compared, and smaller capillaries could be studied (mammalian = 3–6 μm i.d.). A vessel was occluded and the separation (x) between two marker cells (Figure 1a) rather than the position (l) of a single cell was recorded with time. A sample of systemic venous blood was taken from the animal and the colloid osmotic pressure (Π_{c1}) was measured in a membrane osmometer. The occluding probe was then released and the animal's plasma colloid osmotic pressure was changed by injecting a bolus of 25% albumin intravenously. After steady-state conditions were reached the vessel was reoccluded in the same spot. Another blood sample was taken, and Π_{c2} was measured. The initial relative cell velocities $(dx/dt)_0$ for each occlusion were estimated from tangents drawn by eye through the data at $t = 0$ (Figure 1c), and the initial fluid fluxes corresponding to Π_{c1} and Π_{c2} were calculated from equation 2 using X_0 rather than l_0 to denote the initial cell separation. The values for $J_{v,0}$ were graphed versus Π_c and analyzed in the same way as the Landis procedure (Figure 1d). The slope of the line was equal to L_p, but negative in this case. The X-intercept was again an estimate of the algebraic sum of the unmeasured terms in the Starling relationship, but it was different from P_L'. In this case, the X-intercept is the *occluded effective pressure* $[P_e' = P_c' - P_t + \Pi_t]$. It includes P_c' and equals Π_c in the occluded capillary when $J_{v,0} = 0$. The Zweifach-Intaglietta method (73) has four disadvantages. (*a*) It requires multiple curve-fitting procedures. (*b*) Because Π_c is measured in a membrane osmometer, σ is assumed to be one. This assumption affects the value of P_e'. (*c*) Each capillary must be occluded at least three times in the same location to get a value for L_p and P_e', so damage to the capillary is always a possibility. Because the occluding probe compresses the tissue, an initial occlusion must be done to prefocus the microscope on the capillary with the probe in place. A minimum of two more occlusions are then needed to get L_p and P_e'. (*d*) One blood sample must be taken after each occlusion. Thus, only large animals with sufficient blood volumes to avoid problems of hemodilution and changes in systemic blood pressure can be used. In addition to eliminating the need to cannulate the capillaries, Intaglietta & Zweifach (24) introduced the idea of measuring cell separation. Incomplete occlusions and injury to the capillary can thus be detected from the relative motion of two cells. The occluding probe need not be in the viewing field of the microscope, so higher magnifications can be used. Also, the measurement can be confined to shorter segments of each capillary so the requirement that L_p is constant in the region of the measurement is better satisfied.

In 1970, Smaje, Zweifach & Intaglietta (60) introduced a small modification into the Zweifach-Intaglietta (73) procedure that eliminated both the need to cannulate the capillaries and the need to take multiple blood samples. Rather than change Π_c of the blood, Smaje changed the colloid osmotic pressure of the bathing medium (Π_B) outside the tissues. The analytical procedures were comparable (Figures 1c & 1d), except the initial fluid fluxes were now graphed versus Π_B so the slope of the line (L_p) was

Table 1 Hydraulic conductivities and effective pressures deduced from occluded single capillaries

Investigators, year (ref.)	Animals & tissue	Hydraulic conductivity ($L_p \times 10^4\ \mu m \cdot sec^{-1} \cdot cmH_2O^{-1}$) Mean ± S.D.	(range)	Effective pressure (cmH_2O)	Temp. (C)	Sample size
Landis 1927 (27)	frog mesentery	56	(48–74)	$P'_L = 11.5$	22–26	70
Wind 1937 (72)	toad mesentery	62 ± 90	(14–470)	$P'_c = 22.7$	22–26	28
Zwei. & Intag. 1968 (73)	rabbit omentum	art: — ven: —	(20–80) (160–250)	$P'_e = 24$	37	~25
Smaje et al 1970 (60)	rabbit omentum	65	—	—	37	5
	rat cremaster	10 ± 2	—	art: $(P'_c - P_t) = 32$ ven: $(P'_c - P_t) = 22$	37	10
Smaje et al 1971 (59)	rabbit omentum	art: 250 ± 133 ven: 460 ± 33	— —	$P'_e = 34$ $P'_e = 33$	—	11
Lee et al 1971 (30)	rabbit omentum	art: 306 ± 150 ven: 440 ± 110	(100–560) (350–700)	$P'_e = 34$ $P'_e = 35$	37	10 7

Michel et al	frog mesentery	20	(10–140)	P_t & Π_t are small	14–16	44
1974 (47)		50	(10–360)		22–26	79
Gore et al	rat intestinal	% (ℓ/ℓ_0): 15% 40% 64%	82%[a]	$P_e' = 28.3$	37	15
1976 (16)	muscle	L_p: 80 240 580	1150	$P_e = 20.6$[b]		
Mason et al	frog mesentery	protein: ~90	(10–350)	—	22–26	57
1977 (37)		no protein: 450	—	—		—
Levick & Michel	frog mesentery	89	(40–120)	$(\Pi_t - P_t) = 3.4$	20	6
1977 (33)		protein leak: 276	(210–330)	—		3
Clough & Smaje	guinea pig	control: 170 ± 70	—	—	37	13
1977[c]	mesentery	scorbutic: 240 ± 130	—	—		8
McDonagh & Gore	avian skeletal	postural: 1600 ± 1329	—	$P_e' = 12.9$	41	8
1978 (39)	muscle	locomotor: 590 ± 877	—	$P_e' = 11.5$		8
Fraser et al	cat mesentery	capillary: 132 ± 73	—	$P_e' = 32.5$	37	29
1978 (14)		venule: 199 ± 110	—			21

[a] Percent distance along capillary between arteriole (0%) and venule (100%) where L_p was measured.

[b] $(P_e = 20.6)$ is the average effective pressure in the *unoccluded* capillaries.

[c] Clough, G., Smaje, H. L. 1977. Changes in capillary permeability in scurvy. *Biorheology* 14: 203 (Abstr.)

positive. The X-intercept was different from both P_L' and P_e', and was equal to what we will call the *Smaje occluded effective pressure* $[P_S' = P_c' - P_t - \Pi_c]$. The validity of the method was first tested on rabbit omentum. The results were comparable to data obtained by the Zweifach-Intaglietta (73) procedure (Table 1). It was then applied to a study of capillaries in rat cremaster muscle. Estimates for L_p of cremaster capillaries averaged $10 \times 10^{-4} \mu m \cdot sec^{-1} \cdot cmH_2O^{-1}$. This value was the only one available for single capillaries in skeletal muscle until the recent studies by McDonagh & Gore (39). Values of P_S' were not reported directly (60). Rather, a measure of Π_c from each animal was added to P_S' and the results were reported as the net occluded hydrostatic pressure $[(P_S' + \Pi_c) = (P_c' - P_t)]$. Estimates of $(P_c' - P_t)$ measured on the arterial and venous sides of the occluding probe averaged 32 and 22 cmH_2O, respectively. The method of Smaje, Zweifach & Intaglietta (60) has several disadvantages. Like the Zweifach-Intaglietta (73) approach it requires a minimum of three occlusions per capillary and assumes $\sigma = 1$. It also assumes that the tissues equilibrate rapidly with the bathing medium so that $\Pi_B = \Pi_t$. This assumption is a potential source of error. If Π_B is greater than Π_t, then L_p will be consistently underestimated. Two recent papers by Fraser, Smaje & Verrinder (14) and Clough & Smaje (5) clearly show that hydration and equilibration of cat mesentery with an external bathing medium takes several hours or more. Indeed, there is doubt whether equilibrium is ever reached. Thus it is very likely that Π_B of a solution over a fairly thick heterogeneous tissue such as cremaster muscle remains significantly greater than Π_t for hours. Hence, L_p's measured with this method will be underestimated unless it is clearly established that $\Pi_B = \Pi_t$. Interestingly, the L_p's measured by Smaje et al (60) for cremaster muscle capillaries are the smallest values reported in the literature (Table 1).

Two more methodologic improvements were introduced in 1971 (30, 59). Smaje et al (59) described an analytical procedure that reduced the number of required occlusions to one, after the initial occlusion to focus the microscope. Lee et al (30) then added a clever improvement in the form of an analytical model that yields values for L_p and P_e' from one curve-fitting procedure without the need to graph the data, except as a visual aid. The Lee method also requires only one occlusion. The need to perform multiple occlusions was eliminated by simply assuming that the capillary was impermeable to protein ($\sigma = 1$). If $\sigma = 1$, then the protein mass is conserved and the concentration of protein (C_t) between two marker cells at any time ($0 \leqslant t \leqslant \infty$) is inversely proportional to the relative cell separation (X_t/X_0):

$$C_t = C_0 \, (1-H_0)/[(X_t/X_0)-H_0]. \quad 3.$$

Subscript 0 denotes $t = 0$ and H_0 is the initial hematocrit in the capillary between the two marker cells. In the procedure reported by Smaje et al (59), the relationship between Π_c and C_t was represented by the Landis & Pappenheimer (29) equation:

$$\Pi_c = 2.1C_t + 0.16C_t^2 + 0.009C_t^3. \quad 4.$$

By substituting equation 4 into 3, an expression relating Π_c to the relative cell separation (X_t/X_0) as a function of time was obtained. Moreover, the flux at any time was related to the cell separation by the expression:

$$(J_v)_t = -(D/4X_0)\,(dX_t/dt). \quad 5.$$

The cell separation from a single occlusion was graphed versus time. Values of dX_t/dt were measured from multiple tangents drawn to the X_t versus t curve at different times after the occlusion. The fluxes and Π_c's corresponding to the different times were then calculated from dX_t/dt, X_t/X_0 and equations 3–5. The calculated values for $(J_v)_t$ were finally plotted versus the calculated values of Π_c, and estimates of L_p and P_e' were computed from the slope and X-intercept in a way similar to the Landis procedure. Although only a single occlusion was needed to acquire a single data set, the analytical procedure was cumbersome and rather subjective because multiple curve-fitting and graphical procedures were involved. However, Lee et al (30) streamlined the final analytical procedure.

In Lee's method, the relationship between Π_c and C_t was represented by an empirical second-order equation,

$$\Pi_c = aC_t + bC_t^2, \quad 6.$$

that is as accurate as equation 4, given the errors inherent in the methods available to measure Π_c and C_t. Equations 3, 5, and 6 were combined and substituted into the Starling relationship. The resulting differential equation was nondimensionalized, and an exact solution was obtained. The solution (the Lee equation) accurately predicts the relative distance between two cells as a function of time following a single occlusion. The final analytical procedure, unlike the procedure described by Smaje et al (59), simply involves doing a nonlinear least squares fit of the Lee equation to the X_t/X_0 versus time data, as depicted in Figure 1c for $\sigma = 1$. A unique pair of best fit values of L_p and P_e' is obtained. Lee (30) used a direct search method to fit his equation to experimental data. A more accurate and efficient algorithm employing a Newton-Raphson method has since been developed (58) and used in studies of intestinal muscle (16) and skeletal muscle capillaries (39). The practical disadvantage of the Lee method, besides the assumption that $\sigma = 1$, is that the curve-fitting procedure requires the use of a computer. The Lee method, however, is the most objective and efficient of the techniques currently in use. It yields the most information from the least number of experimental manipulations. The experiments result in the least amount of trauma to the tissues and capillaries (one occlusion per measurement, no cannulations). Its validity rests upon relatively few assumptions. And it requires the least number of subjective investigator decisions in the analytical procedure. Values for L_p and P_e' can be measured at different locations on the same capillary. Because relative cell separation is measured, shorter regions in a capillary can be studied and the point condition in equation 1 can be better satisfied than in other methods (27, 47). Multiple estimates of L_p and P_e' can be made easily on the same capillary so that measurement variability can be quantitated. Many different capillaries within the same tissue can be sampled in a reasonable time so the variability among capillaries can be measured before significant tissue deterioration occurs. Finally, the methods (30, 59) are applicable to any viewable microvascular bed in amphibians, birds, and mammals. However, the Lee method yields values for L_p that tend to be larger than results recorded by other methods (see Table 1). It is true that the Lee method gives a more accurate and objective fit to the X versus t data at $t = 0$ than a simple tangent drawn by eye (see Figure 1c). Indeed, the larger values for L_p from the Lee and Smaje methods (30, 59) can be partly explained in this way and may therefore be "better" estimates. Yet precisely because the capillary hydrostatic pressure is not measured or manipulated in the Lee and Smaje procedures, in order to "get" results one must select capillaries in which the cells move following an occlusion. Also, one tends to select capillaries with low hematocrits. Thus the methods may force one to select for study only a portion of the total population of capillaries in a given tissue that have either high or low hydrostatic pressures, and hence possibly larger L_p's. The validity of this criticism and its implications have not been tested.

Between 1969 and 1974, Michel et al (47) reintroduced the original Landis method that involved both occlusion and cannulation of the capillaries. They recognized that if properly modified the Landis method could yield the most information from the fewest assumptions. They suggested two methods (*Method I* and *II*). *Method I* is the same as Landis' method except that the micropipette (Figure 1a) is put to more efficient use. It is filled with a protein solution of known composition and measureable colloid osmotic pressure. Human red cells are added as markers. The solution in the pipette can be changed, so Π_c can be controlled. Once the capillary is cannulated, it is perfused from the pipette to introduce the solution of known composition. The capillary is then occluded and the pipette is used both to measure and adjust P_c'. The composition of the medium bathing the tissue can be manipulated to influence Π_t and P_t. The distance (l) between a marker cell and the occluding probe is measured as a function of time. This procedure is repeated in the same capillary at several different hydrostatic pressures, and estimates of L_p and P_L' are then determined using the analytical procedure of the Landis method (Figures 1c & 1d). However, unlike the Landis method, this method obtains results from each capillary studied. Human red cells (4–5 μm) are used as markers because they pass easily through the orifice of the perfusion pipette (~10 μm i.d.) without plugging it. They are thought to serve as good flow indicators, but the smaller cells may lead to an underestimation of L_p. Diameters of amphibian capillaries are as large as 20–25 μm. During the occlusion, when fluid flow is slow, human cells may settle out and roll along the bottom of the capillary. In this case, they would trace the velocity of plasma in the outer one-fourth or one-fifth of the tube cross section. If a velocity profile develops, then the cells would move at approximately half the average velocity. Michel et al (47) discuss this problem for the case of a capillary 10 μm i.d. and conclude that the cells are an accurate marker. Of all the available techniques, *Method I* allows direct control or manipulation of the greatest number of terms in the Starling relationship. Estimates of L_p, P_L', σ, and solute permeability can all be deduced from the same basic experimental arrangement (8, 11, 12, 31, 32, 41). Thus *Method I* can provide the most quantitative information about the biophysical nature of the fluid exchange barrier—at least in amphibian capillaries, where nearly all the conditions can be defined. *Method I* shows the most promise for combining biophysical and structural data (36, 38, 46) into a detailed, testable, real-time picture of passive transcapillary transport and the nature of the exchange barrier.

Method II (47) is an analytical model that describes the change in the length of a plasma column with time following an occlusion. Presumably, it was developed to reduce the number of occlusions necessary to obtain data from the cannulated capillaries. In this sense it is similar to the Lee model. However, *Method II* is oversimplified and involves assumptions that make it applicable only to amphibian mesenteric capillaries. The model assumes that the protein mass is conserved, so $\sigma = 1$. It also assumes that Π_t and P_t are zero. Furthermore, it assumes that Π_c is a simple linear function of the plasma protein concentration. Finally, one must guess what the equilibrium distance (l_∞) between a marker cell and the occluding probe will be in order to complete the data analysis. The assumption that Π_c and C_t are linearly related is not unreasonable for frog plasma because initial concentrations are only 1–3 g%. But in mammals, initial protein concentrations are 4–7 g% and in a range where the relationship between Π_c and C_t is nonlinear. The assumptions about the tissue pressures are questionable. The recent papers by Fraser, Smaje & Verrinder (14) and Clough & Smaje (5) provide convincing evidence that tissue pressures in cat mesentery change dramatically with time during an experiment and are not zero unless conditions over the mesentery are carefully controlled. But the major drawback of *Method II,* as Michel has discussed (47), is the need to guess l_∞. Indeed, the experimental data shown by Michel et al (47) never reached equilibrium, because either the experiments were not carried out far enough, the vessels were injured by the cannulation procedure, or σ was significantly less than one. Interestingly, Michel (41) reported an average value of σ for albumin of 0.825 ± 0.035 (S.E.) in 7 frog mesenteric capillaries. These results were confirmed in a more recent study on 15 capillaries (42) where an average value of 0.815 ± 0.023 (S.E.) was found. *Method II* has been used in a number of studies, and selected values for L_p compare favorably with those recorded by *Method I* (Table 1). It has also been used to examine the effect of plasma proteins on measured values of L_p (37). Because of the many questionable assumptions in *Method II,* it might be worth repeating the more important experiments (37) that employed it and this time analyze the data with the Lee model. The Lee model would eliminate the need to guess l_∞ and all the questionable assumptions except that $\sigma = 1$.

Although intravascular dyes have been used for many years to view solute movement across single capillaries, Wiederhielm (67, 68) was the first to use an impermeable dye in conjunction with a video densitometric method to quantitate the *relative* water permeability between arterial and venous capillaries. Single capillaries in frog mesentery were perfused with plasma albumin tagged with Evans blue dye. The capillary under study was occluded and the perfusion stopped. An osmotic transient was then induced by dropping a sucrose solution onto the mesentery, and the optical density of the tagged albumin was measured with time. Relative filtration coefficients, or hydraulic conductivities, were then computed from the results. The experimental design required no major assumptions except that the Starling relationship was valid. Both solute and solvent exchange could be studied, but only *relative* values for water permeability could be measured unless additional assumptions were inserted into the analysis. Wiederhielm (67, 68) found that the average *relative* water permeability of venous capillaries was twice that of arterial capillaries. The densitometric measurements (68) were comparable to the results of Intaglietta (22), who used the RBC tracking method and found that L_p of venous capillaries in frog mesentery was 1.6 times L_p in arterial capillaries.

Levick & Michel (33) recently described two densitometric methods for computing L_p in frog mesenteric capillaries. We will call them *Methods A* and *B.* They are similar to *Methods I* and *II* (47). Single capillaries are cannulated and perfused with frog Ringer's solution containing T-1824-labeled albumin. In *Method A,* a capillary is occluded and step changes in capillary pressure are applied through the perfusion pipette. The optical density of the dye complex is measured as a function of time from photographs taken every 5 seconds and is related to the protein concentration. The initial fluid flux at each pressure is calculated from the initial change in optical density and plotted versus P_c'. An estimate of L_p is computed from the slope of the graph. The analysis is essentially the same as the Landis method and Michel's *Method I.* One simply measures dye or protein concentration rather than cell separation or distance. Because the results are computed from photographs taken only every 5 seconds, the initial change in fluid flux at $t = 0$ is missed. Thus L_p will be underestimated unless faster sampling rates are used. Another problem with *Method A* and all similar methods is that it assumes that L_p is independent of pressure (P_c'). Levick & Michel (33) used *Method B* to test this assumption [Figure 8 in (33)] and found in the same capillary that L_p increased from 67×10^{-4} to $95 \times 10^{-4} \mu m \cdot sec^{-1} \cdot cmH_2O^{-1}$ when P_c' was increased from 18 to 26 cmH_2O. Even though L_p increased by 42%, they concluded that the change was not significant. Regardless of whether the assumption inherent in *Method A* is valid, it is clearly not the method to use in a study of the relationship between L_p and changes in capillary hydrostatic pressure. *Method B* (33) is simply the densitometric version of *Method II* (47). All the same assumptions about $P_t = 0$, $\Pi_t = 0$, $\sigma = 1$, and the linear relationship between Π_c and C_t are made, but unlike *Method II* it is not necessary to guess the equilibrium condition.

Existing densitometric techniques for evaluating filtration parameters are presently limited either to large capillaries that can be cannulated (33) or to the measurement of *relative* water permeabilities (67, 68). However, Blake & Gross (2) recently introduced a fluid-exchange model of the occluded capillary that is directly applicable to densitometric experiments. It is more sensitive than the Lee model, and the general form considers axial variations in filtration parameters. Application of the Blake-Gross model to densitometric occlusion experiments would add the same sort of efficiency to densitometric experiments and data analysis that the Lee model contributed to the Landis-type experiments, but with added advantages. The Blake-Gross model was developed from a system of one-dimensional equations that described postocclusion fluid transport including the influences of fluid filtration and solute transport. For the case when transcapillary fluid flow is small relative to capillary blood flow, a condition also required in the Lee model, Blake & Gross obtained an exact solution that predicts the concentration of an intravascular impermeable dye or protein as a function of time following a single occlusion:

$$I/I_0 = \left[1 + \frac{P_e'(x) - (aC_0 + bC_0^2)}{(aC_0 + 2bC_0^2)}\right]\left\{1 - \exp\left[\frac{-4L_p(x)t}{D}(aC_0 + 2bC_0^2)\right]\right\} \qquad 7.$$

where I is the intravascular dye concentration, I_0 is the initial dye concentration, C_0 is the initial total protein concentration, and a and b are best-fit coefficients relating Π_c and C_0. The dependence of $L_p(x)$ and $P_e'(x)$ on the axial distance along the capillary is explicitly indicated by the argument notation. This particular solution assumes that $\sigma = 1$, so an equilibrium condition can be predicted. A value for $P_e'(x)$ over a small interval (Δx) in a capillary can be found from the large time asymptote of equation 7, and L_p can then be evaluated from a best fit of the exponential relationship describing I and t. If an equilibrium is not clearly established in an experiment, then best-fit values of L_p and P_e' can be obtained, without guessing the equilibrium condition, in a manner similar to the procedures used in the application of the Lee model. The Blake-Gross model is to date the most complete, usable fluid exchange model. If properly implemented, it would require only a single occlusion from which L_p and P_e' could be deduced at different sites along the capillary. No cannulation would be needed, and the subjectivity involved in tracking the relative motion of two red cells would be eliminated. The above solution of the model requires that the length scale for $L_p(x)$ be long relative to the region of the measurement, but all models presently available have this constraint. With densitometric methods, the sampling region can be limited to 1–5% of the capillary length. Measureable axial variations in permeability probably do not occur over a scale less than 2–3% of the length of most capillaries. However, in studies designed to quantitate the axial variation in L_p, Gore et al (16) found nearly a 10-fold change in L_p along the length of rat intestinal muscle capillaries, and Wiederhielm (67) observed in several cases nearly an 11-fold change along the length of frog mesenteric capillaries. Thus, care must be taken to determine over what interval L_p may be treated as a constant.

RESULTS AND IMPLICATIONS OF SOME RECENT SINGLE-CAPILLARY STUDIES

A number of recent studies of capillary hydraulic conductivity and permeability (8, 9, 11, 12, 31, 32, 36–38, 42, 43, 46) have given direction to current interpretations of the fluid exchange process, and added some interesting insights into the probable physical nature of the exchange barrier. For example, Michel (43) examined the effect of temperature on the hydraulic conductivity of single capillaries in frog mesentery using *Method I* (47) and found that the ratio of the L_p's measured at two different temperatures was equal to the inverse ratio of the viscosities of water at the different temperatures. One interpretation of this observation is that the pathways for water transport are stable membrane structures that are not significantly altered by temperature variations in the physiological range. Curry (9) repeated these measurements and examined the effect of temperature on L_p with and without albumin in the capillary perfusion medium. He confirmed Michel's observation (43) and also found that the relationship between L_p and water viscosity at different temperatures was unaffected by albumin. Thus the apparent stability of the membrane channels was independent of the presence of albumin in the perfusate. However, in an earlier study, Mason, Curry & Michel (37) found that the magnitude of L_p increased 4–5-fold when the protein concentration was reduced to zero from 0.1 g%. L_p was independent of protein concentration above 0.1 g%. The implication of the combined observations of Michel (43), Curry (9), and Mason et al (37) is that albumin apparently does not influence the structure or geometry of the fluid channels, yet its presence in the capillary determines the magnitude of L_p and is necessary for maintenance of a normal water permeability across the capillary wall. Presumably, albumin determines the magnitude of L_p by coating the capillary wall or by filling the fluid channels. Protein-concentration polarization effects may also be a determinant of the final magnitude of L_p. Curry (10) recently developed a model to describe fluid movement through a fiber-filled network that can account for the effects of surface coats on capillary permeability. The model accounts for the hydraulic conductivity in terms of the physical nature of a fibrous protein network and does not depend on a specific geometry for a hypothetical pore.

Not only are the plasma proteins important for maintaining the normal magnitude of L_p (37) and permeability (31, 32), but they also appear to help maintain the integrity of the endothelial layer within all segments of the vasculature (49). It is interesting that whole-organ studies of transvascular exchange are often performed on organs perfused with physiological salt solutions containing no protein (17). The results of such studies are open to serious question in view of the single vessel studies (32, 37, 49), and ought to be reevaluated.

It has been known for years that there is a permeability gradient along the capillary length, but a quantitative expression for L_p as a function of capillary length in different tissues has been difficult to obtain. Recently, Gore, Schoknecht & Bohlen (16) measured L_p's at different known positions along capillaries in rat intestinal muscle and found a very steep gradient that increased exponentially from the arterial to the venous end. An empirical expression was developed from the data (52) and was used to predict the different effects that a variable hydraulic conductivity might have on transcapillary fluid exchange. It is still uncertain what happens to fluid permeability at the extreme ends of capillaries and in venules. Wiederhielm (68) showed that the *relative* permeability in frog mesentery increases along the capillaries but decreases again in the venules. Other measurements in the cat mesentery (14) indicate that L_p remains elevated in the venules. Regional differences in L_p both within and among capillaries can be explained by assuming a difference in either pore density or pore size. Michel (42) did a series of experiments designed to test which factor was the more probable explanation for the variability in L_p among single capillaries in frog mesentery. Both L_p and σ for albumin were measured. In 15 capillaries, L_p ranged from 15×10^{-4} to $120 \times 10^{-4} \mu m \cdot sec^{-1} \cdot cmH_2O^{-1}$, while σ for albumin remained remarkably constant at 0.815 ± 0.023 (S.E.). The fact that L_p was relatively independent of σ for albumin implies that the size of the hypothetical pores is small and probably uniform, so the variability in L_p is more likely explained by differences in pore density. Additional studies (36, 38, 46) have since attempted to identify structural features in capillaries where the filtration parameters are known. Svensjö et al (65) studied the effect of bradykinin on vascular leakage of large-molecular-weight fluorescent dextrans and protein. Both morphological and physiological measurements were made. The results suggested that an increase in the venular efflux of large molecules induced by bradykinin was caused by an increase in the density of large pores. The increase in macromolecular efflux caused by bradykinin could be greatly reduced by the application of isoproterenol or norepinephrine.

Two recent papers on small-solute exchange contain important implications about fluid exchange and the general nature of the capillary exchange barrier. Curry et al (12) made an imaginative modification of *Method I* and measured the reflection coefficients of frog mesenteric capillaries to NaCl, urea, sucrose, and cyanocobalamin. They found no significant correlation between σ and the molecular size of the test molecules. One interpretation of this observation is that water is able to cross capillary walls by a route unavailable to small hydrophilic molecules. Curry et al (12) used the parallel-channel model described by Lifson (34) to interpret the results. They concluded that exclusive channels for water are arranged in parallel with channels shared by both water and small hydrophilic solutes. Presumably, the exclusive water channels are associated with the endothelial cells, and the shared channels are intercellular junctions. Their results indicate that the exclusive water channels account for about 10% of the total hydraulic conductivity in frog mesenteric capillaries. The remaining 90% of the average, or total, hydraulic conductivity is indicative of the channels shared by solutes and water. In an extension of this work, Curry (8) measured the permeabilities of the capillary wall to low-molecular-weight hydrophilic solutes. The results provide additional evidence to support the hypothesis that the variability in L_p and solute permeability within and among capillaries is caused by differences in pore density rather than pore size and geometry.

McDonagh & Gore (39) have used the Lee method (30) to make comparative measurements of L_p in single capillaries in postural (*red*) and locomotor (*white*) skeletal muscle with the idea of relating single-capillary data to whole-organ function. They found that L_p in *red* muscle capillaries was consistently 2–3 times greater than L_p in *white* muscle capillaries. These results raise a number of questions about the validity and interpretation of previous whole-organ exchange studies. For example, Folkow & Halicka (13) measured the capillary filtration coefficient (CFC) of *red* and *white* skeletal muscles using standard whole-organ volumetric methods. They found that the CFC in *red* muscle was twice that in *white* muscle and concluded that the difference was due entirely to differences in the functional surface area (S_f). However, CFC measured by whole-organ procedures is the product of L_p and S_f, and the volumetric method cannot separate the two variables experimentally. Hence, Folkow & Halicka (13) had to assume that the L_p's in *red* and *white* skeletal muscle capillaries were identical. The observations of McDonagh & Gore (39) show that this assumption is not valid and that the differences in CFC can be explained equally well in terms of measured variations in L_p. Clearly, whole-organ CFC measurements provide only a poor comparative estimate of S_f, or L_p, especially when applied to mixed muscle types or to organs with parallel vascular networks such as the intestine.

Recent measurements of hydrostatic pressures in single capillaries also indicate the need to reexamine previous interpretations of whole-organ experiments. For example, Gore & Bohlen (15) made direct measurements of microvascular pressures in the intestinal muscle layers, the surface of the submucosa, and the mucosal villi of the rat. When systemic arterial blood pressure was maintained at 100–110 mmHg, capillary pressures in the intestinal muscle layers averaged 23.8 ± 1.5 (S.E.) mmHg, while capillary pressures in the mucosal villi averaged 13.8 ± 2.2 (S.E.) mmHg. The results show that significant regional differences in capillary pressures normally exist between the intestinal muscle and mucosal vasculatures and imply that long-term steady-state regional differences in transcapillary fluid balance also occur in the intestine. Precapillary to postcapillary resistance ratios were calculated for the different microvascular regions from the pressure data and measurements of relative blood flow. The measured pressures, flows, and calculated resistance ratios in the individual microvascular regions of the intestine indicated that several major assumptions, upon which the validity of volumetric estimates of whole organ exchange parameters depends, are not correct when applied to the intestine. Indeed, direct observations from single-capillary studies (15, 39) raise questions about the meaning of whole-organ CFC measurements in the intestine and skeletal muscle and indicate the need to reevaluate the results from previous whole-organ studies (64) as they pertain to questions about regulation and exchange. Attempts have been made to combine data from a variety of sources into a coherent picture of the total fluid exchange process (20, 69). Very recently, Wiederhielm (71) completed a series of studies on the dynamics of capillary fluid exchange in both physiological and pathological conditions. The study is an extension of his earlier work (69) and uses a nonlinear computer simulation model based on recent experimental data. The results show the integrated effects of all the factors that comprise the Starling relationship.

SUMMARY

The Landis occlusion experiment has been modified in many ways and applied in studies of fluid exchange to amphibians, birds and mammals. It is presently limited in application to thin tissues and vessels that can be cannulated. If the technical problems of using video densitometry and low-light-level tracer methods are solved, then thicker stationary tissues such as load bearing skeletal muscle and the arrested heart can be studied at the single capillary level. Current capabilities in this area of study would be greatly extended if an experimentally usable mathematical model, like the Blake-Gross model, were developed that described fluid exchange in the occluded or unoccluded capillary with $\sigma \leqslant 1$. "Leaky" capillary beds could then be studied with confidence and our knowledge of whole-body and whole-organ fluid balance could be extended. Physiological studies on intestinal mucosa are required to extend our knowledge of fluid exchange in the intestine. More information about skeletal muscle at the single capillary level is needed, and improved estimates of functional exchange surface area are needed to correlate single-vessel studies with whole-organ measurements. Significant advances have been made in our understanding of the biophysics of the capillary membrane, but information about morphological correlates still lags far behind. Indeed, there is a serious need for more hard data and less speculation. The recent studies by Michel and his colleagues (36, 38, 46) are encouraging in this regard because of the possibilities for obtaining physiological, biophysical, and morphological information from the same series of experiments under controlled, quantitative, defined conditions.

Literature Cited

1. Apelblat, A., Katzir-Katchalsky, A., Silberberg, A. 1974. A mathematical analysis of capillary-tissue fluid exchange. *Biorheology* 11:1–49
2. Blake, T. R., Gross, J. F. 1976. Fluid exchange from a microoccluded capillary with axial variation of filtration parameters. *Biorheology* 13:357–66
3. Brenner, B., Baylis, C., Deen, W. M. 1976. Transport of molecules across renal glomerular capillaries. *Physiol. Rev.* 56:502–34
4. Caro, C. G., Pedley, T. J., Schroter, R. C., Seed, W. A. 1978. The systemic microcirculation. In *The Mechanics of the Circulation,* Chap. 13. NY: Oxford Univ. Press
5. Clough, G., Smaje, L. H. 1978. Simultaneous measurement of pressure in the interstitium and the terminal lymphatics of the cat mesentery. *J. Physiol. London* 283:457–68
6. Crone, C., Christensen, O. 1979. Transcapillary transport of small solutes and water. *Int. Rev. Physiol., Cardiovasc. Physiol. III* 18:149–213
7. Curry, F. E. 1974. A hydrodynamic description of the osmotic reflection coefficient with application to the pore theory of transcapillary exchange. *Microvasc. Res.* 8:236–52
8. Curry, F. E. 1979. Permeability coefficients of the capillary wall to low molecular weight hydrophilic solutes measured in single perfused capillaries of frog mesentery. *Microvasc. Res.* 17:290–308
9. Curry, F. E. 1979. The effect of temperature on the hydraulic conductivity of single capillaries of frog mesentery: The role of albumin in the perfusate. *Microvasc. Res.* 17: Pt 2, S82, Abstr. #18.3
10. Curry, F. E. 1980. Is the transport of hydrophilic substances across the capillary wall determined by a network of fibrous molecules? *Physiologist.* In press
11. Curry, F. E., Mason, J. C., Michel, C. C. 1974. The measurement in a single capillary of the filtration coefficient and the permeability and osmotic reflexion coefficient to sucrose. *J. Physiol. London* 241:111–12P (Abstr.)
12. Curry, F. E., Mason, J. C., Michel, C. C. 1976. Osmotic reflexion coefficients of capillary walls to low molecular weight hydrophilic solutes measured in single perfused capillaries of the frog mesentery. *J. Physiol. London* 261: 319–36
13. Folkow, B., Halicka, H. D. 1968. A comparison between "red" and "white" muscle with respect to blood supply, capillary surface area and oxygen uptake during rest and exercise. *Microvasc. Res.* 1:1–14
14. Fraser, P. A., Smaje, L. H., Verrinder, A. 1978. Microvascular pressures and filtration coefficients in the cat mesentery. *J. Physiol. London* 283:439–56
15. Gore, R. W., Bohlen, H. G. 1977. Microvascular pressures in rat intestinal muscle and muscosal villi. *Am. J. Physiol.* 233:H685–93
16. Gore, R. W., Schoknecht, W. E., Bohlen, H. G. 1976. Filtration coefficients of single capillaries in rat intestinal muscle. *Microcirculation,* ed. J. Grayson, W. Zingg, 1:331–32. NY: Plenum
17. Grabowski, E. F., Bassingthwaighte, J. B. 1976. An osmotic weight transient model for estimation of capillary transport parameters in myocardium. *Microcirculation,* ed. J. Grayson, W. Zingg, 2:29–50. NY: Plenum
18. Gross, J. F., Aroesty, J. 1972. Mathematical models of capillary flow: A critical review. *Biorheology* 9:225–64
19. Guyton, A. C., Granger, H. J., Taylor, A. E. 1971. Interstitial fluid pressure. *Physiol. Rev.* 51:527–63
20. Guyton, A. C., Taylor, A. E., Granger, H. J. 1975. *Circulatory Physiology II: Dynamics and Control of the Body Fluids,* Chap. 8. Philadelphia: W. B. Saunders
21. Haddy, F. J., Scott, J. B., Grega, G. J. 1976. Peripheral circulation: fluid transfer across the microvascular membrane. *Int. Rev. Physiol., Cardiovasc. Physiol. II* 9:63–109
22. Intaglietta, M. 1967. Evidence for a gradient of permeability in frog mesenteric capillaries. *Bibl. Anat.* 9:465–68
23. Intaglietta, M. 1977. Transcapillary exchange of fluid in single microvessels. *Microcirculation,* ed. G. Kaley, B. M. Altura, Vol. I, Chap. 9. Baltimore: University Park Press
24. Intaglietta, M., Zweifach, B. W. 1966. Indirect method for measurement of pressure in blood capillaries. *Circ. Res.* 19:199–205
25. Intaglietta, M., Zweifach, B. W. 1974. Microcirculatory basis of fluid exchange. *Adv. Biol. Med. Phys.* 15: 111–59
26. Landis, E. M. 1926. The capillary pressure in frog mesentery as determined by

micro-injection methods. *Am. J. Physiol.* 75:548–70
27. Landis, E. M. 1927. Micro-injection studies of capillary permeability. II. The relation between capillary pressure and the rate at which fluid passes through the walls of single capillaries. *Am. J. Physiol.* 82:217–38
28. Landis, E. M. 1930. The capillary blood pressure in mammalian mesentery as determined by the micro-injection method. *Am. J. Physiol.* 93:353–62
29. Landis, E. M., Pappenheimer, J. R. 1963. Exchange of substances through the capillary walls. *Handbook of Physiology, Circulation,* ed. W. F. Hamilton, Sect. 2, Vol. II, Chap. 29. Washington DC: Am. Physiol. Soc.
30. Lee, J. S., Smaje, L. H., Zweifach, B. W. 1971. Fluid movement in occluded single capillaries of rabbit omentum. *Circ. Res.* 28:358–70
31. Levick, J. R., Michel, C. C. 1973. The permeability of individually perfused frog mesenteric capillaries to T1824 and T1824-albumin as evidence for a large pore system. *Q. J. Exp. Physiol.* 58: 67–85
32. Levick, J. R., Michel, C. C. 1973. The effect of bovine albumin on the permeability of frog mesenteric capillaries. *Q. J. Exp. Physiol.* 58:87–97
33. Levick, J. R., Michel, C. C. 1977. A densitometric method for determining the filtration coefficients of single capillaries in the frog mesentery. *Microvasc. Res.* 13:141–51
34. Lifson, N. 1970. Revised equations for the osmotic transient method. In *Alfred Benzon Symposium II. Capillary Permeability,* ed. C. Crone, N. Lassen, pp. 302–5. NY: Academic
35. Linde, B. 1976. Studies on the vascular exchange function in canine subcutaneous adipose tissue. *Acta. Physiol. Scand.* Suppl. 433, pp. 7–43
36. Loudon, M. F., Michel, C. C., White, I. F. 1979. The labelling of vesicles in frog endothelial cells with ferritin. *J. Physiol. London.* In press
37. Mason, J. C., Curry, F. E., Michel, C. C. 1977. The effects of proteins upon the filtration coefficient of individually perfused frog mesenteric capillaries. *Microvasc. Res.* 13:185–202
38. Mason, J. C., Curry, F. E., White, I. F., Michel, C. C. 1979. The ultrastructure of frog mesenteric capillaries of known filtration coefficient. *Q. J. Exp. Physiol.* 64:217–24
39. McDonagh, P. F., Gore, R. W. 1978. Comparison of hydraulic conductivities in single capillaries of red versus white skeletal muscle. *Microvasc. Res.* 15:269 (Abstr. #23)
40. Michel, C. C. 1972. Flows across the capillary wall. In *Cardiovascular Fluid Dynamics,* ed. D. H. Bergel, Vol. 2, Ch. 16. NY: Academic
41. Michel, C. C. 1977. Osmotic reflexion coefficients of single capillaries to myoglobin and serum albumin. *J. Physiol. London* 272:95–96P (Abstr.)
42. Michel, C. C. 1978. The relative uniformity of pore size in frog mesenteric capillaries. *J. Physiol. London* 282:46–47P (Abstr.)
43. Michel, C. C. 1978. The effect of temperature on the filtration coefficient of single capillaries in the frog mesentery. *J. Physiol. London* 284:105P (Abstr.)
44. Michel, C. C. 1978. Flow through capillary walls. *Cardiovascular and Pulmonary Dynamics,* ed. M. Y. Jaffrin, INSERM Symp. 71:209–20. Paris: INSERM
45. Michel, C. C. 1978. The measurement of permeability in single capillaries. *Arch. Int. Physiol. Biochem.* 86:657–67
46. Michel, C. C., Clough, G. 1979. Transport of ferritin through endothelial cell vesicles. In preparation
47. Michel, C. C., Mason, J. C., Curry, F. E., Tooke, J. E., Hunter, P. J. 1974. A development of the Landis technique for measuring the filtration coefficient of individual capillaries in the frog. *Q. J. Exp. Physiol.* 59:283–309
48. Middleman, S. 1972. Transcapillary exchange. *Transport Phenomena in the Cardiovascular System,* Chap. 3. NY: Wiley-Interscience
49. Morrison, A. S., Orci, L., Berwick, L., Winegrad, A. I. 1977. Significance of an intact endothelium with regard to the metabolism of aortic intima-media preparations. In *The Biochemistry of Smooth Muscle,* ed. N. L. Stephens, pp. 83–103. Baltimore: Univ. Park Press
50. Nicoll, P. A., Taylor, A. E. 1977. Lymph formation and flow. *Ann. Rev. Physiol.* 39:73–95
51. Ogston, A. G., Michel, C. C. 1978. General descriptions of passive transport of neutral solute and solvent through membranes. *Prog. Biophys. Molec. Biol.* 34:197–217
52. Papenfuss, H. D., Gore, R. W., Gross, J. F. 1980. Effect of variable hydraulic conductivity on transcapillary fluid exchange. Application to the microcirculation of rat intestinal muscle. *Microvasc. Res.* In press

53. Pappenheimer, J. R., Soto-Rivera, A. 1948. Effective osmotic pressure of the plasma proteins and other quantities associated with the capillary circulation in the hindlimbs of cats and dogs. *Am. J. Physiol.* 152:471–91
54. Parker, J. C., Guyton, A. C., Taylor, A. E. 1979. Pulmonary transcapillary exchange and pulmonary edema. *Int. Rev. Physiol., Cardiovasc. Physiol. III* 18:261–315
55. Renkin, E. M. 1977. Multiple pathways of capillary permeability. *Circ. Res.* 41:735–43
56. Renkin, E. M. 1978. The Microcirculatory Society Eugene M. Landis Award Lecture. Transport pathways through capillary endothelium. *Microvasc. Res.* 15:123–35
57. Renkin, E. M., Curry, F. E. 1979. Transport of water and solutes across capillary endothelium. In *Membrane Transport in Biology. Transport Organs,* ed. G. H. Giebisch, Vol. IV, A, Chap. 1. NY: Springer
58. Schoknecht, W. E., Gore, R. W. 1975. An efficient algorithm for the computation of capillary filtration coefficients. *Bull. Am. Phys. Soc.* 20:824 (Abstr.)
59. Smaje, L. H., Lee, J. S., Zweifach, B. W. 1971. A new approach to the indirect measurement of capillary pressure and filtration coefficient. *6th Eur. Conf. Microcirculation, Aalborg, 1970,* pp. 254–58. Basel: Karger
60. Smaje, L. H., Zweifach, B. W., Intaglietta, M. 1970. Micropressures and capillary filtration coefficients in single vessels of the cremaster muscle of the rat. *Microvasc. Res.* 2:96–110
61. Starling, E. H. 1896. On the absorption of fluids from the connective tissue spaces. *J. Physiol. London* 19:312–26
62. Staub, N. C. 1974. Pulmonary edema. *Physiol. Rev.* 54:678–811
63. Stromberg, D. D., Wiederhielm, C. A. 1977. Intravascular and tissue space oncotic and hydrostatic pressures. *Microcirculation,* ed. G. Kaley, B. M. Altura, Vol. I, Chap. 8. Baltimore: Univ. Park Press
64. Svanvik, J., Lundgren, O. 1977. Gastrointestinal circulation. *Int. Rev. Physiol., Gastrointest. Physiol. II* 12: 1–34
65. Svensjö, E., Arfors, K., Raymond, R. M., Grega, G. J. 1979. Morphological and physiological correlation of bradyinin-induced macromolecular efflux. *Am. J. Physiol.* 236:H600–6
66. Wayland, H., Fox, J. R., Elmore, M. D. 1974. Quantitative fluorescent tracer studies *in vivo. Modern Methods in Microcirculatory Research Applied to Studies of Vascular Permeability and Transport* (Spec. reprint proc. symp. held during 8th Eur. Conf. Microcirc., Le Touquet, France), ed. H. Wayland, pp. 21–28. Los Angeles: Calif. Inst. Technol.
67. Wiederhielm, C. A. 1966. Transcapillary and interstitial transport phenomena in the mesentery. *Fed. Proc.* 25:1789–98
68. Wiederhielm, C. A. 1967. Analysis of small vessel function. In *Physical Bases of Circulatory Transport: Regulation and Exchange,* ed. E. B. Reeve, A. C. Guyton, Chap. 19. Philadelphia: Saunders
69. Wiederhielm, C. A. 1968. Dynamics of transcapillary fluid exchange. *J. Gen. Physiol.* 52:29–61
70. Wiederhielm, C. A. 1972. The interstitial space. *Biomechanics: Its Foundations and Objectives,* ed. Y. C. Fung, N. Perrone, M. Anliker, Ch. 11. NY: Prentice-Hall
71. Wiederhielm, C. A. 1979. Dynamics of capillary fluid exchange. A non-linear computer simulation. *Microvasc. Res.* 18:48–82
72. Wind, F. 1937. Versuche zur unmittelbaren Bestimmung des Flüssigkeitsaustritts aus den Blutkapillären des Mesenteriums und des Nierenglomerulus biem Kaltblüter. *Arch. Exp. Pathol. Pharmacol.* 186:161–84
73. Zweifach, B. W., Intaglietta, M. 1968. Mechanics of fluid movement across single capillaries in the rabbit. *Microvasc. Res.* 1:83–101
74. Zweifach, B. W., Silberberg, A. 1979. The interstitial-lymphatic flow system. *Int. Rev. Physiol., Cardiovasc. Physiol. III* 18:215–60

Ann. Rev. Physiol. 1980. 42:359–71

NEURONAL CONTROL OF MICROVESSELS

❖1273

Sune Rosell

Department of Pharmacology, Karolinska Institutet,
104 01 Stockholm 60, Sweden

INTRODUCTION

Most studies of the neuronal control of the microcirculation have involved whole organ measurements of blood flow, tissue volume, or capillary filtration (61). Consequently, accounts of the responses of the different series-coupled sections of a vascular bed—i.e. the pre- and postcapillary resistance sections, exchange section and postcapillary capacitance section—are usually based on such measurements. Only a few studies have involved direct observations in vivo of single vessels during nerve activity. The present review is thus based mainly on data from whole organ measurements.

Comprehensive descriptions of the cardiovascular control mechanisms emanating from higher brain structures (81) and of homeostatic reflex mechanisms have been published (66). This review is limited to the local nervous control mechanisms, a topic also reviewed in recent years (61, 77). An excellent review (61) discusses in detail the control systems, including nervous control, of the vascular beds of skeletal muscle, skin, and intestine. The present survey summarizes some of the recently developed hypotheses and new data related to (*a*) nervous control of vascular resistance and capacitance; (*b*) nervous control of vascular permeability; and (*c*) the peptidergic nervous control of the microcirculation.

Nervous Control of Vascular Resistance and Capacitance Sections

Approximately 80% of the total resistance in a vascular bed resides in the precapillary vessels. From the results of studies on whole organs it has therefore been inferred that the increased peripheral resistance caused by

0066-4278/80/0315-0359$01.00

sympathetic discharge is due to constriction of the terminal arterioles, precapillary arterioles, and metarterioles. Recent direct in vivo microcirculatory observations in the mesentery of the rat have shown that the principal arteries, small arteries, and terminal arterioles all constrict in response to sympathetic nerve stimulation, whereas the precapillary arterioles with an inner diameter of <18 μm did not respond to such nerve stimulation (30). This indicates that the resistance network of the mesentery is sparsely innervated, which is interesting in view of the finding that sympathetic nerve stimulation hardly reduces the canine mesenteric whole blood flow (4). Thus the nervous control of the mesenteric resistance section seems to be different from that of most other vascular beds. This makes it difficult to draw any conclusions regarding the neuronal control of the resistance section in various vascular beds from data from studies on the mesentery. In skeletal muscle the sympathetic innervation of the precapillary resistance section seems to be of greater importance than in the mesentery, since in the rat cremaster sympathetic activation caused vasoconstriction of all precapillary resistance vessels (34, 43). These findings have been confirmed by observations on the rat spinotrapezius muscle (3, 59). Sympathetic stimulation constricted all sections of the arterial tree, and the vasoconstrictor response was maintained in precapillary vessels down to 13 μm internal diameter throughout the stimulation period, whereas terminal arterioles (7–13 μm internal diameter) began to relax after 10–15 sec (59). This relaxation is in agreement with findings in whole organ studies indicating that the "sphincter section" is to a large extent under local control (26).

Bücherl & Schwab (12) proposed that there is separate sympathetic vasoconstrictor control of arterioles and precapillary sphincters. On bleeding an animal they observed a fall in blood–tissue oxygen transport with no appreciable change in arterial blood pressure or blood flow, which indicated that the number of open capillaries had been diminished even though the arterioles had not been narrowed. Similarly, the difference in changes of transcapillary transport of ^{86}Rb and resistance, respectively, as a result of sympathetic nerve activation in the cat was taken as support for the hypothesis that there is a separate nervous control of precapillary resistance vessels and sphincters (72). Direct observation of the cremasteric microvasculature also revealed that the smaller precapillary vessels, but not the larger arterioles, constricted when the vasomotor nerves were stimulated in the central nervous system (CNS) (3, 34). However, the larger arterioles could be activated when the stimulation parameters were increased, which indicated additional recruitment of nerve fibers or increased release of the transmitter. Thus the apparently independent nervous control of the precapillary sphincters and the arteriolar resistance vessels could be due to differences in sensitivity to noradrenaline. In fact, the precapillary arterioles have been shown to be more sensitive than the larger arterioles to topically applied noradrenaline (1, 59).

Within the same organ there may be regional differences in the adrenergic nervous control. Using microcirculatory techniques, the microvascular red blood cell velocity was measured in cat omental adipose tissue. Three different types of response were found upon stimulation of the sympathetic nerves (76): (*a*) a decrease in flow velocity (75% of the vessels); (*b*) no response (7%); and (*c*) an increase in flow (18%). Both increases and decreases in flow velocity were related to the stimulus frequency. Morphological and hemodynamic evidence indicates the presence of two compartments in adipose tissue (5)—one that is predominantly innervated by adrenergic fibers (and thus responds to sympathetic discharge with increased lipolysis and vascular reactions) and another that is not.

The sympathetic innervation may also vary between tissues on the venous side. Based on whole organ measurements in the cat skeletal muscle, it was calculated that adrenergic nervous stimulation induces a two-fold or greater increase in the pre- to postcapillary resistance ratio (62). This will result in a net transvascular absorption of fluid into the circulatory system due to a fall in the mean hydrostatic pressure. On the other hand, in canine subcutaneous adipose tissue there was no indication of fluid absorption during sympathetic nerve activity (53). Plethysmographic recording of the tissue volume combined with external monitoring of the blood volume revealed that the decrease in total volume could be accounted for by a decrease in the blood volume. After cessation of the nerve stimulation no significant net filtration was found. Thus mobilization of fluid from the interstitial space in adipose tissue into the blood does not seem to be due to sympathetic nerve activity, as is the case in skeletal muscle and skin (62).

The most likely explanation for the absence of net transvascular fluid movement during nerve stimulation in adipose tissue is that the mean hydrostatic capillary pressure is essentially unaltered because the pre- to postcapillary resistance ratio does not change. This means that there is an increased resistance in both pre- and postcapillary resistance vessels during sympathetic nerve stimulation. The differences between skeletal muscle and adipose tissue as regards venous responses to sympathetic nerve stimulation have not been confirmed by direct observations of the microvessels.

The absence of fluid mobilization in adipose tissue during nerve stimulation may constitute a protective mechanism to maintain local fluid homeostasis, as has been suggested for the splanchnic organs (64). Mechanical blood flow reduction did not cause net transvascular fluid movement either, which implied that "autoregulation" of the mean capillary pressure occurs under these circumstances. Elevation of the transmural pressure in human subcutaneous adipose tissue caused an active constrictor response in the resistance vessels, counteracting a rise in mean capillary pressure (38). Thus the mean capillary pressure in adipose tissue appears to be carefully balanced under several conditions that might disturb the local balance. The inability of baroreceptor mechanisms to activate the sympathetic nerves to adipose tissue (36, 63) may perhaps be looked upon as an additional protective mechanism.

In the intestine the nervous vascular control as regards the series-coupled vascular sections and the flow distribution in the different layers has been analyzed in several reports (9, 25, 41) and literature on the circulatory system in the alimentary canal has been reviewed recently (55). It has now been shown experimentally that the sympathetic nervous control of the intestinal blood flow is qualitatively and quantitatively similar in cat and human (42).

Thus the autoregulatory escape from the vasoconstrictor fiber influence has been demonstrated in humans. After the escape, the intestinal blood flow leveled off at a constant, somewhat reduced value; in comparison to resting conditions, blood from the muscularis was redistributed to the mucosa-submucosa. This redistribution may be due to a nervously induced closure of precapillary sphincters.

Nervous Control of Vascular Permeability

It is generally agreed that the sympathetic nervous system controls the transvascular exchange of fluid and solutes (*a*) by regulating the number of open capillaries and (*b*) by adjusting the pre- to postcapillary resistance ratio and thereby the capillary hydrostatic pressure (see 61). Another possible mechanism is that sympathetic nerves control the vascular permeability by adjusting the number of pores and their dimensions. Experimental evidence in favor of such a mechanism was lacking until it was found that sympathetic nerve stimulation can change vascular permeability in adipose tissue. The finding that sympathetic nerve stimulation induced an increase in the capillary filtration coefficient (CFC) in canine adipose tissue, despite a concomitant vasoconstriction (65), led to a series of investigations aimed at evaluating this possibility. The hydrodynamic conductivity, as measured by the CFC, is dependent on the total capillary surface area available for exchange processes and on the permeability. Therefore alterations in the CFC do not provide information about which of these two factors has changed (73). Indirect support for the idea that sympathetic nerve activity may actually increase the pore size was provided by the fact that the high CFC values found in subcutaneous adipose tissue following sympathetic nerve stimulation could only be produced by infusion of vasodilator substances known to increase permeability in other tissues—e.g. histamine and bradykinin (29). On the other hand, infusion of prostaglandin E_1, acetylcholine, or isoprenaline in concentrations high enough to produce maximal vasodilation (and consequently a maximal capillary surface area) caused only a moderate increase in CFC. To induce pronounced increments in the CFC, like those found on sympathetic nerve stimulation, more factors must be operating. Increased permeability may be one such factor. This hypothesis is also supported by the finding that when nerve stimulation was superimposed during infusion of prostaglandin E_1, acetylcholine, or isoprenaline, a further increase in CFC was obtained. This was not the case when sympathetic nerve activity was induced during infusion of histamine or bradykinin (29). The average isovolumetric pressure (Pci) in canine subcutaneous adipose tissue decreased from 9.4 mm Hg to 5.6 mm Hg upon sympathetic nerve stimulation with frequencies between 1 and 10 Hz (76). The decrease in Pci may be explained in several ways, including reduction in blood flow due to the vasoconstriction or absorption of fluid from the extravascular space due to a decrease in the capillary pressure during sympathetic nerve activity. The latter would tend to reduce the colloid osmotic pressure difference between blood and tissue and thus reduce the hydrostatic pressure necessary to keep the tissue isovolumetric. Another possibility is that sympathetic nerve activity may induce the formation or release of osmotically active substances that accumulate in the extravascular space and thus reduce the blood-tissue osmotic gradient. After it had been shown experimentally that such mechanisms were less likely to account for the effect, it was suggested that the decrease in Pci was a result of an increased capillary permeability that allowed osmotically active substances to cross the capillary membrane to a greater extent. As a consequence, the blood-tissue difference in osmotic pressure would diminish and the hydrostatic pressure, which counterbalances all pressures tending to cause fluid absorption in an isovolumetric state, may decrase. The observation that histamine, but not prostaglandin E_2, also decreased Pci supports this hypothesis, since histamine, but not prostaglandin E_2, is known to increase permeability in other vascular beds (60, 82).

The diffusion capacity for molecules that pass from the vessels into the tissue has been determined in subcutaneous adipose tissue (54). A single injection-indicator diffusion method (16, 17) was used to determine the PS-products (permeability–surface area products) for two molecules of different sizes, ^{14}C-sucrose (mol wt 342), and polyethylene glycol, ^{3}H-PEG (mol wt 800–900), during and after nerve stimulation at 0.5–6 Hz. Determinations were performed both during vasoconstriction and in the escape phase after the vasoconstriction had subsided or at low stimulation frequencies producing no vasoconstriction. During sympathetic nerve stimulation the PS-product for sucrose increased by 15% in spite of a vasoconstriction. When superimposed on a maximal vasodilatation, sympathetic nerve stimulation increased the PS-product for sucrose by approximately 40% and that for PEG by about 20%. The increases in the PS-products are probably not due to changes in blood flow, since the transvascular diffusion was predominantly barrier-limited. It is also unlikely that the increases in the PS-products are due to an increase in capillary surface area, since significant increases in the PS-products were also found during vasoconstriction—i.e. when the capillary surface area was decreased. Increases in the PS-product were even greater than those produced by a maximal vasodilatation. It is also possible that during nerve stimulation blood flow was distributed to parts of the adipose tissue having higher permeability. Although this possibility cannot entirely be excluded, it appears unlikely. The shapes of the concentration-time curves were similar under control conditions and during nerve stimulation, which indicated a similar distribution of transit times under these conditions. Thus the changes in the PS-products for sucrose and polyethylene glycol also indicate that in subcutaneous adipose tissue sympathetic nerve stimulation causes an increase in the vascular permeability for solutes.

The vessels at the far venous end of the exchange system, where smooth muscle cells are present, comprise a possible site for a permeability increase. Contraction of such vessels might occur without a measurable change in the total vascular resistance, which resides to only a minor extent in the post-capillary vessels. However, owing to the small surface area of these vessels in relation to the entire exchange surface area (88), it seems unlikely that a permeability increase in these vessels alone would be measureable as an increase in the PS-product for small molecules. In contrast, an increase in filtration capacity should be found even if a permeability change took place over only a small part of the surface area, provided that there was a change in pore size. This influences filtration to a much larger extent than diffusion, since filtration depends on the fourth and diffusion on the second power of the pore radius. Increased hydrostatic pressure has been advanced as a possible mediator of increased permeability produced by the histamine-type mediators, the "stretched pore phenomenon" (78, 87). However, it was later shown that this permeability increase also occurred without changes in hydrostatic capillary pressure (11, 56). Furthermore, the mean capillary pressure does not seem to change during sympathetic nerve activation in adipose tissue (53).

The permeability increase caused by histamine occurs predominantly in venules, particularly in those lacking smooth muscle cells (57). In fact, it has been suggested that the increased permeability induced by histamine occurs by contraction of endothelial cells (58). Use of fluorescein-labelled antibodies indicated (7) the presence of a contractile protein, actomyosin, in endothelial cells. In the rabbit ear chamber in vivo (80), sympathetic nerve-induced changes in capillary endothelial cells were described of the type later found with histamine and bradykinin (58). This suggests endothelial cell contraction. Moreover, histamine, bradykinin, and several prostaglandins applied topically on the everted hamster cheek pouch increased the leakage of fluorescein dextran (mol wt 145,000) into the microcirculation at postcapillary venules only (83). Electron microscopy of leaking postcapillary venules indicated that the leakage was due to endothelial cell contraction. One hypothesis is therefore that increased vascular permeability in adipose tissue during sympathetic nerve stimulation is due to endothelial cell contraction, possibly towards the venous end of the exchange section where the intercellular junctions seem to be looser (58).

The increase in vascular permeability is probably mediated by α-adrenoceptors, possibly on endothelial cells. The increase in the filtration coefficient and the decrease in the isovolumetric capillary pressure during nerve stimulation were blocked by α-adrenergic blocking agents (65, 75). Evidence exists for α-adrenergic receptors on endothelial cells from rabbit aorta (8). Moreover, the leakage produced by histamine, bradykinin, and prostaglandins when applied topically on the everted hamster cheek pouch was reduced in the presence of the adrenergic β_2-agonist terbutaline (84). Although a direct adrenergic effect on endothelial cells is a likely possibility, other mediators of the effect of sympathetic nerve stimulation on permeability should be considered. As has been pointed out already, histamine is commonly believed to increase vascular permeability, and adipose tissue is richly supplied with mast cells (19) containing large amounts of histamine (28). In canine subcutaneous adipose tissue histamine also caused increases in the PS-products for sucrose and PEG above the PS values produced by prostaglandin E_2 and papaverine, in doses giving vasodilatation of the same magnitude (54). However, the increase in vascular permeability following sympathetic nerve activity does not appear to be mediated by histamine, since the H_1-blocker mepyramine did not change the characteristic CFC increase following sympathetic nerve stimulation (65). Furthermore, when the histamine H_2-blocker cimetidine has been given in combination with mepyramine in such amounts as to completely abolish the vascular and metabolic effects of histamine, the CFC increase induced by sympathetic nerve stimulation still remained (E. Belfrage, unpublished observations).

A possible function of an increase in vascular permeability during nerve stimulation may be to promote the transvascular transport of large molecules, such as albumin, which are barrier-limited under physiological conditions. Although direct measurements of protein transport have not yet been carried out, indirect measurements, by means of determining the Pci, support this idea (75). Greater availability of albumin in the extracellular water compartment may increase the probability of fatty acid diffusion from the fat cells to blood. Fatty acids are water-insoluble. In blood they are transported by albumin. Albumin may also act as an acceptor of fatty acids in the extravascular compartment. Moreover, Rodbell (74) has shown in vitro that fatty acids act as regulators of lipolysis. The addition of albumin, acting as an acceptor of fatty acids, markedly enhanced the lipolytic rate. The effect on fatty acids is presumably due to inhibition of adenylate cyclase, leading to a decreased accumulation of cyclic AMP (23, 24). The effect will be appreciable when the fatty acid/albumin molar ratio exceeds three (23). The interstitial space of adipose tissue, where the fatty acids may accumulate during increased lipolysis and where the albumin concentration is lower than in blood, is the most likely location of a high concentration ratio. The fatty acid concentration in canine subcutaneous adipose tissue in vivo is elevated by sympathetic nerve stimulation (27). Therefore an increased outward diffusion of albumin due to increased permeability during sympathetic nerve activity may counteract a rise in the fatty acid/albumin molar ratio in the interstitial space. Consequently, the lipolytic rate may not be reduced, as would otherwise be the case, and the outward diffusion of fatty acids may also be facilitated. Thus, the permeability change may constitute a link between lipid mobilization from the adipocytes and the diffusion of fatty acids to the blood circulation. Quantitative data on fatty acid and albumin concentrations in the interstitial space of adipose tissue during different degrees of lipolysis are lacking. Such data will test the validity of the proposed function of permeability changes.

Adrenergic nerves also seem to regulate brain vascular permeability. Stimulation of the locus coeruleus in chronically sympathectomized rhesus monkeys increased the brain's water permeability concomitantly with a decrease in cerebral blood flow (70, 71). The permeability increase was presumably caused by stimulation of noradrenergic nerves originating in the brain stem that reach capillaries of the cerebral hemispheres (37). In addition to this, stimulation of the peripheral sympathetic system also increased the brain's water permeability, which was measured as an increase in brain's PS-product for water (35).

In rhesus monkeys, bilateral cervical sympathetic stimulation produced a prompt increase in the brain's PS-product for water of 19%, and a decrease in cerebral blood flow of 11%. Larger changes in the PS-product were registered after stimulation of locus coeruleus. The peripheral sympathetic and central noradrenergic vasomotor nerves may regulate the water permeability of cerebral vessels at two different levels, with the peripheral sympathetic nerves supplying the pial vessels and larger intraparenchymal vessels of the microcirculation, while the central vasomotor nerves supply the capillaries (35, 39). The adrenergic control of water permeability may contribute to fluid and electrolyte homeostasis in the brain and thus determine brain volume and osmolality. These parameters are obviously important to brain function.

Peptidergic Nervous Control of the Microcirculation

During recent years several peptides with biological activity have been shown to be present in the central nervous system and in the gastrointestinal tract. The vasoactive intestinal peptide (VIP) is found in the gastrointestinal tract in neurons, particularly in the muscularis of the stomach and in the mucosa of the large and small bowel where VIP neurons often accompany the small blood vessels (10, 31, 51, 52, 79). As is indicated by its name, VIP is a potent vasodilator peptide (79). The vasodilator effects of VIP in the gastrointestinal tract have been demonstrated in several studies (48, 85). VIP was released into the venous outflow from the colon upon electrical stimulation of the pelvic nerves and a simultaneous transient vasodilatation occurred in the colon (20–22). A marked increase in venous plasma VIP concentration was demonstrated (20) when the vasodilatation was activated reflexly by mechanical stimulation of the rectal mucosa. This vasodilatation was not blocked by cholinergic or adrenergic blocking agents (21).

Hyperemia in the small intestine of the cat, elicited by mechanical stimulation of the intestinal mucosa, was accompanied by a marked release of VIP from the small intestine into the venous blood (21). The intestinal hyperemia could not be blocked by cholinergic or adrenergic blocking agents. However, both the vasodilatation in the small intestine and the release of VIP were suppressed after close intra-arterial administration of tetrodotoxin, which suggests a nervously mediated effect. Thus there is experimental support for the view that VIP may be a neurotransmitter functionally related to vascular reflexes in the gastrointestinal tract. So far, the circulatory effects of VIP in the gastrointestinal canal have been investigated only with regard to the resistance vessels.

Substance P is another vasoactive peptide that has localized to nerves. Experimental data indicate that Substance P may be involved in the vasodilatation caused by antidromic stimulation of sensory nerves. It has long been known that antidromic stimulation of sensory fibers may cause vasodilatation in the skin of different species (6, 14, 18). The blood flow increase is not blocked by atropine or any adrenergic blocking agent and is probably mediated via pain fibers and related to axonal reflexes (13).

Substance P may be involved in the antidromic vasodilatation produced in the tooth pulp by electrical stimulation of the inferior alveolar nerve in the cat with a stimulation strength within the range known to activate afferent C-fibers involved in vasodilator responses (32).

Immunohistochemical data indicate that fine-caliber afferent fibers in the cat pulp contain Substance P (67). Evidence for release of Substance P has been obtained by radioimmunoassay of Substance P in pulp superfusates during electrical stimulation of the inferior alveolar nerve (68). In addition, electrical nerve stimulation enhanced the blood flow in the dental pulp (86), and this increase was not blocked by adrenergic or cholinergic blocking agents (33). The vascular response in the dental pulp does not seem to be due to release of histamine, since neither mepyramine nor cimetidine influenced the response.

The fact that Substance P was released into the superfusate following nerve stimulation indicates that vasodilatation may be caused by this peptide. In addition to vasodilatation, antidromic stimulation increases the vascular permeability, at least upon antidromic stimulation of the saphenous and trigeminal nerves in rats (15, 46, 47). Substance P has an overall vasodilatory action but does not seem to affect capillary permeability (69), and therefore it may not be the only biologically active substance released. In fact, the increased vascular permeability has been related to a number of inflammatory mediators. For example, plasma kinins have been implicated in neurogenic edema (2, 49), and a bradykinin-like substance has been found in superfusates from dental pulps of dogs after electrical stimulation of the pulp or the mandibular nerve (44, 45, 50). Vasodilatation can also be produced in skeletal muscle by antidromic stimulation of its sensory nerve supply (40). Indomethacin given by close intra-arterial injection (80–160 μg) or intraperitoneally (2 mg kg^{-1}) produced a substantial reduction of the vasodilatation. This suggested to the authors that prostaglandins are involved.

Literature Cited

1. Altura, B. M. 19 . Chemical and humoral regulation of blood flow through the precapillary sphincter. *Microvasc. Res.* 3:361–84
2. Arvier, P. T., Chahl, L. A., Ladd, R. J. 1977. Modification by capsaicin and compound 48/80 of dye leakage induced by irritants in the rat. *Brit. J. Pharmacol.* 59:61–68
3. Baez, S., Feldman, S. M., Gootman, P. M. 1977. Central neuronal influence on precapillary microvessels and sphincter. *Am. J. Physiol.* 233:H141–47
4. Ballard, K., Rosell, S. 1969. The unresponsiveness of lipid metabolism in canine mesenteric adipose tissue to biogenic amines. *Acta Physiol. Scand.* 77:442–48
5. Ballard, K., Malmfors, T., Rosell, S. 1974. Adrenergic innervation and vascular patterns in canine adipose tissue. *Microvasc. Res.* 8:164–71
6. Bayliss, W. M. 1901. On the origin from the spinal cord of the vasodilator fibres of the hind-limb and on the nature of the fibres. *J. Physiol. London* 26:173–209
7. Becker, C. G., Murphy, G. E. 1969. Demonstration of contractile protein in endothelium and cells of the heart valves, endocardium, intima, arteriosclerotic plaques, and aschoff bodies of rheumatic heart disease. *Am. J. Pathol.* 55:1–29
8. Bevan, J. A., Duckles, S. P. 1975. Evidence for α-adrenergic receptors on intimal endothelium. *Blood Vessels* 12:307–10
9. Biber, B. 1973. Vasodilator mechanism in the small intestine. *Acta Physiol. Scand.* (*Suppl.*). 401:1–31
10. Bryant, M. G., Bloom, S. R., Polak, J. M., Albuquerque, R. H., Modlin, I., Pearse, A. G. E. 1976. Possible dual role for vasoactive intestinal peptide as gastrointestinal hormone and neurotransmitter substance. *Lancet i*: 991–93
11. Buckley, I. K., Ryan, G. B. 1969. Increased vascular permeability. The effect of histamine and serotonin on rat mesenteric blood vessels in vivo. *Am. J. Pathol.* 55:329–38
12. Bücherl, E., Schwab, M. 1952. Der Sauerstoffverbrauch des ruhenden Skelettmuskels bei reflektorisch-nervöser Vasokonstriktion. *Pfluegers Arch.* 254: 337–44
13. Celander, O., Folkow, B. 1953. The nature and the distribution of efferent fibres provided with the axon reflex arrangement. *Acta Physiol. Scand.* 29: 359–70
14. Celander, O., Folkow, B. 1953. The correlation between the stimulation frequency and the dilator response evoked by "antidromic" excitation of the thin afferent fibres in the dorsal roots. *Acta Physiol. Scand.* 29:371–76

15. Chahl, L. A., Ladd, R. J. 1976. Local oedema and general excitation of cutaneous sensory receptors produced by electrical stimulation of the saphenous nerve in the rat. *Pain* 2:25–34
16. Chinard, F. P., Vosburgh, G. J., Enns, T. 1955. Transcapillary exchange of water and of other substances in certain organs of the dog. *Am. J. Physiol.* 183:221–34
17. Crone, C. 1963. The permeability of capillaries in various organs as determined by use of the "indicator diffusion" method. *Acta Physiol. Scand.* 58:292–305
18. Dale, H. H., Gaddum, J. H. 1930. Reactions of denervated voluntary muscle and their bearing on the mode of action of parasympathetic and related nerves. *J. Physiol. London* 70:109–44
19. Diculescu, I., Stoica, M. 1970. Fluorescence histochemical investigation on the adrenergic innervation of the white adipose in the rat. *J. Neuro-Visc. Rel.* 32:25–36
20. Fahrenkrug, J., Galbo, H., Holst, J. J., Schaffalitzky de Muckadell, O. B. 1978. Influence of the autonomic nervous system on the release of vasoactive intestinal polypeptide (VIP) from the porcine gastrointestinal tract. *J. Physiol. London* 280:405–22
21. Fahrenkrug, J., Haglund, U., Jodal, M., Lundgren, O., Olbe, L., Schaffalitzky de Muckadell, O. B. 1978. Is vasoactive intestinal polypeptide (VIP) a neurotransmitter in the gastrointestinal tract? *Acta Physiol. Scand.* 102:22–23A
22. Fahrenkrug, J., Schaffalitzky de Muckadell, O. B. 1977. Radioimmunoassay of vasoactive intestinal polypeptide (VIP) in plasma. *J. Lab. Clin. Med.* 89:1379–88
23. Fain, J. N., Shepherd, R. E. 1975. Free fatty acids as feed back regulators of adenylate cyclase and cyclic 3'-5'-AMP accumulation in rat fat cells. *J. Biol. Chem.* 250:6586–92
24. Fain, J. N., Shepherd, R. E. 1976. Inhibition of adenosine 3'-5'-monophosphate accumulation in white fat cells by short chain fatty acids, lactate, and β-hydroxybutyrate. *J. Lipid Res.* 17: 377–85
25. Folkow, B., Lewis, D. H., Lundgren, O. et al. 1964. The effect of graded vasoconstrictor fibre stimulation on the intestinal resistance and capacitance vessels. *Acta Physiol. Scand.* 61:445–57
26. Folkow, B., Öberg, B., Rubinstein, E. H. 1964. A proposed differentiated neuroeffector organization in muscle resistance vessels. *Angiologica* 1:197
27. Fredholm, B. B. 1970. Studies on the sympathetic regulation of circulation and metabolism in isolated subcutaneous adipose tissue. *Acta Physiol. Scand.* 354:4–47
28. Fredholm, B. B., Frisk-Holmberg, M. 1971. Lipolysis in canine subcutaneous adipose tissue following release of endogenous histamine. *Eur. J. Pharmacol.* 13:254–58
29. Fredholm, B. B., Öberg, B., Rosell, S. 1970. Effects of vasoactive drugs on circulation in canine subcutaneous adipose tissue. *Acta Physiol. Scand.* 79:565–74
30. Furness, J. B., Marshall, J. M. 1974. Correlation of the directly observed responses of mesenteric vessels of the rat to nerve stimulation and noradrenaline with the distribution of adrenergic nerves. *J. Physiol. London* 239:75–88
31. Fuxe, K., Hökfelt, T., Said, S. I., Mutt, V. 1977. Vasoactive intestinal polypeptide and the nervous system: immunohistochemical evidence for localization in central and peripheral neurons, particularly intracortical neurons of the cerebral cortex. *Neurosci. Lett.* 5:241–46
32. Gazelius, B., Olgart, L., Edwall, L., Trowbridge, H. O. 1977. Effects of Substance P on sensory nerves and blood flow in the feline dental pulp. In *Pain in the Trigeminal Region,* ed. D. J. Anderson, B. Matthews, pp. 95–101. Amsterdam: Elsevier/North-Holland
33. Gazelius, B., Olgart, L. 1979. Vasodilatation in the dental pulp produced by electrical stimulation of the inferior alveolar nerve in the cat. *Acta Physiol. Scand.* In press
34. Gootman, P. M., Baez, S., Feldman, S. M. 1973. Microcirculatory responses to central nerve stimulation in the rat. *Am. J. Physiol.* 225:1375–83
35. Grubb, R. L. Jr., Raichle, M. E., Eichling, J. O. 1978. Peripheral sympathetic regulation of brain water permeability. *Brain Res.* 144:204–7
36. Hanley, H. G., Sachs, R. G., Skinner, N. S. Jr. 1971. Reflex responsiveness of vascular bed of dog subcutaneous adipose tissue. *Am. J. Physiol.* 220:993–99
37. Hartman, B. K., Zide, D., Udenfriend, S. 1972. The use of dopamine β-hydroxylase as a marker for the central noradrenergic nervous system in rat brain. *Proc. Natl. Acad. Sci. USA* 69:2722–26
38. Henriksen, O. 1977. Local sympathetic reflex mechanism in regulation of blood

flow in human subcutaneous tissue. *Acta Physiol. Scand.* Suppl. 450, pp. 1–48

39. Herbst, T. Y., Raichle, M. E., Ferrendelli, J. A. 1979. β-Adrenergic regulation of adenosine 3',5'-monophosphate concentration in brain microvessels. *Science* 204:330–32
40. Hilton, S. M., Marshall, J. M. 1975. Antidromic dilatation in skeletal muscle. *J. Physiol. London* 251:18–19P
41. Hultén, L., Jodal, M., Lundgren, O. 1969. Extrinsic nervous control of colon blood flow. *Acta Physiol. Scand. (Suppl.)* 335:39–50
42. Hultén, L., Lindhagen, J., Lundgren, O. 1977. Sympathetic nervous control of intramural blood flow in the feline and human intestines. *Gastroenterology* 72: 41–48
43. Hutchins, P. M., Bond, R. F., Green, H. D. 1974. The response of skeletal muscle arterioles to common carotid occlusion. *Microvasc. Res.* 7:321–25
44. Inoki, R., Matsumoto, K. Kudo, T., Kotoni, Y., Oka, M. 1979. Bradykinin as an algesic (pain producing substance in the pulp). *Naunyn-Schmiedeberg's Arch. Pharmacol.* 306:29–36
45. Inoki, R., Toyoda, T., Yamamoto, I. 1973. Elaboration of a bradykinin-like substance in dog's canine pulp during electrical stimulation and its inhibition by narcotic and nonnarcotic analgesics. *Naunyn-Schmiedeberg's Arch. Pharmacol.* 279:387–98
46. Jancsó, N., Jancsó-Gábor, A., Szolcsányi, J. 1967. Direct evidence for neurogenic inflammation and its prevention by denervation and by pretreatment with capsaicin. *Brit. J. Pharmacol.* 31:138–51
47. Jancsó, N., Jancsó-Gábor, A., Szolcsányi, J. 1968. The role of sensory nerve endings in neurotenic inflammation induced in human skin and in the eye and paw of the rat. *Brit. J. Pharmacol.* 32:32–41
48. Kachelhoffer, J., Eloy, M. R., Pouse, A., Hohmatter, D., Greiner, J. F. 1974. Mesenteric vasomotor effects of vasoactive intestinal polypeptide. Study on perfused isolated canine jejunal loops. *Pfluegers Arch.* 352:37–46
49. Kiernan, J. A. 1975. A pharmacological and histological investigation of the involvement of mast cells in cutaneous axon reflex vasodilatation. *Q. J. Exp. Physiol.* 60:123–30
50. Kroeger, D. C. 1968. Possible role of neurohumoral substances in the pulp. In *Biology of the Dental Pulp Organ,* ed. S. B. Finn, pp. 333–46. Birmingham, Ala.: Univ. Alabama Press
51. Larsson, L.-I. 1977. Ultrastructural localization of a new neuronal peptide (VIP). *Histochemie* 54:173–76
52. Larsson, L.-I., Fahrenkrug, J., Schaffalitzky de Muckadell, O. B., Sundler, F., Håkansson, R., Rehfeld, J. F. 1976. Localization of vasoactive intestinal polypeptide (VIP) to central and peripheral neurons. *Proc. Natl. Acad. Sci. USA* 73:3197–200
53. Linde, B. 1976. Effect of sympathetic nerve stimulation on net transvascular movement of fluid in canine adipose tissue. *Acta Physiol. Scand.* 97:166–74
54. Linde, B., Chisolm, G., Rosell, S. 1974. The influence of sympathetic activity and histamine on the blood-tissue exchange of solutes in canine adipose tissue. *Acta Physiol. Scand.* 92:145–55
55. Lundgren, O. 1978. The alimentary canal. In *Peripheral Circulation,* ed. P. C. Johnson, pp. 255–83. NY: Wiley
56. Majno, G., Gilmore, V., Leventhal, M. 1967. On the mechanism of vascular leakage caused by histamine-type mediators. *Circ. Res.* 21:833–47
57. Majno, G., Palade, G. E., Schoefl, G. I. 1961. Studies on inflammation. II. The site of action of histamine and serotonin along the vascular tree: A topographic study. *J. Biophys. Biochem. Cytol.* 11:607–26
58. Majno, G., Shea, S. M., Leventhal, M. 1969. Endothelial contraction induced by histamine type mediators. An electron microscopic study. *J. Cell Biol.* 42:647–72
59. Marshall, J. M. 1976. The influence of the sympathetic nervous system on the microcirculation of skeletal muscle. *J. Physiol. London* 258:118–19P
60. McNamee, J. E., Grodins, F. S. 1975. Effect of histamine on microvasculature of isolated dog gracilis muscle. *Am. J. Physiol.* 229:119–25
61. Mellander, S., Johansson, B. 1968. Control of resistance exchange, and capacitance functions in the peripheral circulation. *Physiol. Rev.* 20:117–96
62. Mellander, S. 1960. Comparative studies on the adrenergic neuro-hormone control of resistance and capacitance blood vessels in the cat. *Acta Physiol. Scand* 50 (Suppl. 176):1–86
63. Ngai, S. H., Rosell, S., Wallenberg, L. R. 1966. Nervous regulation of blood flow in the subcutaneous adipose tissue in dogs. *Acta Physiol. Scand.* 68:397–403

64. Öberg, B. 1964. Effects of cardiovascular reflexes on net capillary fluid transfer. *Acta Physiol. Scand.* 62: (Suppl. 229) 1–98
65. Öberg, B., Rosell, S. 1967. Sympathetic control of consecutive vascular sections in canine subcutaneous adipose tissue. *Acta Physiol. Scand.* 71:47–56
66. Öberg, B. 1976. Overall cardiovascular regulation. *Ann. Rev. Physiol.* 38: 537–70
67. Olgart, L., Hökfelt, T., Nilsson, G., Pernow, B. 1977. Localization of Substance P–like immunoreactivity in nerves in the tooth pulp. *Pain* 4:153–59
68. Olgart, L., Gazelius, B., Brodin, E., Nilsson, G. 1977. Release of Substance P–like immunoreactivity from the dental pulp. *Acta Physiol. Scand.* 101:510–12
69. Pernow, B., Rosell, S. 1975. Effect of Substance P on blood flow in canine adipose tissue and skeletal muscle. *Acta Physiol. Scand.* 93:139–41
70. Raichle, M. E., Hartman, B. K., Eichling, J. O., Sharpe, L. G. 1975. Central noradrenergic regulation of cerebral blood flow and vascular permeability. *Proc. Natl. Acad. Sci. USA* 72:3726–30
71. Raichle, M. E., Eichling, J. O., Grubb, R. L. Jr., Hartman, B. K. 1976. Central noradrenergic regulation of brain microcirculation. In *Dynamics of Brain Edema,* ed. H. M. Pappius, W. Freidel, pp. 11–17. Berlin: Springer
72. Renkin, E. M., Rosell, S. 1962. Independent sympathetic vasoconstrictor innervation of arterioles and precapillary sphincters. *Acta Physiol. Scand.* 54:381–84
73. Rippe, B., Kamiya, A., Folkow, B. 1978. Simultaneous measurements of capillary diffusion and filtration exchange during shifts in filtration-absorption and at graded alterations in the capillary permeability surface area products (PS). *Acta Physiol. Scand.* 104:318–36
74. Rodbell, M. 1965. Modulation of lipolysis in adipose tissue by fatty acid concentration in fat cell. *Ann. NY Acad. Sci.* 131:302–14
75. Rosell, S., Intaglietta, M., Chisolm, G. M. 1974. Adrenergic influence on isovolumetric capillary pressure in canine adipose tissue. *Am. J. Physiol.* 227:692–96
76. Rosell, S., Intaglietta, M., Tuma, R. F. 1974. Microvascular flow velocity in cat omental adipose tissue as affected by sympathetic nerve stimulation. *Acta Physiol. Scand.* 92:399–403
77. Rosell, S. 1978. Nervous control of the microcirculation. *Microcirculation,* ed. G. Kaley, B. M. Altura, II: 371–400. Baltimore, Md: University Park Press
78. Rowley, D. A. 1965. Venous constriction as the cause of increased vascular permeability produced by 5-hydroxytryptamine, histamine, bradykinin and 48/80 in the rat. *Brit. J. Exp. Pathol.* 45:56–67
79. Said, S. I., Mutt, V. 1970. Polypeptide with broad biological activity: isolation from small intestine. *Science* 169: 1217–18
80. Sanders, A. G., Ebert, R. H., Florey, H. W. 1940. The mechanism of capillary contraction. *Q. J. Exp. Physiol.* 30: 218–87
81. Smith, O. A. 1974. Reflex and central mechanisms involved in the control of the heart and circulation. *Ann. Rev. Physiol.* 36:93–123
82. Spector, W. G. 1958. Substances which affect capillary permeability. *Pharm. Rev.* 10:475–505
83. Svensjö, E. 1978. Bradykinin and prostaglandin E_1, E_2 and $F_{2\alpha}$-induced macromolecular leakage in the hamster cheek pouch. *Prostagl. Med.* 1:394–410
84. Svensjö, E., Persson, C. G. A., Rutili, G. 1977. Inhibition of bradykinin induced macromolecular leakage from post-capillary venules by a β_2-adrenoreceptor stimulant, terbutaline. *Acta. Physiol. Scand.* 101:504–6
85. Thulin, L., Olsson, P. 1973. Effects of intestinal peptide mixture G2 and vasoactive intestinal peptide VIP on splanchnic circulation in the dog. *Acta Chir. Scand.* 139:691–97
86. Tönder, K. H., Naess, G. 1978. Nervous control of blood flow in the dental pulp in dogs. *Acta Physiol. Scand.* 104:13–23
87. Wasserman, K., Loeb, L., Mayerson, H. S. 1955. Capillary permeability to macromolecules. *Circ. Res.* 3:594–603
88. Wiedeman, M. P. 1963. Dimensions of blood vessels from distributing artery to collecting vein. *Circ. Res.* 12:375–78

Ann. Rev. Physiol. 1980. 42:373–82

LOCAL CONTROL OF MICROVASCULAR FUNCTION: ROLE IN TISSUE OXYGEN SUPPLY

❖1274

Brian R. Duling[1]

Department of Physiology, University of Virginia School of Medicine, Charlottesville, Virginia 22908

Bruce Klitzman

University of Arizona College of Medicine, Tuscon, Arizona 85724

INTRODUCTION

Local processes within tissues match vascular function to tissue metabolic needs. In this review we examine the functional elements of the microcirculation, how they may be controlled and interact, and especially how local control mechanisms regulate tissue oxygenation by coordinating the responses of arterioles and capillaries, and the distribution of red cells. We limit our discussion to cardiac and striated muscle and to the regulation of oxygen delivery, considering four types of local control: responses to hyperoxia or hypoxia, autoregulation, reactive hyperemia, and functional hyperemia.

Investigators of microcirculatory physiology concentrated formerly on three elements of microvascular function—arteriolar diameter, red cell velocity, and capillary numbers—as separate parameters. Now it is becoming apparent that processes intrinsic to tissues manipulate these variables in concert, emphasizing one element of microvessel function at one time, and another under a different set of circumstances (18, 32). Here we review current knowledge about the behavior of various microvessel elements dur-

[1]This work was conducted during Dr. Duling's tenure as an Established Investigator of the American Heart Association.

0066-4278/80/0315-0373$01.00

ing local regulatory responses. First, we review control of flow and velocity in microvessels; second, we examine how total flow is distributed within the capillaries; and third, we discuss a possible role for control of the oxygen carrying capacity of the capillary blood in local regulatory processes.

REGULATION OF MICROVESSEL FLOW AND VELOCITY

Much recent research on the local control of the microcirculation has focused either on the dimensions of the arterioles, which are primarily responsible for the control of flow, or on the velocity of flow through the capillaries. Increasing the blood oxygen tension or the oxygen tension of a fluid covering a microvessel preparation causes constriction of arterioles and a decrease in the flow velocity in the capillaries (6, 15, 35, 45, 53). This appears to be related to an effect of oxygen on the parenchyma rather than an effect directly on the smooth muscle (6, 7, 15).

Studies of autoregulation have found, as anticipated, that the arterioles dilate as perfusion pressure decreases (29, 34). Assuming that flow varies with the fourth power of the radius (40), Johnson & Intaglietta calculated that the dilation following hypotension actually caused an increase in flow with reduced pressure (29). How this "super-regulation" is related to the behavior of intact tissues remains to be seen.

In spite of a long-term interest in the problem, the contribution of the various series elements of the arteriolar tree to local regulatory processes remains unclear. Kontos et al found that pial microvessels in the 100–200 μm range were most reactive following an alteration in perfusion pressure (35). It is unexpected that such large vessels appear to be the major contributors to the regulatory response, but this is consistent with the fact that a large fraction of the total resistance of the cerebral vasculature lies upstream from the vessels regarded as the true arterioles in striated muscle (13).

A general finding evolving from these and previous studies on the mesentery is that of a linear relation between aortic pressure and pressure at various microvessel sites (17, 35). The fact that pressure at a particular location in the microcirculation remains a constant fraction of the arterial pressure implies that somehow the control of flow by a given vessel segment is in direct proportion to the fractional contribution of that segment to the total resistance. This differs from the typical view that flow is controlled almost entirely by a small population of "resistance vessels." How do vasoactive substances influence these relations in muscle? In the one study where the appropriate pressure measurements were made, simultaneous alterations in systemic arterial pressure make analysis difficult (13).

Various forms of local control of blood flow have been studied in relation to the possible role of oxygen in the regulatory process. The magnitudes of functional hyperemia (15), reactive hyperemia (41, 53), and autoregulation (34) are all sensitive to oxygen, and the magnitude of a dilation induced during any of the three types of regulatory processes can be diminished by the application of a high P_{O_2} solution to the surface of the microcirculatory preparation. The simplest interpretation of these findings is that oxygen is involved in regulating the diameter of the microvessels or the number of open vessels and, thus, that tissue oxygen tension contributes to the control process. However, these experiments fail to consider the possibility that oxygen might act as a nonspecific vasoconstrictor substance that overrides a vasodilation induced locally by the accumulation of a metabolite.

Velocity measurements in capillaries and arterioles and diameter measurements of the arterioles are typically used in microcirculatory experiments as quantitative indexes of the behavior of the regulatory process. Unfortunately, both of these may provided erroneous quantitative information on flow if changes in the number of vessels perfused are ignored. Capillary closure and the resulting intermittent flow are well known, but recent evidence indicates that changes in the number of arterioles may also be an important factor in local blood flow control (9, 10, 16). As a rule, arteriolar closure has not been quantitated in microvascular investigations; in the future, counts of perfused arterioles must be included among quantitative data related to flow control. Furthermore, reports in which changes in capillary velocity are related to whole organ blood flow measurements should include concomitant determination of capillary density (16, 31, 33).

CAPILLARY PERFUSION

The regulation of capillary function consists basically of modulating the distribution of the total blood flow which enters the tissues among various capillary pathways, thereby adjusting the diffusion distance between cells and perfused capillaries. Three elements of capillary behavior are significant: (*a*) the number of open capillaries (capillary density); (*b*) the presence of noncapillary pathways from artery to vein (shunts); and (*c*) the range of variation in type, length, and flow pattern of the capillary bed (heterogeneity).

Capillary Density

Since Krogh's time, short-term intermittency of capillary perfusion has been known at least in some tissues (36). Two of the current concerns of the workers in this area are to determine in which tissues capillary recruitment does occur and to determine what fraction of the capillaries are unperfused at rest. Capillary density in skeletal muscle varies, but the amount of variation is in question. In Krogh's early work it was reported that the density of resting skeletal muscle could increase 11–35-fold (36). However, more recent results have failed to confirm the magnitude of this change. In striated muscle, direct counts of capillaries recruited during contraction show no more than double the capillary density (16, 19). Similar increments of 2–4-fold were observed using either indicator dilution methods (2, 46) or measurement of capillary filtration coefficient (30). These findings suggest that Krogh's earlier recruitment figures were excessively large and that only a 2–3-fold increase in the capillary density may be expected with a transition from rest to maximal perfusion. However, in one of the more recent examinations of capillary recruitment, Lassen found a 15-fold increment in the capillary density of the human forearm (38). Lassen's report suffers from the difficulty that the measurement technique (dilution of a hyperoncotic protein bolus) is a relatively untried one, and also from the fact that the measurements were made on such a heterogeneous tissue as the human forearm. Controversy exists regarding capillary recruitment in cardiac muscle as well. Honig and his associates have documented changes in spacing of capillaries that are observable on the surface of the in situ beating heart. They have found consistently that myocardial capillary density can be significantly augmented (5, 12). Furthermore, they report that the capillary reserve is a function of the age of the animal and a variety of other environmental factors (5, 23).

Results on capillary density in rat heart obtained recently with an improved optical system show no capillary recruitment with hypoxia (52). The discrepancy between these data and other investigations of the intact heart was attributed to the use of an improved optical system, giving an improved capacity to estimate the true capillary density of the tissue. However, the technique required penetration of the hearts with a mechanical support device, and an epi-illuminator system was used that touched the myocardial surface. These manipulations may have disturbed normal capillary function and artificially diminished the ability of the myocardium to open unperfused capillaries.

Thus the role of capillary recruitment as a means of locally enhancing oxygen delivery capacity in myocardium requires further investigation. Indicator-dilution data suggest that capillary recruitment does occur in myocardium (8, 47).

It is not known how microvascular elements open and close capillaries. Many investigators have failed to observe a precapillary sphincter in striated muscle, and control of capillary perfusion has been attributed to closure of the terminal arterioles (10, 16, 24, 33). However, this concept is difficult to reconcile with the fact that capillary recruitment and hyperemia may respond differently to the same stimuli (18, 32). In cardiac muscle the site of capillary closure must be determined. At this time, only very indirect methods indicate the presence of a precapillary sphincter (12).

Shunting

Accurate modeling of tissue Po_2 distributions in cardiac muscle requires the presence of a small shunt fraction (20, 49). Little is known, however, about the site of such shunting or about whether it is anatomical or diffusional in origin. It is well documented that there are no anatomical shunts in skeletal muscle (22).

Whatever the magnitude of shunting in skeletal or cardiac muscle, there is no evidence to date that it is under specific and direct physiological control by local regulatory processes. However, it will be indirectly affected both by the total flow into a tissue and by the proximity of small arterioles to venules. The latter is likely to be constant, but the former is certainly regulated by local control processes. Thus as the flow rate decreases, the diffusional shunting will increase. The tissue transfer of oxygen and other small solutes will thereby be lowered more than it would be lowered as the result of a flow reduction alone.

Heterogeneity of Capillary Perfusion

Intercapillary distances, capillary lengths, and the flow velocities in capillaries all have statistical distributions about some average value, and capillary perfusion waxes and wanes. The extremes of the statistical distributions may be closely related to the points where oxygen availability limits tissue oxygenation even though the average blood flow and average tissue metabolic rate may appear adequate to supply all cells within a tissue (5, 23).

The heterogeneity in muscle is evidenced by the facts that various intravascular tracers are not randomly distributed (11, 44, 47, 50), that there is an irregular distribution of tissue Po_2s (20, 39) that there is a wide spectrum of oxygen saturations in the blood of the cardiac venules (43), and that hypoxic areas of the saline-perfused myocardium develop in a patchy pattern as arterial Po_2 is lowered. (51).

Local regulatory processes in the tissues may have an important impact on perfusion heterogeneity. In an early consideration of this problem, Renkin pointed out that optimization of capillary exchange could be achieved only by a local control process that would match flow and capillary anatomy (46). This follows from the fact that long capillaries, while having a greater exchange area, would automatically receive a lower flow as a result of the higher resistance imposed by their length. A local control mechanism might act to match flow to capillary exchange capacity and thus optimize capillary transport and tissue oxygenation.

A wide variety of observations indicate that vasomotor phenomena modulate the uniformity of distribution of blood flow within muscle. The marginal microcirculation of striated muscle shows a reduction in flow velocity in the capillaries when the total flow to the muscle is enhanced by the infusion of vasodilators (54). Similarly, it has been observed that the distribution of transit times in striated muscle, as estimated from measurements of capillary geometry and flow velocity, is expanded by changes in vasomotor tone (25, 26). Stimulation of striated muscle fibers to induce maximal vasodilation (46) and administration of vasodilators (2, 46) dissociate total blood flow and capillary exchange capacity, at times increasing the former and decreasing the latter. In fact, vasodilators administered to a working muscle perfused at constant flow can diminish muscle contractile function, presumably as a result of perfusion heterogeneity sufficient to compromise the tissue supply in some areas of the muscle (55).

In direct contrast to the preceding reports in striated muscle, Rose & Goresky have reported that the transit-time heterogeneity in the heart is decreased by vasodilation and that the normal condition of the heart is one of enhanced heterogeneity due to vasomotor activity (47). Bourdeau-Martini et al linked perfusion heterogeneity to local control of the microcirculation by showing that heterogeneity of the myocardial intercapillary distances observed in the in situ rat heart was dependent on the level of oxygenation (5).

Evaluation of the possible role of perfusion heterogeneity in local control of blood flow is difficult because the experimental methods for dealing with the problem of heterogeneity are presently inadequate. Microspheres and other tissue-sample techniques provide important information on the large-scale tissue heterogeneity (11, 44, 51) but lack the resolution to tell us what may be happening at the capillary level. Direct observation of the microcirculation provides information about capillary heterogeneity, but in most cases this technique can be utilized only on tissues whose environments are grossly disturbed. Sophisticated statistical techniques for the analysis of microvessel heterogeneity are being considered (5, 12), but these have yet to be accurately validated by direct comparison of predictions with measured performance of the microcirculation.

BLOOD OXYGEN CONTENT

An examination of the role of various microvascular elements in the local control of blood flow would be incomplete without a consideration of the possible impact of local hematocrit changes. Various methods of estimation of capillary hematocrit (including visual observation of the capillaries) yield estimates well below those for the systemic circulation (28, 33, 42, 48).

Typically, capillary hematocrits in the range of 10–20%, or one fifth to one half of the arterial value, are observed.

The reasons for the low capillary hematocrit have not been fully developed. The hematocrit of the blood flowing in small tubes is consistently lower than the feed hematocrit, probably reflecting axial accumulation of the red cells and a resulting velocity differential for red cells and plasma (3). However, the velocity difference of only about 30% between cells and plasma in capillaries is far too small to induce the hematocrit reductions observed (14).

An obvious explanation for the diminished hematocrit in the capillaries is that the red cells are somehow shunted from arterioles to venules. This is likely to explain the behavior of the intestine and carotid body (1, 27), but in skeletal muscle no evidence of significant anatomical shunting of red cells exists (10, 33). Furthermore, total red cell flux through the capillaries of cremaster muscle is approximately equal to the bulk red cell flow into the feed arteries (33). The equality of capillary red cell flux and total tissue red cell flux clearly implies a lack of shunting.

An alternate explanation for a low capillary hematocrit is that the capillaries might possess a relatively slow-moving plasma sleeve surrounding a high-hematocrit core of rapidly moving blood (4, 33). We have calculated that the plasma layer would have to be about 1 μm thick to explain the observed hematocrits (33).

The role of variations in hematocrit in local control of oxygen delivery is not known. Capillary hematocrit does vary: It changes cyclically with spontaneous vasomotion (28), it is decreased by stimulation of the sympathetic nerves (37), it is reduced by tissue hyperoxia (33), and it is increased during functional hyperemia (33). However, it has not been established that physiological variation in the hematocrit will result in the alteration of tissue oxygen delivery. To the extent that low capillary hematocrit is the result of shunting, it will, of course, determine the rate of delivery of red cells to the vicinity of parenchymal cells and thereby alter tissue oxygen delivery. However, if the hematocrit reduction reflects only a velocity difference between plasma and red cells, it would have little effect on the tissue oxygenation (21). This follows from the fact that oxygen delivery at the capillary level is related to the time-averaged red cell passage rate and not to the hematocrit per se. If the hematocrit reduction is solely the result of an increased red cell velocity relative to plasma, then the velocity increment exactly balances the hematocrit reduction, red cell flux is unaltered, and mean tissue oxygenation is unchanged.

One aspect of this problem that seems not to have been examined theoretically is the possibility that transient increments in oxygen consumption may be influenced by the low hematocrit, in spite of a high red cell velocity.

In a tissue such as the heart, where oxidative phosphorylation is tightly coupled to metabolism, the low intravascular hematocrit might limit the rate at which oxygen consumption can be increased with each beat.

SUMMARY

The rate at which oxygen can be transported to tissues is closely tied to the status of the microcirculation. Conversely, microcirculatory function seems to be coupled to tissue metabolic needs. Most microvascular studies have of necessity taken a rather simplistic view of the coupling process and have relied on simple measurements of a single parameter as indexes of regulation. The number, size, and organization of vessels in the tissue, and the distribution of red cells may contribute significantly to regulation. The relative contributions of these elements may vary with the status of the tissue. With the exception of capillary hematocrit, we do not propose any new variables for examination. More careful consideration must be given to well known variables when quantitating microvessel function.

Specific problem areas have been highlighted. Arteriolar closure may be an important factor in inducing local regulatory phenomena in some cases. Arteriolar diameter plays a major role in regulating tissue flow, and this role may be greatest during conditions of low oxygen supply. In contrast to arteriolar function, capillary recruitment seems to be more important during conditions of high oxygen availability. While there is no evidence that shunting is controlled by local processes, its magnitude increases as flow decreases; thus the importance of shunting will vary with blood flow. Perfusion heterogeneity is only beginning to be appreciated as (*a*) significant, and (*b*) possibly under physiological control. Finally, capillary hematocrit, as measured with present techniques, clearly varies with local stimuli. The importance of this fact to microvessel oxygen delivery remains to be established.

Literature Cited

1. Acker, H., Lübbers, D. W. 1976. Oxygen transport capacity of the capillary within the carotid body. *Pflügers Arch.* 366:241–46
2. Appelgren, L. 1972. Perfusion and diffusion in shock. *Acta Physiol. Scand.* 378: (Suppl.) 5–72
3. Barbee, J. H., Cokelet, G. R. 1971. Prediction of blood flow in tubes with diameters as small as 29 μ. *Microvasc. Res.* 3:17–21
4. Bloch, E. H. 1962. A quantitative study of the hemodynamics in the living microvascular system. *Am. J. Anat.* 110: 125–53
5. Bourdeau-Martini, J., Odoroff, C. L., Honig, C. R. 1974. Dual effect of oxygen on magnitude and uniformity of coronary intercapillary distance. *Am. J. Physiol.* 226:800–10
6. Duling, B. R. 1974. Oxygen sensitivity of vascular smooth muscle. II. In vivo studies. *Am. J. Physiol.* 227:42–49
7. Duling, B. R., Pittman, R. N. 1975. Oxygen tension: dependent or independent variable in local control of blood flow? *Fed. Proc.* 34:2012–19
8. Duran, W. N., Marsicano, T. H., Anderson, R. W. 1977. Capillary reserve in

isometrically contracting dog hearts. *Am. J. Physiol.* 232:H276–81
9. Dusseau, J. W., Hutchins, P. M. 1979. Stimulation of arteriolar number by salbutamol in spontaneously hypertensive rats. *Am. J. Physiol.* 236:H134–40
10. Eriksson, E., Lisander, B. 1972. Changes in precapillary resistance in skeletal muscle vessels studied by intravital microscopy. *Acta Physiol. Scand.* 84:295–305
11. Falsetti, H. L., Carroll, R. J., Marcus, M. L. 1975. Temporal heterogeneity of myocardial blood flow in anesthetized dogs. *Circulation* 52:848–53
12. Feldstein, M. L., Henquell, L., Honig, C. R. 1978. Frequency analysis of coronary intercapillary distances: Site of capillary control. *Am. J. Physiol.* 235: H321–25
13. Fronek, K., Zweifach, B. W. 1975. Microvascular pressure distribution in skeletal muscle and the effect of vasodilation. *Am. J. Physiol.* 228: 791–96
14. Gaehtgens, P., Benner, K. U., Schickendantz, S., Albrecht, K. H. 1976. Method for simultaneous determination of red cell and plasma flow velocity *in vitro* and *in vivo*. *Pflügers Arch.* 361:191–95
15. Gorczynski, R. J., Duling, B. R. 1978. Role of oxygen in arteriolar functional vasodilation in hamster striated muscle. *Am. J. Physiol.* 235:H505–15
16. Gorczynski, R. J., Klitzman, B., Duling, B. R. 1978. Interrelations between contracting striated muscle and precapillary microvessels. *Am. J. Physiol.* 235:H494–504
17. Gore, R. W. 1974. Pressures in cat mesenteric arterioles and capillaries during changes in systemic arterial blood pressure. *Circ. Res.* 34:581–91
18. Granger, H. J., Goodman, A. H., Granger, D. N. 1976. Role of resistance and exchange vessels in local microvascular control of skeletal muscle oxygenation in the dog. *Circ. Res.* 38:379–85
19. Gray, S. D., Carlsson, E., Staub, N. C. 1967. Site of increased vascular resistance during isometric contraction. *Am. J. Physiol.* 213:683–89
20. Grunewald, W. A., Sowa, W. 1978. Distribution of the myocardial tissue Po_2 in the rat and the inhomogeneity of the coronary bed. *Pflügers Arch.* 374:57–66
21. Gutherman, H. E. 1977. *Modeling of oxygen autoregulation in canine skeletal muscle.* Ph.D. thesis. Northwestern Univ., Chicago. 384 pp.
22. Hammersen, F. 1970. The terminal vascular bed in skeletal muscle with special regard to the problem of shunts. In *Capillary Permeability,* ed. C. Crone, N. A. Lassen, pp. 351–65. NY: Academic
23. Henquell, L., Odoroff, C. L., Honig, C. R. 1976. Coronary intercapillary distance during growth: relation to Pto_2 and aerobic capacity. *Am. J. Physiol.* 231:1852–59
24. Henrich, H., Johnson, P. C. 1978. Influence of arterial pressure on reactive hyperemia in skeletal muscle capillaries. *Am. J. Physiol.* 234:H352–60
25. Honig, C. R. 1977. Hypoxia in skeletal muscle at rest and during the transition to steady work. *Microvasc. Res.* 13: 377–98
26. Honig, C. R., Feldstein, M. L., Frierson, J. L. 1977. Capillary lengths, anastomoses, and estimated capillary transit times in skeletal muscle. *Am. J. Physiol.* 233:H122–29
27. Jodal, M., Lundgren, O. 1970. Plasma skimming in the intestinal tract. *Acta Physiol. Scand.* 80:50–60
28. Johnson, P. C., Blaschke, J., Burton, K. S., Dial, J. H. 1971. Influence of flow variations on capillary hematocrit in mesentery. *Am. J. Physiol.* 221:105–12
29. Johnson, P. C., Intaglietta, M. 1976. Contributions of pressure and flow sensitivity to autoregulation in mesenteric arterioles. *Am. J. Physiol.* 321:1686–98
30. Kjellmer, I. 1964. The effect of exercise on the vascular bed of skeletal muscle. *Acta Physiol. Scand.* 62:18–30
31. Klabunde, R. E., Johnson, P. C. 1977. Reactive hyperemia in capillaries of red and white skeletal muscle. *Am. J. Physiol.* 232:H411–17
32. Klitzman, B. M. 1979. *Microvascular determinants of oxygen supply in resting and contracting striated muscle.* Ph.D. thesis. Univ. Virginia, Charlottesville. 126 pp.
33. Klitzman, B., Duling, B. R. 1979. Microvascular hematocrit and red cell flow in resting and contracting striated muscle. *Am. J. Physiol.* 237:H481–90
34. Kontos, H. A., Wei, E. P., Navari, R. M., Levasseur, J. E., Rosenblum, W. I., Patterson, J. L. Jr. 1978. Responses of cerebral arteries and arterioles to acute hypotension and hypertension. *Am. J. Physiol.* 234:H371–83
35. Kontos, H. A., Wei, E. P., Raper, A. J., Rosenblum, W. I., Navari, R. M., Patterson, J. L. Jr. 1978. Role of tissue hypoxia in local regulation of cerebral microcirculation. *Am. J. Physiol.* 234: H582–91

36. Krogh, A. 1918–1919. The number and distribution of capillaries in muscles with calculations of the oxygen pressure head necessary for supplying the tissue. *J. Physiol. London* 52:409–15
37. Krogh, A. 1919. The supply of oxygen to the tissues and regulation of the capillary circulation. *J. Physiol. London* 52:457–74
38. Lassen, N. A. 1977. Recruitment of muscle capillaries in man. *Biblio. Anat.* 15:504–5
39. Leniger-Follert, E., Lübbers, D. W., Wrabetz, W. 1975. Regulation of local tissue Po_2 of the brain cortex at different arterial O_2 pressures. *Pflügers Arch.* 359:81–95
40. Lipowsky, H. H., Zweifach, B. W. 1978. Application of the "two-slit" photometric technique to the measurement of microvascular volumetric flow rates. *Microvasc. Res.* 15:93–101
41. Lombard, J. H., Duling, B. R. 1977. Relative importance of tissue oxygenation and vascular smooth muscle hypoxia in determining arteriolar responses to occlusion in the hamster cheek pouch. *Circ. Res.* 41:546–51
42. Mayrovitz, H. N., Tuma, R. F., Wiedeman, M. P. 1977. Relationship between microvascular blood velocity and pressure distribution. *Am. J. Physiol.* 232: H400–5
43. Monroe, R. G., Gamble, W. J., LaFarge, C. G., Benoualid, H., Weisul, J. 1975. Transmural coronary venous O_2 saturations in normal and isolated hearts. *Am. J. Physiol.* 228:318–24
44. Paradise, N. F., Swayze, C. R., Shin, D. H., Fox, I. J. 1971. Perfusion heterogeneity in skeletal muscle using tritiated water. *Am. J. Physiol.* 220: 1107–15
45. Prewitt, R. L., Johnson, P. C. 1976. The effect of oxygen on arteriolar red cell velocity and capillary density in the rat cremaster muscle. *Microvasc. Res.* 12: 59–70
46. Renkin, E. M. 1969. Exchange of substances through capillary walls. In *Ciba Foundation Symposium on Circulatory and Respiratory Mass Transport,* ed. G. E. W. Wolstenholme, J. Knight, pp. 50–64. London: Churchill
47. Rose, C. P., Goresky, C. A. 1976. Vasomotor control of capillary transit time heterogeneity in the canine coronary circulation. *Circ. Res.* 39:541–54
48. Schmid-Schoenbein, G. W., Zweifach, B. W. 1975. RBC velocity profiles in arterioles and venules of the rabbit omentum. *Microvasc. Res.* 10:153–64
49. Schubert, R. W., Whalen, W. J., Nair, P. 1978. Myocardial PO_2 distribution: relationship to coronary autoregulation. *Am. J. Physiol.* 234:H361–70
50. Sestier, F. J., Mildenberger, R. R., Klassen, G. A. 1978. Role of autoregulation in spatial and temporal perfusion heterogeneity of canine myocardium. *Am. J. Physiol.* 235:H64–71
51. Steenbergen, C., Deleeuw, G., Barlow, C., Chance, B., Williamson, J. R. 1977. Heterogeneity of the hypoxic state in perfused rat heart. *Circ. Res.* 41:606–15
52. Steinhausen, M., Tillmanns, H., Thederan, H. 1978. Microcirculation of the epimyocardial layer of the heart: I. A method for in vivo observation of the microcirculation of superficial ventricular myocardium of the heart and capillary flow pattern under normal and hypoxic conditions. *Pflügers Arch.* 378:9–14
53. Tuma, R. F., Lindbom, L., Arfors, K. E. 1977. Dependence of reactive hyperemia in skeletal muscle on oxygen tension. *Am. J. Physiol.* 233:H289–94
54. Vetterlein, F., Schmidt, G. 1975. Effects of vasodilating agents on the microcirculation in marginal parts of the skeletal muscle. *Arch. Int. Pharmacodyn.* 213: 4–16
55. Wright, D. L., Sonnenschein, R. R. 1965. Relations among activity, blood flow, and vascular state in skeletal muscle. *Am. J. Physiol.* 208:782–89

Ann. Rev. Physiol. 1980. 42:383-97

NEUROEFFECTOR MECHANISMS

❖1275

Thomas C. Westfall

Department of Pharmacology, St. Louis University Medical Center, St. Louis, Missouri 63104

INTRODUCTION

The neural systems that regulate the circulation are anatomically complex and employ a variety of transmitters and vasoactive substances. The most important pathway for the central control of blood vessels is mediated by sympathetic adrenergic neurons of the autonomic nervous system, which utilizes norepinephrine (NE) as its transmitter. Several control mechanisms regulate the adrenergically mediated effects of vascular smooth muscle, including (*a*) nerve impulse frequency via receptors located on the soma and dendrites of the sympathetic ganglion cell, and (*b*) binding of NE or its metabolites to neuronal or extraneuronal sites, including postjunctional receptors. Recently it has been discovered that neural and hormonal substances can influence the quantitative release of NE per nerve impulse by an action on receptors located on adrenergic nerve terminals (presynaptic receptors) and thereby greatly influence the concentration of transmitter at the neuroeffector junction. Substances reported to decrease adrenergic neurotransmission include: α-adrenoceptor agonists, including NE itself; purines, such as ATP and adenosine; prostaglandins (PG) of the E series; acetylcholine (Ach), via muscarinic receptors; dopamine (DA); histamine; serotonin (5-HT); and morphine and opioid peptides. Substances facilitating adrenergic neurotransmission include: β-adrenergic agonists; Ach via nicotinic receptors; angiotensin (ANG); and possibly PG of the F series as well as thromboxanes. These substances may also contribute to the regulation of vascular tone by acting directly on vascular smooth muscle and/or by influencing the activity of other vasoactive substances. Here I review the

0066-4278/80/0315-0383$01.00

involvement of these substances in adrenergic transmission at the vascular neuroeffector junction. The reader is referred to several extensive recent reviews for additional details (41, 42, 69, 72, 85).

INHIBITION OF ADRENERGIC NEUROTRANSMISSION

α-Adrenoceptors

Of the many substances that can influence the stimulation-induced release of the adrenergic transmitter, the most firmly established as having physiological significance is a negative-feedback system mediated by NE itself via α-inhibitory adrenoceptors. There is convincing evidence that during nerve transmission the level of NE in the synapse continues to rise until a critical threshold is reached that shuts off further liberation of the transmitter by an action on α-adrenoceptors presumably located on the adrenergic nerve terminal. The evidence supporting the existence of α-inhibitory adrenoceptors has been thoroughly discussed in several recent reviews (41, 42, 69, 72, 85). α-Adrenoceptor agonists diminish the neurogenic release of transmitter, and α-adrenoceptor antagonists facilitate the neurogenically induced release of NE, an effect completely separate from their ability to block neuronal uptake. These effects of α-adrenoceptor agonists and antagonists are seen irrespective of the postjunctional nature of the receptor and even in the absence of a postjunctional neuroeffector cell (81), which provides strong evidence for the presynaptic nature of the response. Moreover, the binding of α-adrenoceptor ligands decreases markedly following denervation of adrenergic neurons with 6-hydroxydopamine (77). Although most studies determining the influence of α-adrenoceptor agonists and antagonists on adrenergic neurotransmission have been carried out in vitro, similar effects have been obtained in vivo (71, 87).

The inhibitory effect of α-adrenoceptor agonists is most pronounced at low, physiological frequencies of nerve stimulation (76), is potentiated by low extracellular calcium, and is attenuated by high extracellular calcium (43). Basal efflux of transmitter is not altered nor is the release induced by substances that induce release in the absence of extracellular calcium (68). Presynaptic inhibition of release by exogenous NE is more effective if uptake is simultaneously blocked (5), which suggests that the α-adrenoceptor is located close to the high affinity uptake carrier. The negative feedback process may be more important in blood vessels with narrow synaptic cleft widths (5).

The molecular mechanism by which activation of presynaptic α-adrenoceptors results in a decreased release of NE during nerve stimulation is unknown. Evidence such as that mentioned above is consistent with the hypothesis that activation of presynaptic α-adrenoceptors (as well as other presynaptic receptors, see below) limits the availability of calcium, a necessary ingredient of secretion coupling. How α-adrenoceptor or other presynaptic receptor activation limits the availability of calcium is unknown. It could be mediated by an increased efflux, decreased influx, or an alteration in calcium utilization. Evidence for an increased efflux has recently been obtained. It has been proposed that α-adrenoceptor agonists inhibit the release of NE from adrenergic neurons and the adrenal medulla by activation of a Na,K-ATPase (31). Another hypothesis with experimental backing suggests that cGMP may be linked to the events triggered by the activation of the inhibitory presynaptic α-adrenoceptors in the rat pineal gland (59). It is not known if a similar mechanism exists in other adrenergically innervated tissues.

Impressive evidence suggests that pre- and postjunctional receptors are not homogeneous. Both agonists (16, 70) and antagonists (11, 20) have preferential effects on the two types of adrenoceptors. These studies have led to the proposal that the postjunctional α-adrenoceptor be referred to as α_1 and the presynaptic α-adrenoceptor as α_2 (4, 41). Unfortunately this is an oversimplification because there are both tissue and species differences in the ability of various drugs to affect α_1 and α_2 adrenoceptors (2). It is also of interest that various vascular beds may respond differently to α agonists and antagonists. There may be a predominance of presynaptic α-adrenoceptor (α_2) in the rabbit basilar artery, and a similar predominance of α_1 and α_2 receptors in other vascular neuroeffector junctions also appears possible (18, 45).

It is of interest that α-adrenoceptors that mediate sympathetic ganglionic hyperpolarization (7), inhibition of Ach release from preganglionic cholinergic neurons (17), inhibition of Melanocyte-Stimulated-Hormone–induced darkening of the frog skin (4), and inhibition of renin release from the kidney (4), all have the characteristics of the α_2 adrenoceptor, while the α-adrenoceptor that mediates an increase in the release of Ach from the somatic nerve at the skeletal neuromuscular junction has characteristics of the α_1 adrenoceptor (53).

Purines (ATP; Adenosine)

Adenosine and ATP inhibit the neurogenically induced release of NE from a wide variety of vascular (56, 79) and nonvascular tissues (10, 35). Thus purines might participate in the modulation of adrenergic neurotransmission, though the physiological role of adenosine or ATP in such modulation is unclear and supporting in vivo data are lacking. As a participant in the normal modulation of adrenergic neurotransmission, ATP and/or adenosine could originate from the adrenergic neuron itself, from postjunctional tissue such as the vascular smooth muscle, or from nonadrenergic (purinergic) neurons. Considerable data support the hypothesis that the adrenergic neuron is the source of the released ATP and adenosine (78). Whether ATP or adenosine is the primary modulator is not known, but this seems immaterial since adenosine and ATP are nearly equipotent in decreasing adrenergic transmission (56, 79).

Adenosine-like material may also be released by an action of NE on postjunctional sites or following nerve stimulation (28). A third possible source of adenosine-like material is from nonadrenergic, purinergic nerves that have been observed at some neuroeffector junctions (8) and could modulate adrenergic transmission by axonal-dendritic or axonal-axonal interaction.

The mechanism of the inhibitory action of ATP and/or adenosine is obscure; but, like the negative feedback induced by α-adrenoceptor agonists, the purines appear to limit the availability of calcium for secretion coupling. Furthermore, it appears certain that the inhibitory effect of adenosine is not mediated via other known inhibitory mediators such as muscarinic, prostaglandin, or α-inhibitory receptors (56, 79). The inhibitory effect by adenosine can be prevented by the administration of theophylline, which suggests an effect on a specific adenosine receptor.

Despite the fact that adenosine has been shown to inhibit adrenergic neurotransmission in a wide variety of sympathetically innervated tissues, it has also been reported that adenosine can facilitate transmission in the cat spleen (57).

Prostaglandin E_1 and E_2

The exogenous administration of PGs of the E series will inhibit neurotransmission in a wide variety of adrenergically innervated tissues [see (34, 69, 72, 74) for recent reviews]. This effect is species-dependent and also varies in different vascular beds within the same species (50). PGE_1 and PGE_2 also reduce the vasoconstrictor response to sympathetic nerve stimulation in concentrations devoid of direct vascular actions (51). Increased PG synthesis by the administration of arachidonic acid inhibited the vasoconstrictor response to sympathetic nerve stimulations (26). Sympathetic nerve stimulation results in the formation and release of PG of the E series [for references see (26)]. Moreover, inhibition of PG synthesis results in a facilitation of adrenergic neurotransmission as well as augmentation of the vascular responses to adrenergic nerve stimulation, though like the effect of exogenously applied PGEs this effect is also species- and tissue-dependent [see (26, 85) for references]. These results have lead to the suggestion that endogenous PGEs contribute to the regulation of vascular tone by local modulation of adrenergic neurotransmission at some neuroeffector junctions (34). The site of origin of the PGE_1 or PGE_2 that may participate in such modulation is controversial. Evidence exists for their formation in postjunctional tissue and in adrenergic nerve terminals themselves (74). The evidence available to date is most consistent with (*a*) formation from postjunctional sites following activation of an adrenoceptor and (*b*) exertion of its effects on the release of NE via a transynaptic action.

The precise adrenoceptor involved in mediating the release of PG appears to vary with the tissue. In the spleen it appears to be an α-adrenoceptor; in the rabbit heart both α- and β-adrenoceptors may contribute to this action (84).

In contrast to the situation regarding the α-adrenoceptor-mediated inhibition of adrenergic neurotransmission (PG-independent), doubts have been expressed about the physiological importance of the PG-mediated effect on NE release. Arguments against the importance of this system are: (*a*) The mechanism is not general, since PGs do not inhibit the release of NE from all adrenergically innervated tissue (19); (*b*) PG release by sympathetic nerve stimulation has been studied mostly in isolated saline perfused organs and in such preparations both the resting and nerve-stimulation-induced output of PG increases with time perhaps because of tissue deterioration (19); and (*c*) the effect of PG in decreasing NE release is quantitatively far less marked than that of the PG-independent α-adrenoceptor mechanism (see 69, 72, 85). Further work must clarify the physiological importance of the PG effect.

The mechanism of the PG-induced inhibition of NE release is unknown. Like α-adrenoceptor agonists, PGE_2 appears to interfere somehow with the availability of calcium for secretion coupling (34). PGE_2 inhibited the activation of adenylate cyclase evoked by acetylcholine or a β-adrenoceptor agonist in the adrenal medulla. This resulted in a reduction in intracellular cAMP with a simultaneous reduction in the rate of ^{45}Calcium efflux from adrenal medullary slices preloaded with calcium (32). It has been suggested that PG may also act as a calcium ionophore (38, 74).

Prostacycline (PGI_2)

In contrast to the effect of PGs of the E series, prostacycline (PGI_2), which is the major vasodilator metabolite of arachidonic acid formed by blood vessels, apparently does not alter the release of NE during nerve stimulation of adrenergically innervated tissues (3). On the other hand, PGI_2 did reduce the increase in contractile force of isolated rabbit atrial strips produced by the exogenous administration of NE or ANG and does inhibit the neurogenically induced contraction of the guinea pig vas deferens (3, 83), though it is much less effective than PGE_2.

Dopamine

DA decreases the effector cell response to adrenergic nerve stimulation in vascular (37) and nonvascular tissue (23, 66). Moreover, DA decreases the nerve-stimulation-induced release of NE in several of these preparations (29, 37, 66). These observations suggest that DA may also have the ability to modulate adrenergic neurotransmission. DA inhibition of NE release is clearly not present in all tissues with adrenergic innervation, however (21, 69, 73).

In tissues where DA does cause an inhibition of adrenergic neurotransmission, the effect is thought to be mediated via specific DA receptors located on adrenergic nerve terminals and not via the well known inhibitory α-adrenoceptors (37). It is controversial whether DA antagonists do (37) or do not (66) increase NE release during nerve stimulation. It seems unlikely that dopamine reaches concentrations high enough to influence transmitter release at adrenergic neuroeffector junctions during nerve stimulation. However, the conversion of DA to NE by dopamine β-hydroxylase can become rate limiting with an increase in the proportion of DA under conditions of marked increases in the frequency of nerve stimulation (40).

The DA receptor on adrenergic nerve terminals is apparently different from the well known DA receptors that induce vasodilation in certain blood vessels (30).

Acetylcholine

Ach has been shown to inhibit the stimulation-induced release of NE from adrenergically innervated tissue and is selectively blocked by muscarinic antagonists [see (58, 69, 85) for references]. This has generated the hypothesis that Ach released from cholinergic fibers stimulates muscarinic inhibitory receptors on terminal adrenergic fibers found in close proximity to cholinergic nerves. This then would represent an example of axonal-dendritic or axonal-axonal interaction between peripheral neurotransmitters. This type of mechanism is suggested by the observation that muscarinic agonists decrease while muscarinic antagonists increase the electrically induced or potassium-induced release of NE from a wide variety of adrenergically innervated tissues and species both in vitro and in vivo. A parallel decrease in the postjunctional response to adrenergic nerve stimulation is also seen. Like that of several other inhibitory release modulating substances, the effect of Ach is most pronounced at low frequencies of nerve stimulation and is active only against release mechanisms requiring extracellular calcium. The mechanism of Ach may thus be similar to that of other inhibitory substances (58).

The physiological significance of the muscarinic-induced inhibition of adrenergic transmission at adrenergic neuroeffector junctions such as the SA node of the heart is supported by the observation that vagal stimulation decreases the release of NE produced by sympathetic nerve stimulation in vivo and in vitro (47, 48). The muscarinic-induced inhibition of NE release is also seen in numerous blood vessel and other smooth muscle preparations, irrespective if whether there is dual adrenergic-cholinergic innervation (67). A physiological role of cholinergic nerves in modulating NE release from blood vessels receiving dual innervation is possible. The significance of such an Ach-mediated effect in blood vessels receiving only adrenergic innervations is unclear.

Unlike α-adrenoceptors, these muscarinic inhibitory receptors appear to be similar to postjunctional muscarinic receptors (24), specifically to the ganglionic receptor mediating hyperpolarization rather than the one inducing depolarization (25).

The mechanism of the muscarinic-induced inhibition of NE release is unknown. Like most other release modulating substances, muscarinic agonists inhibit the release of NE only by calcium-dependent processes. It has been postulated that the mechanism involves a hyperpolarization of adrenergic nerve terminals (33) or an enhancement of potassium permeability (39).

Histamine

Several recent studies suggest that histamine can produce an inhibitory effect on adrenergic neurotransmission by an action on H_2 histamine receptors (49, 55, 60). The presence of H_2 receptors on adrenergic nerve terminals is in contrast to the presence of both types of histamine receptors (H_1 and H_2) in vascular smooth muscle, where they appear to lower blood pressure via direct vasodilation (61).

A physiological role for histamine in modifying adrenergic neurotransmission has not yet been established. However, histamine is present in high concentrations in the blood vessel wall (22) and in cardiac tissue in close proximity to the sinoatrial and atrioventricular nodes (46). Histamine is also present in sympathetic nerves (64). It is released into the circulation during the sudden withdrawal of sympathetic tone (36) and during direct stimulation of the sympathetic nerves and spinal roots (80). Evidence against a physiological role of histamine on adrenergic transmission is the fact that neither H_1 nor H_2 receptor antagonists altered the response to sympathetic nerve stimulation (49). Further, it does not appear that dilation caused by histamine is due to reduction in tonic sympathetic tone (61).

5-Hydroxytryptamine

5-HT has been shown to inhibit the contractile response of vascular smooth muscle to nerve stimulation and potassum depolarization of the sympathetic nerves but not that of tyramine in concentrations that have no direct vascular effect (54). In addition, 5-HT decreases the release of NE evoked by nerve stimulation or potassum depolarization in several adrenergically innervated tissues (54, 65). The effect is not blocked by muscarinic, α-adrenoceptor, histamine, or β-adrenoceptor antagonists or following the inhibition of PG synthesis or following the administration of morphine. Differences in the presynaptic 5-HT receptors on vascular adrenergic neurons compared to postjunctional 5-HT receptors may exist (68, 84). The physiological importance of these 5-HT receptors is unclear.

FACILITATION OF ADRENERGIC NEUROTRANSMISSION

Positive Feedback via β-Adrenoceptors

Several in vitro studies have demonstrated that β-adrenoceptor agonists enhance (*a*) adrenergic neurotransmission in a variety of adrenergically innervated tissues independently of the α or β nature of the postjunctional receptors (1, 9, 75, 86) and (*b*) the release of ^{3}H-NE induced by potassium chloride from the rat superior cervical ganglia grown in organ culture (82). In addition, a facilitation of NE release into the circulation from the heart during cardio-accelerator nerve stimulation has been observed in the anesthetized dog (87). The facilitation induced by β-adrenoceptor agonists is antagonized by β-adrenoceptor blocking agents, which suggests that the effect is mediated by β-adrenoceptors.

The observation that β-adrenoceptor agonists can enhance adrenergic neurotransmission has given rise to a positive feedback hypothesis (1) that the release of NE may be modulated by both a positive and negative feedback process. The positive feedback would be activated by low concentrations of the transmitter leading to an increase in the release of NE per stimulus. As the concentration of NE in the synapse rises, the positive feedback via β-adrenoceptors would then be replaced by the negative feedback process mediated by presynaptic α-adrenoceptors (α_2). An alternative hypothesis suggests that the β-mediated enhancement of NE release is an example of hormonal modulation mediated by circulating epinephrine of adrenal medullary origin. The alternate hypothesis suggests that the physiological role of these exquisitely sensitive β-adrenoceptors may be concerned with the detection of circulating epinephrine, rather than released NE, to mediate enhanced NE secretion from the sympathetic nerves under conditions of increased adrenal medullary activity (75).

The nature of the β-adrenoceptor (β_1 or β_2) that enhances adrenergic transmission is not completely settled. However, there is strong support for it's being of the β_2 type (75, 82, 86). Epinephrine is 100 times more potent than NE in enhancing NE overflow (14). NE itself is a weak agonist at β_2 adrenoceptors, while epinephrine is very active on both β_1 and β_2 adrenoceptors. These findings argue against a neuronally mediated positive feedback system in adrenergic neurons in vascular smooth muscle. They are more consistent with the concept of hormonal modulation of NE release.

At least one report suggests that the β-adrenoceptor enhancing NE release is a β_1 adrenoceptor (13). Both types of β-adrenoceptors may be present on adrenergic nerve terminals with wide species and tissue variations in the relative concentration of β_1 and β_2 adrenoceptors.

The facilitation of NE release observed with β agonists is not nearly as pronounced as that seen after interruption of the α inhibitory system with α-adrenoceptor antagonists, which suggests that the α-adrenoceptor inhibitory pathway is quantitatively a more important pathway. Nevertheless, enhancement of transmitter release by β-agonists is seen at extremely low concentrations (15); during stress, concentrations of epinephrine may be reached that could activate the β-adrenoceptor-mediated release of NE.

The β-adrenoceptor-mediated enhancement of adrenergic transmission may also be important in pathophysiological conditions such as hypertension. A positive correlation has been reported between human hypertension and blood epinephrine but not NE levels; circulating epinephrine is significantly increased in both labile and other types of hypertension (27). If circulating levels of epinephrine are increased, this is reflected by a greater proportion of epinephrine stored in adrenergic nerve endings (44). Moreover, the epinephrine concentration doubles in blood vessels of the spontaneously hypertensive rat. When epinephrine and NE are mixed in adrenergic neurons, the β-adrenoceptor blocking drugs propranolol and metroprolol significantly reduce transmitter release; they had no effect when epinephrine was absent (62). These findings suggest that hypertension may be due to a change in the transmitter released from sympathetic vasomotor nerves that increases the proportion of epinephrine.

As with other release-modulating receptors, the mechanism of the β-adrenoceptor enhancement of the evoked release of NE is still unclear. The demonstration that cyclic AMP can increase adrenergic neurotransmission

(12) and the fact that β-receptor activation increases adenylate cyclase activity resulting in an increased formation of cAMP (63) have given rise to the hypothesis that the presynaptic β-adrenoceptor enhancement of NE release utilizes cAMP as a second messenger (1, 9). Evidence consistent with this hypothesis is available (9, 59).

Angiotensin

ANG enhances the responses evoked by stimulation of adrenergic nerves in a variety of vascular and nonvascular preparations in vitro and in vivo (69, 85, 89). In several but not all types of preparations, enhancement of nerve-stimulated responses is greater than enhancement of the response to exogenous NE (88, 89). ANG has also been shown to enhance the release of NE evoked by nerve stimulation of several adrenergically innervated tissues both in vivo and in vitro [see (69, 85, 89) for references].

The facilitation of NE release appears unrelated to a blockade of reuptake and is thought to be due to activation of ANG receptors located on adrenergic nerve terminals (88). Evidence is available suggesting that subtle differences exist between pre- and postjunctional ANG receptors (6). The angiotensin-induced potentiation of the vasoconstrictor effect on nerve stimulation in the arterial segments of the perfused canine hind paw is greater than that induced by the exogenous administration of NE. Potentiations by the two agents in the venous segments (89), on the other hand, are similar.

The physiological significance of the angiotensin-induced facilitation of adrenergic transmission is not clear. Such facilitation is seen at low frequencies of nerve stimulation well within the physiological range, both in vivo and in vitro (89). Moreover, angiotensin is probably formed within blood vessels in concentrations within the range observed to enhance the nerve-stimulation-induced release of NE [see (85) for references].

Prostaglandins of the F Series; Thromboxane A_2 and B_2

PGs of the F series, like other PGs, are synthesized in blood vessels. They cause vasoconstriction in some but not all such vessels (52). They appear to enhance the effector cell response to adrenergic nerve stimulation or NE administration in a wide variety of tissues in several species [references in (50, 85)]. These results have led to the suggestion that $PGF_{2\alpha}$ may facilitate adrenergic neurotransmission. However, the evidence is indirect; enhancement of release has not been demonstrated.

Thromboxane B_2 has recently been shown to cause vasoconstriction and to potentiate the vascular response to nerve stimulation in the perfused rat spleen (50). This suggests that TXB_2 and its precursor TXA_2 may also participate in modulating the vascular response to adrenergic stimuli. In this regard TXB_2 resembles $PGF_{2\alpha}$. Both of these substances may in certain species and vascular beds oppose or contribute to the modulatory role of PGE_2 on vascular reactivity to adrenergic stimuli.

SUMMARY

Many neural and hormonal agents have been observed to influence the concentration of NE at the vascular neuroeffector junction by decreasing or enhancing adrenergic neurotransmission. Most of these substances act via discrete receptors; their actions are blocked by specific antagonists. These receptors are most likely located on the adrenergic nerve varicosities, though this has not been proven unequivocally in all cases. The mechanism of action of these release-modulating substances is still unknown. Several appear to increase or decrease the availability of calcium for secretion coupling.

Although all of these receptors have important pharmacological implications, their physiological roles are unclear. The most firmly established as having a modulatory role is the α-adrenoceptor inhibitory system, which appears to modulate the pulse-to-pulse release of NE at all adrenergic neuroeffector junctions. Both purines and PGE_2 may participate as inhibitory modulators at selected neuroeffector junctions. Ach can modulate adrenergic transmission following its release from cholinergic neurons, which it appears to do in the sino-atrial area of the heart. During stress the β-adrenoceptor and ANG facilitory systems may be functional. Little information is available on the pathophysiological role of any presynaptic receptors, but the involvement of β and ANG receptors in hypertension is an intriguing possibility.

ACKNOWLEDGMENT

The author's research described in this article was supported by USPHS-NINCDS 10260 and NIHL 19242 and carried out in the Department of Pharmacology, University of Virginia School of Medicine.

Literature Cited

1. Adler-Graschinsky, E., Langer, S. Z. 1975. Possible role of a β-adrenoceptor in the regulation of noradrenaline release by nerve stimulation through a positive feedback mechanism. *Brit. J. Pharmacol.* 53:43–50
2. Arbilla, S., Langer, S. Z. 1978. Differences between presynaptic and postsynaptic α-adrenoceptors in the isolated nictitating membrane of the cat: effects of metanephrine and tolazoline. *Brit. J. Pharmacol.* 64:259–64
3. Armstrong, J. M., Thirsk, G. 1979. Effects of prostacyclin (PGI_2), PGE_2 and 6-OXO-$PGF_{1\alpha}$ on sympathetic nerve function in rabbit mesenteric arteries superfused with Krebs solution *in vitro.* In *Presynaptic Receptors,* ed. S. Z. Langer, pp. 305–9. NY: Pergamon
4. Berthelsen, S., Pettinger, W. A. 1977. A functional basis for the classification of α adrenergic receptors. *Life Sci.* 21:595–606
5. Bevan, J. A. 1978. Norepinephrine and the presynaptic control of adrenergic transmitter release. *Fed. Proc.* 37: 187–90
6. Blumberg, A. L., Ackerly, J. A., Peach, M. J. 1975. Differentiation of neurogenic and myocardial angiotensin II receptors in isolated rabbit atria. *Circ. Res.* 36:719–26
7. Brown, D. A., Canfield, M. P. 1979. Hyperpolarizing α_2 adrenoceptors in rat sympathetic ganglia. *Brit. J. Pharmacol.* 65:435–45
8. Burnstock, G. 1975. Purinergic transmission. *Handb. Psychopharmacol.* 5: 131–94
9. Celuch, S. M., Dubocovich, M. L., Langer, S. Z. 1978. Stimulation of presynaptic β-adrenoceptors enhances ^{3}H-NA release during nerve stimulation in the perfused cat spleen. *Brit. J. Pharmacol.* 63:97–109
10. Clanachan, A. S., Johns, A., Paton, D. M. 1977. Presynaptic inhibitory actions of adenine nucleotides and adenosine on neurotransmission in the rat vas deferens. *Neuroscience* 2:597–602
11. Cubeddu, L. X., Barnes, E. M., Langer, S. Z., Weiner, N. 1974. Release of norepinephrine and dopamine β-hydroxylase by nerve stimulation I. Role of neuronal and extraneuronal uptake and of alpha presynaptic receptors. *J. Pharmacol. Exp. Ther.* 190:431–50
12. Cubeddu, L. X., Barnes, E., Weiner, N. 1975. Release of norepinephrine and dopamine β-hydroxylase by nerve stimulation IV. An evaluation of a role for cyclic adenosine monophosphate. *J. Pharmacol. Exp. Ther.* 193:105–27
13. Dahlöf, C., Äblad, B., Borg, K. O., Ek, L., Waldeck, B. 1975. Prejunctional inhibition of adrenergic nervous vasomotor control due to β-receptor blockade. In *Chemical Tools in Catecholamine Research,* ed. O. Almgren, A. Carlsson, J. Engel, pp. 201–10. Amsterdam: North Holland
14. Dahlöf, C., Ljung, B., Äblad, B. 1979. Evidence for the existence of a presynaptic β-adrenoceptor mediated positive feedback mechanism. See Reference 3
15. Dixon, W. R., Musimann, W. F., Weiner, N. 1979. The role of presynaptic feedback mechanisms in regulation of norepinephrine release by nerve stimulation. *J. Pharmacol. Exp. Ther.* 209:196–204
16. Drew, G. M. 1976. Effects of α adrenoceptor agonists and antagonists on pre- and postsynaptically located α adrenoceptors. *Eur. J. Pharmacol.* 36: 313–20
17. Drew, G. M. 1978. Pharmacological characterization of the presynaptic α adrenoceptors regulating cholinergic activity in the guinea pig ileum. *Brit. J. Pharmacol.* 64:293–300
18. Duckles, S. P., Bevan, J. A. 1976. Pharmacological characterization of adrenergic receptors of a rabbit cerebral artery *in vitro. J. Pharmacol. Exp. Ther.* 197:371–78
19. Dubocovich, M. L., Langer, S. Z. 1975. Evidence against a physiological role of prostaglandins in the regulation of noradrenaline release in the cat spleen. *J. Physiol. London* 251:737–62
20. Dubocovich, M. L., Langer, S. Z. 1974. Negative feedback regulation of noradrenaline release by nerve stimulation in the perfused cat's spleen: Differences in potency of phenoxybenzamine in blocking the pre- and postsynaptic adrenergic receptors. *J. Physiol. London* 237:505–19
21. Earnhardt, J. T., Westfall, T. C. 1979. Role of dopamine in the modulation of norepinephrine release from the rat portal vein. In *Peripheral Dopamine Receptors,* pp. 309–15. NY: Pergamon
22. Elkad, T. M., Brody, M. J. 1975. Evidence for non-mast cell histamine in the vascular wall. *Blood Vessels* 12:181–91
23. Enero, M. A., Langer, S. Z. 1975. Inhibition by dopamine of ^{3}H-norepinephrine release elicited by nerve stimulation in the isolated cat's nictitating mem-

brane. *Naunyn-Schmiedeberg's Arch. Pharmacol.* 289:179–203
24. Fozard, J. R., Muscholl, E. 1972. Effects of several muscarinic agonists on cardiac performance and the release of norepinephrine from sympathetic nerves of the perfused rabbit heart. *Brit. J. Pharmacol.* 45:616–29
25. Fozard, J. R., Muscholl, E. 1974. Atropine resistant effects of the muscarinic agonists McN-A-343 and AHR-602 on cardiac performance and the release of noradrenaline from sympathetic nerves of the perfused rabbit heart. *Brit. J. Pharmacol.* 50:531–41
26. Frame, M. H., Hedqvist, P. 1975. Evidence for prostaglandin mediated prejunctional control of renal sympathetic transmitter release and vascular tone. *Brit. J. Pharmacol.* 54:189–96
27. Franco-Morselli, F., Elghozi, J. L., Joly, E., DiGiulio, S., Meyer, P. 1977. Increased plasma adrenaline concentrations in benign essential hypertension. *Brit. Med. J.* 2:1251–54
28. Fredholm, B. B., Hedqvist, P. 1978. Relase of ^{3}H-purines from ^{3}H-adenine labelled rabbit kidney following sympathetic nerve stimulation and its inhibition by α-adrenoceptor blockade. *Brit. J. Pharmacol.* 63:239–45
29. Fuder, H., Muscholl, E. 1978. The effect of dopamine on the overflow of endogenous noradrenaline from the perfused rabbit heart evoked by sympathetic nerve stimulation. *Naunyn-Schmiedeberg's Arch. Pharmacol.* 305: 109–15
30. Goldberg, L. I. 1978. Vascular dopamine receptors as a model for other dopamine receptors. *Adv. Biochem. Psychopharmacol.* 19:119–29
31. Gutman, Y., Boonyaviroj, P. 1977. Inhibition of catecholamine release by alpha adrenergic activation: interaction with Na/K-ATPase. *J. Neural Transmiss.* 40:245–52
32. Gutman, Y., Boonyaviroj, P. 1979. Mechanism of PGE inhibition of catecholamine release from adrenal medulla. *Eur. J. Pharmacol.* 55:129–36
33. Haeusler, G., Thoenen, H., Haefely, W., Huerlimann, A. 1968. Electrical events in cardiac adrenergic nerves and noradrenaline release from the heart induced by acetylcholine and KC1. *Naunyn-Schmiedeberg's Arch. Pharmacol.* 261:389–411
34. Hedqvist, P. 1977. Basic mechanisms of prostaglandin action on autonomic neurotransmission. *Ann. Rev. Pharmacol. Toxicol.* 17:259–79
35. Hedqvist, P., Fredholm, B. B. 1976. Effects of adenosine on adrenergic transmission: Prejunctional inhibition and postjunctional enhancement *Naunyn-Schmiedeberg's Arch. Pharmacol.* 293:217–23
36. Heitz, D. C., Brody, M. J. 1975. Possible mechanism of histamine release during active vasodilation. *Am. J. Physiol.* 225:1351–57
37. Hope, W., McCulloch, M. W., Rand, M. J., Story, D. F. 1978. Modulation of noradrenergic transmission in the rabbit ear artery by dopamine. *Brit. J. Pharmacol.* 64:527–37
38. Kirtland, S. J., Baurn, H. 1972. Prostaglandin E_1 may act as a "calcium ionophore." *Nature New Biol.* 236:47–49
39. Kirpekar, S. M., Prat, J. C., Puig, M., Wakade, A. R. 1972. Modification of the evoked release of noradrenaline from the perfused cat spleen by various ions and agents. *J. Physiol. London* 221:601–15
40. Kopin, I. J., Breese, G. R., Krauss, K. R., Weiss, V. K. 1968. Selective release of newly synthesized norepinephrine from the cat spleen during sympathetic nerve stimulation. *J. Pharmacol. Exp. Ther.* 161:271–78
41. Langer, S. Z. 1974. Presynaptic regulation of catecholamine release. *Biochem. Pharmacol.* 23:1793–1800
42. Langer, S. Z. 1977. Presynaptic receptors and their role in the regulation of transmitter release. *Brit. J. Pharmacol.* 60:481–97
43. Langer, S. Z., Dubocovich, M. L., Celuch, S. M. 1975. Prejunctional regulatory mechanisms for noradrenaline release elicited by nerve stimulation. See Ref. 14, Vol. II, pp. 183–91
44. Langer, S. Z., Vogt, M. 1971. Noradrenaline release from isolated muscles of the nictitating membrane of the cat. *J. Physiol. London* 214:159–71
45. Lee, T. J. F., Su, C., Bevan, J. A. 1976. Neurogenic sympathetic vasoconstriction of the rabbit basilar artery. *Circ. Res.* 39:120–26
46. Levi, R., Allan, G., Zavecz, J. H. 1976. Cardiac histamine receptors. *Fed. Proc.* 35:1942–47
47. Levy, M. N., Blattberg, B. 1976. Effect of vagal stimulation on the overflow of norepinephrine into the coronary sinus during cardiac sympathetic nerve stimulation in the dog. *Circ. Res.* 38:81–85
48. Löffelholz, K., Muscholl, E. 1970. Inhibition of parasympathetic nerve stimulation of the release of the adrener-

gic transmitter. *Naunyn-Schiedeberg's Arch. Pharmacol.* 267:181–84
49. Lokhandwala, M. F. 1978. Inhibition of sympathetic nervous system by histamine with H_1 and H_2 receptor antagonists. *J. Pharmacol. Exp. Ther.* 206: 115–22
50. Malik, K. U. 1978. Prostaglandin mediated inhibition of the vasoconstrictor response of the isolated perfused rat splenic vasculature of adrenergic stimuli. *Circ. Res.* 43:225–33
51. Malik, K. U., McGiff, J. C. 1975. Modulation by prostaglandins of adrenergic transmission in the isolated perfused rabbit and rat kidney. *Circ. Res.* 36:599–609
52. Malik, K. U., McGiff, J. C. 1976. Cardiovascular actions of prostaglandins. In *Advances in Prostaglandin Research. Prostaglandins: Physiological Pharmacological and Pathological Aspects,* ed. S. M. M. Karin, pp. 103–200. Lancaster: MIT Press
53. Malta, E., McPherson, G. A., Raper, C. 1979. Comparison of prejunctional α adrenoceptors at the neuromuscular junction with vascular postjunctional α receptors in the cat skeletal muscle. *Brit. J. Pharmacol.* 65:249–56
54. McGrath, M. A. 1977. 5-Hydroxytryptamine and neurotransmitter release in canine blood vessels: inhibition by low and augmentation by high concentrations. *Circ. Res.* 41:428–35
55. McGrath, M. A., Shepherd, J. T. 1976. Inhibition of adrenergic neurotransmission in canine vascular smooth muscle by histamine. Mediation by H_2 receptors. *Circ. Res.* 39:566–73
56. Moyland, R., Westfall, T. C. 1979. Effect of adenosine on adrenergic neurotransmission in the superfused rat portal vein. *Blood Vessels.* In press
57. Mueller, A. L., Mosimann, W. F., Weiner, N. 1979. Effects of adenosine on neurally mediated NE release from the cat spleen. *Eur. J. Pharmacol.* 53:329–33
58. Muscholl, E. 1978. Presynaptic muscarine receptors and inhibition of release. In *The Release of Catecholamines from Adrenergic Neurons,* ed D. M. Paton, pp. 87–110. NY: Pergamon
59. Pelayo, F., Dubocovich, M. L., Langer, S. Z. 1978. Possible role of cyclic nucleotides in regulation of noradrenaline release from rat pineal through presynaptic adrenoceptors. *Nature* 274: 76–78
60. Powell, J. R. 1979. Effects of histamine on vascular sympathetic neuroeffector transmission. *J. Pharmacol. Exp. Ther.* 208:360–65
61. Powell, J. R., Brody, M. J. 1976. Identification and specific blockade of two receptors for histamine in the cardiovascular system. *J. Pharmacol. Exp. Ther.* 196:1–14
62. Rand, M. J., Majewski, H., McCullrich, M. W., Story, D. F. 1979. Prejunctional receptors of peripheral adrenergic nerves as sites of antihypertensive drug action. See Ref. 3, pp. 263–69
63. Robison, G. A., Dobbs, J. W., Sutherland, E. W. 1970. On the nature of the receptor sites for biogenic amines. In *Biogenic Amines as Physiological Regulators,* ed. J. J. Blurn, pp. 3–34. Englewood Cliffs, NJ: Prentice Hall
64. Ryan, M. J., Brody, M. J. 1970. Distribution of histamine in canine autonomic nervous system. *J. Pharmacol. Exp. Ther.* 174:123–32
65. Sax, R., Westfall, T. C. 1976. Effect of 5-hydroxytryptamine on the spontaneous and stimulation induced release of ^{3}H-norepinephine from rat heart and vein. *Pharmacology* 19:336
66. Sharabi, F. M., Long, J. P., Cannon, J. G. 1977. Inhibition of canine adrenergic transmission by an analog of dopamine: GJH-166. *J. Pharmacol. Exp. Ther.* 202:97–104
67. Shepherd, J. T., Lorenz, R. R., Tyca, G. M., Vanhoutte, P. M. 1978. Acetylcholine—inhibition of transmitter release from adrenergic nerve terminals mediated by muscarinic receptors. *Fed. Proc.* 37:191–94
68. Starke, K. 1972. Alpha sympathomimetic inhibition of adrenergic and cholinergic transmission in the rabbit heart. *Naunyn-Schmiedeberg's Arch. Pharmacol.* 274:18–45
69. Starke, K. 1977. Regulation of noradrenaline release by presynaptic receptor systems. *Rev. Physiol. Biochem. Pharmacol.* 77:1–124
70. Starke, K., Endo, T., Taube, D. 1975. Relative pre and postsynapitc potencies of α adrenoceptor agonists in the rabbit pulmonary artery. *Naunyn-Schmiedeberg's Arch. Pharmacol.* 291:55–78
71. Steppeler, A., Tanaka, T., Starke, K. 1979. Pre and postsynaptic alpha-adrenergic effects of phenylephrine and tramazoline on blood vessels *in vivo.* See Ref. 3, pp. 99–104
72. Stjärne, L. 1975. Basic mechanisms and local feedback control of secretion of adrenergic and cholinergic neurotransmitters. *Handb. Psychopharmacol.* 6: 179–233

73. Stjärne, L. 1975. Selectivity for catecholamines of presynaptic alpha-receptors involved in feedback control of sympathetic neurotransmitter secretion in guinea pig vas deferens. *Naunyn-Schmiedeberg's Arch. Pharmacol.* 228: 296–303
74. Stjärne, L. 1978. Role of prostaglandin and cyclic adenosine monophosphate in release. See Ref. 58, pp. 111–142
75. Stjärne, L., Brundin, J. 1976. β_2-adrenoceptors facilitating noradrenaline secretion from human vasoconstrictor nerves. *Acta Physiol. Scand.* 97: 88–93
76. Stjärne, L., Brundin, J. 1977. Frequency dependence of ^{3}H-noradrenaline secretion from human vasoconstrictor nerves: modification by factors interfering with α or β adrenoceptor or prostaglandin E_2 mediated control. *Acta Physiol. Scand.* 101:199–210
77. Story, D. F., Briley, M. S., Langer, S. Z. 1979. The effects of 6-hydroxydopamine treatment on the binding of ^{3}H-quinuclidinylbenzilate, ^{3}H-dehydroergocryptine, and ^{3}H-WB 4101 to rat heart ventricular membranes. See Ref. 3, pp. 105–9
78. Su, C. 1975. Neurogenic release of purine compounds in blood vessels. *J. Pharmacol. Exp. Ther.* 195:159–60
79. Su, C. 1978. Purinergic inhibition of adrenergic transmission in rabbit blood vessels. *J. Pharmacol. Exp. Ther.* 204:351–61
80. Tuttle, R. S., McCleary, M. 1970. Effect of sympathetic nerve activity on labeling and release of histamine in the cat. *Am. J. Physiol.* 218:143–48
81. Vogel, S. A., Silberstein, S. D., Berv, V. K. R., Kopin, I. J. 1972. Stimulation induced release of norepinephrine from rat superior cervical ganglia *in vitro*. *Eur. J. Pharmacol.* 20:308–11
82. Weinstock, N., Thoa, N. B., Kopin, I. J. 1978. Beta-adrenoceptors modulate noradrenaline release from axonal sprouts in cultured rat superior cervical ganglia. *Eur. J. Pharmacol.* 47:297–302
83. Wennmalm, A. 1978. Prostaglandin mediated inhibition of noradrenaline release. V. A comparison of the inhibitory effect of three prostaglandins: E_2, I_2 and 6-Keto-$PGF_{1\alpha}$. *Prostagl. Med.* 1:49–54
84. Wennmalm, A., Brundin, T. 1978. Prostaglandin mediated inhibition of norepinephrine release IV. Prostaglandin synthesis is stimulated by myocardial adrenoceptors differing from the α and β type. *Acta Physiol. Scand.* 102:374–81
85. Westfall, T. C. 1977. Local regulation of adrenergic neurotransmission. *Physiol. Rev.* 57:659–728
86. Westfall, T. C., Peach, M. J., Tittermary, V. 1979. Enhancement of the electrically induced release of norepinephrine from the rat portal vein: Mediation by β_2 adrenoceptors. *Eur. J. Pharmacol.* 58:67–74
87. Yamaguchi, N., DeChamplain, J., Nadeau, R. A. 1977. Regulation of norepinephrine release from cardiac sympathetic fibers in the dog by presynaptic α and β receptors. *Circ. Res.* 41:108–17
88. Zimmerman, B. G. 1973. Blockade of adrenergic potentiating effect of angiotensin by 1-Sar-8-ala-angiotensin II. *J. Pharmacol. Exp. Ther.* 185:486–92
89. Zimmerman, B. G. 1978. Actions of angiotensin on adrenergic nerve endings. *Fed. Proc.* 37:199–202

Ann. Rev. Physiol. 1980. 42:399–411

CENTRAL NERVOUS REGULATION OF VASCULAR RESISTANCE

❖1276

S. M. Hilton and K. M. Spyer

Department of Physiology, The Medical School, University of Birmingham, Birmingham B15 2TJ, England

CARDIOVASCULAR PATTERNS INTEGRATED BY THE CENTRAL NERVOUS SYSTEM

It is some years since it was proposed that the central nervous system (CNS) initiates or sustains patterns of cardiovascular response appropriate to particular sets of physiological conditions (39). Initially, this idea was based on studies of the defense reaction, since it had been shown that arousal is accompanied by a pattern of response in anticipation of severe muscular exertion [see (37) for references]. Muscle vasodilatation is a constant feature, together with vasoconstriction in splanchnic and renal beds and in skin, while venoconstriction and increased cardiac activity ensure an increased cardiac output. A decreased compliance of the pulmonary arteries will contribute to the mobilization of blood reservoirs (79).

Each component of this overall pattern of change is expressed to a different extent in different individuals, and thus their combined effect on arterial blood pressure varies. Usually, however, both mean pressure and pulse pressure are increased. The various features of the response are mainly brought about by the sympathetic outputs, as confirmed by recent studies of the postganglionic innervation of skin and muscle (47). The vasoconstrictor nerve fibers to skeletal muscle are apparently inhibited when the vasodilator fibers are excited (11). This inhibition is independent of the baroreceptor reflex. Indeed, an investigation of cardiac and renal sympathetic nerve activity (in addition to heart-rate, blood pressure, and muscle blood flow) recently confirmed that the baroreceptor reflex can be inhibited completely on electrical stimulation within the hypothalamic defense area (10).

0066-4278/80/0315-0399$01.00

It is particularly interesting to contrast this pattern of response with that found during sleep. For example, the profound fall in arterial blood pressure occurring during desynchronized sleep in cats results from vasodilatation in the splanchnic and renal beds, any change in muscle vascular conductance being in the opposite direction—i.e. vasoconstriction (60). After sinoaortic deafferentation, the arterial blood pressure during desynchronized sleep falls to levels below that seen in normal animals (53). The blood pressure was thought to be prevented from reaching dangerously low levels during sleep by the chemoreceptor afferents (34); but it would be most important to know what part the baroreceptors may play, particularly in view of the evidence in humans of exaggerated baroreceptor reflex responses in the sleeping state (75). In other words, to what extent can the central nervous equilibrium in desynchronized sleep be regarded as the opposite of that in arousal, at least so far as cardiovascular control is concerned?

CORTICAL MODULATION OF PATTERNS OF CARDIOVASCULAR RESPONSE

The strong impression gained from studies of this kind is that the CNS is not organized to control single cardiovascular variables (39, 40). Recent work on cerebral cortical effects on the circulation has pointed to the same conclusion. Changes in arterial blood pressure on stimulation of the motor cortex have been reported often (see 46). Reports also exist of muscle vasodilatation mediated in one way or another by the sympathetic system (23, 32, 85). Even vasodilatation in a single limb has been reported in baboons and monkeys (9), though such responses have been denied in man (22).

A study in the cat in which the stimulation of the motor cortex was carefully controlled to avoid reflex effects through stimulation of meningeal afferents or current spread to noncortical structures (45) found no vasodilator effects in skeletal muscles evoked via their sympathetic outflow. When vasodilatation occurred, it was always secondary to muscle contraction: It was simply a functional hyperaemia. On the other hand, some cortical regions can influence muscle blood flow through the vasomotor innervation, and these effects are all brought about by modulation of the defense reaction elicited from lower parts of the brain (82, 83). Sites have been located in the anterior and lateral sigmoid gyri and the rostral part of the orbital gyrus that are without effect on cardiovascular variables when stimulated alone, but that cause a significant reduction of an amygdaloid test response evoked simultaneously, and can almost abolish it, the muscle vasodilatation being affected most. There is also a facilitatory region on the medial aspect of the frontal cortex which may project in the median forebrain bundle. Stimulation in these cortical regions does not alter test responses evoked from the hypothalamic defense area, so one of the main sites of interaction must be in, or near, the hypothalamus itself.

EFFECTS ELICITED FROM THE VENTRAL SURFACE OF THE MEDULLA—THE EFFERENT PATHWAY FOR THE DEFENSE REACTION

In early work on the defense reaction, the areas in the hypothalamus and mid-brain that integrate the many and varied features of this response were anatomically defined, and the efferent pathway for its cardiovascular components was established (1). In the mid-brain, it runs as a narrow band in the substantia nigra just dorsal to the cerebral peduncles. As it continues caudally, it becomes gradually more superficial: In the more rostral medulla it lies 1–2 mm above the ventral surface, while more caudally still it appears to be even closer to the surface (54, 72). In the most recent study, it has been shown to run caudal to the trapezoid body, less than 500 μm from the surface and 3–3.5 mm from the mid-line (35). This almost certainly corresponds to one of the hypothalamofugal pathways demonstrated with up-to-date neuroanatomical techniques (71).

This pathway is readily affected by locally applied pharmacological agents. Pentobarbitone sodium, when placed bilaterally onto the ventral surface of the medulla caudal to the trapezoid bodies, causes a profound fall in arterial blood pressure (24). This and other evidence led to the suggestion that nerve cells situated near the surface tonically maintain blood pressure at its normal level. This idea was substantiated by further experiments showing that glycine bilaterally applied to a relatively well-localized area had the same vasodepressor effect, as had bilateral, electrolytic lesions made by electrodes applied 2 mm caudal to the trapezoid bodies and 4 mm from the mid-line (36). This contrasts markedly with the much smaller effects on arterial blood pressure of much more extensive lesions in the dorsal medulla (8, 62).

The bilateral application of glycine to the sensitive area has now been shown to block all the autonomic components otherwise seen on stimulation within the defense regions of the amygdala, hypothalamus, or mid-brain (35, 43). The block deepens over 5–10 min, as the arterial blood pressure falls; the splanchnic vasoconstrictor component of the pattern of arousal response is abolished first.

Small-current electrical stimulation applied to, or just below, the surface of the medulla elicits all the autonomic components of the defense reaction, including the characteristic pattern of cardiovascular response, notably muscle vasodilatation and splanchnic vasoconstriction. These are elicited from the narrow longitudinal strip described above, which is extremely superficial within the glycine-sensitive area, where it lies less than 500 μm from the surface. After a small lesion restricted to this superficial section of the strip on one side, glycine applied to the contralateral medullary area produces all the changes that, without the lesion, are seen only after bilateral application of the amino acid. It was concluded that the resting level of blood pressure in the normal, awake animal is set mainly by the on-going arousal activity generated in the brainstem defense areas (35, 43).

If glycine acts only at synapses, then its effect is exerted on relay neurons near the medullary surface that form a final link in the efferent pathway to the various autonomic effectors. A group of neurons in this area has been shown by means of the retrograde transport of horseradish peroxidase to project to the intermediolateral column of the spinal cord (5); but the area of their distribution is much wider than that of the medullary strip, and the neurons are deeper, being 450–1100 μm from the surface.

EFFECTS OF STIMULATION OF PERIPHERAL CHEMORECEPTORS

Carotid body stimulation in the high decerebrate cat with the hypothalamus intact evokes a defense reaction; the characteristic pattern of cardiovascular response is well displayed (42). Marshall (63) has now demonstrated a similar result in cats anaesthetized with althesin (81). Thus the chemoreceptor afferent input is a potential arousing or alerting stimulus. This agrees with the reported activation of neurons in the medial hypothalamus on sinus nerve stimulation [presumably of chemoreceptor fibers (80)]. It also raises the question how artefactual may be studies on the pattern of cardiovascular response to chemoreceptor stimulation in animals anaesthetized with traditional agents (chloralose, urethane, and barbiturates) that block or distort transmission through the hypothalamus and mid-brain. These agents clearly depress the muscle vasodilator response and can also alter the cardiac response.

THE SO-CALLED VASOMOTOR CENTER IN THE MEDULLA

The longitudinal form of anatomical arrangement along the neuraxis of the areas integrating the defense reaction, from the hypothalamus through the mid-brain and pons to the medulla, may well exemplify the common mode of organization of cardiovascular control (39). The evidence for a medullary vasomotor center was always tenuous [see (38, 67) for references]; yet the idea remains firmly entrenched and dies hard. Current thinking about vasodepressor responses, in particular, is still dominated by the concept of reciprocally organized half-centers in the medulla consisting of a depressor area (an extensive, medially located region) interacting with more laterally placed pressor centers (4). Despite the lack of any real data, baroreceptor mechanisms have been thought to be mediated through this depressor 'center'. Plentiful evidence now excludes an involvement of the depressor area in the baroreceptor reflex [see discussion below and (6)]. The role of central nervous structures in the mediation of overall vasodepressor responses is probably best elucidated by investigations on regions that evoke patterns of response analogous to that accompanying the activation of peripheral baroreceptors.

THE HYPOTHALAMIC DEPRESSOR AREA

Since the 1930s it has often been stated that the hypothalamus can be divided into rostral parasympathetic and caudal sympathetic centers, at least for its control of the cardiovascular system (see 30). Though the regional organization of hypothalamic circulatory control is much more sophisticated than this, there is no doubt that stimulation within the dorsal part of the anterior hypothalamus evokes vagal activation (30) and sympatho-inhibition (25, 26, 59): In fact, it evokes both together (44). Hilton & Spyer (44) drew attention to the similarity of the pattern of this response, by virtue of the effects on vascular resistance, heart rate, and respiration, to that evoked by baroreceptor stimulation. Destruction of this area reduces the efficacy of the baroreceptor reflex (44, 50). Subsequently, Spyer (77) described neurons in this area of the hypothalamus that are influenced by baroreceptor stimulation. This area may also relay the inhibitory effects from the cerebral cortex outlined above.

The efferent connections of this area are as yet poorly described, but a connection with the medullary depressor area has been assumed on the basis of a similarity of response to stimulation in the two areas (26, 59). This cannot be so, however, since lesions in the medial reticular formation of the medulla, encompassing the whole depressor area, have no effect on the baroreceptor reflex (6). On the other hand, sufficient information already exists about the location and properties of other bulbospinal sympatho-inhibitory pathways to evaluate their roles in mediating the baroreceptor reflex.

MEDULLARY SYMPATHO-INHIBITORY CONNECTIONS

Stimulation at several sites in the medulla can evoke an inhibition of ongoing sympathetic activity and so affect peripheral vascular resistance and heart-rate. It is not surprising that stimulation within the nucleus of the tractus solitarius (NTS) can produce sympatho-inhibition and that destruction of this area can evoke a maintained systemic hypertension (20) since baroreceptor afferents are known to terminate in this area (48, 56, 65, 78). These effects are broadly analogous to baroreceptor stimulation or denervation, respectively, and may thus provide little additional information for determining the efferent connections for baroreceptor control of sympathetic efferent discharge. In this context it is interesting that the major effect of NTS lesions is a marked lability of blood pressure (20, 21, 66) equivalent to the chronic effect of sino-aortic denervation (18). There are, however, indications of pathways descending from the NTS to the spinal cord (58). Thus although their major component is more directly concerned with respiratory control, the NTS may also through such respiratory effects exert an excitatory control over sympathetic activity (see below). In addition, nonrespiratory neurons in the NTS connect to at least the level of the cervical cord. Baroreceptor-sensitive neurons in the NTS with axons in the cervical cord have been described (57). This pathway has a conduction velocity of 29 m sec^{-1}. Further, a pathway has been suggested between the NTS and the intermediomedial cell column (IMM) of the thoracic cord with a conduction velocity of 15 m sec^{-1} (64). Neurons in the NTS and IMM have similar patterns of discharge. Further, the IMM sends projections to the intermediolateral cell column that contains the sympathetic preganglionic neurons. However, a discrepancy exists. The central delay of such a pathway would be an order of magnitude smaller than that quoted for the baroreceptor-sympathetic reflex (see 51).

From the NTS there are neuroanatomically defined projections to several areas of the medulla, and especially to three areas from which sympatho-inhibitory effects can be evoked—the ventromedial medulla, the raphe complex, and the lateral reticular nucleus (58). As mentioned already, however, the ventromedial reticular formation and raphe complex, which encompass the classical 'depressor' area, are not involved in the baroreceptor control of sympathetic activity (6). Whether they receive baroreceptor input either directly or indirectly is also controversial; the consensus is that they do not (78). The ventromedial area, which includes the paramedian reticular nucleus, certainly can evoke a powerful sympatho-inhibition but recent investigations suggest that it only mediates tonic inhibition of the spinal component of the somatic-sympathetic reflexes (17). Section of its descending pathway in the ventrolateral portion of the spinal cord does not abolish baroreceptor control of sympathetic activity (14). Similarly, destruction of the pathway from the raphe nuclei to spinal cord, and particularly that of the 5-HT pathway (14, 16), has little or no effect on ongoing sympathetic activity or on baroreceptor-mediated inhibition.

This latter pathway, which passes in the dorsolateral funiculus, is closely associated with another descending inhibitory pathway consisting of a group of axons arising from catecholamine-containing neurons with cell bodies located diffusely within the lateral reticular nucleus (12, 13). These neurons exert sympatho-inhibitory actions (12, 13). Their pharmacological destruction results in a heightened sympathetic activity and a reduction in the effectiveness of the baroreceptor control of sympathetic activity (15). The pathway may well represent at least a part of the bulbo-spinal component of the baroreceptor reflex. Its axons are small, and mainly unmyelinated, which could contribute to the relatively long central delay of the reflex. This pathway, like the former two, can also contribute to the brainstem control of spinal sympathetic reflexes.

These observations suggest that many of the interactions within the CNS that determine the excitability of sympathetic neurons, and hence vascular resistance, actually take place at the spinal level. There are clearly defined inhibitory systems and indications of descending excitatory pathways within the dorsolateral funiculus [see (84) for review], so that prevailing sympathetic activities may well depend on the interactions among these various descending systems. Interestingly, some pathways, which may be either excitatory or inhibitory or both, may descend without brainstem connections from the hypothalamus to the spinal cord (71), though the same hypothalamic areas send efferent connections to many areas of the medulla, including all the sites that send descending inhibitory connections to the spinal cord. The descending hypothalamic pathway appears to originate from, or close to, the area that integrates the defense reaction, in which case it would have sympathoinhibitory functions (see above). These findings imply a longitudinal arrangement of interconnections having sympatho-inhibitory outputs, with important functional implications for the overall regulation of vascular resistance. This agrees with the previous suggestion of a parallel arrangement of sympatho-excitatory and inhibitory systems through the length of the brainstem (41, 44).

DESCENDING EXCITATORY CONTROL OF SYMPATHETIC EFFERENT ACTIVITY

Regions of the brainstem other than the defense area influence sympathetic activity. Two distinct neuronal systems appear to be involved, since stimulation at sites in the medulla (28, 29, 49, 76), midbrain, and hypothalamus (29, 76) excites sympathetic activity with two distinct patterns of response. The first is a short-latency response that is largely resistant to baroreceptor stimulation; the second is a variable, longer-latency response that is suppressed by baroreceptor stimulation. Since the efferent pathways for these responses, and for excitatory responses from the cerebellum (2), relay in the dorsolateral funiculus of the spinal cord [see (84) for review], these relatively stereotyped systems may have a particular functional significance. However, hardly any attention has yet been paid to the pattern of cardiovascular response that they evoke.

In addition to these excitatory pathways of unresolved physiological function, it is now well established that the neuronal mechanisms responsible for the generation of central respiratory activity also influence sympathetic activity. From the first recordings of sympathetic activity it has been apparent that sympathetic activity is modulated by respiration (3) even in vagotomized animals (68). This activity in preganglionic and postganglionic nerves appears to be differentiated in different postganglionic sympathetic neurons. Respiration has a powerful effect on the discharge of individual vasoconstrictor neurons to skeletal muscle, but the influence is less prominent in the vasoconstrictor supply to the skin (33). The splanchnic sympathetic supply also shows a marked respiratory rhythm (31).

The rhythm is such that firing is most conspicuous in inspiration; it appears to survive reserpine pretreatment (67). Since the rhythm is apparent in vagotomized, thoractomized, and artifically ventilated animals, bulbospinal inspiratory neurons may well be involved in its mediation. The antidromic latency to stimulation of the axon of a preganglionic neuron fluctuates with the respiratory cycle in a manner indicating heightened excitability during inspiration (55). This confirms the autocorrelogram data of Mannard & Polosa (61) but is in part questioned by Gebber & Barman (27), who suggest that the apparent respiratory rhythm of postganglionic elements may in some cases survive the silencing of central inspiratory activity (as judged by phrenic nerve discharge) that accompanies hyperventilation. They argue for an entrainment of two independent oscillators of broadly similar frequency (i.e. a sympathetic 'tone' generator and a respiratory oscillator). These workers have indicated the same type of entrainment for the cardiac rhythm of sympathetic neurons—i.e. entrainment of the baroreceptor effect on sympathetic discharge to a central oscillator. Since the evidence for this latter mechanism has been seriously questioned (7), and since a more plausible explanation has been provided (7), the concept of entrainment, which is in any case a mechanical concept difficult to express in neurophysiological terms, may not be very useful. The excitability of sympathetic efferent neurons seems to be determined by many of the influences on the activity of the reticular formation (7).

When considering the control of the sympathetic supply to the vasculature and heart, these fluctuations in excitability of the preganglionic elements offer an explanation for the cyclic variability of reflex effects. The effectiveness of the baroreceptor influence on sympathetic activity is clearly modified during the respiratory cycle (19, 69, 73, 74). The duration of the silencing of sympathetic activity evoked by the baroreceptors is minimal in the middle of the phrenic nerve burst and maximal shortly after the end of inspiration (74). Such quantitative fluctuations in effectiveness seem best explained by the inhibitory effects of the baroreceptor input arriving at a time of relative disfacilitation of the preganglionic neuron. Obviously, the timing of any input, either inhibitory or excitatory, can have considerable implications for its effectiveness.

CONCLUSIONS

This review has emphasized the ubiquity of cardiovascular effects exerted by central nervous structures and, by implication, has stressed the role of preganglionic neurons of the autonomic nervous system in the processing of incoming signals and the production of a physiologically balanced output. The central nervous structures that we understand, however imperfectly, seem concerned with responses of basic biological significance. Their cardiovascular effects, though of fundamental importance, constitute only a part of their overall function. We have referred frequently to the defense (or arousal) reaction and the response to the baroreceptor input. These seem to be the main activating and deactivating systems, respectively, in constant interplay in the daily lives of higher animals and humans. In principle, the same type of experimental analysis could be made of other major biological response patterns, chiefly those concerned with alimentary and sexual reactions, which are more intermittent features of diurnal activity.

On the other hand, another continually active control process is that for temperature regulation where, once again, a pattern of cardiovascular response is an essential feature. Although little has been done in the way of precise localization, the anterior hypothalamus has long been known to play a major role in the central nervous organization of this response. Recent work has been concerned with elucidating the patterns of cardiovascular response to heating and cooling (52, 70). Muscle blood flow was found to change in the same direction as skin blood flow, though to a lesser extent, while splanchnic blood flow changes in the opposite direction. These changes are so balanced that there is no change of total peripheral resistance; but it is all organized centrally in the nervous system, as in the arousal reaction, and is independent of the baroreceptor reflex.

All in all, this new approach places much less emphasis on the role, and even the concept, of the simple reflex as an important element in cardiovascular regulation. In particular, it shows how misleading has been the traditional notion of a vasomotor center. Though reasonable when first proposed (some 100 years ago), it has now become an impediment to research and is, in any case, untenable. The question of the mode of generation of apparent tone of cardiovascular effectors by the CNS is one that can now be reopened in the confident expectation that alternative explanations will be found.

Literature Cited

1. Abrahams, V. C., Hilton, S. M., Zbrozyna, A. W. 1960. Active muscle vasodilatation produced by stimulation of the brainstem: its significance in the defence reaction. *J. Physiol. London* 154:491–513
2. Achari, N. K., Al-Ubaidy, S. S., Downman, C. B. B. 1978. Spinal sympathoexcitatory pathways activated by stimulating fastigial nuclei, hypothalamus, and lower brain stem in cats. *Exp. Neurol.* 62:230–40
3. Adrian, E. D., Bronk, D. W., Phillips, G. 1932. Discharges in mammalian sympathetic nerves. *J. Physiol. London* 74:115–33
4. Alexander, R. S. 1946. Tonic and reflex functions of medullary sympathetic cardiovascular centres. *J. Neurophysiol.* 9:205–17
5. Amendt, K., Czachurski, J., Dembowsky, K., Seller, H. 1978. Neurones within the "Chemosensitive Area" on the ventral surface of the brainstem which project to the intermediolateral column. *Pflügers Arch.* 375:289–92
6. Barman, S. M., Gebber, G. L. 1978. Tonic sympathoinhibition in the baroreceptor denervated cat. *Proc. Soc. Exp. Biol. Med.* 157:648–55
7. Camerer, H., Stroh-Werz, M., Krienke, B., Langhorst, P. 1977. Postganglionic sympathetic activity with correlation to heart-rate and central cortical rhythms. *Pflügers Arch.* 370:221–26
8. Chai, C. Y., Wang, S. C. 1968. Integration of sympathetic cardiovascular mechanisms in medulla oblongata of the cat. *Am. J. Physiol.* 215:1310–15
9. Clarke, N. P., Smith, O. A., Shearn, D. W. 1968. Topographical representation of vascular smooth muscle of limbs in primate motor cortex. *Am. J. Physiol.* 214:122–29
10. Coote, J. H., Hilton, S. M., Perez-Gonzalez, J. F. 1979. Inhibition of baroreceptor reflex on stimulation in the brainstem defence centre. *J. Physiol. London* 288:549–60
11. Coote, J. H., Hilton, S. M., Zbrożyna, A. W. 1973. The ponto-medullary area integrating the defence reaction in the cat and its influences on muscle blood flow. *J. Physiol. London* 229:257–74
12. Coote, J. H., Macleod, V. H. 1974. The influence of bulbospinal monoaminergic pathways on sympathetic nerve activity. *J. Physiol. London* 241:453–75
13. Coote, J. H., Macleod, V. H. 1974. Evidence for the involvement of the baroreceptor reflex of a descending inhibitory pathway. *J. Physiol. London* 241: 477–96
14. Coote, J. H., Macleod, V. H. 1975. The spinal route of sympathoinhibitory pathways descending from the medulla oblongata. *Pflügers Arch.* 359:335–47
15. Coote, J. H., Macleod, V. H. 1977. The effect of intraspinal microinjections of 6-hydroxydopamine on the inhibitory influence exerted on spinal sympathetic activity by the baroreceptors. *Pflügers Arch.* 371:271–77
16. Coote, J. H., Macleod, V. H., Martin, I. L. 1978. Bulbospinal tryptaminergic neurones: a search for the role of bulbospinal tryptaminergic neurones in the control of sympathetic activity. *Pflügers Arch.* 377:109–16
17. Coote, J. H., Sato, A. 1978. Supraspinal regulation of spinal discharge into cardiac sympathetic nerves. *Brain Res.* 142:425–37
18. Cowley, A. W., Liard, J. F., Guyton, A. C. 1973. Role of the baroreceptor reflex in daily control of arterial blood pressure and other variables in the dog. *Circ. Res.* 32:564–76
19. Davis, A. L., McCloskey, D. I., Potter, E. K. 1977. Respiratory modulation of baroreceptor and chemoreceptor reflexes affecting heart rate through the sympathetic nervous system. *J. Physiol. London* 272:691–703
20. Doba, N., Reis, D. J. 1973. Acute fulminating neurogenic hypertension produced by brainstem lesions in the rat. *Circ. Res.* 32:584–93

21. Doba, N., Reis, D. J. 1974. Role of central and peripheral adrenegic mechanisms in neurogenic hypertension produced by brainstem lesions in the rat. *Circ. Res.* 34:293–301
22. Dornhorst, A. C. 1963. Hyperaemia induced by exercise and ischaemia. *Br. Med. Bull.* 19:137–40
23. Eliasson, S., Lindgren, P., Uvnäs, B. 1952. Representation in the hypothalamus and the motor cortex in the dog of the sympathetic vasodilator outflow to the skeletal muscles. *Acta Physiol. Scand.* 27:18–37
24. Feldberg, W., Guertzenstein, P. G. 1972. A vasodepressor effect of pentobarbitone sodium. *J. Physiol. London* 224:83–103
25. Folkow, B., Johansson, B., Öberg, B. 1959. A hypothalamic structure with a marked inhibitory effect on tonic sympathetic activity. *Acta Physiol. Scand.* 47:262–70
26. Folkow, B., Langston, J., Öberg, B., Prerovsky, I. 1964. Reactions of different series coupled vascular sections upon stimulation of the hypothalamic sympatho-inhibitory area. *Acta Physiol. Scand.* 61:476–83
27. Gebber, G. L., Barman, S. M. 1977. Brainstem vasomotor circuits involved in genesis and entrainment of sympathetic nervous rhythms. *Prog. Brain Res.* 47:61–75
28. Gebber, G. L., McCall, R. S. 1976. Identification and discharge patterns of spinal sympathetic interneurones. *Am. J. Physiol.* 231:722–33
29. Gebber, G. L., Taylor, D. G., Weaver, L. C. 1973. Electrophysiological studies on organisation of central vasopressor pathways. *Am. J. Physiol.* 224:470–51
30. Gellhorn, E. 1957. *Autonomic Mechanisms and the Hypothalamus.* Minneapolis: Univ. Minnesota Press
31. Gootman, P. M., Cohen, M. I. 1973. Periodic modulation (cardiac and respiratory) of spontaneous and evoked sympathetic discharge. *Acta Physiol. Polon.* 24:97–109
32. Green, H. D., Hoff, E. C. 1937. Effects of faradic stimulation of the cerebral cortex on limb and renal volumes in the cat and monkey. *Am. J. Physiol.* 118:641–58
33. Gregor, M., Jänig, W., Wiprich, L. 1977. Cardiac and respiratory rhythmicities in cutaneous and vasoconstrictor neurones to the cat's hindlimb. *Pflügers Arch.* 370:299–302
34. Guazzi, M., Baccelli, G., Zanchetti, A. 1968. Reflex chemoceptive regulation of arterial pressure during natural sleep in the cat. *Am. J. Physiol.* 214:969–78
35. Guertzenstein, P. G., Hilton, S. M., Marshall, J. M., Timms, R. J. 1978. Experiments on the origin of the vasomotor tone. *J. Physiol. London* 275:78–79P
36. Guertzenstein, P. G., Silver, A. 1974. Fall in blood pressure produced from discrete regions of the ventral surface of the medulla by glycine and lesions. *J. Physiol. London* 242:489–503
37. Hilton, S. M. 1965. Hypothalamic control of the cardiovascular responses in fear and rage. In *The Scientific Basis of Medicine Annual Reviews,* pp. 217–238.
38. Hilton, S. M. 1966. Hypothalamic regulation of the cardiovascular system. *Br. Med. Bull.* 22:243–48
39. Hilton, S. M. 1971. A critique of current ideas of the nervous system control of circulation. In *Cardiovascular Regulation in Health and Disease,* ed. C. Bartorelli, A. Zanchetti, pp. 57–62. Milano: Ist. Rech. Cardiovasc.
40. Hilton, S. M. 1974. The role of the hypothalamus in the organization of patterns of cardiovascular response. In *Recent Studies of Hypothalamic Function,* ed. K. Lederis, & K. E. Cooper, pp. 306–314. Basel: Kager
41. Hilton, S. M. 1975. Ways of viewing the central nervous control of the circulation—old and new. *Brain Res.* 87: 213–19
42. Hilton, S. M., Joels, N. 1965. Facilitation of chemoreceptor reflexes during the defence reaction. *J. Physiol. London* 176:20–22P
43. Hilton, S. M., Marshall, J. M., Timms, R. J. 1979. The central nervous regulation of arterial blood pressure. *Acta Physiol. Polon.* In press
44. Hilton, S. M., Spyer, K. M. 1971. Participation of the anterior hypothalamus in the baroreceptor reflex. *J. Physiol. London* 218:271–93
45. Hilton, S. M., Spyer, K. M., Timms, R. J. 1980. The origin of the hind limb vasodilatation evoked by stimulation of the motor cortex in the cat. *J. Physiol. London* 287:545–57
46. Hoff, E. C., Kell, J. F., Carroll, M. N. 1963. Effects of cortical stimulation and lesions on cardiovascular function. *Physiol. Rev.* 43:68–114
47. Horeyseck, G., Jänig, W., Kirchner, F., Thämer, V. 1976. Activation and inhibition of muscle and cutaneous postganglionic neurones to hindlimb during hypothalamically induced vasoconstriction and atropine-sensitive vasodilation. *Pflügers Arch.* 361:231–40

48. Humphrey, D. R. 1967. Neuronal activity in the medulla oblongata of the cat evoked by stimulation of the carotid sinus nerve. In *Baroreceptors and Hypertension,* ed. P. Kezdi, pp. 131–68. NY: Pergamon Press
49. Kahn, N., Mills, E. 1967. Centrally evoked sympathetic discharge: a functional study of medullary vasomotor areas. *J. Physiol. London* 191:339–52
50. Kent, B. B., Drake, J. W., Manning, J. W. 1971. Suprapontine contributions to the carotid sinus reflex in the cat. *Circ. Res.* 29:534–41
51. Kezdi, P., Geller, E. 1968. Baroreceptor control of postganglionic sympathetic nerve discharge. *Am. J. Physiol.* 214: 427–35
52. Kullman, R., Schonung, W., Simon, E. 1970. Antagonistic changes of blood flow and sympathetic activity in different vascular beds following central thermal stimulation. I. Blood flow in skin, muscle and intestine during spinal cord heating and cooling in anaesthetised dogs. *Pflügers Arch.* 319:146–61
53. Kumazawa, T., Baccelli, G., Guazzi, M., Mancia, G., Zanchetti, A. 1969. Hemodynamic patterns during desynchronized sleep in intact cats and in cats with sino-aortic deafferentation. *Circ. Res.* 34:923–37
54. Lindgren, P., Uvnäs, B. 1953. Activation of sympathetic vasodilator and vasoconstrictor neurones by electrical stimulation in the medulla of the dog and cat. *Circ. Res.* 1:479–85
55. Lipski, J., Coote, J. H., Trzebski, A. 1977. Temporal patterns of antidromic invasion latencies of sympathetic preganglionic neurons related to central inspiratory activity and pulmonary stretch receptor reflex. *Brain Res.* 155:162–66
56. Lipski, J., McAllen, R. M., Spyer, K. M. 1975. The sinus nerve and baroreceptor input to the medulla of the cat. *J. Physiol. London* 251:61–78
57. Lipski, J., Trzebski, A. 1975. Bulbospinal neurones activated by baroreceptor afferents and their possible role in inhibition of preganglionic sympathetic neurones. *Pflügers Arch.* 356:181–92
58. Loewy, A. D., Burton, H. 1978. Nuclei of the solitary tract. Efferent projections to the lower brainstem and spinal cord of the cat. *J. Comp. Neurol.* 181:421–50
59. Löfving, B. 1961. Cardiovascular adjustments induced from the rostral cingulate gyrus. *Acta Physiol. Scand.* 53:(Suppl. 184) 1–82
60. Mancia, G., Baccelli, G., Adams, D. B., Zanchetti, A. 1970. Vasomotor regulation during sleep in the cat. *Am. J. Physiol.* 220:1086–93
61. Mannard, D. A., Polosa, C. 1973. Analysis of background firing of single sympathetic preganglionic neurones of cat cervical nerve. *J. Neurophysiol.* 36:398–408
62. Manning, J. W. 1965. Cardiovascular reflexes following lesions in medullary reticular formation. *Am. J. Physiol.* 208:283–88
63. Marshall, J. 1977. The cardiovascular response to stimulation of carotid chemoreceptors. *J. Physiol. London* 266:48–49P
64. McCall, R. S., Gebber, G. L., Barman, S. M. 1977. Spinal interneurones in the baroreceptor reflex arc. *Am. J. Physiol.* 232:H657–65
65. Miura, M., Reis, D. J. 1969. Termination and secondary projections of carotid sinus nerve in the cat brain stem. *Am. J. Physiol.* 217:142–53
66. Nathan, M. A., Reis, D. J. 1976. Chronic labile hypertension produced by lesions of the nucleus tractus solitarii in the cat. *Circ. Res.* 40:72–81
67. Peiss, C. N. 1965. Concepts of cardiovascular regulation: past, present and future. In *Nervous Control of the Heart,* ed. W. C. Randall, pp. 154–97. Baltimore: Williams & Williams
68. Preiss, G., Kirchner, F., Polosa, C. 1975. Patterning of sympathetic preganglionic firing by the central respiratory drive. *Brain Res.* 87:363–74
69. Richter, D. W., Keck, W., Seller, H. 1969. The course of inhibition of sympathetic activity during various patterns of carotid sinus nerve stimulation. *Pflügers Arch.* 317:110–23
70. Riedel, W., Iriki, M., Simon, E. 1972. Regional differentiation of sympathetic activity during peripheral heating and cooling in anaesthetised rabbits. *Pflügers Arch.* 332:239–47
71. Saper, C., Loewy, A. D., Swanson, L. W., Cowan, W. N. 1976. Direct hypothalamo-autonomic connections. *Brain Res.* 117:305–12
72. Schramm, L. P., Bignall, K. E. 1971. Central neural pathways mediating active sympathetic muscle vasodilatation in cats. *Am. J. Physiol.* 221:754–67
73. Seller, H., Langhorst, P., Richter, D., Koepchen, H. P. 1968. Über die Abhängigkeit der pressoreceptorischen Hemmung des Sympathicus von der Atemphase und ihre Auswirkung in der

Vasomotorik. *Pflügers Arch.* 302: 300–14

74. Seller, H., Richter, D. W. 1971. Some quantitative aspects of the central transmission of the baroreceptor activity. In *Research in Physiology,* ed. F. F. Kas, K. Koizumi, M. Vassalle, pp. 541–49. Bologna: Aulo Gaggi
75. Smyth, H. S., Sleight, P., Pickering, G. W. 1969. The reflex regulation of arterial pressure during sleep in man; a quantitative method of assessing baroreflex sensitivity. *Circ. Res.* 24: 109–21
76. Snyder, D. W., Gebber, G. L. 1973. Relationships between medullary depressor region and central vasopressor pathways. *Am. J. Physiol.* 225:1129–37
77. Spyer, K. M. 1972. Baroreceptor sensitive neurones in the anterior hypothalamus of the cat. *J. Physiol.* 224: 245–57
78. Spyer, K. M. 1975. Organisation of baroreceptor pathways in the brainstem. *Brain Res.* 87:221–26
79. Szidon, J. P., Fishman, A. P. 1971. Participation of pulmonary circulation in the defense reaction. *Am. J. Physiol.* 220:364–70
80. Thomas, M. R., Calaresu, F. R. 1972. Responses of single units in the medial hypothalamus to electrical stimulation of the sinus nerve in the cat. *Brain Res.* 44:49–62
81. Timms, R. J. 1976. The use of the anaesthetic steroids alphaxalone-alphadolone in studies of the forebrain in the cat. *J. Physiol. London* 256:71–72P
82. Timms, R. J. 1977. *Influences of the frontal cerebral cortex and corticospinal tract on the cardiovascular system.* Ph.D. thesis. Univ. of Birmingham, England
83. Timms, R. J. 1977. Cortical inhibition and facilitation of the defence reaction. *J. Physiol. London* 266:98–99P
84. Wurster, R. D. 1977. Spinal sympathetic control of the heart. In *Neural Regulation of the Heart,* ed. W. C. Randall, pp. 211–46. NY: Oxford Univ. Press
85. Zwirn, P., Corriol, J. 1962. Fibres corticopyramidales dilatrices des membres. *Archs. Sci. Physiol.* 16:325–45

Ann. Rev. Physiol. 1980. 42:413–27

CARDIOVASCULAR AFFERENTS INVOLVED IN REGULATION OF PERIPHERAL VESSELS ❖1277

Hazel M. Coleridge and John C. G. Coleridge

Cardiovascular Research Institute and Department of Physiology, University of California San Francisco, San Francisco, California 94143

INTRODUCTION

This chapter deals with mechanosensitive and chemosensitive nerve endings in the cardiovascular system that are involved in the reflex control of peripheral vessels. The central connections and the reflex effects that result from engagement of these afferent mechanisms are dealt with in other chapters of this volume, and we refer to them only in passing. Our concern is with the endings themselves, and with the way in which new knowledge of their properties may shed light on their reflex function. For reasons of space we have had to exclude certain recent advances. We say nothing about carotid and aortic chemoreceptors, choosing instead to deal with chemosensitive endings in the heart; similarly, we say nothing about pulmonary stretch receptors even though they provide an afferent input capable of evoking appreciable changes in peripheral vascular resistance.

We deal first with arterial baroreceptors with myelinated fibers, including recent studies of the ionic events leading to baroreceptor excitation, the response of aortic baroreceptors to static and dynamic pressure changes, and the phenomenon of baroreceptor resetting. Mechanoreceptor input is not confined to A fibers, for it is becoming increasingly clear that much of the vagal input from mechanoreceptors in the atria and aorta, and the major part of that from mechanoreceptors in the ventricles, is carried by C fibers. Recent comparisons of the properties of these C fiber mechanoreceptors

0066-4278/80/0315-0413$01.00

with those of their A fiber counterparts has thrown some light on their respective roles in reflex vascular regulation.

Although the powerful inhibitory influence of the vagal and carotid sinus mechanoreceptors is usually thought to dominate the sympathetic vasoconstrictor neurons of the lateral horn under most circumstances, it is now recognized that these neurons may be influenced more directly by an afferent input that travels along sympathetic nerve branches to reach the spinal cord. Much of this input arises from cardiovascular mechanoreceptors whose properties have been found to differ in a number of respects from those of the cardiovascular mechanoreceptors supplied by the IXth and Xth nerves.

An interesting advance in the general area of chemosensitive afferents that evoke reflex vascular effects has been the discovery in the heart and great vessels of vagal C fibers with endings that are stimulated by bradykinin and the prostaglandins, substances that are formed in these organs in a variety of physiological and pathological conditions. Bradykinin and the prostaglandins also excite sympathetic afferent endings in the heart to evoke reflex effects opposite in sign to those resulting from chemical stimulation of the vagal endings.

MECHANORECEPTORS

Baroreceptors with Myelinated Fibers

Increasingly sophisticated analysis of aortic baroreceptor characteristics (1–3, 7) and detailed examination of the basic mechanisms of baroreceptor excitation (26, 27) have been made possible by the development of perfused aortic arch–aortic nerve preparations. Both adaptation and postexcitatory depression of carotid baroreceptors have been tentatively ascribed to reversible visco-elastic changes induced by stretch of the connective tissue attachments of the receptor terminals. Using the rat aortic arch preparation, Saum, Brown & Tuley (27) analyzed these two phenomena and concluded that although baroreceptor adaptation is an expression of visco-elastic changes in the vessel wall, postexcitatory depression results from the operation of Na^+/K^+ pumps in the generator membrane. Postexcitatory depression was clearly confined to the generator region, for the axons were still electrically excitable. Measures known to inhibit Na^+/K^+ pumps (addition of ouabain to the solution perfusing the aorta, removal of K^+ from the perfusate, or substitution of Li^+ for Na^+) left adaptation virtually unaffected but abolished postexcitatory depression. These measures also lowered the threshold of baroreceptors and increased their sensitivity, effects that the authors suggest are also best explained by partial inhibition of electrogenic membrane pumps. Changing $[Na^+]$ and $[K^+]$ in the perfusing medium was later found to alter the behavior of aortic baroreceptors, much as it alters the behavior of other kinds of mechanoreceptors (26). Reducing $[Na^+]$ by 25–50% caused reversible increases in threshold and decreases in sensitivity; increasing $[K^+]$ had the opposite effect; changes in $[Cl^-]$ had no effect. None of these procedures altered the mechanical properties of the aortic wall. These results suggest that activation of baroreceptors, like that of other mechanoreceptors, depends upon a progressive increase in gNa/gK as the generator region is distorted by an increase in pressure above threshold. Changes in the external $[Na^+]$ and $[K^+]$ are believed to act through effects on the respective equilibrium potentials.

These results raise the possibility that baroreceptor reflexes are sensitive to changes in extracellular $[Na^+]$ and $[K^+]$. Indeed reducing $[Na^+]$ by as little as 5% in the solution perfusing an innervated carotid sinus in cats, the other buffer nerves being cut, caused an increase in mean arterial pressure of 15–20 mm Hg and an increase in urine flow (19). The investigators suggested that these changes might be due to a decrease in sensitivity of carotid sinus baroreceptors, but they were unable to show that such small changes in $[Na^+]$ actually decreased the sensitivity of baroreceptors studied individually in the rat aortic arch preparation. The increase in urine output, unexpected in view of known baroreflex effects on ADH and on renal blood flow, was felt to be secondary to the increase in arterial pressure. Evidence that the sensitivity of cardiovascular reflexes can be altered by increases in extracellular $[Na^+]$ might be of equal physiological importance. A recent report describes an increase in carotid baroreceptor activity in cats when the isolated sinus was perfused with 300 mM NaCl but attributes the effect to an increase in osmolarity (35). However, perfusion of the sinus with hyperosmotic glucose solutions did not increase baroreceptor discharge, so the increase in activity may have been due to the increase in Na^+.

The carotid baroreceptors are believed to exert a more powerful buffering action than do the aortic baroreceptors; indeed the latter have been thought to contribute appreciably to control of peripheral resistance and heart rate only when arterial pressure is higher than normal (3, 25). Thus in an in vivo study in dogs, baroreceptor activity was recorded from the entire aortic nerve, and threshold and sensitivity were estimated by counting the spikes that rose above the baseline at various levels of arterial pressure (25); in an in vitro study in cats, activity of individual baroreceptors was recorded during sinusoidal stretch of the whole aortic arch (3). The results of these two quite different experimental approaches led the respective investigators to conclude that at normal arterial pressures the majority of aortic baroreceptors are either inactive or are operating near threshold.

These views have been challenged by the observation that dogs deprived of carotid baroreceptors continue to regulate arterial pressure unchanged, whereas dogs deprived of aortic baroreceptors regulate arterial pressure less precisely and at a level significantly higher than normal (14). Moreover, recordings from individual aortic baroreceptors indicate that approximately 90% of baroreceptors with myelinated fibers in rabbits (33) and 96% of those in dogs (16) are active at normal mean arterial pressures (83 and 100 mm Hg, respectively).

The notion has been revived that the intermittency of baroreceptor discharge at normal arterial pressures implies that receptor threshold is exceeded only by the systolic peak in pressure (3). The opinion that baroreceptors normally operate close to threshold is not supported by the observations described above of aortic baroreceptor activity in rabbits and dogs: For example, in dogs aortic baroreceptors continued to discharge at mean arterial pressures 15 mm Hg below the normal level (16). The more continuous discharge observed once the threshold of excitation was exceeded (3) was probably a result of the less physiological method of evoking receptor activity. Baroreceptors in the rat aortic arch preparation discharge intermittently at pulsatile pressures maintained well above threshold, apparently as a result of the dynamic behavior of the receptor complex (7). When pulse frequencies were increased, baroreceptors fired progressively less during the falling phase; maximum discharge increased to a resonant peak at 4–5 Hz, but mean discharge remained constant over a wide range of pulse frequencies (0.2–20.0 Hz).

Aortic Baroreceptors with Unmyelinated Fibers

The aortic nerve contains many afferent C fibers, some of which arise from baroreceptors in the aortic wall. When examined in vivo in rabbits (33) and dogs (11, 16) and in vitro in rats (34), these baroreceptors were found to have (*a*) thresholds 30–50 mm Hg higher than those of their A fiber counterparts, and (*b*) sensitivities and maximum frequencies much lower. Nevertheless, 25% were active in rabbits at normal arterial pressures, firing a single impulse with each pressure pulse (33). Thereafter, as pressure increased, already active fibers were stimulated to fire several impulses with each cardiac cycle, and previously silent fibers were progressively recruited (11, 16, 33). Clearly C fiber aortic baroreceptors can play little part in opposing a decrease in blood pressure below the normal level, but they come into action when pressure increases above normal.

In the rat aortic arch preparation, C fiber baroreceptors were seen to have overdamped and phase-lagging dynamic characteristics, such as might be expected of relatively simple structures with loose attachments to connective tissue elements (7). Unlike the discharge of A fiber baroreceptors, which was rectified over a wide range of pulse frequencies, that of C fiber baroreceptors increased at high pulse frequencies: The firing of one C fiber baroreceptor, for example, increased from 5 to 10 impulses sec^{-1} when pulse frequency increased from 2 to 10 Hz (the resting heart rate in rats is 4–5 beats sec^{-1}). If these findings can be applied to intact animals, then a large increase in C fiber input, occurring in conditions in which both heart rate and arterial pressure increase, may exert an additionally useful reflex restraint on the cardiovascular system.

Baroreceptor Resetting

Baroreceptor resetting occurs in hypertension. Its essential features include an increase in threshold, a decrease in sensitivity, and usually a decrease in maximal impulse frequency. Resetting has been examined in individual baroreceptors in rabbits (15) and dogs (28), and in aortic arch preparations of rabbits (2) and rats (1, 6, 7, 26, 27). It develops progressively as hypertension develops (2), it can be reversed if the hypertension is reversed at a relatively early stage (28), and it is generally believed to result from decreased arterial distensibility, itself a result of the structural changes that occur in the arterial wall in response to increased transmural pressure (2). In congestive heart failure in dogs, the response of atrial receptors to cardiac filling is reset in analogous fashion as the atrial wall thickens (39). Debate continues whether baroreceptor resetting is entirely secondary to the increase in pressure that results from other causes, or whether, in some forms of hypertension, resetting plays a permissive role in allowing the regulation of arterial pressure at successively higher levels (2, 28). When wall changes are fully established, nerve endings themselves may degenerate (2, 39). An examination (15) of the effect of renal hypertension on aortic baroreceptors in rabbits revealed that resetting was less in the case of C fiber baroreceptors than in the case of A fiber baroreceptors. This suggested that the former play a greater part in the moment-by-moment regulation of arterial pressure in hypertensive animals than in normal animals.

Studies in spontaneously hypertensive (SHRs) and normotensive rats (NTRs) showed that the dynamic characteristics of baroreceptors, when tested with pressure sine waves of amplitudes limited to the linear response range for each receptor, were unchanged by resetting (7). These results were thought to indicate that the nature of the mechanical filter between receptor and vessel wall is unaltered in hypertension (1, 7). The difference in static pressure responses between baroreceptors in SHRs and NTRs (6) was attributed at least in part to some intrinsic defect of the SHR baroreceptors themselves. This was thought to be apparent only at an early stage, before structural changes in the aortic wall were fully developed (1, 7, 26). Thus when baroreceptor distortion was computed as wall stress (tension/thickness) and static pressure responses were examined at 10 weeks, greater wall stress was needed to produce a given baroreceptor discharge in SHRs than in NTRs. At 20 weeks the aortic wall of SHRs had become significantly thickened, and curves relating baroreceptor frequency to wall stress were virtually superimposable for SHRs and NTRs (1).

In these studies, both wall stress and wall strain (the increment of radius for each increment of distending pressure) were used as mathematical expressions for the distortion of the receptor complex, and studies were extended to include an examination of baroreceptor activity and aortic wall properties in normal rats before and after the rapid growth period of puberty (1). Theoretically, wall stress or wall strain can be used interchangeably as expressions of baroreceptor distortion, so long as baroreceptor behavior is studied in animals whose aortic walls have similar structural characteristics; results become more difficult to interpret, however, when comparisons of baroreceptor behavior are made between control animals and animals whose aortic walls have undergone structural modification, either because of hypertension or as part of the normal growth process. For instance, these studies (1) showed that between the ages of 10 and 20 weeks the aortic walls of normal rats become much more distensible. If wall strain is used to compute baroreceptor distortion, more strain is needed to produce a given baroreceptor frequency in 20 week old NTRs than in 10 week old NTRs. The authors refer to this changed relationship as resetting, but the term is somewhat confusing when used in this context, since neither the pressure-response curves nor the stress-response curves [shown in (1), figures 7 and 9] are changed by the growth process. These observations only serve to underline the difficulties of making an accurate assessment of receptor distortion. In developing hypertension, for example, stress at the receptor region may be less than that predicted from the overall change in wall thickness, if elastic layers are added to the luminal side of the media in parallel with the receptors. Similarly, in growth, strain on the receptors may be less than predicted if it is taken up disproportionately by new wall elements added in series with the receptors.

Cardiac Mechanoreceptors with Unmyelinated Fibers

The cardiac ventricles receive few myelinated afferent fibers from the vagus nerve but many unmyelinated fibers, the left ventricle being more profusely innervated than the right (13). Many of these ventricular C fibers have mechanosensitive endings (13, 32); afferent vagal C fibers with mechanosensitive endings have also been identified in the atria (30, 31). The discharge from both groups of cardiac mechanoreceptors is described as being sparse and irregular under control conditions. When activated, ventricular receptors usually fire in systole, probably when myocardial tension reaches a critical level (32). Thus they are stimulated not only when diastolic volume is increased [e.g. by aortic occlusion (32)] but also when the heart beats vigorously round a small diastolic volume, after a sudden decrease in venous return [for references see (13)]. Atrial C fibers are usually activated during the v wave of the venous pressure pulse and are stimulated by intravenous infusion; hence they are probably stimulated by stretch of the atrial wall.

Most action potential studies are carried out in animals with open chests and hence with small cardiac volumes. When activity of a sample of cardiac C fiber mechanoreceptors was recorded in cats, first during spontaneous breathing and later after the chest was opened and artificial ventilation established, ventricular C fiber discharge was unchanged (30). Moreover, approximately half the receptors in the two cardiac chambers were silent under control conditions, whether the chest was intact or open. Some atrial receptors, however, discharged rhythmically during spontaneous breathing, firing an impulse with the cardiac cycles when atrial pressure was at its highest at the end of inspiration and the onset of expiration. With hyperpnea, this phasic activity increased to 2–3 impulses cycle^{-1} and expanded to include more cardiac cycles (30). Thus although one may question whether activity in cardiac afferent C fibers is sufficient under normal resting conditions to have a tonic influence on reflex vascular control, there is little doubt that it will increase sharply in exercise; atrial C fibers are stimulated by an increase in breathing and venous return, and ventricular C fibers by an increase in the vigor of cardiac contraction.

Mechanoreceptors with Fibers in Sympathetic Nerves

Histological studies have shown that branched nerve endings, often indistinguishable from those of the vagal aortic baroreceptors and atrial receptors, but with afferent fibers in sympathetic nerve branches and cell bodies in the dorsal root ganglia, are widely distributed in the heart and great vessels. Electrophysiological studies have shown the endings to be scattered diffusely over the atria, ventricles, venae cavae, pulmonary artery, pulmonary veins, and pericardium (9, 23, 38), and distributed along the aorta from heart to diaphragm (9, 10, 20). This widespread and diffuse distribution contrasts with the more restricted distribution of vagal endings within circumscribed vasosensory areas and is partly explained by the finding that many sympathetic fibers branch in their peripheral course to supply several sensitive terminals, not necessarily on the same anatomical structure (9, 10, 20, 23). Branching fibers with multiple sensitive terminals appear to be a general feature of visceral afferent innervation by spinal nerves; they have also been found to supply the mesentery and intestine (9).

Generally speaking, sympathetic mechanoreceptors with cardiovascular endings have only a sparse control discharge, comparable to that of vagal mechanoreceptors with C fibers, and have thresholds higher than those of vagal cardiovascular endings with myelinated fibers. Many fibers are silent;

others discharge an occasional impulse that often (but not invariably) has a constant relation to the cardiac cycle, though it may miss several cycles at a time in apparently random fashion. The great majority of sympathetic mechanoreceptors in the heart and great vessels are extremely sensitive to light touch, and the high frequency of discharge evoked by stroking the region of the ending is in marked contrast to the often modest discharge evoked by even a large increase in transmural pressure (9, 20). Perhaps the simplest explanation is the correct one, namely that the receptors are close to the surface of the structures they innervate, sometimes even in the overlying pleura or pericardium.

Sympathetic mechanoreceptors are supplied by A or C fibers but it has not been possible to distinguish the two types of fiber by the response of their respective endings. In a study of sympathetic aortic mechanoreceptors, both A and C fibers were found to be inactive at systolic pressures below 100 mm Hg; A fibers first became active at an average systolic pressure of 139 mm Hg and C fibers at one of 132 mm Hg; A fibers had a control discharge of 0.29 impulses sec^{-1} and C fibers one of 0.23 impulses sec^{-1} (20). Even at pressures above threshold, fibers were not invariably activated with each cardiac cycle. By contrast, once arterial pressure reaches the appropriate threshold for activation of vagal aortic baroreceptors, A and C fibers alike fire regularly with each cardiac cycle; moreover, C fibers can be distinguished from A fibers by the higher threshold of their endings.

Cardiovascular mechanoreceptors with sympathetic fibers can be stimulated, according to their location, by increases in arterial pressure, cardiac volume, or the vigor of cardiac contraction. Endings in the ventricles, for example, have been shown to fire a brief burst of 3–4 impulses with the augmented beat that follows a ventricular extrasystole (38). However, although the most sensitive aortic mechanoreceptors (9, 20) might briefly discharge bursts of as many as 12 impulses with each cardiac cycle in response to an abrupt increase in aortic pressure, reaching a maximum while arterial pressure was still increasing, such discharges were found to "adapt" within 5–7 sec, sometimes reverting to control level. Even at mean arterial pressures of 180–200 mm Hg, sustained activity rarely exceeded 2 impulses $cycle^{-1}$ and was often less than one impulse $cycle^{-1}$. A similar rapid decline in receptor response to an increase in transmural pressure has been described in sympathetic mechanoreceptors elsewhere in the heart and great vessels and is obvious in many published records of activity from these endings. Whether the transient response is due to a peculiarity of the coupling between receptor and vessel wall elements, or whether it is due to an intrinsic property of the generator region, is a matter for conjecture.

Langley believed that the only function of these "sympathetic afferent fibers" (a term he introduced) was to transmit a poorly localized sense of visceral pain, but as we have seen, sympathetic endings in the cardiovascular system are activated in circumstances that are unlikely to be perceived as painful. Present evidence indicates that the endings are well designed to signal sudden increases in cardiovascular performance but poorly designed to provide continuing, exact information. In general their reflex effects are excitatory to the cardiovascular system. As far as endings on the high-pressure side of the circulation are concerned, they may be regarded as competing with the vagus and sinus nerve baroreceptors for a final common path. The part they play in the reflex control of the cardiovascular system is still not completely clear. At the transition from rest to exercise it may be of some functional advantage to have a surge of excitatory input arriving at spinal cardiovascular neurons at segmental level to offset the inhibitory influence of descending pathways activated by input from the vagus and sinus nerve. Until more is known about the central connections and interactions of the two afferent systems, cranial and spinal, any conclusions are purely speculative.

CHEMOSENSITIVE NERVE ENDINGS

Chemosensitive Vagal Endings

A variety of foreign chemicals stimulate afferent vagal endings in the heart and lungs and produce reflex vasodilatation (11, 12). Some of these chemicals, such as the veratrum alkaloids, have a depolarizing action on excitable membranes generally, and the reflexes they evoke probably result from sensitization or stimulation of an assortment of vagal afferents. However, other foreign chemicals, capsaicin and phenyl diguanide being the most commonly used, stimulate only certain afferent vagal C fibers, their effect apparently depending upon the pharmacological specificity of the nerve endings themselves. When injected in doses that produce profound depressor responses, these chemicals do not stimulate cardiovascular mechanoreceptors in the atria, ventricles or aorta, neither those with A fibers nor those with C fibers (11–13, 16). Moreover, chemicals of this type demonstrate marked species differences in their ability to stimulate particular groups of chemosensitive vagal C fiber endings and to evoke depressor effects (12). We use the term "chemosensitive endings" to distinguish these vagal C fiber endings from the conventional chemoreceptors of the aortic and carotid bodies, which may have either myelinated or unmyelinated fibers and may also be stimulated by foreign chemicals. Chemosensitive endings, by this definition, are not stimulated by hypoxia of a degree and duration sufficient to cause intense stimulation of conventional chemoreceptors.

Two main concentrations of chemosensitive endings provide vagal afferent inputs capable of evoking reflex vasodilatation (11, 12). One comprises the pulmonary C fiber endings or "J receptors," which are located in the respiratory exchange area of the lung and whose stimulation is responsible for the pulmonary depressor chemoreflex (12). The second, with which we are concerned, comprises the chemosensitive endings in the heart and great vessels, which are accessible to chemicals injected into the coronary circulation and whose stimulation results in the coronary chemoreflex (12). Although these endings are most plentiful in the left ventricular wall, similar endings are found in the right ventricle, atria, great veins, pulmonary artery, and aorta (8, 12, 13). There is no reason to suppose that endings in these latter sites have a function different from that of endings in the left ventricle, but, as might be expected from the relative numbers of endings in the different chambers of the heart, chemoreflexes are evoked most readily from the left ventricle.

The vagal endings whose presence in the heart and great vessels is revealed by their response to foreign chemicals are seldom sensitive to changes in cardiac volume or arterial pressure. For example, few of the chemosensitive endings in the left ventricle or aorta were stimulated when left ventricular end diastolic pressure was increased to between 15 and 25 mm Hg and mean aortic pressure was increased to between 200 and 235 mm Hg. Moreover, the discharge evoked by such large increases in pressure was usually irregular, and impulse frequency did not vary consistently with ventricular or aortic pressure (8, 11–13, 16). These endings, therefore, seem unlikely to have a conventional role in the regulation of arterial blood pressure. Their importance must lie elsewhere. Chemosensitive vagal endings are now known to be stimulated by chemicals such as the prostaglandins and bradykinin that are formed and released in the tissues.

Prostaglandins are released by the myocardium in response to hypoxia, myocardial ischemia, and an increase in pre-load; they produce effects on heart rate, cardiac contractility, vascular smooth muscle, and arterial blood pressure that vary with the prostaglandin and the animal species (21). Some of these cardiovascular effects may have a vagal reflex component (21), indeed $PGF_{2\alpha}$ has been shown to evoke a coronary chemoreflex in cats (18). In dogs, left atrial injection of PGE_2 (1 μg kg^{-1}) was found to stimulate many chemosensitive endings in the atria, ventricles, pulmonary artery, and aorta; activity increased ten-fold on average (4). Surprisingly, firing often remained above control for 2–10 min, even though prostaglandins injected into the blood stream are rapidly destroyed. Stimulation was clearly not secondary to the cardiovascular effects of the prostaglandin, for firing was unchanged when the inferior vena cava was occluded to produce a decrease in pressure equal to that caused directly by PGE_2. $PGF_{2\alpha}$, by contrast, stimulated only a few of the chemosensitive endings, although the response, when it occurred, was as vigorous as that evoked by PGE_2. The cardiovascular effects of the two prostaglandins vary in different species; it remains to be determined whether there are also species differences in the effects on afferent nerve endings. Neither PGE_1 nor $PGF_{2\alpha}$ stimulated atrial, ventricular, or arterial mechanoreceptors with A or C fibers, nor did they stimulate aortic chemoreceptors: Any changes in firing that did occur were secondary to the cardiovascular effects of the prostaglandins.

Bradykinin also is released in the heart. Not only has it a direct vasodilator action, but as little as 1 μg injected into the coronary artery of dogs evokes a coronary depressor chemoreflex (22). Like PGE_2, bradykinin stimulates vagal C fibers with chemosensitive endings in the heart and great vessels of dogs (17). Again like PGE_2, bradykinin has only indirect effects on aortic chemoreceptors and cardiovascular mechanoreceptors with A or C fibers. The effects of bradykinin on the chemosensitive endings differ from those of PGE_2 only in their duration: Whereas the discharge evoked by PGE_2 lasted for several minutes, that evoked by bradykinin lasted on average only 30 sec.

Chemical Stimulation of Sympathetic Afferent Endings

Studies of the chemosensitivity of sympathetic afferent nerve endings in the heart have largely been concerned with the effect of algesic agents such as lactic acid and bradykinin, which, applied topically to the ventricular epicardium of anesthetized animals, evoke reflex vasoconstriction and a pseudoaffective response (29, 36). It seems reasonable to suggest that the pain of angina for example, results mainly from stimulation of chemosensitive nerve endings by substances released in the ischemic myocardium rather than from stimulation of sympathetic mechanoreceptors by purely mechanical events. Moreover, sympathetic afferent pathways, like vagal afferent pathways, have a large C fiber component that might be expected to include fibers with chemosensitive endings. Coronary arterial occlusion in dogs increased the activity of ventricular mechanoreceptors with myelinated fibers, but the effects appeared to be largely secondary to postocclusive bulging of the ventricular wall (37); occlusion also evoked an irregular discharge in sympathetic afferent C fibers that had previously been silent (37) and were later found to be highly sensitive to local application of lactic acid. Thus one might conclude that stimulation of sympathetic afferent C fibers with chemosensitive endings is mainly responsible for pain of cardiac origin and for the associated pressor reflexes. However, unlike vagal mechanoreceptors, sympathetic mechanoreceptors also are stimulated by chemical agents.

Bradykinin applied to the ventricular epicardium excites the endings of both myelinated and unmyelinated sympathetic afferent fibers (5, 24, 36). Application of bradykinin (1 μg/ml) to the epicardium caused many mechanoreceptors with myelinated fibers to fire 1–2 impulses with each heart beat; the most sensitive endings, which had either myelinated or unmyelinated fibers, fired at high frequency, either continuously or in bursts, sometimes for as long as 2–3 min (T. Nerdrum, D. G. Baker, H. M. Coleridge, J. C. G. Coleridge, unpublished observations). Thus both mechanosensitive and chemosensitive sympathetic afferents in the heart are probably involved in the pressor response to locally applied chemicals, but since mechanoreceptors are also stimulated by mechanical changes that are unlikely to be perceived as painful, it is probable that recruitment of C fibers is essential for the sensation of pain.

There is now good evidence that prostaglandins are involved as mediators in the response of sympathetic afferent endings to bradykinin. Not only is the pressor response to bradykinin reduced by prior administration of indomethacin, an inhibitor of the biosynthesis of prostaglandins, but it is also potentiated by prior application of PGE_1 in concentrations that alone have no pressor effect (29). In recent action-potential studies in cats, PGE_1 applied to the epicardium potentiated the stimulation of sympathetic afferent endings by locally applied bradykinin (5).

Significance of Chemosensitive Nerve Endings in the Heart

The functional implications of a dual chemosensitive innervation of the heart by vagal and sympathetic afferent nerves capable of evoking reflex effects of opposite sign is hard to assess, particularly since the two afferent inputs are engaged by the same chemicals, released locally. A possible sequence of events that accommodates many of the experimental findings has been postulated (21): Myocardial ischemia or hypoxia causes local synthesis of bradykinin, which in turn stimulates local production of PGE; these substances, acting alone or together, cause coronary vasodilatation and pain; they also stimulate afferent nerves that reflexly decrease arterial pressure and heart rate, reducing the oxygen requirements of the myocardium.

This hypothesis acknowledges the reflex depressor influence of the vagal afferent input but overlooks the excitatory influence of the sympathetic afferent input. The experimental observation that bradykinin evokes either reflex depressor effects of vagal afferent origin or reflex pressor effects of sympathetic afferent origin, depending on its route of administration, may merely imply that vagal endings are distributed more liberally within the substance of the ventricular wall, whereas sympathetic endings are mainly located near the epicardial surface. When bradykinin is released into the ventricular wall as a result of infarction, however, it probably has access to both vagal and sympathetic nerve endings. Pain will almost certainly result from sympathetic afferent stimulation; but because the reflex effects of the two afferent inputs are opposite in sign, the circulatory outcome is unpredictable, and it could be argued that undue predominance of either afferent input might have harmful consequences for an already threatened myocardium. For example, reflex slowing of a dilated heart may further increase its volume, and a reflex decrease in arterial pressure may reduce coronary flow. Conversely, although sympathetically evoked vasoconstriction may help to divert a reduced cardiac output to the essential circuits of myocardium and brain, a reflex increase in myocardial excitability may cause arrhythmias and even lead to ventricular fibrillation.

CONCLUSION

The information furnished to the central nervous system by the vasosensory areas within the thorax now seems to approach in complexity that from the body surface. Sensitive mechanoreceptors with myelinated fibers in the IXth and Xth nerves play the major role in controlling the caliber of peripheral vessels. When arterial blood pressure increases above the normal level, their influence is reinforced by input from vagal mechanoreceptors with unmyelinated fibers. A large proportion of the vagal afferents that supply the heart and great vessels have chemosensitive terminals that are stimulated by chemicals known to be released in the heart. Unlike the chemoreceptors proper, which respond to chemical changes in the general bloodstream, these chemosensitive endings probably respond to purely local chemical changes, for the substances that stimulate them (bradykinin, prostaglandins) are rapidly broken down. The heart and great vessels have a dual innervation, and mechanosensitive and chemosensitive afferents travel directly to the spinal cord in sympathetic nerve branches. Mechanoreceptors can be sensitized and chemosensitive endings stimulated by bradykinin. Generally speaking, the input from the vagal endings we have described has depressor effects upon the cardiovascular system, and the input from sympathetic endings has excitatory effects.

Literature Cited

1. Andresen, M. C., Krauhs, J. M., Brown, A. M. 1978. Relationship of aortic wall and baroreceptor properties during development in normotensive and spontaneously hypertensive rats. *Circ. Res.* 43:728–38
2. Angell James, J. E. 1973. Characteristics of single aortic and right subclavian baroreceptor fiber activity in rabbits with chronic renal hypertension. *Circ. Res.* 32:149–61
3. Arndt, J. O., Dörrenhaus, A., Wiecken, H. 1975. The aortic arch baroreceptor response to static and dynamic stretches in an isolated aorta-depressor nerve preparation of cats in vitro. *J. Physiol. London* 252:59–78
4. Baker, D. G., Kaufman, M. P., Coleridge, H. M., Coleridge, J. C. G. 1979. Prostaglandin E_2 stimulates vagal chemically-sensitive C-fiber endings in the heart and great vessels. *Fed. Proc.* 38:1322 (Abstr.)
5. Baker, D. G., Nerdrum, T., Coleridge, H. M., Coleridge, J. C. G. 1978. Potentiating role of prostaglandin E_1 in the action of bradykinin on sympathetic afferent endings in the heart. *Fed. Proc.* 37:701 (Abstr.)
6. Brown, A. M., Saum, W. R., Tuley, F. H. 1976. A comparison of aortic baroreceptor discharge in normotensive and spontaneously hypertensive rats. *Circ. Res.* 39:488–96
7. Brown, A. M., Saum, W. R., Yasui, S. 1978. Baroreceptor dynamics and their relationship to afferent fiber type and hypertension. *Circ. Res.* 42:694–702
8. Coleridge, H. M., Coleridge, J. C. G., Dangel, A., Kidd, C., Luck, J. C., Sleight, P. 1973. Impulses in slowly conducting vagal fibers from afferent endings in the veins, atria and arteries of dogs and cats. *Circ. Res.* 33:87–97
9. Coleridge, H. M., Coleridge, J. C. G., Kidd, C. 1978. Afferent innervation of the heart and great vessels: a comparison of the vagal and sympathetic components. *Acta Physiol. Pol.* 29: (Suppl. 17) 55–79
10. Coleridge, H. M., Kidd, C., Coleridge, J. C. G., Banzett, R. B. 1975. Multiterminal sympathetic afferent fibers supplying the thoracic organs of cats and dogs. *Physiologist* 18:173 (Abstr.)
11. Coleridge, J. C. G., Coleridge, H. M. 1977. Afferent C-fibers and cardiorespiratory chemoreflexes. *Am. Rev. Resp. Dis.* 115:251–60
12. Coleridge, J. C. G., Coleridge, H. M. 1979. Chemoreflex regulation of the heart. In *Handbook of Physiology, Sect. 2, Vol. 1, Circulation,* ed. R. M. Berne, pp. 653–76. Washington DC: Am. Physiol. Soc. 2nd ed.
13. Coleridge, J. C. G., Coleridge, H. M., Baker, D. G. 1979. Vagal afferent C-fibres from the ventricle. In *Cardiac Receptors,* ed. R. Hainsworth, C. Kidd, R. J. Linden, pp. 117–37. Cambridge, England: Cambridge Univ. Press
14. Ito, C. S., Scher, A. M. 1979. Hypertension following denervation of aortic baroreceptors in unanesthetized dogs. *Circ. Res.* 45:26–34
15. Jones, J. V., Thorén, P. N. 1977. Characteristics of aortic baroreceptors with non-medullated afferents arising from the aortic arch of rabbits with chronic renovascular hypertension. *Acta Physiol. Scand.* 101:286–93
16. Kaufman, M. P., Baker, D. G., Coleridge, H. M., Coleridge, J. C. G. 1978. Activity of C-fiber baroreceptors in the aortic arch of dogs. *Fed. Proc.* 37:703 (Abstr.)
17. Kaufman, M. P., Baker, D. G., Coleridge, H. M., Coleridge, J. C. G. 1979. Stimulation of vagal chemically-sensitive C-fiber endings in the heart and aorta by bradykinin. *Fed. Proc.* 38:1322 (Abstr.)
18. Koss, M. C., Nakano, J. 1976. Reflex bradycardia and hypotension produced by prostaglandin $F_{2\alpha}$ in the cat. *Br. J. Pharmacol.* 56:245–53
19. Kunze, D. L., Saum, W. R., Brown, A. M. 1977. Sodium sensitivity of baroreceptors mediates reflex changes of blood pressure and urine flow. *Nature* 267: 75–78
20. Malliani, A., Pagani, M. 1976. Afferent sympathetic nerve fibres with aortic endings. *J. Physiol. London* 263:157–69
21. Needleman, P. 1976. The synthesis and function of prostaglandins in the heart. *Fed. Proc.* 35:2376–81
22. Neto, F. R., Brasil, J. C. F., Antonio, A. 1974. Bradykinin-induced coronary chemoreflex in the dog. *Arch. Exp. Pathol. Pharmakol.* 283:135–42
23. Nishi, K., Sakanashi, M., Takenaka, F. 1974. Afferent fibres from pulmonary arterial baroreceptors in the left cardiac sympathetic nerve of the cat. *J. Physiol. London* 240:53–66
24. Nishi, K., Sakanashi, M., Takenaka, F. 1977. Activation of afferent cardiac sympathetic nerve fibers of the cat by pain producing substances and by noxious heat. *Pfluegers Arch.* 372:53–61

25. Pelletier, C. L., Clement, D. L., Shepherd, J. T. 1972. Comparison of afferent activity of canine aortic and sinus nerves. *Circ. Res.* 31:557–68
26. Saum, W. R., Ayachi, S., Brown, A. M. 1977. Actions of sodium and potassium ions on baroreceptors of normotensive and spontaneously hypertensive rats. *Circ. Res.* 41:768–74
27. Saum, W. R., Brown, A. M., Tuley, F. H. 1976. An electrogenic sodium pump and baroreceptor function in normotensive and spontaneously hypertensive rats. *Circ. Res.* 39:497–505
28. Sleight, P., Robinson, J. L., Brooks, D. E., Rees, P. M. 1977. Characteristics of single carotid sinus baroreceptor fibers and whole nerve activity in the normotensive and the renal hypertensive dog. *Circ. Res.* 51:750–58
29. Staszewska-Barczak, J., Ferreira, S. H., Vane, J. R. 1976. An excitatory nociceptive cardiac reflex elicited by bradykinin and potentiated by prostaglandins and myocardial ischaemia. *Cardiovasc. Res.* 10:314–27
30. Thames, M. D., Donald, D. E., Shepherd, J. T. 1977. Behavior of cardiac receptors with nonmyelinated vagal afferents during spontaneous respiration in cats. *Circ. Res.* 41:694–701
31. Thorén, P. N. 1976. Atrial receptors with nonmedullated vagal afferents in the cat. *Circ. Res.* 48:357–62
32. Thorén, P. N. 1977. Characteristics of left ventricular receptors with nonmedullated vagal afferents in cats. *Circ. Res.* 40:415–21
33. Thorén, P., Jones, J. V. 1977. Characteristics of aortic baroreceptor C-fibres in the rabbit. *Acta Physiol. Scand.* 99:448–56
34. Thorén, P., Saum, W. R., Brown, A. M. 1977. Characteristics of rat aortic baroreceptors with nonmedullated afferent nerve fibers. *Circ. Res.* 40:231–37
35. Trzebski, A., Chruscielewski, L., Majcherczyk, S. 1978. Effect of osmotic stimuli on the carotid baroreceptor and chemoreceptor discharges in cats. *Acta Physiol. Pol.* 29:373–77
36. Uchida, Y., Murao, S. 1974. Bradykinin-induced excitation of afferent cardiac sympathetic nerve fibers. *Jpn. Heart J.* 15:84–91
37. Uchida, Y., Murao, S. 1974. Excitation of afferent cardiac sympathetic nerve fibers during coronary occlusion. *Am. J. Physiol.* 226:1094–99
38. Ueda, H., Uchida, Y., Kamisaka, K. 1969. Distribution and responses of the cardiac sympathetic receptors to mechanically induced circulatory changes. *Jpn. Heart J.* 10:70–81
39. Zucker, I. H., Earle, A. M., Gilmore, J. P. 1977. The mechanism of adaptation of left atrial stretch receptors in dogs with chronic congestive heart failure. *J. Clin. Invest.* 60:323–31

Ann. Rev. Physiol. 1980. 42:429–39

AUTONOMIC REGULATION OF THE PERIPHERAL CIRCULATION

❖1278

David E. Donald and John T. Shepherd[1]

Mayo Clinic and Foundation, Rochester, Minnesota 55901

INTRODUCTION

The response of the cardiovascular system to stress is achieved through coordination of local and reflex adjustments of vascular resistance, venous capacitance, and cardiac output (28). This brief review examines recent work on the physiological roles of the arterial baroreceptors, the mechanoreceptors in the heart and lungs, and the chemoreceptors.

Alteration in both heart rate and contractility, and the degree of contraction of the smooth muscle of both the resistance and capacitance vessels are governed by (*a*) the adrenergic nerves that when excited activate the cardiovascular system, and (*b*) the cholinergic nerves that when excited inhibit the activity of the heart and certain blood vessels. Recent work in the cat has shown that the preganglionic origin of the cholinergic vasodilator fibers is limited to ventral roots L2–L5; the sympathetic vasoconstrictor fibers emerge from ventral roots T12–L4 (46).

Studies in anesthetized dogs (13, 26) have confirmed the earlier observation (19) in conscious dogs that myocardial blood flow is lower in the chronically denervated heart than in the innervated heart at the same levels of heart rate and arterial pressure. Cardiac denervation was accompanied by increases in oxygen (42%) and lactate consumption, with no consistent changes in glucose and free fatty acid uptake. External left ventricular work per cm^3 oxygen and μmole lactate consumed was decreased. It was concluded that the conversion of substrate and oxygen into mechanical energy was controlled by the tonic release of norepinephrine from cardiac sympathetic nerve terminals (13). Another study in the anesthetized dog indicated that myocardial oxygen tension may be regulated by coronary sympathetic vasomotion (17).

[1]Supported in part by Research Grants HL-06143 and HL-05883 from the National Institutes of Health

0066-4278/80/0315-0429$01.00

The cardiac sympathetic nerves also influence the course of events following myocardial ischemia. Acute coronary occlusion in dogs with chronic cardiac denervation resulted in a near-zero incidence of ventricular ectopic activity and fibrillation (14). This effect appeared more dependent on the absence of myocardial catecholamines than on the interruption of cardiac sympathetic nerve activity (9). Infarct size also was reduced, possibly owing to reduced flow demand as well as to increased collateral perfusion (26).

Sympathetic nerves are distributed to all blood vessels except the umbilical and placental. The density of innervation of the peripheral vessels varies widely and reflects the degree of participation of the vessels in centrally controlled responses. Present interest centers on receptors on the presynaptic fibers which, when activated, modulate the release of neurotransmitter (45). The role of the sympathetic fibers to the cerebral vessels remains controversial, though most studies have shown that alteration in the activity of the sympathetic nerves to these vessels normally has little or no effect on cerebral blood flow (20, 23, 32).

The sympathetic nerves when activated cause a release of renin into the bloodstream from the juxtaglomerular cells, a process that involves a beta-adrenergic receptor. When the decentralized renal nerves in anesthetized cats and dogs are stimulated at frequencies less than 1 Hz, renin release increases without a change in renal blood flow, glomerular filtration rate, or the excretion of sodium and potassium. This suggests that the release is due to a direct action of the sympathetic nerves on the juxtaglomerular cells, rather than to activation of an intrarenal vascular mechanism or a decrease in sodium load to the macula densa. Though stimulation at still lower frequencies (0.25 Hz) did not result in an increase in renin release, this low-level excitation augmented the increase in renin release due to nonneural perturbations such as supra-renal aortic constriction and the intravenous infusion of furosemide (11).

PERIPHERAL SENSORS

Arterial Baroreceptors and Vagally Innervated Cardiopulmonary Receptors

SYMPATHETIC EFFERENTS TO THE CAROTID SINUS In anesthetized dogs, electrical stimulation of the cut distal fibers of the cervical sympathetic nerve increased the carotid mechanoreceptor activity at pressures in the isolated carotid sinus of about 50–100 mm Hg, whereas at pressures above 150 mm Hg the activity was decreased (7). In normal circumstances is there increased traffic in the sympathetic nerves to the carotid sinus and, if so, what is its role in modulating baroreceptor activity?

SODIUM EFFECTS ON ARTERIAL MECHANORECEPTORS A 5% reduction in the sodium concentration of fluid perfusing the carotid sinus baroreceptors causes a rise in blood pressure, heart rate, and renal sympathetic discharge. The effects are related not to a change in sinus distensibility but to an increase in baroreceptor threshold and a reduction in suprathreshold sensitivity. A diuresis occurs with no change in total sodium excretion. The mechanism of the diuresis has not been established. It is not dependent on intact renal sympathetic nerves and might be due to the increase in arterial pressure since increases in perfusion pressure cause diuresis in isolated kidneys. Thus small reductions in extracellular sodium could, via this sodium-sensitive baroreceptor reflex, result in the excretion of a relatively hyponatriuretic urine and thus restore the extracellular sodium to the normal level (31).

Exposure of conscious dogs to a low sodium diet reduced the normal increase in arterial blood pressure due to bilateral carotid occlusion. This small pressure response in the sodium-depleted dog was not reduced further by blocking the conversion of angiotensin I to angiotensin II. Vascular reactivity to exogenous norepinephrine was not impaired in the sodium-depleted dog, but release of endogenous norepinephrine from sympathetic nerve endings was reduced (40). However, in dog saphenous vein strips, decreases in extracellular sodium from 5–23% did not alter basal tension, but progressively increased tension developed during electrical stimulation. This enhancement was due to a direct effect of the sodium on the smooth muscle cells (3).

DIGITALIS: ACTION ON MECHANORECEPTORS Administration of ouabain or acetylstrophanthidin to the isolated carotid sinus of the cat increased both the depressor response to a given increase in carotid sinus pressure and the increase in carotid sinus nerve discharge at sinus pressures above threshold. This is in keeping with an increase in baroreceptor sensitivity possibly due to blockage of an electrogenic sodium pump that contributes to the resting potential of the baroreceptor (38, 43, 44).

Acetylstrophanthidin augmented the inhibitory influence of cardiac receptors with vagal afferents and resulted in reflex bradycardia, hypotension, and withdrawal of renal sympathetic nerve activity. This occurred whether the acetylstrophanthidin was applied to the epicardial surface of the heart or injected into the circumflex coronary artery (48).

RESETTING OF RECEPTORS The arterial mechanoreceptors are subserved by medullated and nonmedullated fibers, the latter only being activated when the blood pressure rises abnormally. In the carotid sinus, the pressure at which one half of the maximum firing rate of the medullated fibers is obtained corresponds to the normal blood pressure. In the anesthetized dog the threshold pressure of the medullated fibers from aortic arch receptors is higher and the pressure-response curve is displaced to the right. This may not be the case in the conscious animal (24). In animals with experimental hypertension the baroreceptors have higher pressure thresholds. This is more evident in those with medullated than nonmedullated afferents (27, 50). In spontaneously hypertensive rats the aortic baroreceptors have an increased pressure threshold, but the distensibility of the excised aortic arch was the same as in normotensive controls. This implies that the resetting might be due to differences between the properties of the receptors themselves (2), Sapru & Krieger, however, found that in spontaneously hypertensive rats baroreceptor resetting could be due either to adaptation of the baroreceptors to persistent high arterial pressure or to induced vascular wall hypertrophy (42).

STUDIES IN HUMANS Use of neck suction to stimulate the carotid baroreceptors in humans showed that the reflex response of heart rate to carotid sinus distension was proportional to the rate of pressure change, that saturation of the reflex occurred at distending pressures of about 160 mm Hg, and that the magnitude of the response increased linearly with the duration of a standard carotid sinus distension and reached a maximum level with stimuli lasting 0.5 sec and more. Peak responses occurred at about 1.25 sec after the onset of baroreceptor stimulation and were proportional to the intensity of stimulation. The response declined to a steady state during the remaining period of stimulation. Beta-adrenergic blockade did not alter the rate of decay of the sinus node inhibition (15, 16).

Increase and decrease in pressure within a sealed neck chamber were used to vary carotid sinus transmural pressure in normotensive and hypertensive humans. In normotensives the pressor response that followed unit reduction in transmural pressure from the resting state was greater than the depressor response to unit increase in transmural pressure from the same resting level. In the hypertensives where the resting level was much higher the reverse occurred. These findings are compatible with alteration of the pressure-volume characteristics of the carotid sinus in hypertensive man. In normotensives the reflex changes in heart rate due to change in arterial blood pressure from injection of vasoactive drugs were three times those induced by similar changes in blood pressure due to manipulation of carotid sinus transmural pressure. In hypertensives similar reflex changes in heart rate attended alteration in arterial pressure by either method. The authors concluded that the sensitivity of extra-carotid baroreceptors was reduced in hypertension (34, 35).

RELATION OF RESPONSE TO CHANGES IN CAROTID SINUS PRESSURE TO PHASE OF RESPIRATION The sensitivity of the cardiac vagal motoneurons in the nucleus ambiguus to the arterial baroreceptor input has been studied during the respiratory cycle. The neurons are inactive during inspiration and fire only in expiration. The contour of their firing pattern suggests that during inspiration these neurons are inhibited by the central inspiratory drive. It is proposed that the baroreceptor-cardiac reflex is ineffective during inspiration as a result of a summation of influences on the cardiac vagal motorneuron cell membrane (36).

CARDIAC RECEPTORS WITH VAGAL AFFERENTS Extensive current reviews are available and only some recent work is mentioned here (12, 33, 39, 50).

In animals the cardiopulmonary receptors are linked more to renal than to muscle blood vessels; in humans the muscle resistance vessels appear to be more under the control of the cardiopulmonary than the carotid barore-flexes (1, 12).

The role of vagally innervated cardiopulmonary receptors during coronary occlusion continues to be of interest. Two studies in anesthetized dogs have shown a preferential distribution of inhibitory cardiac receptors to the inferoposterior wall of the left ventricle and suggest that in both humans and dogs posterior myocardial ischemia evokes more frequent and more intense cardioinhibitory and vasodepressor responses than anterior myocardial ischemia (49, 52). In conscious dogs occlusion of the left circumflex coronary artery resulted in tachycardia and a minor decrease in arterial blood pressure. This decrease in arterial pressure was greater with occlusion in sino-aortic denervated dogs. In both circumstances vagal cold block resulted in an increase in arterial pressure due in part to an increase in peripheral resistance. It was concluded that vagal afferent activity contributed to the depressor responses observed during myocardial ischemia (6).

INTERACTION OF CAROTID AND CARDIOPULMONARY RECEPTORS IN RENIN RELEASE The varying results of renin release during carotid sinus hypotension can be explained by the interaction between the carotid and the cardiopulmonary baroreceptors. In anesthetized mechanically ventilated dogs with aortic nerves cut but carotid sinuses intact, vagal cold block caused an increase in arterial blood pressure and in carotid sinus nerve activity but not in renin release. Vagal cold block caused an increase in renin release only when the buffering activity of the carotid baroreceptors was prevented by their vascular isolation. Conversely, reduction of carotid sinus pressure to 40 mm Hg in dogs with renal arterial pressure maintained constant failed to cause an increase in renin release with the vagal nerves intact. After cervical vagotomy carotid sinus hypotension increased the release of renin.

Thus although withdrawal of the inhibitory activity of each system separately can increase renin release, if reduction in activity of one system results in concomitant activation of the other, then the expected increase in renin release may not occur. In dogs with aortic nerves cut but carotid sinuses intact a nonhypotensive hemorrhage (4 ml kg^{-1}) caused an increase in renin release. A similar hemorrhage after vagotomy failed to cause an increase. Hemorrhage of this modest amount caused a fall in right atrial pressure but not in arterial blood pressure, and there was no reduction in carotid sinus nerve activity. The experiments allow the following conclusions: An increase in renin release will occur on reduction in inhibitory activity of one of the three peripheral receptor systems if such withdrawal does not change the activity of the other two. Vagally innervated cardiopulmonary receptors exert a tonic inhibition of renin release. Cardiopulmonary receptors are more sensitive to modest decreases in blood volume than are the carotid baroreceptors (11).

THE ROLE OF THE CAROTID SINUS AND CARDIOPULMONARY REFLEXES IN CIRCULATORY REGULATION IN HUMANS Deactivation of human cardiopulmonary and arterial baroreceptors by lower body suction at 40 mm Hg decreased central venous pressure and arterial pulse pressure and increased splanchnic and forearm vascular resistance. Simultaneous application of neck suction (40 mm Hg) prevented the tachycardia and most of the splanchnic vasoconstriction but did not significantly attenuate the forearm vasoconstriction. It was concluded that the splanchnic vasoconstrictor response during venous pooling is mediated primarily through carotid baroreceptors and that cardiopulmonary receptors exert the predominant influence on forearm vascular resistance (1).

The heart rate response to neck suction or to intravenous phenylephrine was not altered by lower body negative pressure, but the peak-to-peak fluctuations of arterial pressure in response to sinusoidal neck suction between 10 and 40 mm Hg were increased by application of 40 mm Hg lower body negative pressure (4). However, with smaller degrees of negative pressure such that variations in central venous pressure and hence of cardiopulmonary receptor activity were within the normal range, there was no modulation of sinus node responses to arterial baroreceptor stimulation (47).

While decreased activity of the arterial mechanoreceptors may contribute to the circulatory adjustments on changing from a lying to a standing position, the available evidence indicates that the cardiopulmonary receptors, probably those with nonmedullated vagal afferents, play the major role. In the sodium-depleted subject, blood pressure is maintained during tilting before, but not after, blocking the conversion of angiotensin I to angiotensin II. These findings indicate that angiotensin II is required for blood pressure homeostasis in sodium-depleted humans and suggest that cardiovascular mechanoreceptors are less effective in regulating systemic blood pressure in the sodium-depleted state (41).

Cardiopulmonary Sympathetic Afferents

Measurement of conduction velocity in cardiac sympathetic afferent nerves showed that 69% were medullated A fibers and 31% nonmedullated C-fibers. Most medullated fibers are spontaneously active, often exhibiting cardiac rhythmicity. Cardiac receptors with nonmedullated afferents discharge irregularly and with no apparent relation to cardiac events (51).

Electrical stimulation of cardiac sympathetic afferents mainly has a pressor effect on the cardiovascular system. There is increased activity in cardiac and renal efferent sympathetic nerves (29, 53) and simultaneously a decrease in activity in efferent cardiac vagal fibers. Stimulation at frequencies greater than 10 Hz resulted in modest increases in heart rate, left ventricular dP/dt, renal resistance, and aortic pressure and blood flow. The pressor responses were greater after bilateral carotid sinus denervation. Pressor responses were small when the stimulation parameters were such as to excite only medullated sympathetic afferents; they became larger when the stimulus intensity was increased to excite both medullated and nonmedullated fibers. Stimulation frequencies of less than 10–15 Hz resulted in depressor responses. In the kidney the magnitude of the reflex decrease in vascular resistance was significantly augmented after removal of vagal inhibitory activity (37).

In cats and dogs occlusion of a major coronary artery resulted in increased discharge in afferent sympathetic fibers (mainly medullated) from receptors located in or near the ischemic myocardium. Efferent cardiac sympathetic nerve activity also was increased during coronary occlusion in vagotomized cats after section of the spinal cord at C-1. A peculiarity is that several receptors may be connected to the same afferent fiber. It is likely that these fibers constitute the afferent pathway of the pain response to coronary occlusion (8).

An increase in heart rate has been reported following expansion of the blood volume in the vagotomized cat with spinal cord section at C-1 (5). However, the role of this spinal reflex in naturally occurring stresses is unknown.

The medullated (A type) fibers in the lung parenchyma that are activated by lung inflation have a threshold of about 1 mm Hg, and their discharge frequency increases linearly with increase in tracheal pressure (30).

Chemoreceptors

Afferent fibers from peripheral chemoreceptors project to the ventral surface of the medulla (18).

TRANSLATION OF CHANGES IN BLOOD GASES TO NERVOUS ACTIVITY The type I cell is the most prevalent type in the carotid body and may be involved in the genesis of chemoreceptor afferent discharge. Histochemical studies reveal the presence of catecholamines and dense-cored storage vesicles. Catecholamines inhibit the activity of the carotid sinus nerve endings. Several putative neurotransmitters including acetylcholine, dopamine, norepinephrine, and serotonin have been identified and measured in the carotid body, but their involvement in the chemosensory response mechanism remains to be elucidated. The number of dense-cored vesicles decreases with hypoxia, as does the content of dopamine (22).

Stimulation of the chemoreceptors causes respiration to quicken and deepen. This activates the lung mechanoreceptors, causing reflex changes that partly obscure the changes due to stimulation of the chemoreceptors. When respiration is controlled, stimulation of the chemoreceptors causes (*a*) slowing of the heart and decreased cardiac output due to increased vagal activity; (*b*) dilatation of the coronary vessels due to activation of the vagal fibers; (*c*) constriction of the resistance vessels in the skeletal muscle, splanchnic bed, and kidney, and of the splanchnic capacitance vessels, due to activation of their sympathetic nerves; and (*d*) dilatation of cutaneous arterioles and veins due to decreased activity of their sympathetic nerves (10).

In anesthetized dogs, perfusion of the carotid bodies with venous or hypoxic blood resulted in a negative inotropic response of the left ventricle and a decrease in heart rate due to decreased activity of the cardiac sympathetic nerves. The vagus nerves played no significant role. The response was abolished by crushing both carotid bodies or by raising carotid pressure (21).

DIVING REFLEX When the face is immersed in water, the sensory endings of the trigeminal nerve areas are activated. This elicits cessation of respiration, vagal bradycardia, and constriction of systemic vessels in the splanchnic region, skeletal muscles, and kidneys. The splanchnic and cutaneous capacitance vessels constrict. The apnea is followed quickly by a decrease in P_{O_2} and an increase in P_{CO_2} in the arterial blood, which stimulates the arterial chemoreceptors. The continued sensory input from the trigeminal nerve overrides the action of the chemoreceptors on the respiratory center. The circulatory effects of chemoreceptor stimulation augment those of the trigeminal reflex, leading to further cardiac slowing and constriction of systemic vessels. There is a reflex dilatation of the coronary vessels mediated by the vagal nerves. Thus the arterial blood pressure is maintained and the blood is made available to the heart and brain (10).

CORONARY CHEMOREFLEXES Injection of 5-hydroxytryptamine into the coronary arteries at their origin activated vagal afferents and led to transient hypertension and tachycardia (25). Activation of this reflex by 5-hydroxytryptamine derived from platelet aggregation would explain the transient hypertension that occasionally accompanies angina pectoris and acute myocardial infarction. Injection of 5-hydroxytryptamine into the distal coronary circulation stimulates other vagal afferents and induces reflex bradycardia and hypotension. The activation of this reflex may help to explain the hypotension and bradycardia observed in most cases of coronary infarction.

Literature Cited

1. Abboud, F. M., Eckberg, D. L., Johannsen, U. J., Mark, A. L. 1979. Carotid and cardiopulmonary baroreceptor control of splanchnic and forearm vascular resistance during venous pooling in man. *J. Physiol. London* 286:173–84
2. Andresen, M. C., Krauhs, J. M., Brown, A. M. 1978. Relationship of aortic wall and baroreceptor properties during development in normotensive and spontaneously hypertensive rats. *Circ. Res.* 43:728–38
3. Beaty, O. III, Lorenz, R. R., Shepherd, J. T. 1978. Increased reactivity of venous smooth muscle by small decreases in extracellular sodium. *Am. J. Physiol.* 235:H581–86
4. Bevegård, S., Castenfors, J., Lindblad, L. E., Tranesjö, J. 1977. Blood pressure and heart rate regulating capacity of the carotid sinus during changes in blood volume distribution in man. *Acta Physiol. Scand.* 99:300–12
5. Bishop, V. S., Lombardi, F., Malliani, A., Pagani, M., Recordati, G. 1976. Reflex sympathetic tachycardia during intravenous infusions in chronic spinal cats. *Am. J. Physiol.* 230:25–29
6. Bishop, V. S., Peterson, D. F. 1978. The circulatory influences of vagal afferents at rest and during coronary occlusion in conscious dogs. *Circ. Res.* 43:840–47
7. Bolter, C. P., Ledsome, J. R. 1976. Effect of cervical sympathetic nerve stimulation on canine carotid sinus reflex. *Am. J. Physiol.* 230:1026–30
8. Brown, A. M., Malliani, A. 1971. Spinal sympathetic reflexes initiated by coronary receptors. *J. Physiol. London.* 212:685–705
9. Corr, P. B., Gillis, R. A. 1978. Autonomic neural influences on the dysrhythmias resulting from myocardial infarction. *Circ. Res.* 43:1–9
10. Daly, M. de B., Korner, P. I., Angell-James, J. E., Oliver, J. R. 1978. Cardiovascular-respiratory reflex interactions between carotid bodies and upper-airways receptors in the monkey. *Am. J. Physiol.* 234:H293–99
11. Donald, D. E. 1979. Studies on the release of renin by direct and reflex activation of renal sympathetic nerves. *Physiologist* 22:39–42
12. Donald, D. E., Shepherd, J. T. 1978. Reflexes from the heart and lungs: physiological curiosities or important regulatory mechanisms. *Cardiovasc. Res.* 12:449–69
13. Drake, A. J., Stubbs, J., Noble, M. I. M. 1978. Dependence of myocardial blood flow and metabolism on cardiac innervation. *Cardiovasc. Res.* 12:69–80

14. Ebert, P. A., Vanderbeek, R. B., Allgood, R. J., Sabiston, D. C. Jr. 1970. Effect of chronic cardiac denervation on arrhythmias after coronary artery ligation. *Cardiovasc. Res.* 4:141–47
15. Eckberg, D. L. 1977. Baroreflex inhibition of the human sinus node: importance of stimulus intensity, duration, and rate of pressure change. *J. Physiol. London* 269:561–77
16. Eckberg, D. L. 1977. Adaptation of the human carotid baroreceptor-cardiac reflex. *J. Physiol. London* 269:579–89
17. Feigl, E. O. 1975. Control of myocardial oxygen tension by sympathetic coronary vasoconstriction in the dog. *Circ. Res.* 37:88–95
18. Fukuda, Y., Loeschcke, H. H. 1977. Effect of H^+ on spontaneous neuronal activity in the surface layer of the rat medulla oblongata in vitro. *Pfluegers Arch.* 371:125–34
19. Gregg, D. E., Khouri, E. M., Donald, D. E., Lowenshohn, H. S., Pasyk, S. 1972. Coronary circulation in the conscious dog with cardiac neural ablation. *Circ. Res.* 31:129–44
20. Gross, P. M., Heistad, D. D., Strait, M. R., Marcus, M. L., Brody, M. J. 1979. Cerebral vascular responses to physiological stimulation of sympathetic pathways in cats. *Circ. Res.* 44:288–94
21. Hainsworth, R., Karim, F., Sofola, O. A. 1979. Left ventricular inotropic responses to stimulation of carotid body chemoreceptors in anaesthetized dogs. *J. Physiol. London* 287:455–66
22. Hanbauer, I., Hellstrom, S. 1978. The regulation of dopamine and noradrenaline in the rat carotid body and its modification by denervation and by hypoxia. *J. Physiol. London* 282:21–34
23. Heistad, D. D., Marcus, M. L. 1978. Evidence that neural mechanisms do not have important effects on cerebral blood blow. *Circ. Res.* 42:295–302
24. Ito, C. S., Scher, A. M. 1978. Regulation of arterial blood pressure by aortic baroreceptors in the unanesthetized dog. *Circ. Res.* 42:230–36
25. James, T. N., Urthaler, F., Hageman, G. R., Isobe, J. N. 1978. Further analysis of components in a cardiogenic hypertensive chemoreflex. In *Neural Mechanisms in Cardiac Arrhythmias (Perspectives in Cardiovascular Research)*, ed. P. J. Schwartz, A. M. Brown, A. Malliani, A. Zanchetti, 2:251. NY: Raven Press. 440 pp.
26. Jones, C. E., Beck, L. Y., DuPont, E., Barnes, G. E. 1978. Effects of coronary ligation on the chronically sympathectomized dog ventricle. *Am. J. Physiol.* 235:H429–34
27. Jones, J. V., Thorén, P. N. 1977. Characteristics of aortic baroreceptors with non-medullated afferents arising from the aortic arch of rabbits with chronic renovascular hypertension. *Acta Physiol. Scand.* 101:286–93
28. Korner, P. I. 1971. Integrative neural cardiovascular control. *Physiol. Rev.* 51:312–67
29. Kostreva, D. R., Hess, G. L., Zuperku, E. J., Neumark, J., Coon, R. L., Kampine, J. P. 1976. Cardiac responses to stimulation of thoracic afferents in the primate and canine. *Am. J. Physiol.* 231:1279–84
30. Kostreva, D. R., Zuperku, E. J., Hess, G. L., Coon, R. L., Kampine, J. P. 1975. Pulmonary afferent activity recorded from sympathetic nerves. *J. Appl. Physiol.* 39:37–40
31. Kunze, D. L., Brown, A. M. 1978. Sodium sensitivity of baroreceptors: reflex effects on blood pressure and fluid volume in the cat. *Circ. Res.* 42:714–20
32. Lee, T. J.-F., Hume, W. R., Su, C., Bevan, J. A. 1978. Neurogenic vasodilation of cat cerebral arteries. *Circ. Res.* 42:535–42
33. Linden, R. J. 1975. Reflexes from the heart. *Prog. Cardiovasc. Dis.* 18:201–21
34. Mancia, G., Ferrari, A., Gregorini, L., Valentini, R., Ludbrook, J., Zanchetti, A. 1977. Circulatory reflexes from carotid and extracarotid baroreceptor areas in man. *Circ. Res.* 41:309–15
35. Mancia, G., Ludbrook, J., Ferrari, A., Gregorini, L., Zanchetti, A. 1978. Baroreceptor reflexes in human hypertension. *Circ. Res.* 43:170–77
36. McAllen, R. M., Spyer, K. M. 1978. The baroreceptor input to cardiac vagal motoneurones. *J. Physiol. London* 282:365–74
37. Purtock, R. V., von Colditz, J. H., Seagard, J. L., Igler, F. O., Zuperku, E. J., Kampine, J. P. 1977. Reflex effects of thoracic sympathetic afferent nerve stimulation on the kidney. *Am. J. Physiol.* 233:H580–86
38. Quest, J. A., Gillis, R. A. 1974. Effect of digitalis on carotid sinus baroreceptor activity. *Circ. Res.* 35:247–55
39. Recordati, G. M. 1978. Type A atrial receptors in the cat: effects of changes in atrial volume and contractility. *J. Physiol. London* 380:303–17
40. Rocchini, A. P., Cant, J. R., Barger, A. C. 1977. Carotid sinus reflex in dogs with low- to high-sodium intake. *Am. J. Physiol.* 233:H196–202

41. Sancho, J., Re, R., Burton, J., Barger, A. C., Haber, E. 1976. The role of the renin-angiotension-aldosterone system in cardiovascular homeostasis in normal human subjects. *Circulation* 53:400–5
42. Sapru, H. N., Krieger, A. J. 1979. Role of receptor elements in baroreceptor resetting. *Am. J. Physiol.* 236:H174–82
43. Saum, W. R., Ayachi, S., Brown, A. M. 1977. Actions of sodium and potassium ions on baroreceptors of normotensive and spontaneously hypertensive rats. *Circ. Res.* 41:768–74
44. Saum, W. R., Brown, A. M., Tuley, F. H. 1976. An electrogenic sodium pump and baroreceptor function in normotensive and spontaneously hypertensive rats. *Circ. Res.* 39:497–505
45. Shepherd, J. T. (Chairman). 1978. Symposium. Alteration in activity of vascular smooth muscle by local modulation of adrenergic transmitter release. *Fed. Proc.* 37:179–211
46. Sonnenschein, R. R., Weissman, M. L. 1978. Sympathetic vasomotor outflows to hindlimb muscles of the cat. *Am. J. Physiol.* 235:H482–87
47. Takeshita, A., Mark, A. L., Eckberg, D. L., Abboud, F. M. 1979. Affect of central venous pressure on arterial baroreflex control of heart rate. *Am. J. Physiol.* 236:H42–47
48. Thames, M. D. 1979. Acetylstrophanthidin-induced reflex inhibition of canine renal sympathetic nerve activity mediated by cardiac receptors with vagal afferents. *Circ. Res.* 44:8–15
49. Thames, M. D., Klopfenstein, H. S., Abboud, F. M., Mark, A. L., Walker, J. L. 1978. Preferential distribution of inhibitory cardiac receptors with vagal afferents to the inferoposterior wall of the left ventricle activated during coronary occlusion in the dog. *Circ. Res.* 43:512–19
50. Thorén, P. 1979. Role of cardiac vagal C-fibers in cardiovascular control. In *Reviews of Physiology, Pharmacology and Biochemistry.* Heidelberg: Springer. In press
51. Uchida, Y. 1975. Afferent sympathetic nerve fibers with mechanoreceptors in the right heart. *Am. J. Physiol.* 228:223–30
52. Walker, J. L., Thames, M. D., Abboud, F. M., Mark, A. L., Klopfenstein, H. S. 1978. Preferential distribution of inhibitory cardiac receptors in left ventricle of the dog. *Am. J. Physiol.* 235:H188–92
53. Weaver, L. C. 1977. Cardiopulmonary sympathetic afferent influences on renal nerve activity. *Am. J. Physiol.* 233:H592–99

Ann. Rev. Physiol. 1980. 42:441–53

NEURAL MECHANISMS IN HYPERTENSION

◆1279

M. J. Brody,[1] *J. R. Haywood,*[2] *and K. B. Touw*

Department of Pharmacology and Cardiovascular Center,
The University of Iowa College of Medicine, Iowa City, Iowa 52242

INTRODUCTION

Hypertension is a dysfunction of arterial pressure regulation. The mechanisms available for maintaining arterial pressure in the normotensive range are complex and integrated. Many function autonomously—i.e. they do not depend upon the central nervous system (CNS) for regulation. Examples of autonomous cardiovascular phenomena with implications for hypertension are autoregulation of myocardial contractility, local regulation of blood flow produced by changes in vascular smooth muscle activity, and activation of the renin-angiotensin system by a fall in renal perfusion pressure.

Studies on the pathogenesis of hypertension have tended to focus on mechanisms not requiring the nervous system. In recent years interest has increased in the possibility that altered CNS regulation of arterial pressure may be implicated directly in the genesis of high arterial pressure. This brief review examines the prominent findings that have implicated the brain in the development and maintenance of hypertension.

RECENT EVIDENCE FOR THE INVOLVEMENT OF THE CNS IN HYPERTENSION

Evidence exists for the participation of central neural factors in DOCA-salt (26), renal (31), and Dahl-strain hypertension (114). Substantial data also support the contribution of increased sympathetic activity to hypertension

[1]Portions of the work from our laboratories were supported by USPHS Grants HLP14388 and HLO7121.

[2]Current address: Department of Pharmacology, University of Texas Health Science Center at San Antonio, 7703 Floyd Curl Drive, San Antonio, TX 78284.

0066-4278/80/0315-0441$01.00

in Okamoto spontaneously hypertensive rats (SHR). Increased peripheral sympathetic nerve activity has been recorded directly (66), and the development of hypertension can be attenuated by peripheral sympathectomy (36). The blood pressure of the Okamoto strain of SHR appears to be hyperresponsive to environmental stimuli such as immobilization stress (75), temperature (119), and alerting stimuli (53, 54, 118); conversely, the development of hypertension in SHR can be delayed by reducing environmental stimulation (52, 77).

Despite these data, recent evidence suggests that in conscious SHR, removal by ganglionic blockade of sympathetic activity does not produce a greater fall in vascular resistance (of the hindquarter, mesenteric, and renal beds) than that observed in normotensive age-matched controls, either at 8 weeks of age (K. B. Touw, R. A. Shaffer, and M. J. Brody, unpublished observation), or at 3–4 months (8). The technique for demonstrating an exaggerated neural contribution to regional vascular resistance was validated by experiments in conscious rats with hypertension produced by aortic baroreceptor deafferentation (115).

Normal animals can become chronically hypertensive when exposed to environmental stress such as stressful learning situations (58), light, sound, and footshocks (76, 82), isolation (5), and noise exposure (11). Dahl salt-sensitive rats become hypertensive in a conflict-avoidance situation without high salt in their diets (38).

Direct electrical stimulation of the posterior hypothalamus increases arterial pressure (3, 17, 18, 109, 113). The classic paper by Folkow & Rubinstein showing that chronic stimulation of the posterior hypothalamus produces sustained hypertension has not been confirmed (37). Lesions of this area of the hypothalamus cause a small decrease in the blood pressure of SHR and one-kidney Grollman hypertensive rats (16). Pinealectomy induces a high-renin form of hypertension in rats (67).

CENTRAL MECHANISMS OF NEUROGENIC HYPERTENSION

Interference with the afferent components of the baroreceptor reflex pathway produces elevated arterial pressure in several species (33, 71), though not all authors agree that mean pressure is increased (105). Electrolytic destruction of the nucleus tractus solitarii (NTS) in the brainstem, the terminus of the baroreceptor afferent projections, causes, after recovery from anesthesia, a fulminating lethal hypertension sometimes accompanied by increases in heart rate in rats (28, 29) and a sustained hypertension and tachycardia in cats (89) and dogs (19). The elevated arterial pressure is a result of an increased regional vascular resistance (107) maintained by enhanced sympathetic tone (27, 115). Decreases in arterial pressure and heart rate occur when the NTS is electrically activated or chemically stimulated by norepinephrine, epinephrine, or dopamine (29).

The increased sympathetic discharge that follows removal of inhibitory baroreceptor input is dependent, in part, on higher centers in the brain since midcollicular decerebration (28) and electrolytic lesions of the periventricular tissue of the anterior hypothalamus (87) significantly attenuate NTS hypertension in rats. Environmental stimuli can also modify sympathetic output in NTS-lesioned animals. Blood pressure in lesioned cats is significantly higher during the day, though it does not return to control levels at night (89). In addition, NTS-lesioned cats showed over a five-fold greater pressor response to a conditioned tone-shock stimulus than do controls (91). These observations suggest that higher centers of the brain can modulate baroreceptor control of sympathetic activity.

Peripheral (21) and central deafferentation (19, 89) cause increased lability of arterial pressure. Partial lesions with 6-hydroxydopamine of the NTS in rats produce a moderate increase in arterial pressure and lability (108), which indicates that the catecholaminergic innervation of the NTS plays an important physiologic role in arterial pressure regulation. Electrolytic ablation of the brainstem A-2 cell group, the source of catecholamine fibers to NTS (24), did not chronically alter arterial pressure or heart rate but did produce increased lability (102).

RENIN-ANGIOTENSIN SYSTEM—CENTRAL ACTIONS

The renin-angiotensin system contributes to hypertension not only by its direct actions on blood vessels and fluid and electrolyte balance, but also by indirect cardiovascular effects mediated through the CNS (10, 42, 95). In hypertension with elevated plasma renin, angiotensin II may exert some of its effects by acting at sites in the brain that lack the blood-brain barrier (12, 35, 44, 72, 97), or by crossing a disrupted barrier under conditions of elevated pressure (98). It is also possible that angiotensin II is produced within the brain by a specific isorenin (41, 61, 95, 101). Increased renin activity and angiotensin II have been found in certain areas of the SHR brain without an increase in plasma levels (40, 68). Hypertension has been produced in rats (48) and dogs (62) by chronic infusion of angiotensin II into the cerebroventricular system.

The area postrema is an important receptor site for angiotensin in species such as dog or cat but does not have this function in rats (56). Removal of the area postrema either has no effect on blood pressure (121) or causes a chronic mild hypotension (32). The one study showing hypertension following an area postrema lesion is complicated by the fact that the lesion might have extended to the region of the NTS (120).

The role of angiotensin in the CNS has also been studied by administering competitive angiotensin antagonists, such as saralasin, into the ventricular system of hypertensive animals. Most of these investigations have been conducted in the SHR, which shows increased responsiveness to centrally administered angiotensin II (65). In most (60, 81, 99, 100, 112, 116) but not all (30) cases, angiotensin blocking agents administered intraventricularly reduced the blood pressure of SHR. Similar effects of central angiotensin antagonism on blood pressure have been observed in renal hypertension (111) and aortic coarctation hypertension (112), a high-renin model of malignant hypertension. Although there is much evidence that angiotensin acts within the CNS to maintain elevated blood pressure, it is clear that many other mechanisms are involved since the depressor effects of centrally administered angiotensin antagonists are relatively small. Furthermore, removal of the angiotensin-sensitive region of the anteroventral third ventricle (AV3V) does not prevent (47) or lower (46) arterial pressure in SHR.

CENTRAL CATECHOLAMINES

The involvement of CNS catecholamines in hypertension and the regulation of arterial pressure is covered in several recent reviews (1, 2, 20, 59). Most attention has been focused on the role of norepinephrine, epinephrine, and dopamine in the brainstem. Catecholamines involved in blood pressure control are, however, also found in nuclei of the hypothalamus and regions of the spinal cord (25, 39). The role of CNS catecholamines in hypertension has been examined by depletion of catecholamines with the neurotoxin, 6-hydroxydopamine, and measurement of neurotransmitters and their biosynthetic enzymes in individual brain nuclei.

Depletion of whole-brain and spinal-cord norepinephrine prevents hypertension in spontaneously hypertensive rats (50, 73), DOCA-salt treated animals (50, 78), one-kidney renal hypertensive rats (45, 50), and two-kidney renal hypertensive animals (74). These studies clearly indicate the importance of CNS catecholamines for the development of hypertension. More selective destruction of catecholamines in the spinal cord by administration of 6-hydroxydopamine into the cisterna magna or at the level of the fifth cervical vertebrae fails to prevent hypertension in spontaneously hypertensive rats (73, 79), DOCA-salt animals (78), and two-kidney renal hypertensive animals (74). However, destruction of spinal catecholamines prevents hypertension caused by electrolytic lesions of the nucleus tractus solitarii (27), which indicates that spinal cord norepinephrine is necessary for NTS hypertension but not for other models of hypertension.

Measurement of neurotransmitter levels and their synthetic enzymes in various regions of the brain has not provided as clear an indication of the role of catecholamines in specific sites of the brain during hypertension as the depletion studies. In young, spontaneously hypertensive rats, when activity of the peripheral sympathetic nervous system is elevated (117), both increases (88) and decreases (104) in norepinephrine synthesis have been shown in the hypothalamus while norepinephrine production is increased in the brainstem (88, 103). Epinephrine synthesis is also apparently increased in the brainstem at this age (43, 103). In the adult SHR, factors other than neurogenic mechanisms have been shown to sustain the elevated arterial pressure (8). In these animals, hypothalamic norepinephrine synthesis is either suppressed (104) or unchanged (88), while in the brainstem epinephrine synthesis is either elevated (43) or unchanged (103). In one-kidney renal hypertensive animals 3 days after renal artery clipping a similar trend of suppressed hypothalamic catecholamines has been shown with no apparent changes occurring in the brainstem (93, 94). At 7 and 28 days after clipping, however, indexes of epinephrine synthesis are increased in the NTS (93). Although these studies suggest an impairment in brain catecholamine function characterized by a decrease in hypothalamic catecholamines and an increase in brainstem norepinephrine and epinephrine, the critical site(s) of central catecholamines in hypertension remains unclear.

CENTRAL NEUROENDOCRINE FACTORS

The CNS can regulate the cardiovascular system by the release of neuroendocrine humoral factors as well as through the autonomic nervous system. Vasopressin (antidiuretic hormone) is presently the major candidate for a role in hypertension (83), though most evidence points to its participation in the accelerating malignant form of the disease. Plasma vasopressin levels are elevated in several forms of experimental hypertension including DOCA-salt (23, 86), two-kidney one-clip (85), SHR (22, 84), and Dahl salt-sensitive rats (106). Since the plasma concentrations of vasopressin found in hypertensive rats do not increase pressure in normal rats, it is hypothesized that hypertensive animals are hyperresponsive to vasopressin (83). Alternatively, vasopressin may increase vascular responsiveness to other pressor agents. Rats genetically deficient in vasopressin fail to develop DOCA-salt hypertension (23), and specific vasopressin antagonist and antibody reduce the pressure in DOCA-salt (23, 86), two-kidney one-clip (85), and spontaneously hypertensive rats (84). A critical unanswered question concerns the mechanism responsible for the apparent exaggerated secretion of vasopressin in hypertensive states of varying etiologies.

ANTERIOR HYPOTHALAMUS IN EXPERIMENTAL HYPERTENSION

Direct evidence for the participation of the anterior hypothalamus in the pathogenesis of hypertension has recently been uncovered. A lesion in the lateral anterior hypothalamus produces an acute hypertensive reaction that is mediated primarily by excessive release of adrenal catecholamines (90). This region appears to represent, therefore, an inhibitory regulator of adrenal medullary function.

Another series of studies has demonstrated that a lesion of periventricular tissue in the preoptic region of the anterior hypothalamus prevents a number of forms of experimental hypertension with diverse etiologies. The region was first identified as containing angiotensin receptors mediating drinking and pressor activity (14, 63). It encompasses the immediate periventricular tissue in the most anterior and ventral portion of the third ventricle, referred to as the AV3V. An electrolytic lesion in this area obliterates the dipsogenic and pressor activity of angiotensin II and hypertonic sodium chloride administered intraventricularly and attenuates the pressor response to angiotensin administered intravenously (6). The electrical activation of the AV3V elicits an integrated peripheral cardiovascular response consisting of vasodilation in the hindquarters and vasoconstriction in the mesenteric and renal vascular beds (34). The pathways carrying information about cardiovascular responses descend from the AV3V through the region of the ventromedial hypothalamus and median eminence (34) and probably relay in the dorsomedial central gray of the mesencephalon (69, 110).

The AV3V lesion protects rats against the development of one-kidney and two-kidney renal hypertension (6) and against deoxycorticosterone (DOC) hypertension (6). It prevents hypertension in Dahl strain salt-sensitive rats (7) and attenuates the hypertension produced by lesion of the nucleus tractus solitarius and cutting of the sino-aortic nerves (M. Mow, M. J. Brody, unpublished observation) while protecting animals from the lethal effects of the NTS lesion (87). Reversal of established renal hypertension with the AV3V lesion has also been described (13). The lesion is not uniformly effective in experimental hypertension since the blood pressure of SHR is neither lowered (46) nor prevented from increasing (47) by an AV3V lesion. Lesions in other areas of the brain thought to be involved with the CNS effects of angiotensin in the rat, such as the supraoptic nucleus (K.

B. Touw, M. J. Brody, unpublished observation) and the area postrema (56), do not affect the development of renal hypertension.

These findings represent the first demonstrations that the integrity of a small and discrete region of the brain is required for the expression of high arterial pressure. Studies on the physiological role of the AV3V region and on the mechanisms by which this area is involved in the pathogenesis of hypertension are still in preliminary stages. However, in reference to overall fluid and electrolyte homeostasis, the AV3V appears to be intimately involved with sodium balance. Chronically lesioned rats exhibit hypernatraemia (15), lack the capacity to excrete an isotonic sodium chloride load normally (4), and appear to have a deficit in the elaboration of a natriuretic hormone (4). The deficit in natriuretic hormone release could participate in the protective effects of the lesion in experimental hypertension since such a substance has been theorized to play both a natriuretic and pressor role in the same forms of hypertension protected by the lesion (49). Despite chronically elevated plasma sodium concentrations, rats with chronic AV3V lesions exhibit elevated plasma renin concentrations although plasma renin activity is in the normal range (9). The release of vasopressin is attenuated in the acute adipsic phase after an AV3V lesion leading to in appropriate diuresis (9). Although chronically lesioned animals exhibit normal fluid intake and excretion, vasopressin release provoked by intraventricular administration of angiotensin is attenuated (64).

Since protection from the development of hypertension is seen in both low- and high-renin forms of the disease, it is difficult to attribute the antihypertensive effects of the lesion to removal of angiotensin receptors per se. In the case of renal hypertension where activation of the renin-angiotensin system is observed at least initially, interference with the central pressor activity of blood-borne angiotensin may contribute to the protective action (6). Angiotensin appears to reach the region of the AV3V through the carotid rather than vertebral arterial supply of the brain (35).

Electrical activation of the sensory or afferent nerves arising from the kidney produces an integrated hemodynamic response qualitatively identical to that of AV3V stimulation, and the effects of stimulation of the renal afferent nerves are significantly attenuated by an acute AV3V lesion (80). Total renal denervation in rats produced by autotransplantation delayed for over two months the appearance of renal but not DOC hypertension (57). This suggests that renal hypertension may be elicited in part by signals reaching the AV3V from sensory fibers originating in the manipulated kidney.

Increases in plasma concentrations of vasopressin have been observed in virtually all forms of experimental hypertension (see above). While the evidence for a pressor role of vasopressin is better in malignant forms of experimental hypertension than in the benign state, the possibility must be entertained that attenuation of vasopressin release by the AV3V lesion could participate in the protective effect of the lesion. The lesion does not appear to interrupt renal hypertension by blocking the elaboration of renin (55).

Close similarities exist between the antihypertensive effects of the AV3V lesion and the protective actions of central catecholamine depletion. Both procedures produce acute adipsia (51), attenuation of central pressor activity of angiotensin (45), and protection against the development of most forms of experimental hypertension (51). Although no direct cause/effect relationship can be ascribed to an interaction between the AV3V lesion and central catecholaminergic systems, the fact that periventricular tissue of the anterior third ventricle is invested richly with noradrenergic and dopaminergic fibers is of considerable interest (92, 96).

The reader is referred to an extensive review of the AV3V (9) for details about its role in the pathogenesis of hypertension. The evidence suggests that this small region of the anterior hypothalamus is an important integrating area for regulation of neuroendocrine mechanisms that are critical to the development of high arterial pressure.

Literature Cited

1. Antonaccio, M. J. 1977. Neuropharmacology of central mechanisms governing the circulation. In *Cardiovascular Pharmacology,* ed. M. J. Antonaccio, pp. 131–65. NY: Raven Press. 534 pp.
2. Axelrod, J. 1976. Catecholamines and hypertension. *Clin. Sci. Mol. Med.* 51: (Suppl. 3) 415–21S
3. Baum, T., Shropshire, A. T. 1969. Stimulation of central cardiovascular centers in hypertension. *Arch. Int. Pharmacodyn.* 181:405–13
4. Bealer, S., Haywood, J. R., Johnson, A. K., Gruber, K. A., Buckalew, V. M., Brody, M. J. 1979. Impaired natriuresis and secretion of natriuretic hormone (NH) in rats with lesions of the anteroventral third ventricle (AV3V). *Fed. Proc.* 38:1232
5. Bennett, T., Gardiner, S. M. 1979. Prevention and reversal of isolation induced systolic arterial hypertension in rats by treatment with beta-adrenoceptor antagonists. *Brit. J. Pharmacol.* 65:205–14
6. Brody, M. J., Fink, G. D., Buggy, J., Haywood, J. R., Gordon, F. J., Johnson, A. K. 1978. The role of anteroventral third ventricle (AV3V) region in experimental hypertension. *Circ. Res.* 43: (Suppl. I) I2–13
7. Brody, M. J., Fink, G. D., Buggy, J., Haywood, J. R., Gordon, F. J., Kneupfer, M. M., Mow, M., Mahoney, L., Johnson, A. K. 1978. Critical role of the anteroventral third ventricle (AV3V) region in development and maintenance of experimental hypertension. In *Nervous System and Hypertension,* ed. H. Schmitt, P. Meyers, pp. 76–84. NY: Wiley. 383 pp.
8. Brody, M. J., Haywood, J. R., Shaffer, R. A. 1979. Contribution of neurogenic vasoconstrictor tone to arterial pressure and vascular resistance in spontaneously hypertensive rats. *Fed. Proc.* 38:1232
9. Brody, M. J., Johnson, A. K. 1980. Role of the anteroventral third ventricle (AV3V) region in fluid and electrolyte balance, arterial pressure regulation, and hypertension. In *Frontiers of Neuroendocrinology,* ed. W. F. Ganong, L. Martini. NY: Raven Press. In press
10. Buckley, J. P., Ferrario, C. M., eds. 1977. *Central Actions of Angiotensin and Related Hormones.* NY: Pergamon Press. 606 pp.
11. Buckley, J. P., Smookler, H. H. 1970. Cardiovascular and biochemical effects

of chronic intermittent neurogenic stimulation. In *Physiological Effects of Noise,* ed. B. L. Welch, A. S. Welch, pp. 75–84. NY: Plenum Press. 365 pp.

12. Buckley, J. P., Smookler, H. H., Severs, W. B., Deuben, R. R. 1977. See Ref. 10, pp. 149–56
13. Buggy, J., Fink, G. D., Haywood, J. R., Johnson, A. K., Brody, M. J. 1978. Interruption of the maintenance phase of established hypertension by ablation of the anteroventral third ventricle (AV3V) in rats. *Clin. Exp. Hypertens.* 1:337–53
14. Buggy, J., Fink, G. D., Johnson, A. K., Brody, M. J. 1977. Prevention of the development of renal hypertension by anteroventral third ventricular tissue lesions. *Circ. Res.* 40: (Suppl. I) I110–17
15. Buggy, J., Johnson, A. K. 1977. Preoptic-hypothalamic periventricular lesions: thirst deficits and hypernatremia. *Am. J. Physiol.* 233:R44–52
16. Bunag, R., Eferakeya, A. 1976. Immediate hypertensive after effects of posterior hypothalamic lesions in awake rats with spontaneous, renal, or DOCA hypertension. *Cardiovasc. Res.* 10:663–71
17. Bunag, R. D., Eferakeya, A. E., Langdon, D. S. 1975. Enhancement of hypothalamic pressor responses in spontaneously hypertensive rats. *Am. J. Physiol.* 288:217–22
18. Bunag, R. D., Riley, E., Montello, M. 1976. Sustained pressor responsiveness to prolonged hypothalamic stimulation in awake rats. *Am. J. Physiol.* 231:1708–15
19. Carey, R. M., Dacey, R. G., Jane, J. A., Winn, H. R., Ayers, C. R., Tyson, G. W. 1979. Production of sustained hypertension by lesions of the nucleus tractus solitarii of the American Foxhound. *Hypertension* 1:246–54
20. Chalmers, J. P. 1978. Nervous system and hypertension. *Clin. Sci. Mol. Med.* 55: (Suppl. 4) 45–56S
21. Cowley, A. W., Laird, J. F., Guyton, A. C. 1973. Role of the baroreceptor reflex in daily control of arterial blood pressure and other variables in dogs. *Circ. Res.* 32:564–76
22. Crofton, J. T., Share, L., Shade, R. E., Allen, C., Tarnowski, D. 1978. Vasopressin in the rat with spontaneous hypertension. *Am. J. Physiol.* 235: H361–66
23. Crofton, J. T., Share, L., Shade, R. E., Lee-Kwon, W. J., Manning, M., Sawyer, W. J. 1979. The importance of vasopressin in the development and maintenance of DOC-salt hypertension in the rat. *Hypertension* 1:31–38
24. Dahlstrom, A., Fuxe, K. 1964. Evidence for the existence of monoamine-containing neurons in the central nervous system. I. Demonstration of monoamines in the cell bodies of brainstem neurons. *Acta Physiol. Scand.* 62: (Suppl. 232) 1–55
25. Dahlstrom, A., Fuxe, K. 1965. Evidence for the existence of monoamine neurons in the central nervous system. II. Experimentally induced changes in the intraneuronal amine levels of bulbosipinal neuron system. *Acta Physiol. Scand.* 64: (Suppl. 247) 1–36
26. deChamplain, J. Jr., Van Amerigen, M. R. 1973. Role of sympathetic fibers and of adrenal medulla in the maintenance of cardiovascular homeostasis in normotensive and hypertensive rats. In *Frontiers in Catecholamine Research,* ed. E. Usdin, S. Snyder, pp. 859–64. NY: Pergamon Press. 1219 pp.
27. Doba, N., Reis, D. J. 1974. Role of central and peripheral adrenergic mechanisms in neurogenic hypertension produced by brainstem lesions in rat. *Circ. Res.* 34:293–301
28. Doba, N., Reis, D. J. 1973. Acute fulminating neurogenic hypertension produced by brainstem lesions in the rat. *Circ. Res.* 32:584–93
29. DeJong, W., Zandberg, P., Wignen, H., Nijkamp, F. P., Bohhus, B., Versteeg, D. H. G. 1979. See Ref. 7, pp. 165–72
30. Elghozi, J. L., Altman, J., Devynck, M. A., Liard, J. F., Grunfeld, J. P., Meyer, P. 1976. Lack of hypotensive effect on central injections of angiotensin inhibitors in spontaneously hypertensive (SH) and normotensive rats. *Clin. Sci. Mol. Med.* 51: (Suppl. 3) 385–89s
31. Estrugamou, M., de la Riva, I. J. 1978. Cardiovascular reactivity and neurogenic tone in hypertension derived from renal artery stenosis and contralateral nephrectomy in rats. *Acta Physiol. Lat. Am.* 27:231–38
32. Ferrario, C. M., Barnes, K. L., Szilagy, J. E., Conomy, J. P. 1979. See Ref. 7, pp. 85–101
33. Ferrario, C. M., McCubbin, J. W., Page, I. H. 1969. Hemodynamic characteristics of chronic experimental neurogenic hypertension in unanesthetized dogs. *Circ. Res.* 24:911–22
34. Fink, G. D., Buggy, J., Haywood, J. R., Johnson, A. K., Brody, M. J. 1978. Hemodynamic responses to electrical stimulation of areas of rat forebrain containing angiotensin on osmosensi-

tive sites. *Am. J. Physiol.* 235:H445–51

35. Fink, G. D., Haywood, J. R., Bryan, W. J., Packwood, W., Brody, M. J. 1979. Central site for pressor activity of blood-borne angiotensin in rat. *Fed. Proc.* 38:1233
36. Folkow, B. G., Hallback, M. I. L. 1977. Physiopathology of spontaneous hypertension in rats. In *Hypertension—Physiopathology and Treatment,* ed. J. Genest, E. Koiw, O. Kuchel, pp. 507–29. NY: McGraw-Hill. 1208 pp.
37. Folkow, B., Rubinstein, E. H. 1966. Cardiovascular effects of acute and chronic stimulation of the hypothalamic defense area in the rat. *Acta Physiol. Scand.* 68:48–57
38. Friedman, R., Iwai, J. 1976. Genetic predisposition and stress-induced hypertension. *Science* 193:161–62
39. Fuxe, K. 1965. Evidence for the existence of monoamine neurons in the central nervous system. IV. Distribution of monoamine nerve terminals in the central nervous system. *Acta Physiol. Scand.* 64: (Suppl. 247) 37–85
40. Ganten, D., Hutchinson, J. S., Schelling, P. 1975. The intrinsic brain iso-renin-angiotensin system in the rat: its possible role in central mechanisms of blood pressure regulation. *Clin. Sci. Mol. Med.* 48: (Suppl. 2) 265–68s
41. Ganten, D., Speck, G. 1978. Commentary: The brain renin-angiotensin system: a model for the synthesis of peptides in the brain. *Biochem. Pharmacol.* 27:2379–90
42. Ganten, D., Stock, G. 1978. Humoral and neurohumoral aspects of blood pressure regulation: focus on angiotensin. *Klin. Wochenschr.* 56: (Suppl. I) 31–42
43. Gianutsos, G., Moore, K. E. 1978. Epinephrine contents of sympathetic ganglia in brain regions of spontaneously hypertensive rats at different ages. *Proc. Soc. Exp. Biol. Med.* 158:45–49
44. Gildenberg, P. L., Ferrario, C. M. 1977. See Ref. 10, pp. 157–64
45. Gordon, F. J., Brody, M. J., Fink, G. D., Buggy, J., Johnson, A. K. 1979. Role of central catecholamines in the control of blood pressure and drinking behavior. *Brain Res.* In press
46. Gordon, F. J., Haywood, J. R., Brody, M. J., Mann, J. F. E., Ganten, D., Johnson, A. K. 1979. Effect of anteroventral third ventricle (AV3V) lesions on Okamoto strain and stroke-prone spontaneously hypertensive rats. *Jpn. Heart J.* In press
47. Gordon, F. J., Haywood, J. R., Johnson, A. K., Brody, M. J. 1979. Effect of anteroventral third ventricle (AV3V) lesions on the development of hypertension in spontaneously hypertensive rats (SHR). *Fed. Proc.* 38:1233
48. Gronon, R. J., York, D. H. 1979. Effects of chronic intraventricular administration of angiotensin II on drinking behavior and blood pressure. *Pharmacol. Biochem. Behav.* 10:121–26
49. Haddy, F., Pamnani, M., Clough, D. 1978. Review: The sodium-potassium pump in volume expanded hypertension. *Clin. Exp. Hypertens.* 1:295–336
50. Haeusler, G. 1976. Central adrenergic neurons in experimental hypertension. In *Regulation of Blood Pressure by the Central Nervous System,* ed. G. Onesti, M. Fernandez, K. E. Kim, pp. 53–64. NY: Grune & Stratton. 484 pp.
51. Haeusler, G., Finch, L., Thoenen, H. 1972. Central adrenergic neurons and the initiation and development of experimental hypertension. *Experientia* 28: 1200–3
52. Hallback, M. 1975. Consequence of social isolation on blood pressure, cardiovascular reactivity, and design in spontaneously hypertensive rats. *Acta Physiol. Scand.* 93:455–65
53. Hallback, M. 1975. Interaction between central neurogenic mechanisms and changes in cardiovascular design in primary hypertension. *Acta Physiol. Scand.* (Suppl. 424) 1–59
54. Hallback, M., Folkow, B. 1974. Cardiovascular responses to acute mental "stress" in spontaneously hypertensive rats. *Acta Physiol. Scand.* 90:684–98
55. Hartle, D. K., Haywood, J. R., Shaffer, R. A., Johnson, A. K., Brody, M. J. 1979. The effect of anteroventral third ventricle (AV3V) lesions on plasma renin activity in the Grollman model of renal hypertension. *Fed. Proc.* 38:1233
56. Haywood, J. R., Fink, G. D., Buggy, J., Phillips, M. I., Brody, M. J. 1979. The area postrema plays no role in the pressor action of angiotensin in the rat. *Am. J. Physiol.* Submitted
57. Haywood, J. R., Patel, N. P., Mahoney, L. T., Touw, K. B., Johnson, A. K., Corry, R. J., Brody, M. J. 1979. Afferent renal nerves in the pathogenesis of experimental hypertension. *Fed. Proc.* 38:883
58. Hecht, K., Van-Hai, N., Moritz, V., Hecht, T. 1976. The importance of stress intensity for the emotional and vascular reactivity, in particular for

blood pressure regulation. *Acta Biol. Med. Germ.* 35:23–33

59. Henning, M. 1975. Central sympathetic transmitters and hypertension. *Clin. Sci. Mol. Med.* 48: (Suppl. 2) 195–203S
60. Hutchinson, J. S., Schelling, P., Ganten, D. 1975. Effect of centrally administered angiotensin II and P113 on blood pressure in conscious rats. *Pfluegers Arch.* 355: (Suppl.) R28
61. Inagami, T., Yokosawa, H., Hirose, S. 1978. Definitive evidence of renin in rat brain by affinity chromatographic separation from portease. *Clin. Sci. Mol. Med.* 55: (Suppl. 4) 121–24S
62. Jandhyala, B. S., Lokhandwala, M. F., Nandiwada, P., Buckley, J. P. 1979. Circulatory effects of chronic administration of angiotensin II into the cerebrolateral ventricles of dogs: studies on the development of an experimental model of hypertension. *Hypertension* 1:219–27
63. Johnson, A. K., Buggy, J. 1977. A critical analysis of the site of action for the dipsogenic effect of angiotensin II. See Ref. 10, pp. 357–86
64. Johnson, A. K., Hoffman, W. E., Buggy, J. 1978. Attenuated pressor responses to intracranially injected stimuli and altered antidiuretic activity following preoptic-hypothalamic periventricular ablation. *Brain Res.* 157: 161–66
65. Johnson, A. K., Simon, W., Schaz, K., Ganten, U., Ganten, D., Mann, J. F. E. 1978. Increased blood pressure responses to central angiotensin II in spontaneously hypertensive rats. *Klin. Wochenschr.* 56: (Suppl. I) 47–49
66. Judy, W. V., Watanabe, A. M., Henry, D. P., Besch, H. R. Jr., Murphy, W. R., Hockel, G. M. 1976. Sympathetic nerve activity: role in regulation of blood pressure in the spontaneously hypertensive rat. *Circ. Res.* 38: (Suppl. II) II21–29
67. Karppanen, H., Lahovaara, S., Mannisto, P., Vapaatalo, H. 1975. Plasma renin activity and *in vitro* synthesis of aldosterone by the adrenal glands of rats with spontaneous, renal, or pinealectomy-induced hypertension. *Acta Physiol. Scand.* 94:184–88
68. Kiprov, D., Orbetzova, V., Dimitrov, T. 1977. Brain and kidney renin-angiotensin activity in spontaneously hypertensive rats. *Cor Vasa* 19:141–50
69. Kneupfer, M. M., Gordon, F. J., Johnson, A. K., Brody, M. J. 1979. Identification of descending cardiovascular pathways from the anteroventral third ventricle (AV3V) region. *Fed. Proc.* 38:1446
70. Deleted in proof
71. Krieger, E. M. 1964. Neurogenic hypertension in the rat. *Circ. Res.* 15:511–21
72. Kirsch, B., Leonhardt, H., Buckheim, W. 1978. The functional and structural border between the CSF and blood milieu in the circumventricular organs (organum vasculosum, laminae terminalis, subfornical organs, area postrema) of the rat. *Cell Tiss. Res.* 195:485–98
73. Kubo, T., Hashimoto, M. 1978. Effects of intraventricular and introspinal 6-hydroxydopamine on blood pressure of spontaneously hypertensive rats. *Arch. Int. Pharmacodyn.* 232:166–76
74. Kubo, T., Hashimoto, M., Ohashi, T. 1978. Effects of intraventricular and intraspinal 6-hydroxydopamine on blood pressure of renal hypertensive rats. *Arch. Int. Pharmacodyn.* 234:270–78
75. Kvetnancky, R., McCarty, R., Thoa, N. B., Lake, C. R., Kopin, I. J. 1979. Sympatho-adrenal responses of spontaneously hypertensive rats to immobilization stress. *Am. J. Physiol.* 236: H457–62
76. Laborit, H., Valette, N., Laurent, J. 1975. Effect of a monoamine oxidase inhibitor (nialamide) on arterial hypertension following exposure to aversive stimuli and on cerebral beta-glucuronidase activity. *Aggressologie* 16:355–60
77. Lais, L. T., Bhatnagar, R. K., Brody, M. J. 1974. Inhibition by dark adaptation of the progress of hypertension in the spontaneously hypertensive rat (SHR). *Circ. Res.* 34/35: (Suppl. I) I155–60
78. Lamprecht, R., St. Richardson, J., Williams, R. B., Kopin, I. J. 1977. 6-Hydroxydopamine destruction of central adrenergic neurons prevents or reverses developing DOCA-salt hypertension in rats. *J. Neural Transm.* 40:149–58
79. Loewy, A. D., Panneton, W. M. 1979. Effects of 6-hydroxydopamine on development of hypertension in the spontaneously hypertensive rat. *Fed. Proc.* 38:1447
80. Mahoney, L. T., Haywood, J. R., Packwood, W. J., Johnson, A. K., Brody, M. J. 1978. Effect of anteroventral third ventricle (AV3V) lesions on regional hemodynamic responses to renal afferent nerve stimulation. *Circulation* 58: (Suppl. II) II68
81. Mann, J. F. E., Phillips, M. I., Dietz, R., Haebara, H., Ganten, D. 1978. Effects of central and peripheral angio-

tensin blockade in hypertensive rats. *Am. J. Physiol.* 234:H629–37

82. McCarty, R., Kopin, I. J. 1978. Changes in plasma catecholamines and behavior of rats during the anticipation of foot shock. *Horm. Behav.* 11:248–57
83. Mohring, J. 1978. Neurohypophyseal vasopressor principle: vasopressor hormone as well as antidiuretic hormone? *Klin. Wochenschr.* 56: (Suppl.) 71–80
84. Mohring, J., Kintz, J., Schoun, J. 1978. Role of vasopressin in blood pressure control of spontaneously hypertensive rats. *Clin. Sci. Mol. Med.* 55: (Suppl. 4) 247–50s
85. Mohring, J., Mohring, B., Petri, M., Haack, D. 1978. Plasma vasopressin concentrations and effects of vasopressin antiserum on blood pressure in rats with malignant two-kidney Goldblatt hypertension. *Circ. Res.* 42:17–22
86. Mohring, J., Mohring, B., Petri, M., Haack, D. 1977. Vasopressor role of ADH in the pathogenesis of malignant DOC hypertension. *Am. J. Physiol.* 232:F260–69
87. Mow, M. T., Haywood, J. R., Johnson, A. K., Brody, M. J. 1978. The role of the anteroventral third ventricle (AV3V) in development of neurogenic hypertension. *Soc. Neurosci. Abstr.* 4:23
88. Nagaoka, A., Lovenberg, W. 1977. Regional changes in the activities of of the adrenergic biosynthetic enzymes in the brains of hypertensive rats. *Eur. J. Pharmacol.* 43:297–306
89. Nathan, M. A., Reis, D. J. 1977. Chronic labile hypertension produced by lesions of the nucleus tractus solitarii in the cat. *Circ. Res.* 40:72–81
90. Nathan, M. A., Reis, D. J. 1975. Fulminating arterial hypertension with pulmonary edema from release of adrenomedullary catecholamines after lesions of the anterior hypothalamus in the rat. *Circ. Res.* 37:226–35
91. Nathan, M. A., Severini, W. H., Tucker, L. W., Reis, D. J. 1978. Enhancement of conditioned arterial pressure responses in cats after brainstem lesion. *Science* 201:71–73
92. Olson, L., Fuxe, K. 1972. Further mapping out of central noradrenaline neuron systems: projections of the "subcoeruleus" area. *Brain Res.* 43:289–95
93. Petty, M. A., Reid, J. L. 1979. Catecholamine synthesizing enzymes in brainstem and hypothalamus during the development of renovascular hypertension. *Brain Res.* 163:277–88
94. Petty, M. A., Reid, J. L. 1977. Changes in noradrenaline concentration in brainstem and hypothalamic nuclei during the development of renovascular hypertension. *Brain Res.* 136:376–80
95. Phillips, M. I. 1978. Current review: angiotensin in the brain. *Neuroendocrinology* 25:354–70
96. Phillips, M. I., Felix, D., Hoffman, W. E., Ganten, D. 1977. Angiotensin-sensitive sties in the brain ventricular systems. In *Neuroscience Symposia,* ed. W. Cowan, J. A. Ferendilli, Vol. 2, pp. 308–39. Bethesda Md: Soc. Neurosci.
97. Phillips, M. I., Hoffman, W. E. 1977. See Ref. 10, pp. 325–56
98. Phillips, M. I., Deshmukh, P., Larsen, W. 1977. Are the central effects of angiotensin due to peripheral angiotensin II crossing the blood brain barrier? *Soc. Neurosci. Abstr.* 3:510
99. Phillips, M. I., Mann, J. F., Haebara, H., Hoffman, W. E., Dietz, R., Schelling, P., Ganten, D. 1977. Lowering of hypertension by central saralasin in the absence of plasma renin. *Nature* 270:445–47
100. Phillips, M. I., Phipps, J., Hoffman, W. E., Leavitt, M. 1975. Reduction of blood pressure by intracranial injection of angiotensin blocker (P113) in spontaneously hypertensive rats (SHR). *Physiologist* 18:350
101. Ramsay, D. J. 1979. The brain renin angiotensin system: a reevaluation. *Soc. Neurosci.* 4:313–22
102. Reis, D. J., Joh, T. H., Nathan, M. A., Renaud, B., Snyder, D. W. Talman, W. T. 1979. Nucleus tractus solatarii: catecholaminergic innervation in normal and abnormal control of arterial pressure.
103. Saavedra, J. M. 1979. Adrenalin levels in brainstem nuclei and effects of a PNMT inhibitor on spontaneously hypertensive rats. *Brain Res.* 166:283–92
104. Saavedra, J. M., Grobecker, H., Axelrod, J. 1978. Changes in central catecholinergic neurons in the spontaneously (genetic) hypertensive rat. *Circ. Res.* 42:529–34
105. Scher, A. M. 1977. Carotid and aortic regulation of arterial blood pressure. *Circulation* 56:521–28
106. Schmid, P. G., Mark, A. L., Takeshita, A., Van Orden, D. 1979. Plasma vasopressin in the Dahl strain of genetically hypertensive rat. *Fed. Proc.* 38:1302
107. Snyder, D. W., Doba, N., Reis, D. J. 1978. Regional distribution of blood flow during arterial hypertension produced by lesion of the nucleus tractus solitarii in rats. *Circ. Res.* 42:87–91

108. Snyder, D. W., Nathan, M. A., Reis, D. J. 1978. Chronic lability of arterial pressure produced by selective destruction of the catecholamine innervation of the nucleus tractus solitarii in the rat. *Circ. Res.* 43:662–71
109. Sudakov, K. V. 1977. Acute experimental emotional stress and natural history of arterial hypertension. *Physiol. Behav.* 19:213–21
110. Swanson, L. W., Kucharczyk, J., Mogenson, G. J. 1978. Autoradiographic evidence for pathways from the medial preoptic area to the midbrain involved in the drinking response to angiotensin II. *J. Comp. Neurol.* 178:645–60
111. Sweet, C. S., Columbo, J. M., Gaul, S. L. 1976. Central antihypertensive effects of inhibitors of the renin-angiotensin system in rats. *Am. J. Physiol.* 231:1794–99
112. Sweet, C. S., Columbo, J. M., Gaul, S. L., Weitz, D., Wenger, H. C. 1977. See Ref. 10, pp. 283–92
113. Takeda, K., Bunag, R. D. 1978. Sympathetic hyperactivity during hypothalamic stimulation in spontaneously hypertensive rats. *J. Clin. Invest.* 62: 642–48
114. Takeshita, A., Mark, A. L. 1978. Neurogenic contribution to hindquarters vasoconstriction during high sodium intake in the Dahl strain of genetically hypertensive rat. *Circ. Res.* 43: (Suppl. I) I86–91
115. Touw, K. B., Fink, G., Haywood, J. R., Shaffer, R. A., Brody, M. J. 1979. Elevated neurogenic vasoconstrictor tone is the mechanism of hypertension in rats with aortic baroreceptor deafferentation. *Fed. Proc.* 38:1232
116. Wickre, C., McDonald, W. J., Ban, D., Moffitt, B., Aumann, S. K. 1978. Blood pressure reduction in the spontaneously hypertensive rats induced by chronic intracerebroventricular infusion of angiotensin antagnoist. *Endocrin. Soc. Program* 60:178
117. Yamori, Y. 1976. Neurogenic mechanisms of spontaneous hypertension. See Ref. 50, pp. 65–76
118. Yamori, Y., Matsumoto, M., Yamabe, H., Okamoto, K. 1969. Augmentation of spontaneous hypertension by chronic stress in rats. *Jpn. Circ. J.* 33:399–409
119. Yen, T. T., Pearson, D. V., Powell, C. E., Kirschner, G. L. 1978. Thermal stress elevates systolic blood pressure of spontaneously hypertensive rats. *Life Sci.* 22:359–62
120. Ylatalo, P., Karppanen, H., Paasonon, M. K. 1974. Is the area postrema a control center of blood pressure? *Nature* 247:58–59
121. Zandberg, P., Palkovits, M., DeJong, W. 1977. The area postrema and control of arterial blood pressure; absence of hypertension after excision of the area postrema in rats. *Pfluegers Arch.* 372:169–73

COMPARATIVE AND INTEGRATIVE PHYSIOLOGY

COMPARATIVE AND INTEGRATIVE PHYSIOLOGY

Introduction

The treatment of the reproductive endocrinology of nonmammalian vertebrates begun in the Comparative Physiology Section of Volume 41 is concluded here with a consideration of birds. New topics introduced in the present section deal with the comparative physiology of temperature regulation and with insect endocrinology. The four reviews comprising this section once again provide us with the opportunity for considering animals whose functional capabilities may differ quantitatively or qualitatively from those evident in more conventional experimental subjects. The reviews on avian reproductive endocrinology and temperature regulation introduce some environmental and behavioral considerations important for the understanding of the various physiological processes under discussion. Those on insect endocrinology deal with mechanisms of chemical coordination and control in a vast and very important group of animals whose physiological processes have evolved quite independently of those of vertebrates. Taken together the four reviews remind us of the resourcefulness of nature and of the fact that choice of experimental animal is an important and frequently very useful variable in physiological studies.

William R. Dawson
Section Editor

Ann. Rev. Physiol. 1980: 42:457–72

REPRODUCTIVE ENDOCRINOLOGY OF BIRDS

❖1280

Donald S. Farner and John C. Wingfield

Department of Zoology, University of Washington, Seattle, Washington 98195

INTRODUCTION

Although the origin of reproductive endocrinology can be traced to the classical transplant experiments of Berthold (14) with roosters, the contemporary research effort in avian reproductive endocrinology is small compared with that on mammals. A conspicuous consequence thereof is the relative unavailability of generally applicable microassays for avian FSH, TSH, ACTH, and prolactin. This is unfortunate since birds, with the same glands, hormones, and hypothalamic components, offer experimental opportunities for the study of certain endocrine functions and relationships that can be approached only with difficulty in mammals.

Despite the much smaller literature, this brief review still cannot do justice to the depth and diversity of the subject. Therefore we concentrate on the reproductive endocrinology of certain temperate-zone finches that use at least some phase of the annual photocycle as predictive information in the primary control of the annual cycle (45, 50–53). Since we have been parsimonious in citation of the literature the reader is referred to several recent reviews of avian reproductive biology (45, 53, 56, 57, 114, 116, 129). We have not considered the extensive and controversial literature, based largely on investigations on the domestic fowl, on ovulation and oviposition. Useful insights into the endocrine basis of these functions may be found in (62, 154).

The survival of species that breed in the annually periodic environments of middle and high latitudes requires neuroendocrine control systems that initiate the annual development of the reproductive system with precision sufficient to assure that young will be produced at a time when trophic resources, and day lengths for their exploitation, are optimal. These systems must also discontinue reproductive effort on a schedule that minimizes late, unsuccessful attempts.

0066-4278/80/0315-0457$01.00

The control systems also have critical roles with respect to other phases and events of the annual cycle—prenuptial molt; vernal migratory hyperphagia, fattening and migration itself; postnuptial molt; the autumnal migratory complex; and hiemal fattening if it occurs in the species. Selection favors a timing of these events that optimizes their sequence and temporal relationships with respect to environmental cycles and avoids coincidence of functions and events that are temporally or ergonically incompatible (50). For example, migration and the active reproductive phase are temporally incompatible. In most species, molt is ergonically incompatible with migration and, in many species, with a wintering phase involving greater thermoregulatory expenditures of energy while trophic resources and day length in which to exploit them are reduced.

The use of day length in the control of annual cycles has been demonstrated in about 60 avian species. It is assumed to be rather general among species of middle and high latitudes, though its role in transequatorial migrants is uncertain. The minimum difference in day length detectable by avian photoperiodic control systems is not known, but probably only a small fraction of the more than 8,000 species of birds inhabit areas where changes in day length are sufficient to serve as effective information. Control systems with photoperiodic components have probably evolved many times among birds. Systems that appear functionally similar may show different characteristics that reflect their differences in origin (50, 54).

ENDOCRINE CONTROL OF REPRODUCTION

For more than two decades the hypothalamus has been known to play a central role in the regulation of secretion of gonadotropins (5). Neural elements in the tuberal region and also in regions dorsal and anterior to it, including supraoptic and preoptic areas, are essentially involved (e.g. 5, 38, 61, 107, 136, 139). It appears that a single gonadotropin-releasing hormone (Gn-RF) is secreted by the avian hypothalamus; factors causing the release of LH and FSH are chromatographically similar, not only to each other, but also to their mammalian counterparts (97, 98, 100); synthetic LHRH increases secretion of LH (18, 19, 64) and FSH (64, 71, 73). LHRH may have a direct role in the induction of female reproductive behavior (33).

The vascular relationship between the hypothalamus and the anterior pituitary gland involves separate portal supplies to the cephalic and caudal lobes (46, 160, 163). Vessels from the capillary bed of the anterior median eminence supply the cephalic lobe, which contains the β cells, a presumed source of FSH; portal vessels from the posterior median eminence supply the caudal lobe wherein occur the γ cells, a presumed source of LH (160). Evidence that Gn-RH from preoptic neurons reaches the anterior median eminence through fibers of the supraoptico-paraventriculo-hypophysial tract (20, 26, 27, 138) and that Gn-RH from neurons of the infundibular nucleus complex reaches the median eminence via fibers of the tubero-infundibular tract (122, 128) may provide a basis for separate controls of the secretion of LH and FSH using a single neurohormone. Purified follicle-stimulating hormone (FSH) and luteinizing hormone (LH) from the domestic fowl and domestic turkey have amino-acid compositions similar to those of mammals and appear to be generally homologous with the latter (49, 66, 74). FSH from the domestic fowl induces proliferation and development of spermatogonia and Sertoli cells, with little effect on the cells of Leydig (22, 96). The effects of avian FSH on the avian ovary have not been studied; mammalian gonadotropins induce development of the ovarian follicle, though less effectively than crude avian pituitary extracts (e.g. 116).

LH in the male primarily induces differentiation of the testicular interstitium (22, 96) and stimulates androgen secretion (119). Mammalian LH increases levels of progesterone and testosterone in the plasma and thecal cells of laying hens but has no effect on plasma levels of estradiol (153), whereas LH and FSH together increase plasma levels of progesterone in female domestic turkeys (29). The effects of avian LH have not been studied.

Testosterone is a major secretory product of the cells of Leydig as is estradiol-17β of the thecal cells of the ovary (130, 131, 141, 142). Sertoli cells may also be steroidogenic (116). Testosterone, possibly secreted by the ovary, has been identified in the plasma of hens (1, 147) and measured by radioimmunoassay in the plasma of females of several feral species (167).

Androgens have been identified definitively in the plasma of only a few avian species. In the plasma of male *Columba livia,* androstenedione and also dehydroepiandrosterone occur in greater concentrations than testosterone (147). Several metabolites of testosterone, including 5α and 5β androstanediol and DHT, have been demonstrated in the plasma of a wild and a domestic strain of mallard, *Anas platyrhynchos* (92). In addition 5α and 5β reductase activity occurs in the secondary sex organs, anterior pituitary, and central nervous system of the European starling (*Sturnus vulgaris*) and domestic fowl (72, 117, 132, 133). Until more species have been studied, caution should be exercised in assuming testosterone to be the major functional androgen in birds. Synthesis of estrogen may occur principally in the small ovarian follicles and/or in the ovarian stroma, though a possible increase in secretion of estradiol by the large follicles at the time of ovulation cannot be precluded (21, 34, 152). Estradiol has been identified definitively only in the plasma of domestic fowl and turkey (1, 142).

Progesterone occurs in the plasma of females (1, 68, 140, 142); the thecal cells of the ovarian follicles appear to be principal sites of synthesis (41, 67). The post-ovulatory follicle does show 3β-hydroxysteroid dehydrogenase activity but this declines rapidly during the first 15 hr after ovulation (2). A corpus luteum is not formed; the follicle regresses within a week (70).

Whether the interrenal gland may also secrete testosterone and estradiol-17β is not yet known, but in the plasma of castrated male white-crowned sparrows, *Zonotrichia leucophrys gambelii,* neither testosterone nor 17β-hydroxy-5α-androstan-3-one (DHT) has been detected (120), which indicates that the interrenal gland is at most a minor source of androgen. However, since the plasma level of progesterone was unaffected, the interrenal gland may be a major source of this hormone, at least in males.

The role of negative feedback by sex hormones in the regulation of secretion of LRF and gonadotropins has not been investigated extensively. In the Japanese quail, *Coturnix coturnix,* as in most birds studied, the "resting" plasma level of immunoreactive LH (irLH) is higher in males than in females (36). Testosterone appears to exert a negative feedback at the hypothalamic level; estrogens in laying females may function mainly at the level of the adenohypophysis, though estrogenic effects at the hypothalamic level are not precluded (36). Further evidence suggests that when gonadal growth is initiated by long days in Japanese quail, the hypothalamo-pituitary complex becomes less sensitive to feedback by androgens, thus allowing the maintenance of gonadotropin secretion under the influence of increasing testosterone levels (39). This is consistent with observations on the white-crowned sparrow (110, 118) and the American tree sparrow, *Spizella arborea* (35, 165, 166). In addition to a negative feedback by testosterone at the hypothalamic level there may be a transient positive feedback on the adenohypophysis that increases its responsiveness to LRF (37).

The functions of prolactin are poorly understood, at least in part because of the lack of a suitable microassay. Published inferences of seasonal changes in rates of secretion based on changes in pituitary concentration must be viewed with great caution (160). Among the functions attributed to this hormone are broodiness (e.g. 160); an antigonadal effect (e.g. 30, 116, 124); development of brood patch in synergy with estrogen (e.g. 116); secretion of crop milk by both sexes in columbiform species (e.g. 146); and induction of migratory metabolism and behavior (e.g. 123). The secretion of prolactin is regulated by a stimulatory factor, PRF (31, 76, 109, 125, 135).

ANNUAL GONADAL CYCLES AND THEIR CONTROL

Annual gonadal cycles result from interplays of information from both external and internal sources. For the so-called photoperiodic species the primary external source of information is day length, which initiates the vernal development of the gonads soon enough to allow the reproductive effort to occur at the most advantageous time for rearing of the young. Secondary external sources include (*a*) seasonal changes in the immediate environment that accelerate or retard the course of the photoperiodically induced gonadal cycle, so that it coincides with the local season and (*b*) conditions essential to the induction, in the females of most birds, of the last few days of ovarian maturation. Abundant field observations indicate that the testes become functional earlier than the ovaries; thus the fine-tuning of the onset of reproductive effort is effected through the interplay of (*a*) and (*b*), above, in the female. Reproduction begins as early as the season permits. Within these categories of information we include the sequential behavioral interactions between male and female of demonstrated importance (88–90, 111, 155) in the final phases of the development of reproductive function in domesticated female canaries and ring doves. Although there are few experimental data (e.g. 79, 145), interactions of this type may be assumed to be common in feral species.

Internal information includes feedback effects of peripheral hormones on the central control system and endogenous rhythms. Among the latter, the most conspicuous are circadian. It is now well established (e.g. 53), for example, that the measurement of day length involves a system with at least one circadian component. The question of endogenous seasonal (circannual) periodicities and their role in the annual gonadal cycle of photoperiodic species is discussed briefly below.

Day Length and Annual Cycles

In the males of at least many photoperiodic species the rates of growth and development of the testis (44, 45, 57, 59) and of its endocrine function (110), respectively mediated through increased plasma levels of FSH and LH, are functions of day length beyond a certain minimum duration. Under constant stimulatory daily photoperiods, testicular growth is an approximately logarithmic function of time until half of ultimate size is attained. The logarithmic growth rate is generally a positive function of day length over the range of natural day length experienced by the species (42, 44, 45, 57, 59). Initially during the logarithmic growth phase in *Z. l. gambelii* a parallel increase occurs in the number of receptor sites for FSH (95). In *Z. l. gambelii* and domesticated *C. coturnix* long days cause increases in plasma levels of LH over several days, after which levels are stabilized by negative feedback from the testes (60, 65, 118). A somewhat similar pattern has been described for FSH in *C. coturnix* (60), though the final stable level after the logarithmic phase of testicular growth is considerably lower than the initial maximum level. The fragmentary information about photostimulated female *C. coturnix* suggests that the temporal patterns for levels of FSH and LH are similar (60). In several photoperiodic species the response to artificial photostimulation is immediate; a single long day causes a measurable increase in LH. However, a change from long to short days is followed by a relatively slow decline (63–65). During both natural testicular development and that induced by artificial long days the increases in plasma levels of LH are followed by increases in gonadal steroid hormones. Maximal levels of testosterone in males of at least several species occur at the time of establishment and defense of territory, courtship, and nesting activity (8, 75, 99, 143, 159, 168–170). These elevated levels are also involved in the induction of secondary sex characteristics, expression of reproductive behavior (115), and vernal migratory fattening and behavior (164, 118). Testosterone, in the presence of FSH, also has a role in the regulation and maintenance of spermatogensis (23, 40).

Little is known of the role of the plasma levels of gonadotropic and sex hormones in the development of the ovary in feral species. In captive females of most species development ceases just short of the phase of yolk deposition (105). Female *Z. leucophrys* under natural conditions attain plasma levels of LH as much as five times greater than those of captives; furthermore, increases in the levels of both DHT and testosterone occur during the time of establishment and defense of territory in which the females participate (168–170).

Plasma estrogen levels also become maximal during ovarian development and egg laying (108, 168–170), during which they have roles in the synthesis of yolk proteins, the development of the oviduct (116, 176, 177), and the induction of female reproductive behavior, including nest building (88, 89, 116, 156). Estrogens also induce the defeatherization and vascularization of the brood patch in passeriform species (7, 88, 155), whereas both progesterone and testosterone appear to be important in nonpasseriforms (102). Estrogens apparently occur only in extremely low concentrations (<40 pg ml^{-1}) in the plasma of males (108, 167–170).

Although termination of the reproductive period in some nonmigratory multiple-clutch photoperiodic species may be effected by decreasing day length (52, 115), it is apparently caused in most species by development of a photorefractory state in which somehow at the hypothalamic or higher level (48) the effect of long days is blocked so that plasma levels of gonadotropins and gondal steroid hormones decrease to minimal levels (65, 118, 158). The various hypotheses of its etiology have been reviewed (55, 57, 115). Except for a revival of the exhaustion hypothesis (158) and the hypothesis of Meier, discussed below, no novelties have appeared since these reviews. Since photostimulated castrates become photorefractory on almost the same schedule as intact birds (118, 157, 166), the mechanism cannot be solely based on feedback effects of gonadal hormones. Photorefractoriness is terminated somehow by short days (25, 45, 50, 55, 87, 161, 173).

Photoreception for the photoperiodic induction of gonadal development in birds is encephalic. The demonstration more than four decades ago (e.g. 9–11) of encephalic photoreceptors in the mallard has been confirmed in at least five additional species (91, 121, 127, 137, 150, 162, 174, 175). The receptors, localized at least primarily in the ventral hypothalamus, have not been identified; they may be structurally unspecialized neural elements (175).

Although not so interpreted by the authors, the first evidence of a circadian component in an avian (*J. hyemalis*) photoperiodic control system was that of Jenner & Engels (101). Since the subsequent demonstration by Hamner (86) of such in *Carpodacus mexicanus,* similar evidence has accumulated for at least six other species (53, 54, 84, 123). It can be assumed therefore that a circadian component is involved in the photoperiodic control of synthesis and release of FSH; indeed, such has been directly demonstrated for LH in domesticated *C. coturnix* (134). It is our view (53, 54) that the chronometric components involved in the photoperiodic control of gonadal function conform generally with the external coincidence model of Bünning (24), as refined by Pittendrigh & Minis (144). In its simplest form as applied to photoperiodic birds, this model assumes an entrainable circadian periodicity in "photosensitivity" in some component of the response system so that each cycle passes through photosensitive and nonphotosensitive phases. Under natural conditions the daily photophase has two functions: (*a*) It entrains the photosensitivity cycle of the bird to a period of 24 hr. (*b*) When it is long enough to coincide with the photosensitive phase of the bird it causes the release of LH and FSH at rates that are positive functions of the duration of the coincidence (53). The same mechanism is apparently used to measure the short days that terminate photorefractoriness (148, 161).

A more elaborate model developed by Meier (123) involves the entrainment of photosensitive phases for release of FSH, LH, and prolactin by a rhythm in plasma concentration of corticosterone, the phase of which is a function of day length. Applied to *Zonotrichia albicollis* the model also proposes that vernal and autumnal migratory fattening, as well as behavior, are functions of changes in phase angle between daily cycles in plasma concentrations of prolactin and corticosterone.

Modifying and Essential Supplementary Information

The literature is replete with evidence of the importance of modifying information and essential supplementary information in the fine-tuning of the reproductive effort to the appropriate phenological phase of the environment and in the culmination of the female cycle (e.g. 57, 88–90, 93, 94, 111). Unfortunately, only a small fraction is derived from experimental investigations and a still smaller fraction contains information on endocrine correlates. A quantitative endocrine indication of the role of modifying information can be obtained by comparison of male *Z. leucophrys* held in outdoor aviaries under natural conditions or subjected to artificial long days in indoor cages, with males in breeding territories (65, 105, 110, 112, 118,

157, 168–171). Testes of males in breeding territories become 10–20% larger and remain functional 10–40 days longer than those in photostimulated caged birds. The plasma concentrations of LH and testosterone are significantly greater in territorial than in captive males, presumably primarily because of the presence of sexually active females. Environmental temperature has a relatively slight effect on testicular growth (113). The possibility that some aspect of conditions of captivity constitutes inhibitory information cannot be excluded.

Since the onset of breeding is controlled by the female it is not surprising that she is affected more by captivity: The development of the ovary in captives rarely proceeds into the phase of yolk deposition (105, 112, 168–171). The ovaries of females in breeding territories require about 10 days to develop to the onset of laying from the stage ordinarily attainable with artificial photostimulation. It is tempting to attribute this to essential supplemental information from a sexually active male, as seems to be the case in several species (e.g. 32, 88–90, 111), and perhaps to other phenological attributes of the environment. However, in captive *Z. l. gambelii,* at least, the final development of the ovary seems to be suppressed by inhibitory information from the retina, for in photostimulated blinded females the ovary and oviduct undergo essentially normal development with plasma levels of LH about twice as great as in caged photostimulated intact females (174).

Many species have the capability of renesting after the loss of a clutch or brood. This is especially important in normally single-clutch species that breed at high latitudes. There the short summer precludes the possibility of rearing two consecutive broods, but it permits a successful replacement clutch and brood if the first is lost early in the season. The only information on the endocrine correlates of renesting comes from studies on female mallards (47) and on *Z. l. gambelii* (171). In mallards the plasma level of LH is conspicuously elevated within 12 hr after loss of clutch, and redevelopment of the ovary begins within three days; a second maximum in plasma testosterone and LH occurs in renesting white-crowned sparrows (171). In *Z. leucophrys,* plasma levels of LH and sex hormones decrease to basal levels at the time of the postnuptial molt and remain so until late winter when the cycle begins anew. In some species, however, the levels of LH and/or testosterone increase in autumn (28, 69, 85, 151). At least in the mallard these autumnal increases are accompanied by sexual behavior.

Endogenous Circannual Periodicities and Photoperiodic Control Systems

Aschoff (3) was first to develop a clear hypothesis specifying that day length in photoperiodic species serves as a *Zeitgeber* that entrains endogenous circannual rhythms into precisely annual cycles (3, 15, 16, 43, 45, 78, 81,

82, 93, 94). This is an attractive hypothesis because the systems that control reproduction have negative feedback components that induce oscillations and because natural selection should favor systems with circannual periods. Although much evidence can be mustered in support of this hypothesis (4, 81, 82), its general applicability to periodic breeding in birds remains controversial (58, 104, 125, 149). Support is derived primarily from extensive demonstration of periodicities, usually somewhat less than annual, in molt, migratory behavior, body weight, and testicular size in birds held on selected constant daily photocycles, such as 12L 12D (15–17, 45, 77–82). The hypothesis rests on formalistic demonstrations that these cycles resemble the outputs of self-sustained oscillators (4, 81); it lacks as yet a statement of the underlying physiological mechanisms. Whether constant daily photocycles constitute the "information-free" environment ultimately necessary for a rigid test of the hypothesis must, in our view, remain open (e.g. 149). To our knowledge, the only experiments on birds conducted in truly constant photic conditions are those on Pekin drakes held in constant light or constant dark (12, 13). The data on the irregular fluctuations in the diameters of the testes have been analyzed by Assenmacher (6). Although an effect of an endogenous circannual periodicity cannot be precluded, the evidence is weak.

We find the photoperiodic induction of as many as five testicular cycles in a year (83, 172) difficult to rationalize with Aschoff's hypothesis, although Gwinner (81, 82, 84) believes that such are consistent with general oscillator theory. Although it may ultimately prove to be only semantic, it is important for now to bear in mind a clear distinction between (*a*) the formal treatment of fluctuations and cycles from the standpoint of oscillator theory and (*b*) their treatment from the standpoint of the causal sequences of physiologic events involved (45, 50, 52, 126). A distinction should also be made between the natural periods and damping properties of control systems, on the one hand, and the overt cycles and fluctuations in gonadal function, molt, migratory function, etc generated by them, on the other (58, 104). We support the suggestion that the role of circadian functions as a basis for circannual cycles deserves further investigation (78, 103, 106, 126).

ACKNOWLEDGMENTS

Some of the investigations on which this chapter is based were supported by the National Science Foundation and The National Institutes of Health. The preparation of the chapter was supported, in part, by Grant No. BMS74-13933 from the National Science Foundation. This review was prepared, in part, while the senior author held an Award for Senior U.S. Scientists, from the Alexander von Humboldt-Stiftung. The authors are grateful to Professor Dr. J. Aschoff and Doctor E. Gwinner (Max-Planck-

Institut für Verhaltensphysiologie, Erling-Andechs) and to Professor Dr. A. Oksche (Zentrum für Anatomie and Cytobiologie, Giessen) for helpful suggestions and discussions. Without assistance in many ways from Mrs. Dorothy C. Farner the preparation of this manuscript would have been impossible. We are most grateful to her.

Literature Cited

1. Arcos, M. 1975. Steroid hormones in the ovarian blood of the laying turkey. *Steroids* 25:169–76
2. Armstrong, D. G., Davidson, M. F., Gilbert, A. B., Wells, J. W. 1977. Activity of 3β-hydroxysteroid dehydrogenase in the post-ovulatory follicle of the domestic fowl (*Gallus domesticus*). *J. Reprod. Fertil.* 49:253–59
3. Aschoff, J. 1955. Jahresperiodik der Fortpflanzung beim Warmblütern. *Stud. Gen.* 8:742–76
4. Aschoff, J., Berthold, P., Gwinner, E., Pohl, H., St. Paul, U. 1980. Biological clocks in birds. In *Proc. Int. Ornithol. Congr. 17th.* In press
5. Assenmacher, I. 1958. Recherches sur le contrôle hypothalamique de la fonction gonadotrope préhypophysaire chez le Canard. *Arch. Anat. Microsc. Morphol. Exp.* 47:447–572
6. Assenmacher, I. 1974. External and internal components of the mechanism controlling reproductive cycles in drakes. *Int. J. Biochron.* 2:117–18
7. Baily, R. E. 1952. The incubation patch of passerine birds. *Condor* 54:121–36
8. Balthazart, J., Hendrick, J. 1976. Annual variation in reproductive behavior, testosterone and plasma FSH levels in the Rouen duck, *Anas platyrhynchos. Gen. Comp. Endocrinol.* 28:171–83
9. Benoit, J. 1935. Nouvelles expériences relatives à la stimulation par la lumière du développement testiculaire chez le Canard. *C. R. Acad. Sci. Paris* 201: 359–62
10. Benoit, J. 1937. Facteurs externes et internes de l'activité sexuelle. II. Étude du mecanisme de la stimulation par la lumière de l'activité testiculaire chez le Canard domestique. Rôle de l'hypophyse. *Bull. Biol. France Belgique* 71: 393–437
11. Benoit, J. 1970. Étude de l'action des radiations visibles sur la gonadostimulation et leur pénétration intracrânienne chez les oiseaux et les mammifères. In *La Photorégulation de la Reproduction chez les Oiseaux et les Mammifères,* ed. J. Benoit, I. Assenmacher, pp. 121–49. Paris: CNRS
12. Benoit, J., Assenmacher, I., Brard, É. 1955. Évolution testiculaire du Canard domestique maintenu à l'obscurité totale pendant une longue durée. *C. R. Acad. Sci. Paris* 241:251–53
13. Benoit, J., Assenmacher, I., Brard, É. 1959. Action d'un éclairement permanent prolongé sur l'évolution testiculaire du Canard pékin. *Arch. Anat. Microsc. Morphol. Exp.* 48:5–12
14. Berthold, A. A. 1849. Transplantation der Hoden. *Arch. Anat. Physiol.* 1849: 42–46
15. Berthold, P. 1974. *Endogene Jahresperiodik.* Konstanz: Universitätsverlag. 46 pp.
16. Berthold, P. 1977. Endogene Steuerung des Vogelzugs. *Vogelwarte* 29: Sonderheft 4–15
17. Berthold, P., Gwinner, E., Klein, H., Westrich, P. 1972. Beziehungen zwischen Zugunruhe und Zugablauf bei Garten- und Mönchsgrasmücke (*Sylvia borin* und *S. atricapilla*). *Z. Tierpsychol.* 30:26–35
18. Bicknell, R. J., Follett, B. K. 1975. A quantitative assay for luteinizing hormone-releasing-hormone (LHRH) using dispersed pituitary cells. *Gen. Comp. Endocrinol.* 26:141–52
19. Bonney, R. C., Cunningham, F. J., Furr, B. J. A. 1974. Effect of synthetic lutenizing hormone releasing hormone on plasma luteinizing hormone in the female domestic fowl, *Gallus domesticus. J. Endocrinol.* 63:539–47
20. Bons, N., Kerdelhue, B., Assenmacher, I. 1978. Immunocytochemical identification of an LHRH-producing system originating in the preoptic nucleus of the duck. *Cell Tiss. Res.* 188:99–106
21. Boucek, R. J., Savard, K. 1970. Steroid formation by the avian ovary *in vitro* (*Gallus domesticus*). *Gen. Comp. Endocrinol.* 15:6–11
22. Brown, N. L., Baylé, J. D., Scanes, C. G., Follett, B. K. 1975. Chicken gonadotrophins: Their effects on the testes of immature and hypophysectomized Japanese quail. *Cell Tiss. Res.* 156:499–520

23. Brown, N. L., Follett, B. K. 1977. Effects of androgen on the testes of intact and hypophysectomized Japanese quail. *Gen. Comp. Endocrinol.* 33: 267–77
24. Bünning, E. 1936. Die endogene Tagesrhythmik als Grundlage der photoperiodische Reaktion. *Ber. Dtsch. Bot. Ges.* 54:590–607
25. Burger, J. W. 1949. A review of experimental investigations on seasonal reproduction in birds. *Wilson Bull.* 61: 211–30
26. Calas, A., Kerdelhue, B., Assenmacher, I., Jutisz, M. 1973. Les axones à LH-RH de l'eminence médiane. Mise en évidence chez le Canard par une technique immunocytochemique. *C. R. Acad. Sci. Paris* 277:2765–68
27. Calas, A., Kerdelhue, B., Assenmacher, I., Jutisz, M., 1974. Les axones à LH-RH de l'èminence médiane. Etude ultrastructurale chez le Canard par une technique immunocytochimique. *C. R. Acad. Sci. Paris* 278:2557–60
28. Campbell, R. R., Ashton, S. A., Follett, B. K., Leatherland, J. F. 1978. Seasonal changes in plasma concentrations of LH in the lesser snow goose (*Anser caerulescens caerulescens*). *Biol. Reprod.* 18:663–68
29. Camper, P. M., Burke, W. H. 1977. Serum estradiol and progesterone levels of the laying turkey hen following acute treatment with mammalian luteinizing hormone or follicle-stimulating hormone. *Gen. Comp. Endocrinol.* 31: 224–32
30. Camper, P. M., Burke, W. H. 1977. The effect of prolactin on reproductive function in female Japanese quail (*Coturnix coturnix japonica*). *Poul. Sci.* 56: 1130–34
31. Chen, C. L., Bixler, E. J., Weber, A. I., Meites, J. 1968. Hypothalamic stimulation of prolactin release from the pituitary of turkey hens and poults. *Gen. Comp. Endocrinol.* 11:489–94
32. Cheng, M.-F. 1974. Ovarian development in the female ring dove in response to stimulation by intact and castrated male ring doves. *J. Endocrinol.* 63: 43–53
33. Cheng, M.-F. 1977. Role of gonadotrophin releasing hormones in the reproductive behaviour of female ring doves (*Streptopelia risoria*). *J. Endocrinol.* 74:37–45
34. Chieffi, G., Botte, V. 1965. The distribution of some enzymes involved in the steroidogenesis of hen's ovary. *Experientia* 21:16–17
35. Cusick, E. K., Wilson, F. E. 1972. On control of spontaneous testicular regression in tree sparrows, *Spizella arborea. Gen. Comp. Endocrinol.* 19:441–56
36. Davies, D. T. 1976. Steroid feedback in the male and female Japanese quail. *J. Endocrinol.* 70:513–14
37. Davies, D. T., Bicknell, R. J. 1976. The effect of testosterone on the responsiveness of the quail's pituitary to luteinizing hormone-releasing hormone (LH-RH) during photoperiodically induced testicular growth. *Gen. Comp. Endocrinol.* 30:487–99
38. Davies, D. T., Follett, B. K. 1975. The neuroendocrine control of gonadotropin release in the Japanese quail. II. The role of the anterior hypothalamus. *Proc. R. Soc. London Ser. B.* 191:303–15
39. Davies, D. T., Goulden, L. P., Follett, B. K., Brown, N. L. 1976. Testosterone feedback on luteinizing hormone (LH) secretion during a photoperiodically induced breeding cycle in Japanese quail. *Gen. Comp. Endocrinol.* 30:477–86
40. Desjardins, C., Turek, F. W. 1977. Effects of testosterone on spermatogenesis and luteinizing hormone release in Japanese quail. *Gen. Comp. Endocrinol.* 33:293–303
41. Dick, H. R., Culbert, J., Wells, J. W., Gilbert, A. B., Davidson, M. F. 1978. Steroid hormones in the postovulatory follicle of the domestic fowl (*Gallus domesticus*). *J. Reprod. Fertil.* 53:103–7
42. Dolnik, V. R. 1963. Kolichestvennoe issledovanie zakonomernostei vesennovo rosta semenikov u neskolkikh vidov vyurkovykh ptits (Fringillidae). *Dokl. Acad. Nauk SSSR* 149:191–93
43. Dolnik, V. R. 1974. Okologodovaya tsiklichnost migratsionnovo otlozheniya zhira, polovoi aktivnosti i linki pri postoyannykh photoperiodakh u zyablika (*Fringilla coelebs*). *Zh. Obshch. Biol.* 34:543–55
44. Dolnik, V. R. 1975. *Migratsionnoe Sostoyaniye Ptits.* Moscow: Akad. Nauk SSSR. 398 pp.
45. Dolnik, V. R. 1976. Fotoperiodizm u ptits. In *Fotoperiodizm Zhivotnykh i Rastenii,* ed. V. A. Zaslavsky, pp. 47–81. Leningrad: Akad. Nauk SSSR
46. Dominic, C. J., Singh, R. M. 1969. Anterior and posterior groups of portal vessels in the avian pituitary. *Gen. Comp. Endocrinol.* 13:22–26
47. Donham, R. S., Dane, C. W., Farner, D. S. 1976. Plasma luteinizing hormone and the development of ovarian follicles after loss of clutch in female mallards

(*Anas platyrhynchos*). *Gen. Comp. Endocrinol.* 29:152–55
48. Erickson, J. E. 1975. *Hypothalamic gonadotropin-releasing hormone and the photoperiodic control of the testes in the white-crowned sparrow,* Zonotrichia leucophrys gambelii. PhD thesis. Univ. Washington, Seattle
49. Farmer, S. W., Papkoff, H., Licht, P. 1975. Purification of turkey gonadotropins. *Biol. Reprod.* 12:415–22
50. Farner, D. S. 1964. The photoperiodic control of reproductive cycles in birds. *Am. Sci.* 52:137–56
51. Farner, D. S. 1970. Predictive functions in the control of annual cycles. *Environ. Res.* 3:119–31
52. Farner, D. S. 1970. Day length as environmental information in the control of reproduction of birds. See Ref. 11, pp. 71–91
53. Farner, D. S. 1975. Photoperiodic controls in the secretion of gonadotropins in birds. *Am. Zool.* 15: Suppl., pp. 117–35
54. Farner, D. S., Donham, R. S., Lewis, R. A., Mattocks, P. W., Darden, T. R., Smith, J. P. 1977. The circadian component in the photoperiodic mechanism of the house sparrow, *Passer domesticus. Physiol. Zool.* 50:247–68
55. Farner, D. S., Follett, B. K. 1966. Light and other environmental factors affecting avian reproduction. *J. Anim. Sci.* 25: Suppl., pp. 90–118
56. Farner, D. S., Follett, B. K. 1979. Reproductive periodicity in birds. In *Hormones and Evolution,* ed. E. J. W. Barrington, pp. 829–72. London: Academic
57. Farner, D. S., Lewis, R. A. 1971. Photoperiodism and reproductive cycles in birds. *Photophysiology* 6:325–70
58. Farner, D. S., Lewis, R. A. 1973. Field and experimental studies of the annual cycles of white-crowned sparrows. *J. Reprod. Fertil.:* Suppl. 19, pp. 35–50
59. Farner, D. S., Wilson, A. C. 1957. A quantitative examination of testicular growth in the white-crowned sparrow. *Biol. Bull.* 113:254–67
60. Follett, B. K. 1976. Plasma follicle-stimulating hormone during photoperiodically induced sexual maturation in male Japanese quail. *J. Endocrinol.* 69:117–26
61. Follett, B. K. 1977. The neuroendocrinology of photoperiodism in birds. In *Proc. First Int. Symp. Avian Endocrinol.,* ed. B. K. Follett, pp. 20–22. Bangor, Wales: Univ. Coll. North Wales
62. Follett, B. K. 1978. Photoperiodism and seasonal breeding in birds and mammals. In *Control of Ovulation,* ed. G. E. Lamming, D. B. Crighton, pp. 267–93. London: Butterworths
63. Follett, B. K., Davies, D. T. 1977. The photoperiodic induction of gonadotrophin release in quail: Events during the first long day and their blockade by sodium pentobarbitone. *J. Endocrinol.* 72:15P
64. Follett, B. K., Davies, D. T., Gledhill, B. 1977. Photoperiodic control of reproduction in Japanese quail: Changes in gonadotrophin secretion on the first day of induction and their pharmacological blockade. *J. Endocrinol.* 74:449–60
65. Follett, B. K., Farner, D. S., Mattocks, P. W. 1975. Luteinizing hormone in the plasma of white-crowned sparrows, *Zonotrichia leucophrys gambelii,* during artificial photostimulation. *Gen. Comp. Endocrinol.* 26:126–34
66. Follett, B. K., Scanes, C. G., Nicholls, T. J. 1972. Hormones-glycoproteiques-hypophysaires. *Colloq. Inserm (Paris),* pp. 193–211
67. Furr, B. J. A. 1969. Identification of steroids in the ovaries and plasma of laying hens and the site of production of progesterone in the ovary. *Gen. Comp. Endocrinol.* 13:506
68. Furr, B. J. A., Pope, G. S. 1970. Identification of cholesterol, 7-oxocholesterol, pregnenolone, progesterone, 20-hydroxypregn-4-en-3-one-epimers and 5β-androstane-3,17-dione in plasma and ovarian tissue of the domestic fowl. *Steroids* 16:471–85
69. Garnier, D. 1972. *Étude de la fonction endocrine du testicule chez le Canard Pékin au cours du cycle saisonnier. Aspects biochimiques et cytologiques.* Thèse de Doctorat Etat. Univ. Paris
70. Gilbert, A. B. 1971. The endocrine ovary. In *Physiology and Biochemistry of the Domestic Fowl,* ed. D. J. Bell, B. M. Freeman, 3:1449–68. London: Academic
71. Gledhill, B. 1977. *In-vitro* studies on pulsatile gonadotropin secretion in Japanese quail. *J. Endocrinol.* 72:14P
72. Gloyna, R. E., Wilson, J. D. 1969. A comparative study of the conversion of testosterone to 17β-hydroxy-5α-androstan-3-one(dihydrotestosterone) by prostate and epididymis. *J. Clin. Endocrinol. Metab.* 29:970–77
73. Godden, P. M., Luck, M. R., Scanes, C. G. 1977. Effect of LHRH and steroids on release of LH and FSH from in-

cubated turkey pituitary cells. *Acta Endocrinol.* 85:713–17

74. Godden, P. M., Scanes, C. G. 1975. Studies on the purification and properties of avian gonadotrophins. *Gen. Comp. Endocrinol.* 27:538–42
75. Gorman, M. L. 1977. Sexual behaviour and plasma androgen concentrations in the male eider duck (*Somateria mollissima*). *J. Reprod. Fertil.* 49:225–30
76. Gourdji, D., Tixier-Vidal, A. 1966. Mise en évidence d'un contrôle hypothalamique stimulant de la prolactine hypophysaire chez le Canard. *C. R. Acad. Sci. Paris* 283:162–65
77. Gwinner, E. 1968. Circannuale Periodik als Grundlage des jahreszeitlichen Funktionswandels bei Zugvögeln. *J. Ornithol.* 109:71–95
78. Gwinner, E. 1973. Circannual rhythms in birds: Their interaction with circadian rhythms and environmental photoperiod. See Ref. 58, pp. 51–65
79. Gwinner, E. 1975. Die circannuale Periodik der Fortpflanungsperiodik beim Star (*Sturnus vulgaris*) unter Einfluss gleich- und andersgeschlechtiger Artgenossen. *Z. Tierpsychol.* 38:34–43
80. Gwinner, E. 1975. Circadian and circannual rhythms in birds. In *Avian Biology,* ed. D. S. Farner, J. R. King, 5:221–8. NY: Academic
81. Gwinner, E. 1977. Circannual rhythms in bird migration. *Ann. Rev. Ecol. Syst.* 8:381–405
82. Gwinner, E. 1977. Photoperiodic synchronization of circannual rhythms in the European starling (*Sturnus vulgaris*). *Naturwissenschaften* 64:44–45
83. Gwinner, E. 1977. Über die Synchronisation circannualer Rhythmen bei Vögeln. *Vogelwarte* 29: Sonderheft, pp. 16–32
84. Gwinner, E., Eriksson, L.-O. 1977. Circadiane Rhythmik und photoperiodische Zeitmessung beim Star (*Sturnus vulgaris*). *J. Ornithol.* 118:60–67
85. Haase, E., Sharp, P. J., Paulke, E. 1975. Annual cycle of plasma luteinizing hormone concentrations in wild mallard drakes. *J. Exp. Zool.* 194:553–58
86. Hamner, W. M. 1963. Diurnal rhythm and photoperiodism in testicular recrudescence of the house finch. *Science* 142:1294–95
87. Hamner, W. M. 1968. The photorefractory period of the house finch. *Ecology* 49:212–27
88. Hinde, R. A. 1965. Interaction of internal and external factors in integration of canary reproduction. In *Sex and Behavior,* ed. F. A. Beach, pp. 381–415. NY: Wiley
89. Hinde, R. A. 1970. *Animal Behavior.* NY: McGraw-Hill. 534 pp. 2nd ed.
90. Hinde, R. A., Steel, E. 1976. The effect of male song on an estrogen-dependent behavior pattern in the female canary (*Serinus canarius*). *Horm. Behav.* 7: 293–304
91. Homma, K., Sakakibara, Y. 1971. Encephalic photoreceptors and their significance in photoperiodic control of sexual activity in Japanese quail. In *Biochronometry,* ed. M. Menaker, pp. 333–41. Washington DC: Natl. Acad. Sci.
92. Horst, H.-J., Paulke, E. 1977. Comparative study of androgen uptake and metabolism in domestic and wild mallard drakes (*Anas platyrhynchos L.*) *Gen. Comp. Endocrinol.* 32:138–45
93. Immelmann, K. 1963. Tierische Jahresperiodik in ökologischer Sicht. *Zool. Jahrb. Abt. 1, Syst. Oekol.* 91:91–200
94. Immelmann, K. 1967. Periodische Vorgänge in der Fortpflanzung tierischer Organismen. *Stud. Gen.* 20:15–33
95. Ishii, S., Farner, D. S. 1976. Binding of follicle-stimulating hormone by homogenates of testes of photostimulated white-crowned sparrows, *Zonotrichia leuchophrys gambelii. Gen. Comp. Endocrinol.* 30:443–50
96. Ishii, S., Furuya, T. 1975. Effects of purified chicken gonadotropins on the chick testis. *Gen. Comp. Endocrinol.* 25:1–8
97. Jackson, G. L. 1971. Comparison of rat and chicken luteinizing hormone-releasing factor. *Endocrinology* 89: 1460–63
98. Jackson, G. L. 1972. Partial purification and characterization of chicken and rat follicle stimulating hormone releasing factors. *Endocrinology* 91:1090–94
99. Jallageas, M., Assenmacher, I., Follett, B. K. 1974. Testosterone secretion and plasma luteinizing hormone concentration during a sexual cycle in the Pekin duck, and after thyroxine treatment. *Gen. Comp. Endocrinol.* 23:472–75
100. Jeffcoate, S. L., Sharp, P. J., Fraser, H. M., Holland, D. T., Gunn, A. 1974. Immunochemical and chromatographic similarity of rat, rabbit, chicken and synthetic luteinizing hormone releasing hormones. *J. Endocrinol.* 62:85–91
101. Jenner, C. E., Engels, W. L. 1952. The significance of the dark period in the photoperiodic response of male juncos and white-throated sparrows. *Biol. Bull.* 103:345–55

102. Jones, R. E. 1969. Hormonal control of incubation patch development in the California quail *Lophortyx californicus. Gen. Comp. Endocrinol.* 13:1–13
103. King, J. R. 1968. Cycles of fat deposition and molt in white-crowned sparrows in constant environmental conditions. *Comp. Biochem. Physiol.* 24:827–837
104. King, J. R., Farner, D. S. 1974. Biochronometry and bird migration. In *Chronobiology,* ed. L. E. Scheving, F. Halberg, J. E. Pauly, pp. 625–30. Tokyo: Igaku Shoin
105. King, J. R., Follett, B. K., Farner, D. S., Morton, M. L. 1966. Annual gonadal cycles and pituitary gonadotropins in *Zonotrichia leucophrys gambelii. Condor* 68:476–87
106. King, J. R., Sansum, E. L. 1976. Long-term effects of constant photoperiods on testicular cycles of white-crowned sparrows (*Zonotrichia leucophrys gambelii*). *Physiol. Zool.* 49:407–16
107. Kobayashi, H., Wada, M. 1973. Neuroendocrinology in birds. See Ref. 80, 3:287–348
108. Korenbrot, C. C., Schomberg, D. W., Erickson, C. J. 1974. Radioimmunoassay of plasma estradiol during the breeding cycle of ring doves (*Streptopelia risoria*). *J. Endocrinol.* 94: 1126–32
109. Kragt, C. L., Meites, J. 1965. Stimulation of pigeon pituitary prolactin release by pigeon hypothalamic extract *in vitro Fed. Proc.* 24:347–52
110. Lam, F., Farner, D. S. 1976. The ultrastructure of the Cells of Leydig in the white-crowned sparrow (*Zonotrichia leucophrys gambelii*) in relation to plasma levels of luteinizing hormone and testosterone. *Cell Tiss. Res.* 169: 93–100
111. Lehrman, D. S. 1965. Interaction between internal and external environments in the regulation of the reproductive cycle of the ring dove. See Ref. 88, pp. 355–80
112. Lewis, R. A. 1971. *The temporal organization of reproductive and associated cycles of the Puget Sound sparrow,* Zonotrichia leucophrys pugetensis. PhD Thesis. Univ. Washington, Seattle. 163 pp.
113. Lewis, R. A., Farner, D. S. 1973. Temperature modulation of photoperiodically induced vernal phenomena in white-crowned sparrows (*Zonotrichia leucophrys*). *Condor* 75:279–86
114. Lofts, B., Follett, B. K., Murton, R. K. 1970. Temporal changes in the pituitary-gonadal axis. *Mem. Soc. Endocrinol.* 18:545–75
115. Lofts, B., Murton, R. K. 1968. Photoperiodic and physiological adaptations regulating avian breeding cycles and their ecological significance. *J. Zool. London* 112:327–96
116. Lofts, B., Murton, R. K. 1973. Reproduction in birds. See Ref. 80, 3:1–107
117. Massa, R., Cresti, L., Martini, L. 1977. Metabolism of testosterone in the anterior pituitary gland and the central nervous system of the European starling (*Sturnus vulgaris*). *J. Endocrinol.* 75:347–54
118. Mattocks, P. W., Farner, D. S., Follett, B. K. 1976. The annual cycle in luteinizing hormone in the plasma of intact and castrated white-crowned sparrows, *Zonotrichia leucophrys gambelii. Gen. Comp. Endocrinol.* 30:156–61
119. Maung, Z. W., Follett, B. K. 1977. Effects of chicken and ovine luteinizing hormone on androgen release and cyclic AMP production by isolated cells from the quail testis. *Gen. Comp. Endocrinol.* 33:242–53
120. McCreery, B. R., Farner, D. S. 1979. Progesterone in male white-crowned sparrows, *Zonotrichia leucophrys gambelii. Gen. Comp. Endocrinol.* 37:1–5
121. McMillan, J. P., Underwood, H. A., Elliott, J. A., Stetson, M. H., Menaker, M. 1975. Extraretinal light perception in the sparrow. IV. Further evidence that the eyes do not participate in photoperiodic photoreception. *J. Comp. Physiol.* 97:205–13
122. McNeill, T. H., Kozlowski, G. P., Abel, J. H. Jr., Zimmerman, E. A. 1976. Neurosecretory pathways in the mallard duck (*Anas platyrhynchos*) brain: localization by aldehyde fuchsin and immunoperoxidase techniques for neurophysin (NP) and gonadotropin releasing hormone (Gn-RH). *Endocrinology* 99:1323–32
123. Meier, A. H. 1976. Chronoendocrinology of the white-throated sparrow. *Proc. 16th Int. Ornithol. Congr.,* ed. H. J. Frith, J. H. Calaby, pp. 355–82. Canberra: Austr. Acad. Sci.
124. Meier, A. H., Dusseau, J. W. 1968. Prolactin and the photoperiodic gonadal response in several avian species. *Physiol. Zool.* 41:95–103
125. Meites, J., Nicoll, C. S. 1966. Adenohypophysis: prolactin. *Ann. Rev. Physiol.* 28:57–58
126. Menaker, M. 1974. Circannual rhythms in circadian perspective. In *Circannual*

Clocks, ed. E. T. Pengelley, pp. 507–20. NY: Academic
127. Menaker, M., Keatts, H. 1968. Extraretinal light perception in the sparrow. II. Photoperiodic stimulation of testicular growth. *Proc. Natl. Acad. Sci. USA* 60:146–51
128. Mikami, S.-I., Tokado, H., Farner, D. S. 1978. The hypothalamic neurosecretory systems of the Japanese quail as revealed by retrograde transport of horseradish peroxidase. *Cell Tiss. Res.* 194:1–15
129. Murton, R. K., Westwood, N. J. 1977. *Avian Breeding Cycles.* Oxford: Clarendon. 594 pp.
130. Nakamura, T., Tanabe, Y. 1972. *In vitro* steroidogenesis by testes of the chicken (*Gallus domesticus*). *Gen. Comp. Endocrinol.* 19:432–40
131. Nakamura, T., Tanabe, Y. 1972. Pathways for androgen synthesis *in vitro* by the testes of Japanese quail (*Corturnix coturnix japonica*). *J. Endocrinol.* 55: 499–506
132. Nakamura, T., Tanabe, Y. 1973. Dihydrotestosterone formation *in vitro* in the epididymis of the domestic fowl. *J. Endocrinol.* 59:651–52
133. Nakamura, T., Tanabe, Y. 1975. *In vitro* metabolism of steroid hormones by chicken brain. *Acta Endocrinol.* 75: 410–16
134. Nicholls, T. J., Scanes, C. G., Follett, B. K. 1973. Plasma and pituitary luteinizing hormone in Japanese quail during photoperiodically induced gonadal growth and regression. *Gen. Comp. Endocrinol.* 21:84–86
135. Nicoll, C. S. 1965. Neural regulation of adenohypophysial prolactin secretion in tetrapods. *J. Exp. Zool.* 158:203–10
136. Novikov, B. G., Rudneva, L. M. 1964. Zavisimost funktsii yaichnika u utok ot gipotalamusa. *Zh. Obshch. Biol.* 25: 390–93
137. Oishi, T., Konishi, T., Kato, M. 1966. Investigations on photorecepting mechanism to control gonadal development in Japanese quail. *Environ. Cont. Biol.* 3:87–90
138. Oksche, A. 1978. Evolution, differentiation and organization of hypothalamic systems controlling reproduction. In *Brain-Endocrine Interaction III. Neural Hormones and Reproduction,* ed. D. E. Scott, G. P. Kozlowski, A. Weindl, pp. 1–15. Basel: Karger
139. Oliver, J. 1972. *Étude expérimentale des structure hypothalamique impliquées dans le réflexe photosexuel chez la Caille.* Thèse, Univ. Sci. Techn. du Languedoc
140. O'Malley, B. W., Kirschner, M. A., Bardin, C. 1968. Estimation of plasma androgenic and progestational steroids in the laying hen. *Proc. Soc. Exp. Biol. Med.* 127:521–23
141. Ozon, R. 1972. Androgens in fishes, amphibians, reptiles and birds. In *Steroids in Non-Mammalian Vertebrates,* ed. D. R. Idler, pp. 329–89. NY: Academic
142. Ozon, R. 1972. Estrogens in fishes, amphibians, reptiles and birds. See Ref. 141, pp. 390–413
143. Paulke, E., Haase, E. 1978. A comparison of seasonal changes in the concentrations of androgens in the peripheral blood of wild and domestic ducks. *Gen. Comp. Endocrinol.* 34:381–90
144. Pittendrigh, C. S., Minis, D. H. 1964. The entrainment of circadian oscillations by light and their role as photoperiodic clocks. *Am. Nat.* 98:261–94
145. Polikarpova, E. 1940. Influence of external factors upon the development of the sexual gland of the sparrow. *C. R. (Dokl.) Acad. Sci. URSS* 26:91–95
146. Riddle, O. 1963. Prolactin in vertebrate function and organization. *J. Natl. Cancer Inst.* 31:1039–110
147. Rivarola, M. A., Snipes, C. A., Migeon, C. J. 1968. Concentrations of androgens in systemic plasma of rats, guinea pigs, salamanders and pigeons. *Endocrinology* 82:115–21
148. Sansum, E. L., King, J. R. 1975. Photorefractoriness in a sparrow: Phase of circadian photosensitivity elucidated by skeleton photoperiods. *J. Comp. Physiol.* 98:183–88
149. Sansum, E. L., King, J. R. 1976. Long-term effects of constant photoperiods on testicular cycles of white-crowned sparrows (*Zonotrichia leucophrys gambelii*). *Physiol. Zool.* 49:407–16
150. Sayler, A., Wolfson, A. 1968. Influence of the pineal gland on gonadal maturation in the Japanese quail. *Endocrinology* 83:1237–46
151. Scanes, C. G., Cheeseman, P., Phillips, J. G., Follett, B. K. 1974. Seasonal and age variation of circulating immunoreactive luteinizing hormone in captive herring gulls, *Larus argentatus. J. Zool* (London) 174:369–75
152. Senior, B. E., Furr, B. J. A. 1975. A preliminary assessment of the source of oestrogen within the ovary of the domestic fowl, *Gallus domesticus. J. Reprod. Fertil.* 43:241–48

153. Shahabi, N. A., Bahr, J. M., Nalbandov, A. V. 1975. Effect of LH injection on plasma and follicular steroids in the chicken. *Endocrinol.* 96:969–72
154. Sharp, P. J. 1980. The endocrine control of ovulation in birds. *Proc. Int. Ornithol. Congr. 17th* In press
155. Silver, R. 1978. The parental behavior of ring doves. *Am. Sci.* 66:209–15
156. Steel, E., Hinde, R. A. 1972. Influence of photoperiod on oestrogenic induction of nest-building in canaries. *J. Endocrinol.* 55:265–78
157. Stetson, M. H., Erickson, J. E. 1971. Endocrine effects of castration in white-crowned sparrows. *Gen. Comp. Endocrinol.* 17:105–14
158. Storey, C. R., Nicholls, T. J. 1976. Some effects of manipulation of daily photoperiod on the rate of onset of a photorefractory state in canaries, *Serinus canarius. Gen. Comp. Endocrinol.* 30:204–8
159. Temple, S. A. 1974. Plasma testosterone titers during the annual reproductive cycle of starlings, *Sturnus vulgaris. Gen. Comp. Endocrinol.* 22:470–79
160. Tixier-Vidal, A., Follett, B. K. 1973. The adenohypophysis. See Ref. 80, 3:109–82
161. Turek, F. W. 1972. Circadian involvement in termination of the refractory period in two sparrows. *Science* 178: 1112–13
162. Turek, F. W. 1975. Extraretinal photoreception during the gonadal photorefractory period in the golden-crowned sparrow. *J. Comp. Physiol.* 96:27–36
163. Vitums, A., Mikami, S.-I., Oksche, A., Farner, D. S. 1964. Vascularization of the hypothalamo-hypophysial complex in the white-crowned sparrow, *Zonotrichia leucophrys gambelii. Z. Zellforsch.* 64:541–69
164. Weise, C. M. 1967. Castration and spring migration in the white-crowned sparrow. *Condor* 69:49–68
165. Wilson, F. E. 1970. The tubero-infundibular region of the hypothalamus: A focus of testosterone sensitivity in male tree sparrows (*Spizella arborea*). In *Aspects of Neuroendocrinology,* ed. W. Bargmann, B. Scharrer, pp. 274–86. Berlin-Heidelberg-New York: Springer
166. Wilson, F. E., Follett, B. K. 1974. Plasma and pituitary luteinizing hormone in intact and castrated tree sparrows, *Spizella arborea,* during a photoinduced gonadal cycle. *Gen. Comp. Endocrinol.* 23:82–93
167. Wingfield, J. C., Farner, D. S. 1975. The determination of five steroids in avian plasma by radioimmunoassay and competitive protein-binding. *Steroids* 26: 311–27
168. Wingfield, J. C., Farner, D. S. 1977. Zur Endokrinologie einer brutenden Population von *Zonotrichia leucophrys pugetensis. Vogelwarte* 29: Zonderheft 25–32
169. Wingfield, J. C., Farner, D. S. 1978. The endocrinology of a natural breeding population of the white-crowned sparrow (*Zonotrichia leucophrys pugetensis*). *Physiol. Zool.* 51:188–205
170. Wingfield, J. C., Farner, D. S. 1979. The annual cycle of plasma irLH and steroid hormones in feral populations of the white-crowned sparrow *Zonotrichia leucophrys gambelii. Biol. Reprod.* 19:1046–56
171. Wingfield, J. C., Farner, D. S. 1980. Temporal aspects of the secretion of luteinizing hormone and androgen in the white-crowned sparrow, *Zonotrichia leucophrys. Proc. Int. Ornithol. Congr. 17th.* In press
172. Wolfson, A. 1954. Production of repeated gonadal, fat, and molt cycles within one year in the junco and white-crowned sparrow by manipulation of day length. *J. Exp. Zool.* 125:353–76
173. Wolfson, A. 1964. Animal photoperiodism. In *Photophysiology,* ed. A. C. Giese, 2:1–49. NY: Academic
174. Yokoyama, K., Farner, D. S. 1976. Photoperiodic responses in bilaterally enucleated female white-crowned sparrows. *Zonotrichia leucophrys gambelii. Gen. Comp. Endocrinol.* 30:528–33
175. Yokoyama, K., Oksche, A., Darden, T. R., Farner, D. S. 1978. The sites of encephalic photoreception in photoperiodic induction of the growth of the testes in the white-crowned sparrow, *Zonotrichia leucophrys gambelii. Cell Tiss. Res.* 189:441–67
176. Yu, J. Y.-L., Marquardt, R. R. 1973. Effects of estradiol and testosterone on the immature female chicken (*Gallus domesticus*). 1. Quantitative changes in nucleic acids, proteins and lipids in the liver. *Comp. Biochem. Physiol.* 46B: 749–57
177. Yu, J. Y.-L., Marquardt, R. R. 1973b. Interaction of estradiol and testosterone in the regulation of growth and development of the chicken (*Gallus domesticus*) oviduct. *Comp. Biochem. Physiol.* 44B:769–77

Ann. Rev. Physiol. 1980. 42:473–91

TEMPERATURE REGULATION IN VERTEBRATES

❖1281

Larry I. Crawshaw

Depts. of Rehabilitation Medicine and Pharmacology, College of Physicians & Surgeons, Columbia University, New York, New York 10032

INTRODUCTION

Vertebrates moderate the stresses associated with varying temperatures through subdivisions of the nervous system that sense skin and deep body temperatures and compare these temperatures with a neuronally represented reference. Resultant output responses characteristically involve systems that subserve or compete with other physiological functions, thereby establishing a strong interdependence between regulations of body temperature and of cardiovascular, respiratory, energetic, ionic, and osmotic variables. The precisely adjusted effector outputs have been carefully documented (13, 42) and characterized by a number of models (11) relating thermal input and output functions. When the participating brain structures are closely investigated, however, it is apparent that the precision of the total thermoregulatory system involves a complex overlay of neuronal networks evolved at different times and performing differing functions (112, 123).

Recent reviews on thermoregulatory physiology support particular viewpoints and initiate access to the earlier literature (12, 13, 17, 29, 52, 112, 123). Various volumes provide comprehensive overviews of related areas (57, 62, 68, 73, 83). Hibernation was reviewed by several authors in the 1978 *Annual Review of Physiology* and in (140). Topics of historical and current interest regarding fever and hyperthermia have been treated in a recent symposium (80).

Vertebrates deal with thermal stresses by adjustments in behavior, autonomic alterations, and acclimation. Mechanisms of the first two types are largely complementary, being activated in seconds and minutes. Tempera-

0066-4278/80/0315-0473$01.00

ture acclimation occurs over hours and days and represents a long-term adjustment to chronic thermal changes involving both physiological and biochemical processes. The three response categories probably exist in all vertebrates. The behavioral and autonomic categories constitute the major subjects of this review. Acclimation will be treated in detail by other authors in a subsequent volume of the *Annual Review of Physiology.* Important differences in the way behavioral and autonomic responses are utilized depend upon whether a vertebrate breathes air or water, and upon whether metabolic heat is utilized in maintaining a constant internal temperature (endothermy) or external heat is the predominant energy source (ectothermy). These differences form subdivisions that reflect the physical constraints placed upon each response category.

TEMPERATURE SENSING AND INTEGRATION

Although most work has been performed on mammals, sufficient data exist to justify the assumption that the neural components integrating thermal responses are similar throughout the vertebrate subphylum. A change in the ambient thermal environment is first detected by peripheral warm- and cold-receptors, which extend several micrometers into the basal epidermal cells. These receptors show a particular static discharge rate at a given temperature and also respond with a dynamic overshoot following sudden temperature shifts. The dynamic response is greatest at the temperature where the static discharge rate is maximal (52, 131). Another type of skin receptor, the thermal nociceptors, are active only at relatively high or low temperatures and likely mediate thermal pain (28, 60). Experiments involving frogs (130) and rats (95) indicate that temperature transduction by the cold-receptors may involve an electrogenic sodium pump (95) or a sodium potassium pump (130). The pump mechanism in these small fibers appears highly active and very temperature-sensitive. Thermally induced decreases in pump activity would allow the membrane to depolarize and initiate discharges in the nerve. Ouabain (which blocks Na^+-K^+ or electrogenic Na^+ pumps) elicits a discharge from cold-receptors (95, 130), and variations in external $[K^+]$ affect the response. Cold-receptors are particularly sensitive to anoxia, which can be produced simply by pressing an object against the skin (59).

The spinal cord is a site both of thermosensitivity and of subsidiary control (123). Certain ascending neurons in the lateral funiculus of the pigeon spinal cord are sensitive to both local cooling and local warming and respond both statically and dynamically (88). A high degree of convergence of peripheral thermal input on spinal thermosensitive neurons occurs in cats (122), though this relationship is much less evident in intact than in spinalized animals (38). For noxious thermal input, descending inhibition can be detected at the dorsal horn neurons (90), but this is not the case for the conventional warm- and cold-receptors (50).

Numerous loci in the brainstem are implicated in the regulation of body temperature—e.g. the medulla, the midbrain, the pons, the posterior and lateral hypothalamus, and the preoptic/anterior hypothalamic [PO/AH] area (111). The PO/AH area is the predominant site of thermoregulatory integration (42, 112) and is an important sensor of core temperature in all vertebrates except birds (104). The pathways from sensors to response mechanisms are to some extent separate: PO/AH lesions abolish heat-induced body extension but do not affect heat-induced locomotion, grooming, or tail vasodilation (109).

BEHAVIORAL RESPONSES

All motile organisms possess the ability to respond to adverse temperatures. This capability is particularly well developed in vertebrates and under appropriate conditions obviates the involvement of autonomic or biochemical mechanisms. The overall similarity of behavioral thermoregulation among the vertebrate classes is emphasized in this section.

Water-Breathing Ectotherms

Cyclostomes, cartilagenous fish, and bony fish regulate body temperature when given a choice of water temperatures (22, 77). In bony fish these responses are influenced by both anterior brainstem temperature and peripheral temperature (22). Heating the anterior brainstem of bony fish and sharks leads to their selecting cooler water (23, 24), while lesions in the preoptic area of goldfish and sunfish severely disrupt behavioral thermoregulation (92). Temperature-sensitive neurons have also been located in this portion of the brain (91). The regulated body temperature of fish is altered by intracerebral chemical injections: Cholinergic stimulation lowers escape temperatures, whereas increased levels of catecholamines and histamine raise them (36). Fish will select warmer temperatures following the injection of certain gram-negative bacteria (108). Thus similarities in thermally sensitive loci, integration of thermal inputs, and sensitivity to pyrogens and putative transmitter substances indicate important similarities between water breathers and other vertebrates in the behavioral regulation of body temperature.

Water-breathing ectotherms are particularly susceptible to problems in ion and osmoregulation because of the thermal dependence of ion uptake mechanisms and the intimate association between water and blood at the gills (22). Osmotic stress can affect temperature selection by fish: Salt-water–adapted threespine sticklebacks select 18°C in salt water and 16°C in fresh water (34). The selection of cooler water presumably reduces the overall metabolic and ionic stress on the animal.

Air-Breathing Ectotherms

Adult amphibians can regulate their body temperature reasonably well (70), though desiccation may obscure this ability if the animals are tested in air. The frog *Rana esculenta* normally regulates its body temperature at 26°C in an aquatic temperature gradient. Heating the spinal cord to 35°C results in the maintenance of body temperature below 15°C, while the injection of killed pathogenic bacteria is followed by the selection of warmer water and subsequent increase in colonic temperature of 6.5°C (82).

Reptiles in the field or in a thermal gradient cluster about a particular temperature. Repeated measurements of the temperature where a particular animal is found typically exhibit a unimodal distribution skewed toward lower temperatures (30). From this information it is often inferred that the reptilian thermoregulatory system involves a set point (the peak of the distribution) and a proportional controller. Indeed, reptiles possess both anterior brainstem and peripheral thermosensitivity, which interact to determine thermoregulatory behavior (81). When given the opportunity to choose a warmer environment, lizards also develop endotoxin fevers of 2–3°C that can be abolished by the administration of the anti-pyretic drug, sodium salicylate (9). Since observations of lizards in the field and in shuttleboxes often indicate a neutral zone of up to 7°C within which the animals fail to regulate body temperature precisely, a dual-threshold system of temperature control has been suggested for these animals (7, 8, 46). If the temperature of the hot end of a shuttlebox is increased, the colonic and brain temperatures at which lizards exit decrease linearly, though the skin temperature at which they exit remains constant. This suggests that peripheral skin temperature provides the major sensory input in the shuttlebox situation (8).

Several authors have emphasized the "costs" associated with behavioral thermoregulation (58, 99, 113). An animal's involvement in such behavior may preclude other necessary activities, and excessive movement produces substantial energy costs. Thus the Puerto Rican lizard *Anolis cristatellus* regulates body temperature in an open park where varied thermal microhabitats are readily available but tolerates variable temperatures in an adjacent forest where basking sites are sparse (58).

The left portion of Figure 1 depicts how response costs, response competition, and sympathetic activation could affect thermoregulatory output functions. The three factors are seen as inhibitory inputs that raise thresholds for the response outputs. Following this schema, a shuttlebox would produce higher "costs" than a thermal gradient, thereby widening the neutral zone. The underlying regulatory system, however, is seen as similar to that of other vertebrates.

Endotherms

Figure 1 also applies to endotherms. For instance, the introduction of a lever that allows rats to obtain food decreases bar pressing for the acquisition of radiant heat in a cold environment (67). In the case of endotherms, however, inadequacies in behavioral regulation are made up by the activation of autonomic thermoregulatory mechanisms, as has been demonstrated for monkeys (1) and pigeons (116). In the pigeon (118) behavioral and autonomic responses are complementary, and an inverse relationship exists between the capacity for autonomic thermoregulation and the drive for behavioral thermoregulation (119). Birds quickly adjust behavioral responses to changes in the external thermal load, and it has been suggested that because of the rapidity of the response the appropriate input signals

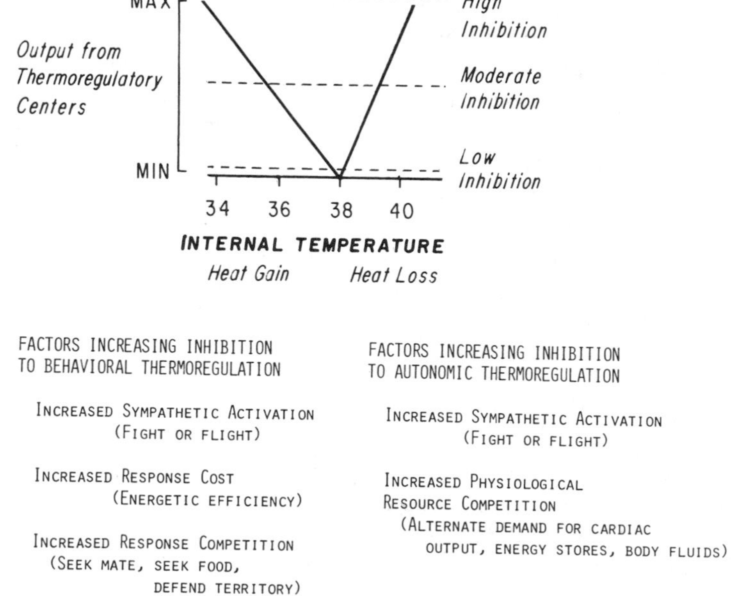

Figure 1 A schematic diagram of certain nonthermal influences on the vertebrate thermoregulatory system. Inhibitory inputs are seen as raising a hypothetical baseline, which has the effect of decreasing the threshold for heat-gain responses and increasing the threshold for heat-loss responses. For simplicity, the output from the thermoregulatory centers is depicted as depending only on central temperature, though peripheral temperature is important. In addition, inhibitory inputs may change the gain as well as the thresholds.

carry information about the rate of change of temperature in unfeathered areas. Autonomic responses to heat (for which primary inputs to the integrating center arise from displacements of body temperature) are activated more slowly (116). Warming or cooling the hypothalamus or spinal cord produces appropriate corrective behavior in the pigeon. However, the accompanying autonomic responses are paradoxical in part: Hypothalamic cooling and warming lead to panting and shivering, respectively. Autonomic changes produced by heating or cooling the spinal cord occur in the expected direction (117).

Interaction between behavioral and autonomic systems can affect the classical definition of thermoneutrality (the ambient temperatures over which metabolism is minimum and constant). Poole & Stephenson (98) have argued that commonly accepted values for the thermoneutral zone of the rat (28–32°C) actually represent a temperature range where heat stress has inhibited behavior and consequently produced a low metabolic rate. They propose an alternative range (18–28°C) wherein behavioral thermoregulation is absent and neither metabolic heat production nor evaporative water loss (saliva spreading) is elevated.

Rat pups, with little autonomic capability for theroregulation, actively huddle and regulate body temperature by controlling the compactness of the huddle (3). Newborn rabbits injected with an exogenous pyrogen are unable to generate a fever when kept at 32°C. However, when placed in a thermal gradient, they do become warmer than controls (114). Adult squirrel monkeys, although fully capable of producing a fever by shivering and peripheral vasoconstriction, instead use behavioral means of elevating body temperature following injections of Prostaglandin E_1 into the PO/AH area (25). Similar results occur with injections of leucocyte pyrogen into the PO/AH area of guinea pigs (128).

AUTONOMIC RESPONSES

Vertebrates use autonomic responses either to anticipate thermally induced physiological changes, to maintain acid-base balance and avoid lethal temperatures, or to keep internal temperature constant. These autonomic responses are subject to modification by nonthermal events, as indicated on the right side of Figure 1. Thus electrical stimulation of the upper medial brainstem or intracerebroventricular injection of 25 μg of noradrenaline in the rabbit activates sympathetic "fight or flight" responses and inhibits thermoregulatory responses both in warm and in cold environments (134, 136). Cardiac output of humans is maintained during increased levels of exercise in the heat by the initiation of peripheral vasoconstriction (84).

Water-Breathing Ectotherms

Fish respond to heating or cooling of the anterior brainstem or spinal cord with respective increases and decreases of gill ventilation (26) and heart rate (85). These changes appear linked with the absolute level of temperature and not to the rate of change in local tissue temperature. Respiration in carp (21) and lampreys (69) is rapidly affected by changes in water temperature. These adjustments are rate sensitive, with decreases in water temperature producing rapid decreases in respiratory activity. Warming the water leads to the opposite effect. The lampreys show similar trends in heart rate. All these results may reflect input to the respiratory centers from the thermoregulatory centers in the anterior brainstem of aquatic ectotherms. This could aid in the maintenance of arterial oxygen levels during heating and minimize the expenditure of energy necessary for gill ventilation and active ion transport during cooling (22).

Pigment aggregation in fish is controlled by sympathetic neurons and has been used to monitor sympathetic activity. Temperature changes at the body surface (138), in the spinal column (87), and in the anterior brainstem (L. I. Crawshaw, unpublished observations), lead to alterations in the color of fish. Warming always leads to a darkening of the skin surface. Injection of lipopolysaccharide into the anterior brainstem of carp caused blanching (86). Thus, in fish, both autonomic and behavioral responses are affected by pyrogens. The lipopolysaccharide effect is consistent with an elevation in the thresholds for thermoregulatory outputs from the anterior brainstem.

Thermoregulation has not been implicated in vasomotor activity in most fish, though changes in peripheral blood flow are apparently affected by local temperature (22). Circumstantial evidence suggests that large tuna can alter the efficiency of their vascular countercurrent heat exchanger, but it is not known if this response is mediated via the anterior brainstem thermoregulatory centers (8, 31, 133).

Air-Breathing Ectotherms

The mucous glands of the bullfrog (*Rana catesbeiana*) are sympathetically innervated, and discharge rates are influenced by the rate of change of peripheral temperature and the temperature of the head. Brain transections caudal but not rostal to the optic chiasma abolish mucous discharge, so the anterior hypothalamus appears involved in the response (71).

Peripheral blood flow increases in reptiles following the local application of heat (22, 127); such changes in blood flow may augment the abilities of reptiles to maintain body temperature near preferred levels (127, 141). No evidence exists that the reptile CNS regulates body temperature by controlling peripheral blood flow. Peripheral blood flow during temperature shifts has been little investigated in amphibians. However, the peripheral circulation appears important in preventing integumentary desiccation in basking frogs (72). The rapid changes in heart rate that occur during heating and cooling in reptiles likely represent a combination of the baroreceptor reflex in response to alterations in local blood flow (141) and the direct effect of temperature on the heart (132). The large changes in blood pressure following relatively small changes in hypothalamic temperature (47, 110) may indicate a thermally activated compensatory mechanism (J. E. Heath, personal communication).

Many reptiles utilize autonomic responses in surviving otherwise lethal environmental temperatures. The panting response receives thermal inputs from the skin, the anterior brainstem, and other deep body sensors in both lizards (19) and turtles (79). The panting threshold in the lizard *Amphibolurus muricatus* rises with increased acclimation temperature and lengthened photoperiods; however, it is also higher in summer than in winter, even when acclimation temperature and photoperiod are held constant (48).

In the lizard *Sauromalus obesus* long bouts of panting result in respiratory hypocapnia and alkalosis (20). However, within the usual range of body temperature, reptiles alter pulmonary ventilation to maintain an appropriate acid-base balance. As with other ectotherms, acid-base regulation during changes in body temperature generally seems to involve the maintenance of a constant state of protein ionization (termed alphastat regulation) rather than a constant hydrogen ion activity (106). Such regulation requires that blood and intracellular pH increase ($dpH/dt \cong -0.016$ units/°C) as body temperature falls. This pH increase and a concomitant decrease in P_{CO_2} take place automatically in a closed system (with constant total CO_2 content), largely because of the temperature-induced decrease in the dissociation of histidine imidazole groups of proteins. Normal respiration involves an open system, and air breathing ectotherms maintain their acid-base balance by altering the relative ventilation—i.e. the ratio of pulmonary ventilation to CO_2 production (106). Decreasing the pH of a solution perfusing the cerebral ventricles of a turtle increased the relative ventilation (53). This response continued for the duration of the perfusion, which indicates the dominance of central chemosensors over any peripheral inputs. Altering the temperature of the perfusion solution while keeping the pH constant produced no changes in respiration.

The relative abundance of oxygen in the atmosphere and the ability to make rapid and precise adjustments for temperature-induced shifts in acid-base levels allow many air-breathing ectotherms to initiate actively large, rapid changes in body temperature. During early morning basking the iguanid lizard *Liolaemus multiformis* can raise its body temperature from 5°C to 30°C in about 30 min (94), and turtles (*Chrysemys scripta*) acclimated to 3°C for three weeks select water above 30°C less than one hour after being placed in a thermal gradient (27). The primacy of acid-base regulation during periods of body-temperature change in air-breathing ectotherms mitigates against the development of a system to anticipate metabolic alterations, as appears to be present in water breathers.

Some exceptions to the concept of alphastat regulation have been observed in reptiles. A monitor lizard (*Varanus exanthematicus*) maintained a constant arterial pH at body temperature between 20°C and 35°C (143), and changes in the arterial pH of chronically catheterized lizards (*Uromastyx acanthinurus*) during the usual daily fluctuations in body temperature (25–38°C) were about half those predicted by strict alphastat regulation (2). However, appropriate acid-base changes are difficult to demonstrate when pH is measured over a range smaller than 20°C. Measurements of total CO_2 content in the blood are especially important under these conditions (R. B. Reeves, personal communication).

Endotherms

Acid-base regulation is also important for endotherms. The automatic pH shifts that occur following temperature changes in a closed system provide for alphastat regulation in perfused extremities that are often much cooler than the body core (107). At elevated temperatures, the high respiratory frequency necessary for heat loss by panting animals introduces a possible acid-base disturbance. When inspired CO_2 and ambient temperatures are varied in rabbits, tidal volume is controlled by the level of blood P_{CO_2}, respiratory frequency is controlled by thermoregulatory requirements, and the reciprocal relationship between the two is regulated such that the mean expiratory volume is appropriate for both gas exchange and heat loss (76). Panting chukar partridges (64) develop a slight (0.04 pH unit) respiratory alkalosis, and that observed in the Saluki dog (65) is somewhat higher (0.065 pH unit) at a similar ambient temperature (45°C).

Birds are somewhat anomalous among the vertebrates: The temperature of the PO/AH area is relatively unimportant in the elicitation of shivering or panting (115, 125, 129), though vasomotor responses are typically altered in an appropriate manner (10, 129). The avian PO/AH area does apparently function as an integrating center, for injections of PO/AH cholinergic substances produce hypothermia in the pigeon (102) just as similar injections of bacterial pyrogen or prostaglandin E_1 cause fever in the chicken (96). Feathered areas of the skin are highly thermosensitive in pigeons. In inhibiting ongoing shivering, the back is more sensitive than the wing, which in turn is more sensitive than the breast (89).

The spinal cord is a major site of deep body thermosensitivity in birds (104, 123), though a major portion of the central thermosensitivity lies outside of it and the hypothalamus (43). Heating and cooling the spinal cord evoked and suppressed panting in pigeons (105). Associated electrophysiological observations indicate that the firing rate of most spinal cord neurons sensitive to spinal warming was linearly related to the absolute level of local tissue temperature but was unaffected by the rate of temperature change. PO/AH neurons responsive to spinal cord heating often evidenced a steep nonlinear increase in firing rate in the temperature range where panting was observed (42–45°C).

In mammals both the spinal cord (123) and the hypothalamus (13, 42) are thermosensitive. Hypothalamic and spinal thermodes as well as an intravascular heat exchanger implanted in goats revealed that input signals to heat production from the residual inner body were nearly the same order of magnitude as those emanating from the spinal cord and hypothalamus (78). Thus, in addition to areas of demonstrated thermosensitivity in the medulla oblongata and abdominal viscera, temperature sensing elements are probably diffusely distributed throughout the body core.

Heating the hypothalamus (66), spinal cord (39), or skin (39, 41) redistributes blood flow in a manner favoring areas subserving heat exchange. These changes are mediated both by alterations in efferent sympathetic nervous activity and by the direct effects of heat upon local vessels. These two effects are largely separate (40, 41): Neuronal influences affect blood flow through arteriovenous anastomoses and local heating affects capillary blood flow. Under normal conditions the two mechanisms work in concert; neuronally mediated increases in flow through the arteriovenous anastomoses increase the local tissue temperature, thereby facilitating capillary blood flow.

Stitt's quantitative model for the interaction of skin and hypothalamic temperature in the control of heat production (135) may reconcile divergent aspects of previous explanations (51, 61, 137). This model describes metabolic rate in toto, with decreases in skin temperature increasing the thermosensitivity of the PO/AH area. Cutaneous thermal inputs can thus influence both the gain and the threshold of the relation between hypothalamic temperature and heat production. Although Stitt's model may characterize the commonly used laboratory mammals, certain small rodents have developed alternate modes of hypothalamic thermosensitivity that may assist in coping with thermally extreme environments. The antelope ground squirrel (*Ammospermophilus nelsoni*), a diurnal desert rodent, exhibits decreases in hypothalamic thermosensitivity when the ambient temperature is decreased, and this unusual response has been interpreted as a change in the organization of thermoregulatory centers to facilitate appropriate behavioral heat loss responses (49).

In addition to appropriate thermoregulatory responses, hypothalamic temperature changes may produce nonspecific effects. For instance, heating the PO/AH area in ducks (124) increases nasal salt gland secretion, and posterior hypothalamic heating increases heat production in the goat (101).

The differences in autonomic response utilization and and the longer term responses involved in thermal acclimation by vertebrates are shown in Figure 2. Also emphasized are the similarities in thermal sensing and integrating and in behavioral thermoregulation.

ACCLIMATION

Following chronic alteration of the environmental temperature, physiological and biochemical changes are induced that occur over hours, days, and weeks. These changes, termed acclimation, are complex and occur at many levels of organization (45, 54). Certain of the responses are due to local temperature effects and apparently occur in all the vertebrate classes. One such example involves thermally induced alterations in the fatty acid composition of membrane lipids (45). Aspects of acclimation that highlight the differences between subdivisions of this review are emphasized below.

Water-Breathing Ectotherms

Thermal acclimation in fish produces major changes in physiological and biochemical systems, in temperature selection, and in overt thermal capabilities (54, 100). Changes in passive diffusion of solutes and active uptake mechanisms in the fish gill often show different thermal coefficients, leading to major problems in ion and osmoregulation following a shift in temperature (22). There is evidence that the endocrine system is involved in certain of the adaptive adjustments in ionic regulation that occur during thermal acclimation of fish (139).

Following an alteration in body temperature, water-breathing ectotherms face acid-base disturbances as described earlier for reptiles. Fish, however, regulate arterial P_{O_2} rather than P_{CO_2} (103); due to the high solubility of CO_2 in water, arterial P_{CO_2} typically remains at a fixed level, slightly (2–5 mm Hg) above the P_{CO_2} of the inspired water. Adjustments appropriate to altered body temperature involve alterations in bicarbonate excretion (103, 106) and likely utilize ion exchange mechanisms (Cl^-/HCO_3^- and Na^+/NH_4^+ or H^+) found on the fish gill (14). Since these adjustments occur over hours and days, they may be considered one aspect of thermal acclimation in fish.

Air-Breathing Ectotherms

Although in amphibians the skin is of major importance in ion and water balance, active acid-base adjustments in the bullfrog are accomplished only

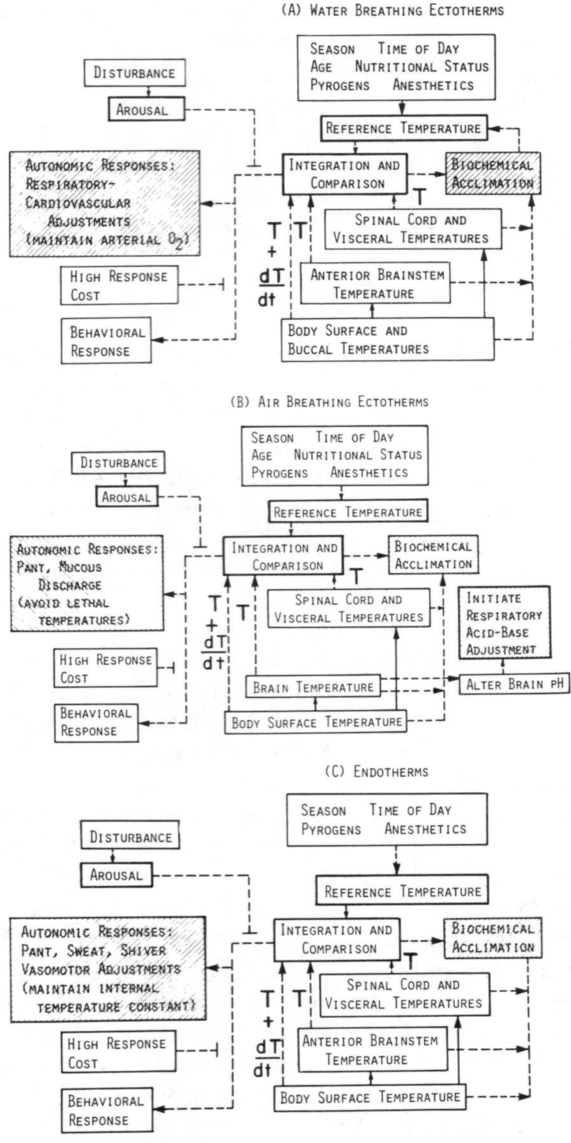

Figure 2 Schema depicting how water-breathing ectotherms (a), air breathing ectotherms (b), and endotherms (c) deal with variations in the thermal environment. Dashed lines indicated informational flow or direct stimulation, while solid lines indicate the involvement of significant amounts of energy. Boxes with heavy borders indicate processing that occurs in the central nervous system. Cross-hatching highlights major differences between groups a, b, and c. All responses are assumed to correct the initiating deficits.

by ventilatory alterations. Skin CO_2 conductance (skin CO_2 loss/transcutaneous P_{CO_2} is not significantly affected by temperature (75).

Thermal acclimation has definite effects on the metabolic rates of various reptilian tissues (56), but temperature effects on oxygen uptake and on acid-base, ionic, and osmotic regulation are less severe than those imposed on water breathers. Thus many temperate-zone reptiles actively initiate changes of body temperature that would rapidly prove fatal to nearly all water breathing vertebrates. Patterson & Davies (93) suggest that acclimation in temperate-zone lizards functions mainly to lower metabolic rates and conserve energy during inactive periods. They placed four species of lizards in a room with the temperature set at the mean night time temperature for spring, summer, autumn, or winter. Heat lamps were turned on in accordance with the mean photoperiod of each season, which allowed the animals to regulate behaviorally their body temperature for that period. Oxygen consumption, measured at 5°C intervals from 5°C to 35°C, was not affected by the "seasonal acclimation" at the higher temperatures. However, low-temperature metabolic rates were lowest for autumn and winter acclimation groups.

Endotherms

Many responses of thermal acclimation in endotherms involve central coordination, since body temperature is typically not altered. Rather, more efficient thermal effector responses are substituted as exposure continues. Local thermal effects are also important, as exposed extremities often undergo large changes in temperature. Tissues in the feet of cold-exposed arctic birds and mammals contain more unsaturated fats, and nerve block in the same peripheral neuron can occur at lower temperatures in distal segments (100). Other alterations, such as increases in effector organ size and capacity, may occur as a result of tissue hyperplasia stimulated by increased effector activity. Thus rats raised in cold showed an increased oxygen uptake, which in turn led to a lung volume 24% greater than that of animals kept at room temperature (35). Hyperplasia of the submaxillary gland (utilized to effect evaporative heat loss) was produced by exposure to heat (55).

The increase in nonshivering thermogenesis seen in rats following prolonged cold exposure is an example of central coordination. In rats this efficient form of heat production involves an increased sensitivity of various organs, especially brown fat, to the synergistic metabolic stimulation of noradrenaline and thyroid hormones (16). Both shivering and nonshivering thermogenesis are influenced by PO/AH and spinal temperatures (6); the PO/AH exerts greater control over nonshivering thermogenesis, while the spinal cord dominates the control of shivering (6, 33).

SUMMARY AND CONCLUSIONS

Vertebrate thermoregulatory systems are similar in overall organization. All vertebrates appear to sense surface and core temperatures, compare these temperatures with a neuronally mediated reference temperature, and effect appropriate behavioral and autonomic output responses. Certain differences exist. Following a temperature change, water-breathing ectotherms activate autonomic responses. These responses may function to avoid disruptions of oxygen uptake following temperature increases and to conserve the energy expended for gill ventilation and active ion uptake during temperature decreases. Thermal acclimation produces major biochemical, physiological, and behavioral changes in these animals. Air-breathing ectotherms activate autonomic thermoregulatory responses only at near-lethal temperatures. Normal variations in body temperature induce respiratory adjustments that maintain a constant ionization state of proteins. In air breathers the consequences of thermal acclimation are less profound than in aquatic ectotherms. Endotherms utilize autonomic responses to maintain a constant internal temperature; long-term biochemical acclimation results in more efficient effector responses and is strongly influence by central neuronal mechanisms.

ACKNOWLEDGMENTS

Drs. M. E. Heath, E. R. Nadel, and L. J. Côté, and Mr. D. E. Lemons provided criticism of the rough draft. During the preparation of this review, the author was supported by NIH Grant 1 RO1 NS15318–01 and the general fund of the Department of Rehabilitation Medicine.

Literature Cited

1. Adair, E. R., Wright, B. A. 1976. Behavioral thermoregulation in the squirrel monkey when response effort is varied. *J. Comp. Physiol. Psychol.* 90: 179–84
2. Albers, C., Gotz, K. H., Welbers, P. 1978. Adaptation of blood gases to diurnal temperature changes in a desert lizard, *Uromastyx ancanthinurus. J. Physiol. London* 277:80–81P
3. Alberts, J. R. 1978. Huddling by rat pups: group behavioral mechanisms of temperature regulation and energy conservation. *J. Comp. Physiol. Psychol.* 92 (2):231–45
4. Deleted in proof
5. Deleted in proof
6. Banet, M., Hensel, H., Liebermann, H. 1978. The central control of shivering and nonshivering thermogenesis in the rat. *J. Physiol. London* 283:569–84
7. Barber, B. J., Crawford, E. C. Jr. 1977. A stochastic dual-limit hypothesis for behavioral thermoregulation in lizards. *Physiol. Zool.* 50 (1):53–60
8. Barber, B. J., Crawford, E. C. Jr. 1979. Dual threshold control of peripheral temperature in the lizard, *Dipsosaurus dorsalis. Physiol. Zool* 52:250–63
9. Bernheim, H. A., Kluger, M. J. 1976. Fever: Effect of drug-induced antipyresis on survival. *Science* 193:237–39
10. Bernstein, M. H. 1974. Vascular responses and foot temperature in pigeons. *Am. J. Physiol.* 226:1350–55
11. Bligh, J. 1973. *Temperature Regulation in Mammals and Other Vertebrates.* Amsterdam: North-Holland. 436 pp.

12. Bligh, J. 1978. Thermoregulation: What is regulated and how? See Ref. 57, pp. 1–10
13. Cabanac, M. 1975. Temperature regulation. *Ann. Rev. Physiol.* 37:415–39
14. Cameron, J. N. 1976. Branchial ion uptake in arctic grayling: Resting values and effects of acid-base disturbance. *J. Exp. Biol.* 64:711–25
15. Deleted in proof
16. Chaffee, R. R. J., Roberts, J. C. 1971. Temperature acclimation in birds and mammals. *Ann. Rev. Physiol.* 33:155–202
17. Corbit, J. D. III. 1974. Control of thermoregulatory behavior. In *Control of Metabolism,* ed. J. D. Sink, pp. 153–93. University Park, Pa: Pennsylvania State Univ. Press
18. Deleted in proof
19. Crawford, E. C. Jr., Barber, B. J. 1974. Effects of core, skin and brain temperature on panting in the lizard, *Sauromalus obesus. Am. J. Physiol.* 226:569–73
20. Crawford, E. C. Jr., Gatz, R. N. 1974. Respiratory alkalosis in a panting lizard, *Sauromalus obesus. Experientia* 30:638–39
21. Crawshaw, L. I. 1976. Effect of rapid temperature change on mean body temperature and gill ventilation in carp. *Am. J. Physiol.* 231:837–41
22. Crawshaw, L. I. 1979. Responses to rapid temperature change in vertebrate ectotherms. *Am. Zool.* 19:225–37
23. Crawshaw, L. I., Hammel, H. T. 1973. Behavioral temperature regulation in the California horn shark, *Heterodontus francisci. Brain Behav. Evol.* 7:447–52
24. Crawshaw, L. I., Hammel, H. T. 1974. Behavioral regulation of internal temperature in the brown bullhead, *Ictalurus nebulosus. Comp. Biochem. Physiol. A* 47:51–60
25. Crawshaw, L. I., Stitt, J. T. 1975. Behavioural and autonomic induction of prostaglandin E fever in squirrel monkeys. *J. Physiol. London* 244:197–206
26. Crawshaw, L. I., Hammel, H. T., Garey, W. L. 1973. Brainstem temperature affects gill ventilation in the California scorpionfish. *Science* 181:579–81
27. Crawshaw, L. I., Johnson, M. H., Lemons, D. E. 1978. Temperature selection and responses to rapid temperature change in the turtle. *Pseudemys scripta. Fed. Proc.* 37:622
28. Croze, S., Duclaux, R., Kenshalo, D. R. 1976. The thermal sensitivity of the polymodal nociceptors in the monkey. *J. Physiol. London* 263:539–62
29. Darian-Smith, I. 1977. Peripheral neural mechanisms of thermal sensibility. *Proc. Aust. Physiol. Pharmacol. Soc.* 8:17–27
30. DeWitt, C., Friedman, R. M. 1979. Significance of skewness in ectotherm thermoregulation. *Am. Zool.* 19:195–220
31. Dizon, A. E., Brill, R. W. 1979. Thermoregulation in tunas. *Am. Zool.* 19:249–66
32. Deleted in proof
33. Fuller, C. A., Horowitz, J. M., Horwitz, B. A. 1977. Spinal cord thermosensitivity and sorting of neural signals in cold exposed rats. *J. Appl. Physiol. Respir. Environ. Exer. Physiol.* 42:154–58
34. Garside, E. T., Heinze, D. G., Barbour, S. E. 1977. Thermal preference in relation to salinity in the threespine stickleback, *Gasterosteus aculeatus L.* with an interpretation of its significance. *Can. J. Zool.* 55:590–94
35. Gehr, P., Hugonnaud, C., Burri, P. H., Bachofen, H., Weibel, E. R. 1978. Adaptation of the growing lung to increased $\dot{V}O_2$. III. The effect of exposure to cold environment in rats. *Respir. Physiol.* 32 (3):345–53
36. Green, M. D., Lomax, P. 1976. Behavioural thermoregulation and neuroamines in fish, *Chromus chromus. J. Thermal. Biol.* 1:237–40
37. Deleted in proof
38. Hackmann, E., Simon, E. 1975. Single unit activity in spinal anterolateral tracts influenced by cold stimulation of spinal cord and skin. In *Depressed Metabolism and Cold Thermogenesis,* ed. L. Janský, X. J. Musacchia, pp. 197–201. Springfield, Ill: C. C. Thomas
39. Hales, J. R., Iriki, M. 1975. Integrated changes in regional circulatory activity evoked by spinal cord and peripheral thermoreceptor stimulation. *Brain Res.* 87 (2–3):267–79
40. Hales, J. R., Iriki, M. 1977. Differential thermal influences in skin blood flow through capillaries and arteriovenous anastomoses, and on sympathetic activity. *Bibl. Anat.* 16 (Pt. 2):189–91
41. Hales, J. R. S., Iriki, M., Tsuchiya, K., Kozawa, E. 1978. Thermally-induced cutaneous sympathetic activity related to blood flow through capillaries and arteriovenous anastomoses. *Pfluegers Arch.* 375:17–24
42. Hammel, H. T. 1968. Regulation of internal body temperature. *Ann. Rev. Physiol.* 30:641–710
43. Hammel, H. T., Maggert, J., Kaul, R., Simon-Oppermann, C., Simon, E. 1976.

Effects of altering spinal cord temperature on temperature regulation in the Adélie penguin, *Pygoscelis adeliae*. *Pfluegers Arch.* 362 (1):1–6
44. Deleted in proof
45. Hazel, J. R., Prosser, C. L. 1974. Molecular mechanisms of temperature compensation in poikilotherms. *Physiol. Rev.* 54:620–77
46. Heath, J. E. 1970. Behavioral regulation of body temperature in poikilotherms. *Physiologist* 13:399–410
47. Heath, J. E., Gasdorf, E., Northcutt, R. G. 1968. The effect of thermal stimulation of anterior hypothalamus on blood pressure in the turtle. *Comp. Biochem. Physiol.* 26:509–18
48. Heatwole, H., Firth, B. T., Stoddart, H. 1975. Influence of season, photoperiod and thermal acclimation on the panting threshold of *Amphibolurus muricatus*. *J. Exp. Zool.* 191:183–92
49. Heller, H. C., Henderson, J. A. 1976. Hypothalamic thermosensitivity and regulation of heat storage behavior in a day-active desert rodent, *Ammospermophilus nelsoni*. *J. Comp. Physiol.* 108B: 255–70
50. Hellon, R. F., Rosenberg, M. F. 1977. Is there modulation of thermal input from the rat scrotum through descending spinal pathways? *J. Physiol. London* 271 (2):63P–64P
51. Hellstrom, B., Hammel, H. T. 1967. Some characteristics of temperature regulation in the unanesthetized dog. *Am. J. Physiol.* 213:547–56
52. Hensel, H. 1976. Functional and structural basis of thermoreception. *Prog. Brain Res.* 43:105–18
53. Hitzig, B. M., Jackson, D. C. 1978. Central chemical control of ventilation in the unanesthetized turtle. *Am. J. Physiol.* 235 (5):R257–64
54. Hochachka, P. W., Somero, G. N. 1973. *Strategies of Biochemical Adaptation.* Philadelphia, Pa: Saunders. 358 pp.
55. Horowitz, M., Soskolne, W. A. 1978. Cellular dynamics of rats submaxillary gland during heat acclimatization. *J. Appl. Physiol.* 44 (1):21–24
56. Hoskins, M. A. H., Aleksiuk, M. 1973. Effects of temperature, photoperiod and season on *in vitro* metabolic rates of tissues from *Thamnophis sirtalis parietalis*, a cold climate reptile. *Comp. Biochem. Physiol.* 45A:737–56
57. Houdas, Y., Guieu, J. D., eds. 1978. *New Trends in Thermal Physiology.* NY: Masson. 204 pp.
58. Huey, R. B. 1974. Behavioral thermoregulation in lizards: Importance of associated costs. *Science* 184:1001–3
59. Iggo, A., Paintal, A. S. 1977. The metabolic dependence of primate cutaneous cold-receptors. *J. Physiol. London* 272 (1):40P–41P
60. Iggo, A., Young, D. W. 1975. Cutaneous thermoreceptors and thermal nociceptors. In *The Somatosensory System*, ed. H. H. Kornhuber, pp. 5–22. Stuttgart: Thieme
61. Jacobson, F., Squires, R. D. 1970. Thermoregulatory responses of the cat to preoptic and environmental temperatures. *Am. J. Physiol.* 218:1575–82
62. Jansk ý, L., Musacchia, X. J., eds. 1976. *Regulation of Depressed Metabolism and Thermogenesis.* Springfield, Ill: Thomas. 276 pp.
63. Deleted in proof
64. Krausz, S., Bernstein, R., Marder, J. 1977. The acid-base balance of the rock partridge, *Alectoris chukar* exposed to high ambient temperatures. *Comp. Biochem. Physiol. A* 57:245–47
65. Krausz, S., Marder, J., Eylath, U. 1978. Blood chemistry changes in the saluki dog exposed to high environmental temperatures. *Physiol. Zool.* 51 (1):33–41
66. Kronert, H., Pleschka, K. 1976. Lingual blood flow and its hypothalamic control in the dog during panting. *Pfluegers Arch.* 367:25–31
67. Laties, V. G. 1971. Effects of d-amphetamine on concurrent schedules of heart and food reinforcement. *J. Physiol. Paris* 63:315–18
68. Lederis, K., Veale, W. L.. eds. 1978. *Current Studies of Hypothalamic Function.* Basel: Karger. Vols. I, II. 218 pp., 210 pp.
69. Lemons, D. E., Crawshaw, L. I. 1978. Temperature regulation in the Pacific lamprey. *Fed. Proc.* 37:929
70. Lillywhite, H. B. 1970. Behavioral temperature regulation in the bullfrog, *Rana catesbeiana*. *Copeia* 1970 (1): 158–68
71. Lillywhite, H. B. 1971. Thermal modulation of cutaneous mucus discharge as a determinant of evaporative water loss in the frog, *Rana catesbeiana*. *Z. Vergl. Physiologie* 73:84–104
72. Lillywhite, H. B. 1975. Physiological correlates of basking in amphibians. *Comp. Biochem. Physiol. A* 52:323–30
73. Lomax, P., Schönbaum, E., eds. 1979. *Body Temperature: Regulation, Drug Effects and Therapeutic Implications.* NY: Marcel Dekker
74. Deleted in proof

75. Mackenzie, J. A., Jackson, D. C. 1978. The effect of temperature on cutaneous CO_2 loss and conductance in the bullfrog. *Respir. Physiol.* 32:313–24
76. Maskrey, M., Nicol, S. C. 1976. Respiratory and thermoregulatory responses of rabbits breathing carbon dioxide during heat exposure. *J. Physiol. London* 261 (2):375–86
77. McCauley, R. W., Reynolds, W. W., Huggins, N. H. 1977. Photokinesis and behavioral thermoregulation in adult sea lampreys, *Petromyzon marinus. J. Exp. Zool.* 202 (3):431–37
78. Mercer, J. B., Jessen, C. 1978. Effects of total body core cooling on heat production on conscious goats. *Pfluegers Arch.* 373 (3):259–68
79. Morgareidge, K. R., Hammel, H. T. 1975. Evaporative water loss in box turtles: Effects of rostral brainstem and other temperatures. *Science* 187:366–68
80. Musacchia, X. J. 1979. Chairman: Symposium on fever and hyperthermia. *Fed. Proc.* 38:27–63
81. Myhre, K., Hammel, H. T. 1969. Behavioral regulation of internal temperature in the lizard, *Tiliqua scincoides. Am. J. Physiol.* 217:1490–95
82. Myhre, K., Cabanac, M., Myhre, G. 1977. Fever and behavioural temperature regulation in the frog, *Rana esculenta. Acta. Physiol. Scand.* 101 (2): 219–29
83. Nadel, E. R., ed. 1977. *Problems With Temperature Regulation During Exercise.* NY: Academic. 141 pp.
84. Nadel, E. R., Cafarelli, E., Roberts, M. F., Wenger, C. B. 1979. Circulatory regulation during exercise in different ambient temperatures. *J. Appl. Physiol. Respirat. Environ. Physiol.* 46:430–37
85. Nagai, M., Iriki, M. 1977. Characteristics of heart rate responses elicited by thermal stimulation of the spinal cord of the carp. *Cyprinus carpio. Comp. Biochem. Physiol. A* 57:417–21
86. Nagai, M., Iriki, M. 1978. Autonomic response of the fish to pyrogen. *Experientia* 34 (9):1177–78
87. Nagai, M., Iriki, M., Iwata, K. S. 1977. Body color changes induced by spinal thermal stimulation of the crucian carp. *Carassius carassius. J. Exp. Biol.* 68: 89–97
88. Necker, R. 1975. Temperature-sensitive ascending neurons in the spinal cord of pigeons. *Pfluegers Arch.* 353 (3):275–86
89. Necker, R. 1977. Thermal sensitivity of different skin areas in pigeons. *J. Comp. Physiol.* 116:239–46
90. Necker, R., Hellon, R. F. 1978. Noxious thermal input from the rat tail: Modulation by descending inhibitory influences. *Pain* 4 (3):231–42
91. Nelson, D. O. 1978. Temperature sensitive neurons in the preoptic region of sunfish. *Physiologist* 21:84
92. Nelson, D. O., Prosser, C. L. 1979. Effects of preoptic lesions on behavioral thermoregulation of green sunfish, *Lepomis cyanellus,* and of goldfish, *Carassius auratus. J. Comp. Physiol.* 129:193–97
93. Patterson, J. W., Davies, P. M. 1978. Thermal acclimation in temperate lizards. *Nature* 275 (5681):646–47
94. Pearson, O. P., Bradford, D. F. 1976. Thermoregulation of lizards and toads at high altitudes in Peru. *Copeia* 1976: 155–70
95. Pierau, F.-K., Torrey, P., Carpenter, D. O. 1974. Mammalian cold-receptor afferents: Role of an electrogenic sodium pump in sensory transduction. *Brain Res.* 73:156–60
96. Pittman, Q. J., Veale, W. L., Cockeram, A. W., Cooper, K. E. 1976. Changes in body temperature produced by prostaglandins and pyrogens in the chicken. *J. Physiol. London* 230 (5):1284–87
97. Deleted in proof
98. Poole, S., Stephenson, J. D. 1977. Body temperature regulation and thermoneutrality in rats. *J. Exp. Physiol.* 62 (2): 143–49
99. Porter, W. P., Mitchell, J. W., Beckman, W. A., DeWitt, C. B. 1973. Behavioral implications of mechanistic ecology. *Oecologia* 13:1–54
100. Prosser, C. L. 1973. *Comparative Animal Physiology.* Philadelphia, Pa: Saunders. pp. 362–428
101. Puschmann, S., Jessen, C. 1978. Anterior and posterior hypothalamus: Effects of independent temperature displacements on heat production in conscious goats. *Pfluegers Arch.* 373 (1): 59–68
102. Pyornila, A., Lahti, H., Hissa, R. 1977. Thermoregulatory changes induced by intrahypothalamic injections of cholinomimetic substances in the pigeon. *Neuropharmacology* 16 (11):737–41
103. Randall, D. J. 1974. The regulation of H^+ concentration in body fluids. *Proc. Can. Soc. Zool. Ann. Meet.,* pp. 89–94
104. Rautenberg, W., Necker, R., May, B. 1972. Thermoregulatory responses of the pigeon to changes of the brain and the spinal cord temperatures. *Pfluegers Arch.* 338:31–42

105. Rautenberg, W., May, B., Necker, R., Rosner, G. 1978. Control of panting by thermosensitive spinal neurons in birds. In *Respiratory Function in Birds, Adult and Embryonic,* ed. J. Piiper, pp. 204–10. Berlin/Heidelberg: Springer
106. Reeves, R. B. 1977. The interaction of body temperature and acid-base balance in ectothermic vertebrates. *Ann. Rev. Physiol.* 39:559–86
107. Reeves, R. B., Rahn, H. 1979. Patterns in vertebrate acid-base regulation. In *The Lung in Health and Disease,* Vol. 13: *Evolution of Respiratory Processes; A Comparative Approach,* pp. 831–2741. NY: Marcel Dekker
108. Reynolds, W. W., Casterlin, M. E., Covert, J. B. 1976. Behavioural fever in teleost fishes. *Nature* 259 (5538):41–42
109. Roberts, W. W., Martin, J. R. 1977. Effects of lesions in central thermosensitive areas on thermoregulatory responses in rat. *Physiol. Behav.* 19 (4): 503–11
110. Rodbard, S., Samson, F., Ferguson, D. 1950. Thermosensitivity of the turtle brain as manifested by blood pressure changes. *Am. J. Physiol.* 160:402–8
111. Satinoff, E. 1974. Neural integration of thermoregulatory responses. In *Limbic and Autonomic Nervous Systems Research,* ed. L. V. DiCara, pp. 41–83. NY: Plenum
112. Satinoff, E. 1978. Neural organization and evolution of thermal regulation in mammals. *Science* 201 (4350):16–22
113. Satinoff, E., Hendersen, R. 1977. Thermoregulatory behavior. In *Handbook of Operant Behavior,* ed. W. K. Honig, J. E. R. Staddon, pp. 153–73. Englewood Cliffs, NJ: Prentice-Hall
114. Satinoff, E., McEwen, G. N. Jr., Williams, B. A. 1976. Behavioral fever in newborn rabbits. *Science* 193 (4258): 139–40
115. Schmidt, I. 1976. Paradoxical changes of respiratory rate elicited by altering rostral brain stem temperature in the pigeon. *Pfluegers Arch.* 367 (1):111–13
116. Schmidt, I. 1978. Interactions of behavioral and autonomic thermoregulation in heat stressed pigeons. *Pfluegers Arch.* 374 (1):47–55
117. Schmidt, I. 1978. Behavioral and autonomic thermoregulation in heat stressed pigeons modified by central thermal stimulation. *J. Comp. Physiol.* 127A:75–87
118. Schmidt, I., Rautenberg, W. 1975. Instrumental thermoregulatory behavior in pigeons. *J. Comp. Physiol.* 101: 225–35
119. Schmidt, I., Graf, R., Rautenberg, W. 1978. Diurnal variations in the cooperation of shivering and instrumental behavior for cold defense in the pigeon. *Proc. Satell. Symp.: Thermal Regulation,* ed. Y. Houdas, J. D. Guieu, pp. 135–38. Paris: Masson
120. Deleted in proof
121. Deleted in proof
122. Simon, E. 1972. Temperature signals from skin and spinal cord converging on spinothalamic neurons. *Pfluegers Arch.* 337:323–32
123. Simon, E. 1974. Temperature regulation: The spinal cord as a site of extrahypothalamic thermoregulatory functions. *Rev. Physiol. Biochem. Pharmacol.* 71:1–76
124. Simon-Oppermann, C., Hammel, H. T., Simon, E. 1979. Hypothalamic temperature and osmoregulation in the Pekin duck. *Pfluegers Arch.* 378:213–21
125. Simon-Oppermann, C., Simon, E., Jessen, C., Hammel, H. T. 1978. Hypothalamic thermosensitivity in conscious Pekin ducks. *Am. J. Physiol.* 235 (3):R130–40
126. Deleted in proof
127. Smith, E. N. 1979. Behavioral and physiological thermoregulation in crocodilians. *Am. Zool.* 191 19:239–48
128. Smith, K. A., Blatteis, C. M. 1979. Behavioral fever induced in guinea pigs by intrapreoptic leucocytic pyrogen (LP). *Fed. Proc.* 38:1296
129. Snapp, B. D., Heller, H. C., Gospe, S. M. Jr. 1977. Hypothalamic thermosensitivity in California quail, *Lophortyx californicus. J. Comp. Physiol.* 117B (31):345–57
130. Spray, D. C. 1974. Metabolic dependence of frog cold-receptor sensitivity. *Brain Res.* 72:354–59
131. Spray, D. C. 1976. Pain and temperature receptors of anurans. In *Frog Neurobiology,* ed. R. Llinas, W. Precht, pp. 607–28. NY: Springer
132. Spray, D. C., Belkin, D. B. 1972. Heart rate cloacal temperature hysteresis in iguana is a result of thermal lag. *Nature* 239:337–38
133. Stevens, E. D., Neill, W. H. 1978. Body temperature relations of tunas, especially tunas. In *Fish Physiology,* ed W. S. Hoar, D. J. Randall, 3:315–59. NY: Academic
134. Stitt, J. T. 1976. Inhibition of thermoregulatory outflow in conscious rabbits during periods of sustained arousal proceedings. *J. Physiol. London* 260 (2):31P–32P

135. Stitt, J. T. 1978. Hypothalamus and thermoregulation: Control of metabolic heat production and the determinants of a normal regulated body temperature in rabbits in the cold. In *Current Studies of Hypothalamic Function,* ed. W. L. Veale, K. Lederis, 2:44–54. Basel: Karger

136. Stitt, J. T., Crawshaw, L. I. 1975. Brainstem stimulation elicits changes in body temperature which can be modified by ambient temperature. *Fed. Proc.* 34:456

137. Stolwijk, J. A. J., Hardy, J. D. 1966. Temperature regulation in man—a theoretical study. *Pfluegers Arch.* 291: 129–62

138. von Frisch, K. 1911. Über den Einfluss der Temperatur auf die schwarzen Pigmentzellen der Fischhaut. *Biol. Zentralbl.* 31:236–48

139. Umminger, B. L. 1978. The role of hormones in the acclimation of fish to low temperatures. *Naturwissenschaften* 65:144–50

140. Wang, L. C., Hudson, J. W., eds. 1978. *Strategies in the Cold: Natural Torpidity and Thermogenesis.* NY: Academic. 715 pp.

141. Weathers, W. W., White, F. N. 1971. Physiological thermoregulation in turtles. *Am. J. Physiol.* 221:704–10

142. Deleted in proof

143. Wood, S. C., Glass, M. L., Johansen, K. 1977. Effects of temperature on respiration and acid-base balance in a monitor lizard. *J. Comp. Physiol.* 116B:287–96

Ann. Rev. Physiol. 1980. 42:493–510

INSECT ENDOCRINOLOGY: Regulation of Endocrine Glands, Hormone Titer, and Hormone Metabolism

❖1282

Lawrence I. Gilbert, Walter E. Bollenbacher, and Noelle A. Granger

Department of Biological Sciences, Northwestern University, Evanston, Illinois 60201

INTRODUCTION

The cyclical processes of growth and molting in insects are brought about by two hormones, one produced by specific neurosecretory cells (NSC) in the brain and the other by paired glands in the prothorax, the prothoracic glands (PG). The product of the NSC, prothoracicotropic hormone (PTTH), is secreted periodically in response to environmental cues and activates the PG. Activation of the PG results in an increased rate of synthesis of the prohormone, ecdysone, which is then converted in peripheral tissues to the molting hormone (MH, ecdysterone, 20-hydroxyecdysone). The action of MH on the epidermal cells results in the initiation of the molting process: retraction of the epidermis from the old cuticle (apolysis); deposition of a new cuticle; and ultimate shedding of the remnant of the old cuticle (ecdysis). A third hormone, the juvenile hormone (JH), is secreted by the corpora allata (CA), paired endocrine glands located near the insect's brain. The role of JH in the molting process is to determine the character of the molt initiated by MH. It is generally believed that a high JH titer dictates a larval-larval molt, while a low JH titer permits a larval-pupal molt (first metamorphic molt); in the presumed absence of JH, pupal-adult metamorphosis occurs. In many adult insects, JH is again synthesized by the CA and this time functions as a gonadotropin (26, 51, 101).

0066-4278/80/0315-0493$01.00

From a half century of research in insect endocrinology it is clear that precise quantities of these three hormones must be secreted at critical stages and titers maintained for specific periods of time in order for normal development to proceed. Thus we discuss the chemistry, biosynthesis, and catabolism of these hormones; endocrine gland regulation; and, most importantly, how the insect regulates its hormone titer and, consequently, its development.

Although only the three hormones controlling post-embryonic development (PTTH, MH, JH) are considered, these and a variety of largely uncharacterized hormones, presumably peptides, control an array of homeostatic and behavioral events in the life of the insect (32, 45, 124, 136) —e.g. hyperglycemic hormone, gut activation hormone, diuretic hormone, antidiuretic hormone, eclosion hormone, embryonic hormone, tanning hormone (bursicon), cardioaccelerating hormone, diapause hormone, pupariation factor, adipokinetic hormone, etc. The adipokinetic hormone, a decapeptide, is the only one thus far purified, sequenced, and synthesized (125, 126). In addition. the insect nervous system contains substances immunochemically similar to several vertebrate regulatory factors—e.g. vasopressin and oxytocin (99, 127); enkephalin (50, 99); somatostatin (25); and glucagon (130).

PROTHORACICOTROPIC HORMONE (PTTH)

Kopeć (72), on the basis of ligation and surgical experiments with larvae of the gypsy moth, concluded nearly 60 years ago that "it is, therefore, most possible that the brain does not influence the general process of metamorphosis through the nerves, but that it has rather the function of an organ of internal secretion, in that it affects the organism by means of a substance (or substances) which may be supposed to pass into the blood of the caterpillar from the brain at a certain stage of the larval life." Further, he conceived the idea of critical periods and implied that the brain does not act alone in stimulating the molting process. These suppositions have been corroborated. This was the first indication of an endocrine function for the nervous system in any organism.

The cerebral endocrine complex includes the brain, containing a variety of NSC (104); the adjoining corpora cardiaca, containing the axon terminals and thus a neurohemal organ for some of these cells (45); and the distal corpora allata, the site of JH synthesis and possibly the neurohemal organ for PTTH in some insects (17, 62). PTTH is synthesized in the perikarya of specific cerebral NSC, transported down the axons, and stored in the enlarged axon terminals of the neurohemal organ. The arrangement of this neuroendocrine axis indicates several points at which the titer of PTTH could be regulated, such as synthesis, storage, axonal transport, and release.

Chemistry of PTTH

Based on limited data, PTTH appears to be a peptide having a molecular weight of ~5000, though higher molecular weight forms have been reported (36, 37, 61, 63, 64, 70, 84, 90, 128, 147, 148). A variety of insects have been used as the source of PTTH and different methods of extraction and purification have been utilized, so the types and number of peptide forms of PTTH are currently obscure. Enzymatic degradation and chemical analysis of PTTH fractions from different insects have: confirmed the peptide nature of the hormone; suggested that the N and C termini of the molecule may be blocked; and indicated that disulfide bonds may be present (64, 84). The major problem in the elucidation of the structure of PTTH has been the lack of a sensitive, specific, rapid, and reproducible bioassay. An in vitro assay using isolated PG (13) has resolved this problem and progress should now be more rapid.

Synthesis and Release of PTTH

Although ultrastructural analyses indicate that some neurosecretory products are released from the corpora cardiaca by granule breakdown and exocytosis (91, 108–110, 115), the mechanism for PTTH release is only understood by analogy. The problem is compounded since the chemical structure of PTTH is unknown and the NSC responsible for PTTH synthesis have only been identified by indirect means (e.g. extirpation, implantation, cautery, etc). Indeed, in a variety of insects almost every group and combination of cerebral NSC has been implicated (43). The lateral group of seven NSC in *Manduca sexta* was cited recently as the area of PTTH production (38). An improved in vitro assay in which a single NSC could be analyzed for PTTH activity showed that a single lateral NSC in each brain hemisphere was the source of PTTH (3).

Studies of the physiology of insect NSC have generally relied on cytology, cytochemistry, and autoradiography; but, unfortunately, the relationship between staining intensity and NSC activity remains unresolved (45). However, use of several of these techniques in one system has determined the flow rate from the perikaryon to the axon terminal in the bee, and most of the neurosecretory material released appeared to be newly synthesized rather than stored (56).

In the well studied cerebral NSC system of the bloodsucking bug, *Rhodnius,* the posterior NSC have been indirectly identified as the source of PTTH (83, 122, 123, 141). These cells are presumably activated by abdominal stretch receptors following a blood meal. Within 2 hr after feeding, their ultrastructural appearance suggests increased synthesis and transport of neurosecretory material from the perikaryon. Ultrastructural observations also revealed developmental alterations in the rates of synthesis, storage, and transport of this material during the first week after the blood meal, which suggests that different processes are emphasized at different times.

By the eighth day after feeding, both the electrical activity in the NSC axons to the CC and the axonal transport of neurosecretory material decline to the pre-feeding level in *Rhodnius,* apparently as a result of inhibition of release by a high MH level in the hemolymph. Here MH may be exerting a negative feedback effect on the neurons concerned with the synaptic control of the NSC, as occurs in the vertebrate brain (122).

CYCLIC NUCLEOTIDES Cyclic AMP (cAMP) is present in the insect brain (102, 138), and a direct correlation between cAMP levels and PTTH activity of the brain exists in silkmoth pupae and developing adults (95, 96). Cyclic nucleotides may act either in the synthesis of PTTH or in its transport and release. However, no such temporal relationship is evident in the brain of the army worm, *Mamestra configurata* (12). Thus the relationship between cyclic nucleotides and PTTH synthesis and/or release is still unclear.

ENVIRONMENTAL AND HUMORAL CONTROL Several stimuli can elicit the synthesis and/or release of PTTH, including nutritional state, crowding, wounding, and especially photoperiod and temperature (24). Neural pathways by which these stimuli are transduced to affect the PTTH-NSC are unknown; control may be exerted indirectly via synaptic inhibition or activation by other neurons, or may act directly on the NSC (24).

Insects possess the capacity for "extra-retinal" photoreception, and the cerebral lobes generally appear to be the neural region that detects photoperiodic change (135). In pupae of the oak silkmoth, *Antheraea pernyi,* the photoperiodic receptor affecting PTTH activity lies in a lateral area of the brain and controls PTTH release rather than synthesis (143). Even when normal neural activity is inhibited by the injection of tetrodotoxin, these pupae respond normally to varying photoperiodic regimens. This suggested that the entire photoperiodic mechanism resides in the lateral NSC (143). In another moth, *Manduca sexta,* specific lateral NSC have been identified as the source of PTTH (3), so perhaps the photoperiod mechanism resides in the PTTH-NSC. In the aphid, a neuronal photoperiodic clock and photoperiodic receptors also appear to lie in a lateral area of the brain (121).

In certain insects, humoral factors may elicit or inhibit PTTH synthesis and release. For example, (33, 146) the CA of the rice stem borer, *Chilo suppressalis,* are active during the larval diapause, and JH inhibited PTTH synthesis and/or release. This concept has been extended to the control of larval and pre-pupal diapause in other insects (131, 149) and to the control of larval pupal development in nondiapausing lepidopteran larvae (59, 87–89).

The mechanisms by which PTTH release is terminated and its synthesis then initiated in preparation for the next molting cycle seem quite complex and may vary between species. Based on observations of hormonal effects on cerebral neurosecretion, release and/or synthesis are probably regulated at various levels by both MH and JH (4, 5, 57, 58, 77, 79, 80, 119, 120, 132) and perhaps by other factors (1). This may occur under both diapausing and nondiapausing conditions and at different stages of the insect's life.

ECDYSTEROIDS

Ecdysteroids are polyhydroxylated ketosteroids having a common tetracyclic nucleus; they are ubiquitous in arthropods (48). Ecdysone (2β,3β,14α,-22R,25-pentahydroxy-5β-cholest-7-en-6-one) was the first of these steroids identified and is the parent molecule for nomenclatural purposes. Ecdysteroids have also been found in nematodes, annelids, and molluscs; a distinct class of ecdysteroids has been identified in plants (39).

Seven ecdysteroids have been identified in various stages of the insect life cycle. With a single exception (makisterone A, a C_{28} steroid), they are C_{27} steroids varying only in the number and/or stereochemistry of the hydroxyl groups present (82). The principal ecdysteroids in insects are ecdysone (α-ecdysone) and 20-hydroxyecdysone (β-ecdysone, ecdysterone, crustecdysone). They initiate post-embryonic development and metamorphosis (101, 116).

Secretory Product of the Prothoracic Glands

The chemical nature of the product synthesized by the PG was not known until recently. Extraction of a substance having MH activity from isolated glands was unsuccessful because the glands do not store the material (39). However, with the development of in vitro culture methods for lepidopteran PG (2, 20, 69), enough of the product was synthesized to permit its identification as ecdysone (20, 69). The PG appear to be the only physiological source of this hormone during larval-larval and larval-pupal development (69), even though other larval tissues apparently can synthesize it (35, 85). Ecdysone is the ecdysteroid synthesized by the PG of cockroaches, locusts, beetles, and flies (15, 39), and now appears to be the only ecdysteroid produced by the larval PG (20, 69). However, this may not be true of PG in general since the product(s) of the glands from other stages of insect development has not been identified.

Following synthesis, ecdysone is released into the hemolymph (69) and metabolized by other tissues to 20-hydroxyecdysone (16, 68), the "true"

MH (116). The observation that 20-hydroxyecdysone is biologically more active than ecdysone suggests that ecdysone acts as a pro(pre)-hormone for 20-hydroxyecdysone (68, 69, 116). However, this may not be true for all orders of insects or for any one insect at all stages of development.

Endocrine Regulation of the PG

Studies on the endocrine regulation of the PG in insects show that PTTH is the major trophic hormone for these glands (45). The direct activation of the PG by PTTH has recently been established in vitro (13). This in vitro approach has shown that, in contrast to the tenet that PTTH activates biosynthetically inactive glands (45), PTTH simply elicits an increase in a basal rate of ecdysone synthesis by the PG.

PTTH appears to stimulate the PG via cAMP in a manner analogous to that of the ACTH-adrenal cortex axis in vertebrates. Correlations between cAMP levels in the PG and the biosynthetic activity of the glands during larval-pupal development suggest that the changes in gland activity may be both cAMP-dependent and -independent (137). Proof that cAMP is involved in the regulation of PG activity by PTTH must await the purification of this neurohormone.

Suggested stimulatory effects of JH on the PG may be restricted to specific developmental states, whereas PTTH activates the glands throughout development (58). However, the physiological basis for a JH-mediated stimulation of the PG is conjectural. The innervation of the PG by both nervous and neurosecretory fibers from the thoracic ganglia has suggested direct regulation of the PG as well, but a function for this innervation has not been demonstrated (8, 10, 57, 117).

Biosynthesis of Ecdysone and 20-Hydroxyecdysone

Research on the biosynthesis of ecdysteroids has focused on the biosynthetic pathways for ecdysone and 20-hydroxyecdysone during larval-pupal development (129). An in vivo approach has generally been utilized in which possible sterol precursors are injected into an insect and the metabolites then analyzed. Sterols are required, for insects cannot synthesize the steroid nucleus (39, 129). These studies indicate that various species of insects at the same developmental stage may utilize various biosynthetic pathways and that individual insects may use various biosynthetic arrangements to produce the same or different ecdysteroids during their life cycles.

The early steps in ecdysone and 20-hydroxyecdysone biosynthesis involve saturation of the Δ^5 bond of cholesterol, establishment of a Δ^7 bond, the addition of a 6-keto group and *cis* fusion of the A/B rings (5 β proton) (129). However, the detailed mechanisms by which these early reactions occur are not known, and they probably cannot be resolved using an in vivo approach.

The later steps in the biosynthetic pathway for ecdysone and 20-hydroxyecdysone are better understood and involve hydroxylations at C-2, 14, 22, and 25 for ecdysone and, in addition, at C-20 for 20-hydroxyecdysone. These hydroxylations apparently occur in a preferred sequence: C-14, C-2, C-25. and ultimately at C-22 to form ecdysone (39, 129). After release by the PG, ecdysone is hydroxylated at C-20 in other tissues to form 20-hydroxyecdysone (68).

An in vitro approach has been utilized recently to elucidate ecdysone biosynthesis by the PG and has thus far corroborated most of the conclusions from the in vivo studies (14). Since the in vitro system permits direct analysis of individual steps in the pathway, it also provides information on the early steps in the biosynthesis. For example, a monohydroxylated 5α-analog (A/B *trans* fusion) of ecdysone (3β-hydroxy-5-β-cholestan-6-one) has been identified in cultured PG of silkmoth larvae and may function as an early biosynthetic intermediate (106). In the larval tobacco hornworm, *Manduca sexta,* the precursor for ecdysone synthesis by the PG may be a steroid more highly oxygenated than cholesterol or the 5α-analog (14). These two proposed precursors are incompatible with a common biosynthetic scheme, which suggests that ecdysone biosynthesis may differ even in insects of the same order.

The most thoroughly characterized step in the synthesis of ecdysteroids is the hydroxylation of ecdysone to 20-hydroxyecdysone (16). Use of a cell-free system has revealed that the enzyme involved in the reaction, ecdysone 20-monooxygenase, is a steroid mixed-function oxidase catalyzed by cytochrome P-450 and is either mitochondrial or microsomal, depending on the insect species (16, 30, 31, 66, 78). The monooxygenase is distributed in various tissues (fat body, Malpighian tubules, midgut, etc). Its activity varies during development, so it may be a regulatory point for controlling the relative titers of ecdysone and 20-hydroxyecdysone (31) and thus postembryonic development.

Catabolism of Ecdysteroids

Degradation of ecdysteroids in insects results from three kinds of catabolic mechanisms: conjugations, oxidations (dehydrogenations and hydroxylations), and isomerizations (epimerizations).

Conjugation, the most common mechanism, produces sulfate and glycoside esters. Although one conjugate has been chemically identified (20-hydroxyecdysone-22-sulfate) (105), the enzyme systems involved have not been described. Two ecdysteroid dehydrogenations are known. The primary one involves a soluble ecdysone oxidase that generates 3-dehydro derivatives of both ecdysone and 20-hydroxyecdysone (71). An enzyme system that catalyzes C-20-C-22 side-chain fission also exists (34), but its biological significance remains questionable. The hydroxylation of ecdysone and 20-

hydroxyecdysone to 26-hydroxy derivatives has been considered a catabolic mechanism because these compounds have reduced biological activities (129). However, an endocrinological function for these ecdysteroids cannot be eliminated. Isomerization is mediated by an ecdysone dehydrogenase-isomerase localized in the midgut of the insect and catalyzes the epimerization of ecdysone to its less active 3α-epimer (86).

Regulation of the Ecdysteroid Titer

The dynamic interaction of four physiological processes—synthesis, degradation (inactivation), excretion, and sequestration—determines the titer of ecdysone and 20-hydroxyecdysone at a specific developmental stage. Synthesis (which encompasses the regulation of the PG and substrate availability) and degradation, are the most critical processes for titer regulation. Sequestration and excretion are the least understood. Sequestration may only involve the formation and storage of conjugates (145). Thus this process may be a major factor in determining the level of biologically active hormone present. Direct excretion of ecdysone, 20-hydroxyecdysone, and 3-dehydro derivatives also occurs (82), but the degree to which this pathway controls the hormone titer is not clear.

A specific hemolymph binding protein for 20-hydroxyecdysone has been identified recently (29). Its function is unknown, but it may protect the hormone from degradation and therefore contribute to the control of the ecdysteroid titer.

Alternative Sources of Ecdysteroids

Ecdysteroids occur in large quantities at specific times during postembryonic development. They also have been found during adult reproduction and embryogenesis (39), when structurally distinct ecdysteroids are synthesized by tissues other than the PG.

During reproduction, ecdysone and 2-deoxyecdysone are synthesized in the ovaries (46, 92), presumably by the follicle cells (46), and then are either sequestered by the developing eggs for later use or are released into the hemolymph where they may initiate vitellogenin synthesis (39, 52). Several unique ecdysteroids have also been identified in insect embryos—e.g. 20-26-dihydroxyecdysone, 26-hydroxyecdysone, and makisterone A (39, 82, 129). Their presence may be a result of sequestration of maternal ecdysteroids and/or synthesis by the developing embryo. The possible site(s) of synthesis in the embryo is not known, nor is the function of these hormones, though serosal cuticle deposition in early embryonic development may be initiated by these ecdysteroids (46).

Although the endocrinology of the ecdysteroids present in these other developmental stages is poorly understood, their presence suggests a complex system involving structurally distinct ecdysteroids controlling a variety of functions during the entire life cycle of the insect. The insect steroid hormone system may be as complex as that of the vertebrates.

JUVENILE HORMONES (JH)

Chemistry of JH

The three juvenile hormones (JH) identified in insects are synthesized and released by the corpora allata (CA). They are homologous sesquiterpenes containing an epoxide function, designated, in order of their discovery, JH I (methyl-(2E,6E)-3,11-dimethyl-7-ethyl-*cis*-10,11-epoxy-trideca-2,6-dienoate) (103); JH II (methyl-(2E,6E)-3,7,11-trimethyl-*cis*-10,11-epoxy-trideca-2,6-dienoate) (81); and JH III (methyl-(2E,6E)-3,7,11-trimethyl-10,11-epoxy-dodeca-2-6-dienoate) (67). The JH produced by the CA have now been isolated and identified in moths, bees, locusts, beetles, and cockroaches, primarily by in vitro culture (111). With a single exception (76), only JH III appears to be synthesized by the CA of insects other than moths.

Function of JH

The JH appear to have numerous roles in insect development, such as in polymorphism (42, 142), larval diapause (21, 33, 146), ovarian diapause (44), coloration (42), locomotory activity (19), and various aspects of behavior (136). However, they function primarily in the control of metamorphosis and reproduction (101, 116). JH I and II have been suggested as the metamorphic hormones and JH III as a gonadotropin in the adult female (76). However, in the honey bee (53) and the grasshopper (11), only JH III has been identified in all developmental stages, implying that it acts as a morphogenetic hormone as well. It must be emphasized that thus far the tentative roles assigned the JH have been inferred from quantitative and qualitative studies of the homologs, which have in most cases been examined only in the adult.

Biosynthesis of JH

With one exception (22), JH biosynthesis occurs only in the CA. In vivo investigations of the biosynthesis of the homosesquiterpenoid structures of JH I and II have been marginally successful and have not revealed the origin of the extra carbons on the side chains of these unique hormones. The development of in vitro culture methods for the CA of *Manduca sexta* (67), which resulted in the discovery of JH III, permitted direct investigation of JH biosynthesis. It was demonstrated that the putative precursors propionate, mevalonate, and acetate are incorporated into JH I and II (65, 113), whereas for JH III, acetate is utilized through a normal isoprenoid pathway. The identification of specific intermediates in this pathway depended on the use of supplemented cell-free CA enzyme systems. With this approach the syntheses of homomevalonate and mevalonate in the presence of acetyl and propionyl-CoA and the existence of derivatives of 3-hydroxy-3-ethylglutarate and 3-hydroxy-3-methylglutarate were demonstrated (112). The subsequent discovery of these two compounds in incubations of CA enzymes with acetyl and propionyl-CoA, and in molar ratios consistent with the physiological levels of JH II and III in the CA donor, suggests that these compounds are actually intermediates in the biosynthetic pathway (112). On the basis of these results, it is generally accepted that the carbon skeleton of JH I is synthesized from one mevalonate and two homomevalonate molecules, and that of JH II from one homomevalonate and two mevalonate molecules. The JH III congener is synthesized from three mevalonate molecules.

The terminal steps in the JH biosynthesis involve methylation at C-1 and epoxidation at the C-10, C-11 positions. A methyl ester transferase, apparently microsomal and selective for JH I and JH III, catalyzes the carboxyl alkylation of the JH acid (98); a mixed-function oxidase, as yet uncharacterized, is presumably responsible for the epoxidation (6, 98).

The exact sequence of these terminal steps in the pathway has not yet been resolved. Based on the accumulation of putative precursors in cell-free systems, alkylation of the epoxy acid appears to be the final step (98). The presence of esterases specific for the hydrolysis of the JH methyl ester function in CA homogenates (54) indicates the rapid alkylation and release of the hormone. Alternatively, accumulation of methyl farnesenate in intact glands in vitro suggests that epoxidation is the terminal step (94). Both pathways may exist, but they may be species specific and/or may occur only at certain developmental stages.

Mechanisms for the Control of JH Titer

The precise and temporally acute manner in which the JH titer is modulated during postembryonic development and reproduction clearly demonstrates that mechanisms for the regulation of the hormone (9, 28, 60) exist and could occur at one or more levels: synthesis, release, catabolism, transport, uptake, and excretion.

REGULATION OF SYNTHESIS AND RELEASE Both the brain and the subesophageal ganglion innervate the CA. This innervation involves both neurosecretory and nonneurosecretory axons, suggesting the existence of both nervous and neurohormonal control (40). Most of the research on the CA that has provided evidence for nervous and/or neuroendocrine regulatory mechanisms has utilized adult insects and has been concerned with the control of the CA during reproduction and diapause. Activation of the glands is generally associated with the medial cerebral NSC of the pars intercerebralis (7, 26, 40, 44), whereas inhibition usually appears to be a nervous phenomenon (26, 40). Exceptions to these generalizations exist, but these regulatory mechanisms probably apply for the larval CA as well (40). In vivo investigations emphasize the central role of the brain in the control of the CA and have indicated that this involves a complex process integrating both neural and humoral inputs. It is unfortunate that an in vivo approach cannot distinguish unequivocally between these two types of control, since both types of stimuli can affect the CA via the same nerve bundle. In vitro techniques have been combined recently with the in vivo approach and have provided evidence for (*a*) a humoral allatotropin (a CA-stimulating factor) (114), and an allatohibin (a CA-inhibiting factor) (144) in larvae of two moths (*Galleria mellonella* and *Manduca sexta,* respectively) and (*b*) nervous inhibition of the CA during the reproductive cycle of the grasshopper, *Schistocerca gregaria,* (133) and of a cockroach, *Diploptera punctata* (118). The probable development in the near future of a completely in vitro system should allow assessment of humoral and even nervous control of JH synthesis by the CA (49).

The possibility that release is a key regulatory point controlling the JH titer has been eliminated by the demonstration that JH is not stored in the CA and that it is released immediately following synthesis (49, 134).

CATABOLISM AND TRANSPORT Insects possess effective and specific mechanisms for the inactivation of JH; these contribute to the modulation of JH titer. JH degradation appears to occur via two major pathways: hydrolysis by general and specific esterases in the hemolymph (39); and hydration of the epoxide group by epoxide hydratases in the fat body, wing discs, and midgut (18, 39, 54). Tissue oxidases may be involved in the catabolism of JH as well (150).

Two types of hemolymph esterases, general and JH-specific, have been identified in insects (6, 39, 40, 73, 140). A specific JH binding protein (JHBP) discovered in the hemolymph protects JH from esterase degradation (39, 40, 54, 74, 107), and in fact the two types of JH esterases are distinguishable by their capacities to hydrolyze JH bound to JHBP. The general esterases are present throughout larval development, are inhibited by organophosphates (93), and cannot hydrolyze JH bound to JHBP. By contrast, the JH-specific esterases appear at particular developmental times, are organophosphate-insensitive, and can hydrolyze either bound or free JH (73, 107). Consequently the JH titer can be dramatically reduced during development by the temporally precise interaction of the JHBP and the specific esterases (6, 54, 75, 139). This interaction, in conjunction with changing rates of JH synthesis by the CA, can regulate the JH titer. Such a role for the hemolymph JH esterases may not be ubiquitous among insects, since in the honey bee and the flesh fly esterases do not appear to be involved in the regulation of the JH titer (23, 140). JH-specific esterases themselves appear to be under some form of endocrine regulation, either direct or indirect, which further increases the complexity of the mechanisms for the control of JH titer (97, 100).

In addition to the high-affinity, high-specificity and low-capacity JHBP found thus far in 14 species of insects (73), low-affinity, low-specificity and high-capacity lipoproteins also exist (39–41). In insects where both the JHBP and the lipoprotein are present, the latter probably plays a minor role in the transport and protection of the hormone. Although JHBP may effectively protect JH I from catabolism and excretion, its affinity for JH II and III is considerably lower (39). Thus the latter homologs may more often exist either in the free state or bound to the high molecular weight lipoprotein and may be metabolized more rapidly to the JH acid.

In insects that have JHBP, fluctuations in its titer during development may also affect the catabolism of JH—i.e. low concentrations of binding protein would result in free JH. This possibility has been investigated in one species; the level of JHBP in the hemolymph appears relatively constant and is higher than the highest titer of JH (47).

EXCRETION AND UPTAKE OF JH Little information exists on the uptake of JH by various tissues, because these tissues may contain degradative enzymes for JH, and because the lipophilic and surface-active characteristics of this hormone make it difficult to study in whole tissue systems (55). Similarly, little is known about excretory rates for JH (27).

Despite many recent studies, no general model for the regulation of JH titer has emerged. Regulation may be achieved by a variety of mechanisms that are themselves subject to regulation. This is apparently also the case for MH and PTTH.

Acknowledgments

Cited research from this laboratory and the writing of this chapter were aided by grants from NIH (AM-02818), NSF (PCM 76–23291), and the Whitehall Foundation. We thank Nancy Grousnick for her expert help in the preparation of this manuscript.

Literature Cited

1. Adams, T. S., Grugel, S., Ittycheriah, P. I., Olstad, G., Caldwell, J. M. 1975. Interactions of the ring gland, ovaries, and juvenile hormone with brain neurosecretory cells in *Musca domestica*. *J. Insect Physiol.* 21:1027–43
2. Agui, N. 1976. Attempts to establish insect endocrine system *in vitro*. In *Invertebrate Tissue Culture*, ed. K. Maramorosch, pp. 133–60. NY: Academic
3. Agui, N., Granger, N., Gilbert, L. I., Bollenbacher, W. E. 1979. Cellular localization of the insect prothoracicotropic hormone: *In vitro* assay of a single neurosecretory cell. *Proc. Natl. Acad. Sci. USA.* In press
4. Agui, N., Hiruma, K. 1977. Ecdysone as a feedback regulator for the neurosecretory brain cells in *Mamestra brassicae*. *J. Insect Physiol.* 23:1393–96
5. Agui, N., Hiruma, K. 1977. *In vitro* activation of neurosecretory brain cells

in *Mamestra brassicae* by β-ecdysone. *Gen. Comp. Endocrinol.* 33:467–72

6. Akamatsu, Y., Dunn, P. E., Kezdy, F. J., Kramer, K. J., Law, J. H., Reibstein, D., Sanburg, L. L. 1975. Biochemical aspects of juvenile hormone action in insects. In *Control Mechanisms in Development,* ed. R. H. Meints, E. Davies, pp. 123–49. NY: Plenum
7. Baehr, J. C. 1973. Controle neuroendocrine du fonctionnement du corpus allatum chez *Rhodnius prolixus. J. Insect Physiol.* 19:1041–55
8. Beaulaton, J. 1968. Étude ultrastructurale et cytochimique des glandes prothoracique de vers à soie aux quatrième et cinquième ages larvaires II. Les cellules interstitielles et les fibres nerveuses. *J. Ultrastruct. Res.* 23:499–515
9. Bergot, B. J., Schooley, D. A., Chippendale, G. M., Yin, C.-M. 1976. Juvenile hormone titer determinations in the southwestern corn borer, *Diatraea grandiosella,* by electron capture–gas chromatography. *Life Sci.* 18:811–20
10. Blazsek, I., Balázs, A., Novák, V. J. A., Malá, J. 1975. Ultrastructural study of the prothoracic glands of *Galleria mellonella* L. in the penultimate, last larval and pupal stages. *Cell Tissue Res.* 158:269–80
11. Blight, M. M., Wenham, M. J. 1976. Identification of JH III in haemolymph from adults and larvae of *Schistocerca gregaria. Insect Biochem.* 6:35–38
12. Bodnaryk, R. P. 1978. Levels of brain cyclic AMP and cyclic GMP during the initiation of adult development in the Bertha army worm, *Mamestra configurata* WLK. *Insect Biochem.* 8:383–87
13. Bollenbacher, W. E., Agui, N., Granger, N., Gilbert, L. I. 1979. *In vitro* activation of insect prothoracic glands by the prothoracicotropic hormone. *Proc. Natl. Acad. Sci. USA* 76:5148–52
14. Bollenbacher, W. E., Galbraith, M. N., Gilbert, L. I., Horn, D. H. S. 1977. *In vitro* metabolism of 3β-hydroxy-, and 3β,14α-dihydroxy- [3α-^{3}H]-5β-cholest-7-en-6 one by the prothoracic glands of *Manduca sexta. Steroids* 29:47–63
15. Bollenbacher, W. E.. Goodman, W., Vedeckis, W. V., Gilbert, L. I. 1976. *In vitro* synthesis and secretion of α-ecdysone by the ring glands of the fly, *Sarcophaga bullata. Steroids* 27:309–24
16. Bollenbacher, W. E., Smith, S. L., Wielgus, J. J., Gilbert, L. I. 1977. Evidence for an α-ecdysone cytochrome P-450 mixed function oxidase in insect fat body mitochondria. *Nature* 268:660–63
17. Bounhiol, J. J., Gabe, M., Arvy, L. 1954. Données histophysiologiques sur la neuro-sécrétion chez *Bombyx mori* L. et sur ses rapports avec les glandes endocrines. *Pubbl. Stn. Zool. Napoli Suppl.* 24:52–53
18. Brooks, G. T. 1977. Epoxide hydratase as a modifier of biotransformation and biological activity. *Gen. Pharmacol.* 8:221–26
19. Caldwell, R. L., Rankin, M. A. 1972. Effects of a juvenile hormone mimic on flight in the milkweed bug, *Oncopeltus fasciatus. Gen. Comp. Endocrinol.* 19:601–5
20. Chino, H., Sakurai, S., Ohtaki, T., Ikekawa, N., Miyazaki, H., Ishibashi, M., Abuki, H. 1974. Biosynthesis of α-ecdysone by prothoracic glands *in vitro. Science* 183:529–30
21. Chippendale, G. M. 1977. Hormonal regulation of larval diapause. *Ann. Rev. Entomol.* 22:121–38
22. Dahm, K. H., Bhaskaran, G., Peter, M. G., Shirk, P. D., Seshan, K. R., Röller, H. 1976. On the identity of the juvenile hormone in insects. In *The Juvenile Hormones,* ed. L. I. Gilbert, pp. 19–47. NY: Plenum
23. deKort, C. A. D., Wieten, M., Kramer, S. J., Goewie, E. 1977. Juvenile hormone degradation and carrier proteins in honey bee larvae. *Proc. K. Ned. Akad. Wet. Ser. C* 80:297–301
24. Doane, W. E. 1972. Role of hormones in insect development. In *Insects: Developmental Systems,* ed. S. J. Counce, C. H. Waddington, 2:291–497. NY: Academic
25. Doerr-Schott, J., Joly, L., Dubois, M. P. 1978. Sur l'existence dans la pars intercerebralis d'un insecte (*Locusta migratoria* R. et F.) de cellules neurosécrétices fixant un antisérum antisomatostatine. *C. R. Acad. Sci. Paris* 286:93–95
26. Engelmann, F. 1970. *The Physiology of Insect Reproduction,* pp. 143–89. Oxford: Pergamon. 307 pp.
27. Erley, D., Southard, S., Emmerich, H. 1975. Excretion of juvenile hormone and its metabolites in the locust, *Locusta migratoria. J. Insect Physiol.* 21:61–70
28. Fain, M. J., Riddiford, L. M. 1975. Juvenile hormone titers in the hemolymph during late larval development of the tobacco hornworm, *Manduca sexta* (L.). *Biol. Bull. Woods Hole* 149:506–21
29. Feyereisen, R. 1977. A specific binding protein for the moulting hormone ecdysterone in locust haemolymph. *Experientia* 33:1111

30. Feyereisen, R., Durst, F. 1978. Ecdysterone biosynthesis: a microsomal cytochrome P-450-linked ecdysone 20-monooxygenase from tissues of the African migratory locust. *Eur. J. Biochem.* 88:37–47
31. Feyereisen, R., Hoffmann, J. A. 1977. Regulation of ecdysone hydroxylation in *Locusta migratoria:* rôle of the moulting hormone level. *J. Insect Physiol.* 23:1175–81
32. Frontali, N., Gainer, H. 1977. Peptides in invertebrate nervous systems. In *Peptides in Neurobiology.* ed. H. Gainer, pp. 259–94. NY: Plenum
33. Fukaya, M., Mitsuhashi, J. 1961. Larval diapause in the rice stem borer with special reference to its hormonal mechanism. *Bull. Natl. Inst. Agric. Res. Jpn;* 13:1–30
34. Galbraith, M. N., Horn, D. H. S., Middleton, E. J. 1969. The catabolism of crustecdysone in the blowfly, *Calliphora stygia. Chem. Commun.* 1134–35
35. Galbraith, M. N., Horn, D. H. S., Middleton, E. J. 1973. Ecdysone biosynthesis in the blowfly, *Calliphora stygia. Chem. Commun.* 203–4
36. Gersch, M. 1961. Insect metamorphosis and the activation hormone. *Am. Zool.* 1:53–57
37. Gersch, M., Eckert, M., Baumann, E., Birkenbeil, H. 1977. Immunological investigations of the neuroendocrine system of insects. V. Characterization of activation factor II by immunological, biochemical and physiological methods. *Zool. Jahrb. Physiol.* 81:153–64
38. Gibbs, D., Riddiford, L. M. 1977. Prothoracicotropic hormone in *Manduca sexta:* localization by a larval assay. *J. Exp. Biol.* 66:255–66
39. Gilbert, L. I., Goodman, W., Bollenbacher, W. E. 1977. Biochemistry of regulatory lipids and sterols in insects. In *International Review of Biochemistry. Biochemistry of Lipids II,* ed. T. H. Goodwin, 14:1–50. Baltimore: University Park Press
40. Gilbert, L. I., Goodman, W., Granger, N. 1978. Regulation of juvenile hormone titer in Lepidoptera. In *Comparative Endocrinology,* ed. P. J. Gaillard, H. H. Boer. pp. 471–86. Amsterdam: Elsevier/North Holland
41. Gilbert, L. I., Goodman, W., Nowock. J. 1976. The possible roles of binding proteins in juvenile hormone metabolism and action. In *Actualités sur les Hormones d'Invertébrés, Colloque Internation aux CNRS No. 251,* pp. 413–30. Paris: CNRS
42. Girardie, A. 1975. Le polymorphisme phasaire des Acridiens et son controle endocrine. *J. Endocrinol. Toulouse,* pp. 13–17
43. Girardie, A., De Reggi, M. 1978. Moulting and ecdysone release in response to electrical stimulation of protocerebral neurosecretory cells in *Locusta migratoria. J. Insect Physiol.* 24:797–802
44. Girardie, A., Mouline, M., Girardie, J. 1974. Rupture de la diapause ovarienne d'*Anacridium aegyptium* par stimulation électrique des cellules neurosécrétrices médianes de la pars intercerebralis. *J. Insect Physiol.* 20:2261–75
45. Goldsworthy, G. J., Mordue, W. 1974. Neurosecretory hormones in insects. *J. Endocrinol.* 60:529–58
46. Goltzené, F., Lagueux, M., Charlet, M., Hoffmann, J. A. 1978. The follicle cell epithelium of maturing ovaries of *Locusta migratoria:* a new biosynthetic tissue for ecdysone. *Hoppe-Seyler's Z. Physiol. Chem.* 359:1427–34
47. Goodman, W., Gilbert, L. I. 1978. The hemolymph titer of juvenile hormone binding protein and binding sites during the fourth larval instar of *Manduca sexta. Gen. Comp. Endocrinol.* 35: 27–34
48. Goodwin, T. W., Horn, D. H. S., Karlson, P., Koolman, J., Nakanishi, K., Robbins, W. E., Siddall. J. B., Takemoto, T. 1978. Ecdysteroids: a new generic term. *Nature* 272:122
49. Granger, N. A., Bollenbacher, W. E., Vince, R., Gilbert, L. I., Baehr, J. C., Dray, F. 1979. *In vitro* biosynthesis of juvenile hormone by the larval corpora allata of *Manduca sexta:* Quantification by radioimmunoassay. *Mol. Cell. Endocrinol.* 16:1–17
50. Gros, C., Lafon-Cazal, M., Dray, F. 1978. Présence de substances immunoréactivement apparentées aux enképhalines chez un Insecte, *Locusta migratoria. C. R. Acad. Sci. Paris* 287:647–50
51. Hagedorn, H. H., Kunkel, J. G. 1979. Vitellogenin and vitellin in insects. *Ann. Rev. Entomol.* 24:475–505
52. Hagedorn, H. H., O'Connor, J. D., Fuchs, M. S., Sage, B., Schlaeger, D. A., Bohm, M. K. 1975. The ovary as a source of α-ecdysone in an adult mosquito. *Proc. Natl. Acad. Sci. USA* 72:3255–59
53. Hagenguth, H., Rembold, H. 1978. Identification of juvenile hormone 3 as the only JH homolog in all developmen-

tal stages of the honey bee. *Z. Naturforsch.* 33:847–50
54. Hammock, B. D. 1975. NADPH dependent epoxidation of methyl farnesoate to juvenile hormone in the cockroach, *Blaberus giganteus* L. *Life Sci.* 17:323–28
55. Hammock, B., Nowock, J., Goodman, W., Stamoudes, V., Gilbert, L. I. 1975. The influence of hemolymph-binding protein on juvenile hormone stability and distribution in *Manduca sexta* fat body and imaginal discs *in vitro*. *Mol. Cell. Endocrinol.* 3:167–84
56. Heinzeller, T., Vogel, H. 1978. Daily release of neurosecretory material produced in the pars intercerebralis of *Apis mellifica* L. with and without training to a foraging schedule. *J. Comp. Physiol.* 126:327–31
57. Herman, W. S., Gilbert, L. I. 1966. The neuroendocrine system of *Hyalophora cecropia* (L.) (Lepidoptera:Saturniidae) 1. The anatomy and histology of the ecdysial glands. *Gen. Comp. Endocrinol.* 7:275–91
58. Hiruma, K., Shimada, H., Yagi, S. 1978. Activation of the prothoracic gland by juvenile hormone and prothoracicotropic hormone in *Mamestra brassicae*. *J. Insect Physiol.* 24:215–20
59. Hiruma, K., Yagi, S., Agui, N. 1978. Action of juvenile hormone on the cerebral neurosecretory cells of *Mamestra brassicae in vivo* and *in vitro*. *Appl. Entomol. Zool.* 13:149–57
60. Hsiao, T. H., Hsiao, C. 1977. Simultaneous determinations of molting and juvenile hormone titers of the greater wax moth. *J. Insect Physiol.* 23:89–93
61. Ichikawa, M., Ishizaki, H. 1963. Protein nature of the brain hormone of insects. *Nature* 198:308–9
62. Ichikawa, M., Nishiitsutsuji-Uwo, J. 1959. Studies on the role of the corpus allatum in the Eri-silkworm, *Philosamia cynthia richini*. *Biol. Bull. Woods Hole* 116:88–94
63. Ishizaki, H., Ichikawa, M. 1967. Purification of the brain hormone of the silkworm *Bombyx mori*. *Biol. Bull. Woods Hole* 133:355–68
64. Ishizaki, H., Suzuki, A., Isogai, A., Nagasawa, H., Tamura, S. 1977. Enzymatic and chemical inactivation of partially purified prothoracicotropic (brain) hormone of the silkworm, *Bombyx mori*. *J. Insect Physiol.* 23:1219–22
65. Jennings, R. C., Judy, K. J., Schooley, D. A., Hall, M. S., Siddall, J. B. 1975. The identification and biosynthesis of two juvenile hormones from the tobacco budworm moth (*Heliothis virescens*). *Life Sci.* 16:1033–40
66. Johnson, P., Rees, H. H. 1977. The mechanism of C-20 hydoxylation of α-ecdysone in the desert locust, *Schistocerca gregaria*. *Biochem. J.* 168:513–20
67. Judy, K. J., Schooley, D. A., Dunham, L. L., Hall, M. S., Bergot, B. J., Siddall, J. B. 1973. Isolation, structure and absolute configuration of a new natural insect juvenile hormone from *Manduca sexta*. *Proc. Natl. Acad. Sci. USA* 70:1509–13
68. King, D. S. 1972. Metabolism of α-ecdysone and possible intermediate precursors by insects *in vivo* and *in vitro*. *Gen. Comp. Endocrinol. Suppl.* 3:221–24
69. King, D. S., Bollenbacher, W. E., Borst, D. W., Vedeckis, W. V., O'Connor, J. D., Ittycheriah, P. I., Gilbert, L. I. 1974. The secretion of α-ecdysone by the prothoracic glands of *Manduca sexta in vitro*. *Proc. Natl. Acad. Sci. USA* 71:793–96
70. Kobayashi, M., Yamazaki, M. 1966. The proteinic brain hormone in an insect, *Bombyx mori* L. (Leipidoptera:-Bombycidae). *Appl. Entomol. Zool.* 1:53–60
71. Koolman, J., Karlson, P. 1978. Ecdysone oxidase: reaction and specificity. *Eur. J. Biochem.* 89:453–60
72. Kopeć, S. 1922. Studies on the necessity of the brain for the inception of insect metamorphosis. *Biol. Bull. Woods Hole* 42:323–42
73. Kramer, K. J., Childs, C. N. 1977. Interaction of juvenile hormone with carrier proteins and hydrolases from insect haemolymph. *Insect Biochem.* 7:397–403
74. Kramer, K. J., Sanburg, L. L., Keźdy, F. J., Law, J. H. 1974. The juvenile hormone binding protein in the hemolymph of *Manduca sexta*. *Proc. Natl. Acad. Sci. USA* 71:493–97
75. Kramer, S. J., Wieten, M., de Kort, C. A. D. 1977. Metabolism of juvenile hormone in the Colorado potato beetle, *Leptinotarsa decemlineata*. *Insect Biochem.* 7:231–36
76. Lanzrein, B., Hashimoto, M., Parmakovich, V., Nakanishi, K., Wilhelm, R., Lüscher, M. 1975. Identification and quantification of juvenile hormones from different developmental stages of the cockroach, *Nauphoeta cinerea*. *Life Sci.* 16:1271–84
77. Marks, E. P., Ittycheriah, P. I. Leloup, A. M. 1972. The effect of β-ecdysone on

insect neurosecretion *in vitro*. *J. Insect Physiol.* 18:847–50

78. Mayer, R. T., Svoboda, J. A., Weirich, G. F. 1978. Ecdysone 20-hydroxylase in midgut mitochondria of *Manduca sexta* (L.). *Hoppe-Seyler's Z. Physiol. Chem.* 359:1247–57
79. McCaffery, A. R., Highnam, K. C. 1975. Effects of corpora allata on the activity of the cerebral neurosecretory system of *Locusta migratoria migratorioides* R. & F. *Gen. Comp. Endocrinol.* 25:358–72
80. McCaffery, A. R., Highnam, K. C. 1975. Effects of corpus allatum hormone and its mimics on the activity of the cerebral neurosecretory system of *Locusta migratoria migratoriodes* R. & F. *Gen. Comp. Endocrinol.* 25: 373–86
81. Meyer, A. S., Schneiderman, H. A., Hanzmann, E., Ko, J. H. 1968. The two juvenile hormones from the Cecropia silk moth. *Proc. Natl. Acad. Sci. USA* 60:853–60
82. Morgan, E. D., Poole, C. F. 1977. Chemical control of insect moulting. *Comp. Biochem. Physiol.* 57B:99–109
83. Morris, G. P., Steel, C. G. H. 1977. Sequence of ultrastructural changes induced by activation in the posterior neurosecretory cells in the brain of *Rhodnius prolixus* with special reference to the role of lysosomes. *Tissue & Cell* 9:547–61
84. Nagasawa, H., Isogai, A., Suzuki, A., Tamura, S., Ishizaki, H. 1979. Purification and properties of the prothoracicotropic hormone of the silkworm, *Bombyx mori, Dev. Growth Differ.* 21: 29–38
85. Nakanishi, K., Moriyama, H., Okauchi, T., Fujioka, S., Koreeda, M. 1972. Biosynthesis of α- and β-ecdysone from cholesterol outside of the prothoracic glands in *Bombyx mori. Science* 176:51–52
86. Nigg, H. N., Svoboda, J. A., Thompson, M. J., Kaplanis, J. N., Dutkey, S. R., Robbins, W. E. 1974. Ecdysone metabolism: ecdysone dehydrogenase-isomerase. *Lipids* 9:971–74
87. Nijhout, H. F. 1975. A threshold size for metamorphosis in the tobacco hornworm, *Manduca sexta* (L.) *Biol. Bull. Woods Hole* 149:214–25
88. Nijhout, H. F., Williams, C. M. 1974. Control of moulting and metamorphosis in the tobacco hornworm, *Manduca sexta* (L.): growth of the last instar larva and the decision to pupate. *J. Exp. Biol.* 61:481–91
89. Nijhout, H. F., Williams, C. M. 1974. Control of mounting and metamorphosis in the tobacco hornworm, *Manduca sexta* (L.): cessation of juvenile hormone secretion as a trigger for pupation. *J. Exp. Biol.* 61:493–501
90. Nishiitsutsuji-Uwo, J. 1972. Purification and some properties of insect brain hormone extracted from silkworm heads. *Botyu-Kagaku* 37:93–102
91. Normann, T. C. 1969. Experimentally induced exocytosis of neurosecretory granules. *Exp. Cell Res.* 55:285–87
92. Ohnishi, E., Mizuno, T., Chatani, F., Ikekawa, N., Sakurai, S. 1977. 2-Deoxy-α-ecdysone from ovaries and eggs of the silkworm, *Bombyx mori. Science* 197:66–67
93. Pratt, G. E. 1975. Inhibition of juvenile hormone carboxylesterase of locust haemolymph by organophosphates *in vitro. Insect Biochem.* 5:595–607
94. Pratt, G. E., Tobe, S. S. 1974. Juvenile hormones radiobiosynthesized by corpora allata of adult female locusts *in vitro. Life Sci.* 14:575–86
95. Rasenick, M. M., Neuburg, M., Berry, S. J. 1976. Brain cyclic AMP levels and the initiation of adult development in the Cecropia silkmoth. *J. Insect Physiol.* 22:1453–56
96. Rasenick, M. M., Neuburg, M., Berry, S. J. 1978. Cyclic nucleotide activation of the silkmoth brain—cellular localization and further observations on the patterns of activation. *J. Insect Physiol.* 24:137–39
97. Reddy, G., Hwang-Hsu, K., Kumaran, A. K. 1979. Factors influencing juvenile hormone esterase activity in the wax moth, *Galleria mellonella. J. Insect Physiol.* 25:65–71
98. Reibstein, D., Law, J. H., Bowlus, S. B., Katzenellenbogen, J. A. 1976. Enzymatic synthesis of juvenile hormone in *Manduca sexts.* See Ref. 22, pp. 131–46
99. Remy, C., Girardie, J., Dubois, M. P. 1979. Vertebrate neuropeptide-like substances in the subesophageal ganglion of two insects: *Locusta migratoria* R. and F. (Orthoptera) and *Bombyx mori* L. (Lepidoptera) immunocytological investigation. *Gen. Comp. Endocrinol.* 37:93–100
100. Retnakaran, A., Joly, P. 1976. Neurosecretory control of juvenile hormone inactivation in *Locusta migratoria* L. See Ref. 41, pp. 317–23
101. Riddiford, L. M. 1980. Insect endocrinology: action of hormones at the cellular level. *Ann. Rev. Physiol.* 42:511–28

102. Rojakovick, A. S., March, R. B. 1972. The activation and inhibition of adenyl cyclase from the brain of the Madagascar cockroach (*Gromphadorhina portentosa*). *Comp. Biochem. Physiol. B* 43:209–15
103. Röller, H., Dahm, K. H., Sweeley, C. C., Trost, B. M. 1967. The structure of juvenile hormone. *Angew. Chem. Int. Ed. Engl.* 6:179–80
104. Rowell, H. F. 1976. The cells of the insect neurosecretory system: constancy, variability and the concept of the unique identifiable neuron. *Adv. Insect Physiol.* 12:63–123
105. Russell, G. B., Price, G. M. 1977. Metabolism of β-ecdysone during the larval and white puparial stage of the blowfly, *Calliphora erythrocephala. Insect Biochem.* 7:197–202
106. Sakurai, S., Ikekawa, N., Ohtaki, T., Chino, H. 1977. 3β-Hydroxy-5α-cholestan-6-one: A possible precursor of α-ecdysone biosynthesis. *Science* 198:627–29
107. Sanburg, L. L., Kramer, K. J., Keźdy, F. J., Law, J. H., Oberlander, H. 1975. Role of juvenile hormone esterases and carrier proteins in insect development. *Nature* 253:266–67
108. Scharrer, B. 1968. Neurosecretion XIV. Ultrastructural study of sites of release of neurosecretory material in blattarian insects. *Z. Zellforsch.* 89:1–16
109. Scharrer, B., Wurzelmann, S. 1974. Observations on synaptoid vesicles in insect neurons. *Zool. Jb. Physiol.* 78: 387–96
110. Scharrer, B., Wurzelmann, S. 1978. Neurosecretion XVII. Experimentally induced release of neurosecretory material by exocytosis in the insect *Leucophaea maderae. Cell Tiss. Res.* 190: 173–80
111. Schooley, D. A. 1977. Analysis of the naturally occurring juvenile hormones —their isolation, identification, and titer determination at physiological levels. In *Analytical Biochemistry of Insects,* ed. R. B. Turner, pp. 241–87. NY: Elsevier
112. Schooley, D. A., Judy, K. J., Baker, F. C., Lee, E., Bergot, B. J., Hall, M. S. 1978. Biosynthesis of the juvenile hormones: the role of the homoisoprenoid intermediates. See Ref. 40, pp. 499–502
113. Schooley, D. A., Judy, K. J., Bergot, B. J., Hall, M. S., Siddall, J. B. 1973. Biosynthesis of the juvenile hormones of *Manduca sexta:* labelling pattern from mevalonate, propionate and acetate. *Proc. Natl. Acad. Sci. USA* 70:2921–25
114. Sehnal, F., Granger, N. A. 1975. Control of corpora allata function in last instar larvae of *Galleria mellonella. Biol. Bull. Woods Hole* 148:106–16
115. Smith, U. 1970. The origin of small vesicles in neurosecretory axons. *Tissue & Cell* 2:427–33
116. Sridhara, S., Nowock, J., Gilbert, L. I. 1978. Biochemical endocrinology of insect growth and development. *Int. Rev. Biochem.:* 20:133–88
117. Srivastava, K. P., Tiwari, R. K., Kumar, P. 1977. Effect of sectioning the prothoracic gland nerves in the larva of the lemon-butterfly, *Papilio demoleus* L. *Experientia* 33:98–99
118. Stay, B., Tobe, S. S. 1977. Control of juvenile hormone biosynthesis during the reproductive cycle of a viviparous cockroach I. Activation and inhibition of corpora allata. *Gen. Comp. Endocrinol.* 33:531–40
119. Steel, C. G. H. 1973. Humoral regulation of the cerebral neurosecretory system of *Rhodnius prolixus* (Stal.) during growth and moulting. *J. Exp. Biol.* 58:177–87
120. Steel, C. G. H. 1975. A neuroendocrine feedback mechanism in the insect moulting cycle. *Nature* 253:267–69
121. Steel, C. G. H. 1976. Neurosecretory control of polymorphism in aphids. In *Phase and Caste Determination in Insects,* ed. M. Lüscher. pp. 117–30. Oxford: Pergamon
122. Steel, C. G. H. 1978. Nervous and hormonal regulation of neurosecretory cells in the insect brain. See Ref. 40, pp. 327–30
123. Steel, C. G. H., Harmsen, R. 1977. Dynamics of the neurosecretory system in the brain of an insect, *Rhodnius prolixus,* during growth and moulting. *Gen. Comp. Endocrinol.* 17:125–41
124. Steele, J. E. 1976. Hormonal control of metabolism in insects. *Adv. Insect Physiol.* 12:239–323
125. Stone, J. V., Mordue, W., Batley, K. E., Morris, H. R. 1976. Structure of locust adipokinetic hormone, a neurohormone that regulates lipid utilisation during flight. *Nature* 263:207–11
126. Stone, J. V., Mordue, W., Broomfield, C. E., Hardy, P. M. 1978. Structure-activity relationships for the lipid-mobilising action of locust adipokinetic hormone. *Eur. J. Biochem.* 89:195–202
127. Strambi, C., Strambi, A., Cupo, A., Rougon-Rapuzzi, G., Martin, N. 1978. Étude des taux d'une substance apparentée à la vasopressine dans le systém nerveux de Grillons soumis à

différentes conditions hygrométriques. *C.R. Acad. Sci. Paris* 287:1227–30

128. Suzuki, A., Isogai, A., Hori, T., Ishizaki, H., Tamura, S. 1975. A simple procedure for partial purification of silkworm brain hormone. *Agric. Biol. Chem.* 39:2157–62
129. Svoboda, J. A., Kaplanis, J. N., Robbins, W. E., Thompson, M. J. 1975. Recent developments in insect steroid metabolism. *Ann. Rev. Entomol.* 20: 205–20
130. Tager, H. S., Markese, J., Spiers, R. D., Kramer, K. J. 1975. Glucagon-like immunoreactivity in insect corpus cardiacum. *Nature* 254:707–8
131. Takeda, N. 1978. Hormonal control of prepupal diapause in *Monema flavescens* (Lepidoptera). *Gen. Comp. Endocrinol.* 34:123–31
132. Thomsen, E., Lea, A. O. 1968. Control of the medial neurosecretory cells by the corpus allatum in *Calliphora erythrocephala. Gen. Comp. Endocrinol.* 12:51–57
133. Tobe, S. S., Chapman, C. S., Pratt, G. E. 1977. Decay in juvenile hormone biosynthesis by insect corpus allatum after nerve transection. *Nature* 268:728–30
134. Tobe, S. S., Pratt, G. E. 1974. Dependence of juvenile hormone release from corpus allatum on intraglandular content. *Nature* 252:474–76
135. Truman, J. W. 1976. Extraretinal photoreception in insects. *Photochem. Photobiol.* 23:215–25
136. Truman, J. W., Riddiford, L. M. 1977. Invertebrate systems for the study of hormonal effects on behavior. *Vitam. Horm.* 35:283–325
137. Vedeckis, W. V., Bollenbacher, W. E., Gilbert, L. I. 1976. Insect prothoracic glands: a role for cyclic AMP in the stimulation of α-ecdysone secretion. *Mol. Cell. Endocrinol.* 5:81–88
138. Vedeckis, W. V., Gilbert, L. I. 1973. Production of cyclic AMP and adenosine by the brain and prothoracic glands of *Manduca sexta. J. Insect Physiol.* 19:2445–57
139. Vince, R. K., Gilbert, L. I. 1977. Juvenile hormone esterase activity in precisely timed last instar larvae and pharate pupae of *Manduca sexta. Insect Biochem.* 7:115–20
140. Weirich, G., Wren, J. 1976. Juvenile hormone esterase in insect development: A comparative study. *Physiol. Zool.* 49:341–50
141. Wigglesworth, V. B. 1934. The physiology of ecdysis in *Rhodnius prolixus* (Hemiptera) II. Factors controlling moulting and "metamorphosis." *Q. J. Microsc. Sci.* 77:191–222
142. Wigglesworth, V. B. 1970. *Insect Hormones,* p. 125. Edinburgh: Oliver and Boyd. 159 pp.
143. Williams, C. M. 1969. Photoperiodism and the endocrine aspects of insect diapause. *Symp. Soc. Exp. Biol.* 23:285–300
144. Williams, C. M. 1976. Juvenile Hormones—In Retrospect and in Prospect. See Ref. 22, pp. 1–14
145. Willig, A., Rees, H. H., Goodwin, T. W. 1971. Biosynthesis of insect moulting hormones in isolated ring glands and whole larvae of *Calliphora. J. Insect Physiol.* 17:2317–26
146. Yagi, S., Fukaya, M. 1974. Juvenile hormone as a key factor regulating larval diapause of the rice stem borer, *Chilo suppressalis* (Lepidoptera:Pyralidae). *Appl. Entomol. Zool.* 9:247–55
147. Yamazaki, M., Kobayashi, M. 1969. Purification of the proteinic brain hormone of the silkworm, *Bombyx mori. J. Insect Physiol.* 15:1981–90
148. Yamazaki, M., Kobayashi, M. 1971. Studies on the purification of the brain hormone in an insect. *Bombyx mori. Bull. Seric. Exp. Stn. Tokyo* 24:499–524
149. Yin, C.-M., Chippendale, G. M. 1973. Juvenile hormone regulation of the larval diapause of the southwestern corn borer, *Diatraea grandiosella. J. Insect Physiol.* 19:2403–20
150. Yu, S. J., Terriere, L. C. 1978. Metabolism of juvenile hormone I by microsomal oxidase, esterase, and epoxide hydrase of *Musca domestica* and some comparisons with *Phormia regina* and *Sarcophaga bullata. Pestic. Biochem. Physiol.* 9:237–46

Ann. Rev. Physiol. 1980. 42:511–28

INSECT ENDOCRINOLOGY: Action of Hormones at the Cellular Level ❖1283

Lynn M. Riddiford

Department of Zoology, University of Washington, Seattle, Washington 98195

The endocrine regulation of the life of the insect is based on the ecdysteroids (ecdysone, 20-hydroxyecdysone), juvenile hormone (JH), and a myriad of neurosecretory peptide hormones, most of which have yet to be purified and sequenced. Ecdysteroids and JH control both growth and development and later reproductive maturation. The neurohormones regulate the release of these two hormones and also a variety of homeostatic activities and behavior.

The preceding review in this volume (47) discusses the regulation of the endocrine glands and the chemistry and metabolism of the hormones. This review is concerned with the hormonal regulation of physiological processes. Since there have been many recent reviews of various aspects of insect endocrinology and insect hormone action (13, 26, 36, 48, 50–52, 60, 99, 111, 112, 120) I concentrate here on a few systems that promise to better our understanding of the action of ecdysteroids and juvenile hormone at the cellular level, in both morphogenesis and reproduction. I then discuss the actions of two identified peptide hormones.

MORPHOGENETIC ACTIONS OF ECDYSONE AND JUVENILE HORMONE

Since an insect lives within a rigid exoskeleton or cuticle, growth necessitates the periodic shedding of this cuticle and the production of a larger one. This process of molting is controlled by ecdysone from the prothoracic glands, which is converted to 20-hydroxyecdysone, the active hormone, by

0066-4278/80/0315-0511$01.00

the peripheral tissues (47). Since growth always occurs in the larval stages and is terminated at metamorphosis, a second hormone, juvenile hormone, from the corpora allata ensures larval molting. When the insect approaches its maximum size, the JH titer declines, allowing the ecdysteroids to initiate metamorphosis. The cellular changes associated with larval molting occur primarily in the epidermis; but at metamorphosis internal changes also occur.

Epidermis and Cuticle Formation

The insect epidermis is a single cell layer of electrically coupled cells (21) that produces the overlying cuticle, each cell molding the surface pattern of the cuticle lying above it (127). Although epidermal cells are regarded as differentiated cells that make the cuticle, they can further differentiate into specialized structures such as bristles or hairs at the time of the molt (128). Most insect epidermal cells can produce various kinds of cuticle—i.e. larval, pupal, or adult, depending on the hormonal milieu.

The cytological events occurring in the epidermis in preparation for the molt have been described in detail (reviewed in 73, 86, 133). The following sequence of events generally occurs: The cells detach from the overlying cuticle (apolysis); an ecdysial membrane is secreted that separates the old cuticle from the one to be made; the molting gel is secreted, followed by the new epicuticle, consisting primarily of proteins and lipids, and the new procuticle of chitin and protein (4). Usually late in this sequence the enzymes in the molting fluid, often including enzymes in the cuticle itself (7), are activated and digest the old procuticle leaving the epicuticle to be shed at ecdysis. After ecdysis the new cuticle is sclerotized by a cross-linking of the proteins with each other and with chitin (4), a process often accelerated by the hormone bursicon (86, 99). Thus the insect epidermal cell is primarily a secretory unit that makes and releases various products in a defined sequence in response to a hormonal stimulus. The cell must also undergo any cell division and/or differentiation dictated by the hormonal milieu at the beginning of this sequence. Ecdysone, which initiates cuticle formation and directs its progress, is present in the insect through the beginning of procuticle deposition (35, 99).

The hormonal control of this cuticular deposition is now being studied primarily in tissue culture. Irrespective of whether the epidermis is from embryos (16, 17), body wall (20, 39, 78, 82, 83, 101), or from imaginal discs or their derivatives (76, 78, 81, 85, 88, 129), cuticle formation complete with differentiated bristles requires exposure to about 10^{-6} to 10^{-7} M 20-hydroxyecdysone (β-ecdysone or ecdysterone) [similar to the titers being reported in the hemolymph (126)] for a defined length of time. In most systems a definite concentration-time relationship governs cuticle formation (20, 78, 82, 85). Furthermore, ecdysone (α-ecdysone), the hormone secreted by the prothoracic glands (47, 48), appears to be about 1% as effective as 20-hydroxyecdysone on epidermis (20, 39, 76, 78, 98), which indicates that it is a prohormone (47, 48). Whether ecdysone has any role itself in activating the epidermis is still an open question; several workers have suggested that it may be important in stimulating very early cellular changes—e.g. DNA synthesis (18, 67), appearance of rough endoplasmic reticulum, and increased mitochondrial number (20). Low concentrations of 20-hydroxyecdysone can also cause these changes. (20). Thus before any definite conclusions can be drawn the role of the epidermis in the metabolism of ecdysone to 20-hydroxyecdysone must be clarified.

The biochemistry of 20-hydroxyecdysone-stimulated cellular events leading up to cuticle production is being pursued profitably in the imaginal disc system (discussed below). The hormonal regulation of the type of cuticle deposited can be studied best in other kinds of epidermis. Thus far, two lepidopteran systems seem ideal for studying the morphogenetic role of JH in cuticle deposition: pupal wing epidermis (129) and larval abdominal epidermis (83, 101). In response to 20-hydroxyecdysone the former forms either adult cuticle with scales and hairs in the absence of JH or pupal cuticle in its presence. Similarly, the larval epidermis forms either new larval cuticle in the presence of JH or pupal cuticle in its absence. In both cases, the pattern of proteins synthesized in the presence of JH and 20-hydroxyecdysone differs from that synthesized in the presence of 20-hydroxyecdysone alone (100, 129). What these differences mean remains unclear, especially since some do not seem to be cuticular proteins (129).

Sclerotization and Tanning of the Cuticle

After ecdysis the newly formed cuticle hardens and often darkens in a process called sclerotization (3, 4). This process is governed usually by neurosecretory hormones, though the ecdysteroids may also be involved in some instances (59, 99).

At the time of metamorphosis in flies, the last stage larval cuticle hardens and darkens to form the puparium within which the pupa develops. At first the ecdysteroids were thought to initiate this process by turning on the gene for dopa decarboxylase (59), a key enzyme in quinone tanning (3). Yet dopa decarboxylase activity increases before the release of ecdysone to initiate puparium formation (109). This apparent paradox is resolved by the finding that 20-hydroxyecdysone serves mainly to increase the rate of synthesis of this enzyme (42) in the epidermis, probably by increasing the rate of mRNA synthesis. Ecdysone then later causes the release into the hemolymph of a neurosecretory hormone, "puparium tanning factor" (PTF), which initiates the tanning process (109). PTF appears to act via cAMP (41, 109), which can substitute for the factor in the presence of an RNA synthesis inhibitor (actinomycin) but not in the presence of protein synthesis inhibitors. Since the addition of dopa or dopamine but not of tyrosine has the same effect, Fraenkel et al (41) have speculated that PTF acts somehow on the initial step in the pathway to convert tyrosine to dopa.

In most insects, the tanning of the new cuticle after ecdysis is controlled by another neurosecretory hormone, bursicon (86, 99). In the tobacco hornworm, *Manduca sexta,* bursicon is released from two identified neurons in each abdominal ganglion (P. Taghert, personal communication) into the hemolymph immediately after adult eclosion (95). It causes the increased plasticization of the wings that allows full wing expansion (93). This plasticization is then followed by tanning of the wings. Bursicon from *M. sexta* has now been purified to near homogeneity and appears to be a peptide of about 9000 daltons (P. Taghert, personal communication).

The precise mode of action of bursicon is not known, but it is thought to affect transport of tanning precursors into the hemocytes and/or the epidermal cells (86). It appears to increase cAMP levels in both of these cells (34, 86), though in the epidermal cells the evidence is only correlative. The critical experiments await a pure hormone preparation whose action on isolated cells can be defined.

Cellular Reprogramming of the Epidermis

The larval epidermis of Lepidoptera and probably also Coleoptera seems ideal for the study of the hormonal control of cellular reprogramming. In these insects metamorphosis begins in two discrete steps: a decline in JH, followed by two releases of ecdysone (35, 55, 99). In the tobacco hornworm and probably in other species, the first release initiates metamorphosis by changing the commitment of the epidermis from that for larval differentiation to that for pupal differentiation (98, 122). The second and larger release promotes pupal cuticle synthesis (122). Both actions of 20-hydroxyecdysone are also seen when *M. sexta* larval epidermis is exposed to the hormone in vitro (82, 83, 98). Juvenile hormone can prevent the change to pupal commitment only if given during the initial exposure to 20-hydroxyecdysone (83, 98, 101, 122). After an exposure to 20-hydroxyecdysone in the absence of JH, the epidermis becomes insensitive to JH and produces pupal cuticle irrespective of the presence or absence of JH. Before such an exposure the epidermis remains capable of producing larval cuticle when induced to molt by 20-hydroxyecdysone in the presence of JH (98, 101). Thus, contrary to a recent suggestion (55), neither the decline of JH nor the appearance of "JH-specific" esterases (47, 48) causes the reprogramming of the epidermis. Rather this reprogramming must be initiated by 20-hydroxyecdysone in the absence of JH.

The cellular and molecular events that cause the change in commitment are only superficially understood at present. In *Tenebrio molitor* epidermis at the time of the ecdysone releases (35), changes in ionic coupling occur (21) that can also be induced by 20-hydroxyecdysone in vitro (22). These changes may be important for the regulation of the development of pupal cuticular pattern (21, 22). In *M. sexta* DNA synthesis in the epidermis peaks during the first rise in ecdysteroids (100, 126), but this also occurs on the day preceding the ecdysteroid rise (126). Furthermore, similar increases in DNA synthesis leading to octaploidy are seen in epidermis cultured in vitro in both the presence and absence of hormone (100). Inhibition of this DNA synthesis by cytosine arabinoside does not inhibit the 20-hydroxyecdysone-induced change of commitment (100). This process of DNA synthesis and subsequent cell division (125) is undoubtedly important for the surface morphology of the new pupal cuticle (104), but it seems unnecessary for the switching of the cellular commitment.

By contrast, the altered patterns of RNA and protein synthesis initiated by 20-hydroxyecdysone in *M. sexta* epidermis are necessary for the change in commitment (97, 100). At least one or two new mRNAs and proteins appear, whereas at least six or seven mRNAs and proteins present in the larvally committed cell are no longer synthesized. Quantitative changes in other mRNAs and proteins also occur. Presumably some of these latter proteins are larval cuticular proteins, for major endocuticular synthesis ceases when the animal stops feeding (97, 125). The new mRNAs appearing during the change in commitment do not appear to be for pupal cuticular proteins (A. C. Chen, L. M. Riddiford, manuscript in preparation). Whether some of the changes seen in response to 20-hydroxyecdysone in the absence of JH involve nuclear regulatory proteins, as might be expected for a change in programming, awaits further investigation.

Imaginal Discs

Imaginal discs are groups of relatively undifferentiated cells found in holometabolous larvae. These discs grow during larval life but at metamorphosis undergo differentiation into adult structures such as eyes, wings, legs, genitalia, etc (46). Their growth appears to be continuous throughout larval life; it stops soon after the beginning of pupal development (37, 67, 89, 110). Apparently JH has a permissive effect on this growth; it seems necessary for growth in vitro (32), though the critical concentrations and times of exposure have not been ascertained. Visible evagination and differentiation do not occur until 20-hydroxyecdysone in the absence of JH initiates pupal development.

In the Lepidoptera these imaginal structures (or parts of them) respond to the early decline in JH titer in the last larval instar by becoming committed to pupal differentiation before the first release of ecdysone [(64, 66, 87); L. M. Riddiford, unpublished studies], thus behaving somewhat differently from the abdominal epidermis discussed above (98). Yet no visible differentiation of the discs is seen until the wandering stage, when tracheolar migration occurs (89), presumably in response to the first release of ecdysone. An increase in DNA synthesis in lepidopteran (66, 67) and dipteran discs (124) occurs before the wandering stage and may be a consequence of the earlier decline in JH. Pupal differentiation of these structures, at least in some Lepidoptera, must occur in the presence of JH: Removal of the corpora allata during the last larval instar permits precocious adult development of some of these structures [(64) and references therein]. Pupal cuticle can be formed by lepidopteran wing discs in vitro in response to 20-hydroxyecdysone when no JH is present (85, 88, 89). The concentration of 20-hydroxyecdysone and the time of exposure appear to determine whether the cuticle formed is pupal or adult (85). Unfortunately, normal metamorphosis (i.e. pupal then adult cuticle formation) by these discs has not yet been achieved in vitro. Further in vivo and in vitro investigation will settle whether or not the apparent differences between the responses to hormones of imaginal discs and abdominal epidermis are real.

By contrast to the Lepidoptera, the complete sequence of development of *Drosophila melanogaster* imaginal discs from larval to pupal to adult can be induced by two days' exposure of larval discs to 20-hydroxyecdysone in vitro (76, 81). Furthermore, since these discs can be readily mass-isolated, much is known about the early cellular and biochemical changes that occur in response to 20-hydroxyecdysone and culminate in evagination and the beginning of pupal cuticle synthesis (76, 107, 110). This material has been reviewed recently in detail (110, 111). 20-Hydroxyecdysone stimulates DNA, RNA, and protein synthesis in discs ready to metamorphose, and JH appears to prevent these hormone-induced increases. Furthermore, the pattern of protein synthesis that occurs in discs exposed to JH and 20-hydroxyecdysone differs from that in discs exposed to either hormone alone or to no hormone. This indicates that JH is not simply inhibitory; it directs cellular processes in discs as it does in other types of epidermis (see above).

Cellular receptors for the ecdysteroids have been obtained recently from imaginal discs (132). About 1000 receptors per cell seem to be associated primarily with the crude nuclear fraction. Thus they appear to differ from the predominant cytoplasmic steroid receptors of vertebrates. More work is necessary with purified nuclei to confirm this difference.

Salivary Glands and Chromosome Puffs

In 1960 Clever & Karlson (27) demonstrated that ecdysone induced specific "puffs" in the polytene chromosomes of dipteran salivary glands. These puffs have been used ever since in the study of ecdysteroid action. At the end of larval life the salivary glands synthesize a glycoprotein glue that fixes the old larval skin (which will become the puparium) to the substrate; the glands then degenerate (9). A specific puff seen early in the third (final) larval instar of *Drosophila melanogaster* appears to be responsible for one of these proteins (65); this puff disappears when the ecdysone titer rises prior to pupariation.

More interest has recently been centered on the sequence of puffs that appears around the time of pupariation (5). In *D. melanogaster* this whole sequence can be induced by two exposures of isolated salivary glands to 20-hydroxyecdysone separated by a minimal 3-hr period in hormone-free medium (reviewed in 5, 99). The early puffs are thought to be induced directly by 20-hydroxyecdysone and to code for proteins that induce the late puffs and repress the early puffs (6). The synthesis of these proteins is postulated to occur only in the presence of 20-hydroxyecdysone so that the later obligatory 3-hr absence of hormone is necessary to derepress some of these genes. Thus the temporal appearance and disappearance of 20-hydroxyecdysone regulates the normal puffing sequence. JH has no apparent effect on the early sequence induced by 20-hydroxyecdysone (5, 96) but inhibits the late sequence when given during the hormone-free period (96).

The identity of the proteins encoded by the two early puffs is unknown. Newly synthesized RNA from both salivary glands and imaginal discs exposed to 20-hydroxyecdysone has been hybridized to the salivary gland chromosomes (15). The RNA from salivary glands hybridizes to the sites of the early puffs and also to some other regions (both hormone-insensitive puffs and unpuffed regions). The RNA from the imaginal discs does not hybridize to the early puff sites. Thus if the products of the early puffs are regulatory proteins they must differ from tissue to tissue. Recent studies on another dipteran, *Acricotopus lucidus,* which has two cell types in its salivary gland, have suggested that 20-hydroxyecdysone can have differential effects on RNA synthesis in the two cell types (90).

Fat Body

Among the viscera, the larval-pupal transformation of the fat body offers a good experimental system in which to study the role of the two morphogenetic hormones. The insect fat body is essentially equivalent to the liver and the adipose tissue of vertebrates. During larval life it processes incoming nutrients and, in preparation for metamorphosis, stores material not needed for growth. In several Diptera and Lepidoptera the larval fat body synthesizes and secretes several large proteins (~500,000 daltons) that accumulate in the hemolymph; these are then taken back into the fat body and are concentrated into granules at the cessation of feeding (130). The disappearance of these proteins during metamorphosis indicates their consumption during this process.

Recent studies on the blowfly, *Calliphora vicina*, show that calliphorin is synthesized by the fat body up to two days before pupariation; then synthesis ceases but its mRNA remains until shortly before pupariation (108). Since the highest rate of synthesis occurs early in the last larval stage, JH may direct this synthesis (108). By contrast, in both *Bombyx mori* (116) and *Manduca sexta* (A. C. Chen, unpublished studies in this laboratory) the storage proteins appear to accumulate in the hemolymph in response to a declining JH titer. Although fat body is notorious for its rapid metabolism of JH (47, 48), the role of JH in the synthesis of these proteins should be readily clarified using an in vitro system.

That the reuptake of these proteins and the formation of storage granules are induced by ecdysteroids at metamorphosis is most convincingly demonstrated in *Drosophila melanogaster* (72, 102). In the temperature-sensitive *ecd*[1] mutant, which cannot pupariate at the restrictive temperature due to lack of sufficient ecdysone (45), the addition of exogenous 20-hydroxyecdysone causes the larval serum proteins to be taken up into the fat body (72). The hormone also initiates the synthesis of several new proteins by the fat body at this time.

During the onset of metamorphosis, autophagic vacuoles appear in the fat body (33, 106, 123). This appearance can be induced precociously by 20-hydroxyecdysone in vivo only after the decline of JH (106) or in vitro at the very end of the instar (33, 106, 123).

Cells In Vitro

Hormonally responsive insect cell lines have been developed recently and utilized to study the biochemical mechanism of action of the ecdysteroids (29, 69, 77). A cell of *Drosophila melanogaster* Kc line responds to ecdysteroids by cessation of DNA synthesis and mitosis (105); a series of morphological changes occurs, consisting first of elongation of cellular processes and then of clumping; finally, within three to four days, the cell dies (10, 25, 29). During this hormone-induced differentiation, the spectrum of surface glycoproteins synthesized changes (80). Other new proteins are produced (10), including acetyl cholinesterase (11, 25) and β-galactosidase (12). The physiological basis for these enzyme inductions is unclear. Yet they provide a ready means for studying the molecular action of ecdysteroids in a morphological system.

Ecdysteroid-binding protein(s) has been found in the cytosol of these *D. melanogaster* cells (79). Apparently the receptors translocate rapidly to the nucleus. Most of the labeled hormone is found in the crude nuclear pellet after a 30 min incubation. The binding data agree remarkably well with those obtained for the ecdysteroid receptors in imaginal discs (132), but the question of the normal cellular location of these unbound receptors has not been resolved.

Juvenile hormone and certain JH mimics inhibit the morphological differentiation induced by 20-hydroxyecdysone in several of the *Drosophila*

Kc cell lines (30, 131). Although the mechanism of action of JH has not been elucidated, the *D. melanogaster* system has been effectively used recently in the search for a cellular receptor for JH (23). The preliminary results suggest the presence of cytoplasmic receptors (about 2000 sites per cell).

An interesting sidelight on JH action is its ability to inhibit phytohemagglutinin phorbol ester (12-0-tetradecanoylphorbol-13-acetate) induced mitogenesis in bovine lymphocytes (62), apparently by preventing the phorbol ester induced ornithine decarboxylase synthesis (63). It is unknown whether JH prevents the action of the phorbol ester on the cell membrane or acts later in the sequence of events leading to increased enzyme activity. The effective JH concentrations (5×10^{-5} M or higher) were at least 100- to 1000-fold above the apparent physiological level of the hormone in insects.

HORMONAL CONTROL OF REPRODUCTION

Unlike the vertebrates, the insects have utilized the hormones that govern growth and development to control reproduction in adult life. In the adult the corpora allata again secrete JH, which usually directs some aspect of oogenesis in the female (36, 99) and in a few cases is important in the maturation of accessory glands (36, 71, 99) or reproductive behavior (120) in the male. The prothoracic glands usually degenerate during adult development. The surprise of the past few years, however, is the finding that the adult ovary becomes an endocrine organ and secretes ecdysone, either into the hemolymph or into the egg (47, 111) where it may be used to control oogenesis or embryonic development, respectively.

Juvenile Hormone and Oogenesis

The role of JH in oogenesis varies but may affect one or more of the following processes: (*a*) maturation of previtellogenic oocytes; (*b*) initiation of female-specific yolk protein (vitellogenin) synthesis in the fat body; (*c*) induction of vitellogenin uptake into the oocyte.

In some insects (2, 52, 84, 115) JH stimulates previtellogenic growth of the follicles so that they become competent to take up the vitellogenin at a later stage. The cellular events that occur in this development of competence have not been described exactly.

The hormonal regulation of vitellogenesis may involve the synthesis and/or uptake of vitellogenin into the oocytes. Since this subject has been reviewed recently (52, 130), a brief summary of two systems that promise more information about the mode of the gonadotropic action of JH suffices to illustrate the complexities involved. In the locust *Locusta migratoria* JH appears to be necessary for the normal maturation of the female fat body into a protein-secreting organ (24, 28). In allatectomized females, a JH mimic causes the initiation of vitellogenin synthesis within 48 hr after the first exposure and nearly immediately after subsequent exposures (24), a phenomenon similar to primary and secondary hormonal stimulation in vertebrates. Also, a cytosolic receptor for JH has been found in vitellogenic fat body (P. Roberts, G. R. Wyatt, personal communication). Thus it appears that JH may directly induce mRNA synthesis in this system, but this conclusion cannot be confirmed until the whole process can be performed in vitro. One major problem here (as in using the fat body to study the action of JH in larval life) is rapid metabolism of the added hormone (47).

In *Rhodnius prolixus* JH is important in oogenesis, primarily in promoting vitellogenin uptake into the oocyte (31). Ovarian follicle cells incubated in vitro with JH I exhibit an increase in the size of intercellular spaces due to a 50% decrease in cellular volume (2). Thus JH is postulated to stimulate a membrane-related pump to expel fluid from the cell, but no definitive experiments as to the nature of this pump or its interaction with JH have been reported. Inhibitor studies suggest that RNA and protein synthesis are not involved in this response to JH (1), but no direct measurements have been made. Thus this effect of JH could be entirely different from its induction of vitellogenesis in the fat body.

Role of Ecdysone in Female Reproduction

It was first shown in the mosquito *Aedes aegypti* that ecdysone played a direct role in insect reproduction (see 52 for review). After a blood meal ecdysone is released from the ovary and converted to 20-hydroxyecdysone, which acts on the fat body to stimulate vitellogenin synthesis and release. Whether this stimulation involves initiation of vitellogenin mRNA synthesis or some aspect of translation or processing [as recently shown for JH in *Oncopeltus* (61)] has not been resolved (52). Prior exposure of the fat body to JH is necessary to render it competent to respond to 20-hydroxyecdysone (40). JH may initiate changes similar to those seen in locust fat body (24, 28), possibly including synthesis of vitellogenin mRNA; it may thus act as the primary stimulus for vitellogenesis in this as in most other insect systems. This interesting two-hormone system requires further exploration.

Since these initial findings in mosquitoes an increasing number of adult female insects have been found to contain ecdysteroids (47). So far ecdysteroids have been implicated in the process of egg maturation in only one other insect, *Drosophila melanogaster.* The temperature-sensitive *ecd*^{1} mutant matures eggs only at the permissive temperature (45). Also, 20-hydroxyecdysone injected into isolated female *Drosophila* abdomens causes about a three-fold increase in newly synthesized vitellogenin in the hemolymph but does not permit its uptake into the oocyte (53). JH is necessary for the latter process (91) and by itself can stimulate both the synthesis and uptake in the isolated abdomen (53). Consequently JH is thought to stimulate a tissue in the abdomen to secrete ecdysone, which then increases vitellogenin synthesis in the fat body (53). This tissue could well be the ovary, for mature adult ovaries stimulate vitellogenesis when implanted into males [(57) but see (52) for a critique]. This role of the ovary has yet to be tested by experiments to determine whether isolated ovariectomized female abdomens synthesize vitellogenin in response to JH.

In the Orthoptera and Lepidoptera (14, 54, 56, 68, 70) the ovary also produces ecdysone but not until the terminal phases of oogenesis just before chorion formation. In *Locusta migratoria* this ecdysone is produced by the follicle cells (49, 68), secreted into the egg, and apparently utilized to initiate the formation of the serosal cuticle (M. Lagueux, J. Hoffmann, personal communication). In the Lepidoptera and the cockroach most of the ecdysteroids are also put into the egg (14, 54, 56, 70), but their function in embryonic development is unclear. In these species some ecdysteroids are also found in the hemolymph but have no apparent function.

NEUROSECRETORY HORMONES

Neurosecretory hormones abound in the insect (13, 51). They are released in response to environmental signals, either external or internal, to maintain homeostasis [regulation of carbohydrate (43, 60, 112) and lipid (50, 60) metabolism, water balance (75), etc]; to alter the structural properties of the cuticle (92, 93, 109); to initiate various behaviors (120); and in one well-documented case, that of the prothoracicotropic hormone (PTTH), to direct the activity of an endocrine gland, the prothoracic gland (47). Presumably the activity of the corpora allata is also controlled by neurohormonal factors as well as by direct nervous signals (47). Yet in spite of their importance only one neurosecretory hormone, the adipokinetic hormone of locusts, a peptide, has thus far been isolated and sequenced. The action of this hormone and of the partially purified eclosion hormone are discussed here.

Adipokinetic Hormone (AKH)

Flight in locusts relies on both carbohydrate and lipid as fuel (58). At the outset of flight, hemolymph trehalose (the insect blood sugar) is utilized. Within 5–10 min this carbohydrate reserve is depleted and AKH is released from the grandular lobe of the corpora cardiaca to mobilize the stored triglycerides from the fat body (8, 50). Diglycerides are then released into the hemolymph and taken up by the muscle.

AKH was recently isolated and sequenced (PCA-Leu-Asn-Phe-Thr-Pro-Asn-Trp-Gly-Thr-NH_2) (113). Synthetic AKH has been found to stimulate a two–three-fold increase in cAMP in locust fat body about 6 min after injection of 10 pmol (44). Presumably this increase in cellular cAMP causes the activation of a cAMP-dependent protein kinase (8), which in turn activates a triglyceride lipase (50), a sequence analogous to the stimulation of lipolysis in mammalian adipose tissue by epinephrine and glucagon (38). But this cascade of enzyme reactions has not yet been demonstrated with AKH, though cAMP is known to mimic the lipolytic action of the hormone (8).

In working flight muscle itself, AKH-containing extracts of the glandular lobes of the corpora cardiaca have been reported to cause an increase in fatty acid oxidation (103). AKH was postulated to act directly on the mitochondrial enzyme carnitine acyl transferase to stimulate lipid metabolism and thereby acyl group uptake into the mitochondria. Recently, however, Candy (19) has been unable to repeat these results, though he did find that octopamine stimulated both lipid and carbohydrate metabolism in these muscles. These experiments must be repeated with pure hormone before any direct action on the muscle can be claimed.

Eclosion Hormone

Eclosion, the emergence of adult holometabolous insects from their pupal cases, is initiated by a neurosecretory hormone from the brain. In moths this hormone is produced by certain medial neurosecretory cells in the brain during the latter part of adult development and sent to the corpora cardiaca for storage (117). On the final day of adult development in response to a circadian clock set by the photoperiod regime, the hormone is released into the hemolymph (95) and triggers a species-specific series of behaviors that result in the emergence of the moth and the assumption of adult behavior (118). The hormone has been partially purified and is thought to be a peptide of about 9000 daltons (94).

The purified eclosion hormone has been shown to induce the stereotyped series of abdominal movements associated with eclosion by acting directly on the abdominal nervous system to elicit the readout of a behavioral program (119). The animal (presumably its nervous system) only becomes responsive to the hormone on the day before or the day of eclosion, depending on the species (95, 118). In *Manduca sexta* the onset of responsiveness occurs suddenly about 4 hr before the hormone is released (95). Whether this is simply part of the developmental program of the adult nervous system or is due to some other neurohormonal release that synchronizes the synthesis of hormonal receptors or other cellular events necessary for the response is unknown. Once the animal or the isolated nervous system has been exposed to the hormone it permanently loses the ability to respond again to the hormone (119). This loss occurs immediately, which suggests a rapid loss of cellular receptors, followed in some species by degeneration of certain neurons that may or may not be the target cells for the hormone [(114); J. W. Truman, personal communication].

When crude corpora cardiaca extracts were used in this system, eclosion hormone appeared to act on the nervous system by triggering an increase in cAMP (121). With the purified hormone no increase in cAMP could be elicited (121a). Instead, a two-fold rise in cGMP was observed. Furthermore, cGMP was found to be more than 100 times more potent in provoking eclosion than was cAMP. Therefore, it was concluded that the hormone acts via an increase in cGMP. Both the role of cGMP in triggering the behavioral program and the target cells for the hormone are unknown.

The eclosion hormone also acts on other target organs in the pharate moth, namely the wings and the intersegmental muscles. It acts on the wings to increase their extensibility by plasticizing the cuticle (93), a necessary preparation for their expansion immediately after eclosion. It also initiates the breakdown of the abdominal intersegmental muscles (L. Schwartz, personal communication), which are used in emergence and wing inflation, then degenerate within 24–28 hr (74). In both of these instances the hormone is thought to act via cGMP (J. W. Truman, L. Schwartz, personal communication), but the subsequent cellular events are unknown. Inhibitor studies indicate that both RNA and protein synthesis are necessary for the muscle breakdown (74).

Acknowledgments

I wish to thank Professor James Truman for helpful suggestions and a critical reading of this manuscript, Ms. Jackie Cho for the typing, and Ms. Anna Curtis and Dr. Karen Dyer for the final proofreading. The unpublished work from my laboratory was supported by NSF (PCM 76-18800), NIH (AI 12459), and the Rockefeller Foundation (RF 73019).

Literature Cited

1. Abu-Hakima, R., Davey, K. G. 1977. Effects of hormones and inhibitors of macromolecular synthesis on the follicle cells of *Rhodnius. J. Insect Physiol.* 23:913–17
2. Abu-Hakima, R., Davey, K. G. 1977. The action of juvenile hormone on the follicle cells of *Rhodnius prolixus*: The importance of volume changes. *J. Exp. Biol.* 69:33–44
3. Andersen, S. O. 1976. Cuticular enzymes and sclerotization in insects. In *The Insect Integument,* ed. H. R. Hepburn, pp. 121–44. Amsterdam: Elsevier. 571 pp.
4. Andersen, S. O. 1979. Biochemistry of insect cuticle. *Ann. Rev. Entomol.* 24: 29–61
5. Ashburner, M., Berendes, H. D. 1978. Puffing of polytene chromosomes. In *The Genetics and Biology of Drosophila,* ed. M. Ashburner, T. R. F. Wright, 2b:315–95. NY: Academic. 601 pp.

6. Ashburner, M., Richards, G. 1976. The role of ecdysone in the control of gene activity in the polytene chromosomes of *Drosophila. Symp. R. Entomol. Soc. London* 8:203–25
7. Bade, M. L. 1975. The time of appearance and disappearance of active molting chitinase in *Manduca* cuticle. The endogenous activity. *FEBS Lett.* 51: 161–63
8. Beenakkers, A. M. Th., Van der Horst, D. J., Van Marrewijk, W. J. A. 1978. Regulation of release and metabolic function of the adipokinetic hormone in insects. In *Comparative Endocrinology*, ed. P. J. Gaillard, H. H. Boer, pp. 445–48. Amsterdam: Elsevier/North-Holland. 538 pp.
9. Berendes, H. D., Ashburner, M. 1978. The salivary glands. See Ref. 5, pp. 453–98
10. Berger, E., Ringler, R., Alahiotis, S., Frank, M. 1978. Ecdysone-induced changes in morphology and protein synthesis in *Drosophila* cell cultures. *Dev. Biol.* 62:498–511
11. Best-Belpomme, M., Courgeon, A. M. 1977. Ecdysterone and acetylcholinesterase activity in cultured *Drosophila* cells—inducible, noninducible and constitutive clones or lines. *FEBS Lett.* 82:345–47
12. Best-Belpomme, M., Courgeon, A. M., Rambach, A. 1978. β-galactosidase induced by hormone in *Drosophila melanogaster* cell cultures. *Proc. Natl. Acad. Sci. USA* 75:6102–6
13. Bodnaryk, R. P. 1978. Structure and function of insect peptides. *Adv. Insect Physiol.* 13:69–132
14. Bollenbacher, W. E., Zvenko, H., Kumaran, A. K., Gilbert, L. I. 1978. Changes in ecdysone content during postembryonic development of the wax moth, *Galleria mellonella*: The role of the ovary. *Gen. Comp. Endocrinol.* 34:169–79
15. Bonner, J. J., Pardue, M. L. 1977. Ecdysone-stimulated RNA synthesis in salivary glands of *Drosophila melanogaster*. Assay by in situ hybridization. *Cell* 12:219–25
16. Bulliére, F. 1977. Effects of moulting hormone on RNA and cuticle synthesis in the epidermis of cockroach embryos cultured in vitro. *J. Insect Physiol.* 23:393–401
17. Bulliére, F., Bulliére, D. 1977. Régenerátion, differenciation et hormones de mues chez l'embryon de blatte en culture in vitro. *Wilhelm Roux Arch. Entwicklungsmech. Org.* 182:255–75
18. Bulliére, F., Bulliére, D. 1977. DNA synthesis and epidermal differentiation in the cockroach embryo and pharate 1st instar: moulting hormone and mitomycin. *J. Insect Physiol.* 23:1475–89
19. Candy, D. J. 1978. The regulation of locust flight muscle metabolism by octopamine and other compounds. *Insect Biochem.* 8:177–82
20. Caruelle, J. P., Cassier, P., Joulie-Delorme, C. 1978. Activités sécrétrices et remaniements cellulaires du tégument larvaire de *Schistocerca gregaria* Forsk.: actions des ecdysones in vitro; relations doses-effets. *Ann. Sci. Nat. Zool. Paris* 20:53–78
21. Caveney, S. 1976. The insect epidermis: a functional syncytium. See Ref. 3, pp. 259–74
22. Caveney, S. 1978. Intercellular communication in insect development is hormonally controlled. *Science* 199:192–95
23. Chang, E. S., O'Connor, J. D., Law, J. 1979. Demonstration of a juvenile hormone binding protein in an established cell line of *Drosophila melanogaster. West. Region. Conf. Comp. Endocrinol.*, p. 21 (Abstr.)
24. Chen, T. T., Couble, P., Abu-Hakima, R., Wyatt, G. R. 1979. Juvenile hormone–controlled vitellogenin synthesis in *Locusta migratoria* fat body. Hormonal induction in vivo. *Dev. Biol.* 69:59–72
25. Cherbas, P., Cherbas, L., Williams, C. M. 1977. Induction of acetylcholinesterase activity by β-ecdysone in a *Drosophila* cell line. *Science* 197:275–77
26. Chippendale, G. M. 1977. Hormonal regulation of larval diapause. *Ann. Rev. Entomol.* 22:121–38
27. Clever, U., Karlson, P. 1960. Induktion von Puff-veränderungen in den Speicheldrüsen Chromosomen von *Chironomus tentans* durch Ecdyson. *Exp. Cell Res.* 20:623–26
28. Couble, P., Chen, T. T., Wyatt, G. R. 1979. Juvenile hormone–controlled vitellogenin synthesis in *Locusta migratoria* fat body. Cytological development. *J. Insect Physiol.* 25:327–37
29. Courgeon, A. M. 1972. Morphological changes of the diploid cell line of *Drosophila melanogaster* treated with ecdysone and several analogs in vitro. *Exp. Cell Res.* 74:327–36
30. Courgeon, A. M. 1975. Action conjugée de l'hormone juvenile et de l'ecdysterone sur des ligneés cellulaires de *Drosophila* in vitro. *C. R. Acad. Sci.* 280D:2563–65

31. Davey, K. G. 1978. Hormonal stimulation and inhibition in the ovary of an insect, *Rhodnius prolixus.* See Ref. 8, pp. 13–20
32. Davis, K. T., Shearn, A. T. 1977. In vitro growth of imaginal discs from *Drosophila melanogaster. Science* 196:438–40
33. Dean, R. L. 1978. The induction of autophagy in isolated insect fat body by β-ecdysone. *J. Insect Physiol.* 24: 439–47
34. Delachambre, J., Delbecque, J. P., Provansal, A., Grillot, J. P., DeReggi, M. L., Cailla, H. L. 1979. Total and epidermal cyclic AMP levels related to variations of ecdysteroids and bursicon during metamorphosis of the mealworm *Tenebrio molitor. Insect Biochem.* 9:95–100
35. Delbecque, J.-P., Hirn, M., Delachambre, J., DeReggi, M. 1978. Cuticular cycle and molting hormone levels during the metamorphosis of *Tenebrio molitor* (Insecta Coleoptera). *Dev. Biol.* 64: 11–30
36. De Wilde, J., De Loof, A. 1973. Reproduction—endocrine control. In *The Physiology of Insecta,* ed. M. Rockstein, 1:97–157. NY: Academic. 2nd ed. 512 pp.
37. Egberts, D. J. N. 1979. Late larval and prepupal DNA synthesis in imaginal wing discs of *Calliphora erythrocephala. Insect Biochem.* 9:89–93
38. Fain, J. N. 1977. Cyclic nucleotides in adipose tissues. In *Cyclic 3',5' Nucleotides: Mechanism of Action,* ed. H. Cramer, J. Schultz, pp. 207–28. London: Wiley. 554 pp.
39. Fain, M. J., Riddiford, L. M. 1977. Requirements for molting of the crochet epidermis of the tobacco hornworm larva in vivo and in vitro. *Wilhelm. Roux Arch. Entwicklungsmech. Org.* 181:285–307
40. Flanagan, T. R., Hagedorn, H. H. 1977. Vitellogenin synthesis in the mosquito: the role of juvenile hormone in the development of responsiveness. *Physiol. Entomol.* 2:173–78
41. Fraenkel, G., Blechl, A., Blechl, J., Herman, P., Seligman, M. I. 1977. 3',5'-cAMP and hormonal control of puparium formation in the fleshfly, *Sarcophaga bullata. Proc. Natl. Acad. Sci. USA* 74:2182–86
42. Fragouli-Fournogeraki, M. E., Fragoulis, E. G., Sekeris, C. E. 1978. Protein synthesis by polysomes from the epidermis of blowfly larvae: dependence of formation of dopa-decarboxylase on developmental stage. *Insect Biochem.* 8:435–41
43. Friedman, S. 1978. Trehalose regulation, one aspect of metabolic homeostasis. *Ann. Rev. Entomol.* 23:389–407
44. Gäde, G. 1979. Studies on the influence of synthetic adipokinetic hormone and some analogs on cyclic AMP levels in different arthropod systems. *Gen. Comp. Endocrinol.* 37:122–30
45. Garen, A., Kauvar, L., Lepesant, J.-A. 1977. Roles of ecdysone in *Drosophila* development. *Proc. Natl. Acad. Sci. USA* 74:5099–103
46. Gehring, W. J., Nöthiger, R. 1973. The imaginal discs of *Drosophila.* In *Developmental Systems: Insects,* ed. S. J. Counce, C. H. Waddington, 2:211–90. NY: Academic. 615 pp.
47. Gilbert, L. I., Bollenbacher, W. E., Granger, N. A. 1980. Insect endocrinology: regulation of endocrine glands, hormone titer, and hormone metabolism. *Ann. Rev. Physiol.* 42:493–510
48. Gilbert, L. I., Goodman, W., Bollenbacher, W. E. 1978. Biochemistry of regulatory lipids and sterols in insects. In *Biochemistry of Lipids II,* ed. T. W. Goodwin, 14:1–50. Baltimore: University Park Press. 386 pp.
49. Glass, H., Emmerich, H., Spindler, K. D. 1978. Immunohistochemical localization of ecdysteroids in follicular epithelium of locust oocytes. *Cell Tissue Res.* 194:237–44
50. Goldsworthy, G. J., Cheeseman, P. 1978. Comparative aspects of the endocrine control of energy metabolism. See Ref. 8, pp. 423–36
51. Goldsworthy, G. J., Mordue, W. 1974. Neurosecretory hormones in insects. *J. Endocrinol.* 60:529–58
52. Hagedorn, H. H., Kunkel, J. G. 1979. Vitellogenin and vitellin in insects. *Ann. Rev. Entomol.* 24:475–505
53. Handler, A. M., Postlethwait, J. H. 1978. Regulation of vitellogenin synthesis in *Drosophila* by ecdysterone and juvenile hormone. *J. Exp. Zool.* 206: 247–54
54. Hsiao, T. H., Hsiao, C. 1979. Ecdysteroids in the ovary and the egg of the greater wax moth. *J. Insect Physiol.* 25:45–52
55. Hwang-Hsu, K., Reddy, G., Kumaran, A. K., Bollenbacher, W. E., Gilbert, L. I. 1979. Correlations between juvenile hormone esterase activity, ecdysone titer, and cellular reprogramming in *Galleria mellonella. J. Insect Physiol.* 25:105–11

56. Imboden, H., Lanzrein, B., Delbecque, J. P., Lüscher, M. 1978. Ecdysteroids and juvenile hormone during embryogenesis in the ovoviviparous cockroach *Nauphoeta cinerea*. *Gen. Comp. Endocrinol.* 36:628–35
57. Kambysellis, M. P. 1977. Genetic and hormonal regulation of vitellogenesis in *Drosophila*. *Am. Zool.* 17:535–51
58. Kammer, A. E., Heinrich, B. 1978. Insect flight metabolism. *Adv. Insect Physiol.* 13:133–228
59. Karlson, P., Sekeris, C. E. 1976. Control of tyrosine metabolism and cuticle sclerotization by ecdysone. See Ref. 3, pp. 145–56
60. Keeley, L. L. 1978. Endocrine regulation of fat body development and function. *Ann. Rev. Entomol.* 23:329–52
61. Kelly, T. J., Telfer, W. H. 1977. Antigenic and electrophoretic variants of vitellogenin in *Oncopeltus* blood and their control by juvenile hormone. *Dev. Biol.* 61:58–69
62. Kensler, T.W., Mueller, G. C. 1978. Inhibition of mitogenesis in bovine lymphocytes by juvenile hormones. *Life Sci.* 22:505–9
63. Kensler, T. W., Verma, A. K., Boutwell, R. K., Mueller, G. C. 1978. Effects of retinoic acid and juvenile hormone on induction of ornithine decarboxylase activity by 12-0-tetradecanoylphorbol-13-acetate. *Cancer Res.* 38:2896–99
64. Kiguchi, K., Riddiford, L. M. 1978. A role of juvenile hormone in the pupal development of the tobacco hornworm, *Manduca sexta*. *J. Insect Physiol.* 24:673–80
65. Korge, G. 1977. Direct correlation between a chromosome puff and the synthesis of a larval saliva protein in *Drosophila melanogaster*. *Chromosoma* 62:155–74
66. Kurushima, M., Ohtaki, T. 1975. Relation between cell number and pupal development of wing disks in *Bombyx mori*. *J. Insect Physiol.* 21:1705–12
67. Lafont, R., Mauchamp, B., Blais, C., Pennetier, J. L. 1977. Ecdysones and imaginal disk development during last larval instar of *Pieris brassicae*. *J. Insect Physiol.* 23:277–83
68. Lagueux, M., Hirn, M., Hoffmann, J. A. 1977. Ecdysone during ovarian development in *Locusta migratoria*. *J. Insect Physiol.* 23:109–19
69. Lanir, N., Cohen, E. 1978. Studies on the effect of the moulting hormone in a mosquito cell line. *J. Insect Physiol.* 24:613–21
70. Legay, J. M., Calvez, B., Hirn, M., DeReggi, M. L. 1976. Ecdysone and oocyte morphogenesis in *Bombyx mori*. *Nature* 262:489–90
71. Leopold, R. A. 1976. The role of male accessory glands in insect reproduction. *Ann. Rev. Entomol.* 21:199–221
72. Lepesant, J.-A., Kejzlarova-Lepesant, J., Garen, A. 1978. Ecdysone-inducible functions of larval fat bodies in *Drosophila*. *Proc. Natl. Acad. Sci. USA* 75:5570–74
73. Locke, M. 1976. The role of plasma membrane plaques and Golgi complex vesicles in cuticle deposition during the moult/intermoult cycle. See Ref. 3, pp. 237–58
74. Lockshin, R. A., Beaulaton, J. 1974. Programmed cell death. *Life Sci.* 15: 1549–65
75. Maddrell, S. H. P. 1976. Functional design of the neurosecretory system controlling diuresis in *Rhodnius prolixus*. *Am. Zool.* 16:131–39
76. Mandaron, P., Guillermet, C., Sengel, P. 1977. In vitro development of *Drosophila* imaginal discs: Hormonal control and mechanism of evagination. *Am. Zool.* 17:661–70
77. Marks, E. P. 1978. Responses of a lepidopteran cell line to treatment with ecdysones. *In Vitro* 14:373–74
78. Marks, E. P., Sowa, B. A. 1976. Cuticle formation in vitro. See Ref. 3, pp. 339–58
79. Maroy, P., Dennis, R., Beckers, C., Sage, B. A., O'Connor, J. D. 1978. Demonstration of an ecdysteroid receptor in a cultured cell line of *Drosophila melanogaster*. *Proc. Natl. Acad. Sci. USA* 75:6035–38
80. Metakovskii, E. V., Cherdantseva, E. M., Gvozdev, V. A. 1977. Action of ecdysterone on surface membrane glycoproteins of *Drosophila melanogaster* cells in culture. *Mol. Biol.* 11:128–33
81. Milner, M. J. 1977. The eversion and differentiation of *Drosophila melanogaster* leg and wing imaginal discs cultured in vitro with an optimal concentration of β-ecdysone. *J. Embryol. Exp. Morphol.* 37:105–17
82. Mitsui, T., Riddiford, L. M. 1976. Pupal cuticle formation by *Manduca sexta* epidermis in vitro: patterns of ecdysone sensitivity. *Dev. Biol.* 54:172–86
83. Mitsui, T., Riddiford, L. M. 1978. Hormonal requirements for the larval-pupal transformation of the epidermis of *Manduca sexta* in vitro. *Dev. Biol.* 62:193–205

84. Moobola, S. M., Cupp, E. W. 1978. Ovarian development in the stable fly, *Stomoxys calcitrans,* in relation to diet and juvenile hormone control. *Physiol. Entomol.* 3:317–21
85. Nardi, J. B., Willis, J. H. 1979. Control of cuticle formation by wing imaginal discs in vitro. *Dev. Biol.* 68:381–95
86. Neville, A. C. 1975. *Biology of the Arthropod Cuticle.* NY: Springer. 448 pp.
87. Nijhout, H. F. 1975. Dynamics of juvenile hormone action in larvae of the tobacco hornworm, *Manduca sexta. Biol. Bull.* 149:568–79
88. Oberlander, H. 1976. Hormonal control of growth and differentiation of insect tissues cultured in vitro. *In Vitro* 12:225–35
89. Oberlander, H., Silhacek, D. L. 1976. Action of juvenile hormone on imaginal discs of the Indian meal moth. In *The Juvenile Hormones,* ed. L. I. Gilbert, pp. 220–33. NY: Plenum. 572 pp.
90. Panitz, R. 1978. Cell specific effect of ecdysone on RNA synthesis in the differentiated salivary gland of *Acricotopus lucidus. Cell Diff.* 7:387–98
91. Postlethwait, J. H., Handler, A. M. 1978. Non-vitellogenic female sterile mutants and the regulation of vitellogenesis in *Drosophila melanogaster. Dev. Biol.* 67:202–13
92. Reynolds, S. E. 1976. Hormonal regulation of cuticle extensibility in newly emerged adult blowflies. *J. Insect Physiol.* 22:529–34
93. Reynolds, S. E. 1977. Control of cuticle extensibility in the wings of adult *Manduca* at the time of eclosion: effects of eclosion hormone and bursicon. *J. Exp. Biol.* 70:27–39
94. Reynolds, S. E., Truman, J. W. 1979. Eclosion hormone. In *Insect (Peptide) Neurohormones,* ed. T. Miller. NY: Springer. In press
95. Reynolds, S. E., Taghert, P. H., Truman, J. W. 1979. Eclosion hormone and bursicon titer and the onset of hormonal responsiveness during the last day of adult development in *Manduca sexta* (L.). *J. Exp. Biol.* 78:77–86
96. Richards, G. 1978. Sequential gene activation by ecdysone in polytene chromosomes of *Drosophila melanogaster.* VI. Inhibition by juvenile hormones. *Dev. Biol.* 66:32–42
97. Riddiford, L. M. 1976. Juvenile hormone control of epidermal commitment in vivo and in vitro. See Ref. 89, pp. 198–219
98. Riddiford, L. M. 1978. Ecdysone-induced change in cellular commitment of the epidermis of the tobacco hornworm, *Manduca sexta,* at the initiation of metamorphosis. *Gen. Comp. Endocrinol.* 34:438–46
99. Riddiford, L. M., Truman, J. W. 1978. The biochemistry of insect hormones and insect growth regulators. In *Biochemistry of Insects,* ed. M. Rockstein, pp. 308–57. NY: Academic. 649 pp.
100. Riddiford, L. M., Chen, A. C., Thornhill, W., Dyer, K., Keily, M., Wolfgang, W. J. 1979. Cellular events during the ecdysone-induced change to pupal commitment of larval *Manduca* epidermis. *Eur. Ecdysone Workshop, 4th, Strasbourg, April, 1979* (abstr.)
101. Riddiford, L. M., Kiguchi, K., Roseland, C. R., Chen, A. C., Wolfgang, W. J. 1979. Cuticle formation and sclerotization in vitro by the epidermis of the tobacco hornworm, *Manduca sexta.* In *Invertebrate Tissue Culture. Applications and Developments,* ed. E. Kurstak, K. Maramorosch. NY: Academic. In press
102. Roberts, D. B., Wolfe, J., Akam, M. E. 1977. The developmental profiles of two major hemolymph proteins from *Drosophila melanogaster. J. Insect Physiol.* 23:871–78
103. Robinson, N. L., Goldsworthy, G. 1977. A possible site of action for adipokinetic hormone on the flight muscle of locusts. *J. Insect Physiol.* 23: 153–58
104. Roseland, C. R., Riddiford, L. M. 1979. Analysis of a cuticular spacing pattern after metamorphosis in vitro of larval integument. See Ref. 101
105. Rosett, R. 1978. Effects of ecdysone on a *Drosophila* cell line. *Exp. Cell Res.* 111:31–36
106. Sass, M., Kovacs, J. 1977. The effect of ecdysone on fat body cells of penultimate larvae of *Mamestra brassicae. Cell Tissue Res.* 180:403–9
107. Scheller, K., Karlson, P., Bodenstein, D. 1978. Effects of ecdysterone and the juvenile hormone analogue methoprene on protein, RNA and DNA synthesis in wing discs of *Calliphora vicina. Z. Naturforsch.* 33C:253–60
108. Sekeris, C. E., Scheller, K. 1977. Calliphorin, a major protein of the blowfly: correlation between the amount of protein, its biosynthesis and the titer of translatable calliphorin m-RNA during development. *Dev. Biol.* 59:12–23
109. Seligman, M., Blechl, A., Blechl, J., Herman, P., Fraenkel, G. 1977. Role of ecdysone, pupariation factors, and cyclic AMP in formation and tanning of

puparium of the fleshfly *Sarcophaga bullata. Proc. Natl. Acad. Sci. USA* 74:4697–701

110. Siegel, J. G., Fristrom, J. W. 1978. The biochemistry of imaginal disc development. In *The Genetics and Biology of Drosophila,* ed. M. Ashburner, T. Wright, 2a:317–94. NY: Academic. 604 pp.
111. Sridhara, S., Nowock, J., Gilbert, L. I. 1978. Biochemical endocrinology of insect growth and development. In *Biochemistry and Mode of Action of Hormones II,* ed. H. Rickenberg, 20:133–88. Baltimore: University Park Press. 265 pp.
112. Steele, J. E. 1976. Hormonal control of metabolism in insects. *Adv. Insect Physiol.* 12:239–324
113. Stone, J. V., Mordue, W., Batley, K. E., Morris, H. R. 1976. Structure of locust adipokinetic hormone: a neurohormone that regulates lipid utilization during flight. *Nature* 263:207–10
114. Taylor, H. M., Truman, J. W. 1974. Metamorphosis of the abdominal ganglia of the tobacco hornworm, *Manduca sexta:* changes in populations of identified motor neurons. *J. Comp. Physiol.* 90:367–88
115. Tobe, S. S., Langley, P. A. 1978. Reproductive physiology of *Glossina. Ann. Rev. Entomol.* 23:283–307
116. Tojo, S., Betchaku, T., Ziccardi, V. J., Wyatt, G. 1978. Fat body protein granules and storage proteins in the silkmoth, *Hyalophora cecropia. J. Cell Biol.* 78:823–38
117. Truman, J. W. 1973. How moths "turn on": a study of the action of hormones on the nervous system. *Am. Sci.* 61:700–6
118. Truman, J. W. 1976. Development and hormonal release of adult behavior patterns in silkmoths. *J. Comp. Physiol.* 107:39–48
119. Truman, J. W. 1978. Hormonal release of stereotyped motor programmes from the isolated nervous system of the *Cecropia* silkmoth. *J. Exp. Biol.* 74: 151–73
120. Truman, J. W., Riddiford, L. M. 1977. Invertebrate systems for the study of hormonal effects on behavior. *Vitam. Horm. NY* 35:283–315
121. Truman, J. W., Fallon, A. M., Wyatt, G. R. 1976. Hormonal release of programmed behavior in silk moths: probable mediation by cyclic AMP. *Science* 194:1432–34

121a. Truman, J. W., Mumby, S. M., Welch, S. K. 1978. Involvement of cGMP in the release of stereotyped behavior patterns in moths by a peptide hormone. *J. Exp. Biol.* In press

122. Truman, J. W., Riddiford, L. M., Safranek, L. 1974. Temporal patterns of response to ecdysone and juvenile hormone in the epidermis of the tobacco hornworm, *Manduca sexta. Dev. Biol.* 39:247–62
123. Tysell, B., Butterworth, F. M. 1978. Different rate of protein granule formation in the larval fat body of *Drosophila melanogaster. J. Insect Physiol.* 24: 201–6
124. Vijverberg, A. J. 1973. Incorporation of ^{3}H-thymidine in the wing and leg discs of *Calliphora erythrocephala.* Short term effects of ecdysterone on DNA synthesis during larval and prepupal development. *Neth. J. Zool.* 23:189–214
125. Wielgus, J. J., Gilbert, L. I. 1978. Epidermal cell development and control of cuticle deposition during the last larval instar of *Manduca sexta. J. Insect Physiol.* 24:629–38
126. Wielgus, J. J., Bollenbacher, W. E., Gilbert, L. I. 1979. Correlations between epidermal DNA synthesis and hemolymph ecdysteroid titre during the last larval instar of the tobacco hornworm, *Manduca sexta. J. Insect Physiol.* 25: 9–16
127. Wigglesworth, V. B. 1973. The role of the epidermal cells in moulding the surface pattern of the cuticle in *Rhodnius* (Hemiptera). *J. Cell. Sci.* 12:683–705
128. Wigglesworth, V. B. 1976. The epidermal cell. In *Insects and the Life of Man,* ed. V. B. Wigglesworth, pp. 149–67. London: Chapman and Hall. 217 pp.
129. Willis, J. H., Hollowell, M. P. 1976. The interaction of juvenile hormone and ecdysone: antagonistic, synergistic, or permissive. See Ref. 88, pp. 270–87
130. Wyatt, G. R., Pan, M. L. 1978. Insect plasma proteins. *Ann. Rev. Biochem.* 47:779–817
131. Wyss, C. 1976. Juvenile hormone analogue counteracts growth stimulation and inhibition by ecdysones in clonal *Drosophila* cell line. *Experientia* 32: 1272–74
132. Yund, M. A., King, D. S. Fristrom, J. W. 1978. Ecdysteroid receptors in imaginal discs of *Drosophila melanogaster. Proc. Natl. Acad. Sci. USA* 75:6039–43
133. Zacharuk, R. Y. 1976. Structural changes of the cuticle associated with moulting. See Ref. 3, pp. 299–321

RENAL PHYSIOLOGY

RENAL PHYSIOLOGY

Introduction

The purpose of this year's narratives in renal physiology is to review some aspects of currently available information about the renal circulation. The first two articles in the series analyze the architecture of the renal vasculature and currently available ways for measuring renal blood flow. In the first article, R. Beeuwkes reviews the vascular topography of the kidney, with particular emphasis on relatively recent data concerning the different branching patterns of efferent glomerular vessels, depending on glomerular location; on nephron perfusion patterns; on the juxtaglomerular apparatus; and on the medullary vascular architecture. Whenever possible, Beeuwkes attempts to relate structure and function, while recognizing that many of the functional consequences of certain structural patterns are as yet undefined.

In the second paper, K. Aukland reviews methods for measuring both total renal blood flow and regional distribution of renal blood flow. Aukland's summary of the various techniques indicates clearly both the advantages and the deficiencies of current techniques for studying renal blood flow. From these observations one deduces that no entirely satisfactory means is presently available for analyzing renal blood flow and its permutations and combinations.

The next three articles are concerned with dynamic aspects of the renal circulation at both an organ and a nephron level, and with how intrarenal and extrarenal hormonal systems modulate these events. In the third article, L. G. Navar et al marshal a persuasive, albeit not definitive, argument in support of the distal tubular feedback hypothesis, i.e. the notion that the composition and/or volume of fluid reaching the macula densa initiates a sequence of events that modulates preglomerular and/or postglomerular resistance, thereby regulating in part both intrinsic renal hemodynamics and, in turn, glomerular filtration rate. These workers analyze in detail the provocative suggestion that either the osmolality and/or the Cl^- concentration of fluid emerging from the thick ascending limb of Henle's loop serves as the primary intraluminal compartment initiating the feedback response. In the next article, R. C. Blantz discusses the segments of nephron vascular resistances in series—including the preglomerular arteriole, the glomerular capillary network, and the efferent arteriole—and the physiologic and/or pharmacologic factors that modulate the various series elements. Blantz also reviews evidence in keeping with the notion that there are probably no functionally important afferent-efferent shunts that bypass glomerular capillaries. In the fifth article, P. G. Baer and J. C. McGiff analyze the ways in which the renin-angiotensin system and the kallikrein-kinin system, both of which have intrarenal origins, contribute to the regulation of the renal circulation. While emphasizing the opposing effects of kinins and angiotensins directly on the renal circulation, Baer & McGiff stress the fact that these seemingly counterbalanced systems also share at least one important property: the ability to promote prostaglandin synthesis and to alter prostaglandin metabolism.

Finally, in the last article, Conger & Schrier analyze the role of factors discussed in the preceding articles, e.g. tubuloglomerular feedback, renal blood flow redistribution, alterations in segmental vascular resistances, and hormonal effects, in the pathogenesis of acute tubular necrosis. These workers conclude that, while circumstantial evidence indicates a possibly primary role for reduced renal blood flow in the induction phase of acute renal failure, its role in maintaining the latter is much less clear.

T. E. Andreoli
Section Editor

Ann. Rev. Physiol. 1980. 42:531–42

THE VASCULAR ORGANIZATION OF THE KIDNEY ❖1284

Reinier Beeuwkes III

Department of Physiology, Harvard Medical School,
Boston, Massachusetts 02115

INTRODUCTION

The last 15 years have witnessed major advances in the understanding of renal vascular and tubular organization. Yet even now some textbooks show structural features known to be erroneous in 1920. The efferent vessel from a single glomerulus is often shown perfusing the entire length of the nephron arising from that same glomerulus, and the vascular zonation of the cortex and medulla is frequently ignored. The persistence of such concepts is perhaps due to the influence of schematic diagrams published by Smith in 1951 (56). Such diagrams were perhaps appropriate for the era in which redistribution of cortical blood flow, intrarenal feedback mechanisms, and the role of the medulla in urine concentration were all unknown. Blood flow redistribution may indicate the existence of regional differences in function and in structure. The search for such differences has revealed the true relationships between efferent blood vessels and nephrons. Studies of the juxtaglomerular apparatus, a vascular-tubular relationship of great potential importance, have been stimulated by an interest in intrarenal feedback control mechanisms. Detailed studies of medullary organization have focussed on the role of countercurrent mechanisms in the development and preservation of medullary hypertonicity. The investigations reviewed in the following pages have been undertaken in the belief that function, if not following directly from structure, must at least be consistent with structure.

0066-4278/80/0315-0531$01.00

INTRARENAL VASCULAR PATTERN

Major Vessels

The patterns of the major arterial and venous pathways in the human kidney (31) and in other species (26) have been reviewed recently. In brief, the renal artery divides to form interlobar, arcuate, and finally interlobular arteries. The term interlobar is used even in single-lobed kidneys. The arcuate vessels, which lie at the junction between cortex and outer medulla, give rise to the interlobular arteries, which rise toward the capsule and from which the afferent vessels bearing glomeruli arise. The peritubular capillary network formed by the glomerular efferent vessels has been described many times (9, 26, 45, 52, 65). Near the interlobular vessels in midcortex a profuse peritubular network surrounds convoluted tubules. Midway between interlobular axes in the "medullary rays" a less dense network, largely oriented perpendicular to the capsule, apparently surrounds the cortical portions of Henle loops. The outer cortex of the subcapsular zone is essentially free of glomeruli in the rat, rabbit, and dog, though very superficial glomeruli are found in human and monkey kidneys [(62), R. Beeuwkes unpublished observation] and in the "Munich-Wistar" rat (20). In the inner cortex many glomeruli have long efferent vessels that extend to the outer medulla, where they divide many times to form vascular bundles. From the margins of these bundles a profuse capillary network is formed in the inner stripe of the outer medulla; from the cores of the bundles, vessels extend to the inner medulla. Venous connections are formed at every level within the cortex and drain laterally both the convoluted peritubular capillaries and the network of the medullary rays. The venous return from the medulla occurs by way of vessels rising both within and beside the vascular bundles. These veins are numerous, as is shown by venous injection studies (65).

Glomerular Efferent Vessels

Although many workers have described the general appearance of the peritubular capillary network, few have attempted to define the glomeruli giving rise to the capillaries of each region or to classify glomeruli on the basis of their efferent branching pattern. Perhaps the first attempts at classification were those of Lee-Brown & Morison (42, 46). Generalizing from studies in human, dog, rabbit, rat, and seven other species, they concluded that four distinct types of efferent vessels existed. These included a "subcapsular" type having a long efferent extending to the kidney surface and dividing there, forming a stellate vessel; a "cortical" type, which divided abruptly to form a peritubular capillary network near the glomerulus; and "cortico-medullary" and "medullary" types, which contributed to the outer medullary bundles. A complete classification of efferent vascular patterns in the dog kidney was attempted by the present author in 1971 (9). Ten characteristic efferent pathways were described: two in the subcapsular cortex, four in midcortex, and four in the inner cortex. The subcapsular types appeared to perfuse highly convoluted nephron segments through long pathways extending to the kidney surface or through the immediate branching of the efferent vessel near the glomerulus. In midcortex, efferent vessels were found either to branch abruptly near the glomerulus and perfuse highly convoluted tubule structures near the interlobular axis or else to extend directly to the long meshed network of the medullary ray. In the inner cortex, glomerular efferents extended downward to form vascular bundles through long or short pathways, with an occasional branch to the region between the bundles. Here few glomeruli were found with efferent vessels dividing close to the glomerulus to form a complex network.

Similar patterns have been seen in other species. Efferent types like those of the dog kidney have been described in the human kidney (11), while five of the ten types seen in the dog have been illustrated in the rat kidney (52). These have recently been condensed into three main families (24). In conjunction with studies of the distribution of microspheres (1, 2, 4), four efferent vascular patterns have been described in the rabbit. These include outer cortical types that extend to the kidney surface before dividing, inner cortical types that descend to form outer medullary vascular bundles, and two less well-defined types.

The classification of efferents into only a few types reflects the view that the branching patterns form a continuum in which precise definition of types is not meaningful. Further, to the extent that the efferent network is freely anastomotic, the details of supply of each tubular segment may be of little importance. The evidence for free anastomosis derives not only from the appearance of the filling patterns but also from the embryology of the peritubular capillary system (34). However, regardless of physical anastomosis, intrarenal pressure relationships in vivo must define whether or not functional anastomoses actually occur. A provocative report (25) has shown that the arterial injection of Sephadex spheres large enough to obstruct single afferent arterioles resulted in highly localized regions of infarction. This suggests that collateral flow from adjacent regions does not prevent tubular ischemia, despite the presence of physical anastomosis, and that the distribution of individual efferents is functionally important.

The existence of several different efferent types within single cortical regions indicates that most studies of regional cortical blood flow may lack sufficient resolution to define functional correlates. For example, although flow in the most superficial or deepest cortex would reasonably reflect superficial peritubular and medullary blood flow respectively, a change in flow within the midcortex could change the perfusion of either convoluted tubules, Henle loops, or both, since efferent types exist that appear to perfuse each of those segments. Similarly, the arbitrary division of the cortex into halves, thirds, or fourths appears to have no anatomical correlate in terms of vascular pattern. Such an arbitrary region could have an internal redistribution of flow between different efferent types while showing no net change in flow.

CORTICAL VASCULAR-TUBULAR RELATIONS

The transport functions of each nephron segment must depend in part on the chemical and osmotic properties of the adjacent interstitium. In turn, this interstitium must reflect the peritubular blood supply. As this supply is derived from glomerular efferent vessels, the exact relationships between efferent vessels and tubular segments are potentially of functional importance. If, by virtue of free anastomosis and high flow rates, the peritubular capillaries and interstitium form an effectively infinite "ocean" of uniform composition, then these details would be of little interest. However, as noted, functional anastomosis may not exist (25), and good evidence for the inhomogeneity of the cortical microenvironment has recently appeared (67, 68).

Nephron Perfusion Patterns

Bowman illustrated a short segment of proximal tubule perfused by the efferent vessel of its parent glomerulus (18), and Cushny extended this association to all of Henle's loop (23). However, Braus clearly showed each nephron to be supplied by many glomerular efferent vessels along its course (19). Smith followed the lead of Cushny (56).

Beginning in 1970, we have reported the attempts of our own laboratory to define the relationships between glomerular efferent vessels and the nephron segments they perfuse (8, 9, 11, 13, 14, 17). These studies were based on the application of a new double-injection technique (9, 14). Canine kidneys were fixed in vivo by arterial perfusion with Tyrode or Ringer solution containing glutaraldehyde so that tubule lumens remained open. The arterial systems of the kidneys were then partially injected with colored silicone rubber so as to fill glomeruli and the early efferent vessels. After dehydration and clearing, tubules arising from selected glomeruli were injected with white silicone by means of micropipettes inserted into Bowman's space. The relationship between the nephron being injected and efferent vascular structures was recorded in motion pictures. The earliest observations showed clearly that, in general, the efferent vessel emerging from a given glomerulus was dissociated from the tubule originating from the same glomerulus (8, 9). Association between efferent vessel and tubule was found only for some proximal convoluted tubules of the superficial cortex.

Extension of these studies to the entire nephron (13, 14) has confirmed this organizational principle. The midcortical efferents extending to the medullary rays perfuse Henle loop segments of about 1 mm length originating from more superficial glomeruli. Midcortical efferent vessels lying close to the interlobular vessel usually perfuse convoluted tubule segments, both proximal and distal, arising from glomeruli deeper in the cortex. Efferents of inner cortical glomeruli generally extend downward to form vascular bundles, though a few efferents of convoluted type are found. The convoluted tubules arising from these glomeruli extend upward into the cortex and are perfused by midcortical efferent vessels of the convoluted pattern. The efferents extending into the medulla form part of the complex vascular and tubular organization of that region. These general relationships are illustrated schematically in Figure 1. Similar studies in human kidneys have revealed essentially identical patterns (11, 17).

Thus the nephron segments perfused by each glomerular efferent vessel may be defined; these relationships are nonrandom and similar in the two species so far examined in detail. The dependence of single-nephron perfusion on the efferents of many glomeruli seems well established. Because the medullary ray is a common pathway for many nephrons, interruption of the perfusion of this area might have major functional consequences. This has been suggested as a possible explanation for the profound effect of localized lesions in some forms of acute renal failure (11, 14) and is consistent with the pre- and postglomerular vasoconstriction recently demonstrated (66).

The functional consequences of vascular-tubular relationships in the superficial cortex of the rat have been examined (67, 68). Sodium, chloride, and inulin were measured in plasma collected from stellate vessels on the kidney surface (68). Compared to systemic plasma, peritubular plasma was low in chloride and inulin, indicating that early proximal reabsorbate had been added to the peritubular plasma even before the efferent vessel reached the kidney surface. Experiments including a nonmetabolizable sugar as a marker of early proximal transport showed that the fluid added to the efferent vessel derived in nearly equal amounts from early and late proximal convolutions (67). Coordinated morphologic studies demonstrated close association between the early efferent vessel in the superficial cortex and both early and late proximal segments (69). Midproximal segments were found to lie away from the welling point in the region over the interlobular axis. These relationships were found to conflict with the countercurrent organization of vessels proposed earlier (59–61), a proposal that had already

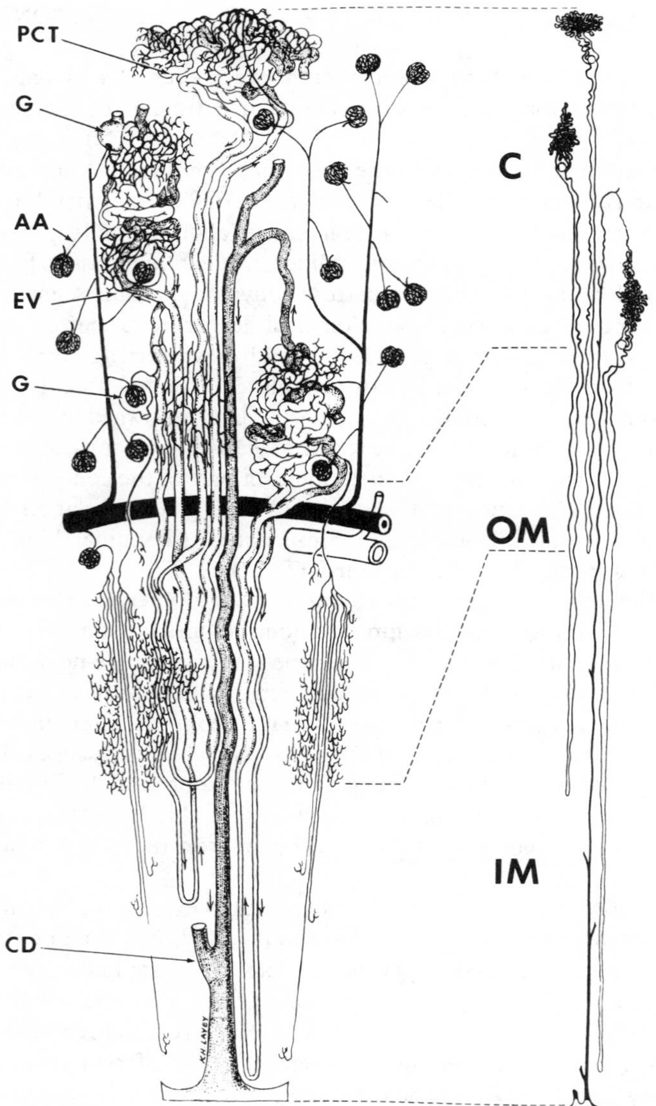

Figure 1 Diagram of renal vascular and tubular organization. Only three nephrons are shown, vascular structures are extensively simplified, and vertical scale is compressed. The same nephrons are shown undistorted to the right. Major zones are: cortex (C), outer medulla (OM), and inner medulla (IM). Afferent arterioles (AA), glomeruli (G), and efferent vessels (EV) are shown together with part of the peritubular capillary network. The proximal convoluted tubules (PCT) and distal convoluted tubules (dark hatching) are generally dissociated from the efferent network arising from their parent glomeruli. Some midcortical efferents directly perfuse Henle loops and collecting ducts in cortical medullary rays. In outer medulla, descending thin limbs of short loops are close to vascular bundles, while thin limbs of long loops are found with thick ascending limbs and collecting ducts (CD) in the interbundle region. [Modified from (12)]

been disputed (57). The origin of the tubules surrounding individual stellate vessels has been studied by two groups (21, 32). These have shown that most such welling points are associated with two or more nephrons.

Juxtaglomerular Apparatus

The relation between the glomerular vascular pole and the distal tubule, the "juxtaglomerular apparatus," has long been known (reviewed in 7). The presence of granular cells in the wall of the afferent arteriole and the specialization of the distal tubule, the "macula densa," suggested the possibility of a feedback mechanism linking some distal tubular parameter with arteriolar function. Although the macula densa cells of the distal tubule are often thought to be in direct contact with the granular cells of the afferent arteriole, the serial-section studies of Barajas have established that this is not an accurate description (5–7). Through careful fixation and avoidance of compression artifacts, it was shown that granular cells are usually not in contact with cells of either the distal tubule in general or the macula densa in particular. Based on these reconstruction studies, Barajas proposed that the macula densa cells serve as an "anchor point" and that the influence of the distal tubule on the arterioles may take place through cellular contacts outside the macula densa region. Studies of the metaplasia of smooth muscle cells into granular cells following renal ischemia (22) confirm that cells of secretory type are typically found far from the macula densa cells at the glomerular vascular pole. A recent study (30) confirms the dissociation between granular cells and macula densa while emphasizing the close relationship between macula densa cells and the cells lying at the glomerular pole. On the other hand, the basement membranes of the distal tubule away from the macula densa region were found to be in contact or actually fused with those of arterioles throughout the region of close apposition. Thus there seem to be morphologic grounds for a direct distal tubular, as opposed to macula densa, influence upon vascular function in the juxtaglomerular region. Since most studies of intrarenal feedback mechanisms have involved study of an entire distal tubule segment, of which the macula densa cells comprise only a small part, both direct tubular and macula densa mediated effects would appear to be equally consistent with the results obtained. Histochemical studies of the macula densa cells themselves have consistently demonstrated only low levels of enzyme systems associated with ion transport. The activity of Krebs cycle enzymes is low even when corrected for the relative lack of mitochondria (28) while the pentose phosphate system appears hyperactive (29). The Na,K-ATPase system was histochemically undetectable in these cells, in marked contrast to high activity in adjacent cells of distal tubular type (15, 16). The histochemically demonstrable ATPase that is present in these cells is ouabain-insensitive (27).

MEDULLARY ORGANIZATION

The zonation of the medulla is based upon tubular rather than vascular criteria (48). The inner border of the outer medulla is defined by the beginning of thick ascending limbs of Henle's loops. The outer margin is usually taken arbitrarily as the level of arcuate arteries or the level of the lowest glomeruli. Within the outer medulla are two zones, the outer and inner stripes. The inner stripe is defined as the region in which thin descending limbs overlap thick ascending limbs (48). This contains the capillary plexus derived from the vascular bundles. The inner medulla, containing thin limbs and collecting ducts, is supplied with blood through the cores of the outer medullary bundles. The venous drainage of the inner medulla occurs through venous pathways ascending within the bundles. The drainage of the outer medulla occurs largely by way of veins running between the bundles, not in countercurrent apposition to the supply (45, 51). This arrangement has led to the suggestion that abrupt changes in solute composition at the border between inner and outer medulla may result from a "washing-out" effect of the outer medullary capillary network (10). However, within the bundles the ultrastructural details are remarkably similar to those found in the retia mirabilia, which isolate the swim bladder and other organs. These ultrastructural specializations go beyond those apparently required for simple countercurrent isolation (43). The descending (arterial) vessels have a continuous endothelium, while the ascending (venous) vessels are fenestrated. [The ultrastructure of renal vessels is briefly reviewed in (38).] These endothelial cell types change at the turning points of the vasa recta (54). The ascending vessels outnumber the descending, and their diameter is larger (33, 44). Although the inner medulla is often regarded as relatively avascular, its capillary volume fraction is more than twice that of the cortex (49).

The detailed organization of the medulla has been described in a superb series of papers (35–37, 39–41). Vascular and tubular structures observed in carefully oriented sections of well-preserved kidneys have been correlated with the medullary location of the section. Studies of the outer medulla showed that the outer parts of the vascular bundles—primarily composed of veins returning from the inner medulla—included many thin descending limbs of Henle loops (35, 36, 40). Through the use of a silicone injection technique to define single nephrons, the thin descending limbs within the bundles were found to belong to nephrons having short loops—i.e. loops turning within the inner stripe of the outer medulla (37, 41). The ascending thick limbs of these loops were separated from the descending thin limbs and were found in the interbundle region together with the thin descending and thick ascending limbs of loops having turning points deep within the inner medulla. In the mouse kidney the same basic pattern was observed, with thin descending limbs of short loops associated with giant vascular bundles in the inner stripe (39). The difference in position of thin limbs was also associated with a difference in thin limb ultrastructure. Such differences have been recently described in the rat (55). In the desert rodent *Psammomys,* outer medullary organization achieves perhaps its most extreme form (3, 33). The inner stripe of the outer medulla contains two separate vascular compartments, one composed of giant vascular bundles, the other containing a capillary network supplied by vessels descending from the outer stripe and drained by venous pathways extending into the cortex (3). The giant bundles contain several times more venous than arterial vasa recta, all of these venous vessels originating within the inner medulla. The bundles also contain descending limbs of short loops in about a 1 : 1 numerical ratio to the venous structures (33). The capillary network of the interbundle region surrounds thick ascending limbs of both short and long Henle loops, together with the thin descending limbs of long loops and the collecting ducts (3). The embryological origin of the separation of short and long loop structures has been addressed by Speller & Moffat, who suggest that, since the short loops arise from the later-developing regions of the cortex, they are added to the periphery of the medullary rays and can thus extend only into the spaces next to the vascular bundles (58). The marked zonation of the outer medulla in *Psammomys* raises the possibility that outer medullary organization rather than papillary length is the morphologic correlate of urine concentrating ability. Many years ago it was noted that the outer medulla was much more highly organized in species of high concentrating ability than it was in the beaver and pig (50). Monkeys, on the other hand, make urine of three times plasma osmolality despite a poorly organized outer medulla (63, 64). A recent study of 21 mammalian species found a positive correlation between urine concentrating capacity and the ratio of cortical to medullary height (47), corresponding to the classical correlation of Schmidt-Nielsen & O'Dell (53). However, an equally good correlation was also found between urine concentrating capacity and the numerical density of outer medullary vasa recta.

Acknowledgments

The work performed in the author's laboratory was supported by NIH grants HL 02493 and AM 18249, and by gifts from Hoechst-Roussel Pharmaceutical Company and R. J. Reynolds Industries, Inc. The author is recipient of NIH Research Career Development Award AM 00224.

Literature Cited

1. Bankir, L., Farman, N. 1973. Glomerular heterogeneity in the rabbit. *Arch. Anat. Microsc. Morphol. Exp.* 62: 281–91
2. Bankir, L., Farman, N., Grunfeld, J.-P., Huet de la Tour, E., Funck-Brentano, J.-L. 1973. Radioactive microsphere distribution and single glomerular blood flow in the normal rabbit kidney. *Pfluegers Arch.* 342:111–23
3. Bankir, L., Kaissling, B., deRouffignac, C., Kirz, W. 1979. The vascular organization of the kidney of *Psammomys obesus. Anat. Embryol.* 155:149–60
4. Bankir, L., Tan, M.-M. T. T., Grunfeld, J.-P. 1979. Measurement of glomerular blood flow in rabbits and rats: Erroneous findings with 15 μm microspheres. *Kidney Int.* 15:126–33
5. Barajas, L. 1970. The ultrastructure of the juxtaglomerular apparatus as disclosed by three-dimensionnal reconstructions from serial sections. *J. Ultrastruct. Res.* 33:116–47
6. Barajas, L. 1971. Renin secretion: an anatomical basis for tubular control. *Science* 172:485–87
7. Barajas, L. 1972. Anatomical considerations in the control of renin secretion. In *Control of Renin Secretion,* ed. T. A. Assaykeen, pp. 1–16. NY: Plenum. 290 pp.
8. Beeuwkes, R. 1970. Dissociation of proximal tubule and efferent peritubular capillaries in the same glomerulus. *Physiologist* 13:146 (Abstr.)
9. Beeuwkes, R. III. 1971. Efferent vascular patterns and early vascular-tubular relations in the dog kidney. *Am. J. Physiol.* 221:1361–74
10. Beeuwkes, R. 1972. Functional anatomy of the medullary vasculature of the dog kidney. In *Recent Advances in Renal Physiology, Int. Symp. Renal Handling of Sodium, Brestenberg, 1971,* pp. 184–89. Basel: Karger. 298 pp.
11. Beeuwkes, R. III. 1980. Vascular-tubular relationships in the human kidney. In *International Symposium on Renal Pathophysiology,* ed. A. Leaf, G. Giebisch, pp. 155–63. NY: Raven
12. Beeuwkes, R. III, Brenner. B. M. 1978. In *Peripheral Circulation,* ed. P. C. Johnson, p. 170. NY: Wiley. 369 pp.
13. Beeuwkes, R. III, Bonventre, J. V. 1973. The organization and vascular perfusion of canine renal tubules. *Physiologist* 16:264 (Abstr.)
14. Beeuwkes, R. III, Bonventre, J. V. 1975. Tubular organization and vascular tubular relations in the dog kidney. *Am. J. Physiol.* 229:695–713
15. Beeuwkes, R. III, Rosen, S. 1980. Renal Na-K-ATPase: localization and quantitation by means of its K^+-dependent phosphatase activity. *Curr. Top. Membr. Transp.* 13:343–54
16. Beeuwkes, R. III, Shahood, J., Rosen, S. 1975. Macula densa: absence of transport ATPase. *Kidney Int.* 8:467 (Abstr.)
17. Bonventre, J. V., Beeuwkes, R. III. 1973. The configuration and vascular perfusion of human proximal tubules. *Physiologist* 16:269 (Abstr.)
18. Bowman, W. 1842. On the structure and use of the malpighian bodies of the kidney with observations on the circulation through that gland. *Philos. Trans. R. Soc. London, Pt. I* 132:57–80
19. Braus, H. 1921. *Anatomie des Menchens.* 2:350–51. Berlin: Julius Springer. 835 pp.
20. Brenner, B. M., Troy, J. L., Daugharty, T. M. 1971. The dynamics of glomerular filtration in the rat. *J. Clin. Invest.* 50:1776–80
21. Briggs, J. P., Wright, F. S. 1979. Feedback control of glomerular filtration rate: site of the effector mechanism. *Am. J. Physiol.* 236:F40–47
22. Cantin, M., Araujo-Nascimento, M., Benchimol. S., Desormeaus, Y. 1977. Metaplasia of smooth muscle cells into juxtaglomerular cells in the juxtaglomerular apparatus, arteries, and arterioles of the ischemic (endocrine) kidney. *Am. J. Pathol.* 87:581–602
23. Cushny, A. R. 1926. In *The Secretion of the Urine,* ed. E. H. Starling, P. 2 London: Longmans, Green. 288 pp.
24. Evan, A. P., Dail, W. G. Jr. 1977. Efferent arterioles in the cortex of the rat kidney. *Anat. Rec.* 187:135–46
25. Faarup, P., Ryo, G., Saelan, H. 1972. Selective capillary vascularization of the nephron in the rat kidney. *Acta Pathol. Microbiol. Scand.* 80:139–41
26. Fourman, J., Moffat, D. B. 1971. *The Blood Vessels of the Kidney.* Oxford: Blackwell. 161 pp.
27. Gomba, Sz., Soltesz, M. B. 1968. A juxtaglomerularis apparatus ATP-ase aktiv kepleteinek histokemiai vizsgalata, kulonos tekintettel az apparatus Na transport functiojara. *Kiserl. Orvostud.* 21:28–33
28. Gomba, Sz., Soltesz, M. B., Szokoly, V., Endes, P. 1968. Dehydrogenase and nucleoproteid histochemistry of the juxtaglomerular complex. *Acta Morphol. Acad. Sci. Hung.* 16:431–38

29. Gomba, Sz., Soltesz, M. B., Szokoly, V., Endes, P. 1970. Histochemical characterization of the juxtaglomerular apparatus. In *Proc. IV Int. Congr. Nephrol., Stockholm,* pp. 120–23. Basel: Karger
30. Gorgas, K. 1978. Structure and innervation of the juxtaglomerular apparatus of the rat. In *Advances in Anatomy, Embryology and Cell Biology,* ed. A. Brodel et al, Vol. 54, Fasc. 2. Berlin: Springer. 84 pp.
31. Graves, F. T. 1971. *The Arterial Anatomy of the Kidney.* Baltimore: Williams & Wilkins. 101 pp.
32. Holzgreve, H., Schrier, R. W. 1975. Evaluation of the peritubular capillary microperfusion method by morphological and functional studies. *Pfluegers Arch.* 356:59–71
33. Kaissling, B., deRouffignac, C., Barrett, J. M., Kriz, W. 1975. The structural organization of the kidney of the desert rodent *Psammomys obesus. Anat. Embryol.* 148:121–43
34. Kazimierczak, J. 1978. Topography and structure of vasculature in developing cortex of rat kidney. *Anat. Embryol.* 153:213–26
35. Kriz, W. 1967. Der architektonische und functionelle Aufbau der Rattenniere. *Z. Zellforsch.* 82:495–535
36. Kriz, W. 1968. Organization of structures within the renal medulla. In *Urea and the Kidney,* ed. B. Schmidt-Nielsen, pp. 342–57. Amsterdam: Excerpta Medica. 495 pp.
37. Kriz, W. 1973. Gefäss- und Kanalchen Architektonik der Niere. *Verh. Anat. Ges.* 67:21–36
38. Kriz, W., Barrett, J. M., Peter, S. 1976. The renal vasculature: anatomical-functional aspects. In *Int. Rev. Physiol. Kidney and Urinary Tract Physiol. II,* ed. K. Thurau, 11:1–22. Baltimore: University Press. 326 pp.
39. Kriz, W., Koepsell, H. 1974. The structural organization of the mouse kidney. *Z. Anat. Entwicklungsgesch.* 144: 137–63
40. Kriz, W., Lever, A. F. 1969. Renal countercurrent mechanisms: structure and function. *Am. Heart J.* 78:101–18
41. Kriz, W., Schnermann, J., Koepsell, H. 1972. The position of short and long loops of Henle in the rat kidney. *Z. Anat. Entwicklungsgesch.* 138:301–19
42. Lee-Brown, R. K. 1924. The renal circulation. *Arch. Surg.* 8:831–52
43. Longley, J. B., Banfield, W. G., Brindley, D. C. 1960. Structure of the rete mirabile in the kidney of the rat as seen with the electron microscope. *J. Biophys. Biochem. Cytol.* 7:103–9
44. Marsh, D. J., Segal, L. A. 1971. Analysis of countercurrent diffusion exchange in blood vessels of the renal medulla. *Am. J. Physiol.* 221:817–28
45. Moffat, D. B., Fourman, J. 1963. The vascular pattern of the rat kidney. *J. Anat. London* 97:543–53
46. Morison, D. M. 1926. A study of the renal circulation, with special reference to its finer distribution. *Am. J. Anat.* 37:53–93
47. Munkacsi, I., Palkovits, M. 1977. Measurements on the kidneys and vasa recta of various mammals in relation to urine concentrating capacity. *Acta Anat.* 98:456–68
48. Peter, K. 1909. *Untersuchungen über Bau and Entwicklung der Niere.* Jena: Fisher. 648 pp.
49. Pfaller, V. W., Rittinger, M. 1977. Quantitative Morphologie der Niere. *Mikrosk. Wien* 33:74–79
50. Plakke, R. K., Pfeiffer, E. W. 1964. Blood vessels of the mammalian renal medulla. *Science* 146:1683–85
51. Pomeranz, B. H., Birtch, A. G., Barger, A. C. 1968. Neural control of intrarenal blood flow. *Am. J. Physiol.* 215:1067–81
52. Rollhauser, H., Kriz, W., Heinke, W. 1964. Der Gefäss-system der Rattenniere. *Z. Zellforsch.* 64:381–403
53. Schmidt-Nielsen, B., O'Dell, R. 1961. Structure and concentrating mechanism in the mammalian kidney. *Am. J. Physiol.* 200:1119–24
54. Schwartz, M. M., Karnovsky, M. J., Venkatachalam, M. A. 1976. Ultrastructural differences between rat inner medullary descending and ascending vasa recta. *Lab. Invest.* 35:161–70
55. Schwartz, M. M., Venkatachalam, M. A. 1974. Structural differences in thin limbs of Henle: physiological implications. *Kidney Int.* 6:193–208
56. Smith, H. W. 1951. *The Kidney.* NY: Oxford Univ. Press. 1049 pp.
57. Solomon, S. 1971. Is there an effective countercurrent system in the superficial renal cortex? *Proc. Soc. Exp. Biol. Med.* 137:1019–20
58. Speller, A. M., Moffat, D. B. 1977. Tubulo-vascular relationships in the developing kidney. *J. Anat.* 123:487–500
59. Steinhausen, M. 1972. Further information on the cortical countercurrent system in rat kidney. *Yale J. Biol. Med.* 45:451–56
60. Steinhausen, M., Eisenbach, G. M., Galaske, R. 1970. A countercurrent system

of the surface of the renal cortex of rats. *Pfluegers Arch.* 318:244–58

61. Steinhausen, M., Eisenbach, G. M., Galaske, R. 1970. Countercurrent system in the renal cortex of rats. *Science* 167:1631–33
62. Tanner, G. A., Selkurt, E. E. 1979. Kidney function in the squirrel monkey before and after hemorrhagic hypotension. *Am. J. Physiol.* 219:597–603
63. Tisher, C. C. 1971. Relationship between renal structure and concentrating ability in the rhesus monkey. *Am. J. Physiol.* 220:1100–6
64. Tisher, C. C., Schrier, R. W., McNeil, J. S. 1972. Nature of urine concentrating mechanism in the macaque monkey. *Am. J. Physiol.* 223:1128–37
65. Trueta, J., Barclay, A. E., Daniel, P. M., Franklin, K. J., Prichard, M. M. L. 1947. *Studies on the Renal Circulation.* Oxford: Blackwell Scientific. 187 pp.
66. Venkatachalam, M. A., Rennke, H. G., Sandstrom, D. J. 1976. The vascular basis for acute renal failure in the rat. Preglomerular and postglomerular vasoconstriction. *Circ. Res.* 38:267–79
67. Weinstein, S. W., Bank, N., Klose, R., Szyjewicz, J. 1979. Effects of tubular reabsorbate on efferent vessel plasma composition. *Am. J. Physiol.* 236: F119–25
68. Weinstein, S. W., Szyjewicz, J. 1976. Early postglomerular plasma concentration of chloride, sodium, and inulin in the rat kidney. *Am. J. Physiol.* 231:822–31
69. Weinstein, S. W., Szyjewicz, J. 1978. Superficial nephron tubular-vascular relationships in the rat kidney. *Am. J. Physiol.* 234:F207–14

Ann. Rev. Physiol. 1980. 42:543–55

METHODS FOR MEASURING RENAL BLOOD FLOW: Total Flow and Regional Distribution

❖1285

Knut Aukland

Institute of Physiology, University of Bergen, Bergen, Norway

INTRODUCTION

This review discusses methods for measuring renal blood flow (RBF), especially its intrarenal distribution. Studies on the regulation of renal perfusion, which has been the subject of several recent reviews (3, 11, 17, 43, 62), are referred to only when they help to elucidate methodological problems.

TOTAL RENAL BLOOD FLOW

New modifications and analytical improvements of renographic techniques (e.g. 14), aiming at an indirect measure of hippuran clearance, are mainly of clinical interest. Attempts are also being made to use the hippuran transit time pattern to estimate intrarenal flow distribution (76).

Two recent noninvasive techniques may offer continuous recording of RBF: detection of ultrasonic Doppler signals from the renal artery (75), and external recording of the $^{81}Rb/^{81m}Kr$ ratio after i.v. injection of ^{81}Rb (29). The latter method is based on the fact that ^{81}Rb taken up in the kidney disintegrates rapidly ($T_{1/2}$ = 4.6 hr) to form ^{81m}Kr gas, which in turn is removed at a rate dependent on blood flow.

Telemetered signals from a Doppler flowmeter chronically implanted on a renal artery permit the study of RBF under circumstances more interesting than those under the conventional Nembutal anesthesia (e.g. 71).

LOCAL AND REGIONAL BLOOD FLOW

Microsphere Method

The microsphere (Ms) technique introduced in 1970 by McNay & Abe (17) is now used extensively (reviewed in 3, 43, 62, 63).

0066-4278/80/0315-0543$01.00

TECHNICAL ASPECTS When used with a reference sampling technique, proper dispersion of the Ms, and injection into the left heart, the method gives a reliable estimate of total RBF (see 30). For estimating local flow, the renal cortex is divided into 2–4 zones parallel to the kidney surface. Ms radioactivity is estimated per g tissue, giving zonal flow in ml per min·g; when the relative volume of the zones has been defined their relative flow fractions are readily calculated. Error due to changes of kidney volume after Ms injection may be avoided by simultaneous measurement of total RBF (64).

If zonal glomerular concentration is measured, average single glomerular flow (GBF) may be estimated for each zone. GBF of anatomically well-defined glomeruli may be obtained after silicone rubber injection and micro-dissection (9). Furthermore, measurements of GBF may be combined with the Hanssen ferrocyanide technique for single nephron filtration rate (SN-GFR) to obtain the zonal filtration fraction (15, 55, 78).

It is often stated that 3M Company microspheres with diameters of 15 ± 5 μm were used. In reality, this means an average diameter anywhere between 12 and 18 μm. Furthermore, the actual SD for a given Ms batch seems to have been 2–3 μm in the early seventies (46, 61) but only about 1.5 μm in the last few years. Accordingly, results obtained with "15 ± 5 μm" Ms are not necessarily comparable.

EVALUATION OF RESULTS In order to obtain correct and reproducible zonal flow measurements:

1. Ms injection should not disturb RBF or its intrarenal distribution.
2. All microspheres should be arrested in the kidney.
3. Even the largest microspheres should be small enough to enter the narrowest afferent arterioles and reach the glomeruli in numbers proportional to glomerular blood flow.

1. In normal dogs good agreement is obtained between two subsequent Ms injections (28, 39, 57, 64), whereas a decrease of the OC/IC (outer cortex/inner cortex) flow ratio was observed after the first injection in dogs with vena cava ligation (28). A preferential reduction of OC flow has been observed in two studies on rats (34, 79), whereas Källskog et al (38) found no change with a narrow 16 μm Ms batch.

2. While in dogs practically no "15 ± 5 μm" Ms appear in the renal vein (see 63), the lower diameter limit for complete extraction has not been well defined: Katz et al (39) reported that from 3 to 30% of Ms "largely 7–10 μm in size" would pass through the kidney. Archie et al (1) found incomplete trapping of Ms under 7 μm in diameter in lambs, and their less explicit data on sheep and dogs suggest a lower limit of about 8 μm. Complete renal extraction of 8.5 ± 0.8 μm Ms has been reported for the rat (18).

3. Ofstad and coworkers (47, 47a, 49, 50) suggest that the low Ms uptake in deep compared to superficial cortex is in part caused by steric restriction at the origin of the afferent arterioles of Ms larger than 15–17 μm. If so, the increased deep Ms fraction under vasodilatation (see 3, 17, 43, 62) could be due to a widening of the afferent arterioles sufficient to admit entrance of large spheres (47a). Ms might also fail to enter deep arterioles in proportion to blood flow because of axial accumulation or a wall-exclusion effect, again mechanisms that might predominantly affect larger spheres.

Evidence for or against such mechanisms is largely indirect: Underestimation of deep cortical flow is likely (*a*) if many Ms are trapped in interlobular arteries or afferent arterioles; (*b*) if the outer cortex contains a greater fraction of large Ms; and (*c*) if deep glomerular Ms flow is conspicuously low compared to SN-GFR or deep flow measured with other methods.

Injecting Ms 10–40 μm in diameter, Ofstad et al (50) found that all spheres over 20 μm had been trapped before reaching the glomeruli; they calculated mean entrance diameters for afferent arterioles and for glomerular capillaries of 19.5 and 17.1 μm, respectively (47a). In clear disagreement, Chenitz et al (19) found all Ms smaller than 18 μm and 50% of 34.5 μm Ms to be located in the glomeruli. The corresponding numbers in rats, 18 and 25 μm, were later shown to be appreciably reduced with injection of increasing numbers of large Ms (35). However, the number of injected Ms seems not to account either for the much lower limiting arteriolar diameter observed by Ofstad et al (47a, 49, 50) in dogs or for the finding by Zillig et al (79) that less than 85% of 12.8 ± 1.1 μm Ms reached the glomeruli in rats. Differences among species, animals, experimental conditions, and techniques may be decisive. Thus, gentle exposure of the rat kidney appreciably reduced the size of Ms reaching the glomeruli (35).

Any size-dependent maldistribution should result in a larger average Ms diameter in outer than in inner cortex. However, with the narrow diameter ranges currently available this is a remarkably insensitive test. Nevertheless, using 18 ± 1.8 μm Ms, Warren & Ledingham (74) found greater Ms diameters in outer than in inner cortex in young, but not in adult, rabbits; Bankir (8) found maldistribution also in adult rabbits with 15 μm Ms. In rats, uneven diameter distribution has been reported with 15 μm (8, 58a) and even with 12.7 ± 1.7 μm Ms [borderline statistical significance (79)] but not with 7–10 μm Ms (58a).

Since Ms radioactivity is proportional to the third power of the sphere radius, maldistribution of large spheres is easily detected by comparing the distribution of radioactivity of two Ms batches of different size: Thus Casellas & Mimran (18) showed that 12.7 ± 1.2 μm Ms overestimated outer cortical flow by 12% compared to that obtained with 8.5 ± 0.8 μm. Even greater discrepancy between 15 and 9 μm Ms was observed by A. Aperia (personal communication) in two groups of young rats (body weight 60 and 170 g). Similarly, in the dog kidney 10.5 ± 1.2 μm Ms gave 26% higher flow in the inner one third of cortex + medulla than that obtained simultaneously with 14.9 ± 1.0 μm Ms (23a). The average extraction was >99% even with the smaller Ms size.

In nine studies of SN-GFR with the Hanssen ferrocyanide method [summarized in (43)], the S/D (superficial/deep) SN-GFR ratio in rats averaged 0.75 (range 0.50–0.87). In comparison, Ms (15 μm) measurements of GBF have given S/D ratios of >3.0 (36), 3.08 (9), 1.50 (79), and 1.26 (38). The ratios above 3 give incredibly high deep filtration fractions, and suggests that deep glomerular flow has been underestimated. Of special interest are simultaneous measurements of GBF and SN-GFR: Using 11.0 ± 2.6 μm Ms, Poujeol et al (55) obtained a S/D flow ratio of 0.66, compatible with a SN-GFR ratio of 0.79. A similar S/D ratio for SN-GFR was observed by Yarger et al (78), but the GBF ratios averaged 2.40 and 1.18 with Ms diameters of 14 and 9 μm, respectively. They concluded that even 9 μm Ms underestimated deep cortical flow in rats.

In dogs, the S/D ratio of 0.80 for SN-GFR reported by Bruns et al (15) corresponds well to the Ms ratio of 0.74 measured in the same animals. Ms ratios in other studies range from 0.79 to 1.80 (39, 46, 61). Again the Ms distribution observed in dogs seems more plausible than that obtained in rats.

Both in rats and dogs, deep cortical (+ medullary) flow measured with Ms is lower than that obtained with diffusible indicators (see Inert Diffusible Tracers, below).

COMPARISON TO RED CELLS AND IN VITRO STUDIES The failure to demonstrate red cell skimming by micropuncture sampling of postglomerular blood has been taken to indicate the absence of Ms skimming (62). However, appreciable skimming of red cells has been observed by a more direct technique in the cat kidney (48). Furthermore, there are no good reasons to presume that rigid 15 μm Ms and discoid, flexible 2 × 7 μm red cells should behave identically. In model experiments, blood flowing in 100 μm channels at velocities similar to that in small arteries shows little or no axial accumulation of red cells (12, 52). However, there is a practically cell-free zone at the vessel wall that is independent of flow velocity but narrows with increasing hematocrit (10, 12). In the dog kidney, the deepest of the 35 arterioles originating from each interlobular artery (72) will drain off only 3–5% of the main stream, possibly with preference for the layers near the wall. In an attempt to mimic this situation, E. S. Øfjord in our laboratory has adopted the glass slit model of Palmer (51), using a main channel with a "diameter" (= slit gap) of 63 μm and a 90° side branch with a "diameter" of 25 μm. With whole blood (Hct 40) flowing at a mean linear velocity of 3 cm sec^{-1}, and a side branch flow fraction of 3–5%, the side-branch hematocrit was about 70% of input Hct, whereas 15 μm Ms suspended in blood showed values of only 25–30% (48a). While this model seems to show more skimming than takes place in the kidney, it does indicate that 15 μm Ms are separated to a much larger extent than erythrocytes.

CONCLUSIONS Because of the indirectness of the evidence presented above, conclusions must be tentative: It seems likely that deep cortical flow in rats is regularly underestimated with the usual "15 ± 5 μm" Ms, and even spheres of 9–12 μm may be maldistributed. In dogs, deep cortical flow is clearly underestimated with Ms diameters greater than 17 μm, and even 15 μm Ms have been shown to be distributed differently from 10 μm Ms. It remains to be seen whether different Ms diameters of 15 μm and less will show similar changes in distribution, e.g. under renal vasodilation.

The attractive idea of a soluble, nonskimmable, glomerular flow indicator was apparently realized in the glomerular basement membrane antibody method of Wallin et al (73). Unfortunately, later investigators have failed to reproduce the technique (63).

Inert Diffusible Tracers

^{85}Kr AND ^{133}Xe The external detection of ^{85}Kr or ^{133}Xe washout (69) has the great attraction of being atraumatic, repeatable, and applicable in humans (see 3, 11, 17, 31). Based on the concept of exponential washout from each of several anatomical regions with parallel perfusion, compartment (Cp) analysis of the composite washout curve was initially believed to give information on local blood flow in ml/min·g in cortex (Cp I), juxtamedullary cortex + outer medulla (Cp II), inner medulla (Cp III), and perirenal fat (Cp IV). Today, nobody seems to subscribe to this interpretation of Cp III and IV; increasing doubts are expressed as to the significance of Cp I and II, partly because of failure to give correct average flow (31) and disagreement with local flow measurements (3, 26, 58, 61), and partly because of the unrealistic calculated tissue volumes (2, 3). The suspicion that maintenance of high Cp I flow rate in low flow states might reflect some compartment-analytical error (3) has recently been corroborated by Hollenberg et al (32), who found much lower Cp I flow with "maximum likelihood analysis" in chronic renal failure.

Recent measurement of local tissue ^{85}Kr concentrations (54) would seem to provide a rational basis for the interpretation of the composite washout curves: In a large number of dogs the kidney was clamped at varying times after intraarterial injection of a standard dose of ^{85}Kr. Tissue samples from outer cortex (A_1), inner cortex + outer stripe of outer medulla (A_2), and inner stripe of outer medulla (B) were analyzed for ^{85}Kr concentration. Despite great scatter among animals, it seems permissible to construct an average washout curve for control dogs, as shown in Figure 1. In order to obtain the total amount of tracer in each zone, tissues A_1, A_2, and B were assigned the relative volumes of 45, 35, and 10% of kidney volume. To the reviewer, the following points seem of special interest: (*a*) The initial washout rate is only about 25% lower in A_2 than in A_1. (*b*) In both cortical layers the washout rate falls to ~ 50–33% of the initial rate after 45 sec. (*c*) Within the period when Cp II is determined, tissues A_1, A_2, and B contribute approximately equal amounts of radioactivity. Accordingly, Cp II has no specific anatomical location.

The unexpected multiexponential washout in A_1 and A_2 might suggest heterogeneous cortical perfusion. In the inner cortex, the medullary rays could represent less-perfused regions, as suggested by Coelho et al (24), but this seems an unlikely cause for retardation of ^{85}Kr washout in the outer cortex. Recirculation of ^{85}Kr may be a more likely explanation: Observations in humans (20, 41, 42) suggest that as much as 0.5–1% of the ^{85}Kr

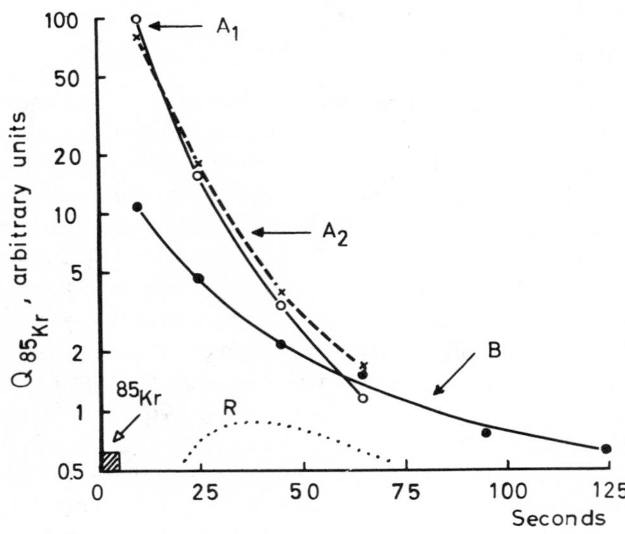

Figure 1 Regional washout of ^{85}Kr after intraarterial injection according to (54). A_1 (open circles): outer cortex. A_2 (crosses): inner cortex + outer stripe of outer medulla. B (closed circles): inner stripe of outer medulla. Zonal amounts of indicator ($Q85_{Kr}$) calculated from average concentrations in Figures 2, 3, and 4 (54), assuming zonal volumes of 45, 35, and 10% of total kidney volumes for A_1, A_2, and B, respectively. R: Recirculation to A_1, and A_2 conjectured by reviewer (see text).

leaving the injected kidney with venous blood may eventually reappear in the renal artery. Recirculation of this magnitude, suggested by the dotted line (R) in Figure 1, might explain the declining cortical washout rate observed by Passmore et al (54). If so, it might account for an appreciable part of Cp II and later components of the external washout curve; this would be compatible with the observations in humans (41, 42) and with the different washout patterns for ^{85}Kr and ^{133}Xe in dogs (16). If this hypothesis is correct, many cases of alleged redistribution of RBF may instead reflect disturbances of gas exchange in the lungs.

In conclusion, it seems doubtful whether the externally recorded ^{85}Kr or ^{133}Xe washout curves can give any information about intrarenal blood flow distribution. The method may still be useful for assessing average RBF, empirically shown to be well represented by the initial washout rate (31). However, the noninvasive inhalation technique, with correction for recirculation (60), seems worth further exploration.

H_2, ^{125}I-IODOANTIPYRINE AND TRITIATED WATER Among methods for local measurement, the recording of H_2 gas washout by implanted platinum electrodes (6) has the advantage of practically unlimited repeatability of simultaneous measurements at several locations in the kidney. As reviewed elsewhere (3), local H_2 clearances in outer medulla and the various cortical layers vary in proportion to total RBF in practically all situations examined. To evaluate the possible flow disturbance due to electrode trauma we have recently studied the uptake of ^{131}I-iodoantipyrine (I-Ap) and tritiated water (THO) after 10–15 sec infusion, recording tracer concentrations in 1 sec arterial blood samples and in the excised kidney (33). In the dog kidney, the flow distribution patterns obtained with I-Ap and THO are practically identical (21, 23) and are similar to that obtained with local H_2 (3, 70) and ^{85}Kr washout (54). Renal vasoconstriction and dilatation, induced by angiotensin II and acetylcholine respectively, cause no change in the distribution pattern of I-Ap or THO (21, 22). Thus, the failure of local H_2 measurements to confirm the microsphere finding of increased deep cortical flow fraction in vasodilatation (70) cannot be blamed on tissue trauma.

Comparison of I-Ap uptake to Ms distribution in dogs shows consistent disagreement in control kidneys: While only 16% of Ms (diameter 16.1 ± 2.4 or 12.9 ± 1.3 μm) were found in the inner one third of cortex + medulla, the corresponding "deep flow fraction" obtained with I-Ap was 25% (22, 23). If Ms measure flow correctly, the inner cortex must have received a large fraction of its I-Ap content by diffusion from the interlobular arteries or via peritubular flow from midcortical glomeruli. (Net inward tubular flow may explain only a small part of the discrepancy.) The alternative explanation, a marked underestimation of deep glomerular flow with Ms, has not been excluded. However, the observations that renal vasodilatation, with or without increased RBF, will increase the deep Ms fraction until it almost equals I-Ap flow (4, 21), and that angiotensin II increases the discrepancy (22), seem most readily explained by a variable net post-glomerular capillary blood flow from superficial to deep layers of the cortex (4). Preliminary measurements of the net flow direction of H_2 gas generated locally in the cortex support this hypothesis (A. Kirkebø, personal communication). In any case, these observations strengthen the suspicion of a variable relationship between glomerular and peritubular "nutrient" flow in a given cortical layer (33, 53, 58).

The uptake and removal of inert diffusible indicators in the inner medulla may be greatly influenced by urine flow (5). Furthermore, owing to counter-current exchange the uptake and washout rates will presumably fall with increasing tracer diffusibility.

^{86}Rubidium Uptake

Measurement of RBF with ^{86}Rb is based on the finding that in the period of 10–120 sec after bolus injection in dogs and rats the fraction taken up by the kidney is fairly constant and similar to the RBF fraction of cardiac output (59, 65). This indicates that the kidney has a ^{86}Rb extraction [E-^{86}Rb = (A-V)/A] similar to the average for the rest of the body. However, the extraction is not complete and depends on RBF: In the dog, the first-passage E-^{86}Rb falls from about 0.8 to 0.6 when RBF increases from 100 to 200 ml min^{-1} (65). Slightly higher extractions. but similar flow dependency, have been observed in rats (L. Rosivall, A. Hope, personal communication). As evidence against regional differences in E-^{86}Rb in the rat kidney, Coelho (24) invoked (*a*) the similarity to local uptake of para-aminohippurate, and (*b*) the similar distribution of ^{86}Rb 6 and 12 sec after bolus injection. The latter evidence seems questionable because redistribution of ^{86}Rb after passage of the first bolus will not depend on local E-^{86}Rb alone: ^{86}Rb will move from regions having attained a high "specific activity" (tissue ^{86}Rb/K) to regions with low activity, i.e. regions with a low (flow· E-^{86}Rb) product will continue to accumulate ^{86}Rb.

The 7 sec ^{86}Rb uptake in the inner medulla of rats, corresponding to a plasma flow of 0.18 ml/min·g, agreed well with ^{125}I-albumin uptake after correction for a reasonable filtration fraction of juxtamedullary glomeruli, suggesting little counter current exchange of ^{86}Rb (25). Several times higher medullary ^{86}Rb flow and increasing values with 15–45 sec infusion were recently reported (78). Also in dogs ^{86}Rb seems to accumulate in the inner medulla almost linearily with time, corresponding to blood flow rates of about 1.0 ml/min·g at 30 sec (7, 65), 1.3 ml/min·g at 60 sec (40, 68), and 2.5 ml/min·g at 120 sec (65) after bolus injection. Transport of ^{86}Rb to the inner medulla by tubular fluid may well add significantly to the effect of systemic recirculation (78). Further studies are needed to clarify the uptake kinetics of ^{86}Rb and to define the optimal procedure for its use as an intrarenal flow indicator.

Albumin and Erythrocyte Accumulation and Transit Times

Counter current exchange of diffusible tracers and inaccessibility to Ms suggest blood elements as tracers for flow in the inner medulla and papilla.

An apparent linear accumulation of labelled plasma albumin in the inner medulla for at least 30 sec following the start of intraarterial infusion was first demonstrated in dogs (45) and was later confirmed in rats (27). If the arterial concentration is constant and no tracer leaves the inner medulla in this period, the accumulation rate will equal "plasma" inflow. However, since the actual arterial concentration curve was not recorded in these studies, the linear accumulation might be fortuitous and would therefore not exclude simultaneous washout. To determine the "true" accumulation curve, Rasmussen (56) introduced a nearly ideal renal arterial step function in rats by a cross-perfusion technique. Because of the scatter of the data he was not able to define the exact uptake function, but he concluded that "the early accumulation is likely to follow a curved rather than a straight line." While questioning the absolute flow values, this conclusion does not exclude "initial slope" as a useful indicator for inner medullary perfusion.

Measurement of the local transit time of labelled albumin or red cells has the great advantage of being repeatable, but it is traumatic and has hitherto been used in dogs only. Analytical difficulties due to changes in local blood volume and "internal recirculation" seem reasonably well resolved (77).

Both accumulation rate and transit time for albumin will give an "equivalent medullary plasma flow" and will overestimate the actual plasma fluid flow to the extent that water is filtered in the juxtamedullary glomeruli (25, 45) and abstracted from the descending vasa recta (56, 77). Furthermore, calculation of whole blood flow should take into account the low hematocrit of inner medullary blood, which is probably caused by erythrocyte skimming somewhere in the outer medulla (56, 77).

Microvascular Red Cell Velocity

Red cell velocities have been determined by cinematographic techniques on postglomerular vessels in the rat cortex (66) and in papillary vasa recta (13, 37) using frame-to-frame analysis (66), microkymographic technique (13), or dual-slit photodetection (37). Even though cortical measurements showed good correspondence to total renal blood flow (66), the question arises to what extent flow rate in these superficial vessels will be representative for a larger region. Somewhat deeper "insight"—up to 1 mm from the surface—may be obtained by the laser-Doppler spectroscopic technique (67), which integrates red cell movements in a large number of microvessels.

CONCLUSION

Because of the many unanswered methodological problems the present survey does not end with an unqualified advocation of any particular method. For some time to come we may have to live with the unpleasant feeling recently expressed by Leaf & Cotran (44): "Writing this paragraph [on intrarenal flow] with 52 articles on the subject in front of me, all of which appeared in the last 4 years, and a limited sample at that—from many highly reputable laboratories, I can only conclude that confusion reigns in this important area of renal physiology." One hopes that laboratories will respond to the challenge by designing definitive tests.

Literature Cited

1. Archie, J. P. Jr., Fixler, D. E., Ullyot, D. J., Hoffman, J. I. E., Utley, J. R., Carlson, E. L. 1973. Measurement of cardiac output with and organ trapping of radioactive microspheres. *J. Appl. Physiol.* 35:148–54
2. Aukland, K. 1975. Intrarenal distribution of blood flow. Are reliable methods available for measurements in man? *Scand. J. Clin. Lab. Invest.* 35:481–86
3. Aukland, K. 1976. Renal blood flow. In *Int. Rev. Physiol., Kidney and Urinary Tract Physiol. II,* ed. K. Thurau, 11:23–79. Baltimore: University Park Press. 326 pp.
4. Aukland, K. 1978. Renal hemodynamics. *Proc. Int. Congr. Nephrol., Montreal, 7th,* pp. 593–99
5. Aukland, K., Berliner, R. W. 1964. Renal medullary counter-current system studied with hydrogen gas. *Circ. Res.* 15:430–42
6. Aukland, K., Bower, B. F., Berliner, R. W. 1964. Measurement of local blood flow with hydrogen gas. *Circ. Res.* 14:164–87
7. Bálint, P., Bartha, J., Fekete, A. 1969. Intrarenal distribution of blood flow in the dog. *Acta Physiol. Acad. Sci. Hung.* 36:1–11
8. Bankir, L., Farman, N., Grünfeld, J.-P., Huet, E., Funck-Brentano, J.-L. 1973. Radioactive microsphere distribution and single glomerular blood flow in the normal rabbit kidney. *Pfluegers Arch.* 342:111–23
9. Bankir, L., Trinh, M.-M., Grünfeld, J.-P. 1979. Measurement of glomerular blood flow in rabbits and rats: Erroneus findings with 15-μm microspheres. *Kidney Int.* 15:126–33
10. Barbee, J. H., Cokelet, G. R. 1971. The Fahraeus effect. *Microvasc. Res.* 3:6–16
11. Barger, A. C., Herd, J. A. 1973. Renal vascular anatomy and distribution of blood flow. In *Handbook of Physiology, Section 8: Renal Physiology,* ed. J. Orloff, R. W. Berliner, pp. 249–313. Washington DC: Am. Physiol. Soc. 1082 pp.
12. Blackshear, P. L. Jr., Forstrom, R. J., Dorman, F. D., Voss, G. O. 1971. Effect of flow on cells near walls. *Fed. Proc.* 30:1600–9
13. Böttcher, W., Steinhausen, M. 1976. Microcirculation of the renal papilla of rats under control conditions and after temporary ischemia. *Kidney Int.* 10: Suppl. 6, pp. S74–S80
14. Brodkey, M. J., Schlegel, J. U., Derouen, T. A. 1977. Determination of renal plasma flow using the gamma scintillation camera. *Invest. Urol.* 14:417–20
15. Bruns, F. J., Alexander, E. A., Riley, A. L., Levinsky, N. G. 1974. Superficial and juxtamedullary nephron function during saline loading in the dog. *J. Clin. Invest.* 53:971–79
16. Carriere, S. 1970. A comparison of the disappearance curves of ^{133}Xe and ^{85}Kr for the measurement of the intrarenal distribution of blood flow. *Can. J. Physiol. Pharmacol.* 48:834–37

17. Carriere, S. 1975. Factors affecting renal cortical blood flow. A review. *Can. J. Physiol. Pharmacol.* 53:1–20
18. Casellas, D., Mimran, A. 1978. The influence of microsphere (MS) size and of the renal hemodynamic status on the estimation of intrarenal blood flow distribution (IRBFD) in the rat. *Int. Symp. Radionuclides Nephrol., Boston* (Abstr.)
19. Chenitz, W. R., Nevins, B. A., Hollenberg, N. K. 1976. Preglomerular resistance and glomerular perfusion in the rat and dog. *Am. J. Physiol.* 231:961–66
20. Chidsey, C. A., Fritts, H. W. Jr., Hardewig, A., Richards, D. W., Cournand, A. 1959. Fate of radioactive krypton (Kr^{85}) introduced intravenously in man. *J. Appl. Physiol.* 14:63–66
21. Clausen, G., Hope, A., Kirkebø, A., Tyssebotn, I., Aukland, K. 1977. Effect of vasodilation on distribution of microspheres and on zonal blood flow measured with diffusible indicators in the dog kidney. *Proc. Int. Union Physiol. Sci.* 13:141 (Abstr.)
22. Clausen, G., Hope, A., Kirkebø, A., Tyssebotn, I., Aukland, K. 1978. Glomerular versus postglomerular capillary blood flow. *Abstr. Int. Congr. Nephrol., 7th, Montreal,* p. F-12
23. Clausen, G., Hope, A., Kirkebø, A., Tyssebotn, I., Aukland, K. 1979. Distribution of blood flow in the dog kidney. I. Saturation rates for inert diffusible tracers, ^{125}I-iodoantipyrine and tritiated water, versus uptake of microspheres under control conditions. *Acta Physiol. Scand.* 107:69–81

23a. Clausen, G., Kirkebø, A., Tyssebotn, I., Øfjord, E. S., Aukland, K. 1979. Erroneous estimates of intrarenal blood flow distribution in the dog with radiolabelled microspheres. *Acta Physiol. Scand.* 107:385–87

24. Coelho, J. B. 1977. Heterogeneity of intracortical peritubular plasma flow in the rat kidney. *Am. J. Physiol.* 233(4):F333–341
25. Coelho, J. B. 1977. Medullary plasma flows and juxtamedullary-glomeruli (JMG) filtration fraction (FF) in the rat kidney. *Kidney Int.* 12:553 (Abstr.)
26. Gagnon, J. A., Grove, D. W., Flamenbaum, W. 1974. Blood flow distribution and tissue solute content of the isolated-perfused kidney. *Pfluegers Arch.* 347: 261–74
27. Ganguli, M., Tobian, L. 1974. Does the kidney autoregulate papillary plasma flow in chronic postsalt hypertension? *Am. J. Physiol.* 226:330–33
28. Gutman, R. A., McRae, R. L. 1975. Renal intracortical blood flow distribution, function, and sodium excretion in unanesthetized dogs following vena caval ligation. *Circ. Res.* 36:216–21
29. Herk, G. van, Zeeuw, D. de. 1978. Unilateral kidney blood flow measurement using the $^{81}Rb/^{81m}Kr$ ratio. *Contrib. Nephrol.* 11:67–72
30. Heymann, M. A., Payne, B. D., Hoffman, J. I. E., Rudolph, A. M. 1977. Blood flow measurements with radionuclide-labeled particles. *Progr. Cardiovasc. Dis.* 20:55–79
31. Hollenberg, N. K., Mangel, R., Fung, H. Y. M. 1976. Assessment of intrarenal perfusion with radioxenon: A critical review of analytical factors and their implications in man. *Semin. Nucl. Med.* 6:193–216
32. Hollenberg, N. K., Sandor, T., Adams, D. F. 1978. Perfusion of the residual renal cortex in patients with chronic renal disease. *Nephron* 22:81–90
33. Hope, A., Clausen, G., Aukland, K. 1976. Intrarenal distribution of blood flow in rats determined by ^{125}I-iodoantipyrine uptake. *Circ. Res.* 39:362–70
34. Hsu, C. H., Kurtz, T. W., Preuss, H. G., Weller, J. M. 1975. Measurement of renal blood flow in the rat. *Proc. Soc. Exp. Biol. Med.* 149:470–72
35. Ishikawa, I., Hollenberg, N. K. 1977. Renal blood flow, afferent vascular resistance, and estimated glomerular capillary pressure in the nonexposed rat kidney. *Circ. Res.* 41:67–73
36. Jaenike, J. R. 1972. The renal functional defect of postobstructive nephropathy. *J. Clin. Invest.* 51:2999–3006
37. Jamison, R. L., Gussis, G. L., Inloes, D. S., Robertson, C. 1977. Time-averaged erythrocyte velocities in vasa recta capillaries of the mammalian renal medulla. *Proc. Int. Union Physiol. Sci.* 13:353 (Abstr.)
38. Källskog, Ö., Lindbom, L. O., Ulfendahl, H. R., Wolgast, M. 1975. Regional and single glomerular blood flow in the rat kidney prepared for micropuncture. A methodological study. *Acta Physiol. Scand.* 94:145–53
39. Katz, M. A., Blantz, R. C., Rector, F. C. Jr., Seldin, D. W. 1971. Measurement of intrarenal blood flow. I. Analysis of microsphere method. *Am. J. Physiol.* 220:1903–13
40. Kövér, G., Bartha, J., Stimácz, E. 1974. Effect of angiotensin on renal function and intra-renal circulation. *Arch. Int. Physiol. Biochim.* 82:285–300

41. Ladefoged, J. 1964. The significance of recirculation for the determination of intrarenal blood flow distribution with krypton-85 and xenon-133. *Scand. J. Clin. Lab. Invest.* 16:479–80
42. Ladefoged, J. 1968. *Renal Circulation in Hypertension,* pp. 67–71. Copenhagen: Munksgaard. 129 pp.
43. Lameire, N. H., Lifschitz, M. D., Stein, J. H. 1977. Heterogeneity of nephron function. *Ann. Rev. Physiol.* 39:159–84
44. Leaf, A., Cotran, R. S. 1976. *Renal Pathophysiology,* p. 11. NY: Oxford Univ. Press. 387 pp.
45. Lilienfield, L. S., Maganzini, H. C., Bauer, M. H. 1961. Blood flow in the renal medulla. *Circ. Res.* 9:614–17
46. McNay, J. L., Abe, Y. 1970. Pressure-dependent heterogeneity of renal cortical blood flow in dogs. *Circ. Res.* 27:571–87
47. Mørkrid, L., Ofstad, J., Willassen, Y. 1976. Effect of steric restriction on the intracortical distribution of microspheres in the dog kidney. *Circ. Res.* 39:608–15
47a. Mørkrid, L., Ofstad, J., Willassen, Y. 1978. Diameter of afferent arterioles during autoregulation estimated from microsphere data in the dog kidney. *Circ. Res.* 42:181–91
48. Nissen, O. I. 1969. *The Function of Superficial and Deep Areas of the Cat Kidney.* Copenhagen: Virum Costers Bogtrykkeri. 59 pp.
48a. Øfjord, E. S., Clausen, G., Aukland, K. 1979. Do microspheres measure correct local blood flow in the renal cortex? In vitro experiments. *Upsala J. Med. Sci. Suppl.* 26:58 (Abstr.)
49. Øfstad, J., Mørkrid, L., Willassen, Y. 1975. Diameter of the afferent arteriole in the dog kidney estimated by the microsphere method. *Scand. J. Clin. Lab. Invest.* 35:767–74
50. Øfstad, J., Willassen, Y., Egenberg, K. E. 1973. Distribution of radioisotope-labeled microparticles in the renal cortex of dogs in hemorrhagic hypotension. *Scand. J. Clin. Lab. Invest.* 31:277–87
51. Palmer, A. A. 1965. Axial drift of cells and partial plasma skimming in blood flowing through glass slits. *Am. J. Physiol.* 209:1115–22
52. Palmer, A. A. 1969. Influence of absolute flow rate and rouleau formation on plasma skimming in vitro. *Am. J. Physiol.* 217:1339–45
53. Passmore, J. C., Leffler, C. W., Neiberger, R. E. 1978. A critical analysis of renal blood flow distribution during hemorrhage in dogs. *Circ. Shock* 5: 327–38
54. Passmore, J. C., Neiberger, R. E., Eden, S. W. 1977. Measurement of intrarenal anatomic distribution of krypton-85 in endotoxic shock in dogs. *Am. J. Physiol.* 232(1):H54–58
55. Poujeol, P., Chabardés, D., Bonvalet, J. P., Rouffignac, C. de. 1975. Glomerular filtration rate and miscrosphere distributions in single nephron of rat kidney. *Pfluegers Arch.* 357:291–301
56. Rasmussen, S. N. 1978. Red cell and plasma volume flows to the inner medulla of the rat kidney. *Pfluegers Arch.* 373:153–59
57. Riley, R. L. 1974. Effects of acute changes in renal cortical blood flow distribution on renal function in dogs. In *Recent Advances in Renal Physiology and Pharmacology,* ed. L. G. Wesson, G. M. Fanelli, pp. 149–73. Baltimore: University Park Press. 388 pp.
58. Rosivall, L., Fasekas. A., Pósch, E., Szabó, G., Hársing, L. 1979. Effect of renal vasodilation on the intrarenal blood flow distribution. *Acta Physiol. Acad. Sci. Hung.* 53:399–408
58a. Sabto, J., Bankir, L., Grünfeld, J. P. 1978. The measurement of glomerular blood flow in the rat kidney: influence of microsphere size. *Clin. Exp. Pharmacol. Physiol.* 5:559–65
59. Sapirstein, L. A. 1958. Regional blood flow by fractional distribution of indicators. *Am. J. Physiol.* 193:161–68
60. Schmitz-Feuerhake, I., Falkenreck-Herbst, I., Coburg, A. J., Wonigkeit, K., Gerhardt, K.. Prévot, H. 1978. Atraumatic method of renal blood flow estimation by ^{133}Xenon inhalation and its application to transplanted kidneys. *Eur. J. Clin. Invest.* 8:75–80
61. Slotkoff, L. M., Logan, A., Jose, P., D'Avella, J., Eisner, G. M. 1971. Microsphere measurement of intrarenal circulation of the dog. *Circ. Res.* 28:158–66
62. Stein, J. H. 1976. The renal circulation. In *The Kidney,* ed. B. M. Brenner, F. C. Rector, 1:215–50. Philadelphia: Saunders. 762 pp.
63. Stein, J. H., Boonjarern, S., Wilson, C. B., Ferris, T. F. 1973. Alterations in intrarenal blood flow distribution. Methods of measurement and relationship to sodium balance. *Circ. Res.* 32–33:Suppl. I, 61–72
64. Stein, J. H., Ferris, T. F., Huprich, J. E., Smith, T. C., Osgood, R. W. 1971. Effect of renal vasodilatation on the distribution of cortical blood flow in the

kidney of the dog. *J. Clin. Invest.* 50:1429–38

65. Steiner, S. H., King, R. D. 1970. Nutrient renal blood flow and its distribution in the unanesthetized dog. *J. Surg. Res.* 10:133–46

66. Steinhausen, M., Eisenbach, G. M., Böttcher, W. 1973. High-frequency microcinematographic measurements on peritubular blood flow under control conditions and after temporary ischemia of rat kidneys. *Pfluegers Arch.* 339:273–88

66a. Stern, M. D., Bowen, P. D., Parma, R.. Osgood, R. W., Bowman, R. L., Stein, J. H. 1979. Measurement of renal cortical and medullary blood flow by laser-Doppler spectroscopy in the rat. *Am. J. Physiol.* 236(1):F80–87

67. Stern, M. D., Lappe, D. L., Bowen, P. D., Chimosky, J. E., Holloway, G. A. Jr., Keiser, H. R., Bowman, R. L. 1977. Continuous measurement of tissue blood flow by laser-Doppler spectroscopy. *Am. J. Physiol.* 232 (4):H441–48

68. Szabó, G., Posch, E., Rosivall, L., Fazekas, A., Hársing, L. 1976. Renal blood flow during ureteral obstruction measured with ^{133}Xe washout, ^{86}Rb uptake techniques and with an electromagnetic flowmeter. *Pfluegers Arch.* 367:33–36

69. Thorburn, G. D., Kopald, H. H., Herd, J. A., Hollenberg, M., O'Morchoe, C. C. C., Barger, A. C. 1963. Intrarenal distribution of nutrient blood flow determined with krypton^{85} in the unanesthetized dog. *Circ. Res.* 13:290–307

70. Tyssebotn, I., Kirkebø, A. 1979. Renal cortical blood flow distribution measured by hydrogen clearance during dopamine and acetylcholine infusion. Effect of electrode thickness and position in cortex. *Acta Physiol. Scand.* 106:385–93

71. Vatner, S. F. 1978. Effects of exercise and excitement on mesenteric and renal dynamics in conscious, unrestrained baboons. *Am. J. Physiol.* 234 (2):H210–14

72. von Kügelgen, A., Kuhle, B., Kuhle, W., Otto, K.-J. 1959. Die Gefässarchitektur der Niere. Untersuchungen an der Hundeniere. In *Zwanglose Abhandlungen aus dem Gebiet der Normalen und Pathologischen Anatomie,* ed. W. Bargmann, W. Doerr, 5:9–111. Stuttgart: Thieme. 111 pp.

73. Wallin, J. D., Rector, F. C. Jr., Seldin, D. W. 1971. Measurement of intrarenal plasma flow with antiglomerular basement-membrane antibody. *Am. J. Physiol.* 221:1621–28

74. Warren, D. J.. Ledingham, J. G. G. 1975. Measurement of intrarenal blood-flow distribution in the rabbit using radioactive microspheres. *Clin. Sci. Mol. Med.* 48:51–60

75. Watanabe, H., Saitoh, M., Igari, D., Tanahashi, Y., Harada, K. 1976. Non-invasive detection of ultrasonic Doppler signals from renal vessels. *Tohoku J. Exp. Med.* 118:393–94

76. Wilkinson, S. P., Smith, I. K., Clarke, M., Arroyo, V., Richardson, J., Moodie, H., Williams, R. 1977. Intrarenal distribution of plasma flow in cirrhosis as measured by transit renography: relationship with plasma renin activity, and sodium and water excretion. *Clin. Sci. Mol. Med.* 52:469–75

77. Wolgast, M. 1973. Renal medullary red cell and plasma flow as studied with labelled indicators and internal detection. *Acta Physiol. Scand.* 88:215–25

78. Yarger, W. E., Boyd, M. A., Schrader, N. W. 1978. Evaluation of methods of measuring glomerular and nutrient blood flow in rat kidneys. *Am. J. Physiol.* 235 (5):H592–600

79. Zillig, B., Schuler, G., Truniger, B. 1978. Renal function and intrarenal hemodynamics in acutely hypoxic and hypercapnic rats. *Kidney Int.* 14:58–67

Ann. Rev. Physiol. 1980. 42:557–71

DISTAL TUBULAR FEEDBACK CONTROL OF RENAL HEMODYNAMICS AND AUTOREGULATION

❖1286

L. G. Navar, D. W. Ploth, and P. D. Bell

Nephrology Research and Training Center, Departments of Physiology & Biophysics and of Medicine, University of Alabama, Birmingham, Alabama 35294

INTRODUCTION

Many studies have indicated that a component of the distal nephron interacts significantly with the glomerular vascular elements of each nephrovascular unit. The structural link that supports this hypothesis is the intimate morphological association between the macula densa cells of the distal tubule and the glomerular structures (13, 56). The distal tubular feedback hypothesis (also referred to as tubulo-glomerular feedback) proposes that a structure in the distal tubule, presumably at the macula densa area, is capable of sensing a physicochemical component of the fluid emerging from the ascending loop of Henle and of initiating a sequence of events that culminates in the local adjustment of vascular resistance (37, 50, 59, 60). Mild to substantive disagreement has met virtually every aspect of this hypothesis including (*a*) the nature of the intraluminal constituent in the distal tubule responsible for initiating feedback signals, (*b*) the mechanism of communication between the tubular cells and the vascular elements, (*c*) the factor responsible for eliciting changes in vascular tone, (*d*) the precise vascular element or elements most responsive to feedback signals, and (*e*) the physiological role of the feedback mechanism. In this review we evaluate

0066-4278/80/0315-0557$01.00

recent experimental findings germane to this issue, and cite primarily recent works reported as full papers since 1976. The reader is referred to several reviews (5, 30, 37, 50, 56, 59, 60) for more comprehensive bibliographies on older work related to this problem and associated aspects. The present review focuses on how the distal tubular feedback mechanism participates in the intrinsic control of hemodynamics. It also considers recent reports related to the general phenomenon of renal autoregulation.

CHARACTERISTICS OF THE DISTAL TUBULAR FEEDBACK MECHANISM

The feedback hypothesis predicts that deviations in concentration or delivery of a constituent of the distal tubule fluid elicit adjustments in vascular resistance that regulate glomerular function. The negative feedback function subserved by this system requires that increases in flow into the distal tubule lead to decreases in glomerular filtration rate (GFR) while decreases in flow elicit increases in GFR. Two specific approaches have been used to test these predictions at the single-nephron level.

Evaluation of Single Nephron GFR (SNGFR) and Glomerular Pressure (GP) Responses to Interruption of Distal Delivery

Several recent studies have confirmed earlier findings that SNGFR calculated on the basis of complete proximal tubule fluid collections ($SNGFR_{prox}$) may be higher than SNGFR values derived from techniques that do not require interruption of distal volume delivery. Studies in rats (28, 48) have provided additional evidence that SNGFR measurements based on distal tubule fluid collections ($SNGFR_{dist}$) are less than $SNGFR_{prox}$. The difference between these values (approximately 5 nl min^{-1}) is not large, and paired measurements from proximal and distal tubule segments are more likely to yield consistent differences (46–48). Rats on normal-to-high salt content diets are less likely to exhibit consistent differences between $SNGFR_{prox}$ and $SNGFR_{dist}$ (28, 59). Furthermore, the level of renal arterial pressure with respect to the coexisting autoregulatory range has been shown to influence the magnitude of the differences observed (37, 48, 58). Most studies in the rat are conducted at arterial pressures toward the lower level of the autoregulatory range in this species, and this factor may partially explain why some studies have reported that differences in SNGFR are often small or undetectable (14, 28). Results in the dog (58) are consistent with this view. At control arterial pressures, SNGFR based on an indicator dilution ($SNGFR_{ID}$) technique that requires only partial proximal tubule fluid collections was consistently lower than $SNGFR_{prox}$. At reduced arterial pressures, $SNGFR_{prox}$ was similar to both $SNGFR_{ID}$ and $SNGFR_{dist}$. Thus interference with distal delivery may lead to an increase in SNGFR under certain conditions. Churchill et al (14) failed to detect differences between $SNGFR_{prox}$ and $SNGFR_{dist}$. However, mean arterial pressure averaged 112 ± 1 mm Hg, a value close to the lower limit of autoregulation in the rat (4, 24, 48). At these pressures, detectable differences between $SNGFR_{prox}$ and $SNGFR_{dist}$ might not be expected.

Interruption of distal delivery may also lead to an increase in glomerular pressure of the blocked nephron, with the magnitude of the increment being dependent on the level of arterial pressure (37, 40). For that reason, the stop flow pressure (SFP) technique may not provide a valid estimation of glomerular pressure, especially at renal arterial pressures substantially above the lower limit of the autoregulatory range. Directly measured values for glomerular pressure in the dog most closely agree with the estimated glomerular pressure values taken at reduced arterial pressure but not with estimated glomerular pressure based on SFP measurements taken at control arterial pressures (55). However, in other studies (43, 44) estimates of glomerular pressure based on the SFP technique were somewhat lower. These discrepancies may reflect differences in preparation of the kidney for micropuncture (11). Studies in the rat have indicated that little or no difference exists between direct measurements of glomerular pressure and glomerular pressure estimates based on SFP (3, 44). Thus in the rat, interruption of distal volume delivery causes little increase in glomerular pressure. In contrast, the dog can sometimes respond to proximal blockade with substantial elevations in glomerular pressure.

Evaluation of SNGFR and Stop Flow Pressure Responses to Increases in Distal Nephron Perfusion Rate

A more direct means to assess the status of the feedback mechanism is to alter the perfusion rate to the distal nephron receptor sites and to measure either SNGFR or SFP at various rates of distal volume delivery. Most studies have utilized an orthograde perfusion technique: A segment of the proximal tubule is blocked, perfusion is initiated into a late proximal tubule segment, and SFP measurements or tubule fluid collections are made from an early proximal tubule segment. Studies in both rats and dogs have demonstrated the presence of a sensitive feedback mechanism capable of eliciting decreases in SNGFR and glomerular pressure in response to increases in distal nephron perfusion rate. In the rat, increases in distal perfusion rate from zero to 25–40 nl min^{-1} lead to reductions in SNGFR of about 10–15 nl min^{-1} (8, 35, 36, 45–48, 50–52, 56, 59). Likewise, SFP also decreases progessively by 8–12 mm Hg as perfusion rate is increased. The basic pattern of the feedback responses is such that a relatively steep and sensitive portion of the response is observed at intermediate flow rates. Less responsiveness is found at the very low or the very high perfusion rates. In general, the SFP responses parallel the SNGFR responses and the observed decreases in SFP, when considered to reflect equivalent decreases in glomerular pressure, are sufficient to account for the observed decreases in SNGFR. Recent studies have reported the application of distal microperfusion techniques to the dog (6, 7, 39, 53). In this species the maximum decreases in SNGFR and SFP are rather dramatic: Decreases in SNGFR of 40–60 nl min^{-1} and decreases in SFP of 15–25 mm Hg occur in response to increases in distal perfusion rate up to 70 nl min^{-1}. Studies in this species have also indicated a parallelism in SFP and SNGFR as the distal perfusion rate is increased. Although the responses in this species have not been characterized as precisely as in the rat, it is clear that alterations in late proximal perfusion rate, both below and above values considered normal, elicit changes in SNGFR and SFP. Thus most investigators agree that increases in distal perfusion rate elicit feedback mediated decreases in glomerular pressure and SNGFR in both species commonly studied. Major questions remain about (*a*) the actual quantitative sensitivity of the feedback mechanism within the precise physiological range of end proximal flow rates and (*b*) the quantitative association between the glomerular pressure and SNGFR responses.

Nature of Intraluminal Component Responsible for Initiation of Feedback Response

Under physiological circumstances, feedback-mediated decreases in SNGFR are associated with increases in distal tubular fluid flow rate and distal tubule sodium, chloride, and total solute concentrations. Consequently the delivery rates of the various tubular fluid constituents also increase. The unique properties of the ascending limb of the loop of Henle allow the delivery of a hypotonic, hypochloremic, hyponatremic solution to the area of the macula densa cells. Furthermore, the degree of hypotonicity appears to be closely linked to the volume delivery rate. Thus as flow rate increases, the concentrations of the tubular fluid constituents increase.

Studies by Schnermann and associates (50, 52, 59, 60) have led to the hypothesis that chloride transport by the receptor cells initiates feedback responses. Chloride rather than sodium was suggested because furosemide, a potent inhibitor of chloride transport in the ascending loop of Henle, inactivates the feedback mechanism (50, 59, 60). However, this problem is complicated and current results are equivocal. For example, using orthograde perfusion techniques, various laboratories have demonstrated that feedback responses can be obtained with a variety of perfusion solutions including sodium-free and chloride-free solutions (7, 35, 39, 52). The simplest and most direct interpretation of the orthograde perfusion studies is that no specific ionic species is essential for the elicitation of feedback responses (7, 35, 39). However, when the macula densa area was perfused retrograde from a distal tubular site (52), not only sodium chloride solutions but also solutions containing potassium chloride, rubidium chloride, cesium chloride, ammonium chloride, sodium bromide, or potassium bromide elicited decreases in early proximal flow rate greater than 10%. In contrast, solutions containing lithium chloride, choline chloride, magnesium chloride, and six chloride-free sodium salt solutions failed to elicit perceptible feedback responses. Schnermann et al (52) concluded that absorption of chloride ions serves as the initiating step of the feedback circuit and that increases in chloride concentration serve as the driving force for the increase in chloride absorption. Accordingly, the magnitude of the feedback response should be closely associated with changes in distal chloride concentration. However, Muller-Suur and Gutsche (35) found that there was no common threshold for either early distal sodium or chloride concentrations associated with activation of the feedback mechanism. Specifically, feedback-mediated decreases in SFP and SNGFR were elicited by sodium acetate solutions. Under these conditions, distal tubule fluid chloride concentration actually decreased slightly. Microperfusion studies in the dog (7, 39) have also provided evidence that seems to be at variance with the concept of a chloride-dependent activation signal. In the dog, orthograde perfusion with solutions containing nonelectrolytes such as mannitol or urea can elicit feedback-mediated decreases in SFP (39). When isotonic and hypotonic mannitol-containing solutions were perfused, all except very hypotonic solutions containing less than 70 mOs kg^{-1} decreased SFP to about the same magnitude as the electrolyte-containing solutions.

Thus the precise nature of the intraluminal component that serves as the initiating stimulus is uncertain. Further studies are necessary to determine the extent of actual species variation. There is need for precise quantitative studies evaluating the changes in distal tubule fluid composition under conditions where the feedback responses are being determined. Such an approach could provide insight into the precise nature of the receptor system involved in the feedback mechanism. Several possibilities other than chloride transport have been suggested, including transmembrane or transepithelial potential (35, 60), total solute entry or transport into the receptor cells, and the osmotic gradient (37, 39).[1]

Vascular Resistance Alterations Responsible for Feedback-Mediated Changes in SNGFR and Glomerular Pressure

Because of the close association between changes in SFP and SNGFR in response to changes in distal flow rate, most investigators have concluded that both are mediated as a consequence of adjustment in afferent arteriolar resistance (37, 56). However, few studies have quantitated the actual changes in single nephron vascular resistances associated with feedback-mediated adjustments in glomerular function. The technical complexity of this question is apparent since the experimental design would require assessment of SNGFR, glomerular pressure, and glomerular plasma flow at several distal perfusion rates. Tucker et al (57) have utilized the carbonic anhydrase inhibitor, benzolamide, as a means of obtaining small increases in distal volume delivery. These were associated with decreases in SNGFR; however, glomerular pressure did not decrease significantly. Both afferent and efferent arteriolar resistance increased following benzolamide administration (See Footnote 1). It was suggested that with very small increases in distal flow rate, decreases in SNGFR can occur in the absence of decreases in glomerular pressure. Other recent studies suggest that SFP does indeed decrease even when distal flow rate is altered within the physiological range (36, 47). Benzolamide may exert additional effects on renal vascular resistance that are not specifically mediated by increases in distal volume delivery.

[1]This problem was discussed in detail at a recent symposium entitled "Feedback control of glomerular filtration rate" held during the 1979 FASEB meeting in Dallas, Texas. Participants in the symposium were F. S. Wright, L. Barajas, L. G. Navar, J. P. Briggs, R. C. Blantz, and J. Schnermann. Briggs & Wright presented data in support of the hypothesis that the sensing system was closely linked to a component of chloride concentration or chloride reabsorption. They suggested that the feedback responses during orthograde perfusion with nonelectrolyte solutions were transient. Navar presented results indicating that sustained feedback-mediated decreases in SFP can be elicited with both electrolyte and nonelectrolyte solutions and that an increase in distal tubule chloride concentration is not essential for the inducement of feedback-mediated decreases in SFP. In other aspects of the problem, Barajas reviewed recent findings on the ultrastructure of the macula densa–juxtaglomerular apparatus. Blantz & Schnermann discussed data concerning the segmental localization of vascular resistance changes that effect the GFR responses; Schnermann concluded that afferent arteriolar responses were predominantly involved while Blantz indicated that both pre- and postglomerular resistance segments responded to feedback signals. The role of the feedback mechanism as a mediator of renal autoregulation was discussed by Navar and by Schnermann. The results of this symposium are scheduled to appear in a future issue of *Federation Proceedings*.

In an effort to obtain a more direct evaluation of the resistance alterations, Briggs & Wright (10) measured the changes in single nephron filtration fraction following an increase in distal nephron flow. The unique aspect of this study was the identification of stellate vessels or "welling points" derived from the nephrons being subjected to alterations in distal volume delivery. In response to an increase in late proximal flow rate from 16–40 nl min^{-1}, average SFP decreased by 7 mm Hg, SNGFR decreased by 12 nl min^{-1}, and single nephron filtration fraction decreased from .38 to .29. A rather complicated nomogram was presented to support the conclusion that "constriction of the afferent arteriole is the dominant vascular response in the feedback pathway linking flow rate through the loop of Henle and SNGFR." A simple analysis can be achieved by pooling the data derived from the different experiments. With this approach, preglomerular resistance increased by 33% in response to an increased distal perfusion rate; efferent resistance was essentially unchanged (7% decrease). These results provide quantitative verification of the premise that the vascular resistance adjustments that occur as a consequence of feedback mediated signals from the distal tubule are localized predominantly to the preglomerular segments.

MEDIATOR MECHANISMS LINKING DISTAL TUBULE TO VASCULAR ELEMENTS AND CONDITIONS ALTERING FEEDBACK RESPONSIVENESS

Possible Role of Renin-Angiotensin System

At least one important mechanism regulating renin release operates through some type of macula densa feedback mechanism similar to that already described (15, 29). Since the release of renin leads to the formation of angiotensin II, a potent vasoconstrictor, some investigators have attempted to integrate the feedback mechanism for the control of vascular resistance with the feedback mechanism for the control of renin release (32, 54, 56). The proposal rests on the finding that the endothelial cells of the renal vasculature contain angiotensin-converting enzyme (12, 56). Thurau and associates have proposed that an increased distal volume delivery and associated increased distal NaCl concentration or delivery result in the local release of renin and the subsequent local formation of angiotensin II, which results in the observed increases in renal vascular resistance. It has also been proposed that angiotensin could exert a local controlling influence on glomerular function independent of the feedback mechanism (21–23).

Several studies have demonstrated reduced feedback responsiveness when renin release is suppressed. Acute extracellular and plasma volume expansion results in reduced feedback responses (45, 47, 50, 56, 60). Treatment with chronic high salt intake has also been shown to result in attenuated feedback sensitivity (28, 50). Similarly, tubuloglomerular feedback activity was impaired in the unclipped renin-depleted kidney of two kidney Goldblatt hypertensive rats (48). The persistence of feedback responsiveness early in the course of acute renal failure has been integrated into a hypothesis by which the tubuloglomerular feedback system contributes to the clearance impairment in acute renal failure (32). Other studies have failed to resolve the precise role for angiotensin in the mediation of feedback responsiveness. Feedback-induced decreases in early proximal flow rate were attenuated but not abolished during blockade of the renin-angiotensin system with either angiotensin II antagonists or a converting enzyme inhibitor (SQ 20881) (54). Muller-Suur et al (36) measured feedback responses in several experimental settings designed to alter renal renin content. The feedback responses were smaller in the DOCA and salt-loaded rats, but in other circumstances there was no obvious correlation between the kidney renin content and the maximum feedback-induced decreases in stop flow pressure. These authors suggested that a minimum intrarenal renin content may be requisite for an intact feedback response, but that other factors might be more important in transmitting the signal from the receptor segment to the muscular effector.

Another approach to the problem (19, 33) revealed that the renin concentration in blood taken from efferent arterioles was lower than in blood from the renal artery, renal vein, or superficial venules. It was suggested that renin is released into the interstitium where it might act directly on the vascular elements. Even when renin secretion was stimulated by hemorrhage, efferent arteriolar renin concentration did not exceed that in arterial blood. When nephrons surrounding a particular superficial venule were blocked with oil, the renin concentration of blood from that venule was decreased. In other experiments (19) single nephron juxtaglomerular apparatus (JGA) renin content was increased by salt depletion. The renin content was also significantly increased in the nephrons perfused with 150 mM NaCl but not in nephrons perfused with a dilute NaCl solution. The authors concluded that there was a direct association between JGA renin content and NaCl delivery to the distal tubule. However, Churchill et al (15) examined the relationship between renin secretion rate and distal tubule Na concentration or load as altered by dietary intake of NaCl. No consistent relationship existed between distal tubule sodium concentration and renin secretion rate; however, an inverse relationship existed between sodium load and renin secretion. This relationship is in general agreement with most whole-kidney experiments evaluating renin secretion, but it is at variance with what would be expected if the renin-angiotensin system were responsible for mediating the increased vascular resistance that occurs with increases in distal tubule flow or sodium chloride delivery. Thus the contradictory experimental findings bearing upon the hypothesis relating renin secretion rate to feedback-mediated alterations in local vascular resistance are difficult to reconcile. Perhaps the overall status of the renin-angiotensin system serves to modulate the sensitivity of the feedback mechanism but does not actually effect the changes in vascular tone.

The renin-angiotensin system could also exert an intrarenal local effect on hemodynamics by regulating efferent arteriolar resistance, perhaps independently of the distal tubule feedback mechanism (9, 21–23). Evidence in support of this possibility has been obtained from whole-kidney autoregulation experiments where it has been shown that chronic sodium loading plus DOCA administration (a condition expected to reduce renal renin content markedly) decreases the capability to autoregulate GFR (22). Blood flow autoregulation may not be altered much (22) or may be attenuated (9). Furthermore, during administration of angiotensin II antagonists, RBF appears to be autoregulated more efficiently than GFR, such that filtration fraction decreases in response to decreases in renal arterial pressure (21, 23). These findings have been interpreted (21–23) as suggestive of an important local role for angiotensin in the control of efferent arteriole resistance. At present, data are insufficient to confirm the validity of this interesting hypothesis. However, recent micropuncture experiments have failed to demonstrate that blockade of the renin-angiotensin system elicits preferential decreases in efferent arteriolar resistance, as might be expected on the basis of the above hypothesis (41, 53b). Also, Murray & Malvin (36a) failed to observe any relationship between GFR and RBF autoregulatory ability and renal renin content.

Other Effector Mechanisms

There have been other suggestions concerning how feedback signals originating at the tubular cells might be transmitted to the vascular elements (50). One such suggestion has been related to adenosine (43, 51). Osswald et al (43) suggested that local concentrations of adenosine, a vasoconstrictor in the kidney, may influence the renal vascular resistance. Schnermann et al (51) recently reported that luminal application of theophylline or methylxanthines, thought to antagonize adenosine effects, impaired the feedback-mediated changes in early proximal tubule fluid flow rate or stop flow pressure. Luminal application of dibutyryl cyclic AMP resulted in only slight attenuation of feedback activity. Yet another possible mediator system has been suggested by the finding that feedback responses are also attenuated by prostaglandin synthetase inhibitors (53a).

In an attempt to determine how the sensitivity of the feedback system might be altered, Persson et al (45) reported that the protein concentration in peritubular capillary perfusate influenced the magnitude of feedback responses to increases in distal perfusion rate. These authors postulated that reduced peritubular capillary protein concentration, and presumably the associated increases in interstitial fluid pressure, could be responsible for reduced feedback activity following extracellular fluid volume expansion. However, plasma volume expansion also results in reductions in the magnitude of the responses, even though peritubular protein concentration would not be expected to be altered (48). Also, tissue pressure per se may not be significant since increases in renal venous pressure that are known to be associated with increases in interstitial hydrostatic pressure do not modify the magnitude of the feedback-mediated decreases in SFP following increases in distal perfusion rate (6). Finally, the distal tubular feedback mechanism is not dependent on systemic influences or on an intact renal innervation. Studies in transplanted rat kidneys (42) and in isolated blood perfused dog kidneys (53) demonstrated the presence of tubuloglomerular feedback responses in these preparations. In addition, tubuloglomerular feedback responses were unaffected by reserpine, 6-OH dopamine, and phenoxybenzamine, though propranolol administration did attenuate feedback activity (54).

RELATIONSHIP BETWEEN DISTAL TUBULAR FEEDBACK MECHANISM AND RENAL AUTOREGULATION

A relatively close association has been demonstrated between the autoregulatory responses of superficial nephrons and those of the total nephron population (38). SNGFR, proximal tubule pressure, distal tubule pressure, and tubular transit times all exhibited autoregulatory responses to decreases in arterial pressure. At the lower level of the autoregulatory range, it appeared that whole-kidney RBF and GFR were maintained even though some decrease in superficial nephron function occurred. These results support the notion that deeper nephrons exhibit autoregulatory efficiency equivalent to or perhaps greater that that of superficial nephrons. A similar conclusion was reached by Morkrid et al (34), who estimated changes in afferent arteriolar diameters, relative flow distribution, and conductance during normotension and after lowering the blood pressure. Progressively larger microspheres entered glomeruli and afferent arterioles with decreases in arterial pressure. It appeared that the same degree of dilation of the afferent arterioles was observed in the three cortical layers.

Several recent studies have inquired into the potential effects of anesthesia and surgery on renal hemodynamics. In one study (25), cardiac output and renal blood flow decreased substantially. Afferent arteriolar resistance, estimated from the size of microspheres reaching the glomeruli, seemed to be increased more than total renal vascular resistance. These investigators suggested that the surgery required to expose the kidney may have a quantitatively significant influence on glomerular capillary pressure and that normal glomerular capillary pressure in the rat is in the range of 50–60 mm Hg. In addition the nature of the anesthesia may influence autoregulation: RBF autoregulation was more frequently impaired during Inactin than during pentobarbital anesthesia in one study (16), though this was not observed in other laboratories (18, 48).

Autoregulatory Responses in Single Nephrons

Interruption of distal volume delivery may lead to an inability of the blocked nephron to exhibit appropriate autoregulatory responses to changes in arterial pressure (37). SNGFR based on proximal collections decreased significantly in response to decreases in renal arterial pressure while SNGFR based on distal collections was not altered when renal arterial pressure was decreased (37, 48). Whole-kidney GFR autoregulation was impaired in contralateral kidneys of animals with one-clip renal hypertension; this was associated with a close association between $SNGFR_{prox}$ and $SNGFR_{dist}$ at both control and reduced arterial pressures (48). Spontaneously hypertensive rats did exhibit autoregulation of whole-kidney GFR but, under these conditions, $SNGFR_{dist}$ but not $SNGFR_{prox}$ exhibited efficient autoregulatory responses (46). Use of an indicator dilution technique to reevaluate the role of distal volume delivery on single nephron autoregulation (46) revealed that $SNGFR_{ID}$ was significantly lower than SNGFR based on complete collections at the control arterial pressures. In response to decreases in renal arterial pressure, $SNGFR_{ID}$ was not significantly altered and exhibited autoregulatory behavior in association with the total nephron population. In contrast, SNGFR based on complete proximal collections failed to exhibit autoregulation. Other results (31) are at variance with these: SNGFR measured from total proximal tubule fluid collections was not significantly different at elevated and reduced arterial pressures in sodium-depleted dogs and only slightly different in sodium-expanded dogs. The basic difference between these studies (31, 58) is in the SNGFR values reported at higher arterial pressures. Nevertheless, evidence from several laboratories indicates that highly efficient autoregulation of SNGFR is seen consistently only when normal flow to the distal tubule is maintained (32a, 37).

Whole-kidney Autoregulation Studies

Autoregulation of vascular flow studied in isolated dog and rat kidneys perfused with oxygenated paraffin oil as compared to oxygenated electrolyte and colloidal containing solutions demonstrated that autoregulatory capability was abolished during oil perfusion (2). A nonfiltering kidney model developed by retrograde filling of the tubular network with apiezon oil demonstrated that autoregulatory capability was markedly attenuated during the "oil block"; however, the autoregulatory index calculated for these oil-blocked kidneys was not indicative of a purely passive system. When blockade of filtration was achieved by complete ureteral obstruction along with intravenous infusion of mannitol, the autoregulatory index was indicative of a purely passive pressure-flow relation.

Most studies have indicated that renal blood flow autoregulation is not affected to a major extent by inhibitors or blockers of the renin-angiotensin system (1, 4, 21, 27). Hall et al (22) have indicated that renal renin depletion induced by high sodium chloride diets plus deoxycorticosterone acetate injections does not impair RBF autoregulation but does affect GFR autoregulation. These investigators (21–23) have suggested that the renin-angiotensin system participates in the local control of GFR through effects on the efferent arteriole. However, Murray & Malvin (36a) concluded that renal renin depletion does not impair RBF or GFR autoregulation.

The role of prostaglandins as mediators of autoregulatory behavior has been examined. Several chemically dissimilar inhibitors of prostaglandin synthetase have been examined. These studies have generally failed to support the suggestion that local prostaglandins may participate in autoregulatory responses (17, 18, 26).

Furosemide administration interferes with RBF autoregulation for about 30 min (17). This finding is of interest since single-nephron feedback responses are also abolished when furosemide is added to the perfusion solution (7, 32a, 59). The effects of furosemide appear to be due to a specific effect on the distal tubule feedback receptor, since increases in distal flow rate elicited by other diuretics such as carbonic anhydrase inhibitors (57, 60) are not associated with attenuated feedback responsiveness or reduced autoregulatory capability.

CONCLUSIONS

Several hormonal, neural, and systemic systems contribute to the basal level of renal vascular resistance (5). Their quantitative contributions are not well understood but probably vary with specific physiological and pathological circumstances. Of the total responsive vascular resistance, only a component is subject to control by the autoregulatory process. Vasodilators can decrease renal vascular resistance even at arterial pressures below the autoregulatory range (20). Thus these other systems presumably contribute to the basal vascular tone of the kidney by operating on a component other than that responsible for autoregulatory adjustments. With regard to autoregulation, the evidence is not highly supportive of a major role for neural factors, adrenergic receptors, the renin-angiotensin system, or the prostaglandin system. Rather, evidence from several laboratories supports the distal tubular feedback system as an intrarenal mechanism that accounts, to a major extent, for the phenomenon of renal autoregulation.

Acknowledgments

The authors are grateful for the excellent secretarial assistance of Ms. Becky Smith.

The authors' research efforts were supported by grants from National Heart, Lung and Blood Institute, the Veterans Administration, and the Alabama Heart Association. Intramural support was provided by the Nephrology Research and Training Center and the Urological Research and Rehabilitation Center.

Dr. Navar was the recipient of a Research Career Development Grant from the National Heart, Lung and Blood Institute.

Literature Cited

1. Abe, Y., Kishimoto, T., Yamamoto, K. 1976. Effect of angiotensin II antagonist infusion on autoregulation of renal blood flow. *Am. J. Physiol.* 231:1267–71
2. Aizawa, C., Waugh, W. H. 1977. Absence of renal circulatory autoregulation during perfusion with paraffin oil. *Blood Vessels* 14:175–88
3. Arendshorst, W. J. 1979. Autoregulation of renal blood flow in spontaneously hypertensive rats. *Circ. Res.* 44:344–49
4. Arendshorst, W. J., Finn, W. F. 1977. Renal hemodynamics in the rat before and during inhibition of angiotensin II. *Am. J. Physiol.* 233(4):F290–97
5. Aukland, K. 1976. Renal blood flow. In *Kidney and Urinary Tract Physiology*, ed. K. Thurau, II:25–79. Baltimore: University Park Press
6. Bell, P. D., Navar, L. G. 1979. Stop-flow pressure feedback responses during reduced renal vascular resistance in the dog. *Am. J. Physiol.* 237:F204–9
7. Bell, P. D., Thomas, C. E., Williams, R. H., Navar, L. G. 1978. Filtration rate and stop-flow pressure feedback responses to nephron perfusion in the dog. *Am. J. Physiol.* 234:F154–65
8. Blantz, R. C., Konnen, K. S. 1977. Relation of distal tubular delivery and reabsorptive rate to nephron filtration. *Am. J. Physiol.* 233:F315–24
9. Brech, W. J. 1976. Über die Beziehungen zwischen Autoregulation des renalen Blutflusses, intrarenaler Hämodynamik, und dem Renin-Angiotensin System. *Klin. Wochenschr.* 54:245–54
10. Briggs, J. P., Wright, F. S. 1979. Feedback control of glomerular filtration rate: site of the effector mechanism. *Am. J. Physiol.* 236:F40–47
11. Burke, T. J., Peterson, L. N., Duchin, K. L. 1978. Effect of kidney surface temperature on single nephron filtration rate. *Proc. Soc. Exp. Biol. Med.* 159:428–31
12. Caldwell, P. R., Seegal, B. C., Hsu, K. C., Das, M., Soffer, R. L. 1976. Angiotensin converting enzyme: vascular endothelial localization. *Science* 191:1050–51
13. Christensen, J. A., Bohle, A. 1978. The juxtaglomerular apparatus in the normal rat kidney. *Virchows Arch. A.* 379:143–50
14. Churchill, P. C., Churchill, M. C., McDonald, F. D. 1977. Tubulo-glomerular feedback in the rat. *Nephron.* 19:53–59
15. Churchill, P. C., Churchill, M. C., McDonald, F. D. 1978. Renin secretion and distal tubule Na^+ in rats. *Am. J. Physiol.* 235:F611–16
16. Conger, J. D., Burke, T. J. 1976. Effects of anesthetic agents on autoregulation of renal hemodynamics in the rat and dog. *Am. J. Physiol.* 230:652–57
17. Duchin, K. L., Peterson, L. N., Burke, T. J. 1977. Effect of furosemide on renal autoregulation. *Kidney Int.* 12:379–86

18. Finn, W. F., Arendshorst, W. J. 1976. Effect of prostaglandin synthetase inhibitors on renal blood flow in the rat. *Am. J. Physiol.* 231:1541–45
19. Gillies, A., Morgan, T. 1978. Renin content of individual juxtaglomerular apparatuses and the effect of diet, changes in nephron flow rate and in vitro acidification on the renin content. *Pflügers Arch.* 375:105–10
20. Gross, R., Kirchheim, H., Brandstetter, K. 1976. Basal vascular tone in the kidney. *Circ. Res.* 38:525–31
21. Hall, J. E., Coleman, T. G., Guyton, A. C., Balfe, J. W., Salgado, H. C. 1979. Intrarenal role of angiotensin II and [des-asp[1]] angiotensin II. *Am. J. Physiol.* 236:F252–59
22. Hall, J. E., Guyton, A. C., Cowley, A. W. 1977. Dissociation of renal blood flow and filtration rate autoregulation by renin depletion. *Am. J. Physiol.* 232:F215–21
23. Hall, J. E., Guyton, A. C., Jackson, T. E., Coleman, T. G., Lohmeier, T. E., Trippodo, N. C. 1977. Control of glomerular filtration rate by renin-angiotensin system. *Am. J. Physiol.* 233: F366–72
24. Heller, J., Horacek, V. 1977. Autoregulation of renal blood flow in the rat. *Pflügers Arch.* 370:81–85
25. Ishikawa, I., Hollenberg, N. K. 1977. Renal blood flow, afferent vascular resistance and estimated glomerular capillary pressure in the non-exposed rat kidney. *Circ. Res.* 41:67–73
26. Kaloyanides, G. J., Ahrens, R. E., Shepherd, J. A., DiBona, G. F. 1976. Inhibition of prostaglandin E_2 secretion. Failure to abolish autoregulation in the isolated dog kidney. *Circ. Res.* 38:67–73
27. Kaloyanides, G. J., DiBona, G. F. 1976. Effect of an angiotensin II antagonist on autoregulation in the isolated dog kidney. *Am. J. Physiol.* 230:1078–83
28. Kaufman, J. S., Hamburger, R. J., Flamenbaum, W. 1976. Tubuloglomerular feedback: effect of dietary NaC1 intake. *Am. J. Physiol.* 231(6):1744–49
29. Kotchen, T. A., Galla, J. H., Guthrie, G. P., Luke, R. G. 1979. Regulation of renin release by chloride. *Cardiovasc. Med.* 4:475–96
30. Leyssac, P. P. 1976. The renin angiotensin system and kidney function: a review of contributions to a new theory. *Acta Physiol. Scand.* 442: Suppl. pp. 1–52
31. Marchand, G. R., Burke, T. J., Haas, J. A., Romero, J. C., Knox, F. G. 1977. Regulation of filtration rate in sodium-depleted and expanded dogs. *Am. J. Physiol.* 232:F325–28
32. Mason, J., Takabatake, T., Olbricht, C., Thurau, K. 1978. The early phase of experimental acute renal failure. III. Tubuloglomerular feedback. *Pflügers Arch.* 373:69–76
32a. Moore, L. C., Schnermann, J., Yarimizu, S. 1979. Feedback mediation of SNGFR autoregulation in hydropenic and DOCA- and salt-loaded rats. *Am. J. Physiol.* 237:F63–74
33. Morgan, T., Gillies, A. 1977. Factors controlling the release of renin: a micropuncture study in the cat. *Pflügers Arch.* 368:13–18
34. Mørkrid, L., Ofstad, J., Willassen, Y. 1978. Diameter of afferent arterioles during autoregulation estimated from microsphere data in the dog kidney. *Circ. Res.* 42:181–91
35. Muller-Suur, R., Gutsche, H. -U. 1978. Effect of intratubular substitution of Na^+ and $C1^-$ ions on the operation of the tubuloglomerular feedback. *Acta Physiol. Scand.* 103:353–62
36. Muller-Suur, R., Gutsche, H. -U., Samwer, K. F., Oelkers, W., Hierholzer, K. 1975. Tubuloglomerular feedback in rat kidneys of different renin contents. *Pflügers Arch.* 359:33–56
36a. Murray, R. D., Malvin, R. L. 1979. Intrarenal renin and autoregulation of renal plasma flow and glomerular filtration rate. *Am. J. Physiol.* 236:F559–66
37. Navar, L. G. 1978. Renal autoregulation: perspectives from whole kidney and single nephron studies. (Editorial review). *Am. J. Physiol.* 234(5): F357–70
38. Navar, L. G., Bell, P. D., Burke, T. J. 1977. Autoregulatory responses of superficial nephrons and their association with sodium excretion during arterial pressure alterations in the dog. *Circ. Res.* 41:487–96
39. Navar, L. G., Bell, P. D., Thomas, C. E., Ploth, D. W. 1978. Influence of perfusate osmolality on stop-flow pressure feedback responses in the dog. *Am. J. Physiol.* 235:F352–58
40. Navar, L. G., Bell, P. D., White, R. W., Watts, R. L., Williams, R. H. 1977. Evaluation of the single nephron glomerular filtration coefficient in the dog. *Kidney Int.* 12:137–49
41. Navar, L. G., LaGrange, R. A., Bell, P. D., Thomas, C. E., Ploth, D. W. 1979. Glomerular and renal hemodynamics during converting enzyme inhibition

(SQ 20881) in the dog. *Hypertension* 1:371–77

42. Norlen, B. J., Muller-Suur, R., Persson, A. E. G. 1978. Tubulo-glomerular feedback response and excretory characteristics of the transplanted rat kidney. *Scand. J. Urol. Nephrol.* 12:27–33
43. Osswald, H., Spielman, W. S., Knox, F. G. 1978. Mechanism of adenosine-mediated decreases in glomerular filtration rate in dogs. *Circ. Res.* 43:465–69
44. Ott, C. E., Marchand, G. R., Diaz-Buxo, J. A., Knox, F. G. 1976. Determinants of glomerular filtration rate in the dog. *Am. J. Physiol.* 231:235–39
45. Persson, A. E. G., Muller-Suur, R., Selen, G. 1979. Capillary oncotic pressure as a modifier for tubulo-glomerular feedback. *Am. J. Physiol.* 236:F97–102
46. Ploth, D. W., Dahlheim, H., Schmidmeier, E., Hermle, M., Schnermann, J. 1978. Tubuloglomerular feedback and autoregulation of glomerular filtration rate in Wistar-Kyoto spontaneously hypertensive rats. *Pflügers Arch.* 375:261–67
47. Ploth, D. W., Rudulph, J., Thomas, C., Navar, L. G. 1978. Renal and tubuloglomerular feedback responses to plasma expansion in the rat. *Am. J. Physiol.* 235:F156–62
48. Ploth, D. W., Schnermann, J., Dahlheim, H., Hermle, M., Schmidmeier, E. 1977. Autoregulation and tubuloglomerular feedback in normotensive and hypertensive rats. *Kidney Int.* 12:253–67
49. Sadowski, J., Wocial, B. 1977. Renin release and autoregulation of blood flow in a new model of non-filtering non-transporting kidney. *J. Physiol. London* 266:219–33
50. Schnermann, J. 1975. Regulation of single nephron filtration rate by feedback—facts and theories. *Clin. Nephrol.* 3:75–81
51. Schnermann, J., Osswald, H., Hermle, M. 1977. Inhibitory effect of methylxanthines on feedback control of glomerular filtration rate in the rat kidney. *Pflügers Arch.* 369:39–48
52. Schnermann, J., Ploth, D. W., Hermle, M. 1976. Activation of tubuloglomerular feedback by chloride transport. *Pflügers Arch.* 362:229–40
53. Schnermann, J., Stowe, N., Yarimizu, S., Magnusson, M., Tingwald, G. 1977. Feedback control of glomerular filtration rate in isolated, blood-perfused dog kidneys. *Am. J. Physiol.* 233:F217–24

53a. Schnermann, J., Schubert, G., Hermle, M., Herbst, R., Stowe, N. T., Yarimizu, S., Weber, P. C. 1979. The effect of inhibition of prostaglandin synthesis on tubuloglomerular feedback in the rat kidney. *Pflügers Arch.* 379:269–79

53b. Steiner, R. W., Tucker, B. J., Blantz, R. C. 1979. Glomerular hemodynamics in rats with chronic sodium depletion. Effect of saralasin. *J. Clin. Invest.* 64:503–12

54. Stowe, N., Schnermann, J., Hermle, M. 1979. Feedback regulation of nephron filtration rate during pharmacologic interference with the renin-angiotensin and adrenergic systems in rats. *Kidney Int.* 15:473–86
55. Thomas, C. E., Bell, P. D., Navar, L. G. 1979. Glomerular filtration dynamics in the dog during elevated plasma colloid osmotic pressure. *Kidney Int.* 15:502–12
56. Thurau, K., Mason, J. 1974. The intrarenal function of the juxtaglomerular apparatus. In *Kidney and Urinary Tract Physiology,* ed. K. Thurau, 6:357–89. Baltimore: University Park Press
57. Tucker, B. J., Steiner, R. W., Gushwa, L. C., Blantz, R. C. 1978. Studies on the tubulo-glomerular feedback system in the rat. The mechanism of reduction in filtration rate with benzolamide. *J. Clin. Invest.* 62:993–1004
58. Williams, R. H., Thomas, C., Bell, D., Navar, L. G. 1977. Autoregulation of nephron filtration rate in the dog assessed by indicator-dilution technique. *Am. J. Physiol.* 233:F282–89
59. Wright, F. S., Briggs, J. P. 1977. Feedback regulation of glomerular filtration rate. (Editorial review). *Am. J. Physiol.* 233:F1–7
60. Wright, F. S. 1978. Regulation of glomerular filtration rate and renal salt excretion by a single-nephron feedback pathway. *Cardiovasc. Med.* 3:731–53

Ann. Rev. Physiol. 1980. 42:573–88

SEGMENTAL RENAL VASCULAR RESISTANCE: SINGLE NEPHRON

❖1287

Roland C. Blantz

Department of Medicine, University of California San Diego School of Medicine, La Jolla, California 92093 and Veterans Administration Medical Center, San Diego, California 92161

This review does not evaluate the autoregulation of total renal blood flow but rather assesses the physiologic influences upon the several resistances in series at the level of the single nephron vascular unit: the afferent arteriole, the glomerular capillary, the efferent arteriole, and the peritubular capillary.

NEPHRON VASCULAR RESISTANCES IN SERIES

The Preglomerular Vascular Resistance— The Afferent Arteriole

Hydrostatic pressure presumably decreases by a finite and significant amount along interlobular and arcuate arteries and along the afferent vessel, but the exact pressure profile has not been defined. (See Note, page 585.) Thus recent data assume that afferent arteriolar resistance is that single nephron resistance defined by (*a*) the pressure gradient between aorta and the glomerular capillary, and (*b*) the rate of nephron blood flow.

Recent developments in micromeasurements and their application in the rat have permitted quantitative definition of afferent arteriolar resistance. Utilizing a servo-nulling device and micropipets of 1–3 μm tip diameter, glomerular capillary hydrostatic pressure has been measured in the surface glomeruli of the Munich-Wistar rat and certain other strains. In the dog and

0066-4278/80/0315-0573$01.00

in strains of rat that do not possess surface glomeruli, glomerular capillary hydrostatic pressure has been estimated indirectly by stop-flow techniques. Several reports in the anesthetized rat have recently shown that afferent arteriolar resistance constitutes approximately 60% of the total series of vascular resistances (9, 14, 50, 60, 78) (Table 1). Certain data obtained in the dog suggest that the afferent arteriolar resistance constitutes only 40% of total renal vascular resistance (52), but other studies from this species have described a higher percentage of total vascular resistance (50–60%) (53, 54).

The Glomerular Capillary—Vascular Resistance and Hydrostatic Pressure

In the water deprived, anesthetized Munich-Wistar rat at micropuncture, glomerular capillary hydrostatic pressure (P_G) ranges from 43–50 mm Hg at mean arterial pressures of 100–125 mm Hg. Tubular pressures under these conditions are 10–16 mm Hg, which requires a pressure gradient from capillary to Bowman's space (ΔP) of approximately 35 mm Hg, a value lower than observed in earlier indirect estimates. Investigators making similar direct measurements have obtained somewhat higher values for P_G (55–60 mm Hg) (3, 64) in other strains of rat.

The direct measurement of glomerular capillary pressure also enables us to estimate the vascular resistance of the capillary. The mammalian glomerulus is a "basket" of parallel channels that are further interconnected by smaller channels too small to admit red blood cells (83). Although total glomerular capillary vascular resistance cannot be computed directly, repeated measurement of pressure within the same glomerulus and in other glomeruli on the surface of the kidney of the Munich-Wistar rat provides values for P_G in a narrow range. This finding at least suggests that the reduction in P_G along a given parallel conduit within the glomerular capillary is small and probably within the range of error of the servo-nulling device, approximately $\pm$1–2 mm Hg. Thus glomerular capillary vascular resistance is probably lower than 2% of total renal resistances in series.

P_G can remain remarkably constant across a wide range of values of nephron blood flows. When the proximal tubule is obstructed with oil, filtration ceases and thus the volume of ultrafiltrate is restored to glomerular blood flow. If P_G is monitored continuously during this maneuver, P_G will rise transiently following cessation of filtration but will then decrease to control values within 20–25 seconds. This implies an alteration in vascular resistance either at afferent or efferent arterioles or within the glomerular capillary (11).

Surface area of the glomerular capillary has not been measured accurately, and the local hydraulic permeability of the glomerular membrane

Table 1 Representative pressures, flows, and renal segmental vascular resistances in various physiologic conditions in the rat (Munich-Wistar)

	MAP (mm Hg)	P_G (mm Hg)	AR ($\times 10^9$ dyn·sec·cm^{-5})	ER ($\times 10^9$ dyn·sec·cm^{-5})	rbf (nl·min^{-1})	sngfr (nl·min^{-1})	HP_E (mm Hg)	HP_S (mm Hg)	DR ($\times 10^9$ dyn·sec·cm^{-5})
Hydropenia	114	47	24	13	236	33	18	10	4.7
Plasma volume expansion	120	59	14	9	377	51	23	19	4.5
Increased ureteral pressure	117	59	28	16	213	27	—	—	15
Increased renal venous pressure	115	48	27	11	200	26	23	19	2
Colloid expansion (low hematocrit)	84	56	8	9	311	56	27	—	6.7
Saline expansion	107	50	19	12	253	50	22	18	5.1
Angiotensin II infusion (plasma expansion)	143	67	38	27	182	35	22	—	9.0

has only been estimated. However, studies in both rat (13, 14, 28) and dog (54) have permitted the quantification of a net permeability–surface area product or a glomerular ultrafiltration coefficient, abbreviated either K_f or L_pA. The values (quantified per glomerulus) for the rat are 0.06–0.12 nl sec^{-1} mm Hg^{-1} (~4–7 nl min^{-1} mm Hg^{-1}) (13, 14, 28), and similar values have been obtained for the dog (54). This value for hydraulic permeability–surface area product is exceedingly high when compared to other nonrenal capillary networks. This high value for K_f or L_pA could be attributed to both the fenestrated character of glomerular endothelial cells and the relatively large glomerular capillary surface area. The L_pA or K_f in the glomerulus is sufficiently large that, at least in the Munich-Wistar rat, the filtration process proceeds to equilibrium within the length of the glomerular capillary [oncotic pressure generated by capillary protein concentration rises to a value within the length of the glomerular capillary equal to the hydrostatic pressure gradient from capillary to Bowman's space (ΔP)] (9, 19, 60).

Recent experimental evidence suggests that the glomerular permeability–surface area product can change within certain limits. In pathophysiologic states of renal dysfunction associated with acute immune injury (16, 17, 48) and acute nephrotoxic renal failure (10) L_pA may be reduced to as low as 0.015 nl sec^{-1} mm Hg^{-1} or approximately 20% of the "normal" observed value. This reduction has been shown to be the consequence of either or both (*a*) reductions in effective capillary surface area and (*b*) decreased local hydraulic permeability secondary to architectural changes in the glomerular membrane. Smaller changes in the glomerular permeability–surface area product have been observed in a variety of other physiologic states (8, 12, 71, 74, 75) and following the infusion of a variety of endogenous hormonal substances (7, 13, 41). Specifically, angiotensin (13), Ca^{2+}, and parathormone (43) may affect L_pA, K_f, in part by altering the surface area of the glomerular capillary.

The Efferent Arteriole

The efferent arteriole is defined by the confluence of parallel conduits constituting the glomerular capillary and a longer conduit that persists adjacent to the afferent arteriole and later branches to make up the peritubular capillary. The contractile elements of the efferent arteriole of the superficial cortical vasculature may be constituted in certain species by myoepithelial cells, related to the mesangial cell, rather than true smooth muscle (36). The deeper, juxtamedullary glomeruli more consistently exhibit smooth muscle within the efferent vessel (33, 65).

Direct observations in the rat suggest that in most physiologic states efferent arteriolar resistance constitutes approximately 30% of total segmental renal vascular resistance (9, 14, 50, 60, 78) (Table 1). Literature written prior to the past few years has suggested that afferent and efferent arteriolar resistances (AR and ER) vary independently in regulating P_G and thereby filtration rate. However, data from our own laboratory derived from a large variety of physiologic, but not markedly pathophysiologic, conditions show that afferent and efferent vascular resistances tend to change in parallel (Figure 1) (75) and not independently. Exceptions exist, such as the autoregulatory response to reductions in renal arterial pressure (60). The mechanism or mechanisms whereby changes in efferent resistance are linked to directional changes in afferent arteriolar resistance have not yet been well defined, but the relationship does seem clear in the rat (75). The efferent resistor may change directly in response to alterations in glomerular capillary hydrostatic pressure, thus maintaining P_G; however, this hypothesis has not been proven unambiguously (11). Andreucci et al have postulated that efferent resistance changes in a way that maintains the peritubular capillary pressure at a constant fraction (0.4) of the glomerular

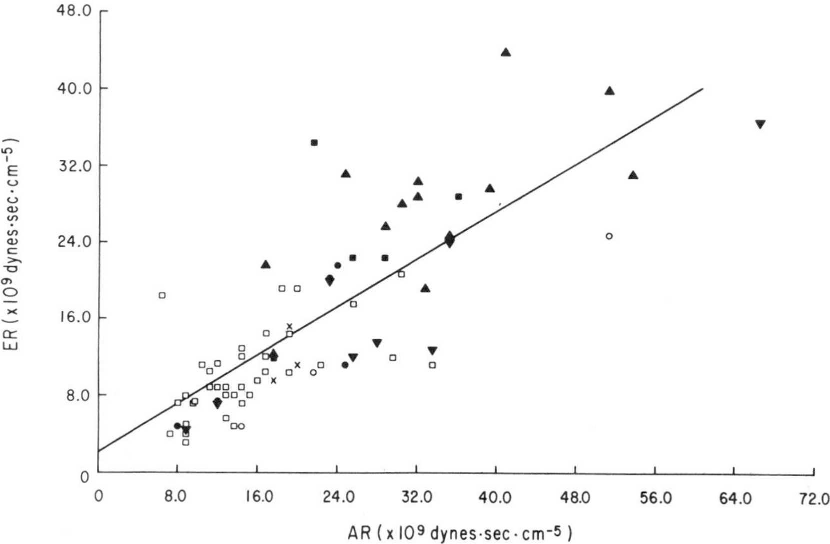

Figure 1 The correlation of absolute values for single nephron afferent (AR) and efferent arteriolar (ER) vascular resistances as evaluated by micropuncture in a variety of physiologic conditions in the Munich-Wistar rat. The various symbols designate a variety of conditions including hydropenia, volume expanded states, infusion of angiotensin II, increased ureteral pressure, etc, for a large range of values for nephron filtration rate and nephron blood flow. Across this wide range of values for single nephron vascular resistances there is a significant tendency for AR and ER to change in parallel. The specific mechanism or mechanisms that link changes in AR to changes in ER have not been elucidated completely.

capillary hydrostatic pressure (1, 2). Increases in P_G, possibly as a result of decreases in AR, could cause a readjustment in ER in an effort to maintain P_G constant. This mechanism could explain for the rat the tendency for AR and ER to change in parallel (Figure 1) (75).

As a result of the high filtration fraction in mammals (as high as 0.45 in the rat), the systemic hematocrit rises to values at the efferent arteriole much higher than in aortic blood. ER could then be a function of not only the length and radius of the efferent arteriole but also the high hematocrit within blood at this segment. At a given shear rate whole blood viscosity is a direct, but nonlinear, function of hematocrit. Viscosity per se is probably not an issue within the glomerular capillary or in vessels of 10 μm diameter or less (however, cellular aggregation could contribute to resistance to flow) (18, 49). In somewhat larger vessels (~20 μm diameter), of the order of the efferent arteriole, viscosity could be greater owing to the higher hematocrit and could contribute to the intrinsic vascular resistance computed as ER. Whole blood viscosity also varies inversely with the velocity or shear rate and influences the relationship of viscosity and hematocrit. The classical description of viscosity increasing moderately with hematocrit at low levels and rising sharply above 60% (58) should be amended, as suggested by Wells & Merrill (82), to include a family of curves that show an inverse relation of viscosity to shear rate but rise most steeply at high hematocrits and lower shear rates. Although hematocrit at the efferent arteriole of the rat is commonly 65% in the hydropenic condition, the rather high estimated rate of shear, in excess of 100 sec^{-1}, could preclude a major influence of increased viscosity on the actual ER (49, 61, 63).

Several studies have examined the renal vascular effects of selective major alterations in hematocrit (51, 62, 63). In general, reduced hematocrit is associated with (*a*) decreased renal vascular resistance, (*b*) increased blood flow, and (*c*) decreased filtration fraction. Supranormal hematocrits are associated with the opposite renal effects. The major single study in which single nephron vascular resistances have been measured (51) demonstrated in the rat that with large decreases in hematocrit, renal vascular resistance decreases significantly and does so primarily via an effect on afferent arteriolar resistance. However, when hematocrit was increased above normal, such that efferent arteriolar hematocrit exceeded 80%, renal vascular resistance increased. This effect was solely the consequence of increases in efferent arteriolar resistance. Even at these high shear rates, shear stress and thereby resistance to flow may increase with markedly increased hematocrit by decreasing red cell deformation and increasing the velocity gradient between red cells and the wall of the vessel (49).

The Potential for Afferent-Efferent Arteriolar Shunts in the Mammalian Kidney

A persistent issue in mammalian renal physiology is the existence and functional importance of low-resistance afferent-efferent arteriolar pathways (shunts) that in certain physiologic conditions might permit blood and plasma flow to enter the secondary capillary network, vasa recta, and peritubular capillaries, bypassing the glomerular ultrafilter, the primary capillary bed. In keeping with the original hypothesis of Trueta et al (73), Ljungquist & Wagemark (47) observed afferent-efferent arteriolar shunts confined to the juxtamedullary glomeruli in the rat. In the dominant cortical glomeruli the afferent arteriole, glomerular capillary, and efferent vessel are in series. Utilizing silicon rubber casts of the vasculature of both rat and dog kidneys, Spinelli and coworkers found no evidence of afferent-efferent shunts in either cortical or juxtamedullary glomeruli (66). O'Dorisio et al evaluated the issue of vascular shunts utilizing 15 μm radioactive microspheres (56). These investigators noted no leak of microspheres into the renal vein during hydropenia and acetylcholine infusion or after hemorrhagic hypotension. The authors did not examine renal histology to determine whether all microspheres were lodged entirely within glomeruli. Such 15 μm particles could have transitted afferent-efferent shunts during acetylcholine or hemorrhagic hypotension and remained lodged in peritubular capillaries or venules. In summary, most investigations find no functionally important shunts bypassing the glomerular capillary.

The Peritubular Capillary

At the efferent arteriole the renal vasculature converts from an ultrafiltering, primary capillary bed, the glomerulus, to the reabsorbing, secondary capillary bed, the peritubular capillary. Initial peritubular capillary flow is diminished by the volume of glomerular ultrafiltrate formed and is characterized by both a hematocrit and a protein concentration significantly higher than those of the systemic blood. When viewed at high microscopic magnification on the kidney surface, the "welling point" or the surface expression of the efferent arteriole branches immediately into several (32, 47, 56) smaller channels, which in turn branch once or twice more on the surface of the kidney. The branches appear to narrow at a distance from the "welling point." Nephron peritubular capillary flow increases owing to the addition of proximal tubular reabsorbate (50–70% of the nephron filtration rate along the course of the proximal tubule). The hematocrit therefore decreases along the course of the peritubular capillaries. The net result of these several opposing influences is a significant decrease in hydrostatic pressure from the large peritubular capillary ("welling point") to the smallest peritubular vessels. Data on such pressures in the rat are provided in Table 1 (15, 76). In the normally hydrated rat approximately 40–50% of the vascular resistance between efferent arteriole and renal vein resides within the peritubular capillary.

We have observed in the rat that the magnitude of decline in hydrostatic pressure along the length of the surface peritubular capillary tends to parallel the magnitude of decline in the colloid osmotic pressure in any given physiologic condition examined (15). The peritubular capillary tends also to operate as a Starling resistor; increases in the proportion of vascular resistance that is more distal in the vasculature are associated with reduction in vascular resistance in the more proximal peritubular capillary.

The surface area–hydraulic permeability product of the peritubular capillary has also been evaluated. Direct evaluations in the rat place the value for this single nephron "reabsorption permeability coefficient" at only somewhat below the values observed for the glomerular ultrafiltration coefficient (15, 76). Other authors have estimated much lower values for this reabsorptive permeability coefficient (27, 59). Deen and co-workers suggest that the peritubular capillary membrane is relatively permeable to molecules the size of albumin (29). In summary, the vascular resistance beyond the efferent arteriole contributes significantly to total renal segmental vascular resistance at 10–20% of the total. The vascular resistance contributed by the peritubular capillary varies between 20 and 60% of this "distal" vascular resistance in a variety of physiologic conditions.

PHYSIOLOGIC INFLUENCES UPON SEGMENTAL RENAL VASCULAR RESISTANCES

Alterations in Volume Status

Extracellular volume expansion with saline (10% body wt. i.v.) results in a proportional reduction in both AR and ER in the rat such as to maintain P_G constant (45–50 mm Hg) and similar to hydropenic values. In general, there is a lesser reduction in vascular resistance beyond the efferent arteriole (Table 1), which is reflected in increased pressure in the peritubular capillaries. When plasma volume is expanded with parenterally administered isoncotic plasma, there also occur major alterations in renal segmental vascular resistance that are not dependent upon major changes in systemic blood pressure. The balance of change in vascular resistances differs qualitatively in plasma volume expansion from that observed with saline in the rat in that the afferent arteriolar resistance is reduced (13, 19, 28); the net effect is a tendency for P_G to rise significantly (55–63 mm Hg) higher than values in both hydropenia and saline expansion. With plasma volume expansion, vascular resistance beyond the peritubular capillary remains relatively high and similar to hydropenic values (13, 19, 28, 53).

The effects of chronic NaCl depletion upon specific renal vascular resistances have also been examined utilizing micropuncture techniques in the rat (71). Significant volume depletion has been produced in the rat by administering a single dose of a potent diuretic (such as furosemide) and maintaining the animals on essentially NaCl-free diets. Under such conditions, nephron filtration rate can be reduced consistently (69, 71, 81). In the study of Steiner, Tucker & Blantz, individual vascular resistances were evaluated during chronic NaCl depletion. Nephron plasma flow was decreased when compared to rats maintained on normal NaCl intake. This decrease in nephron blood flow was the result of increases in both afferent and efferent arteriolar resistances. Pressures within glomerular and peritubular capillaries were similar to those observed in rats maintained on normal NaCl intake (71).

Hemorrhagic hypotension represents the severest form of acute volume depletion. Andreucci et al have provided direct measurements of blood pressure and glomerular capillary hydrostatic pressure during control hydropenia, during hemorrhagic hypotension, and during hemorrhage and the concurrent infusion of norepinephrine, epinephrine, and dopamine, respectively (2). Blood pressure decreased from approximately 120 mm Hg to 65 mm Hg during hemorrhagic hypotension and glomerular capillary hydrostatic pressure decreased concurrently from 49–50 mm Hg to 27–28 mm Hg. Nephron blood flow was not measured in this study and therefore specific values for afferent and efferent arteriolar resistance could not be calculated. However, studies in which the various catecholamines infused indirectly suggested that changes in efferent arteriolar resistance did not help in maintaining glomerular pressure and that afferent arteriolar resistance increased with hemorrhagic hypotension (2). The renal microvascular response to hemorrhagic hypotension is undoubtedly quite different from the autoregulatory responses to reduced renal artery pressure as assessed by Robertson et al (60). These investigators noted the expected major decrease in afferent arteriolar resistance but also an increase in efferent arteriolar resistance that helped to maintain P_G and the nephron filtration rate.

The Influence of Physiologic Vasoconstrictors and Vasodilators

ANGIOTENSIN Blantz, Konnen & Tucker have examined the effects of infusion of both native and synthetic AII in the plasma expanded rat (13). When pressor quantities of native AII were infused, blood pressure rose approximately 20 mm Hg. AR doubled from 16.8 to 37.5 $\times$ 10^9

dyn·sec·cm^{-5} and ER increased to a somewhat greater degree from 10.4 to 27.1 × 10^9 dyn·sec·cm^{-5}. As a result of these effects of AII on AR and ER, P_G rose from approximately 60 to 67 mm Hg while nephron blood flow fell to approximately 50% of control values (Table 1) (13). The changes in AR were not merely the result of autoregulation of nephron blood flow in response to the increase in systemic blood pressure, because similar doses of synthetic AII (Asn-1, Val-5 angiotensin II) produced nearly identical changes in glomerular capillary hydrostatic pressure, nephron blood flow, AR, and ER but had no effect on blood pressure and peripheral resistance. Another important result of AII infusion was a major reduction in the glomerular permeability coefficient (L_pA or K_f).

Myers et al have examined the effects of significantly larger doses of synthetic AII (0.2–0.6 μg kg^{-1}min^{-1}) in hydropenic rats (50). In spite of the larger dose of AII utilized and the different control condition, AII infusion had similar effects upon AR, ER, and P_G. AR increased by approximately 75% while ER increased at least 125%, the net effect being similar to that described by Blantz et al (13): increased P_G and decreased nephron blood flow. One important difference in conclusions was derived from these studies. If the rise in systemic blood pressure was prevented by aortic constriction, AR rose only 25% but ER still increased with AII infusion by more than 100% (50). Later studies by these authors also demonstrated that infused AII produces a significant decrease in the glomerular permeability coefficient (L_pA or K_f).

Infusion of AII into single large peritubular capillaries produced major reductions in the diameter of these vessels as evaluated by photographic techniques (44). This effect of AII may be analogous to the observed effects of AII in glomerular capillaries (13, 38). It may suggest that peritubular capillary vascular diameter must decrease with AII and that receptors for the hormone must be present in peritubular as well as glomerular capillaries (57, 67).

The evaluation of the effects of intrarenally generated AII has been more indirect and has made use of the AII receptor antagonist, saralasin. Steiner et al have examined by micropuncture the efficacy of maximal doses of saralasin in reversing the renal hemodynamic effects of parenterally infused AII (70). In spite of the acute nature of this evaluation not all the effects of parenteral AII infusion were neutralized. Saralasin infusion restored both ER and the decreased L_pA to the normal control values; however, the AII-induced increase in AR was not completely reversed. These studies suggest that the influence of saralasin may be selective and non-uniform, but no specific reason for the inability to restore AR to normal has been provided.

In chronic NaCl depletion, a state in which the activity of the renin-angiotensin system is increased, decreases in nephron blood flow contribute to the decrease in nephron filtration rate (71). When saralasin was infused in this condition, renal plasma flow (rpf) was restored to normal as a consequence of major decreases in AR while ER remained unchanged. Alternatively, the vasoconstriction that occurs as a consequence of activation of the tubulo-glomerular feedback system is associated with increases in both AR and ER (78). When saralasin is infused continuously under these conditions, the AII antagonist prevents the increase in both AR and ER (77).

Therefore there remains some question about the major site of action of AII upon renal vascular resistance. Certain infusion studies suggest that AII acts primarily, if not wholly, at the efferent arteriole, and glomerular and peritubular capillaries. However, studies in which AII is generated endogenously have suggested a major activity for AII at the afferent arteriole as well.

CATECHOLAMINES AND NEUROGENIC VASOCONSTRICTION Both the afferent and efferent arterioles of mammalian kidneys are innervated by adrenergic fibers (35, 47). The issue of the major site of vascular action within the single nephron unit for catecholamines and adrenergic stimulation is analogous to the issues raised for the activity of angiotensin. The effects of parenterally infused norepinephrine may be somewhat different from that observed following normal renal adrenergic stimulation. Myers et al found that the effects of parenterally infused norepinephrine were similar to those observed with angiotensin II (50) except that with norepinephrine all of the observed increase in AR could be accounted for by autoregulation in response to the increase in systemic blood pressure. However, Andreucci et al (1, 2), utilizing similar parenteral infusions of norepinephrine, concluded that the afferent arteriole was the major site of action for catecholamines. The majority of infusion studies place the major site of action for norepinephrine at the efferent arteriole; some disagreement exists about how much of the afferent arteriolar effect is primary and how much secondary. The afferent arteriole is more densely innervated than the efferent arteriole (35, 47), and this may explain a greater sensitivity of the efferent vessel to circulating catecholamines.

VASODILATORS AND RENAL SEGMENTAL VASCULAR RESISTANCE Prostaglandins represent the class of biologically active substances for which there is the best evidence for a major role in regulation of renal vascular resistance (25, 32, 79). Inhibition of prostaglandin synthesis prevents the rise in renal blood flow with hemorrhage (25, 79). Prostaglandins appear to function as normal antagonists and modifiers of biologic vasoconstrictor systems (31).

Prostaglandins antagonize the effects of angiotensin II and other vasoconstrictors (6, 42). Prostaglandin synthesis inhibitors enhance the renal vascular effects of exogenously administered and endogenously generated angiotensin II (6, 42).

In one of the few studies in which segmental vascular resistances and intrarenal pressures were measured before and after the infusion of vasodilators such as prostaglandin E_1, acetylcholine, and bradykinin (7), infusion of 0.4–0.8 $\mu g\ kg^{-1}\ min^{-1}$ of prostaglandin E_1 produced a reduction in both AR and ER, though the reduction in AR was greater than that in ER. This agent also significantly reduced the glomerular permeability coefficient (L_pA or K_f) enough to prevent the attainment of filtration pressure equilibrium. These authors also demonstrated that infusion of both acetylcholine and bradykinin resulted in major reductions in AR and ER, the decrease in AR being consistently greater than in ER (7). Theophylline, too, reduces afferent arteriolar resistance (20).

THE EFFECTS OF INCREASED RENAL VENOUS AND URETERAL PRESSURE It is reasonable to expect that major alterations in either or both renal venous and ureteral pressure should lead to significant changes in segmental renal vascular resistance. Kallskog & Wolgast have examined the effects of increased renal venous pressure in the rat (46). In spite of increases in renal venous pressure to 14.8 mm Hg, nephron blood flow was not altered and afferent and efferent arteriolar resistances were not changed. P_G remained constant (as evaluated by stop-flow methods) but peritubular capillary hydrostatic pressure rose significantly. Tucker & Blantz found strikingly similar results with partial renal venous occlusion in the rat (76). The major abnormality defined by both laboratories was a reduction in nephron filtration rate, which resulted primarily from the reduction in the hydrostatic pressure gradient across the glomerular capillary (ΔP).

Although transient elevations in ureteral pressure in the dog have been associated with increases in total renal blood flow (52), specific vascular responses to sustained elevations in ureteral pressure have only been documented in the rat. Kallskog & Wolgast found that afferent arteriolar resistance decreased while nephron blood remained constant and P_G increased (46). However, the study of Blantz, Konnen & Tucker demonstrated that when all segmental vascular resistances were quantitated there was no change in either AR or ER, and nephron blood flow remained constant (12). The rise in P_G observed was entirely the result of increases in downstream hydrostatic pressure and vascular resistances beyond the peritubular capillaries.

With more chronic and sustained increases in ureteral pressure, Humes et al have demonstrated that P_G is increased but nephron blood flow is markedly reduced. These observations suggest that the increase in ER was greater than that in AR (40). Although the renin level increases with prolonged ureteral obstruction, major vasoconstriction still occurs after ureteral obstruction in renin-depleted rats (39).

Effect of Diuretic Agents on Renal Segmental Vascular Resistance

The literature offers few data on the effects of the various clinical diuretics upon specific renal vascular resistances. Furosemide has been shown to increase renal blood flow and decrease total renal vascular resistance (30, 37, 68), but the specific site of major reductions in segmental vascular resistance has not been elucidated.

Tucker et al have elucidated the mechanisms of reduction in GFR following the administration of Benzolamide, a carbonic anhydrase inhibitor, and have shown that nephron blood flow decreases as a result of parallel increases in both AR and ER (78). The specific renal vascular effects of thiazide diuretics have not been delineated.

The effect of mannitol infusion, a representative osmotic diuretic, has been examined by Blantz utilizing micropuncture techniques in the rat (9). In spite of the fact that plasma osmolality was not altered by mannitol infusion, nephron plasma flow increased from 90.7 ± 2.7 to 158.4 ± 9.8 nl min^{-1}. This increase in nephron blood flow was the consequence of decreases in both AR and ER. Therefore it is apparent that no generalizations can be applied to the effect of all diuretic agents upon segmental renal vascular resistance.

NOTE ADDED IN PROOF: A recent study by K. J. H. Tønder and K. Aukland (personal communication) suggests that as much as 50% of the preglomerular resistance is proximal to the afferent arteriole in the interlobular and arcuate arteries.

Literature Cited

1. Andreucci, V. E., Dal Canton, A., Corradi, A., Migone, L. 1976. Efferent arterioles in glomerular haemodynamics. *Proc. Eur. Dial. Transplant Assoc.* 12:169–73
2. Andreucci, V. E., Dal Canton, A., Corradi, A., Stanziale, R., Migone, L. 1976. *Kidney Int.* 9:475–80
3. Aukland, K., Heyeraas Tonder, K., Naess, G. 1977. Capillary pressure in deep or superficial glomeruli of the rat kidney. *Acta Physiol. Scand.* 101: 418–27
4. Deleted in proof
5. Deleted in proof
6. Baylis, C., Brenner, B. M. 1978. Modulation by prostaglandin synthesis inhibitors of the action of exogenous angiotensin II on glomerular ultrafiltration in the rat. *Circ. Res.* 43:889–98
7. Baylis, C., Deen, W. M., Myers, B. D., Brenner, B. M. 1976. Effects of some vasodilator drugs on transcapillary fluid exchange in the renal cortex. *Am. J. Physiol.* 230:1148–58
8. Baylis, C., Ichikawa, I., Willis, W. T., Wilson, C. B., Brenner, B. M. 1977. Dynamics of glomerular ultrafiltration. IX. Effects of plasma protein concentration. *Am. J. Physiol.* 1:F58–71
9 Blantz, R. C. 1974. Effect of mannitol on glomerular ultrafiltration in the hydropenic rat. *J. Clin. Invest.* 54:1135–43
10. Blantz, R. C. 1975. The mechanism of acute renal failure after uranyl nitrate. *J. Clin. Invest.* 55:621–635
11. Blantz, R. C., Israelit, A. H., Rector, F. C. Jr., Seldin, D. W. 1972. The relation of distal tubular delivery and glomerular hydrostatic pressure. *Kidney Int.* 2:22–32
12. Blantz, R. C., Konnen, K. S., Tucker, B. J. 1975. Glomerular filtration response to elevated ureteral pressure in both the hydropenic and plasma expanded rat. *Circ. Res.* 37:819–29
13. Blantz, R. C., Konnen, K. S., Tucker, B. J. 1976. Angiotensin II effects upon the glomerular microcirculation and ultrafiltration coefficient of the rat. *J. Clin. Invest.* 57:419–34
14. Blantz, R. C., Rector, F. C. Jr., Seldin, D. W. 1974. Effect of hyperoncotic albumin expansion upon glomerular ultrafiltration in the rat. *Kidney Int.* 6:209–21
15. Blantz, R. C., Tucker, B. J. 1975. Determinants of peritubular capillary fluid uptake in hydropenia, saline and plasma expansion. *Am. J. Physiol.* 228:1927–35
16. Blantz, R. C., Tucker, B. J., Wilson, C. B. 1978. The acute effects of antiglomerular basement membrane antibody on the process of glomerular filtration in the rat. II. Influence of dose and complement depletion. *J. Clin. Invest.* 61:910–21
17. Blantz, R. C., Wilson, C. B. 1976. Acute effects of antiglomerular basement membrane antibody on the process of glomerular filtration in the rat. *J. Clin. Invest.* 58:899–911
18. Braasch, D., Jenett, W. 1968. Erythrocyte flexibility, hemoconcentration and blood flow resistance in glass capillaries with diameters between 6 and 50 microns. *Pfluegers Arch.* 302:245–54
19. Brenner, B. M., Troy, J. L., Daugharty, T. M., Deen, W. M., Robertson, C. R. 1972. Dynamics of glomerular ultrafiltration in the rat. II. Plasma flow dependence of GFR. *Am. J. Physiol.* 223:1184–90
20. Cambar, J., Saurel, J. 1978. Influence of theophylline on the diameter of the afferent glomerular arteriole of the rat. *Acta Anat.* 101:255–58
21. Deleted in proof
22. Deleted in proof
23. Deleted in proof
24. Deleted in proof
25. Data, J. L., Chang, L. C. T., Nies, A. S. 1976. Alteration of canine renal vascular response to hemorrhage by inhibitors of prostaglandin synthesis. *Am. J. Physiol.* 230:940–45
26. Deleted in proof
27. Deen, W. M., Robertson, C. R., Brenner, B. M. 1973. A model of peritubular capillary control of isotonic fluid reabsorption by the renal proximal tubule. *Biophys. J.* 13:340–57
28. Deen, W. M., Troy, J. L., Robertson, C. R., Brenner, B. M. 1973. Dynamics of glomerular ultrafiltration in the rat. IV. Determination of the ultrafiltration coefficient. *J. Clin. Invest.* 52:1500–8
29. Deen, W. M., Ueki, I. F., Brenner, B. M. 1976. Permeability of renal peritubular capillaries to neutral dextran and endogenous albumin. *Am. J. Physiol.* 231:283–91
30. Dualun, K. L., Peterson, L. N., Burke, T. J. 1977. Effect of furosimide on renal autoregulation. *Kidney Int.* 12:379–86
31. Dunham, E. W., Zimmerman, B. G. 1970. Release of prostaglandin like material from dog kidney during nerve stimulation. *Am. J. Physiol.* 219: 1279–85

32. Dusing, R., Melder, B., Kramer, H. J. 1976. Prostaglandins and renal function in acute extracellular volume expansion. *Prostaglandins* 12:3–10
33. Edwards, J. G. 1956. Efferent arterioles of glomeruli in the juxtamedullary zone of the human kidney. *Anat. Rec.* 125: 521–29
34. Deleted in proof
35. Fourman, J. 1970. The adrenergic innervation of the efferent arterioles and the vasa recta in the mammalian kidney. *Experientia* 26:293–94
36. Fourman, J., Moffat, D. B. 1964. Observations on the fine blood vessels of the kidney. In *Cardiovascular Anatomy and Pathology, Symp. Zool. Soc. London, No. 11,* ed. R. T. Harrison, K. R. Hill, pp. 57–71. NY: Academic. 188 pp.
37. Hook, J. B., Blatt, A. H., Brady, M. J., Williamson, H. E. 1966. Effects of several saluretic-diuretic agents on renal hemodynamics. *J. Pharmacol. Exp. Ther.* 154:667–73
38. Hornych, H. Beaufils, M., Richet, G. 1972. The effect of exogenous angiotensin on superficial and deep glomeruli in the rat kidney. *Kidney Int.* 2:336–43
39. Huguenin, M., Ott, C. E., Romero, J. C., Knox, F. G. 1976. Influence of renin depletion on renal function after release of 24-hour ureteral obstruction. *J. Lab. Clin. Med.* 87:58–64
40. Humes, H. D., Dieppa, R. A., Brenner, B. M. 1977. A model of hereditary bilateral ureteral obstruction in the rat. *Clin. Res.* 25:436A
41. Ichikawa, I., Brenner, B. M. 1977. Evidence for glomerular actions of ADH and dibutyryl cyclic AMP in the rat. *Am. J. Physiol.* 2:F102–17
42. Ichikawa, I., Brenner, B. M. 1979. Local intrarenal vasoconstrictor-vasodilator interactions in mild partial ureteral obstruction. *Am. J. Physiol.* 236:F131–40
43. Ichikawa, I., Humes, H. D., Dousa, T. P., Brenner, B. M. 1978. Influence of parathyroid hormone on glomerular ultrafiltration in the rat. *Am. J. Physiol.* 234:F393–401
44. Jensen, P. K., Steven, K. 1977. Angiotensin II induced reduction of peritubular capillary diameter in the rat kidney. *Pfluegers Arch.* 371:245–50
45. Deleted in proof
46. Kallskog, O., Wolgast, M. 1975. Effect of elevated interstitial pressure on the renal cortical hemodynamics *Acta Physiol. Scand.* 95:364–72
47. Ljungqvist, A., Wagermark, J. 1970. The adrenergic innervation of intrarenal glomerular and extra-glomerular circulatory routes. *Nephron* 7:218–29
48. Maddox, D. A., Bennett, C. M., Deen, W. M., Glassock, R. J., Knutson, D., Daugharty, T. M., Brenner, B. M. 1975. Determinants of glomerular filtration in experimental glomerulonephritis in the rat. *J. Clin. Invest.* 55:305–18
49. Merrill, W. W. 1969. Rheology of blood. *Physiol. Rev.* 49:863–88
50. Myers, B. D., Deen, W. M., Brenner, B. M. 1975. Effects of norepinephrine and angiotensin II on the determinants of glomerular ultrafiltration and proximal tubule reabsorption in the rat. *Circ. Res.* 37:101–10
51. Myers, B. D., Deen, W. M., Robertson, C. R., Brenner, B. M. 1975. Dynamics of glomerular ultrafiltration in the rat. Effects of hematocrit. *Circ. Res.* 36: 425–35
52. Navar, L. G. 1970. Minimal preglomerular resistance and calculation of normal glomerular pressure. *Am. J. Physiol.* 219:1658–1664
53. Navar, L. G., Bungorn, C., Bell, P. D. 1975. Absence of estimated glomerular pressure autoregulation during interrupted distal delivery. *Am. J. Physiol.* 229:1596–603
54. Navar, L. G., Bell, P. D., White, R. W., Watts, R. L., Williams, R. H. 1977. Evaluation of the single nephron glomerular filtration coefficient in the dog. *Kidney Int.* 12:137–49
55. Deleted in proof
56. O'Dorisio, T. M., Stein, J. H., Osgood, R. W., Ferris, T. F. 1973. Absence of aglomerular blood flow during renal vasodilatation and hemorrhage in the dog. *Proc. Exp. Biol. Med.* 143(3): 612–15
57. Osbourne, M. J., Droz, B., Meyer, P., Morel, F. 1975. Angiotensin II: Renal localization in glomerular mesangial cells by autoradiography. *Kidney Int.* 8:245–54
58. Pirofsky, B. 1953. The determination of blood viscosity in man by a method based on Poiseuille's law. *J. Clin. Invest.* 32:92–100
59. Quinn, M. D., Marsh, D. J. 1979. Peritubular capillary control of proximal tubule reabsorption in the rat. *Am. J. Physiol.* 236:F472–77
60. Robertson, C. R., Deen, W. M., Troy, J. L., Brenner, B. M. 1972. Dynamics of glomerular ultrafiltration in the rat. III. Hemodynamics and autoregulation. *Am. J. Physiol.* 223:1191–1200
61. Schmid-Schoenbein, H., Gaehtgens, P., Hirsch, H. 1968. On the shear rate de-

pendence of red cell-aggregation in vitro. *J. Clin. Invest.* 47:1447–56

62. Schrier, R. W., Earley, L. E. 1970. Effects of hematocrit on renal hemodynamics and sodium excretion in hydropenic and volume expanded dogs. *J. Clin. Invest.* 49:1656–67
63. Schrier, R. W., McDonald, K. M., Wells, R. E., Lauler, D. P. 1970. Influence of hematocrit and colloid on whole blood viscosity during volume expansion. *Am. J. Physiol.* 218:346–52
64. Schwietzer, G., Gertz, K. H. 1979. Changes of hemodynamics and glomerular ultrafiltration in renal hypertension of rats. *Kidney Int.* 15:134–43
65. Smith, J. P. 1956. Anatomical features of the human renal glomerular efferent vessel. *J. Anat.* 90:290–92
66. Spinelli, F. R., Wirz, H., Brudier, C., Pheling, G. 1972. Non-existence of shunts between afferent and efferent arterioles of juxtamedullary glomeruli in dog and rat kidneys. *Nephron* 9:123–28
67. Sraer, J. P., Sraer, J., Ardaillou, R., Mimioun, O. 1974. Evidence for renal glomerular receptors for angiotensin II. *Kidney Int.* 6:241–46
68. Stein, J. H., Mauk, R. C., Boonjarern, S., Ferris, T. F. 1972. Differences in the effect of furosemide and chlorothiazide on the distribution of renal cortical blood flow in the dog. *J. Lab. Clin. Med.* 79:995–1003
69. Stein, J. H., Osgood, R. W., Boonjarern, S., Cox, J. W., Ferris, T. F. 1974. Segmental sodium reabsorption in rats with mild and severe volume depletion. *Am. J. Physiol.* 227:351–60
70. Steiner, R. W., Blantz, R. C. 1979. Acute reversal by Saralasin of multiple intrarenal effects of angiotensin II. *Am. J. Physiol.* 237(5):F386–91
71. Steiner, R. W., Tucker, B. J., Blantz, R. C. 1979. Glomerular hemodynamics in rats with chronic sodium depletion: effect of saralasin. *J. Clin. Invest.* 64: 503–12
72. Deleted in proof
73. Trueta, J., Barday, A. E., Daniel, P. M., Franklin, K. J., Pritchard, M. M. L. 1948. *Studies of the Renal Circulation.* Oxford: Blackwell. 187 pp. 2nd ed.
74. Tucker, B. J., Blantz, R. C. 1977. Factors determining superficial nephron filtration in the mature, growing rat. *Am. J. Physiol.* 232:F97–104
75. Tucker, B. J., Blantz, R. C. 1977. An analysis of the determinants of nephron filtration rate. *Am. J. Physiol.* 232: F477–83
76. Tucker, B. J., Blantz, R. C. 1978. Determinants of proximal tubular reabsorption as mechanisms of glomerulotubular balance. *Am. J. Physiol.* 235: F142–50
77. Tucker, B. J., Blantz, R. C. 1978. Inhibition of tubulo-glomerular feedback induced reduction in nephron filtration rate with Saralasin. *Kidney Int.* 14: 784A
78. Tucker, B. J., Steiner, R. W., Gushwa, L., Blantz, R. C. 1978. Studies on the tubuloglomerular feedback system in the rat. Mechanism of reduction in filtration rate with Benzolamide. *J. Clin. Invest.* 62:993–1004
79. Vatner, S. F. 1974. Effects of hemorrhage on regional blood flow distribution in dogs and primates. *J. Clin. Invest.* 54:225–35
80. Deleted in proof
81. Weiner, M. W., Weinman, J., Kashgarian, M., Hayslett, J. P. 1972. Accelerated reabsorption on the proximal tubule produced by volume depletion. *J. Clin. Invest.* 50:1379–85
82. Wells, R. E. Jr., Merrill, E. W. 1961. The variability of blood viscosity. *Am. J. Med.* 31:505–75
83. Zlabek, K. 1973. Über dünne interkapilläre Anastomosen im Nierenglomerulus der Ratte. *Acta Anat.* 85:177–89

Ann. Rev. Physiol. 1980. 42:589–601

HORMONAL SYSTEMS AND RENAL HEMODYNAMICS

❖1288

Philip G. Baer

Department of Pharmacology, University of Tennessee
Center for the Health Sciences, Memphis, Tennessee 38163

John C. McGiff

Department of Pharmacology, New York Medical College,
Valhalla, New York 10595

INTRODUCTION

Two hormonal systems, the renin-angiotensin and the kallikrein-kinin, contribute to the regulation of the renal circulation and extracellular fluid volume. The enzymes, renin and kallikrein, are formed and stored intrarenally; when released they act on plasma globulins to liberate decapeptides, angiotensin I and lysyl-bradykinin, respectively. A single enzyme acts on both decapeptides, converting angiotensin I to the more active hormone, angiotensin II, and degrading kinins. Blockade of this enzyme by an inhibitor will augment the activity of the kallikrein-kinin system (41) and depress that of the renin-angiotensin system (13). Although kinins and angiotensins have opposing effects on the renal circulation, they share an important property, the ability to promote prostaglandin synthesis and to alter metabolism of prostaglandins (32). In addition, release of renin and kallikrein is partially controlled by a prostaglandin mechanism (12, 44). The interactions of the renin-angiotensin and kallikrein-kinin systems with prostaglandins can result in major modifications of the effects of these hormonal systems on renal hemodynamics and excretion of salt and water—e.g. attenuation of the vasoconstrictor-antidiuretic action of angiotensin and enhancement of the vasodilator-diuretic action of kinins (35). Although renal prostaglandins can also modify the activity of various hormones having

0066-4278/80/0315-0589$01.00

diverse actions on renal function, we address primarily prostaglandin interactions with kinins and angiotensins, since these are of major importance to the regulation of the renal circulation.

THE RENIN-ANGIOTENSIN AND KALLIKREIN-KININ SYSTEMS

Zonal stratifications within the kidney of renin (51) and kallikrein (8) are similar; the concentration is highest in the outer cortex and diminishes progressively on approaching the corticomedullary junction. Despite similar renal cortical gradients for kallikrein and renin, there are important differences in their primary functional localization within the kidney—i.e. renin-angiotensin to the vasculature and kallikrein-kinin to the tubules (35). Compartmentalization of these hormonal systems is evident from examining urine and venous blood. Renin is found in the renal venous effluent, being normally denied access to the urinary compartment, whereas most of the kallikrein of renal origin exits in the urine. Changes in urinary kallikrein excretion have been used as an index of altered activity of the renal kallikrein-kinin system, whereas changes in the activity of the renin-angiotensin system can be estimated by measuring renin activity in plasma.

Kallikrein-Kinin System Interacts With Prostaglandins

Prostaglandins formed within the kidney exit in both urinary (42) and venous effluents (32). Changes in the activity of the renal prostaglandin system have been related to altered efflux of prostaglandins into either urine or renal venous blood. Thus PGE_2 and renin activity in renal venous blood have been positively correlated over a wide range of experimental conditions (49), as have urinary excretion of PGE_2 and kallikrein (42). The renal kallikrein-kinin system appears to be a major determinant of the activity of renal prostaglandins under basal conditions. Nasjletti et al (42) measured changes in urinary prostaglandins and kallikrein simultaneously in long-term studies in the rat. Wide variations in urinary kallikrein activity, induced by activation and inhibition of the renal kallikrein system, were accompanied by corresponding alterations in excretion of PGE_2. It is possible to increase kallikrein excretion by giving mineralocorticoids (31). When given to rats, either aldosterone or deoxycorticosterone (DOC) increased the excretion of kallikrein and PGE_2 two- to four-fold for as long as the mineralocorticoid was administered—two weeks in this study (42). Injections of a kallikrein inhibitor, aprotinin (trasylol), decreased renal kallikrein activity and secondarily reduced PGE_2 excretion. Thus, enhanced excretion of prostaglandins induced by mineralocorticoids is a consequence of activation of the renal kallikrein-kinin system. However, when the animal is stressed, the renin-angiotensin system may supersede the renal kallikrein-kinin system in regulating prostaglandin synthesis within the kidney (49).

The contributions of prostaglandins to the renal action of kinins are uncertain. In the isolated blood-perfused canine kidney, a significant, albeit small, component of the renal vasodilator action of bradykinin was related to a prostaglandin mechanism (34). However, the vasodilator response to bradykinin for the kidney in situ was considered to be independent of a prostaglandin mechanism (29), though demonstration of the latter appears critically dependent on electrolyte balance (M. C. Blasingham, A. Nasjletti, personal communication). In contrast, a prostaglandin contribution to the effects of kinins on salt and water excretion seems more certain. Thus a renal prostaglandin, presumably PGE_2, has been proposed to mediate the effects of bradykinin on free water excretion (34).

Although assignment of the primary renal activity of the kallikrein-kinin system to the tubular compartment and of the renin-angiotensin system to the vascular compartment is useful conceptually, this does not preclude major effects of kinins on the renal circulation or of angiotensin on tubular reabsorption of salt and water. There is evidence supporting each. Thus inhibition of the principal kinin-degradative enzyme of the kidney, kininase II, using a converting enzyme inhibitor, resulted in elevated renal blood flow (41). These renal circulatory changes were accompanied by a ten-fold increase in excretion of urinary kinins and a two-fold increase in the concentration of kinins in renal venous blood.

Control of Renal Hemodynamics by Angiotensin

Renin release, with subsequent generation of angiotensin II, is a major determinant of renal perfusion pressure when renal blood flow is compromised by local factors such as lesions of the renal artery or systemic factors such as diminished extracellular fluid volume. Cowley and co-workers (9, 10) have analyzed and quantified the renin-angiotensin feedback regulation of blood pressure. In the dog, after abolition of neural control of the circulatory system, sustained reductions in renal arterial perfusion pressure, over a pressure range of 100–50 mm Hg, resulted in linearly related increases in plasma renin activity (10). The resultant increases in systemic arterial pressure, when perfusion pressure to both kidneys was reduced, were almost equal to the decreases in renal arterial pressure.

During sodium depletion, elevated renin-angiotensin system activity is requisite for maintenance of systemic blood pressure and glomerular filtration rate (GFR). Infusion of the angiotensin II blocking agent, 1-sar-8-ala angiotensin II, decreased blood pressure and GFR and increased renal blood flow in sodium-depleted dogs but had no such effects in salt-replete dogs (28). Thus under conditions of high release of renin by the kidney, angiotensin II may act as a regulator of renal hemodynamics to maintain GFR (20). Infusion of angiotensin II into the isolated kidney of the rat reproduced the effects of salt depletion; filtration fraction increased, indicating that the efferent arteriole was primarily affected by the polypeptide (13). Purified renin substrate evoked the same renal hemodynamic response as infusion of angiotensin II; this was prevented by inhibiting angiotensin converting enzyme or blocking angiotensin II with an angiotensin analog. Exogenous and endogenous angiotensin II may, therefore, selectively constrict the postglomerular blood vessels and thereby maintain GFR despite decreased renal blood flow. When GFR was depressed by constriction of the renal artery, intravenous infusion of angiotensin II caused large increases in GFR (33).

The importance of the renin-angiotensin system to the regulation of GFR is apparent from studies of renal autoregulation in animals depleted of renin or after administration of an angiotensin II blocking agent. In salt-loaded dogs with undetectable renal venous renin, autoregulation of renal blood flow was not altered; however, autoregulation of GFR was abolished (19). In sodium-replete dogs, influsion of an angiotensin II blocking agent did not alter resting renal blood flow or GFR. When renal arterial perfusion pressure was decreased, filtration fraction fell. GFR remained constant while renal blood flow progressively increased. In sodium-depleted dogs, infusion of the angiotensin II blocking agent had a markedly different effect; renal blood flow remained constant but GFR progressively fell as renal perfusion pressure was decreased (20).

These studies support the conclusion that, under some experimental and physiological conditions, regulation of efferent arteriolar resistance by angiotensin II controls GFR. Acceptance of a primary postglomerular effect of angiotensin II is complicated by the studies (50) concluding that alterations in delivery, or composition, of fluid to the distal nephron, sensed by the macula densa cells of the juxtaglomerular apparatus, caused changes in GFR mediated through effects of angiotensin II on the afferent arteriole. In addition, plasma renin activity of the rat was not greater in blood sampled at the terminus of the efferent arteriole than in aortic blood, though renin activity was greater in renal venous blood than in either aortic or efferent arteriolar blood (37). Reduction of renal arterial pressure stimulated renin release from the kidney but did not alter the ratio of aortic to efferent arteriolar plasma renin activity. The implication of these observations is that, within the kidney, renin enters the blood indirectly, being taken up by the peritubular capillaries after release from the vascular pole of the glomerulus into the interstitial fluid. This has received support from a study in which progressive reduction of renal perfusion pressure caused incremental increases in angiotensin II concentration in the renal lymph, associated with changes in total renal vascular resistance (5).

URETERAL OCCLUSION The responses of the kidney to acute reductions in arterial perfusion pressure and to acute ureteral obstruction show many similarities. Following ureteral obstruction in the anesthetized dog, renal vascular resistance is reduced, and blood flow increases (43, 45); GFR may be decreased (45) or slightly increased (43) if the animal is not volume expanded. Renal autoregulatory capacity is reduced or exhausted by ureteral occlusion (43), suggesting a common site of reduction of renal vascular resistance in response to ureteral pressure elevation and to renal arterial pressure reduction. Ureteral obstruction also stimulates renin release by the kidney; at maximum levels of ureteral pressure, reduction of arterial pressure did not further stimulate renin release (16). Following abrupt release of acute ureteral occlusion, renal blood flow initially rose to levels higher than control, then fell to control levels after 10–30 min (43).

Acute ureteral occlusion also stimulates PGE_2 synthesis within the kidney (45). Following administration of inhibitors of prostaglandin synthesis, in the absence of measurable PGE_2 in renal venous blood, ureteral occlusion no longer caused renal blood flow to increase, and a much greater fall in GFR was observed than that in dogs not treated with an aspirin-like drug. These observations suggest that elevated prostaglandin synthesis may be responsible for the increased renal blood flow evoked by ureteral occlusion in anesthetized dogs, and may explain the observation that, in unanesthetized dogs, ureteral occlusion caused no increase in renal blood flow but, after 1–3 hr, a progressive and sustained decrease (55). Prostaglandin synthesis in the kidney of the anesthetized dog subjected to abdominal surgery is already much greater than in conscious resting dogs (49); thus imposition of ureteral occlusion might evoke a prostaglandin-mediated renal vasodilatation in the former, but not in the latter.

After three days of chronic ureteral obstruction, thromboxane A_2 was found in the renal effluent of rabbit kidneys (38). Not found in the effluent of normal kidneys, thromboxane A_2 is a potent vasoconstrictor. Intrarenal production of thromboxane A_2 in response to prolonged ureteral obstruction might contribute to the marked reduction in renal blood flow in this condition (55), contrasted with the increases in renal blood flow, possibly mediated by PGE_2, seen in response to acute obstruction. In addition, generation of intrarenal thromboxane A_2 could explain the observation that, after release of ureteral obstruction of 24 hours duration, renal blood flow remained 30–50% below control values for several hours. In this same period, radioactive microsphere injection revealed that flow to the outer cortex was decreased but flow to the juxtamedullary region was increased (55). Similarly, in response to acute ureteral occlusion in anesthetized dogs, total renal flow and absolute flow to all cortical zones increased; fractional blood flow to the outer cortex, however, decreased, while that to the inner cortex and juxtamedullary zone increased (1).

Renal Cortical Prostaglandin Synthesis

Zones and structures within the kidney vary quantitatively and qualitatively in their capacity to form prostaglandins. Although previously denied (11), prostaglandin synthesis has been shown to occur in the cortex (26). Indeed, for renal cortical blood vessels the capacity for prostacyclin generation is large, but its demonstration requires removal of blood vessels from the cortical matrix (48). Arterial elements thus far examined include the main renal artery and lobar, lobular, and interlobular arteries, the latter with attached afferent arterioles; all demonstrated similar capacities to convert arachidonic acid to prostaglandins, chiefly prostacyclin. In contrast, isolated convoluted tubules showed a low capacity to generate prostaglandins. The difficulty in demonstrating renal cortical prostaglandin synthesis by slices or homogenates of kidney may be due to a cortical inhibitor of cyclo-oxygenase. The presence of an inhibitor within the renal cortex suggests a possible target for hormones or drugs with repression or stimulation of the inhibitor resulting in changes in renal vascular resistance.

Renin-Angiotensin System Interacts With Prostaglandins

Direct evidence for a major effect of prostaglandins on renal vascular resistance was obtained by Gerber et al (18). They infused arachidonic acid, the precursor of prostaglandins, into the renal artery of the dog; a possible medullary component of the prostaglandin-mediated renal vascular response is abolished in this preparation, the nonfiltering kidney. Arachidonic acid caused renal vasodilatation, which could be prevented by inhibiting prostaglandin synthesis. Because any possible effects of the renal medulla on the cortex have been eliminated in the nonfiltering kidney, the action of arachidonic acid on renal vascular resistance must arise from its conversion to prostaglandins within the cortex. Further, a prostaglandin mechanism that operated intracortically, specifically within the wall of the afferent arteriole, might be a major factor in regulating renin release (12). Renin release and subsequent generation of angiotensin II can in turn affect prostaglandin synthesis at vascular sites distal to the afferent arteriole and in cellular elements in contact with the vasculature, such as the interstitial cells that can synthesize prostaglandins (39). As noted, renin passes into the interstitial space (5) as does kallikrein (36). PGE_2 released from these several sites, both within the vascular and interstitial spaces, can in turn terminate the action of angiotensins (32). The latter probably occurs only in the face of excessive levels of angiotensin II, concentrations that are likely to cause rapid deterioration of renal function if unopposed.

These interactions of the renal prostaglandin and renin-angiotensin systems occur in the vascular and interstitial compartments of the kidney and are important to the regulation of the renal circulation, particularly during stress or in disease. Therefore, prostaglandins have been proposed to serve a primary defensive role; when organ function is threatened, a prostaglandin mechanism may be evoked that sustains function in the face of the noxious agent (49). For example, activation of the renin-angiotensin system by either hypovolemia or laparotomy resulted in increased synthesis of renal prostaglandins as indicated by enhanced renal venous efflux of PGE_2; concentrations of PGE_2 in renal venous blood increased as much as fifteen-fold (49). Changes in renal venous PGE_2 concentrations were highly correlated with the level of plasma renin activity. Under normal conditions, then, the activities of the renin-angiotensin and prostaglandin systems within the kidney are coupled. The contribution of prostaglandins to the support of the renal circulation in acutely stressed animals can be uncovered by administration of indomethacin. In the surgically stressed dog a large reduction in renal blood flow occurred rapidly in response to indomethacin, despite an attendant increase in renal perfusion pressure (49). A simultaneous decline in renal efflux of PGE_2 was proportional to the reduction of renal blood flow. Administration of indomethacin to the rabbit, after constricting a single renal artery, can precipitate malignant hypertension associated with rapid deterioration in renal function (46). Further, administration of indomethacin after giving a potent diuretic, such as a "loop diuretic," can result in a precipitous fall in GFR (44). Thus, during acute stress or when renal blood flow is compromised, the renal circulation is supported by a major prostaglandin component, withdrawal of which results in decreased renal blood flow.

PROSTACYCLIN There is one complicating factor, however, in estimating the contribution of prostaglandins to the renal circulation, namely, determining the importance of prostacyclin (PGI_2). Definition of the role of PGI_2 in regulating the renal circulation is complicated by its instability and rapid metabolism. Spontaneous hydrolysis of prostacyclin to an inactive product, 6-keto-$PGF_{1\alpha}$, will occur during preparation of blood or urine samples for assay. Assaying blood or urine for 6-keto-$PGF_{1\alpha}$ as an index of renal production of PGI_2 may be unreliable, for prostacyclin is rapidly metabolized by the kidney to other products (54).

We conclude that a prostaglandin mechanism is more important when the renal circulation is affected by disease or stress; the latter includes surgery, extracellular fluid volume depletion, and stress induced by drugs. However, the importance of prostaglandins, particularly prostacyclin, to the renal circulation under physiological conditions remains uncertain. Because indomethacin did not affect renal blood flow in the conscious resting dog even at doses more than ten-fold those that had major vascular effects in the stressed dog (49), it was concluded that renal prostaglandins did not contribute significantly to the renal circulation at rest. In the conscious rabbit, however, indomethacin administration increased renal vascular resistance two-fold (6). PGE_2 levels in renal venous blood apparently reflect the contribution of a prostaglandin mechanism to the renal circulation over a wide range of experimental conditions and are positively correlated with the activity of the renin-angiotensin system. The concentration of PGE_2 in arterial blood is normally less than 40 pg ml^{-1}, and any present is destroyed intrarenally; it follows that PGE_2 in renal venous effluent arises from prostaglandin synthesis by the kidney (15).

THE DUALITY OF THE RENAL CIRCULATION

The renal circulation was first described as having a "dual nature" because blood flow to the cortex and the medulla were considered to respond differently during hemorrhagic hypotension and shock (52). The morphological basis for the functional duality of the renal circulation derives from the morphological continuity of the postglomerular blood vessels of the inner cortical or juxtamedullary nephrons; the vasa recta arise from the efferent arterioles of these nephrons. Further, the caliber of these blood vessels is larger than that of similar vessels of cortical nephrons; this is reflected in calculated pressures of 50 mm Hg in the efferent arterioles as opposed to 16 mm Hg in those of the outer cortex (51). The studies of Trueta et al (52) were the first to indicate that juxtamedullary shunting of blood, bypassing the cortex, may occur during hemorrhagic shock. These studies and others have excluded arteriovenous anastomoses as the basis for the capability of the kidney to divert blood to the inner cortex and medulla. They have anticipated the concept, advanced recently, of control of the intrarenal circulation through hormonal regulation of blood flow to the medulla and inner cortex, whereby a stimulus causes a proportionately greater or lesser fraction of total renal blood flow to be distributed to the inner cortex and medulla by producing corresponding changes in prostaglandin synthesis in this zone (23).

The vasa recta can be directly affected by prostaglandins released in the medulla. The principal renal prostaglandin, PGE_2, is synthesized in large amounts in the medulla; because of the low activity of medullary prostaglandin degradative enzymes, local levels of PGE_2 are presumed to be high (26). PGE_2 formed in the medulla not only by interstitial cells but also by tubular and vascular elements enters the medullary interstitium and diffuses into both vascular and tubular compartments, affecting blood flow and salt and water reabsorption in this zone. The ability of vasoactive hormones to affect prostaglandin synthesis in the medulla may explain some of the anomalous effects of vasoconstrictor hormones—e.g. angiotensin II can result in increased blood flow to this zone, an effect mediated by PGE_2 (22).

Regulation of Intrarenal Distribution of Blood Flow

An intrarenal mechanism that controls the partition of blood flow within the kidney has been considered to be important to the regulation of salt and water excretion. The contribution of prostaglandins to the regulation of the intrarenal distribution of blood flow was first described in the isolated blood-perfused kidney of the dog by Itskovitz et al (23). The concentration of PGE_2 in the blood recirculating through the isolated kidney increased progressively during the entire period of perfusion (4–6 hr) and was associated with a gradual increase in renal blood flow, particularly that fraction to the inner cortex. Over a period of several hours, the fraction of blood flow to the inner cortex increased three- to four-fold. Administration of either indomethacin or meclofenamate decreased the levels of PGE_2 in the perfusate by over 70% and concomitantly reduced renal blood flow, particularly the inner cortical component, which declined from 34% to 19% (24). Infusion of PGE_2 did not prevent the decrease in blood flow to the inner cortex after indomethacin treatment, suggesting that loss of the local action of endogenous PGE_2 determines the effect of inhibitors of prostaglandin synthesis on the distribution of renal blood flow. In contrast to PGE_2, infusion of arachidonic acid, the precursor to PGE_2, increased inner cortical blood flow selectively, an effect abolished by indomethacin (27).

Angiotensin I: An Intrarenal Hormone?

In these studies, the renin-angiotensin system was shown to participate in the regulation of blood flow to the same zone, the inner cortex, affected by PGE_2. Infusion of synthetic renin substrate, the tetradecapeptide, decreased inner cortical blood flow, an effect mimicked by angiotensin I but not by angiotensin II (21). Infusions of angiotensin II decreased outer cortical blood flow without producing consistent changes in inner cortical blood flow. As angiotensin I decreased inner cortical blood flow, despite inhibition of angiotensin-converting enzyme, it was suggested that these effects of angiotensin I were direct—i.e. did not require its conversion to angiotensin II. The possibility exists, however, that tonin (7) or a related peptidase generated angiotensin II from the infused angiotensin I during inhibition of converting enzyme.

These studies taken together suggest that a balanced mechanism involving both angiotensin I and PGE_2 participates in the regulation of the partition of renal blood flow (22), with PGE_2 dilating and angiotensin constricting the medullary circulation. In this regard, elimination of the prostaglandin mechanism that participates in the maintenance of blood flow to the medulla may contribute to the development of analgesic nephropathy; inhibition of prostaglandin synthesis by aspirin-like drugs may produce medullary ischemia and lead to papillary necrosis, events described in those who use analgesics excessively (40).

ADH and Intrarenal Distribution of Blood flow

Renewed interest in the possible role of antidiuretic hormone (ADH) in regulation of renal blood flow distribution derived from observations in dogs with chronic diabetes insipidus after hypothalamic-hypophyseal tract section. During the initial diuretic phase, ^{85}Kr washout measurements and intravascular silicone rubber injection indicated that, in the absence of ADH, blood flow shifted toward the outer cortex (17). Recent evidence supporting the above observations derives from radioactive microsphere determinations of renal cortical blood flow distribution (25), in combination with ^{133}Xe washout measurements (2) before and after ADH administration to dogs undergoing water diuresis. In both studies, antidiuresis ensued without alteration of total renal blood flow. Cortical distribution was altered, however; ADH caused decreases in outer cortical and increases in juxtamedullary blood flow. In Brattleboro rats with hereditary diabetes insipidus, antidiuretic doses of ADH increased juxtamedullary nephron filtration rate while decreasing outer cortical nephron filtration rate (14). Such a response might be attributed to increases in blood flow in the juxtamedullary nephrons and/or increases in glomerular filtration pressure secondary to efferent arteriolar constriction.

ADH Interacts With Prostaglandins

ADH has been shown to increase synthesis of PGE_2 by the kidney, presumably within the medulla (53). Interactions of PGE_2 and ADH within the medulla may determine the effect of ADH on redistribution of renal blood flow within the cortex; namely, PGE_2-mediated dilatation of the medullary circulation evoked by ADH causes increased blood flow to the inner cortex by virtue of the morphological unity of the efferent arterioles and vasa recta. In addition, a direct effect of ADH on prostaglandin synthesis by cortical blood vessels must be considered. A close link between ADH and intrarenal prostaglandin production has been demonstrated in rats with hereditary diabetes insipidus (53). These Brattleboro rats have a reversible deficiency in renal prostaglandin production. Following chronic administration of ADH for 12 days, urinary PGE_2 excretion in Brattleboro rats rose from 39 ng per 24 hr to 228 ng per 24 hr, a value similar to that of normal Long-Evans rats; in normal Long-Evans rats, chronic ADH administration produced similar increases in urinary PGE_2 excretion. Although PGE_2 causes renal vasoconstriction in the rat (4), administration of inhibitors of prostaglandin synthesis has been reported to cause vaosconstriction in the rat renal medulla, which suggests that endogenous prostaglandins may be dilators in this region (47). Altered rates of synthesis of endogenous renal prostaglandins may, thus, contribute to the effects of ADH on intrarenal blood flow distribution. Further, because renal prostaglandin levels were decreased in the rat with hereditary diabetes insipidus and were restored to normal levels by injecting ADH, synthesis of renal prostaglandins may be dependent upon the concentration of ADH in the renal medulla.

The anomalous effect of PGE_2 on renal blood flow in the rat (4) may constitute the basis for the intriguing hypothesis that prostaglandins could contribute to the elevation of blood pressure in the genetically hypertensive rat (3). Prostaglandins are generally considered to be anti-hypertensive in all species, the rat possibly excepted. The basis for the proposed exception is the direct renal vasoconstrictor effect of prostaglandins in the rat (4, 30). It should be stressed, however, that the most important renal effects of prostaglandins are probably indirect, manifested as interactions with vasoactive hormones. As modulators, prostaglandins can affect the vascular actions of hormones or neurotransmitters at concentrations that have no direct vascular action. For example, exogenous PGE_2 can influence renal adrenergic neurotransmission at concentrations less than one one-hundredth of those that have a direct vascular action (30). This modulatory activity, by which small amounts of a prostaglandin affect the vascular actions of hormones for periods in excess of the half-life of the prostaglandin, may be of greatest importance to prostaglandin mechanisms affecting the circulation of the kidney and other organs.

Acknowledgments

The authors extend their sincere appreciation and apologies to the many researchers whose contributions to the literature, invaluable in the preparation of this manuscript, could not be cited because of editorial limitations on the acceptable number of references. We also wish to thank Ms. Mary Finney, Ms. Patti Norton, and Ms. Sue Hatton for their patience and expert secretarial work.

Literature Cited

1. Abe, Y., Kishimoto, T., Yamamoto, K., Ueda, J. 1973. Intrarenal distribution of blood flow during ureteral and venous pressure elevation. *Am. J. Physiol.* 224:746–51
2. Akatsuka, N., Moran, W. H., Morgan, M. L., Wilson, M. F. 1977. Effects of steady-state plasma vasopressin levels on the distribution of intrarenal blood flow on electrolyte excretion. *J. Physiol. London* 266:567–86
3. Armstrong, J. M., Blackwell, G. J., Flower, R. J., McGiff, J. C., Mullane, K. M., Vane, J. R. 1976. Genetic hypertension in rats is accompanied by a defect in renal prostaglandin catabolism. *Nature* 260:582–86
4. Baer, P. G., McGiff, J. C. 1979. Comparison of effects of prostaglandins E_2 and I_2 on rat renal vascular resistance. *Eur. J. Pharmacol.* 54:359–63
5. Bailie, M. D., Loutzenhiser, R., Moyer, S. 1972. Relation of renal hemodynamics to angiotensin II in renal hilar lymph of the dog. *Am. J. Physiol.* 222:1075–78
6. Beilin, L. J., Bhattacharya, J. 1977. The effect of prostaglandin synthesis inhibitors on renal blood flow distribution in conscious rabbits. *J. Physiol. London* 269:395–405
7. Boucher, R., Asselin, J., Genest, J. 1974. A new enzyme leading to the direct formation of angiotensin II. *Circ. Res.* 34/35: (Suppl. I) I-203–12

8. Carretero, O. A., Scicli, A. G. 1976. Renal kallikrein: its localization and possible role in renal function. *Fed. Proc.* 35:194–98
9. Cowley, A. W. Jr., Guyton, A. C. 1972. Quantification of intermediate steps in the renin-angiotensin-vasoconstrictor feedback loop in the dog. *Circ. Res.* 30:557–66
10. Cowley, A. W. Jr., Miller, J. P., Guyton, A. C. 1971. Open-loop analysis of the renin-angiotensin system in the dog. *Circ. Res.* 28:568–81
11. Crowshaw, K. 1971. Prostaglandin biosynthesis from endogenous precursors in rabbit kidney. *Nature New Biol.* 231:240–42
12. Data, J. L., Gerber, J. G., Crump, W. J., Frolich, J. C., Hollifield, J. W., Nies, A. S. 1978. The prostaglandin system: A role in canine baroreceptor control of renin release. *Circ. Res.* 42:454–58
13. Davalos, M., Frega, N. S., Saker, B., Leaf, A. 1978. Effect of exogenous and endogenous angiotensin II in the isolated perfused rat kidney. *Am. J. Physiol.* 235:F605–10
14. Davis, J. M., Schnermann, J. 1971. The effect of antidiuretic hormone on nephron filtration rates in rats with hereditary diabetes insipidus. *Pflügers Arch.* 330:323–34
15. Dunn, M. J., Liard, J. F., Dray, F. 1978. Basal and stimulated rates of renal secretion and excretion of prostaglandins E_2, F_α, and 13,14-dihydro-15-keto F_α in the dog. *Kidney Int.* 13:136–43
16. Eide, I., Loyning, E., Langard, O., Kiil, F. 1977. Mechanism of renin release during acute ureteral constriction in dogs. *Circ. Res.* 40:293–99
17. Fisher, R. D., Grunfeld, J.-P., Barger, A. C. 1970. Intrarenal distribution of blood flow in diabetes insipidus: role of ADH. *Am. J. Physiol.* 219:1348–58
18. Gerber, J. G., Data, J. L., Nies, A. S. 1978. Enhanced renal prostaglandin production in the dog. *Circ. Res.* 42: 43–45
19. Hall, J. E., Guyton, A. C., Cowley, A. W. Jr. 1977. Dissociation of renal blood flow and filtration rate autoregulation by renin depletion. *Am. J. Physiol.* 232:F215–21
20. Hall, J. E., Guyton, A. C., Jackson, T. E., Coleman, T. G., Lohmeier, T. E., Trippodo, N. C. 1977. Control of glomerular filtration rate by renin-angiotensin system. *Am. J. Physiol.* 233:F366–72
21. Itskovitz, H. D., Hebert, L. A., McGiff, J. C. 1973. Angiotensin as a possible intrarenal hormone in isolated dog kidneys. *Circ. Res.* 32:550–55
22. Itskovitz, H. D., McGiff, J. C. 1974. Hormonal regulation of the renal circulation. *Circ. Res.* 34/35: (Suppl. I) I-65–73
23. Itskovitz, H. D., Stemper, J., Pacholoczyk, D., McGiff, J. C. 1973. Renal prostaglandins: determinants of intrarenal distribution of blood flow in the dog. *Clin. Sci. Mol. Med.* 45:321s–24
24. Itskovitz, H. D., Terragno, N. A., McGiff, J. C. 1974. Effect of a renal prostaglandin on distribution of blood flow in the isolated canine kidney. *Circ. Res.* 34:770–76
25. Johnson, M. D., Park, C. S., Malvin, R. L. 1977. Antidiuretic hormone and the distribution of renal cortical blood flow. *Am. J. Physiol.* 232:F111–16
26. Larsson, C., Änggård, E. 1973. Regional differences in the formation and metabolism of prostaglandins in the rabbit kidney. *Eur. J. Pharmacol.* 21:30–36
27. Larsson, C., Änggård, E. 1974. Increased juxtamedullary blood flow and stimulation of prostaglandin biosynthesis. *Eur. J. Pharmacol.* 25:327–34
28. Lohmeier, T. E., Cowley, A. W. Jr., Trippodo, N. C., Hall, J. E., Guyton, A. C. 1977. Effects of endogenous angiotensin II on renal sodium excretion and renal hemodynamics. *Am. J. Physiol.* 233:F388–95
29. Lonigro, A. J., Hagemann, M. H., Stephenson, A. H., Fry, C. L. 1978. Inhibition of prostaglandin synthesis by indomethacin augments the renal vasodilator response to bradykinin in the anesthetized dog. *Circ. Res.* 43:447–55
30. Malik, K. U., McGiff, J. C. 1975. Modulation by prostaglandins of adrenergic transmission in the isolated perfused rabbit and rat kidney. *Circ. Res.* 36:599–609
31. Margolius, H. S., Horwitz, D., Pisano, J. J., Keiser, H. R. 1976. Relationships among urinary kallikrein, mineralocorticoids and human hypertensive disease. *Fed. Proc.* 35:203–6
32. McGiff, J. C., Itskovitz, H. D. 1973. Prostaglandins and the kidney. *Circ. Res.* 33:479–88
33. McGiff, J. C., Lynch, J. R., Leinicke, J. A., Strand, J. C., Aboosi, A. 1969. Some determinants of the effects of VAL-5-angiotensin II amide on glomerular filtration rate and sodium excretion in dogs. *J. Clin. Invest.* 48:146–55
34. McGiff, J. C., Nasjletti, A. 1976. Kinins, renal function and blood pressure

regulation. Introduction. *Fed. Proc.* 35:172–74
35. McGiff, J. C., Wong, P. Y-K. 1979. Compartmentalization of prostaglandins and prostacyclin within the kidney: implications for renal function. *Fed. Proc.* 38:89–93
36. Mills, I. H., Macfarland, N. A. A., Ward, P. E., Obika, L. F. O. 1976. The renal kallikrein-kinin system and the regulation of salt and water excretion. *Fed. Proc.* 35:181–88
37. Morgan, T., Davis, J. M. 1975. Renin secretion at the individual nephron level. *Pflügers Arch.* 359:23–31
38. Morrison, A. R., Nishikawa, K., Needleman, P. 1977. Unmasking of thromboxane A_2 synthesis by ureteral obstruction in the rabbit kidney. *Nature* 267:259–60
39. Muirhead, E. E., Germain, G., Leach, B. E., Pitcock, J. A., Stephenson, P., Brooks, B., Brosius, W. L., Daniels, E. G., Hinman, J. W. 1972. Production of renomedullary prostaglandins by renomedullary interstitial cells grown in tissue culture. *Circ. Res.* 30/31: (Suppl. II) II-161–72
40. Nanra, R. S., Chirawong, P., Kincaid-Smith, P. 1973. Medullary ischemia in experimental analgesic nephropathy. The pathogenesis of renal papillary necrosis. *Aust. N. Z. J. Med.* 3:580–85
41. Nasjletti, A., Colina-Chourio, J., McGiff, J. C. 1975. Disappearance of bradykinin in the renal circulation of dogs. *Circ. Res.* 37:59–65
42. Nasjletti, A., McGiff, J. C., Colina-Chourio, J. 1978. Interrelations of the renal kallikrein-kinin system and renal prostaglandins in the conscious rat. Influence of Mineralocorticoids. *Circ. Res.* 43:799–807
43. Navar, L. G., Baer, P. G. 1970. Renal autoregulatory and glomerular filtration responses to gradated ureteral obstruction. *Nephron* 7:301–16
44. Olsen, U. B. 1977. The pharmacology of bumetanide: a review. *Acta Pharmacol. Toxicol.* 41: (Suppl. III) 1–31
45. Olsen, U. B., Magnussen, M. P., Eilertsen, E. 1976. Prostaglandins, a link between renal hydro- and hemodynamic in dogs. *Acta Physiol. Scand.* 97:369–76
46. Romero, J. C., Strong, C. G. 1977. The effect of indomethacin blockade of prostaglandin synthesis on blood pressure of normal rabbits and rabbits with renovascular hypertension. *Circ. Res.* 40: 35–41
47. Solez, K., Fox, J. A., Miller, M., Heptinstall, R. H. 1974. Effects of indomethacin on renal inner medullary plasma flow. *Prostaglandins* 7:91–98
48. Terragno, N. A., Terragno, A., Early, J. A., Roberts, M. A., McGiff, J. C. 1978. Endogenous prostaglandin synthesis inhibitor in the renal cortex. Effects on production of prostacyclin by renal blood vessels. *Clin. Sci. Mol. Med.* 55:199s–202
49. Terragno, N. A., Terragno, D. A., McGiff, J. C. 1977. Contribution of prostaglandins to the renal circulation in conscious, anesthetized, and laparotomized dogs. *Circ. Res.* 40:590–95
50. Thurau, K. 1974. Intrarenal action of angiotensin. In *Handbook of Experimental Pharmacology,* ed. I. M. Page, F. M. Bumpus, 37:475–89. NY: Springer
51. Thurau, K. 1964. Renal hemodynamics. *Am. J. Med.* 36:698–719
52. Trueta, J., Barclay, A. E., Daniel, P. M., Franklin, K. J., Prichard, M. M. L. 1947. *Studies of the Renal Circulation.* Springield, Ill: Thomas
53. Walker, L. A., Whorton, A. R., Smigel, M., France, R., Frolich, J. C. 1978. Antidiuretic hormone increases renal prostaglandin synthesis in vivo. *Am. J. Physiol.* 235:F180–85
54. Wong, P. Y-K., McGiff, J. C., Cagen, L., Malik, K. U., Sun, F. F. 1979. Metabolism of prostacyclin in the rabbit kidney. *J. Biol. Chem.* 254:12–14
55. Yager, W. E., Griffith, L. D. 1974. Intrarenal hemodynamics following chronic unilateral ureteral obstruction in the dog. *Am. J. Physiol.* 227:816–26

Ann. Rev. Physiol. 1980. 42:603–14

RENAL HEMODYNAMICS IN ACUTE RENAL FAILURE ❖1289

John D. Conger and Robert W. Schrier

Department of Medicine, University of Colorado Medical Center, Denver, Colorado 80262

INTRODUCTION

Numerous laboratory and clinical observations have indicated an association between major changes in systemic or renal hemodynamics and acute renal failure (ARF) (6, 7, 14, 47). However, the exact role of changes in renal blood flow (RBF) in the initiation and maintenance of ARF continues to be controversial, since in experimental acute renal failure RBF may have returned to normal, either spontaneously or by pharmocological maneuvers, and yet the ARF persists as assessed by a continued marked reduction in glomerular filtration rate (GFR) (22, 23, 71). This disparity in the ratio of RBF to GFR has suggested to many workers that other pathogenetic factors, such as tubular fluid back-leak and tubular obstruction, may play more important roles than a reduction in RBF in various forms of ARF.

Two difficulties confront the reviewer of RBF in ARF. First, we must distinguish the induction from the maintenance phase of ARF. While it is clear that a reduction in RBF may be the immediate cause of ARF, its role in the maintenance phase is much less clear. Renal artery cross-clamping, intrarenal norepinephrine, and intramuscular glycerol injection all produce marked reductions in RBF and subsequent ARF. However, in these same models of acute renal failure RBF frequently returns to 50% or more of the control value without a substantial change in GFR. Second, information concerning the pathogenesis of ARF comes from various experimental models in which ARF has been induced by a variety of manipulations and nephrotoxic agents. Furthermore, responses to ischemia and nephrotoxic drugs differ in various animal species, particularly the dog and the rat.

0066-4278/80/0315-0603$01.00

Here we focus on the role of changes in RBF in the induction and maintenance of ARF and consider the importance of renal vascular hemodynamic changes in the various models of ARF. Various pathogenetic theories of ARF are listed below. We are concerned primarily with the vascular theories.

Pathogenetic Theories of ARF:

- Backleak of glomerular filtrate
- Tubular obstruction
- Vascular theories
  - Renin-angiotensin system stimulation
  - Tubuloglomerular feedback
  - Redistribution of RBF
  - Increased adrenergic activity
  - Selective alterations in afferent and efferent arteriolar resistances
  - Altered vascular reactivity
  - Altered renal prostaglandin activity
  - Cellular swelling theory
  - Intrarenal coagulation
  - Altered glomerular permeability

RENIN ANGIOTENSIN SYSTEM STIMULATION

During World War II a pathogenetic role for the renin-angiotensin system in acute renal failure was suggested because of the pathological finding of increased juxtaglomerular cell granularity in kidneys of autopsied patients (41). Experimental studies in support of this hypothesis have showed increased plasma renin activity in ischemic as well as nephrotoxic forms of acute renal failure (13, 57, 59, 65, 88). Glycerol-, uranyl nitrate-, and mercuric chloride–induced ARF all have shown elevation of plasma renin levels (52, 60, 65). With the exception of the level observed in uranyl nitrate–induced disease in the dog (31), peripheral renin levels have been found to peak early after the experimental insult and return toward normal within one to two days while ARF persists.

Experimental studies have attempted to manipulate the renin-angiotensin system and observe the effects upon ARF. Plasma renin activity has been suppressed by chronic saline loading (25, 44, 61, 76, 83), by active and passive immunization against renin-angiotensin (67), and by infusion of competitive antagonists of angiotensin and angiotensin-converting enzyme (10, 52, 69). While chronic saline loading is effective in protecting kidneys from glycerol- and mercuric chloride–induced ARF, the more specific techniques of renin-angiotensin suppression were not effective (10, 15, 16, 52, 69, 82). Chronic saline loading was ineffective in protecting the kidney from norepinephrine-induced ARF (8).

In summary, intrarenal renin activity may be a factor in the increased renovascular resistance and decreased renal blood flow that occur in the initiation stage of ARF. However, most recent studies suggest that the renin-angiotensin system is not critical to the maintenance phase of either ischemic or nephrotoxic forms of ARF. The protection against both glycerol- and mercuric chloride–induced ARF that has been noted with chronic saline loading is likely due to the ensuing solute diuresis or to some consequence thereof that attenuates the severity of acute renal failure.

TUBULOGLOMERULAR FEEDBACK

The tubuloglomerular feedback hypothesis has been invoked to explain the initiation if not the maintenance phase of acute renal failure. Damage to proximal tubular cells is thought to decrease sodium reabsorption and increase the sodium delivery to the macula densa. The increased uptake of sodium or another cation or anion by the macula densa stimulates renin release and the local generation of angiotensin II (9, 48). The increased angiotensin II then causes afferent arteriolar constriction and a reduction in glomerular filtration rate. Several factors support this hypothesis. First, there is a close anatomic association between the macula densa and the afferent arteriolar juxtaglomerular apparatus. Second, an increase in juxtaglomerular renin activity has been observed after the initiation of acute renal failure (32, 33). In addition, micropuncture studies have shown that increased sodium concentrations in the tubular fluid near the macula densa are associated with activation of renin in the juxtaglomerular apparatus of the same nephron (42, 84a). Moreover, in a study (33) of ARF induced by uranyl nitrate in the rat, whole kidney GFR fell to less than half of the control value as did the single nephron filtration rate, while distal tubular sodium delivery increased 57% and peripheral and juxtaglomerular apparatus renin activity rose.

Other studies, however, suggest that the tubuloglomerular feedback mechanism may not be involved in ARF pathogenesis. Renin release has been found to be increased by a lower concentration of sodium delivered to the macula densa rather than by an increased delivery of sodium (32). In a study of the role of arterial pressure and macula densa sodium on renin release in the dog (89), osmotic diuretics, chlorthiazide, and acetazolamide given during or before reduction of arterial pressure by aortic constriction prevented the expected release of renin (89). These authors speculated that the diuretic-induced increase in sodium delivery to the macula densa inhibited the renin release. Micropuncture studies have shown a reduction, rather than an increase, in distal tubular sodium delivery following a reduction in renal perfusion (40, 58). In addition, tachyphylaxis to the vasoconstrictor effect of angiotensin has been demonstrated (12, 45). Direct measurement of glomerular capillary pressures and glomerular hemodynamics showed that angiotensin increased both afferent and efferent arteriolar resistances and elevated single nephron filtration fraction without altering single nephron filtration rates (24). In these studies the systemic pressor effect of angiotensin on the kidney was eliminated by maintaining renal perfusion pressure constant by adjusting a suprarenal aortic clamp. A final argument against the tubuloglomerular feedback mechanism in the pathogenesis of acute renal failure is the finding (11) that, after the intravenous infusion of uranyl nitrate, GFR decreased without an appreciable change in renal plasma flow. Glomerular capillary pressures actually increased in these animals and the decreased GFR was considered to be due to a decrease in the glomerular capillary permeability. A tubuloglomerular feedback mechanism that constricted the afferent arteriole would be expected to decrease both RBF and GFR.

REDISTRIBUTION OF RBF

Techniques using radioactive gases and radiolabeled microspheres have allowed assessment of intrarenal distribution of blood flow as well as total RBF. Microsphere (31, 35, 55), xenon wash-out (7, 14, 31, 35, 51), and angiographic (56, 78) techniques in both ischemic and nephrotoxic forms of ARF have shown a decrease in outer cortical blood flow. Since 80% of RBF is distributed to cortical glomeruli, the finding of cortical pallor and redistribution of renal blood flow away from the cortex supports a possible role for redistribution of RBF in producing the functional lesion of ARF. Animal models of ARF also have shown cortical ischemia using the technique of silicon rubber injection (14, 34, 53). The return of cortical perfusion in both human and animal studies of ARF has been shown in some instances to correlate with a return of renal function (14, 34, 67a, 68).

In contrast, at 48 hr after norepinephrine-induced ARF in the dog, RBF was 60% of the control, and microsphere redistribution from the outer to the inner cortex did not occur (22). In another study of norepinephrine-induced ARF in the rat, outer cortical RBF was greater than 90% of the control value 48 hr after the ischemic insult (19). Despite this return of RBF to the outer portion of the cortex, renal function as measured by inulin clearance was still markedly reduced. Studies that examine distribution of blood flow and superficial and deep nephron function will be required to define more precisely the role of renal blood flow redistribution in ARF.

INCREASED ADRENERGIC ACTIVITY

Enhanced adrenergic activity has been proposed as a pathogenetic factor in RBF. For example, shock, surgery, and anesthesia all have been associated with ARF and increased sympathetic nerve activity. Moreover, it has been shown that prior renal denervation and treatment with phenoxybenzamine afford considerable functional protection when administered in glycerol-, norepinephrine-, and methemoglobin-induced ARF in the dog (46, 62, 75).

Mercuric chloride, although usually described as causing a nephrotoxic rather than circulatory form of ARF, has been reported to cause an immediate and lasting reduction of RBF (77). Recent in vitro data suggest that this effect is adrenergically mediated, since vascular smooth muscle contraction in response to mercuric chloride administration is considerably reduced by alpha adrenergic blockade with phentolamine and phenoxybenzamine (80). Adrenergic mechanisms also appear to be important in the two-hour renal artery clamp model in the dog, since splanchnic nerve sectioning (28), chlorpromazine treatment (81), and infiltration of the renal hilum with procaine (27) all significantly improved survival over nontreated animals. Perhaps by its anesthetic and/or renin suppressing effect, d,l-propanolol is of value in reducing the severity of ARF induced by renal artery cross-clamping in rats (26, 49, 50, 54) and rabbits (79). A recent study of renal artery cross-clamping in rats for 70 min showed a marked lessening of the degree of uremia with the use of the B_1-adrenergic blocking agent practolol (1). In contrast, the occurrence of ARF in transplanted, noninnervated kidneys (3) and the failure of phenoxybenzamine to increase the RBF in established ARF in humans (84) are arguments against a significant adrenergic mechanism in acute renal failure in man.

SELECTIVE ALTERATIONS IN AFFERENT AND EFFERENT ARTERIOLAR RESISTANCES

A pathogenetic model has been proposed (73) in studies of human ARF following shock. RBF was markedly reduced in occasional patients, but on the average it was 40% of normal. These values were not different from those seen in patients with stable chronic renal failure. Results from the use of radioactive sodium and radioactive EDTA were compatible with a mild degree of afferent arteriolar vasoconstriction and, more importantly, with the additional occurrence of efferent arteriolar relaxation. By combining these oppositely directed changes in resistance RBF could be relatively well preserved, but glomerular capillary pressure would be reduced markedly. Such selective efferent arteriolar dilatation could explain the finding of continued RBF with a near absence of GFR. At the present time no confirmatory data directly support this suggestion. However, such a pathogenetic mechanism could explain in part the lack of protection or lack of recovery after the use of vasodilator drugs that have their effect primarily at the efferent arteriolar level (72).

ALTERED VASCULAR REACTIVITY

Thomson & Fung (84) have provided evidence that adrenergic and probably humoral mechanisms are unimportant in maintaining their model of norepinephrine-induced ARF. Following a two-hour intrarenal infusion of norepinephrine, renal vasodilatation in response to acetylcholine was markedly reduced compared with control values. This impairment in vascular tone following norepinephrine-induced ischemia is in sharp contrast to the previously cited failure of renal artery cross-clamping to alter significantly renovascular resistance (74).

ALTERED RENAL PROSTAGLANDIN ACTIVITY

A role for prostaglandins in human and experimental ARF has now been proposed (18, 29, 39, 66, 85, 86, 91). Since intrarenal infusion of norepinephrine and angiotensin II stimulate the release of a prostaglandin E_2-like substance into renal venous blood, prostaglandins may function as physiologic antagonists to the vasoconstrictor activity of vasopressor substances (2, 4). Also, the normal hyperemia following renal artery occlusion can be blocked by indomethacin, a substance that inhibits prostaglandin synthesis. Since reduced RBF appears to be a primary event in ARF, failure to release prostaglandins in response to these stimuli could be important in the initiation of acute renal failure. In this regard, indomethacin enhances the severity of glycerol-induced but not mercuric chloride–induced ARF in rabbits (78, 86). Since glycerol is generally considered a circulatory model, while mercuric chloride is not, this finding does suggest a protective vascular role for endogenous prostaglandin release. Recently, in another circulatory model (43), the severity of the ARF induced by renal artery occlusion could be reduced by the prior autotransplant of renomedullary tissue into the abdominal wall. In contrast to these studies, infusions of prostaglandin into animals and humans at varying times in the course of acute renal failure have not improved renal excretory function (18, 63, 70).

THE CELLULAR SWELLING THEORY

Marked reductions in RBF and glomerular capillary endothelial cell swelling were observed (36) following one hour of total renal ischemia produced by renal artery occlusion in the rat. The investigators concluded that the endothelial cell swelling reduced the effective luminal radius of arteriolar and glomerular capillary vessels within the kidney, thereby markedly increasing renovascular resistance. The cellular swelling was thought to be due to a direct effect of ischemia to reduce the activity of transport mechanisms that pump sodium from cells and return potassium to intracellular sites. In the same study (36), hypertonic but not isotonic mannitol administration during the last 15 min of ischemia prevented both the cell swelling and the reduction of RBF. It was concluded that the hypertonic mannitol reversed the cellular swelling, presumably by osmotically opposing water movement into cells. Thus, in animals not treated with mannitol, tissue ischemia followed by cell swelling resulted in even more ischemia in a self-perpetuating cycle.

While it is an attractive hypothesis, other investigators have not confirmed the "no reflow" phenomenon in the rat (5, 17) or the dog (74). A return to normal renal blood flow was demonstrated (74) in the dog 2 min after releasing 90 min of total renal arterial occlusion. In a glycerol-induced ischemic model of acute renal failure in the rat (17), spontaneous RBF had returned to 85% of control value within 12 hr following the insult. Moreover, an additional study by the workers who originally described the cell swelling phenomenon does not support the original findings and conclusions (37). In the later study, RBF measured 4 hr after releasing the clamp was actually higher than the control values (37). Cell swelling, a constant feature immediately after clamp release, spontaneously disappeared after 24 hr of reflow (37). A recent study (23) found equivalent protection from norepinephrine-induced acute renal failure after isotonic or hypertonic mannitol administration, which, supports a protective effect of a solute diuresis rather than an osmotic effect on cell volume.

INTRARENAL COAGULATION

A pathogenetic role for the coagulation system in ARF also has received attention (90). Increased radiofibrinogen catabolism and altered coagulation indexes have been noted (90) in most forms of ARF. Approximately 10–20% of the patients who developed ARF associated with pregnancy have an atypical course and do not recover renal function (30). These patients usually have diffuse bilateral renal cortical necrosis, and a disturbance in the coagulation mechanism is likely to be involved in the pathogenesis of this lesion. In a recent study (20) examining postpartum ARF in Munich-Wistar rats using intravenous endotoxin, intrarenal fibrin deposition was discovered. However, an acute decline in renal function occurred prior to significant fibrin deposition and was associated with marked increases in afferent and lesser increases in efferent arteriolar resistances with resultant declines in both glomerular plasma flow and glomerular capillary pressure. Thus, while factors that produce an alteration in coagulation (such as endotoxin) may play a pathogenetic role in ARF in the postpartum state, coagulation within the kidney per se does not appear to be the initial event in the decline of renal function.

ALTERED GLOMERULAR CAPILLARY PERMEABILITY

The possibility of an alteration in glomerular capillary permeability was raised (22) as a potential pathogenetic mechanism in ischemic ARF. Dogs were infused for 2 hr with norepinephrine into the renal artery. The kidney developed ischemia and urine flow stopped. When the kidney was examined at 48 hr after the insult, RBF was less than that of the control but could be returned to levels above that of the control with saline infusion. Despite the increased RBF, no urine formation was found. Scanning electron microscopy revealed marked disruption of the normal epithelial podocyte structure. The cell bodies were unstructured and wrinkled; it was not possible to differentiate the primary and secondary processes or the terminal foot processes. It was conjectured that a decrease in glomerular capillary permeability could explain these findings. Also, the calculated ultrafiltration coefficient for single glomeruli decreased in rats 48 hr after uranyl nitrate induction of ARF (11). Not consistent with an altered glomerular permeability theory, however, are the findings that in a norepinephrine-induced ARF model in rats, single nephron filtration was nearly normal in nephrons with normal glomerular capillary pressures if tubular obstruction was relieved (21). In addition, a recent scanning electron microscopic examination in human acute renal failure (64) and in ARF induced by a lower dose of norepinephrine in dogs (23) disclosed no consistent glomerular epithelial abnormalities. Moreover, decreases in glomerular capillary pressure and secondary tubular obstruction appear to be sufficient to explain the pathogenesis of norepinephrine-induced ARF.

Literature Cited

1. Adar, R., Franklin, A., Spark, R. F., Salzman, E. W. 1978. Alleviation of acute anoxic renal failure in rats by B_1-adrenergic blockade with practolol. *Isr. J. Med. Sci.* 14:274–79
2. Aiken, J. W., Vane, J. R. 1973. Intrarenal prostaglandin release attenuates the renal vasoconstrictor activity of angiotensin. *J. Pharmacol. Exp. Ther.* 184: 678–87
3. Almgard, L. E., Ljungqvist, A., Ungerstedt, M. 1971. The reaction of the intrarenal sympathetic nervous system to renal transplantation. *Scand. J. Urol. Nephrol.* 5:65–72
4. Anderson, R. J., Berl, T., McDonald, K. M., Schrier, R. W. 1976. Prostaglandins. Effects on blood pressure, renal blood flow, sodium and water excretion, editorial. *Kidney Int.* 10:205–15
5. Arendshorst, W. J., Finn, W. F., Gottschalk, C. W. 1976. A micropuncture study of acute renal failure following temporary renal ischemia in the rat. *Kidney Int.* 10:S100–5

6. Arendshorst, W. J., Finn, W. F., Gottschalk, C. W. 1975. Pathogenesis of acute renal failure following renal ischemia in the rat. *Circ. Res.* 37:558–68
7. Ayer, G., Grandchamp, A., Wyler, T., Truniger, B. 1971. Intrarenal hemodynamics in glycerol-induced myohemoglobinuric acute renal failure in the rat. *Circ. Res.* 29:128–35
8. Baehler, R. W., Kotchen, T. A., Oh, C. E. 1978. Failure of chronic saline loading to protect against norepinephrine-induced acute renal failure in dogs. *Circ. Res.* 42:23–27
9. Bailie, M. D., Rector, F. C. Jr., Seldin, D. W. 1971. Angiotensin II in arterial and renal venous plasma and renal lymph in the dog. *J. Clin. Invest.* 50:119–26
10. Baranowski, R. L., O'Connor, G. J., Kurtzman, N. A. 1973. The effect of 1-sarcosine, 8-leucyl angiotensin II on glycerol-induced acute renal failure. *Proc. Am. Soc. Nephrol.* 6:7A
11. Blantz, R. C. 1975. The mechanism of acute renal failure after uranyl nitrate. *J. Clin. Invest.* 55:621–35
12. Bock, K. D., Gross, F. 1961. Renin and angiotensin tachyphylaxis. *Circ. Res.* 9:1044–50
13. Brown, J. J., Gleadle, R. I., Lawson, D. H., Lever, A. F., Linton, A. L., Macadam, R. F., Prentice, E., Robertson, J. I. S., Tree, M. 1970. Renin and acute renal failure: studies in man. *Brit. Med. J.* 1:253–58
14. Chedru, M., Baethke, R., Oken, D. E. 1972. Renal cortical blood flow and glomerular filtration in myohemoglobinuric acute renal failure. *Kidney Int.* 1:232–39
15. Chenitz, W. R., Mimran, A., Hollenberg, N. K., Merrill, J. P. 1973. Renal perfusion in acute renal failure: angiotensin mediated cortical vasoconstriction reversed by a competitive antagonist. *J. Clin. Invest.* 52:17A
16. Churchill, P., Bidani, A., Fleischmann, L., Becker-McKenna, B. 1977. Glycerol-induced acute renal failure in the two-kidney Goldblatt rat. *Am. J. Physiol.* 233:F247–52
17. Churchill, S., Zarlengo, M. D., Carvalho, J. S., Gottlieb, M. N., Oken, D. E. 1977. Normal renocortical blood flow in experimental acute renal failure. *Kidney Int.* 11:246–55
18. Cioffi, R. F., O'Connell, J. M. B., Shalhoub, R. J. 1975. Effect of prostaglandin A_1 on acute renal failure in the rat. *Nephron* 15:29–34
19. Conger, J. D., Cronin, R. E., deTorrente, A., Burke, T. J., Schrier, R. W. 1978. *7th Int. Congr. Nephrol.,* Montreal. D-44 (Abstr.)
20. Conger, J. D., Falk, S. A. 1978. *Am. Soc. Nephrol.* 89A (Abstr.)
21. Conger, J. D., Robinette, J. B., Falk, S. A. 1977. *Am. Soc. Nephrol.* 70A (Abstr.)
22. Cox, J. W., Baehler, R. W., Sharma, H., O'Dorisio, T., Osgood, R. W., Stein, J. H., Ferris, T. F. 1974. Studies on the mechanism of oliguria in a model of unilateral acute renal failure. *J. Clin. Invest.* 53:1546–58
23. Cronin, R. E., deTorrente, A., Miller, P. D., Bulgar, R. E., Burke, T. J., Schrier, R. W. 1978. Pathogenic mechanisms in early norepinephrine-induced acute renal failure. Functional and histological correlates of protection. *Kidney Int.* 14:115–25
24. Deen, W. M., Myers, B. D., Troy, J. L., Brenner, B. M. 1974. Effects of vasoactive substances on the preglomerular, glomerular and postglomerular microcirculation in rats. *Kidney Int.* 6:35A
25. DiBona, G. F., McDonald, F. D., Flamenbaum, W., Dammin, G. J., Oken, D. E. 1971. Maintenance of renal function in salt loaded rats despite severe tubular necrosis induced by $HgCl_2$. *Nephron* 8:205–20
26. Eliahou, H. E., Iaina, A., Solomon, S., Gavendo, S. 1977. Alleviation of anoxic experimental acute renal failure in rats by beta-adrenergic blockade. *Nephron* 19:158–66
27. Fekete, A., Taraba, I. 1965. Changes in renal function after procaine treatment in acute renal failure. *Acta. Physiol. Acad. Sci. Hung.* 26:257–62
28. Fekete, A., Taraba, I., Visy, M. 1965. Splanchnicotomy affords protection against acute renal failure in dogs. *Acta. Physiol. Acad. Sci. Hung.* 26:245–49
29. Fine, L. G. 1970. Acquired prostaglandin E_2 (medullin) deficiency as the cause of oliguria in acute tubular necrosis; a hypothesis. *Isr. J. Med. Sci.* 6:346–50
30. Finkelstein, F. O., Kashgarian, M., Hayslett, J. P. 1974. Clinical spectrum of postpartum renal failure. *Am. J. Med.* 57:649–54
31. Flamenbaum, W. 1973. Pathophysiology of acute renal failure. *Arch. Int. Med.* 131:911–28
32. Flamenbaum, W., Hamburger, R., Kaufman, J. 1976. Distal tubule [Na^+] and juxtaglomerular apparatus renin activity in uranyl nitrate induced acute

renal failure in the rat. *Pflügers Arch. Physiol.* 364:209–15
33. Flamenbaum, W., Hamburger, R. J., Huddleston, M. L., Kaufman, J., McNeil, J. S., Schwartz, J. H., Nagle, R., 1976. The initiation phase of experimental acute renal failure: an evaluation of uranyl nitrate induced acute renal failure in the rat. *Kidney Int.* 10: S115–22
34. Flamenbaum, W., Huddleston, M. L., McNeil, J. S., Hamburger, R. J. 1974. Uranyl nitrate acute renal failure in the rat: micropuncture and renal hemodynamic studies. *Kidney Int.* 6:408–18
35. Flamenbaum, W., McNeil, J. S., Kotchen, T. A., Saladino, A. J. 1972. Experimental acute renal failure induced by uranyl nitrate in the dog. *Circ. Res.* 31:682–98
36. Flores, J., DiBona, D. R., Beck, C. H., Leaf, A. 1972. The role of cell swelling in ischemic renal damage and the protective effect of hypertonic solute. *J. Clin. Invest.* 51:118–26
37. Frega, N. S., DiBona, D. R., Leaf, A. 1976. Ischemic renal injury. *Kidney Int.* 10:S17–25
38. Deleted in proof.
39. Gerhard, H., Mulrow, P. J. 1974. The effect of acute renal failure on renal prostaglandin A. *Clin. Res.* 22:528A
40. Glabman, S., Aynedjian, H. S., Bank, N. 1965. Micropuncture study of the effect of acute reductions in glomerular filtration rate on sodium and water reabsorption by the proximal tubules of the rat. *J. Clin. Invest.* 44:1410–16
41. Goormaghtigh, N. 1945. Vascular and circulatory changes in renal cortex in anuric crush-syndrome. *Proc. Soc. Exp. Biol. Med.* 59:303–5
42. Granger, P., Dahlheim, H., Thurau, K. 1972. Enzyme activities of the single juxtaglomerular apparatus in the rat kidney. *Kidney Int.* 1:78–88
43. Held, E. 1976. Protective effects of renomedullary autotransplants upon the course of postischemic acute renal failure in rabbits. *Kidney Int.* 10: S201–7
44. Henry, L. N., Lane, C. E., Kashgarian, M. 1968. Micropuncture studies of the pathophysiology of acute renal failure in the rat. *Lab. Invest.* 19:309–14
45. Hollenberg, N. K., Adams, D. F. 1974. Vascular factors in the pathogenesis of acute renal failure in man. In *Proc. Conf. Acute Renal Failure, Washington DC, DHEW #NIH 74–608,* ed. E. A. Friedman, H. E. Eliahov, pp. 209–29
46. Hollenberg, N. K., Adams, D. F., Oken, D. E., Abrams, H. L., Merrill, J. P. 1970. Acute renal failure due to hephrotoxins. Renal hemodynamic and angiographic studies in man. *N. Engl. J. Med.* 282:1329–33
47. Hollenberg, N. K., Epstein, M., Rosen, S. M., Basch, R. I., Oken, D. E., Merrill, J. P. 1968. Acute oliguric renal failure in man. Evidence for preferential renal cortical ischemia. *Medicine (Baltimore)* 47:455–75
48. Horky, K., Rojo-Ortega, J. M., Rodriguez, J., Boucher, R., Genest, J. 1971. Renin, renin substrate, and angiotensin in 1–converting enzyme in the lymph of rats. *Am. J. Physiol.* 220: 307–11
49. Iaina, A., Solomon, S., Eliahou, H. E. 1976. Beta adrenergic blockade reduces the severity of acute renal failure in rats. *Proc. Eur. Dial. Transplant Assoc.* 12:197
50. Iaina, A., Solomon, S., Eliahou, H. E. 1975. Reduction in severity of acute renal failure in rats by beta-adrenergic blockade. *Lancet* 2:157
51. Iaina, A., Solomon, S., Serban, I., Eliahou, H. E. 1976. Chronic saline loading in anoxic renal failure in rats. *Isr. J. Med. Sci.* 12:1457–61
52. Ishikawa, I., Hollenberg, N. K. 1976. Pharmacologic interruption of the renin-angiotensin system in myohemoglobinuric acute renal failure. *Kidney Int.* 10:S183–90
53. Kashgarian, M., Siegel, N. J., Ries, A. L., Dimeola, H. J., Hayslett, J. P. 1976. Hemodynamic aspects in development and recovery phases of experimental postischemic acute renal failure. *Kidney Int.* 10:S160–68
54. Klein, L. 1978. Propanotol protection in acute renal failure. *Invest. Urol.* 15:401–3
55. Kleinman, J. G., Flamenbaum, W., McNeil, J. S. 1975. Uranyl nitrate acute renal failure: early changes in renal function and hemodynamics. *Clin. Sci. Mol. Med.* 48:9–16
56. Knapp, R., Hollenberg, N. K., Busch, G. J., Abrams, H. L. 1972. Prolonged unilateral acute renal failure induced by intra-arterial norepinephrine infusion in the dog. *Invest. Radiol.* 7:164–73
57. Kokot, F., Kuska, J. 1969. Plasma renin activity in acute renal insufficiency. *Nephron* 6:115–27
58. Landwehr, D. M., Schnermann, J., Klose, R. M., Giebisch, G. 1968. Effect of reduction in filtration rate on renal

tubular sodium and water reabsorption. *Am. J. Physiol.* 215:687–95

59. Massani, Z. M., Finkielman, S., Worcel, M., Agrest, A., Paladini, A. C. 1966. Angiotensin blood levels in hypertensive and non-hypertensive diseases. *Clin. Sci.* 30:473–83
60. Matthews, P. G., Morgan, T. O., Johnston, C. I. 1974. The renin-angiotensin system in acute renal failure in rats. *Clin. Sci. Mol. Med.* 47:79–88
61. McDonald, F. D., Thiel, G., Wilson, D. R., DiBona, G. F., Oken, D. E. 1969. The prevention of acute renal failure in the rat by long term saline loading. A possible role of the renin-angiotensin axis. *Proc. Soc. Exp. Biol. Med.* 131: 610–14
62. McLean, D., Thomson, A. E. 1970. Effect of phenoxybenzamine on glycerol-induced acute renal failure in the rat. *Fed. Proc.* 29:1313
63. Moskowitz, P. S., Korobkin, M., Rambo, O. N. 1975. Diuresis and improved renal hemodynamics produced by prostaglandin E_1 in the dog with norepinephrine-induced acute renal failure. *Invest. Radiol.* 10:284–99
64. Myers, W. D., Langlinais, P., Merrill, R. H. 1977. Glomerular alterations by scanning electron microscopy in acute renal insufficiency in man. *Am. Soc. Nephrol.* 79A (Abstr.)
65. Ochoa, E., Finkielman, S., Agrest, A. 1970. Angiotensin blood levels during the evolution of acute renal failure. *Clin. Sci.* 38:225–31
66. Oken, D. E. 1975. Hypothesis: On the role of prostaglandins in the pathogenesis of acute renal failure. *Lancet* 1:1319–22
67. Oken, D. E., Cotes, S. C., Flamenbaum, W., Powell-Jackson, J. D., Lever, A. F. 1975. Active and passive immunization to angiotensin in experimental acute renal failure. *Kidney Int.* 7:12–18

67a. Oken, D. E., DiBona, G. F., McDonald, F. D. 1970. Micropuncture studies of the recovery phase of myohemoglobinuric acute renal failure in the rat. *J. Clin. Invest.* 49:730–37

68. Pedersen, F., Ladefoged, J. 1973. Renal hemodynamics in acute renal failure in man measured by intra-arterial injection. External counting technique with Xenon-133, and I-131 albumin. *Scand. J. Urol. Nephrol.* 7:187–95
69. Powell-Jackson, J. D., MacGregor, J., Brown, J. J., Lever, A. F., Robertson, J. I. S. 1974. The effect of angiotensin II antisera and synthetic inhibitors of the renin-angiotensin system on glycerol-induced acute renal failure in the rat. See Ref. 45, pp. 281–89
70. Reubi, F. C. 1975. The pathogenesis of anuria following shock. *Kidney Int.* 5:106–10
71. Reubi, F. C., Gossweiler, W., Gurtler, R. 1964. The renal blood flow in acute renal failure. In *Acute Renal Failure,* ed. S. Shaldon, G. C. Cooke, pp. 25–33. Philadelphia: FA. Davis
72. Reubi, F. C., Vorburger, C. 1976. Renal hemodynamics in acute renal failure after shock in man. *Kidney Int.* 10: S137–43
73. Reubi, F. C., Vorburger, C., Tuckman, J. 1973. Renal distribution volumes of indocyanine, ^{51}Cr-EDTA and ^{24}Na in man during acute renal failure. *J. Clin. Invest.* 52:223–35
74. Riley, A. L., Alexander, E. A., Migdal, S., Levinsky, N. G. 1975. The effect of ischemia on renal blood flow in the dog. *Kidney Int.* 7:27–34
75. Ruiz-Guinazu, A. 1971. Alterations of glomerular filtration rate in acute renal failure. In *Pathogenesis and Clinical Findings with Renal Failure,* ed. U. Gessler, K. Schroder, H. Weidinger, pp. 23–32. Stuttgart: G. T. Verlag
76. Ryan, R., McNeil, J. S., Flamenbaum, W., Nagle, R. 1973. Uranyl nitrate induced acute renal failure in the rat: effect of varying doses and saline loading. *Proc. Soc. Exp. Biol. Med.* 143: 289–96
77. Sherwood, T., Lavender, J. P., Russell, S. B. 1974. Mercury-induced renal vascular shutdown: observations in experimental acute renal failure. *Eur. J. Clin. Invest.* 4:1–8
78. Solez, K., Altman, J., Rienhoff, H. Y., Riela, A. R., Finer, P. M., Heptinstall, R. H. 1976. Early angiographic and renal blood flow changes after $HgCl_2$ or glycerol administration. *Kidney Int.* 10:S153–59
79. Solez, K., D'Agonotini, R. J., Stawowy, L., Freedman, M. T., Scott, W. W., Siegelman, S. S., Heptinstall, R. H. 1977. Beneficial effect of propranolol in a histologically appropriate model of postischemic acute renal failure. *Am. J. Pathol.* 88:163
80. Solomon, H. S., Hollenberg, N. K. 1975. Catecholamine release: mechanism of mercury-induced vascular smooth muscle contraction. *Am. J. Physiol.* 229:8–12
81. Taraba, I. 1965. Prevention of experimental renal failure by chlorpromazine. *Acta. Physiol. Acad. Sci. Hung.* 26: 251–56

82. Thiel, G., Brunner, F., Wunderlich, P., Huguenin, M., Bienko, B., Torhorst, J., Peters-Haefeli, L., Kirchertz, E. J., Peters, G. 1976. Protection of rat kidneys against $HgCl_2$-induced acute renal failure by induction of high urine flow without renin suppression. *Kidney Int.* 10:S-191–200
83. Thiel, G., McDonald, F. D., Oken, D. E. 1970. Micropuncture studies of the basis for protection of renin depleted rats from glycerol induced acute renal failure. *Nephron* 7:67
84. Thomson, A. E., Fung, H. Y. M. 1974. Adrenergic and cholinergic mechanisms in acute renal failure in the dog and in man. See Ref. 45, pp. 293–304
84a. Thurau, K., Dalheim, H., Gruner, A., Mason, J., Granger, P. 1972. Activation of renin in the single juxtaglomerular apparatus by sodium chloride in the tubular fluid at the macula densa. *Circ. Res.* 30–31: (Suppl. 2) 182–86
85. Torres, V. E., Romero, J. C., Strong, C. G., Wilson, D. M. Walker, V. R. 1974. Renal prostaglandin E during acute renal failure. *Prostaglandins* 8:353–60
86. Torres, V. E., Strong, C. G., Romero, J. C., Wilson, D. M. 1975 Indomethacin enhancement of glycerol-induced acute renal failure in rabbits. *Kidney Int.* 7:170–78
87. Deleted in proof
88. Tu, W. H. 1965. Plasma renin activity in acute tubular necrosis and other renal diseases associated with hypertension. *Circulation* 31:686–95
89. Vander, A. J., Miller, R. 1964. Control of renin secretion in the anesthetized dog. *Am. J. Physiol.* 207:537–46
90. Wardle, E. N. 1973. Fibrinogen catabolism studies in patients with renal disease. *Q. J. Med.* 42:205–19
91. Werb, R., Clark, W. F., Lindsay, R. M., Jones, E. O. P., Turnbull, D. I., Linton, A. L. 1978. Protective effect of prostaglandin [PGE_2] in glycerol-induced acute renal failure in rats. *Clin. Sci. Mol. Med.* 55:505–7

SPECIAL TOPIC: RECEPTORS IN EXCITABLE CELLS

Ann. Rev. Physiol. 1980. 42:615–27

RECEPTORS FOR AMINO ACIDS

❖1290

Ernest J. Peck, Jr.

Department of Cell Biology, Baylor College of Medicine, Texas Medical Center, Houston, Texas 77030

INTRODUCTION

Free amino acids in the central nervous system (CNS) serve as precursors for proteins, as sources of metabolic energy, and as neurotransmitters or neuromodulators. This diversity of function obscured their role as neurotransmitters for some time. It also confused the search by biochemists for specific receptors for amino acids that could play a role in synaptic function. Significant advances within the last decade have allowed the biochemical identification and partial characterization of several receptors for amino acid neurotransmitters. In this mini-review, I examine receptors for gamma-aminobutyric acid (GABA), glycine, and glutamic acid. I discuss biochemical, not neurophysiologic, approaches to their study. The reader is referred to other reviews for comprehensive treatments of amino acids as neurotransmitters (11, 34, 54, 58, 60, 66, 67) and of receptors for amino acids (58, 66).

RECEPTORS FOR AMINO ACIDS

Most investigators have dealt primarily with the capacity of receptors to recognize and associate with a specific amino acid. Thus these studies have examined the association of radioactive ligands (drugs, toxins, or amino acids) with high-affinity, limited-capacity binding or receptive sites located on membranes isolated from nervous tissues.

Such studies often begin by examining ligand binding to intact cells and/or isolated membranes and progress toward the solubilization and

0066-4278/80/0315-0615$01.00

purification of these binding sites. Investigators usually choose (*a*) ligands selective for a given class of receptor, as defined via physiologic response and pharmacologic specificity, and (*b*) tissues likely to possess large quantities of the receptor mechanism under study. The binding of ligand should show specificity with respect to stereochemistry and pharmacology as well as tissue source. The affinity of the receptive site for ligand should be in reasonable agreement with the biological activity of the ligand, and the number of receptive sites per mass of tissue should be small enough to be due to specific proteins embedded in the membrane. Finally, if possible, the binding of ligand to receptive site should be correlated with biological response. Each of these criteria should be applied to any ligand binding system considered to be a neurotransmitter receptor. These criteria have been reviewed extensively for hormone receptors (4) and more recently for neurotransmitter receptors (57, 58, 66).

Neurotransmitter receptors are thought to be macromolecules, probably multimeric complexes, that reside on or within postsynaptic membranes and that possess physiologically relevant binding sites. The receptor mechanism may also include ionophores, enzymes, and/or regulator molecules. The association of radioactive amino acids with receptive sites has been used to study the receptors since often only ligand selectivity and affinity persist in broken-cell preparations. However, such procedures are fraught with difficulty in the study of amino acid systems in the CNS, where high-density, homogeneous innervation is rare. In addition, few ligands are known that interact with amino acid neurotransmitter systems in an ultra-high-affinity manner as do curarimimetic snake toxins with the acetylcholine receptor. Anabolic and catabolic enzymes, transport carriers, and postsynaptic receptors all possess active or binding sites specific for a given amino acid. How can the postsynaptic receptor be distinguished from the multitude of other receptive species having similar properties? This is my primary topic.

Gamma-aminobutyric Acid

Gamma-aminobutyric acid (GABA) is synthesized in nerve endings by L-glutamate decarboxylase and catabolized in mitochondria by GABA transaminase (78). GABA is released from presynaptic cells to effect physiologic responses on postsynaptic membranes (39, 53) and is inactivated by a high-affinity transport mechanism (10, 63). These systems—i.e. enzymes, receptors, and transport processes—are the sources of multiple binding or receptive sites that have obscured the search for the GABA receptor. The recent development of new radiolabelled ligands, and careful analysis of kinetic constants, abundance, specificity, ion dependence, and subcellular distribution of the various receptive sites, now allow reasonable conclusions about their identity.

The enzymes responsible for the synthesis and degradation of GABA are readily distinguished from receptors by their relatively low affinity for GABA (mM range), sensitivity to sulfhydryl reagents, and subcellular distribution (cytoplasmic and mitochondrial). However, in purified synaptic plasma membranes there persist various transport systems (neuronal and glial), the postsynaptic receptor, and perhaps presynaptic receptors, all capable of binding GABA. Thus the positive identification of the postsynaptic receptor on the synaptic plasma membrane is difficult. GABA uptake proceeds via a carrier-mediated process that is strictly dependent on sodium ions and is separate and distinct from the postsynaptic receptor (8, 47). The apparent K_m for GABA uptake into brain slices is about 50 μm (54) and averages about 5 μm for synaptosomes (30, 31, 37, 44, 45, 50, 59). Since the uptake process is sodium-dependent while the interaction of GABA with postsynaptic receptor mechanisms is sodium-independent, ion requirements were among the first criteria employed for distinguishing between the various membrane-bound GABA-receptive sites.

We examined the sodium dependence of GABA binding and transport using synaptosomes, synaptic membranes, and junctional complexes, reasoning that subcellular localization coupled with measurements of ion dependence should help to identify the various receptive sites. A major portion of the GABA bound to synaptic plasma membranes, as well as that taken up by hippocampal synaptosomes, is dependent on sodium ions (43). Both processes, sodium-dependent binding and uptake, are maximal at about 100 millimolar NaCl, and neither is demonstrable in the absence of sodium. Choline chloride will not replace NaCl in either the binding or transport process. In contrast, the binding of ^{3}H-GABA to synaptic plasma membranes treated with low concentrations (0.05–0.1%) of Triton is a sodium-independent process. This sodium-independent binding of GABA to junctional complexes (i.e. Triton-treated synaptic plasma membrane) is similar, kinetically and pharmacologically, to the sodium-independent binding of GABA to synaptic plasma membranes. Since sodium-dependent GABA binding disappears from synaptic plasma membrane upon Triton treatment, this component must be a species loosely associated with the membrane and may be responsible for mediating sodium-dependent transport.

A second criterion for determining the type of GABA receptive site measured, i.e. uptake or postsynaptic, is pharmacologic specificity. A variety of drugs, including 2-fluoro-, 2-chloro,- 2-methyl-, or 2-hydroxyl-GABA, L-2,4-diaminobutyric acid (L-DABA), nipecotic acid, guvacine, and *cis*-1,3-aminocyclohexanecarboxylic acid (3, 32, 35, 40–42, 47, 51, 65) are potent inhibitors of the transport process but show little or no efficacy as postsynaptic GABA agonists or antagonists in neurophysiological studies.

Putative postsynatic receptors in synaptic plasma membranes and junctional complexes may be differentiated using drugs that affect postsynaptic GABA responses physiologically—e.g. bicuculline (an antagonist) and its derivatives, and the agonists muscimol, 3-amino-propanesulfonic acid, imidazole-4-acetic acid, and isoguvacine. These compounds either block or mimic the effects of GABA at the postsynaptic membrane as measured either physiologically (8, 26, 33, 73, 76) or in studies of sodium-independent binding to synaptic plasma membrane (21, 22, 25, 26, 43, 70, 77). Table 1 summarizes the inhibition of sodium-dependent and sodium-independent binding of radiolabelled GABA to synaptic plasma membranes and junctional complexes by a number of pharmacologic agents. Table 1 also contains IC_{50} values for the inhibition of sodium-dependent GABA uptake into synaptosomes by these drugs. Although by no means exhaustive, the list includes the most often employed of the drugs that exhibit reasonable affinities for these sites.

Drugs that affect the postsynaptic receptor and sodium-independent GABA binding (e.g. muscimol, 3-aminopropanesulfonic acid, imidazoleacetic acid and bicuculline) do not inhibit sodium-dependent GABA binding or uptake into synaptosomes, whereas drugs that inhibit sodium-dependent GABA uptake into synaptosomes (e.g. nipecotic acid and L-DABA) do not inhibit sodium-independent GABA binding. Furthermore, there is a correlation between sodium-dependent GABA binding and sodium-dependent GABA uptake in the rank order of displacement by the various inhibitors,

Table 1 Pharmacology of GABA binding and uptake

	IC_{50} (μM)[a]		
	Binding to synaptic plasma membranes		
Analog	NA^+-independent	NA^+-dependent	Uptake by synaptosomes
3-Aminopropane-sulfonic acid	0.035	140	450
Muscimol	0.006	500	320
GABA	0.1–0.2	5	4
Imidazole acetic acid	0.7	1,600	3,300
Bicuculline	15	300	520
β-Alanine	100	2,900	3,700
L-DABA	> 1,000	350	120
Nipecotic acid	> 1,000	40	15

[a] IC_{50} values are that concentration of analog required to inhibit ^{3}H-GABA binding or uptake by 50% when synaptic plasma membranes or synaptosomes are exposed to subsaturating concentrations of label and either specific binding or initial velocity of uptake, respectively, are measured. These data are taken from (43, 58) and unpublished results from our laboratory.

including those of sodium-independent GABA binding. Thus sodium-dependent GABA binding to synaptic plasma membranes and GABA uptake into synaptosomes represent different manifestations of the same process.

Physical separation of GABA binding sites can facilitate the unambiguous assignment of their function. The GABA uptake site has been solubilized using Triton X-100 and reconstituted in artificial liposomes (37, 38). Studies in our laboratory have focused on the postsynaptic receptor within junctional complexes. Detergent disruption of nerve ending particles or synaptosomes results in the formation of junctional complexes (5–7). The resulting complexes are primarily postsynaptic densities since most extrajunctional membranes are dispersed by 0.1% Triton (5). Junctional complexes should possess only sodium-independent GABA-receptive sites—i.e. the putative postsynaptic receptor. The sodium-dependent GABA-receptive sites should be lost upon Triton treatment since they comprise extrajunctional membrane protein. We found this to be the case. In a typical experiment, synaptic plasma membranes are exposed to various concentrations of Triton X-100, and the binding of ^{3}H -GABA to the remaining membrane is measured in the presence and absence of 100 mM NaCl. GABA binding in the presence of sodium is reduced about 90% by treatment of synaptic plasma membranes with 0.1% Triton. Subsequent treatment with higher concentrations of Triton has no effect. The sodium-independent binding of GABA is reduced slightly by this treatment. The amount of GABA bound to Triton-treated synaptic plasma membranes (i.e. junctional complexes) is essentially the same in the presence or absence of sodium; that is, the sodium-independent GABA-receptive sites measured in treated membranes correspond to the 10% of original measured in the presence of sodium. Furthermore, the pharmacologic specificity of GABA binding to the junctional complex preparation in the presence or absence of sodium is identical to that of the sodium-independent GABA-receptive site in synaptic plasma membranes. In the presence or absence of 100 mM NaCl, the binding of ^{3}H -GABA to junctional complexes is inhibited by muscimol ($IC_{50} = 6.5$ nM), imidazoleacetic acid ($IC_{50} = 700$ nM), and bicuculline ($IC_{50} = 26$ μM) but not by nipecotic acid or L-DABA.

The dissociation constant for complexes of GABA with sodium-independent receptive sites in synaptic plasma membranes is variously reported to be between 0.15 and 0.45 μM (21, 26, 43, 70, 81), with a binding capacity of 1–5 pmoles mg^{-1} protein. The K_d of complexes of GABA with junctional complexes is lower (4–150 nM) than that observed for sodium-independent binding to synaptic plasma membrane, and multiple species of these receptive sites have been reported (21, 22, 26, 70, 77). The reduction in the apparent K_d could result from reduction of nonspecific GABA binding, the removal of a contribution to binding by sodium-dependent sites, or the removal of endogenous ligand or inhibitor. It has been reported that multiple binding components cannot be observed unless junctional complex membranes are extensively washed to remove residual Triton, suggesting that Triton inhibits the binding of GABA to these complexes (77). In our experiments, repeated washing of junctional complexes results in a decrease in K_d from 250 nM (no washing) to 60 nM (five washes). However, no inhibition of sodium-independent GABA binding could be observed when Triton was added to washed junctional complexes.

An alternative explanation of this phenomenon suggests that an endogenous inhibitor is present on these membranes (25, 70). In fact, a heat stable, acidic protein of about 15,000 daltons has been characterized that interferes with GABA binding (70). This protein, a noncompetitive inhibitor of sodium-independent GABA binding, may also act as a ligand for benzodiazepine-receptive sites and thereby modulate sodium-independent GABA-receptive sites. Thus, the partially purified protein inhibits the binding of labelled diazepam to synaptic plasma membranes (27). In addition, benzodiazepines may displace the protein from membranes and alter the sodium-independent binding of GABA from moderate affinity ($K_d = 111$–250 nM) to higher affinity ($K_d = 28$–33 nM) (27). However, in these studies a crude synaptosomal-mitochondrial membrane fraction was employed that includes neuronal and glial uptake sites as well as postsynaptic receptors. The presence of such low-affinity and high-capacity sites could produce artifically high estimates of the K_d for the postsynaptic or sodium-independent GABA-receptive sites. Studies with well-defined membrane systems should allow definitive conclusions about the nature of these important interactions.

The characterization of GABA-receptive sites in synaptic plasma membranes and junctional complexes represents the most recent application of subcellular fractionation to the assignment of function to binding sites. Thus the transport site appears loosely associated with extrajunctional membrane while the postsynaptic receptor is an integral protein of the junctional complex. The GABA receptor system probably includes this GABA-receptive site and other components such as ionophores. These may be studied via binding interactions with other ligands—e.g. barbiturates and picrotoxin (55, 59, 68, 69). Studies with these ligands, as well as a systematic search for endogenous ligands, should allow a complete discription of GABA receptor systems in the near future.

Glycine

Valdes & Orrego (72) first reported that strychnine inhibited the binding of glycine to crude mitochondrial-synaptosomal pellets of rat brain. A K_m of about 80 μM was reported, and strychnine apparently inhibited this association competitively. Although two components are apparent in saturation curves and double reciprocal analyses in this report, the presence of sodium (123 mM) and the narrow range of ligand concentrations employed preclude any resolution of these or any assessment of their relation to transport or postsynaptic sites. Strychnine at high concentrations (0.5 mM) reduced the binding of ^{14}C-glycine by only 20–25%, suggesting (but not proving) that postsynaptic sites might represent about one quarter of the total sites measured in this study. More recently these authors reported that the glycine-receptive sites measures in cerebral cortex are primarily transport receptive sites (56) and that moderately high-affinity, sodium-dependent receptive sites for glycine exist on myelin membranes and possibly on other glial plasma membranes but not in synaptosomes (71). The presence of high-affinity ($K_d = 20$ μM) transport systems and receptive sites for glycine in glial elements of cerebral cortex (and undoubtedly spinal cord) suggests that gross dissection should be employed to reduce extraneous binding sites before pursuing the study of postsynaptic sites.

Examination of ^{14}C-glycine binding to synaptosomal-mitochondrial fractions of rat and cat cerebral cortex and spinal cord (13–17) confirms the existence of transport sites for glycine. In addition, caudal-rostral distribution of glycine sites was generally observed. In a study of apparent affinities, "double-affinity" (or two-site) and "triple-affinity" (or three-site) binding processes for these amino acids were reported (17). However, the resolution of multi-component Scatchard analyses was insufficient, and little can be concluded except that multiple processes were observed. Since crude synaptosomal fractions from intact cerebral cortex and spinal cord were employed and since the presence or absence of sodium was not employed to differentiate transport from postsynaptic receptive sites, nothing can be said about the identity of these multiple processes.

Young & Snyder (79) first reported the binding of [^{3}H]-strychnine to crude membrane preparations derived from spinal cord and brain stem. This binding had a K_d for strychnine of about 35 nM and was competitively inhibited by glycine and β-alanine (K_is about 10 μM) (80). Displacement of labelled strychnine by unlabelled strychnine yielded Hill coefficients of 1.0, whereas displacement of labelled strychnine by glycine indicated cooperative or multi-site interactions (Hill coefficient about 1.7). Recent studies have suggested that strychnine interacts with the "ionophore" or ionic conductance mechanism associated with the glycine receptive site and not with the receptive site itself (66, 80). The cooperativity observed with glycine displacement of strychnine may relate either to multiple classes of glycine binding sites for which strychnine might compete or to the apparent cooperativity observed for the interaction of glycine with other physiologic systems (74, 75).

A multitude of glycine-receptive sites have been demonstrated by the binding of labelled glycine and the potent antagonist, strychnine, to membranes of the CNS. Labelled strychnine associates with a high-affinity, limited-capacity receptive site abundant in spinal cord and brain stem but essentially absent in higher centers (79). The glycine postsynaptic receptor may be a complex possessing an ionophore that binds strychnine with very high affinity (nM) and a second receptive site that binds glycine with moderate affinity (μM). These sites may interact to produce complex isotherms. Alternatively, the sodium-dependent transport site for glycine may contribute to these complex binding kinetics. The application of subcellular and membrane fractionation techniques should yield an answer to this question in the near future.

Glutamate

The role of L-glutamate as an excitatory neurotransmitter in the CNS is suggested by neurochemical and neurophysiological evidence (9, 12, 20, 24, 29, 36.) However, to prove that this acidic amino acid is a neurotransmitter has been difficult in view of its ubiquitous distribution as a metabolic intermediate. The demonstration of postsynaptic receptive sites for glutamate has also been hampered by the same heterogeneity of sites as discussed for GABA and glycine and, in addition, by a scarcity of pharmacologic tools.

High- and low-affinity binding sites for glutamate have been demonstrated (49, 61). High-affinity binding, selective for the L-enantiomer, is localized in synaptic membrane fractions and is not solubilized with Triton X-100 (49). Studies employing sodium dependence to differentiate postsynaptic from transport receptive sites suggest that the glutamate antagonists glutamic acid diethylester, L-methionine-DL-sulfoximine, and 1-hydroxyl-3-aminopyrrolid-2-one inhibit the binding of glutamate to the high-affinity (postsynaptic?) receptive site but do not interfere with low-affinity (uptake?) sites (62). The binding of [^{3}H]-kainic acid, a potent glutamate agonist, to membranes isolated from central nervous tissue has also been demonstrated (64). Kainic acid is 50 times more potent than glutamate with respect to binding and about 100 times more active physiologically when applied to central neurons. Multiple classes of kainic acid receptive sites were demonstrated very recently on microsomal, mitochondrial, and synaptic plasma membranes (52). These results suggest that kainic acid does not bind exclusively to synaptic receptors and thus should not be used as the only criterion for postsynaptic receptor identification.

Detergent dispersion, affinity, and concanavalin A Sepharose chromatograpy have been employed in a 200-fold purification of a synaptic membrane glycoprotein that binds glutamate with reasonably high affinity ($K_d = 0.7$ μM) (48). The partially purified protein has no enzymatic activity and differs from the glutamate transport system in its sodium independence. In addition, the binding of glutamate to this site is inhibited by glutamate diethylester, consistent with its identity as a receptive site of the physiologic receptor of L-glutamic acid.

Kainic acid has been utilized (19) to differentiate between glutamate-receptive proteolipids (18) and aspartate-receptive proteolipids (23) isolated by organic solvent extraction of membranes from cerebral cortical tissues of rats. Also employed in these studies were N-methyl-D-aspartate and L-glutamic acid diethylester. Kainic acid (25 μM) inhibited L-glutamate binding but not the binding of L-aspartate. N-methyl-D-aspartate (40 μM) reduced the binding of L-aspartate but not that of L-glutamate. Since these analogs are not substrates for their respective transport systems (1) and since binding to these proteolipids was studied in the strict absence of sodium, these proteolipids may represent postsynaptic receptive sites.

In the mammalian CNS, glutamate dimethylester is much more potent than the diethylester at inhibiting glutamate transport (2, 46), while the diethylester inhibits the excitatory action of glutamate and the dimethylester has little effect on postsynaptic processes (28). This conformational selectivity of postsynaptic and transport receptive sites for analogs of glutamate may allow their separation and characterization. Additional pharmacologic agents, subcellular fractionation techniques, and differential solubilization should reveal the nature of receptive sites for this putative excitatory neurotransmitter.

SUMMARY

Specific receptors for amino acid neurotransmitters can be demonstrated on membranes of central nervous tissue via ligand binding studies. However, while specific ligand binding sites can be demonstrated, these cannot always be assigned a specific physiologic role. Subcellular fractionation and purification of membranes from discrete regions of the CNS together with specific agonists and antagonists of known physiologic function have allowed specific receptive sites to be discerned and assigned roles as transport or postsynaptic receptive species. However, whenever crude membrane preparations have been employed to study a single ligand interaction, such assignments are impossible.

In the future, as purified receptive sites and antibodies to them become available, a number of intriguing questions may be asked. What role do multiple states of a given receptive species and/or multiple species of receptor for a given neurotransmitter play in physiologic processes? How do modulators or endogenous inhibitors modify the functional status of receptors? Does the existence of agonist/antagonist states of receptive sites and/

or endogenous modulators result in an infinite array of receptors for a given transmitter, or are these artifacts of the methods employed for isolating and measuring receptive sites? Can receptive species be reconstituted within defined membrane systems to allow the study of their mechanism of action —i.e. the coupling of receptive sites with ionophores or transport systems? Answers to these questions should be forthcoming the the next few years.

Acknowledgments

The author is indebted to B. R. Lester, K. Kelner, and A. Miller for assistance with this manuscript. Portions of this work were supported by grants from the N.I.H., NS 11753, 5K04-HD-00022, and HD 08389, as well as from the Huntington's Chorea Foundation and the Muscular Dystrophy Association. Any failure to cite the contributions of others is the fault of the author and reflects his incapacity to deal with an exponentially increasing literature.

Literature Cited

1. Balcar, V. J., Johnston, G. A. R. 1972. The structural specificity of the high affinity uptake of L-glutamate and L-aspartate by rat brain slices. *J. Neurochem.* 19:2657–66
2. Balcar, V. J., Johnston, G. A. R. 1973. High affinity uptake of transmitters: Studies on the uptake of L-aspartate, GABA, L-glutamate and glycine in cat spinal cord. *J. Neurochem.* 20:529–39
3. Bowery, N. G., Jones, G. P., Neal, M. J. 1976. Selective inhibition of neuronal GABA uptake by cis-1,3-aminocyclohexanecarboxylic acid. *Nature* 264: 281–84
4. Clark, J. H., Peck, E. J. Jr. 1979. *Female Sex Steroids: Receptors and Function.* Amsterdam: Springer. In press
5. Cotman, C. W., Banker, G., Churchill, L., Taylor, D. 1974. Isolation of postsynaptic densities from rat brain. *J. Cell Biol.* 63:441–55
6. Cotman, C. W., Levy, W., Banker, G., Taylor, D. 1971. An ultrastructual and chemical analysis of the effect of Triton X-100 on synaptic plasma membrane. *Biochim. Biophys. Acta* 249:406–18
7. Cotman, C. W., Matthews, D. A. 1971. Synaptic plasma membranes from rat brain synaptasomes: Isolation and partial characterization. *Biochim. Biophys. Acta.* 249:380–94
8. Curtis, D. R., Duggan, A. W., Felix, D., Johnston, G. A. R. 1970. GABA, bicuculline and central inhibition. *Nature* 226:1222–24
9. Curtis, D. R., Duggan, A. W., Felix, D., Johnston, G. A. R., Tebecis, A. K., Watkins, J. C. 1972. Excitation of mammalian central neurons by acidic amino acids. *Brain Res.* 41:283–301
10. Curtis, D. R., Duggan, A. W., Johnston, G. A. R. 1970. The inactivation of extracellularly administered amino acids in the feline spinal cord. *Exp. Brain Res.* 10:447–62
11. Curtis, D. R., Johnston, G. A. R. 1974. Amino acid transmitters in the mammalian central nervous system. *Ergeb. Physiol.* 69:94–188
12. Davidoff, R. A., Graham, L. T. Jr., Shank, R. P., Werman, R., Aprison, M. 1967. Changes in amino acid concentrations associated with loss of spinal interneurons. *J. Neurochem.* 14:1025–31
13. DeFeudis, F. V. 1973. Binding of ^{3}H-gamma-aminobutyric acid and ^{14}C-glycine to synaptosomal-mitochondrial fractions of rat cerebral cortex and spinal cord. *Can. J. Physiol. Pharmacol.* 51:873–78
14. DeFeudis, F. V. 1974. Preferential "binding" of gamma-aminobutyric acid and glycine to synaptosome-enriched fractions of rat cerebral cortex and spinal cord. *Can. J. Physiol.* 52:138–47
15. DeFeudis, F. V. 1975. "Binding" of gamma-aminobutyric acid and glycine to synaptosome-enriched fractions of

rat cerebral cortex and spinal cord. *Exp. Neurol.* 47:189–93

16. DeFeudis, F. V., Madtes, P., Gervas-Camacho, J. 1977. "Binding" of glycine and gamma-aminobutyric acid to synaptosomal fractions of 6 regions of the feline brain; effects of strychnine. *Experientia* 33:340–42
17. DeFeudis, F. V., Schiff, N. 1975. Comparison of binding affinities and capacities of gamma-aminobutyric acid and glycine in synaptosome-enriched fractions of rat cerebral cortex and spinal cord. *Exp. Neurol.* 48:325–35
18. De Robertis, E., Fiszer de Plazas, S. 1976. Isolation of hydrophobic protein binding amino acids. Stereo-selectivity of the binding of L(^{14}C) glutamic acid in cerebral cortex. *J. Neurochem.* 26: 1237–43
19. De Robertis, E., Fiszer de Plazas, S. 1976. Differentiation of L-aspartate and L-glutamate high affinity binding sites in a protein fraction isolated from rat cerebral cortex. *Nature* 260:347–49
20. Duggan, A. W. 1974. The differential sensitivity of L-glutamate and L-aspartate of spinal interneurons and Renshaw cells. *Exp. Brain Res.* 19:522–28
21. Enna, S. J., Snyder, S. H. 1975. Properties of GABA receptor binding in rat brain synaptic membrane fractions. *Brain Res.* 100:81–97
22. Enna, S. J., Snyder, S. H. 1977. Influences of ions, enzymes and detergents on α-aminobutyric acid-receptor binding in synaptic membranes of rat brain. *Mol. Pharmacol.* 13:442–53
23. Fiszer de Plazas, S., De Robertis, E. 1976. Isolation of hydrophobic proteins binding amino acids: L-aspartic acid-binding proteins from the rat cerebral cortex. *J. Neurochem.* 27:889–94
24. Graham, L. T. Jr., Shank, R. P., Werman, R., Aprison, M. H. 1967. Distribution of some synaptic transmitter suspects in cat spinal cord: glutamic acid, aspartic acid, α-aminobutyric acid, glycine and glutamine. *J. Neurochem.* 14:465–72
25. Greenlee, D. V., Van Ness, P. C., Olsen, R. W. 1978. Endogenous inhibitor of GABA binding in mammalian brain. *Life Sci.* 22:1653–62
26. Greenlee, D. V., Van Ness, P. C., Olsen, R. W. 1978. Gamma-aminobutyric acid binding in mammalian brain: Receptor-like specificity of sodium-independent sites. *J. Neurochem.* 31:933–38
27. Guidotti, A., Toffano, G., Costa, E. 1978. An endogenous protein modulates the affinity of GABA and benzodiazepine receptors in rat brain. *Nature* 275:553–55
28. Haldeman, S., McLennan, H. 1972. The antagonistic action of glutamic acid diethylester towards amino-acid induced and synaptic excitations of central neurons. *Brain Res.* 45:419–25
29. Haldeman, S., McLennan, H. 1973. The action of two inhibitors of glutamic acid uptake upon amino acid-induced and synaptic excitations of thalamic neurons. *Brain Res.* 63:123–29
30. Henke, H., Schenker, T. M., Cuenod, M. 1976. Uptake of neurotransmitter candidates by pigeon optic tectum. *J. Neurochem.* 26:125–30
31. Henn, F. A., Hamberger, A. 1971. Glial cell function: Uptake of transmitter substances. *Proc. Natl. Acad. Sci. USA* 68:2686–90
32. Hitzemann, R. J., Loh, H. H. 1978. A comparison of GABA and β-alanine transport and GABA membrane binding in the rat brain. *J. Neurochem.* 30:471–77
33. Hori, N., Ikeda, K., Roberts, E. 1978. Muscimol, GABA and picrotoxin: Effects on membrane conductance of a crustacean neuron. *Brain Res.* 141: 364–70
34. Huxtable, R., Barbeau, A., eds. 1976. *Taurine.* NY: Raven
35. Iversen, L. L., Johnston, G. A. R. 1971. GABA uptake in rat central nervous system: Comparison of uptake in slices and homogenates and the effects of some inhibitors. *J. Neurochem.* 18: 1939–50
36. Johnston, G. A. R., Curtis, D. R., Davies, J. McCulloch, R. M. 1974. Spinal interneurone excitation by conformationally restricted analogues of L-glutamic acid. *Nature* 248:804–5
37. Kanner, B. I. 1978. Active transport of α-aminobutyric acid by membrane vesicles isolated from rat brain. *Biochemistry* 17:1207–11
38. Kanner, B. I. 1978. Solubilization and reconstitution of the α-aminobutyric acid transporter from rat brain. *FEBS Lett.* 89:47–50
39. Krnjevic, K. 1974. Chemical nature of synaptic transmission in vertebrates. *Physiol. Rev.* 54:418–540
40. Krogsgaard-Larsen, P., Johnston, G. A. R. 1975. Inhibition of GABA uptake in rat brain slices by nipecotic acid, various isoxazoles and related compounds. *J. Neurochem.* 25:797–802
41. Krogsgaard-Larsen, P., Johnston, G. A. R., Curtis, D. R., Game, C. J. A., McCulloch, R. M. 1975. Structure and

biological activity of a series of conformationally restricted analogues of GABA. *J. Neurochem.* 25:803–9
42. Krogsgaard-Larsen, P., Johnston, G. A. R., Lodge, D., Curtis, D. R. 1977. A new class of GABA agonist. *Nature* 268:53–55
43. Lester, B. R., Peck, E. J. Jr. 1979. Kinetic and pharmacologic characterization of gamma-aminobutyric acid receptive sites from mammalian brain. *Brain Res.* 161:79–97
44. Levi, G. 1970. Cerebral amino acid transport *in vitro* during development: A kinetic analysis. *Arch. Biochem. Biophys.* 138:347–49
45. Levi, G., Raiteri, M. 1973. Detectability of high and low affinity uptake systems for GABA and glutamate in rat brain slices and synaptosomes. *Life Sci.* 12:81–88
46. McLennan, H., Haldeman, S. 1973. The actions of the dimethyl and diethyl esters of glutamic acid on glutamate uptake by brain tissue. *J. Neurochem.* 20:629–31
47. Martin, D. L. 1973. Kinetics of the sodium-dependent transport of gamma-aminobutyric acid by synaptosomes. *J. Neurochem.* 21:345–56
48. Michaelis, E. K. 1975. Partial purification and characterization of a glutamate-binding membrane glycoprotein from rat brain. *Biochem. Biophys. Res. Commun.* 65:1004–12
49. Michaelis, E. K., Michaelis, M. L., Boyarsky, L. L. 1974. High-affinity glutamic acid binding to brain synaptic membranes. *Biochim. Biophys. Acta* 367:338–48
50. Miller, A. L., Chaptal, C., McEwen, B. S., Peck, E. J. Jr. 1978. Modulation of high affinity GABA uptake into hippocampal synaptosomes by glucocorticoids. *Physchoneuroendocrinology* 3:155–64
51. Neal, M. J., Bowery, N. G. 1977. Cis-3-aminocyclohexanecarboxylic acid: A substrate for the neuronal GABA transport system. *Brain Res.* 138:169–74
52. Nieto, M., Shelton, D., Cotman, C. W. 1979. Multiple kainic acid binding sites in rat brain. *Trans. Am. Soc. Neurochem.* 10:191
53. Obata, K., Ito, M., Ochi, R., Sato, N. 1967. Pharmacological properties of the postsynaptic inhibition by Purkinje cell axons and the action of γ-aminobutyric acid on Deiter's neurons. *Exp. Brain Res.* 4:43–57
54. Oja, S. S., Kontro, P., Lahdesmaki, P. 1977. Amino acids as inhibitory neurotransmitters. *Prog. Pharmacol.* 1:1–119
55. Olsen, R. W., Ticku, M. K., Miller, T. 1978. Dihydropicrotoxin binding to crayfish muscle sites possibly related to gamma-aminobutyric acid receptor-ionophores. *Mol. Pharmacol.* 14:381–90
56. Orrego, F., Valdes, F. 1973. Proceedings: Glycine receptors in the cerebral cortex are probably transport receptors. *Acta Physiol. Lat. Am.* 23:623–25
57. Peck, E. J. Jr. 1977. GABA receptive sites in the mammalian central nervous system. In *Neurotransmitter Function,* ed. W. Fields, pp. 105–14. NY: Straton Intercontinental Med. Books
58. Peck, E. J. Jr., Lester, B. R. 1979. Amino acid receptors in the central nervous system: identification and properties. In *The Cell Surface and Neuronal Function, Cell Surface Reviews,* Vol. 6, ed. G. Poste, G. L., Nicalson, C. W. Cotman. NY: Elsevier/North-Holland. In press
59. Peck, E. J. Jr., Miller, A. L., Lester, B. R. 1976. Pentobarbital and synaptic high-affinity receptive sites for gamma-aminobutyric acid. *Brain Res. Bull.* 1:595–97
60. Roberts, E., Chase, T. N., Tower, D. B., eds. 1976. *GABA in Nervous System Function.* NY: Raven. p. 554
61. Roberts, P. J. 1974. Glutamate receptors in the rat central nervous system. *Nature* 252:399–401
62. Roberts, P. J. 1975. Glutamate binding to synaptic membranes—detection of post-synaptic receptor sites? *J. Physiol. London* 247:44–45
63. Sano, K., Roberts, E. 1963. Binding of α-aminobutyric acid by mouse brain preparations. *Biochem. Pharmacol.* 12:489–502
64. Simon, J. R., Contrero, J. E., Kuhar, M. J. 1976. Specific [^{3}H]-kainic acid binding to brain membranes: Evidence for association with the L-glutamate receptor. *J. Neurochem.* 26:141–48
65. Simon, J. R., Martin, D. L. 1973. The effects of L-2,4-diaminobutyric acid on the uptake of GABA by a synaptosomal fraction from rat brain. *Arch. Biochem. Biophys.* 157:348–55
66. Snyder, S. H., Bennett, J. P. Jr. 1976. Neuotransmitter receptors in the brain: Biochemical identification. *Ann. Rev. Physiol.* 38:153–75
67. Tebecis, H. K. 1974. *Transmitters and Identified Neurons in the Mammalian Central Nervous System.* Bristol, Engl: Scientechnica. 340 pp.

68. Ticku, M. K., Bar, M. Olsen, R. W. 1978. Binding of ^{3}H-dihydropicrotoxinin, a gamma-aminobutyric acid synaptic antagonist, to rat brain membranes. *Mol. Pharmacol.* 14:391–402
69. Ticku, M. K., Van Ness, P. C., Haycock, J. W., Levy, W. B., Olsen, R. W. 1978. Dihydropicrotoxinin binding sites in rat brain: Comparison to GABA receptors. *Brain Res.* 150:642–47
70. Toffano, G., Guidotti, A., Costa, E. 1978. Purification of an endogenous protein inhibitor of the high affinity binding of α-aminobutyric acid to synaptic membranes of rat brain. *Proc. Natl. Acad. Sci. USA* 75:4024–28
71. Valdes, F., Munoz, C., Feria-Velasco, A., Orrego, F. 1977. Subcellular distribution of rat brain cortex high-affinity, sodium-dependent, glycine transport sites. *Brain Res.* 122:95–112
72. Valdes, F., Orrego, F. 1970. Strychnine inhibits the binding of glycine to rat brain-cortex membranes. *Nature* 226: 761–62
73. Walker, R. J., Woodruff, G. N., Kerkut, G. A. 1971. The effect of ibotenic acid and muscimol on single neurons of the snail, *Helix aspersa*. *Comp. Gen. Pharmacol.* 2:168–74
74. Werman, R. 1969. An electrophysiological approach to drug-receptor mechanisms. *Comp. Biochem. Physiol.* 30: 997–1017
75. Werman, R., Davidoff, R. A., Aprison, M. H. 1968. Inhibitory action of glycine on spinal neurons in the cat. *J. Neurophysiol.* 31:81–95
76. Wheal, H. V., Kerkut, G. A. 1976. The action of muscimol on the inhibitory postsynaptic membrane of the crustacean neuromuscular junction. *Brain Res.* 109:179–83
77. Wong, D. T., Horng, J. S. 1977. Na^+ -independent binding of GABA to the Triton X-100 treated synaptic membranes from cerebellum of rat brain. *Life Sci.* 20:445–51
78. Wu, J.-Y. 1976. Purification, characterization and kinetic studies of GAD and GABA-T from mouse brain. See Ref. 62, pp. 7–55
79. Young, A. B., Snyder, S. H. 1973. Strychnine binding associated with glycine receptors of the central nervous system. *Proc. Natl. Acad. Sci. USA* 70:2832–36
80. Young, A. B., Snyder, S. H. 1974. Strychnine binding in rat spinal cord membranes associated with the synaptic glycine receptor: Cooperativity of glycine interactions. *Mol. Pharmacol.* 10:790–809
81. Zukin, S. R., Young, A. B., Snyder, S. H. 1974. GABA binding to receptor sites in the rat central nervous system. *Proc. Natl. Acad. Sci. USA* 71:4802–7

Ann. Rev. Physiol. 1980. 42:629–41

ROLE OF CYCLIC NUCLEOTIDES IN EXCITABLE CELLS

❖1291

Irving Kupfermann

Division of Neurobiology and Behavior and Department of Psychiatry, College of Physicians and Surgeons of Columbia University and New York State Psychiatric Institute, New York, New York 10032

INTRODUCTION

In the past 15 years substantial research has explored the hypothesis that cyclic nucleotides act as second messengers for some of the effects of neurotransmitters on excitable cells. A recent review (10) cites over 1200 papers, most of them published after 1970. Still, in most experimental systems our knowledge of the precise effect of cyclic nucleotides on excitable cells is quite primitive. This review concentrates on electrophysiological research at the cellular level and does not cover pharmacological, biochemical, and trophic aspects of the action of cyclic nucleotides. No attempt is made to document systematically the history and priorities of the various hypotheses discussed (see 10, 38, 41).

One set of studies has investigated the function of cyclic nucleotides in mediating alterations in resting membrane potential (i.e. synaptic potentials) produced by the action of certain neurotransmitters (6, 20). Unlike those of conventional transmitters, transmitter actions mediated by cyclic nucleotides may be relatively long-lasting and may be mediated by mechanisms other than the direct opening of ionic channels (cf 6). A second set of studies has been concerned with the so-called modulatory effects of neurotransmitters, in which alterations of cell excitability or activity are produced by mechanisms that do not involve substantial changes of resting membrane potential (cf 29, 34).

0066-4278/80/0315-0629$01.00

MODULATION OF RESTING MEMBRANE POTENTIAL

The slow hyperpolarization produced by biogenic amines in many neurons of the nervous system may be mediated by cAMP (6). In addition, the slow depolarization associated with the muscarinic depolarizing action of acetylcholine may be mediated by cGMP (55).

Mammalian Cerebellum and Neocortex

Some of the best evidence for a role of cyclic nucleotides in the nervous system has come from studies of the cerebellar cortex. Earlier data [1970–1975; for review see (6)] indicated that the slow inhibitory effect of noradenaline on Purkinje cells is mediated by cylic adenosine monophosphate (cAMP). Perhaps because of the variety and richness of earlier experimental approaches, in the past few years little additional evidence has been presented in support of this conclusion. One major approach that would be useful, but which has not yet been employed successfully in the cerebellum, is intracellular injection of cyclic nucleotides.

In neocortical neurons the evidence for a role of cyclic nucleotides in the generation of slow potential changes has not been as extensive as for cerebellar cortical cells. A careful study (48) has confirmed that extracellular applications of cAMP and noradenaline (NA) result in inhibition of spontaneous spike activity of most neocortical units. cAMP was not inhibiting the cells by means of an adenosine-sensitive receptor, since aminophylline (a methylxanthine that blocks the actions of adenosine) reduced but did not block the inhibitory effects of cAMP. Most identified pyramidal tract neurons were excited by cyclic guanosine monophosphate (cGMP), whereas depression of activity was seen in some nonpyramidal tract neurons. Of the neurons tested, 83% responded similarly to acetylcholine (ACh) and cGMP.

Intracellular injection techniques have been employed recently to study the possible role of cGMP in mediating the depolarizing action of acetylcholine on neurons in the neocortex (63). This depolarization frequently lasts minutes or longer and is associated with a decrease of membrane conductance. In awake, nonanesthetized cats, neocortical units were impaled and cGMP was injected by means of iontophoretic currents. Changes of membrane potential were not examined, presumably because the recording system did not permit accurate long-term recording of steady potentials. However, in 35 of 111 cells, injection of cGMP produced a long-lasting decrease of membrane conductance, similar to what occurs when neurons are depolarized by means of extracellular iontophoresis of acetylcholine or cGMP. Thus these experiments provide support for a role of cGMP in ACh-induced depolarization in cortical neurons. Several features of this study, however, suggest that caution should be exercised in interpreting the results. The authors utilized two different methods to estimate membrane conductance. Both methods indicated that resistance increased following injection of cGMP in 35 of 111 cells; but for another 24 cells, the measurements using the two methods did not agree in the sign of resistance change. Furthermore, the long duration of the effect following a 30 sec application of cGMP may be due to continual release of cGMP from the electrode. First, some cGMP probably diffused from the electrode, since braking currents were not used. In addition, resistance measurements were continually made by means of brief depolarizing current pulses through the electrode containing the cGMP. Electro-osmotic effects from this current flow might result in some ejection of cGMP during each resistance measurement (23).

Sympathetic Ganglion

Studies of sympathetic ganglia, particularly superior cervical ganglia, supported a postsynaptic role of cGMP and cAMP in mediating the membrane potential changes produced by acetylcholine and dopamine, respectively. Recent data cast serious doubt on this hypothesis, particularly with reference to cAMP. Utilizing the sucrose gap technique to record potentials, McAffee & Greengard (37) reported that perfusion of the sympathetic ganglion with cAMP, cGMP, or their derivatives could produce potential shifts that presumably reflected depolarization or hyperpolarization of principal cells of the ganglion. Subsequent studies utilizing this technique have failed to replicate these results (1, 8, 12, 33). The sucrose gap method often appears to indicate shifts of potential when solution changes of any type are made (33). In addition, studies utilizing intracellular recording and direct injection of cAMP into sympathetic ganglion cells of frog, rat, and rabbit have not found that cAMP produces the hyperpolarization that is evoked by dopamine or preganglionic nerve stimulation (1, 15, 25, 56).

Although recent studies do not support a role of cAMP in mediating hyperpolarizing responses in the sympathetic ganglion, it is premature to rule out a possible role. Application of a cyclic nucleotide does not provide a test equivalent to the extracellular application of a putative transmitter at a synaptic junction. Neither extracellular nor intracellular application of a cyclic nucleotide insures arrival of the nucleotide in the region of the cell where it may normally act. Evidence now exists that cyclic nucleotides need not act diffusely throughout a cell but may act at particular regions within the cell [for examples see (13)].

Results obtained with cGMP in sympathetic ganglia are more positive than results with cAMP. Intracellular injection of cGMP into neurons of the sympathetic ganglia of frogs (56) or rats (15) occasionally produced depolarization. The depolarization, however, was associated with an increase of membrane conductance, unlike what is seen during the synaptically evoked slow excitatory postsynaptic potential (sEPSP). Similar results have been reported for extracellular application of dbcGMP in frog (8) and rabbit (11). One study, however, on rabbit superior cervical ganglion has reported results consistent with a role of cGMP in producing muscarinic depolarization (21). As reported by others, high doses of cGMP applied extracellularly produced cellular depolarization, associated with a nonphysiological increase of membrane conductance. On the other hand, low doses of extracellular cGMP produced depolarization that resembled the synaptically induced sEPSP in two respects. First, the depolarization occurred without any measurable change in conductance. Second, there was an apparent decrease in delayed rectification—i.e. there was a reduction in the steady-state conductance increase that occurs when the cell is depolarized. If an intracellularly applied dose of cyclic nucleotide is excessive and is therefore producing a nonphysiological increase of membrane conductance, then as the nucleotide is broken down the concentration should fall into a physiological range and the cell should eventually go through a phase in which the nucleotide mimics the effects of the normal transmitter (15). It is therefore puzzling that no one has reported that intracellular injection of cGMP into neurons of sympathetic ganglia produces a depolarization without a conductance increase. Perhaps the effects of an excessive dose are not reversed when the concentration falls to a normal range.

It is not clear how cGMP might be causally related to cholinergic depolarization. It is generally thought that the increased synthesis of cGMP (unlike that of cAMP) is not dependent upon a transmitter-sensitive cyclase. Rather, increased synthesis seems to result from an increase of intracellular calcium due to an influx through either voltage-sensitive channels or through transmitter- (or hormone-) sensitive channels (17). If this is so, then in order for ACh to increase cGMP levels it would have to first increase the calcium conductance of the cells. This could (*a*) occur by a direct effect of ACh on transmitter-sensitive calcium channels (27), or (*b*) be due to activation of voltage-sensitive calcium channels that are opened as a secondary consequence of a depolarization evoked by, for example, a decrease in potassium conductance (54). In either case cGMP would at best serve to augment, rather than be a primary cause of, the conductance change. However, a recent report (32) suggests that under appropriate conditions the guanylate cyclase of many tissues (including nervous system) can exhibit transmitter-sensitive stimulation, not involving calcium.

MODULATION OF NEURONAL EXCITABILITY WITHOUT CHANGES OF RESTING MEMBRANE POTENTIAL

Sympathetic Ganglion

In the sympathetic ganglion, cAMP may function to increase the size of the slow excitatory synaptic potentials in principal cells, and the action of cAMP in itself need not involve any changes in membrane potential (34). The original observations were based on the effects of cAMP applied in the bathing solution. With this procedure it is difficult to distinguish presynaptic from postsynaptic actions. A recent study in the superior cervical ganglion of the rabbit suggests that intracellular injection of cAMP can produce effects similar to those produced by extracellular application (25). Of 9 cells injected with cAMP, 4 exhibited a prolonged (around 2 hr) amplification of the sEPSP evoked by stimulation of the preganglionic nerve. Passage of current alone in 10 cells did not result in amplification of the sEPSP. That relatively few cells showed the effect is not surprising in view of the known capriciousness of electrophoretic ejection of cyclic nucleotides. Furthermore, my statistical analysis of the experimental and control data indicates a significant experimental effect ($p < .05$, Fisher exact probability test; assuming the independence of each cell studied). The amplification of the sEPSP was not a result of a nonspecific effect of cAMP, since the initial fast EPSP in the same cells was not enhanced. The mechanism whereby cAMP could amplify a specific class of excitatory synaptic input is not known. Evidence suggests that the sEPSP, at least in some principal cells of the frog, involves the activation of inward calcium currents (27). cAMP may enhance transmitter-sensitive calcium currents in a manner analogous to the means by which cAMP appears to amplify voltage-sensitive calcium currents in cardiac tissue and certain synaptic terminals (see below).

Modulation of Muscle

The effect of cAMP on excitable cells is well documented in cardiac tissue of vertebrates (53, 62). Numerous data indicate that the positive inotropic effects of adrenergic agents on the heart are mediated, in part, by a rise in intracellular cAMP (for review see 53). Somehow increased intracellular cAMP amplifies the slow inward calcium current turned on when the cells are depolarized. A detailed study (44) has explored the means by which epinephrine (and cAMP) amplifies the slow inward current in the heart. The data indicate that the amplification is *not* associated with (*a*) a shift of the activation curve along the voltage axis, (*b*) a shift of activation kinetics, or (*c*) an alteration of channel selectivity. The enhancement of the slow inward calcium current could be explained most simply by an increase in the number of voltage-sensitive calcium channels that can be activated by a given level of depolarization. Although cAMP is known to increase the phosphorylation of certain contractile proteins in cardiac tissue (see Bárány & Bárány, this volume), no convincing evidence indicates that this effect contributes to the positive inotropic action of cAMP and adrenaline. Indeed, one study (3) suggests that at least under some conditions the total positive inotropic action of adrenaline can be accounted for by increased inward current, and therefore any enhanced phosphorylation of contractile proteins cannot contribute to the effect.

The mechanism by which cAMP increases the number of available voltage-sensitive channels in cardiac tissue is not known. By analogy to other systems (19), it has been proposed (43, 46) that cAMP may activate a protein kinase that in turn phosphorylates a protein associated with a calcium channel. In the phosphorylated state the protein allows calcium to pass through the channel if a voltage-sensitive gate is also activated. Studies (58) suggest, however, the interesting possibility that cAMP acts directly on membranes to alter membrane ionic permeability (see 18). Red cell ghosts were exposed to cAMP when no phosophate or energy source was available to phosphorylate proteins. Permeability to calcium was tested by observing the rate at which the ghosts swelled when exposed to a solution containing calcium and a freely permeable anion (chloride). In the presence of cAMP but not cGMP, the ghosts swelled more, which suggested that the cAMP increased their permeability to calcium. When the red cell ghosts were permitted to phosphorylate in the presence of ATP, they swelled less in a calcium chloride solution, which indicated that calcium permeability was decreased. Synaptosomes prepared from brain also apparently exhibit decreased calcium permeability following exposure to conditions that result in protein phosphorylation (59). It is not yet clear how this phosphorylation relates to the cAMP-dependent phosphorylation studied by others (19, 61). Furthermore, control of resting calcium permeability (presumably studied by Weller and colleagues) may differ from the voltage-sensitive calcium conductances that regulate contraction and secretion.

Evidence now indicates that the negative inotropic action of acetylcholine on the heart is in many respects a mirror opposite to that of noradenaline and that cGMP acts as the second messenger. Electrophysiological data suggest that the negative inotropic effect of ACh results from a decrease of the slow inward calcium current (16, 49). In atrial myocardium a direct effect of ACh (decrease of the voltage-sensitive calcium channel conductance) and an indirect effect of ACh (decrease of spike width, due to enhancement of K^+ conductance) on decreasing inward calcium currents have been distinguished (49). This was accomplished by measuring contractions elicited by voltage clamp pulses whose duration is not affected by any changes in outward currents. At low doses of ACh, contractions elicited by voltage clamp pulses were not diminished, which suggests that the inotropic effect of low doses of ACh is due to an enhancement of outward current. At higher doses of ACh both an enhancement of outward K^+ current and a decrease in inward Ca^{2+} current were observed. ACh stimulates the synthesis of cGMP in the heart, and application of cGMP produces a negative inotropic effect (e.g. 50). Studies of ionic flux suggest, however, that the component of ACh action mediated by cGMP may not involve a change in potassium permeability but may be due exclusively to a decrease of the inward calcium current (39).

Several studies indicate that the positive inotropic and chronotropic effect of serotonin on molluscan hearts may also be mediated by cAMP (22, 36a). Furthermore, serotonin-mediated enhanced contraction of the muscle that controls the feeding apparatus in *Aplysia* appears to be mediated by cAMP (57). Analogs of cyclic nucleotides enhanced contraction of buccal muscle, and firing of an individual serotonergic neuron that innervates the buccal muscle enhanced the synthesis (accumulation) of cAMP in the muscle. Interestingly, as far as could be determined by intracellular recording from buccal muscle fibers, activity of the serotonergic input to the muscle never resulted in any detectable change of resting potential. This may represent an extreme example of an effect seen in other systems: Neurotransmitters whose actions are mediated by cAMP produce very small shifts of membrane potential that do not appear to explain the primary action of the transmitter (see 24, 34).

Modulation of Neuronal Burst Activity

Data obtained from studies of single identifiable neurons of invertebrates suggest that cyclic nucleotides may be involved in the modulation of burst activity of neurons. Vertebrate peptide hormones and peptides isolated from the nervous systems of molluscs can increase burst activity in cell R15 of *Aplysia* and similar cells in snails (2, 30). The same peptides stimulate the synthesis of cAMP and cGMP in nervous tissue of molluscs (30, 31). Burst activity of R15 can be suppressed by nerve stimulation (40), which also increases the synthesis of cAMP in the ganglion (9). Application of several phosphodiesterase inhibitors increases burst activity in R15 and other cells (51). In addition, injection of analogs of cAMP directly into R15 increases burst activity. On the other hand, when cAMP levels in the cell are raised by intracellular injection of 5'-guanylyl-imidophosphate (a powerful activator of adenylate cyclase), R15 hyperpolarizes, and burst activity is completely inhibited (52). Thus, depending on how levels of cAMP are raised, cell R15 can show inhibition (mimicking the effect of nerve stimulation) or a form of excitation (mimicking the effect of peptides). Levitan et al (30) propose a highly speculative explanation of these results: Procedures that increase cAMP without increasing cGMP (injection of guanylyl-imido-phosphate) lead to inhibitory effects; procedures that inhibit phosphodiesterase and thereby produce an increase of both cAMP and cGMP, (phosphodiesterase inhibitors, and injection of analogs of cAMP) result in enhancement of the burst activity of the cell.

Modulation of Presynaptic Terminals

Indirect studies indicated that catecholamines may increase the release of catecholamines from synaptic terminals by acting on β autoreceptors and thereby increasing the level of cAMP in the terminal (47, 60). Studies (7, 24) have now provided strong support for the hypothesis that cAMP may be a second messenger that mediates presynaptic facilitation (increased release of transmitter) at the terminals of sensory neurons of *Aplysia.* Facilitation results from presynaptic release of a transmitter (most likely serotonin) at the terminals of the sensory neurons. The mechanism by which serotonin and cAMP enhance increase release at the sensory terminals has been studied (24). The possible role of calcium was investigated by first treating the ganglion with TEA (tetraethylammonium). This partially blocks outward currents, and the action potential thus becomes much broader than normal. The broadening of the spike results in a considerable increase of the relatively slowly activating inward calcium current, and the duration of the spike becomes a sensitive index of the time-course and amplitude of inward calcium currents. Although recorded in the cell body, the spike reflects events occurring at the synaptic terminals. Serotonin, cAMP, phosphodiesterase inhibitors, and presynaptic stimulation increase the release of transmitter and produce a prolongation of the late portion of the spike (see also 26). Thus, the experimental manipulations all appear to increase the release of transmitter by increasing the slow inward calcium current. Additional evidence that the effect is on calcium current is the observation that serotonin broadened the spike in the absence of sodium. Furthermore, the addition of cobalt, which blocks inward calcium current, rapidly narrowed a spike that was previously broadened by presynaptic input (connective nerve stimulation). It is not clear whether spike broadening is a direct effect on calcium channels, or whether it is an indirect effect reflecting a reduction of an outward current—in particular, calcium-dependent potassium current (I-K_{Ca}) that may still be present in the presence of TEA. Indirect data indicated (24) that the primary effect is on the calcium channels. Thus, for example, in a high-calcium/low-sodium solution, connective stimulation (which produces heterosynaptic facilitation) caused an increase in the earliest part of the action potential. Since I-K_{Ca} must be preceded by the influx of calcium (which triggers I-K_{Ca}) a very early increase of inward current suggests that the primary effect may not be on potassium.

Other investigators using *Aplysia* (45) have also concluded that presynaptic facilitation at certain synaptic terminals involves cAMP and that the cAMP is acting on calcium currents. The latter conclusion was based on the observation that if calcium was removed from the bathing solution, facilitation due to extracellular infusion of cAMP at the terminals did not occur until calcium was also infused at the terminals. However, this experiment does not specifically implicate calcium. Since calcium is necessary for transmitter release, the potentiating effects of cAMP will not be seen unless calcium is present, whether or not cAMP affects calcium fluxes.

Studies on *Aplysia* suggest that cAMP mediates a type of synaptic plasticity that underlies sensitization, a simple form of learning. Data obtained from cortical neurons also suggest that cGMP could in principle underlie a form of neuronal plasticity that may be involved in learning. In cortical neurons of the cat, application of ACh extracellularly or cGMP intracellularly could produce a brief decrease in membrane conductance (63). If, however, the ACh or cGMP was applied and the cell was discharged by means of depolarizing pulses, the observed decreases of membrane conductance were greatly prolonged. As discussed above, there may be certain technical problems with the methods used in this experiment. Furthermore, although it was reported that firing the cell without application of cGMP or ACh did not result in a prolonged decrease of cell conductance, Bindman, Lippold & Milne (4) have reported that firing of cortical cells by antidromic activation, but without synaptic input, could produce a prolonged increase in neuronal excitability. Nevertheless, the results of Woody et al (63) are provocative, and it is hoped that these experiments will be replicated, though it is clear that the techniques are difficult. Based on findings of Woody et al the following chain of events at cortical neurons can be envisioned: (*a*) release of ACh onto the cell; (*b*) increase of intracellular level of cGMP; (*c*) depolarization of the cell, associated with a decrease of membrane conductance; (*d*) prolonged decrease of membrane conductance if the depolarization succeeds in firing the cell. Woody et al suggest that such a mechanism might underlie associative learning. However, since an overall decrease of cell conductance would amplify all synaptic inputs to the cell, whether or not they were paired with successful firing of the cell, the mechanism as presented would not provide for specificity of paired input, one of the prime characteristics of associative learning. It is of course possible that a similar mechanism might operate at a restricted locus such that, for example, specific input to a dendrite would result in a conductance decrease restricted to a dendrite exhibiting a local spike. Input to the affected dendrite would be maximally increased without much affecting other synaptic inputs at distant dendrites. Consistent with this notion are the observations that (*a*) the stimulation of the synthesis of cGMP appears to be dependent on calcium (cf 17), (*b*) dendrites can exhibit local calcium spikes (35), and (*c*) intracellular calcium does not diffuse far from its source of entry (cf 36).

SUMMARY AND PERSPECTIVES

Much of the evidence supporting a role of cyclic nucleotides in neural function has come from studies of the hyperpolarizing action of noradenaline on mammalian cerebellar neurons. This work has been criticized on various grounds (41), but most objections have been answered (see e.g. 5, 14). Nevertheless, the precise role of cyclic nucleotides in cerebellar neurons is uncertain. Evidence that cyclic nucleotides may mediate shifts of membrane potential in the "simple" superior cervical ganglion offered a refreshing alternative approach, but increasing evidence indicates that (*a*) the superior cervical ganglion is far from simple (28), and (*b*) cAMP does not mediate physiological shifts of membrane potential. Data have continued to accumulate suggesting that in the sympathetic ganglion cAMP may function postsynaptically to modulate a specific synaptic input to the principal cells. Evidence from studies of *Aplysia* neurons also support a possible postsynaptic role of cyclic nucleotides in modulating burst activity. In addition, studies on *Aplysia* have now provided strong evidence for a presynaptic role of cAMP in modulating transmitter release. Several lines of evidence suggest that both the presynaptic and many of the postsynaptic effects of cyclic nucleotides may arise from their ability to modulate (either directly or indirectly) calcium fluxes through voltage-sensitive ionic gates. The precise ways in which cAMP, calcium, and cGMP (cf 42) act and interact in excitable cells remain to be elucidated.

ACKNOWLEDGMENTS

I greatly appreciate the comments of Drs. T. Carew, P. Kanoff, E. Kandel, J. Koester, J. Schwartz, and K. Weiss on an earlier draft of this paper. Preparation supported, in part, by grant NS 12492.

Literature Cited

1. Akasu, T., Koketsu, K. 1977. Effects of dibutyryl cyclic adenosine 3',5'-monophosphate and theophylline on the bullfrog sympathetic ganglion. *Br. J. Pharmacol.* 60:331–36
2. Baker, J. L., Smith, T. G. Jr. 1977. Peptides as neurohormones. In *Approaches to the Cell Biology of Neurons,* ed. W. M. Cowan, J. A. Ferendelli, Neurosci. Symp. II:340–73. Bethesda, Md: Soc. Neurosci.
3. Beresewicz, A., Reuter, H. 1977. The effects of adrenaline and theophylline on action potential and contraction of mammalian ventricular muscle under "rested-state" and "steady-state" stimulation. *Arch. Pharmacol.* 301:99–107
4. Bindman, L. J., Lippold, O. C. J., Milne, A. R. 1979. Prolonged changes in excitability of pyramidal tract neurons in the cat: A post-synaptic mechanism. *J. Physiol. London* 286:457–77
5. Bloom, F. E., Siggins, G. R., Hoffer, B. J. 1974. Interpreting the failure to confirm the depression of cerebellar Purkinje cells by cyclic AMP. *Science* 185:627–28
6. Bloom, F. E. 1975. The role of cyclic nucleotides in central synaptic function. *Rev. Physiol. Biochem. Pharmacol.* 74:1–103
7. Brunelli, M., Castellucci, V., Kandel, E. R. 1976. Synaptic facilitation and behavioral sensitization in *Aplysia*: Possible role of serotonin and cyclic AMP. *Science* 194:1178–80
8. Busis, N. A., Weight, F. F., Smith, P. A. 1978. Synaptic potentials in sympathetic ganglia: Are they mediated by cyclic nucleotides? *Science* 200:1079–81
9. Cedar, H., Kandel, E. R., Schwartz, J. H. 1972. Cyclic adenosine monophosphate in the nervous system of *Aplysia californica.* I. Increased synthesis in response to synaptic stimulation. *J. Gen. Physiol.* 60:558–69
10. Daly, J. 1977. *Cyclic Nucleotides in the Nervous System.* NY: 401 pp.
11. Dun, N. J., Kaibara, K., Karczmar, A. G. 1978. Muscarinic and cGMP induced membrane potential changes: differences in electrogenic mechanisms. *Brain Res.* 150:658–61
12. Dun, N. J., Karczmar, A. G. 1977. A comparison of the effect of theophylline and cyclic adenosine 3':5'-monophosphate on the superior cervical ganglion of the rabbit by means of the sucrose-gap technique. *J. Pharmacol. Exp. Ther.* 202:89–96
13. Earp, H. S., Steiner, A. L. 1978. Compartmentalization of cyclic nucleotide-mediated hormone action. *Ann. Rev. Pharmacol. Toxicol.* 18:431–59
14. Freedman, R., Hoffer, B. J., Woodward, D. J. 1975. A quantitative microiontophoretic analysis of the responses of central neurons to noradenaline: Interactions with cobalt, manganese, verapamil and dichloroisoprenaline. *Br. J. Pharmacol.* 54:529–39
15. Gallagher, J. P., Shinnick-Gallagher, P. 1977. Cyclic nucleotides injected intracellularly into rat superior cervical ganglion cells. *Science* 198:851–52
16. Giles, W., Noble, S. J. 1976. Changes in membrane currents in bullfrog atrium produced by acetylcholine. *J. Physiol. London* 261:103–23
17. Goldberg, N. D., Haddox, M. K. 1977. Cyclic GMP metabolism and involvement in biological regulation. *Ann. Rev. Biochem.* 46:823–96
18. Green, C. D., Martin, D. W. Jr. 1974. A direct, stimulating effect of cyclic GMP on purified phosphoribosyl pryrophosphate synthetase. *Cell* 2:241–45
19. Greengard, P. 1978. Phosphorylated proteins as physiological effectors. *Science* 199:146–52
20. Greengard, P., Kuo, J. F. 1970. On the mechanism of action of cyclic AMP. In *Advances in Biochemical Psychopharmacology,* ed. P. Greengard, E. Costa, 3:287–306. NY: Raven
21. Hashiguchi, T., Ushiyama, N. S., Kobayashi, H., Libet, B. 1978. Does cyclic GMP mediate the slow excitatory synaptic potential in sympathetic ganglia? *Nature* 271:267–68
22. Higgins, W. J. 1977. 5-Hydroxytryptamine-induced tachyphylaxis of the molluscan heart and concomitant desensitization of adenylate cyclase. *J. Cyclic Nucleotide Res.* 3:293–302
23. Hill-Smith, I., Purves, R. D. 1978. Synaptic delay in the heart: An ionophoretic study. *J. Physiol. London* 279:31–54
24. Klein, M., Kandel, E. R. 1978. Presynaptic modulation of voltage-dependent Ca^{2+} current: Mechanism for behavioral sensitization in *Aplysia californica.* *Proc. Natl. Acad. Sci. USA* 75:3512–16
25. Kobayashi, H., Hashiguchi, T., Ushiyama, N. S. 1978. Postsynaptic modulation of excitatory processes in sympathetic ganglia by cyclic AMP. *Nature* 271:268–70
26. Krnjević, K., Van Meter, W. G. 1976.

Cyclic nucleotides in spinal cells. *Can J. Physiol. Pharmacol.* 54:416–21

27. Kuba, K., Koketsu, K. 1976. Analysis of the slow excitatory postsynaptic potential in bullfrog sympathetic ganglion cells. *Jpn. J. Physiol.* 26:651–69
28. Kuba, K., Koketsu, K. 1978. Synaptic events in sympathetic ganglia. *Prog. Neurobiol.* 11:77–169
29. Kupfermann, I. 1979. Modulatory actions of neurotransmitters. *Ann. Rev. Neurosci.* 2:447–65
30. Levitan, I. B., Harmar, A. J., Adams, W. B. 1979. Synaptic and hormonal modulation of a neuronal oscillator: A search for molecular mechanisms. *J. Exp. Biol.* In press
31. Levitan, I. B., Treistman, S. N. 1977. Modulation of electrical activity and cyclic nucleotide metabolism in molluscan nervous system by a peptide-containing nervous system extract. *Brain Res.* 136:307–17
32. Liang, C. T., Sacktor, B. 1978. The stimulation by catecholamines of guanylate cyclase activity in a cell-free system. *J. Cyclic Nucleotide Res.* 4:97–111
33. Libet, B. 1979. Which postsynaptic action of dopamine is mediated by cyclic AMP? *Life Sci.* 24:1043–58
34. Libet, B. 1979. Slow postsynaptic actions in ganglionic functions. In *Integrative Function of the Autonomic Nervous System,* ed. C. McC. Brooks, K. Koizumi, A. Sata. Tokyo: Tokyo Univ. Press. In press
35. Llinás, R., Sugimori, M. 1978. Dendritic calcium spiking in mammalian Purkinje cells: In vitro study of its function and development. *Neurosci. Abstr.* 4:66
36. Loewenstein, W. R., Rose, B. 1978. Calcium in (junctional) intercellular communication and a thought on its behavior in intracellular communication. *Ann. NY Acad. Sci.* 307:285–307

36a. Mandelbaum, D. E., Koester, J., Schonberg, M. Weiss, K. R. 1979. Cyclic AMP mediation of the excitatory effect of serotonin in the heart of *Aplysia. Brain. Res.* 177:388–94

37. McAfee, D. A., Greengard, P. 1972. Adenosine 3',5'-monophosphate: Electrophysiological evidence for a role in synaptic transmission. *Science* 178: 310–12
38. Nathanson, J. A. 1977. Cyclic nucleotides and nervous system function. *Physiol. Rev.* 57:157–256
39. Nawrath, H. 1977. Does cyclic GMP mediate the negative inotropic effect of acetylcholine in the heart? *Nature* 267:72–74
40. Parnas, I., Armstrong, D., Strumwasser, F. 1974. Prolonged excitatory and inhibitory synaptic modulation of a bursting pacemaker neuron. *J. Neurophysiol.* 37:594–608
41. Phillis, J. W. 1977. The role of cyclic nucleotides in the CNS. *Can. J. Neurol. Sci.* 4:151–95
42. Rasmussen, H., Goodman, D. B. P. 1977. Relationships between calcium and cyclic nucleotides in cell activation. *Physiol. Rev.* 57:421–509
43. Reuter, H. 1979. Properties of two inward membrane currents in the heart. *Ann. Rev. Physiol.* 41:413–24
44. Reuter, H., Scholz, H. 1977. The regulation of the calcium conductances of cardiac muscle by adrenaline. *J. Physiol. London* 264:49–62
45. Shimahara, T., Tauc, L. 1977. Cyclic AMP induced by serotonin modulates the activity of an identified synapse in *Aplysia* by facilitating the active permeability to calcium. *Brain Res.* 127: 168–72
46. Sperelakis, N., Schneider, J. A. 1976. A metabolic control mechanism for calcium ion influx that may protect the ventricular mycardial cell. *Am J. Cardiol.* 37:1079–85
47. Starke, K. 1977. Regulation of noradenaline release by presynaptic receptor systems. *Rev. Physiol. Biochem. Pharmacol.* 77:1–124
48. Stone, T. W., Taylor, D. A. 1977. Microiontophoretic studies of the effects of cyclic nucleotides on excitability of neurons in the rat cerebral cortex. *J. Physiol. London* 266:523–43
49. Ten Eick, R., Nawrath, H., McDonald, T. F., Trautwein, W. 1976. On the mechanism of the negative inotropic effect of acetylcholine. *Pflügers Arch.* 361:207–13
50. Trautwein, W., Trube, G. 1976. Negative inotropic effect of cyclic GMP in cardiac fragments. *Pflügers Arch.* 366:293–95
51. Treistman, S. N, Drake, P. F. 1979. The effects of cyclic nucleotide agents on neurons in *Aplysia. Brain Res.* 168: 643–47
52. Treistman, S. N., Levitan, I. B. 1976. Intraneuronal Guanylyl-imidodiphosphate injection mimics long-term synaptic hyperpolarization in *Aplysia. Proc. Natl. Acad. Sci. USA* 73:4689–92
53. Tsien, R. W. 1977. Cyclic AMP and contractile activity in heart. *Adv. Cyclic Nucleotide Res.* 8:363–420

54. Weight, F. F. 1974. Synaptic potentials resulting from conductance decreases. In *Synaptic Transmission and Neuronal Interaction,* ed. M. V. L. Bennett, pp. 141–52. NY: Raven
55. Weight, F. F., Petzold, G., Greengard, P. 1974. Guanosine 3',5'monophosphate associated with synaptic transmission. *Science* 186:942–44
56. Weight, F. F., Smith, P. A., Schulman, J. A. 1978. Postsynaptic potential generation appears independent of synaptic elevation of cyclic nucleotides in sympathetic neurons. *Brain Res.* 158:197–202
57. Weiss, K. R., Mandelbaum, D. E., Schonberg, M., Kupfermann, I. 1979. Modulation of buccal muscle contractility by serotonergic metacerebral cells in *Aplysia:* Evidence for a role of cyclic adenosine monophosphate. *J. Neurophysiol.* 42:791–803
58. Weller, M., Laing, W. 1978. Cyclic AMP increases the Na^+ permeability of the avian erythrocyte membrane by a process which does not involve protein phosphorylation. *Mol. Cell. Biochem.* 20:119–24
59. Weller, M., Morgan, I. G. 1977. A possible role of the phosphorylation of synaptic membrane proteins in the control of calcium ion permeability. *Biochem. Biophys. Acta* 465:527–34
60. Westfall, T. C. 1977. Local regulation of adrenergic neurotransmission. *Physiol. Rev.* 57:659–728
61. Williams, M., Rodnight, R. 1977. Protein phosphorylation in nervous tissue: possible involvement in nervous tissue function and relationship to cyclic nucleotide metabolism *Prog. Neurobiol.* 8:183–250
62. Wollenberger, A., Will, H. 1978. Protein kinase–catalyzed membrane phosphorylation and its possible relationship to the role of calcium in the adrenergic regulation of cardiac contraction. *Life Sci.* 22:1159–78
63. Woody, C. D., Swartz, B. E., Gruen, E. 1978. Effects of acetylcholine and cyclic GMP on input resistance of cortical neurons in awake cats. *Brain Res.* 158:373–95

Ann. Rev. Physiol. 1980. 42:643–52

BIOPHYSICAL ANALYSIS OF THE FUNCTION OF RECEPTORS

❖1292

Charles F. Stevens

Department of Physiology, Yale University School of Medicine, New Haven, Connecticut 06510

INTRODUCTION

Receptors form a class of intrinsic membrane proteins (or glycoproteins) defined by the high affinity and specificity with which they bind ligands. Usually a receptor is named according to the natural ligand it binds with the highest affinity; we speak, for example of the "ACh (acetylcholine) receptor" and the "GABA (γ-aminobutyric acid) receptor".

Implicit in the definition and naming of receptors is the functional significance of their binding activity. Because TTX (tetrodotoxin) binds with high affinity and specificity to sodium channels in most nerves, we sometimes loosely refer to these channels as "TTX receptors" to emphasize the fact that the channel proteins were, in a particular experiment, identified solely by their ligand binding properties. However, strict usage reserves "receptor" to those instances in which ligand binding plays a normal and essential role in the function of the proteins.

The presence of membrane proteins that do nothing beyond binding specific ligands with high affinity can have implications for cell function. For example, receptors can transiently buffer the surface concentration of a ligand and can alter the rates of diffusion along the membrane surface. Thus binding alone might be of importance to a cell, but most if not all receptors serve some additional function: For example, they are sometimes the regulatory subunit of an enzyme or are associated with a channel that controls the flow of ions through the membrane. The study of receptors, then, can focus either on binding per se or on the functional changes evoked in the protein as a consequence of ligand binding. Although the receptors found in nervous tissue perform a variety of functions other than ligand

0066-4278/80/0315-0643$01.00

binding, many are associated with ion channels. I survey here the biophysical techniques for the study of receptor/channel protein and illustrate some uses of these techniques. I limit the discussion to those methods that relate specifically to the binding and the gating functions of the class of receptor/channels being considered here.

EQUILIBRIUM BINDING: DIRECT STUDIES

Equilibrium binding is typically measured with radiolabeled ligands, though any physical technique for determining the total quantity of ligand present is satisfactory. Two methods are generally used. With the traditional method, the receptors are placed in a compartment (usually a dialysis sack) that the ligand can leave but the receptor cannot. At equilibrium the free ligand concentrations inside and outside the compartment are equal, but the inside compartment contains extra ligand bound to the receptors. A measurement of total ligand within the compartment, minus the free quantity, gives the amount of bound ligand. Conclusions from a number of traditional equilibrium binding studies have been discussed in a recent review (13a). With the second method, the receptor is separated from the solution containing free ligand, and the amount bound is determined directly. What separation method is satisfactory depends on the average lifetime of the bound state. For high-affinity binding with dissociation constants in the picomolar range, the bound state persists for minutes or longer; membrane fragments bearing the receptor can then be separated by centrifugation. This approach can be used, for example, in studying binding of snake toxins to the ACh receptor. Ultrafiltration can be carried out in fractions of a second and can thus be used when dissociation constants are in the nanomolar range or lower (6). Analysis of amount bound as a function of ligand concentration can provide estimates of the dissociation constant or constants and can detect the presence of multiple binding sites.

BINDING KINETICS: DIRECT STUDIES

Some binding reactions are nearly diffusion-limited, which means the association step occurs with a rate constant approaching $10^9 M^{-1} sec^{-1}$. Other binding occurs, however, with much lower association rates. To determine the association rate constant, and therefore the mean lifetime of the bound state [mean bound lifetime = 1/(unbinding rate constant) = 1/(dissociation constant × binding rate constant)], one must carry out kinetic binding studies. Such kinetic studies have the additional advantage of providing a good test for the proposed binding scheme—i.e. whether binding is bimolecular or involves several steps, etc.

Depending on the magnitudes of the rate constants involved, one may use two different methods to study binding kinetics: rapid mixing or perturbation. With the rapid mixing approach, receptor (unbound) and free ligand are rapidly mixed together, and the amount bound as a function of time is measured. The perturbation methods depend on the fact that the equilibrium distribution of the bound and free states of a ligand depends on temperature, pressure, and other variables. With the perturbation techniques, equilibrium binding is established at, for example, one temperature, the equilibrium is "instantaneously" shifted by a stepwise change in temperature, and the approach to the new equilibrium distribution is followed.

Use of these kinetic techniques requires a method for measuring the progress of the binding step. If rates are sufficiently slow, separation of receptor from the solution containing the ligand can be achieved by ultrafiltration, and a determination of bound, radiolabeled ligand can be employed (7). Alternative approaches use a ligand whose fluorescence properties change with binding (4, 8, 13, 16, 29, 30), employ a continuously bound fluorescent probe (12, 23, 25), measure intrinsic fluorescence of the receptor itself (3, 5), or detect some ion (Ca^{2+}, for example) whose dissociation is coupled to binding the ligand under study (22).

EQUILIBRIUM BINDING: PHYSIOLOGICAL STUDIES

The methods for determining binding described so far have relied on some direct measurement of receptor-ligand association. Whenever, as generally is the case, a receptor has a function other than that of being a sponge for the ligand(s) in question, binding can be studied through its consequences. As indicated earlier, I shall focus on a single consequence, channel opening, appropriate for the class of receptor/channel proteins. More specifically, I shall restrict attention to the acetylcholine receptor because it is the most completely studied.

For receptor/channels, ligand binding leads to channel opening, and the number of open channels can be detected by measuring the current passing through them (28). The idea, then, is to infer binding from the number of open channels as a function of ligand concentration (1, 9, 11). Several technical problems complicate studies of this sort, though these problems were not obvious prior to an analysis of the binding (or dose-response) curves determined by this technique [see discussion in (9)]. First, ACh receptors, like many other receptor types, enter a physiologically dead (called "desensitized") state when exposed to ligand for long periods of time (see 14). Therefore ligand may be applied for only brief periods, on the order of seconds, before being removed; otherwise too few channels will open for a given agonist concentration. Second, high agonist doses cause large ion fluxes, which can alter the ionic composition both of the fiber under study and of the medium just outside the synaptic region. Such ion concentration changes can significantly alter the driving force on the ions carrying current through the channels and thus affect the magnitudes of the currents used to estimate numbers of open channels. Finally, high ligand concentrations can have dual effects, both opening and blocking channels. When this blocking effect occurs, more channels are opened than are detected by the current recordings and binding is underestimated.

Binding curves are seldom simple. One significant complication recognized in many studies of ligand binding and it's consequences is cooperativity. For receptor/channels, at least three types of cooperativity must be distinguished, and experiments must be designed to detect each. The first is *binding cooperativity:* When more than one ligand molecule can bind onto a receptor, the presence of ligand molecules already bound can alter the affinity of the receptor for additional ligand binding. Second, and logically independent of binding cooperativity, the consequence of ligand binding can depend on the number of ligand molecules present on the receptor. For example, two ligand molecules (which could themselves bind independently to a receptor) might be required to cooperate in causing channel opening. This phenomenon can be termed *effect cooperativity.* Finally, neighboring receptor/channel proteins can interact to influence each others' behavior, in terms of either ligand binding or its consequences. For example, the opening of one channel could enhance the probability that neighbors would open. This can be called *intermolecular cooperativity.* Each of these forms of cooperativity will, if present, be expressed in the binding curve measured through physiological consequences of binding (e.g. channel opening).

KINETICS: PHYSIOLOGICAL STUDIES

Binding studies can be concerned with either the equilibrium state or the approach to equilibrium. Similarly, studies of the effects of binding can focus on either the equilibrium properties of the system or the transient relaxation to equilibrium. Kinetic studies of binding effects are important because they provide much additional information about the receptor under investigation, but they can be difficult to interpret when the rate-limiting steps in the binding-effect sequence are unknown.

For receptor/channel proteins, two main approaches can be used to investigate the kinetics of relaxation to equilibrium: the perturbation techniques, and fluctuation analysis. Some perturbation methods use a rapid change in ligand concentration; in others, ligand concentration is maintained constant but the equilibrium distribution of channels in the open state is rapidly displaced. In all of these approaches one measures the number of channels open as a function of time by detecting the currents that pass through the open channels. Small changes can accurately be assessed, and time constants in the 100 microsecond and longer range can be determined.

The problem for all perturbation methods is to produce a change in the equilibrium number of open channels that is instantaneous on the time scale of the processes under investigation. Because the reactions associated with ligand-receptor binding can be rapid, the production of sufficiently rapid perturbations in the equilibrium number of open channels can be difficult. Rapid changes in ligand concentration are particularly difficult to produce, and neither of the two methods now used to do so is really satisfactory. The first of these uses nerve stimulation and relies on the rapid removal of ACh from the cleft by diffusion and esterase action; single quantum releases thus give a fairly good approximation to delta function stimulation (17). The difficulties with using nerve-released ACh are that concentrations are unknown, the time course of the cleft ligand concentration transient is uncertain, and ligands other than ACh and acetylmonoethylcholine (15) cannot be studied. The second method uses a ligand, Bis-Q, that has two conformations (*cis* and *trans*) with very different affinities for the receptor. The distribution of these two conformers can be controlled by exposing the agonist to light of the appropriate wavelengths. Rapid changes in the concentration of the active *trans* isomer can thus be achieved by brief light flashes (19). This method has two disadvantages: The time course of the concentration transient is uncertain, and studies are limited to the single ligand *trans*-Bis-Q.

In the second category of perturbation methods, the equilibrium number of open channels is rapidly shifted by a step in the voltage difference across the membrane bearing the ACh-activated channels. This generally more satisfactory method is not without problems. The number of channels open depends, for a fixed ligand concentration, on membrane potential because the conformational change in the channel that is responsible for channel opening and closing is voltage sensitive (10); the extent to which a voltage dependence of the ligand binding plays a role is still unknown. Magleby & Stevens (17) provided the theoretical background for the voltage jump technique, demonstrated that this approach is feasible, and found that the rate constants involved depend instantaneously on membrane potential. These workers, however, used nerve-released ACh rather than exogenously applied ligand and did not exploit the voltage dependence of equilibrium number of channels open. Improved and extended, this method has been used to study the properties of several agonists (1, 20, 26). The voltage jump method is technically difficult because channel blocking, desensitization, and voltage clamp errors can all cause complications. Nevertheless, it is generally the best way to study certain types of ligands and pharmacological agents and is particularly suited to investigations of near-saturation ligand concentrations.

Fluctuation analysis (see 27) provides a complement to the perturbation methods just described. Fluctuation analysis depends on the fact that ligand binding and the consequent channel opening are probabilistic events. With a constant concentration of ligand present, the exact number of channels open fluctuates around the average in a random fashion from instant to instant. The fluctuations are, however, governed by the same physical interactions that express themselves in relaxations toward equilibrium studied with the perturbation methods. This means that the kinetics of receptor/channel behavior can be investigated by studying properties of the spontaneous random fluctuations. Perturbation methods yield a set of relaxation amplitudes and time constants that embody both the binding constants and the rate constants that characterize the conformational changes responsible for channel gating. Fluctuation analysis provides estimates for these same amplitudes and time constants but with different weights.

I emphasize the complementary nature of these two approaches. In certain situations, their combined use can resolve unanswered questions. Specifically, two different kinetic mechanisms that are equally compatable with the results of a perturbation experiment can be differentiated by their quite different predictions about fluctuations. The effectiveness of this combined approach is well illustrated in Ruff's analysis (24) of local anesthetic effects on the ACh receptor/channel; he was able to show that only one of three possible mechanisms of drug action—all equivalent in their predictions for perturbation experiments—was compatable with the observations on fluctuations. Fluctuation analysis can also provide additional information not otherwise available. For example, in most instances fluctuation analysis yields, in addition to kinetic information, estimates for the conductance of a single open channel.

STUDIES ON SINGLE MEMBRANE PROTEINS

The techniques described so far measure properties of populations of receptors. Certain questions, however, require measurements on single molecules. For example, population measurements do not reveal whether a receptor/channel operates in a simple open-shut manner or in a more complicated way with a gate smoothly modulating the channel conductance. As another example, population measurements cannot discriminate between (*a*) the random behavior of individual members of a homogeneous group and (*b*) the deterministic behavior of a heterogeneous group with a particular distribution of properties for individual molecules.

Although no method is available for examining binding to individual receptors, the consequent channel opening and closing can be studied for single receptor/channels. Neher & Sakmann (21) developed a method for measuring currents flowing through small areas of membrane that contain relatively few channels, and have managed to reduce the noise levels in the recording circuitry so that single-channel currents can be detected in certain circumstances. This technique has confirmed the conclusions from fluctuation and perturbation analyses and has supported some of the previously unverified assumptions upon which the interpretation of these earlier studies was based.

SOME RESULTS OBTAINED WITH THESE TECHNIQUES

The ACh receptor/channel is the membrane protein that has been most completely studied with the methods described here. Its properties are complex. Since there is no reason to suspect other receptors will be significantly simpler, the difficulties these complexities cause for the interpretation of binding and other measurements should provide instructive warnings for investigators approaching other receptor types. The important point is that the complexities to be described must be considered when interpreting the observations made by any of the techniques discussed here; failure to do so will lead to incorrect conclusions.

Complementary pictures of the ACh receptor/channel are provided by binding studies and physiological experiments. From an investigation on the binding kinetics, Cohen & Boyd (7) arrived at the following scheme based on the original proposal by Katz & Thesleff (14):

$$\begin{array}{ccc} L + R_1 & \overset{K_D = 1\,\mu M}{\rightleftharpoons} & L \cdot R_1 \\ {\scriptstyle .0028\ sec^{-1}}\uparrow\downarrow{\scriptstyle .005\ sec^{-1}} & & {\scriptstyle .0024\ sec^{-1}}\uparrow\downarrow{\scriptstyle .18\ sec^{-1}} \\ L + R_2 & \underset{.15\ sec^{-1}}{\overset{7 \times 10^{7}\ M^{-1}\ sec^{-1}}{\rightleftharpoons}} & L\ R_2 \end{array} \qquad 1.$$

where L = acetylcholine, and R_1,R_2 = conformations of the ACh receptor.

The functional significance of the various states of the receptor was not determined in this study, but presumably R_2 is the desensitized conformation and R_1 the "normal" form.

Dionne, Steinbich & Stevens (9) have provided, from physiological studies that detected the number of open channels, the following scheme:

$$
\begin{array}{ccccc}
2\,L + R & \underset{}{\overset{K_D = 600\ \mu M}{\rightleftharpoons}} & L + LR & \underset{}{\overset{K_D = 80\ \mu M}{\rightleftharpoons}} & L_2\,R \\
 & & {\scriptstyle .005}\updownarrow & & \updownarrow{\scriptstyle .47} \\
 & & L + LR^* & \underset{.9\ \mu M}{\rightleftharpoons} & L_2\,R^*
\end{array}
\qquad 2.
$$

where L = carbamylcholine, R = receptor/channel in closed conformation, and R* = receptor/channel in open conformation.

It is unclear how these two schemes are to be brought into register. The physiological study did not permit receptors to enter their desensitized state, and the binding study did not detect open channels. The two sets of measurements also used different time scales: "Equilibrium" for the physiological study was achieved after a few milliseconds, whereas in scheme 1 equilibrium was attained after seconds. Presumably scheme 2 is an expansion of the $L+R_1 \leftrightarrow LR_1$ step of scheme 1, but it may be that binding sites for the two schemes are separate and that they represent parallel processes.

Note that observations cannot be correctly interpreted without taking the various steps represented by these schemes into account. For example, "equilibrium" binding experiments must be interpreted in light of the time scale on which the binding measurements were made. On the several-second time scale, a dissociation constant of 15 nM is found for ACh, but a dissociation constant about three orders of magnitude higher is inferred from the more rapidly achieved equilibrium studied in the physiological experiments. Further, binding experiments generally do not distinguish between the forms L_2R and L_2R^* of scheme 2, so the apparent dissociation constant is influenced by the subsequent conformational change that traps ligand on the receptor.

Similar conclusions hold for kinetic studies. Because conformational changes follow binding steps, binding rates can easily be confused with rates for the conformational transition.

The approaches described here—and improvements on them that will follow—are powerful and should finally provide a complete picture of receptor function. At each stage in the analysis, however, we must be aware of the possible complexities inherent in the receptors' properties. Particularly we must attempt to combine the various approaches and interpret our data in light of overall receptor function.

Literature Cited

1. Adams, P. R. 1975. Kinetics of agonist conductance changes during hyperpolarization at frog end-plates. *Br. J. Pharmacol.* 53:308–10
2. Barrantes, F. J. 1976. Intrinsic fluorescence of the membrane-bound acetylcholine receptor: Its quenching by suberyldicholine. *Biochem. Biophys. Res. Commun.* 72:479–88
3. Barrantes, F. J. 1978. Agonist-mediated changes of the acetylcholine receptor in its membrane environment. *Mol. Biol.* 124:1–26
4. Barrantes, F. J., Sakmann, B., Bonner, R., Eibl, H., Jovin, T. M. 1975. 1-Pyrene-butyrylcholine: A fluorescent probe for the cholinergic system. *Proc. Natl. Acad. Sci. USA* 72:3097–3101
5. Bonner, R., Barrantes, F. J., Jovin, T. M. 1976. Kinetics of agonist-induced intrinsic fluorescence changes in membrane-bound acetylcholine receptor. *Nature* 263:429–31
6. Cohen, J. B. 1978. Why smash atoms? In *Molecular Specialization and Symmetry in Membrane Function,* ed. A. K. Solomon, M. Karnovsky, pp. 99–128. Cambridge: Harvard Univ. Press
7. Cohen, J. B., Boyd, N. D. 1979. Conformational transitions of the membrane-bound cholinergic receptor. In *Catalysis in Chemistry and Biochemistry,* ed. B. Pulman, D. Ginsburg. NY: D. Reidel. In press
8. Cohen, J. B., Changeux, J.-P. 1973. Interaction of a fluorescent ligand with membrane-bound cholinergic receptor from *Torpedo marmorata. Biochemistry* 12:4855–64
9. Dionne, V. E., Steinbach, J. H., Stevens, C. F. 1978. An analysis of the dose-response relationship at voltage-clamped frog neuromuscular junctions. *J. Physiol. London* 281:421–44
10. Dionne, V. E., Stevens, C. F. 1975. Voltage dependence of agonist effectiveness at the frog neuromuscular junction: Resolution of a paradox. *J. Physiol. London* 251:245–70
11. Dreyer, F., Peper, K., Sterz, R. 1978. Determination of dose-response curves by quantitative ionophoresis at the frog neuromuscular junction. *J. Physiol. London* 281:395–419
12. Grünhagen, H. H., Changeux, J.-P. 1976. Studies on the electrogenic action of acetylcholine with *Torpedo marmorata* electric organ. V. Qualitative correlation between pharmacological effects and equilibrium processes of the cholinergic receptor protein as revealed by the structural probe quinacrine. *J. Mol. Biol.* 106:517–35
13. Grünhagen, H. H., Changeux, J.-P. 1976. Studies on the electrogenic action of acetylcholine with *Torpedo marmorata* electric organ. IV. Quinacrine: A fluorescent probe for the conformational transitions of the cholinergic receptor protein in its membrane-bound state. *J. Mol. Biol.* 106:497–516

13a. Heidmann, T., Changeux, J.-P. 1978. Structural and functional properties of the acetylcholine receptor protein in its purified and membrane-bound states. *Ann. Rev. Biochem.* 47:317–57

14. Jürss, R., Prinz, H., Maelicke, A. 1979. NBD-5-acylcholine: Fluorescent analog of acetylcholine and agonist at the neuromuscular junction. *Proc. Natl. Acad. Sci. USA* 76:1064–68
15. Katz, B., Thesleff, S. 1957. A study of "desensitization" produced by acetylcholine at the motor end-plate. *J. Physiol. London* 138:63–80
16. Large, W. A., Rang, H. P. 1978. Factors affecting the rate of incorporation of a false transmitter into mammalian motor nerve terminals. *J. Physiol. London* 285:1–24
17. Maelicke, A., Fulpius, B. W., Klett, R. P., Reich, E. 1977. Acetylcholine receptor. Responses to drug binding. *J. Biol. Chem.* 252:4811–30
18. Magleby, K. L., Stevens, C. F. 1972. A quantitative description of end-plate currents. *J. Physiol. London* 223: 173–97
19. Martinez-Carrion, M., Raftery, M. A. 1973. Use of a fluorescent probe for the study of ligand binding by the isolated cholinergic receptor of *Torpedo californica. Biochem. Biophys. Res. Commun.* 55:1156–64
20. Nass, M. M., Lester, H. A., Krouse, M. E. 1978. Response of acetylcholine receptors to photoisomerizations of bound agonist molecules. *Biophys. J.* 24:135–60
21. Neher, E., Sakmann, B. 1975. Voltage-dependence of drug-induced conductance in frog neuromuscular junction. *Proc. Natl. Acad. Sci. USA* 72:2140–44
22. Neher, E., Sakmann, B. 1976. Single-channel currents recorded from membrane of denervated frog muscle fibres. *Nature* 260:799–802
23. Neumann, E., Chang, H. W. 1976. Dynamic properties of isolated acetylcholine receptor protein: Kinetics of the binding of acetylcholine and Ca ions. *Proc. Natl. Acad. Sci. USA* 73:3994–98

24. Quast, U., Schimerlik, M., Raftery, M. A. 1978. Stopped flow kinetics of carbamylcholine binding to membrane bound acetylcholine receptor. *Biochem. Biophys. Res. Commun.* 81:955–64
25. Ruff, R. L. 1977. A quantitative analysis of local anaesthetic alteration of miniature end-plate currents and end-plate current fluctuations. *J. Physiol. London* 264:89–124
26. Schimerlik, M., Raftery, M. A. 1976. A fluorescence probe of acetylcholine receptor conformation and local anesthetic binding. *Biochem. Biophys. Res. Commun.* 73:607–13
27. Sheridan, R. E., Lester, H. A. 1975. Relaxation measurements on the acetylcholine receptor. *Proc. Natl. Acad. Sci. USA* 72:3496–500
28. Stevens, C. F. 1977. Study of membrane permeability changes by fluctuation analysis. *Nature* 270:391–96
29. Takeuchi, A., Takeuchi, N. 1960. On the permeability of end-plate membrane during the action of transmitter. *J. Physiol. London* 154:52–67
30. Waksman, G., Fournie-Zaluski, M.-C., Roques, B., Heidmann, T., Grünhagen, H. H., Changeux, J.-P. 1976. Synthesis of fluorescent acyl-cholines with agonistic properties: Pharmacological activity on electroplaque and interaction in vitro with *Torpedo* receptor-rich membrane fragments. *FEBS Lett.* 67:335–42
31. Weber, G., Borris, D.-P., De Robertis, E., Barrantes, F. J., LaTorre, J. L., Llorente de Carlin, M. C. 1971. The use of a cholinergic fluorescent probe for the study of the receptor proteolipid. *Mol. Pharmacol.* 7:530–37

AUTHOR INDEX

M

N

O

S

Y

SUBJECT INDEX

I

R

S

T

U

V

CUMULATIVE INDEXES

CONTRIBUTING AUTHORS, VOLUMES 38–42

CHAPTER TITLES, VOLUMES 38–42

ORDER FORM ANNUAL REVIEWS INC.

Please list on the order blank on the reverse side the volumes you wish to order and whether you wish a standing order (the latest volume sent to you automatically upon publication each year). Volumes not yet published will be shipped in month and year indicated. Prices subject to change without notice. Out of print volumes subject to special order.

NEW TITLES FOR 1980

ANNUAL REVIEW OF PUBLIC HEALTH — ISSN 0163-7525
Vol. 1 (avail. May 1980): $17.00 (USA), $17.50 (elsewhere) per copy

ANNUAL REVIEWS REPRINTS: IMMUNOLOGY, 1977–1979 — ISBN 0-8243-2502-8
A collection of articles reprinted from recent *Annual Review* series
Avail. Mar. 1980 Soft cover: $12.00 (USA), $12.50 (elsewhere) per copy

SPECIAL PUBLICATIONS

ANNUAL REVIEWS REPRINTS: CELL MEMBRANES, 1975–1977 — ISBN 0-8243-2501-X
A collection of articles reprinted from recent *Annual Review* series
Published 1978 Soft cover: $12.00 (USA), $12.50 (elsewhere) per copy

THE EXCITEMENT AND FASCINATION OF SCIENCE, VOLUME 1 — ISBN 0-8243-1602-9
A collection of autobiographical and philosophical articles by leading scientists
Published 1965 Clothbound: $6.50 (USA), $7.00 (elsewhere) per copy

THE EXCITEMENT AND FASCINATION OF SCIENCE, VOLUME 2: Reflections by Eminent Scientists
Published 1978 Hard cover: $12.00 (USA), $12.50 (elsewhere) per copy — ISBN 0-8243-2601-6
Soft cover: $10.00 (USA), $10.50 (elsewhere) per copy — ISBN 0-8243-2602-4

THE HISTORY OF ENTOMOLOGY — ISBN 0-8243-2101-7
A special supplement to the *Annual Review of Entomology* series
Published 1973 Clothbound: $10.00 (USA), $10.50 (elsewhere) per copy

ANNUAL REVIEW SERIES

Annual Review of ANTHROPOLOGY — ISSN 0084-6570
Vols. 1–8 (1972–79): $17.00 (USA), $17.50 (elsewhere) per copy
Vol. 9 (avail. Oct. 1980): $20.00 (USA), $21.00 (elsewhere) per copy

Annual Review of ASTRONOMY AND ASTROPHYSICS — ISSN 0066-4146
Vols. 1–17 (1963–79): $17.00 (USA), $17.50 (elsewhere) per copy
Vol. 18 (avail. Sept. 1980): $20.00 (USA), $21.00 (elsewhere) per copy

Annual Review of BIOCHEMISTRY — ISSN 0066-4154
Vols. 28–48 (1959–79): $18.00 (USA), $18.50 (elsewhere) per copy
Vol. 49 (avail. July 1980): $21.00 (USA), $22.00 (elsewhere) per copy

Annual Review of BIOPHYSICS AND BIOENGINEERING* — ISSN 0084-6589
Vols. 1–8 (1972–79): $17.00 (USA), $17.50 (elsewhere) per copy
Vol. 9 (avail. June 1980): $17.00 (USA), $17.50 (elsewhere) per copy

Annual Review of EARTH AND PLANETARY SCIENCES* — ISSN 0084-6597
Vols. 1–7 (1973–79): $17.00 (USA), $17.50 (elsewhere) per copy
Vol. 8 (avail. May 1980): $17.00 (USA), $17.50 (elsewhere) per copy

Annual Review of ECOLOGY AND SYSTEMATICS — ISSN 0066-4162
Vols. 1–10 (1970–79): $17.00 (USA), $17.50 (elsewhere) per copy
Vol. 11 (avail. Nov. 1980): $20.00 (USA), $21.00 (elsewhere) per copy

Annual Review of ENERGY — ISSN 0362-1626
Vols. 1–4 (1976–79): $17.00 (USA), $17.50 (elsewhere) per copy
Vol. 5 (avail. Oct. 1980): $20.00 (USA), $21.00 (elsewhere) per copy

Annual Review of ENTOMOLOGY* — ISSN 0066-4170
Vols. 7–24 (1962–79): $17.00 (USA), $17.50 (elsewhere) per copy
Vol. 25 (avail. Jan. 1980): $17.00 (USA), $17.50 (elsewhere) per copy

Annual Review of FLUID MECHANICS* — ISSN 0066-4189
Vols. 1–11 (1969–79): $17.00 (USA), $17.50 (elsewhere) per copy
Vol. 12 (avail. Jan. 1980): $17.00 (USA), $17.50 (elsewhere) per copy

Annual Review of GENETICS — ISSN 0066-4197
Vols. 1–13 (1967–79): $17.00 (USA), $17.50 (elsewhere) per copy
Vol. 14 (avail. Dec. 1980): $20.00 (USA), $21.00 (elsewhere) per copy

Annual Review of MATERIALS SCIENCE — ISSN 0084-6600
Vol. 1–9 (1971–79): $17.00 (USA), $17.50 (elsewhere) per copy
Vol. 10 (avail. Aug. 1980): $20.00 (USA), $21.00 (elsewhere) per copy

(continued on reverse)

*Price will be increased to $20.00 (USA), $21.00 (elsewhere) per copy effective with the 1981 volume.

Annual Review of MEDICINE: Selected Topics in the Clinical Sciences* ISSN 0066-4219
Vols. 1–3, 5–15, 17–30 (1950–52, 1954–64, 1966–79): $17.00 (USA), $17.50 (elsewhere) per copy
Vol. 31 (avail. Apr. 1980): $17.00 (USA), $17.50 (elsewhere) per copy

Annual Review of MICROBIOLOGY ISSN 0066-4227
Vols. 15–33 (1961–79): $17.00 (USA), $17.50 (elsewhere) per copy
Vol. 34 (avail. Oct. 1980): $20.00 (USA), $21.00 (elsewhere) per copy

Annual Review of NEUROSCIENCE* ISSN 0147-006X
Vols. 1–2 (1978–79): $17.00 (USA), $17.50 (elsewhere) per copy
Vol. 3 (avail. Mar. 1980): $17.00 (USA), $17.50 (elsewhere) per copy

Annual Review of NUCLEAR AND PARTICLE SCIENCE ISSN 0066-4243
Vols. 10–29 (1960–79): $19.50 (USA), $20.00 (elsewhere) per copy
Vol. 30 (avail. Dec. 1980): $22.50 (USA), $23.50 (elsewhere) per copy

Annual Review of PHARMACOLOGY AND TOXICOLOGY* ISSN 0362-1642
Vols. 1–3, 5–19 (1961–63, 1965–79): $17.00 (USA), $17.50 (elsewhere) per copy
Vol. 20 (avail. Apr. 1980): $17.00 (USA), $17.50 (elsewhere) per copy

Annual Review of PHYSICAL CHEMISTRY ISSN 0066-426X
Vols. 10–21, 23–30 (1959–70, 1972–79): $17.00 (USA), $17.50 (elsewhere) per copy
Vol. 31 (avail. Nov. 1980): $20.00 (USA), $21.00 (elsewhere) per copy

Annual Review of PHYSIOLOGY* ISSN 0066-4278
Vols. 18–41 (1956–79): $17.00 (USA), $17.50 (elsewhere) per copy
Vol. 42 (avail. Mar. 1980): $17.00 (USA), $17.50 (elsewhere) per copy

Annual Review of PHYTOPATHOLOGY ISSN 0066-4286
Vols. 1–17 (1963–79): $17.00 (USA), $17.50 (elsewhere) per copy
Vol. 18 (avail. Sept. 1980): $20.00 (USA), $21.00 (elsewhere) per copy

Annual Review of PLANT PHYSIOLOGY* ISSN 0066-4294
Vols. 10–30 (1959–79): $17.00 (USA), $17.50 (elsewhere) per copy
Vol. 31 (avail. June 1980): $17.00 (USA), $17.50 (elsewhere) per copy

Annual Review of PSYCHOLOGY* ISSN 0066-4308
Vols. 4, 5, 8, 10–30 (1953, 1954, 1957, 1959–79): $17.00 (USA), $17.50 (elsewhere) per copy
Vol. 31 (avail. Feb. 1980): $17.00 (USA), $17.50 (elsewhere) per copy

Annual Review of SOCIOLOGY ISSN 0360-0572
Vols. 1–5 (1975–79): $17.00 (USA), $17.50 (elsewhere) per copy
Vol. 6 (avail. Aug. 1980): $20.00 (USA), $21.00 (elsewhere) per copy

***Price will be increased to $20.00 (USA), $21.00 (elsewhere) per copy effective with the 1981 volume.**

To ANNUAL REVIEWS INC., 4139 El Camino Way, Palo Alto, CA 94306 USA
(Tel. 415-493-4400)

Please enter my order for the following publications:
(Standing orders: indicate which volume you wish order to begin with)

________________________________, Vol(s). ____ Standing order ____

________________________________, Vol(s). ____ Standing order ____

________________________________, Vol(s). ____ Standing order ____

________________________________, Vol(s). ____ Standing order ____

Amount of remittance enclosed $________ California residents please add applicable sales tax.
Please bill me ☐ Prices subject to change without notice.

SHIP TO (include institutional purchase order if billing address is different)

Name ________________________________

Address ________________________________

____

________________________________ Zip Code ____________

Signed ________________________________ Date ____________

☐ Please add my name to your mailing list to receive a free copy of the current Prospectus each year.
☐ Send free brochure listing contents of recent back volumes for *Annual Review(s)* of

____